84TH CONGRESS, 2D SESSION, HOUSE DOCUMENT NO. 344

1956

the

Yearbook

of

Agriculture

the yearbook of agriculture 1956

THE UNITED STATES GOVERNMENT PRINTING OFFICE

ANIMAL DISEASES

THE UNITED STATES DEPARTMENT

OF AGRICULTURE · WASHINGTON, D.C.

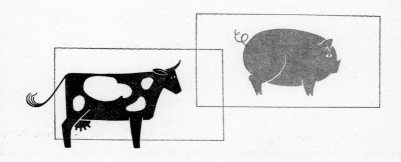

FOR SALE BY THE SUPERINTENDENT OF DOCUMENTS, WASHINGTON 25, D. C., PRICE $2.00

foreword

Ezra Taft Benson
SECRETARY OF AGRICULTURE

I SALUTE the workers in the biological sciences, among whom are our veterinarians. They are in the forefront in our relentless fight against animal diseases, some of which are linked closely to human health.

They have done much for us as individuals and as a Nation, as the chapters in this Yearbook prove.

Their efforts have helped greatly to reduce the risk and uncertainty in raising animals and poultry on our farms and ranches.

Poultry, dairy, beef, pork, and other livestock products provide nutrients that help us to be a strong, healthy, virile people. By their efforts to protect that production, the biological scientists have done much for our national health.

Another direct contribution to our health is their work to curb such diseases as anthrax, brucellosis, rabies, trichinosis, and tuberculosis, which people can get from animals.

Veterinarians have brought a great measure of prosperity over the years to our farmers and the industries that use and process the livestock products.

They have saved us countless dollars and spared us countless instances of inefficiency and loss of milk, eggs, and work time; loss in quality in meat, hides, and wool; morbidity and death among livestock, poultry, pet animals and birds, and wild animals.

They have enlarged our knowledge of zoology, pathology, parasitology, immunology, and other sciences that affect human life no less than the other forms of life.

I salute them also for the affirmative courage with which they face up to the challenges of the future.

They are the first to say that many gaps exist in their knowledge—the pages that follow contain examples of techniques that admittedly are less than perfect, of methods and diagnostic devices that need improvement, of diseases that remain to be conquered, of research that must be undertaken.

They have told me of a procedure that will help meet those lacks, and I mention and endorse it here: A challenge of the next 25 years lies in the ability of our colleges to produce scientists with a high specificity of knowledge and a sharpened desire to follow a career devoted to biological and veterinary research. That would suggest a greater specialization in restricted fields of inquiry during the training period. It should not be at the expense of training the general practitioner but rather in greater selectivity in choosing undergraduates—preferably those with a knowledge born of experience with animals—who show a deep desire to specialize and in providing additional graduate training for definitive fields of veterinary research. A part of the problem is that financial opportunities often favor the general practitioner, but the satisfaction of conducting research toward a solution of disease problems is great, and the work of advancing biological knowledge will develop basic facts that in turn will benefit the general practitioner.

Facilities for biological research have been improved greatly in the past few years, but they are not yet sufficient. As more scientists enter that field, more and better facilities will be needed. Facilities for the study of infectious disease must be good enough to prevent the transmission of diseases from experimental animals to other animals or—when the diseases are transmissible to people—to the laboratory workers. Such facilities are expensive.

The needed research may cost many millions of dollars. The results of the research may save hundreds of millions, for morbidity and mortality from infectious, noninfectious, and parasitic diseases still cause estimated losses of more than 2 billion dollars each year.

vi

preface

Alfred Stefferud
EDITOR

THIS YEARBOOK gives information about the cause, nature, and prevention of the common diseases of animals on American farms.

We have tried to make it useful, practical, and complete within the limits of time, expense, and scope that we had to observe. It is not a "veterinary handbook."

Keeping his animals as healthy as he can is the responsibility of the owner. As many of our chapters emphasize, treatment and cure—if there is a cure—are primarily the responsibility of the veterinarian.

In fact, one of our purposes is to tell the owner how much he can do but also to warn him that there is much he cannot do and should not attempt to do for a sick animal—any more than he should try to treat himself for tuberculosis or a broken leg.

A precursor of this volume was the 1942 Yearbook of Agriculture, *Keeping Livestock Healthy*, which is nearly out of print. The present book was not thought of as a new or revised edition of the earlier volume; it is an entirely different book because knowledge of the subject has developed so greatly in the intervening years. (The foreword to the 1942 Yearbook said the losses caused by diseases, parasites, and insect pests in the United States "amount to well over 400 million dollars a year in spite of an enviable record in working out and applying control methods." The losses have since been placed at more than 2 billion dollars!)

This book follows much the same plan as the earlier work. It is divided into 11 sections: Introduction; basic principles of health and disease of animals; diseases and parasites that affect two or more species; diseases and parasites that affect cattle, swine, sheep and goats, horses and mules, poultry, fur-bearing animals, and dogs and cats. The first three sections are arranged to give a survey of the nature and prevention of disease.

Although we thought of our task as presentation of background details rather than the preparation of a book to be kept in the stable for quick consultation in emergencies, we have added a few devices to help the reader who needs help in a hurry—a table of contents and a full index that lists the items by species of animals, name of the organism, synonyms of the disease, symptoms, and so on.

Readers who now are seeing a Yearbook for the first time may like to know that since 1936 each of the Yearbooks (a century-old institution) has been devoted to one subject. Recent Yearbooks, which still can be bought from the Superintendent of Documents, Government Printing Office, Washington 25, D. C., at the prices given, are: *Science in Farming* ($2); *Grass* ($2); *Trees* ($2); *Crops in Peace and War*—agricultural chemistry ($2.50); *Insects* ($2.50); *Plant Diseases* ($2.50); *Marketing* ($1.75); and *Water* ($2).

The 1956 Yearbook Committee included:

Dr. O. E. Reed
Dr. Hugh C. McPhee
Dr. B. T. Simms
Dr. Benjamin Schwartz
Dr. Ralph E. Hodgson
Dr. Lane A. Moore
Dr. T. C. Byerly
Dr. N. R. Ellis
Dr. E. G. McKibben
Mr. C. P. Heisig
Dr. John R. Matchett
Dr. C. D. Van Houweling
Mr. Samuel B. Detwiler, Jr.
Mr. J. Kendall McClarren
Dr. E. F. Knipling

Since the Committee started its work of planning and outlining the volume, two members retired from the Department of Agriculture after many years of outstanding service. Dr. Reed and Dr. McPhee left a record of devoted and efficient public service to the livestock industry and in the solution of its problems.

contents

Ezra Taft Benson	Foreword	v
Alfred Stefferud	Preface	vii

TO GUARD THE HEALTH OF MAN AND ANIMALS
our goal

C. D. Van Houweling	Our Battle Against Animal Diseases	1
M. R. Clarkson	Food Supplies and Animal Diseases	7
A. V. Nordquist *C. H. Pals*	Economic Losses from Animal Diseases and Parasites	11
James H. Steele	Infectious Diseases Common to Animals and Man	14
Benjamin Schwartz	Parasites That Attack Animals and Man	21

PREVENTION AND TREATMENT OF DISEASES
basic principles

H. W. Schoening *Benjamin Schwartz* *E. F. Knipling* *Aubrey M. Lee*	Causes of Disease	29
H. W. Schoening *Benjamin Schwartz* *Arthur W. Lindquist*	How Diseases and Parasites Are Spread	40
Nelson F. Waters	Genetics and Disease	46
B. T. Simms	Protection Against Transmissible Diseases and Parasites	54
Aubrey M. Lee *Lloyd A. Spindler*	Feeding and Management	60
C. L. Gooding	Quarantining	62

PREVENTION AND TREATMENT OF DISEASES
some methods

B. T. Simms	Treatment of Disease	71
Aurel O. Foster	Special Principles of Parasite Control	75
Aurel O. Foster	Chemotherapeutic Agents, Internal Parasites	80
E. F. Knipling	Chemotherapeutic Agents, External Parasites	85
Oren E. Herl Leigh T. Giltner	Veterinary Biological Products	88
L. Meyer Jones	Antibiotics	94
L. Meyer Jones	The Sulfa Drugs	96
W. L. Mallmann	Disinfection	98

DISEASES AND PARASITES AFFECTING
several species of animals

N. R. Ellis	Urinary Calculi	103
C. L. Davis W. T. Shalkop	Tumors	105
Robert W. Dougherty	Bloat in Ruminants	108
Wayne Binns	Chemical Poisoning	113
Ward T. Huffman Edward A. Moran Wayne Binns	Poisonous Plants	118
R. D. Radeleff G. T. Woodard R. C. Bushland	Toxicity of Insecticides	131
Roscoe H. Carter H. V. Claborn G. T. Woodard Ray E. Ely	Pesticide Residues in Animal Products	143
Emmett W. Price	Liver Flukes of Cattle and Sheep	148
Dale A. Porter Kenneth C. Kates	Tapeworms and Bladderworms	153
Allen McIntosh William C. McDuffie	Ticks That Affect Domestic Animals and Poultry	157
E. F. Knipling William C. McDuffie	Flies That Affect Livestock	166
Gaines W. Eddy R. C. Bushland	Screwworms That Attack Livestock	172
Gaines W. Eddy R. C. Bushland	Fleeceworms	175
Arthur W. Lindquist William C. McDuffie	Mosquitoes on Livestock and Man	177
Arthur W. Lindquist William C. McDuffie	Biting Gnats	181
W. C. Patterson L. O. Mott	Vesicular Stomatitis—V. S.	182

M. S. Shahan J. Traum	Foot-and-Mouth Disease	186
H. W. Schoening	Rabies	195
C. A. Manthei A. K. Kuttler E. R. Goode, Jr.	Brucellosis	202
Howard W. Johnson Albert F. Ranney	Tuberculosis and Its Eradication	213
Aubrey B. Larsen Howard W. Johnson	Paratuberculosis (Johne's Disease)	221
A. H. Frank	Vibriosis of Cattle	224
G. B. Van Ness C. A. Manthei	Leptospirosis	226
C. D. Stein G. B. Van Ness	Anthrax	229
C. D. Stein	Malignant Edema	235
C. D. Stein	Tetanus	237
H. E. Biester L. H. Schwarte	Listeriosis	239

DISEASES AND PARASITES AFFECTING
cattle

W. J. Gibbons	Milk Fever	243
R. W. Brown, Jr.	Bovine Mastitis	245
Joseph A. Dye Robert W. Dougherty	Ketosis in Cattle	250
W. A. Aitken	Shipping Fever	255
R. E. Davis H. R. Crookshank	Grass Tetany and Wheat-Pasture Poisoning	260
C. D. Stein	Blackleg	263
A. W. Monlux C. L. Davis	Actinomycosis and Actinobacillosis	265
John C. Lotze Daniel W. Gates T. O. Roby	Anaplasmosis of Cattle	268
Aubrey M. Lee	Hyperkeratosis	273
Datus M. Hammond Paul R. Fitzgerald J. LeGrande Shupe	Trichomoniasis of the Reproductive Tract	277
Dale A. Porter Harry Herlich Halsey H. Vegors	Roundworm Parasites of the Digestive Tract of Cattle	284
Robert Rubin	Verminous Pneumonia of Cattle	290
Irwin H. Roberts N. G. Cobbett	Cattle Scabies	292
John T. Lucker	Verminous Dermatitis	298

Irwin H. Roberts Arthur W. Lindquist	Cattle Grubs	300
C. L. Smith Irwin H. Roberts	Cattle Lice	307
T. W. Cole Wm. M. MacKellar	Cattle Tick Fever	310
R. S. Sugg	Infectious Keratitis, or Pinkeye, in Cattle	313
Leonard Reid Davis George W. Bowman	Bovine Coccidiosis	314
M. G. Fincher	Diseases of Calves	317
L. O. Mott C. A. Manthei	Miscellaneous Diseases of Cattle	327

DISEASES AND PARASITES AFFECTING
swine

John S. Andrews	Lung Parasites of Swine	335
John S. Andrews Francis G. Tromba	Kidney Worms of Swine	338
Lloyd A. Spindler	The Large Intestinal Roundworm	340
Lloyd A. Spindler	The Intestinal Threadworm	343
Kenneth C. Kates	Thorn-Headed Worm of Swine	344
N. G. Cobbett R. C. Bushland	The Hog Louse	345
N. G. Cobbett	Hog Mange	347
Richard D. Shuman John S. Andrews F. L. Earl	Atrophic Rhinitis in Swine	350
J. P. Torrey	Hog Cholera	354
L. P. Doyle L. M. Hutchings	The Enteritis Complex	362
Richard E. Shope	Swine Influenza	366
F. J. Mulhern W. C. Patterson	Vesicular Exanthema	369
Richard D. Shuman O. L. Osteen	Swine Erysipelas (Diamond Skin Disease)	373
N. R. Ellis Richard D. Shuman	Diseases of Baby Pigs	377
Paul C. Bennett J. P. Torrey C. N. Dale	Miscellaneous Diseases of Swine	382

DISEASES AND PARASITES AFFECTING
sheep and goats

| John C. Lotze | Coccidiosis of Sheep and Goats | 387 |
| Kenneth C. Kates Rex W. Allen James H. Turner | Roundworms of the Digestive Tract | 389 |

Rex W. Allen	Nodular Worms of Sheep and Goats	399
Aaron Goldberg	Lungworms in Sheep and Goats	401
H. E. Kemper H. O. Peterson	Scabies in Sheep and Goats	403
N. G. Cobbett	Head Grubs of Sheep	407
H. O. Peterson R. C. Bushland	Lice of Sheep and Goats	411
C. L. Davis	Sore Mouth in Sheep and Goats	414
C. R. Omer	Scrapie in Sheep	416
D. G. McKercher B. R. McCrory J. L. Hourrigan	Bluetongue of Sheep	418
B. R. McCrory C. L. Davis	Enterotoxemia of Sheep	422
Hadleigh Marsh	Vibriosis of Sheep	425
W. A. Anderson C. L. Davis	Pregnancy Disease	427
O. H. Muth	White Muscle Disease in Lambs and Calves	429
Hadleigh Marsh E. A. Tunnicliff	Other Diseases of Sheep	431

DISEASES AND PARASITES AFFECTING
poultry

Everett E. Wehr Marion M. Farr	Coccidiosis of Chickens and Turkeys	437
Everett E. Lund	Blackhead of Turkeys and Chickens	441
Everett E. Lund	Hexamitiasis of Turkeys	444
J. E. Williams Paul B. Zumbro A. D. MacDonald	Pullorum Disease of Chickens and Turkeys	446
Walter J. Hall	Fowl Typhoid	451
J. E. Williams	Poultry and the Paratyphoids	453
O. L. Osteen	Newcastle Disease	455
John P. Delaplane	Ornithosis and Psittacosis	459
Walter J. Hall G. B. Van Ness	Blue Comb	463
Walter J. Hall	Fowlpox	464
B. R. Burmester Nelson F. Waters	Avian Lymphomatosis	466
Richard D. Shuman O. L. Osteen	Turkey Erysipelas	474
J. F. Sullivan Clarence H. Thompson, Jr. O. L. Osteen	Chronic Respiratory Disease in Chickens	476
J. F. Sullivan Clarence H. Thompson, Jr.	Infectious Sinusitis in Turkeys	479

E. L. Jungherr J. F. Sullivan	Infectious Bronchitis	480
O. L. Osteen	Infectious Laryngotracheitis	483
J. L. Gardiner	Tapeworms of Chickens and Turkeys	484
J. L. Gardiner	Roundworms	486
Irwin H. Roberts C. L. Smith	Poultry Lice	490
Irwin H. Roberts C. L. Smith	Mites on Poultry	493
E. Dougherty III	Diseases of Ducks	496
Everett E. Wehr Marion M. Farr	Parasites Affecting Ducks and Geese	500

DISEASES AND PARASITES AFFECTING
dogs and cats

F. D. Enzie Emmett W. Price	Internal Parasites of Dogs and Cats	503
Carroll N. Smith F. D. Enzie	External Parasites of Dogs and Cats	517
J. E. Greene	Infectious Diseases of Dogs and Cats	523
M. K. Heath W. M. Dillard	Miscellaneous Ailments of Cats and Dogs	528

DISEASES AND PARASITES AFFECTING
horses and mules

T. O. Roby L. O. Mott	Equine Periodic Ophthalmia	531
E. R. Doll	Equine Influenza	534
E. R. Doll	Breeding Problems	536
E. R. Doll	Diseases of Foals	541
C. D. Stein	Equine Infectious Anemia	546
M. S. Shahan H. W. Schoening	Equine Encephalomyelitis	550
F. D. Enzie	Mange and Lice of Horses and Mules	555

DISEASES AND PARASITES AFFECTING
fur-bearing animals

Karl W. Hagen, Jr.	Infectious Diseases of the Rabbit	559
Everett E. Lund	Parasites of the Domestic Rabbit	563
John R. Gorham	Diseases and Parasites of Minks	567
John R. Gorham	Diseases and Parasites of Foxes	573

xiv

ANIMAL

diseases

TO GUARD THE
HEALTH OF MAN
AND ANIMALS

our goal

Our Battle Against Animal Diseases

C. D. VAN HOUWELING

A NEW YORK milkman named Peter Dunn bought a milk cow in 1843 from the captain of the *Washington*, a British ship. It seemed to Peter Dunn that he was getting the cow at a big bargain, but she turned out to be just as expensive as Mrs. O'Leary's cow, which supposedly caused the big fire that destroyed one-third of Chicago in 1871. Peter Dunn's cow introduced contagious pleuropneumonia into these United States—and cost our livestock owners untold dollars.

Before Peter Dunn's time, animal diseases were a minor problem in the United States. Until the colonization of America, native livestock were free of many of the diseases that trouble us today. Stock later imported from Europe brought diseases with them, but lack of transportation limited the spread of the diseases. As the country and the livestock population grew, however, our livestock disease problems grew in proportion.

Enterprising stockmen were continually improving our breeds through importations of the choicest animals from the best herds and flocks of the Old World. The glowing prospects of an extensive export trade in animals and their products gave an impetus to the livestock industry and brought our people to realize more fully the importance of this phase of agriculture.

On the farms of this country in 1883, the year before the establishment of an organized animal-disease-eradication program, there were an estimated 10,838,111 horses, and 1,871,079 mules, 41,171,762 cattle, 49,237,291 sheep, and 43,270,086 hogs—a total of 146,-

388,329 animals valued at 2,338,241,-519 dollars.

But up to 1883 livestock diseases had received little attention from State or National Governments. Contagious pleuropneumonia had existed along the Atlantic coast since Peter Dunn's fateful purchase 40 years before. From 25 million to 30 million dollars' worth of hogs were dying each year from hog cholera. Sheep raising had become precarious in many sections because of scab and other parasitic diseases. Tuberculosis and brucellosis were spreading. Anthrax and blackleg were on the increase in most of the States.

Cattle raisers lived in fear of Texas fever. The causes of the most destructive animal diseases were unknown or in dispute, and livestock owners to a large extent were defenseless, as veterinary science had not been able to provide effectual prophylactic or medical treatment.

Vexatious and expensive quarantines were increasing—some were for protection, but some were only for retaliation. Our system of interstate and export animal transportation was denounced as a disgrace and an outrage on the first principles of humanity. There was a growing demand for protection of the public health in connection with the meat supply.

Contagious pleuropneumonia, introduced by Peter Dunn's cow, developed to such an extent that our export cattle and sheep were denied admission into Great Britain and were condemned to slaughter within a limited time on the docks where they landed. Our pork had been prohibited entrance into most of the markets of Europe.

That was the situation in 1883 when the Veterinary Division of the Department of Agriculture was established to meet the urgent needs for reliable, official information concerning the nature and prevalence of animal diseases and of the means required to control and eradicate them. Dr. D. E. Salmon was appointed chief of the new division, and a 7-acre farm was acquired to be used as an experimental station.

Much more was needed. Livestock men realized soon enough that an executive agency to carry into effect regulations to control and eradicate disease and to protect the growing animal industry at home and abroad had become even more necessary than the research work. Vigorous agitation and insistent demands for governmental assistance finally culminated in the act of Congress of May 29, 1884—"An act for the establishment of a Bureau of Animal Industry, to prevent the exportation of diseased cattle, and to provide means for the suppression and extirpation of pleuropneumonia and other contagious diseases among domestic animals."

THE ACT SPECIFIED that a competent veterinary surgeon should be chief of the Bureau, that the force should not exceed 20 persons at any one time, and that the Commissioner of Agriculture was authorized to appoint two competent agents who should be either practical stockraisers or experienced in livestock business matters. The sum of 150,000 dollars was appropriated to put the law into effect.

The wording of the act indicated that the first duty of the Bureau was to take charge of the eradication of pleuropneumonia in cooperation with the authorities of the States where the disease existed. Massachusetts and Connecticut had succeeded in eradicating the disease, but lack of laws, interest, and funds in other States had permitted the disease to spread from Long Island, where it appeared in 1843, into Pennsylvania, New York, New Jersey, Maryland, Virginia, West Virginia, and the District of Columbia by 1884. Reinfection occurred in Connecticut. Outbreaks in the Western States were reported in 1885.

It cost the National Government 5 years of work and 1,509,100.72 dollars to eradicate contagious pleuropneumonia from the United States. The United States was the first of the large countries to extirpate contagious pleuropneumonia. It was a signal achievement, especially in view of the doubts as to the possibility of eradicating the disease, the fact that the States were unprepared to cooperate effectively, the widespread opposition to "government interference," occasioned by the restrictions and temporary sacrifices experienced by individual owners, and the experiences of the other countries, which had labored a much longer time and made greater expenditures of money without success. Thus the new Bureau of Animal Industry accomplished its first undertaking.

Out of this first experience in disease eradication came an important lesson—control of a contagious disease cannot be left to individual initiative. The clean herd of a good husbandman can be infected by his careless neighbor. A contagion does not stop at political boundaries. Only combined efforts at community, State, national, and international levels give us any degree of security against it.

Pleuropneumonia was only one of many problems. Although the slow boats that brought animals to this country were in one sense a floating quarantine, where many contagions ran their course before infected animals landed, many animal ills of the Old World had been imported with livestock. Anthrax, scab, the mange, blackleg, tuberculosis, the fowl plague, and pox were some of the more important ones. Tick fever had been imported, probably from the West Indies and Mexico. We also developed a disease of our own. Hog cholera appeared in Ohio in 1833 and by 1884 was a real killer.

To FIND THE CAUSE of tick fever was the next task of the Bureau of Animal Industry.

Tick fever probably entered this country as early as the 17th century by way of the West Indies and Mexico. By the 1860's trail herds from Texas had brought pestilence and death to cattle in Indian Territory, Missouri, Kansas, and Arkansas.

Farmers were the first to suspect the cattle tick. Theobald Smith, the Bureau's first pathologist, began systematic experiments with tick fever in 1888. In 1 year he found the disease to be caused by a protozoan parasite in the blood of infected animals. Cooper Curtice, a Bureau zoologist, worked out the life cycle of the tick. F. L. Kilborne, working with Dr. Smith, tested the theory of the relation of ticks to the disease. Bulletin No. 1 of the Bureau of Animal Industry, issued in 1892, announced the momentous discovery that infection can be carried from one animal to another through the agency of an intermediate host—the tick.

This first classic example of animal research cost 65,000 dollars. Today it saves farmers at least 60 million dollars a year. But even more important: The discovery unlocked the mysteries of such human diseases as malaria, yellow fever, typhus, bubonic plague, and Rocky Mountain spotted fever.

Then a means of destroying the tick had to be devised. Experiments were carried out on cattle, using dips containing as the main ingredients carbolic acid, tobacco extract, sodium sulfate, glycerin, lime-sulfur, and many other substances with unsatisfactory results. The use of crude mineral oil was found to be more satisfactory, and it was used almost exclusively from 1903 to 1911 as a spray, a smear, and a dip in freeing cattle of ticks.

Effective July 1, 1906, the Congress made available 82,500 dollars to begin the work of freeing the South of cattle ticks. The area infested with the fever tick had been quarantined a few years earlier, and the enforcement of regulations controlling the movement of cattle from the quarantined area was helpful in preventing the spread of tick fever. Although the more intelligent cattle owners manifested much enthusiasm in tick eradication, it was found impossible to guard against infractions of the regulations in maintaining the quarantine line. Many of the livestock owners did not believe in tick eradication, and inspectors were derided and ridiculed and suspected.

The most discouraging conditions with which the inspectors had to contend were the need of adequate State laws, the disinclination of State authorities to enforce existing law, the lack of State and county funds to carry on the work, and ignorance and prejudice. Nevertheless the work continued to spread, and some of the benefits were being seen in territory freed of ticks.

By 1910 the efforts of the Bureau to eradicate cattle ticks had attracted the attention of the officials of the various railroads in the Southern States, the management of some industrial concerns, and banking institutions interested in the development of the South. Great impetus was given to the work by some of those organizations through the publication and wide distribution of literature stressing tick eradication as an economic measure of national importance, affecting not only cattle owners but all other businesses proportionately.

The development of the arsenical dip also proved a boon to tick eradication.

Experiments with an arsenical dip were first reported in 1906 by Dr. Joseph W. Parker. Other experiments and improvements followed, and in 1911 an order was promulgated to permit the use of the arsenical solution as an official dip for the interstate movement of cattle originating in the quarantined area.

With the perfection of a practicable, economical, speedy, and effectual means for the disinfection of cattle for ticks by dipping, an all-important step was taken. Tick eradication was really underway. Cattle were dipped every 14 days for about a year. This broke the tick's life cycle. Once an area was freed, the disease fighters moved on, working from North to South. Although dipping vats were dynamited by opponents to this eradication program and men were killed in the violent opposition to the eradication program, the dipping schedule was maintained, and persistence paid off. Although occasional infestation is found in a narrow strip of land in Texas along the Mexican border, tick fever has ceased to be a significant disease of cattle in this country.

FOOT-AND-MOUTH DISEASE, the most elusive killer of all, has penetrated our defenses six times since 1900. In all but two outbreaks, the disease was eradicated and quarantines were removed within a few months. It took nearly 2 years, however, to complete the eradication of the 1914 and 1924 outbreaks. The 1924 outbreak was in the Los Angeles and the Bay areas of California and near Houston, Tex.

One infection occurred in 1929 near Los Angeles. The eradication procedure consisted of quarantining, destruction of infected and exposed herds, and cleaning and disinfection of premises after the removal of the animals.

Here again our forces met with resistance from the beginning of the first eradication campaign. Some livestock owners objected to slaughtering as too drastic, but once again the Bureau persisted in its eradication measures.

Cholera threatened to wipe out our swine industry by the 1890's. Research by the Department of Agriculture led to the discovery in 1904 that hog cholera was caused by a filterable virus, accounting for the lack of success in the earlier attempts to produce an effective vaccine or serum. Development and production of the anti-hog-cholera serum was begun, and the serum-virus preventive treatment was initiated. Thus the swine growers of the Nation were given a means of protecting themselves against deadly hog disease, and refinements in the immunizing agents make the eradication of this disease a practical possibility.

Another early drive against disease that took on campaign proportions was the eradication of scabies in western sheep, and, to a lesser extent, in cattle. A dipping regimen together with quarantine had virtually extinguished the threat of scab mite by 1941.

Two contagious diseases of horses that have been brought under control or wiped out are dourine and glanders. Glanders is communicable to man and usually causes death.

Dourine had appeared in so many States by 1903 that it was decided to take agressive steps against it. Dr. John R. Mohler, then chief of the Pathological Division of the Bureau of Animal Industry, was sent to the National Veterinary School at Alfort, France, to study the disease and the methods of combating it. The development of a satisfactory test to locate the diseased horses opened the way to eradication of the disease. Occasionally Indian horses in the Southwest are found to be infected, but otherwise the disease has been eradicated from the horses of this country.

While engaged in the eradication of pleuropneumonia, the inspectors of the Bureau had discovered an unexpected amount of glanders among the horses and mules of the country, and concerted efforts were made in cooperation with the States to combat it. The accurate method of diagnosing glanders and persistent destruction of the reactors to the test led to its eradication.

OUR FARMERS TODAY generally know about the campaigns against bovine tuberculosis and brucellosis (Bang's disease).

The tuberculosis campaign was begun in 1917, and here again the fieldworkers met with opposition. Any control program that brings out the incidence of the disease is regarded with alarm by the industry, for fear that some consumers will be prejudiced against the livestock products and that shipments of their animals will be interfered with.

Despite this temporary opposition, tuberculin testing was continued, and one of the first features of the program was the recognition of accredited herds; that is, herds that had been tested and found to be free of tuberculosis. It was realized from the beginning, however, that tuberculosis could not be eradicated under the accredited herd plan. In 1919 concerted efforts

to test all cattle within a given county were begun. That was the beginning of the modified accredited area plan.

Gradually all the counties in all the States became modified accredited tuberculosis-free areas. The last remaining State to become accredited as being tuberculosis-free attained that status by 1940. To maintain accredited status, an area can not have an infection of more than 0.5 percent, as shown in the tests. The percentage of infection in 1955 was only 0.11.

The disease has been all but wiped out, but experience has shown that as long as tuberculosis exists in the cattle in this country, vigilance must not be relaxed, else the infection will once again be on the increase. Not until the last infected cow has been slaughtered will we consider our campaign at an end.

A campaign to eradicate brucellosis in cattle began in 1934. J. Traum and Alice Evans, research scientists in the Department of Agriculture, led in showing that three separate but related organisms cause the disease.

Other Department workers, J. M. Buck and W. E. Cotton, did much of the early work for the development of Strain 19 vaccine, now used to vaccinate calves against bovine brucellosis. The main features of the program are testing of animals, slaughter of those found to be diseased, and vaccination of young animals to build up their resistance to infection.

The milk-ring test, a recent addition to the official program, is conducted on composite samples of milk collected from the milking cows in the herd. Use of the test thus eliminates the need to take blood samples in many herds. At the beginning of the program, the percentage of infected animals was 2 or 3 times as great as in 1955, when 2.6 percent of the cattle blood tested were found to be reactors. The estimated annual loss from brucellosis in cattle in 1946 was 90 million dollars. This annual loss had been reduced by 1954 to an estimated 45 million dollars. Although the loss to the industry had been cut in half, a loss of 45 million dollars is still a tremendous one. In an effort to eradicate the disease as quickly as possible, an expanded program was begun in 1955.

ANOTHER BIG PROBLEM of the Bureau of Animal Industry was to provide wholesome meat for human consumption in the United States and abroad. Foreign governments had set up restrictions on cattle and meat imported from the United States because of the existence of diseases in this country. In response to appeals from meatpackers, livestock producers, and others, the first Federal meat inspection law was passed on August 30, 1890. It provided for the inspection of salted pork and bacon intended for exportation when the requirements of foreign governments made such inspection necessary. It also provided for the inspection of all cattle, sheep, other ruminants, and swine for export. Over the years this authority was broadened to control sanitation and to provide inspection and supervision of the preparation and labeling of products, which is essential to a comprehensive system of inspection.

Federal inspection was primarily established to meet economic needs, but its hygienic benefits were not limited to the foreign consumer of our products. In fact, the natural and proper development of the service logically made it a national service in hygiene, and this has long been its dominant value, while its importance from the economic viewpoint remains great.

The volume of work done by our meat inspection has increased greatly since the 1890's. Approximately 95 million carcasses are inspected every year. Almost 800 carcasses are inspected every minute of every working day.

WITHOUT THESE LARGE GAINS in disease control and eradication, the livestock industry as we know it today would not be possible. But there are still many problems to be faced.

Some 95 million head of cattle were on United States farms and ranches in 1954, and the losses incurred from livestock diseases, parasites, and insects have been estimated at 2.7 billion dollars a year. Although this is a tremendous loss, it is only a small part of the loss which would have been sustained if there had been no eradication programs. For example, the savings resulting from the tuberculosis eradication program alone are put at 150 million dollars a year.

Today's livestock producer must cope with many diseases to which his predecessor's herds were not exposed. With our modern system of transportation and marketing, diseases can spread faster and farther than ever before. The large number of livestock we must have today also magnifies the problems and greatly complicates things.

Research alone is not enough. Research findings have to be put into practice. Disease control and eradication is the application of research. The present organization of the Agricultural Research Service, which includes the work of the former Bureau of Animal Industry, separates livestock research and livestock regulatory activities. Nevertheless, these two activities are placed close together in practice.

All livestock-disease control and eradication programs are conducted in cooperation with the States, under State laws and regulations. Without the excellent cooperation which has been received from the States, the successful disease eradication drives of the last 75 years would not have been possible.

Our present programs consist of quarantine of imported cattle to keep out diseases; cooperation with the States in the eradication of existing diseases; inspection of meat; control of viruses, serums, and toxins to insure the purity and potency of the products; and continued research.

The goal of all our disease programs is eventual eradication. We hope to eradicate the serious bacterial, viral, and parasitic diseases that challenge us today. We envision areas and countries whose livestock are free of transmissible diseases. This, then, is our goal—to guard the health of the livestock of this country and contribute our full share to an expanding livestock industry so that all our people may be provided with abundant and wholesome food at a reasonable price.

C. D. VAN HOUWELING *is director of the Livestock Regulatory Programs of Agricul-* *tural Research Service and has the responsibility for planning, coordinating, and directing the administration of the Department's program aimed at nationwide control or eradication of diseases of livestock and poultry. Before his appointment to that position in 1954, Dr. Van Houweling was an official of the American Veterinary Medical Association. He obtained the degree of doctor of veterinary medicine from Iowa State College.*

Food Supplies and Animal Diseases

M. R. CLARKSON

A FEW FACTS tell the importance of the food we get from animals.

To supply an average American family of four, farmers produce almost 3 tons of food a year. More than half of it is meat, eggs, poultry, and dairy products. Of those animal foods, we ate 25 percent more in 1956 than we did in 1935. American farms produce a third of the world's recorded yearly total of 80 billion pounds of red meat and a fourth of the 500 billion pounds of milk.

A look at the experience of other countries demonstrates further the importance of meat in the diet and the need to keep animals healthy.

Food supplies in most of the world cannot be taken for granted. Perhaps half of the world's people exist on diets that are nutritionally poor. Several hundred million, notably the people in countries where animal parasites run rampant and epizootics flare up repeatedly, are half-starved.

Every year brings additional evidence of how extensive is protein malnutrition in the world. Where it is most serious, as in tropical and subtropical parts of Africa, a livestock industry is almost nonexistent, and shortages of meat, milk, eggs, and other livestock products are acute. The average person usually has less meat in an entire year than most Americans eat in a week. Milk is not tasted after infancy. Several forms of malignant malnutrition are prevalent as a result.

An effective treatment for kwashiorkor, a form of malnutrition common among infants and young children in those areas, is cow's milk, especially skim milk, according to a study made in 1950 for the Food and Agriculture Organization of the United Nations.

Yet an adequate livestock industry is difficult to maintain. The numerous efforts by various governments to produce breeds adapted to the climate, develop pasturage, and provide water have not given justifiable hope that a marked improvement in livestock production can be expected as long as animal diseases remain unchecked.

So it has been throughout history. Men always have been plagued and driven by animal diseases and sometimes destroyed by them. Their agriculture has suffered; they themselves have become victims of the 80 diseases that can be transmitted from animals to man.

Anthrax, for example, was described in ancient and Biblical literature and is thought to have been the fifth plague of Egypt, believed to have occurred about 1451 B. C. Violent outbreaks were recorded in Rome, Spain, and Greece between 800 and 500 B. C.

While the Black Death was killing many people in Europe in 1348–1349, a plague—probably rinderpest—was attacking their cattle, which perished by the thousands. A great rise in food prices followed, despite an abundant harvest of cereals.

Disease in 1863 nearly exterminated the horned stock of Egypt, paralyzed farm operations, and deprived thousands of people of basic necessities.

Early wars (and the later ones, too) spread disease among the livestock and people wherever the armies went.

When Charlemagne led his army against the Danes in A. D. 810, he was followed back into France by plagues that created great havoc. The repeated raids by Mongols and Huns over several centuries established rinderpest in Russia. The Napoleonic Wars steadily built up the incidence of animal diseases in Europe to a culmination of ravages between 1812 to 1815. Diseases continued to flare and took an average of 10 to 25 percent of all the cattle in Belgium and Holland each year for the next 50 to 60 years. Rinderpest marched through Russia and into Rumania, Bulgaria, Poland, and Greece during the First World War. It caused enormous losses of livestock and had a part in the postwar Russian famine that cost thousands of lives.

WHEN HEAVY LOSSES in cattle and water buffalo occurred during the Second World War, farmers had to abandon many acres of croplands in the Philippines, Indonesia, Burma, and Malaya, where those animals are used to till crops. Severe shortages of food resulted.

Not long ago the loss of one water buffalo brought starvation to a provincial Asian village because it meant failure of the rice crop. Cattle and buffalo still mean meat, milk, transportation, farm power, and in many lands manure for the soil. Keeping them free of disease, therefore, can help insure a better nutrition and a better health for hundreds of millions of people.

Enzootic animal diseases bar the full use of several areas in the world that otherwise are well suited to production of livestock. If rinderpest could be conquered in the great grazing areas of northern Africa, they could become great meat-producing lands. If African swine disease could be conquered in coastal Africa, hog production could become a reality. Better control of cattle diseases in several areas in Asia could increase milk production by about a third without adding a single animal. If mastitis could be driven out of dairy herds in Europe, milk production could be increased by more than 5 million tons a year.

OUR OWN LAND also provides examples of the harm outbreaks of animal disease can bring. No cattle, domestic sheep, or horses existed on this continent when Europeans first arrived; they were brought in. Yet fossil remains indicate that at one time horses and cattle roamed about. We do not know what caused them to vanish, but the possibility that diseases exterminated them is given some support by fossil traces of insects, including the tsetse fly. The tsetse fly is not found here now, but where it does occur, as in some parts of Africa, livestock production is almost impossible because of nagana, a devastating disease it spreads among cattle.

Establishing livestock in North America was a slow process. The early arrivals did not bring cattle and sheep with them, but poor nutrition and high death rates, especially among the children, led to laws that settlers must bring livestock. Later pioneers who journeyed westward from the Atlantic coast as a matter of course took 2 or 3 cattle to each wagon: Livestock production was started, and it expanded with the country.

Up to that point there was little

evidence of widespread outbreaks of livestock diseases. The outbreaks that did occur apparently were of local significance. As long as the wide spaces remained open, stockmen could keep moving and escape disease. But as the country filled up, the practice became no defense at all.

The Civil War demonstrated how widely the effects of a local condition could spread. When Union forces secured the Mississippi, cattle of the Southwest were shut off from markets.

Afterward, when the roads opened, the great herds were driven north to Nebraska and Iowa and east to Pennsylvania. They spread a plague of cattle tick fever. Other diseases also got beyond control, notably contagious pleuropneumonia in cattle and cholera in hogs.

State and Federal measures were developed gradually to combat the diseases. Today this Nation is one of the safest in all the world in which to raise stock.

But diseases, parasites, and insects still exact a heavy tribute. Each year 10 percent of all farm animals can be expected to die from disease or parasitism. Even greater economic losses come from diseases that do not necessarily kill but debilitate or maim the animals and otherwise interfere with efficient production.

To reduce those losses is a growing challenge. Ours is a relatively efficient livestock industry, compared to many other areas of the world. The cow's ability to convert into food for people the materials that man cannot eat has been enhanced by advances in breeding, feeding, and management. We have many more cattle, sheep, hogs, and goats in this country than people. We devote perhaps 70 out of every 100 acres in farms to growing forages and feed grains. Almost all economically usable rural lands not in farms also are providing grazing or hay.

This concentration upon livestock production reflects our dietary preferences and affects our nutrition. Milk, meat, eggs, butter, and lard contribute a major share of several key nutrients in the daily fare of most prople living in the United States. For example, it was estimated in 1955 that those products accounted for roughly 65 percent of the protein, 70 percent of the fat, 80 percent of the calcium, 71 percent of the riboflavin, 49 percent of the niacin, 41 percent of the thiamine, 41 percent of the calories, 40 percent of the iron, 39 percent of the vitamin A value, and 23 percent of the folic acid supplied by food brought into the Nation's home and institutional kitchens. In the 20 years before 1955, per capita consumption of meat per year had increased by 27 pounds, of milk by 5 gallons, of eggs by 9.5 dozen. This followed a trend that had been apparent for more than 40 years.

Studies of the growth of population indicate, however, that livestock production will have to be at least 38 percent greater in 1975 than it was in 1951–1953 if we are merely to maintain our regular supplies of meat and milk for the increased population we can expect by that time.

The total agricultural requirements for maintaining our standards of living in 1975 would require the production equivalent of 300 million to 350 million acres more of pasture and range and up to 100 million acres of cropland measured on the basis of 1951–1953 acre yields and livestock unit production. Only a part of those conflicting land requirements can be met by farming new land or transferring land uses. The obvious solution would be to increase yields per acre and per unit of livestock. A substantial part of the increases must come through better control of animal diseases.

DESPITE THE ADVANCES in veterinary science and the gains in knowledge through research, the task is becoming increasingly difficult.

Paradox that it is, the efficiency that has been developed creates new difficulties. The incidence of tuberculosis among cattle, for instance, still is high enough to be dangerous, but it is low enough to be difficult to detect and stamp out. Complete eradication will first require the devising of new techniques, and studies along this line have been started.

Other complications develop. Communicable disease of livestock can be eradicated only when we prevent diseased animals from mingling with susceptible ones. On the other hand, the freedom we have enjoyed from many diseases makes our cattle highly susceptible should one of them strike.

Then there are the problems generated by increased numbers of animals. Authorities in England have pointed out that disease problems are directly related to the increase in livestock population. When animals double in number, disease problems increase by four times in a geometric progression that piles up troublesome crises faster than they can be resolved.

Modern traffic in livestock accelerates those troubles. Today's livestock producer must cope with many diseases to which his predecessor's herds were not exposed. Modern transportation and marketing mingle livestock from different parts of the country and multiply the opportunities for exposure. A steer these days may live in 3 or 4 States before he is slaughtered in Chicago.

Mobility and mingling magnify problems of disease control. It took 15 years after hog cholera was first diagnosed in 1833 for it to spread across the land. Some States remained free of the disease for 30 years. Tick fever of cattle moved across North Carolina at a rate of 4 miles a year in the 1870's. But when vesicular exanthema of hogs broke out of California in 1952, the disease was diagnosed in 20 States within 3 months.

So diseases of animals become more and more a concern of everyone, not merely the affected livestock owner.

We have been working with hog cholera for 75 years, but only in 1956 did we reach a point where we could experimentally try to achieve complete eradication in an area.

It is not merely a matter of giving medicines to an ailing animal. We need to pay even more attention, for example, to parasites, which take a heavy toll of the livestock industry. Many instances have been reported in which parasites are the main agents in causing outbreaks of disease. We need to control spectacular outbreaks, but frequently that pressing need delays the bringing of available resources to bear on the chronic, nonfatal disorders. Like mastitis, which causes an estimated 5-percent loss in total milk production, many do great damage.

Other problems arise because new diseases arise. Some diseases just appear. Often we do not know where they come from.

Viruses, bacteria, and parasites are prolific, insidious, elusive, and invisible. They strike suddenly, without warning. As livestock populations increase, as diseases and parasites cause new ravages, and as our standards of farm management rise, the task becomes bigger and more exacting.

A livestock industry that can supply an adequate amount of meat, milk, and eggs to maintain good diets for an increasing population is our heritage. An understanding of the threats to this capability that animal diseases present and maintaining ceaseless watch against them are our responsibility.

M. R. CLARKSON *became deputy administrator of the Agricultural Research Service in 1952. A veterinarian, Dr. Clarkson has had long experience in the administration of regulatory programs and in Federal-State cooperative activities. He began his career in the Department of Agriculture in 1930 as a veterinary meat inspector. Among his assignments in the Department's field service and in Washington was work in the fight against foot-and-mouth disease in Mexico from 1947 to 1955. A native of Ferndale, Wash., he holds the degrees of bachelor of science and doctor of veterinary medicine from Washington State College and bachelor of laws from Georgetown University.*

Economic Losses from Animal Diseases and Parasites

A. V. NORDQUIST AND C. H. PALS

DEATH losses from all causes in 1954 included more than 1.5 million cattle, 2.5 million calves, 4 million sheep and lambs, and 10.5 million hogs and pigs.

About 235 million chickens and 7.2 million turkeys died from diseases and other causes that year.

About 250,000 horses and mules and an unknown number of goats, and fur animals, domestic rabbits, and miscellaneous poultry also were lost.

The figures do not measure the full toll of animal diseases: The loss in production, feed, labor, and capital investment is tremendous every year.

Nor do official figures include the deaths of baby pigs and lambs, because estimates of losses relate only to those considered "saved," or raised to about weaning age. Another 30 million pigs and perhaps as many as 3.5 million lambs may have died before weaning. Occasional investigations have indicated losses of baby pigs at 20 to 35 percent of the number born and losses of baby lambs from all causes at 15 percent.

A few surveys have been made to obtain information on the importance of disease and parasites as a cause of death. A Minnesota survey disclosed about 58 percent of the deaths of turkeys in 1951 resulted from disease and parasites.

Earlier surveys in Missouri and Wisconsin showed the disease toll ranging from 27 to 80 percent of the deaths of various species of livestock and poultry. The surveys indicated that about 55 percent of the deaths resulted from disease.

The value of livestock and poultry that were lost in 1954 from all causes, roughly calculated, was more than 1 billion dollars. Death loss from diseases and parasites alone may have exceeded 500 million dollars.

Farmers are most keenly aware of the economic loss from livestock and poultry that die or suffer from illness severe enough to cut production rates or increase the costs of production. They are well aware of the expense of curing the sick animals or protecting animals against disease but less aware of the lower efficiency of production and lower quality of their products as a result of disease and parasites.

Economic loss is not confined strictly to farm operations, although losses discovered after livestock and poultry leave the farm have a way of being reflected in prices received by farmers. Sick animals create losses when they are transported from farm to market and handled at the markets and in packing and processing plants.

Hidden losses from disease and parasites in meat, hides, edible offal, and byproducts because of condemnations or lowered quality, when added to the economic loss from death and sickness on the farm and between the farm and the processor, reach a staggering total.

The best judgment of specialists in the Department of Agriculture on the extent of livestock and poultry losses was reported in *Losses in Agriculture, a Preliminary Appraisal for Review,* issued in June 1954. Annual losses of livestock and poultry from diseases, disorders, parasites, and insect pests for the period 1942-1951 were placed in that report at 2,420 million dollars.

The losses represented about 6 percent of the potential agricultural production and about 15 percent of the average annual value of farm marketings and home consumption of livestock and products. The publication pointed out that the potential return from nearly 20 million acres of cropland and 126 million acres of grassland was lost because of animal diseases, disorders, insect pests, and internal parasites and the downgrading of livestock products because of lowered quality.

Costs of controlling, combating, and preventing diseases may be charged to disease and parasites; so also a large part of the cost of protecting the public from unwholesome meat products.

Protective measures even extend beyond the boundaries of the United States—the campaign against foot-and-mouth disease in Mexico after 1947 cost 134.5 million dollars net. Inspection of exports and imports of live animals cost 850 thousand dollars in 1954. The fight against vesicular exanthema disease in hogs involved nearly 4 million dollars in State and Federal indemnity payments to producers. One item of expense—as an example—was the visits inspectors had to make once a month to 14,000 premises to check a million hogs that were fed garbage, that being a cause of vesicular exanthema.

Besides the expenditures for foot-and-mouth disease and vesicular exanthema, Federal appropriations for the eradication of animal diseases amounted to 7.2 million dollars in 1954. In addition, State agencies spent approximately 23 millions of dollars; that sum included 5.7 million dollars spent to combat tuberculosis and 13.6 million dollars to fight brucellosis.

Deaths and sickness resulting from cattle diseases, including nutritional ailments, have inflicted losses in excess of 650 million dollars a year. Specialists judged the loss to cattle and calves at more than 400 million dollars and the loss in value of milk production at nearly 250 million dollars.

The value of the cattle that died from disease was believed to be around 90 million dollars. Bloat, leptospirosis, and mastitis were responsible for about four-fifths of the deaths of cattle.

Mastitis was responsible also for an additional production loss valued at

225 million dollars. Vibriosis cost nearly 140 million dollars; leptospirosis, more than 100 million dollars; and brucellosis, about 100 million dollars, including a control cost of about 14 million dollars. In addition, brucellosis causes sterility which, if included, would increase the dollar loss about 50 percent.

ABOUT 80 percent of all the livestock slaughtered commercially in the United States are processed in plants operating under Federal meat inspection. The animals receive careful inspection at the plants before and at the time of slaughter. Often the meat inspectors can identify the diseased animals so that they can be traced to their origin. Thus information is had concerning the centers of infection.

Meat inspection records show the incidence of all the disease conditions found by inspectors on antemortem and postmortem inspection. The records are retained for several years and can be used to determine incidence and trends of diseases.

Inspectors of Federal Meat Inspection condemned about 120,000 carcasses of cattle and calves in 1954. Most of the animals were condemned because of diseased, parasitic, or septic conditions. About 330,000 parts of carcasses and 2,400,000 cattle and calf livers were condemned. Cattle livers from approximately 13 percent of the cattle slaughtered under Federal inspection were condemned as unfit for food for people.

ANNUAL LOSSES from swine diseases, including losses of baby pigs, were believed to exceed 500 million dollars at least. The greater part of this dollar loss is represented by losses of baby pigs, which result from infections and parasites and from mismanagement and nutritional disorders.

A reduction in losses of baby pigs in the future would contribute greatly to increased productivity in hog production and lower cost of production per breeding unit. An average of nearly 7 pigs is saved per litter up to weaning age. The average could be close to 10 pigs if the causes contributing to pig losses were eliminated.

Losses from hog cholera cost nearly 50 million dollars a year, despite widespread use of preventive measures. Erysipelas causes losses in production valued at 24 million dollars annually, and atrophic rhinitis (sneezing sickness) at 14 million dollars. Brucellosis cuts hog income by an average of 10 million dollars each year.

Federal meat inspectors condemned 99,000 swine for 50 different causes in 1954. Arthritis, septic conditions such as abscess, and pleurisy or pneumonia accounted for half of the condemnations.

Parts of more than 1.6 million swine carcasses were condemned in 1954. Most of the rejections were due to abscess or pyemia conditions.

Sheep diseases reduced the value of annual production around 12 million dollars in 1942-1951. Vibriosis, with resulting abortion and loss in weight and wool, accounted for more than 70 percent of the annual loss.

About 65,000 sheep and lambs were condemned in 1954.

Diseases inflict losses to horses, mules, goats, fur animals, and rabbits amounting to about another 5 million dollars.

A HEAVY LOSS in value results from poultry diseases. This loss is reflected in mortality, lower egg production and fertility, and inefficient use of feed. Newcastle disease and pullorum disease, once serious threats to the poultry industry, have been brought under control, but the annual loss from disease probably exceeds 240 million dollars. Lymphomatosis causes the heaviest loss, accounting for more than one-fourth of the total.

About 300 kinds of internal parasites are of economic importance. Some are common and abundant. Others are rare. Internal parasites cut into livestock and poultry production by more than 400 million dollars annually. That is a rough estimate, but probably

it is low, because it does not include many hidden losses. It is difficult or impossible to arrive at an accurate evaluation of the economic loss from internal parasites, which affect production and quality of animal and poultry products and involve waste of feed, labor and equipment, and cost of control, treatment, and eradication.

Internal parasites hit swine hardest of all species; the losses are put at more than 275 million dollars annually. Worms of various kinds caused more than 70 percent of the swine losses from internal parasites. Losses from kidney worms were especially serious.

Internal parasites reduced cattle and sheep production by an annual loss valued at nearly 40 million dollars each, and poultry by more than 45 million dollars.

Insect pests take another big chunk out of potential livestock and poultry income; that loss is set at more than 500 million dollars a year. Economic losses show up in damage to hides and meat, loss in weight and milk production, inefficient utilization of feed, and damage to wool and mohair. Labor and other resources also are expended to combat the pests. Hornflies reduce the potential value of cattle and milk production by an estimated 150 million dollars a year. Damage by cattle grubs to hides, loss in carcass meat, and productivity are believed to reach 100 million dollars annually. Insect damage to sheep may be 20 million dollars a year and to poultry 80 million dollars.

EFFECTIVE CONTROL and eradication of livestock diseases, parasites, and insect pests would contribute to greater productivity of the land resources of the United States. The potential return from millions of acres of cropland and grassland represented by the economic tolls from livestock disease and parasites is a significant part of the national agricultural output. It represents a huge economic loss and waste of agricultural resources each year. The reduction of this loss should be a major objective of research to improve efficiency of agricultural production and increase returns to producers.

A. V. NORDQUIST *is chief of Livestock and Poultry Statistics Branch, Agricultural Estimates Division, Agricultural Marketing Service. He started with the Nebraska office*

of Crop and Livestock Estimates in 1933 and was placed in charge of the livestock and poultry statistical work in 1947. He is a graduate of the University of Montana.

C. H. PALS *is assistant chief of the Meat Inspection Branch, which he joined in 1932. He has the degree of doctor of veterinary medicine from Iowa State College.*

Infectious Diseases Common to Animals and Man

JAMES H. STEELE

ZOONOSES are diseases that are transmitted among animals and from animals to man.

Of more than 200 communicable diseases of animals, one-half are considered infectious to man, and more than 80 are transmitted naturally between vertebrate animals and man.

They are grouped according to their morphological characteristics—that is, viral, rickettsial, bacterial, fungal, protozoal, helminthic, and arthropod-insect.

Many other parasitic diseases of animals have occurred only rarely or on single occasions. Of the 120 parasites found both in animals and man, 76 are rare in man. Some of the latter may occur more commonly than is supposed, but others must be thought of as accidental infections.

Animals also are passive carriers of disease organisms, the most common of which are the *bacilli* of tetanus, gas gangrene, and botulism. Animals also transmit toxins, or chemicals, which may be injurious to persons who eat the meat.

Wild animals and birds are important reservoirs of zoonoses. They may be of even greater concern than domestic animals in some countries.

Among them are wild dogs, wildcats, and rodents.

Rabies is the most serious disease that can be attributed to the dog. The dog, as far as man is concerned, is the major reservoir of rabies. Each year in the United States more than 600,000 persons are bitten by dogs; 5 to 10 percent of the victims have to have anti-rabies vaccine because the biting animal is proved rabid or is suspected of being rabid. Even if the dog is not captured or if for some other reason laboratory examination is not possible immediately, the victim must be given the vaccine.

The cost of rabies in our country exceeds 10 million dollars a year.

In the Western Hemisphere, rabies is a problem in the United States and in Alaska, parts of Canada, Mexico, Central America, and most of South America. The only places free of rabies are eastern Canada, the Northeastern States, some localities in the Northwestern States, some parts of the West Indies, Panama, southern Chile, and Argentina. The elimination of canine rabies in the Americas would save millions of dollars. The same probably can be said for the parts of Europe, Africa, and Asia where canine rabies is enzootic, that is, constantly present but of low incidence.

The control of canine rabies in cities is possible in most of the world if people recognize the problem and believe it can be done.

An effective program to control rabies is based on three principles: Public health education, which is necessary to have public support of the technical phases; vaccination of the resident dog population with an effective canine rabies vaccine; and the elimination of stray and homeless dogs and, sometimes, wild animals.

The success of such a program depends on public support, the experience and training of the technical staff, and the effectiveness of the immunizing agent that is used. The cost of a preventive program is not comparable to the cost of living with the disease. Human treatment costs much more than canine immunization; and if the indirect or inestimable values such as mental anguish and loss of productive time are included there is no logic in the apathy that surrounds this disease in many cities, States, and countries.

MANY INVESTIGATORS consider the dog to be the principal mammalian reservoir of the infections that have been grouped under African tickborne fever (rickettsial). Among the diseases included in this group are Boutonneuse fever, South African tick-bite fever, Kenya typhus, and Brazilian and Colombian spotted fever. Dogs also may harbor the ticks that transmit Rocky Mountain spotted fever. Dogs have been known to develop infection, with signs of disease. Under such circumstances, uninfected ticks could become infected from the host dog and give rise to infected progeny, which would transmit the disease among various animals and to man.

The dog harbors a variety of bacterial diseases that occasionally cause human illness. The most important probably is leptospirosis. *Leptospira canicola* is the causative organism commonly found in dogs, but *L. icterohem-*

orrhagiae, the rat type, has been found in infected dogs and farm animals. The infection is spread through the urine of diseased animals. Various methods of control have been attempted. The infection in canines responds to treatment with streptomycin and penicillin. Vaccines also have seemed to be of value.

The most common fungal disease transferable to man from the dog—and the cat—is ringworm caused by *Microsporum canis*. We must control the disease in pets if we are to stop its spread to man. Because no tried and proved medication is available, each series of cases must be treated according to the experience of veterinarians in the area. It is recommended that people avoid intimate association with pets that may have the disease and that communities cooperate in destroying stray dogs. Those measures are important also in the control of other canine zoonoses.

Creeping eruption, an irritating form of dermatitis, plagues man in regions where the dog and cat hookworm, *Ancylostoma braziliense*, exists. It is common in the Southeastern States and parts of South America, Africa, and Asia. The larvae of *A. braziliense* have the ability, as do all hookworm larvae, to penetrate the skin of the host—or accidental host, i. e., man—in which it causes an inflammatory reaction manifested by intense itching.

In man the invasion of the organism is limited to the skin, in contrast to the more extensive invasion of the human type of hookworm, *Ancylostoma duodenale*. In regions where *A. braziliense* is common, many persons become infected at work and play—at beaches and playgrounds, in gardens, and in the close quarters under buildings where plumbers, carpenters, electricians, and other persons sometimes have to work. Often the soil in such places is contaminated with infected dog and cat feces, and exposure is almost unavoidable.

The problem is serious. In one Southeastern State 8,000 cases were reported in one summer, but that number probably was a fraction of the cases that actually occurred.

Prevention in human beings requires that dogs and cats be barred from all recreational areas. Pet owners should make sure that infected animals are treated with an effective vermifuge. Contamination of gardens, yards, and households thereby can be prevented.

THE INFESTATION by the tapeworm *Echinococcus granulosus* is serious in dogs. Echinococcis is transmitted directly to man by the accidental ingestion of the eggs, which are found in dog feces and which in turn contaminate the immediate vicinity. The infection may sometimes be airborne—the eggs are blown around in dust and thus contaminate food, food utensils, and man himself. The disease is one of the major zoonoses in southern South America, the Mediterranean area, the Middle East, Australia, New Zealand, and parts of Alaska and Canada. Some authorities have estimated that more than 50,000 persons in those areas are in some stage of infection at any time.

Echinococcus granulosus has an interesting life cycle between herbivorous and carnivorous animals. The adult worm inhabits the lower intestines of dogs and other Canidae—wolves, foxes, coyotes, and wild dogs. The eggs are passed in the feces. Herbivora (cattle, sheep, goats, deer, and other grass eaters) become infected through the ingestion of contaminated vegetation. Swine also are frequently infected. The larval form of the infection is found in the herbivorous animals and swine, as in man. The infection in cattle, sheep, and other such animals produces hydatids, or cysts, in the lungs, liver, and other sites. The cysts are filled with fluid and infectious daughter cysts. When a dog or other definitive—final—host ingests cyst-bearing flesh or offal from diseased animals, the germinal tissue develops within 50 to 60 days into a sexually mature tapeworm, thus completing the organism's life cycle.

Echinococcosis is a costly public health problem in areas where it is enzootic. If only one-half of the estimated cases are treated, the cost of medical care runs into tens of millions of dollars. The economic losses due to this disease are also sizable when one considers the mortality among farm animals, loss of production resulting from human illness, and condemnation of meat animals or parts of their carcasses because of infection. An intensive control campaign would save millions of dollars and prevent untold illness and death and contribute to an improved animal husbandry and economy.

Control of hydatid disease is based on the elimination of the infection in dogs and the prevention of reinfection. Both in cities and in rural areas dogs should be kept under control. Generally speaking, in areas where the infection is known to occur, the numbers of dogs should be reduced as far as possible, and people should be discouraged from keeping pets within their homes.

Dogs that must be kept within the home should be examined periodically; if they are found to be infected, they should be treated.

ONE CANINE roundworm, *Toxocara canis*, causes severe and sometimes fatal liver damage in young children.

Other parasitic infections of dogs that cause human disease include various other roundworms, tapeworms, and flukes. Strongyloidiasis has been reported frequently in dogs and man. The dog tapeworm, *Dipylidium caninum*, is acquired by man when he accidentally swallows an infected flea, *Ctenocephalides canis*, the intermediate host. Human infections with flukes are major health problems in many areas of the world. Dogs may have a part in maintaining the life cycle of the fluke. The infection of dogs with *Schistosoma japonicum* has often been reported in the Far East.

Prevention of all these parasitic infections is based on proved hygienic principles, on effective control of dogs, and on veterinary medical care of animals closely associated with man.

This discussion would indicate that the dog is probably the most important animal reservoir of disease as far as man is concerned. Probably it is, because of its intimate association with man and its worldwide distribution. But man is exposed to the diseases of many other animals with which he has daily contact. After the dog, the cow is probably the most important of these animals. Unlike the dog, the products of the cow are the usual means of disease transmission, although contact may also be a route of infection.

BOVINE TUBERCULOSIS is a major zoonosis throughout the world. The disease is encountered frequently in cattle-raising areas of the world except in the United States, Canada, and Scandinavia, where the prevalence of bovine tuberculosis in cattle has been reduced to the point that it is no longer a serious animal problem or a public health problem.

In the United States the incidence in 1953 and 1954 was 0.11 percent. More than 10 million animals of a population of more than 90 million were tested; 10,886 reactors were found. In addition, 1,299 carcasses were found by meat inspectors to have lesions of tuberculosis. As a result of control, the savings in animal products that otherwise would have been condemned in recent years have more than paid for all of the control expenditure.

Besides the economic gains, there is the public health accomplishment— the disappearance of the bovine type of tuberculosis in children and adults. This type of infection in man now is exceedingly rare, according to the reports received by the United States Public Health Service. Only six cases were identified in 1950–1955. Five were in adults—one of whom was a recent immigrant from central Europe. When the disease is found in adults, the question can always be raised as to whether the infection is a reactivation of an old lesion. Only one case in a child was reported—on a farm in the Midwest, where all cattle were found to be infected. This latter experience emphasizes the importance of constant surveillance and periodic retesting to prevent reestablishment of the disease in areas where eradication has been accomplished.

The eradication of bovine tuberculosis is an animal and public health objective that is attainable in any area willing to support a program. The salient principles of an animal tuberculosis campaign are tuberculin testing of all cattle, removal from the herd of all reactors, and their consignment to slaughter. It is also important that when, on inspection, tuberculous carcasses are found in the abattoirs and the packinghouses an investigation be undertaken to determine their place of origin. All the cattle on the premises to which an infected animal is traced should be tested.

The question is often asked whether the Bacillus Calmette-Guerin vaccine (BCG) has value in the control of bovine tuberculosis. Information available in 1956 did not lend support to its use in the control of animal tuberculosis.

Investigators in California reported that BCG vaccine conferred enough resistance to protect against the fatal effects of virulent tubercle bacilli; the chief protective effect of BCG seemed to be retardation of the extension of tuberculosis infection. They also reported that the vaccine may be of some value under conditions where an eradication program appears to be hopeless.

Studies by F. M. Hayes, C. M. Haring, and J. Traum, at the University of California, on swine yielded no evidence that BCG injections were of value in the control of tuberculosis in swine. M. M. Kaplan, of World Health Organization, in a report in 1948 stated that repeated injections of BCG confer a high degree of protection in calves up to 2 years of age and that thereafter immunity declines, despite repeated inoculations. He also pointed out that BCG vaccination is worthless in adult animals. Preliminary research reports from Europe indicate that isonicotinic acid, which has been so valuable in treating human infection, is of dubious value in the control of bovine tuberculosis among calves.

CATTLE are one of the chief reservoirs of brucellosis, but goats, sheep, and swine are also noteworthy sources of this disease as far as man is concerned.

Brucellosis, like tuberculosis, is worldwide and has caused serious economic losses and public health problems wherever it has been found. The losses are incalculable. Department of Agriculture officials estimated in 1949 that annual losses in the United States are about 100 million dollars. Authorities who discussed this problem at the First Pan American Veterinary Congress estimated that there may be as many as 100,000 human cases in the Western Hemisphere.

Brucellosis is both an occupational and a public health problem. It will continue to take its toll of human health unless steps are taken to combat it. It has to be eliminated in animals if it is to be ended in man. In cattle that is not an impossible task; there are excellent diagnostic procedures—the blood serum agglutination test and the milk-ring test. The tests have been proved by time. They are used extensively throughout the world. An animal that is identified by test as a positive reactor should be moved to slaughter as soon as possible. Since most reactors are shedders of disease organisms, to hold a reactor in a herd is to invite economic disaster and spread the infection to man and other animals. The development of Strain 19 *Brucella* vaccine for calves has advanced the control and eradication of brucellosis.

The Scandinavian countries have had outstanding success in their eradication programs. Finland and Norway have eradicated the disease. Sweden is reported to have eradicated it in most of the country. The program in Denmark has progressed rapidly and she hopes to eliminate brucellosis in the next few years.

Swine brucellosis is both a serious public health and animal health problem in some communities in the United States. The best control procedure today is to slaughter the herd, clean up the premises, and allow a few months interval before disease-free animals are brought onto the establishment. Recent reports from Denmark state that the European hare is the reservoir of the Danish type of swine brucellosis. In Denmark the disease in swine is controlled by herd slaughter.

Many localities in the United States and Canada have reduced the incidence of brucellosis so that it no longer takes its costly toll of animals and man. The number of human cases dropped from an estimated 10,709 in the United States in 1949 to fewer than 2,000 in 1955. Brucellosis can be controlled and eliminated in areas where people are convinced that its elimination is a worthwhile objective. The effort is costly, but, as the Norwegian authorities have stated, the benefits from resulting increased production can pay for the program in a short time.

MANY OTHER ZOONOSES OF CATTLE should be cited. To mention a few: Cowpox, milkers' nodules, Rift Valley fever, and vesicular stomatitis are viral disease problems of various continents; Q-fever, a rickettsial disease, is commonly found in cattle in widely separated regions; anthrax, leptospirosis, salmonellosis, streptococcus and staphylococcus infections, and vibriosis are bacterial diseases of import. Ringworm of cattle is known to be readily communicable to man. The African trypanosomiasis, a common disease of cattle, is carried to man by the tsetse fly. Among the parasitic infections of cattle that affect human health are beef tapeworm, *Taenia saginata*, and the fluke infections caused by *Fasciola hepatica* and *Schistosoma japonicum*.

Nor should the importance of other domestic and wild animal reservoirs and vectors of disease be overlooked in an outline like this.

For 4,000 years the horse has been close to man. Glanders, the most important disease of Equidae to which man is susceptible, has been eradicated in many parts of the world, but it is still a problem in some areas of the Eastern Hemisphere.

Hogs are probably susceptible to a greater number of diseases than any other domestic animal, and many of their ills are transmissible to man. Among them are brucellosis, leptospirosis, salmonellosis, trypanosomiasis, trichinosis, and cystercercosis. Trichinosis and cystercercosis have been recognized as health problems in many parts of the world and supposedly are the basis of the first food sanitation codes.

Sheep and goats are susceptible to nearly all the diseases of cattle, in addition to a few which are host specific. Of these, probably the most important to man's health is brucellosis, which is found wherever goats are kept and frequently is enzootic among sheep. Sore mouth, or contagious ecthyma, is a problem in the major sheep-raising areas of the world and frequently causes infection in man. Q-fever appears to be an important communicable infection of sheep and goats in southern Europe and western United States. It causes no signs of illness in animals studied in the United States and only occasionally produces clinical signs of infection in man.

The cat often enjoys intimate contact with the human family, an association which allows him to expose man to his maladies. Many of the diseases of the dog are commonly found in cats. Rabies is the most serious of these—a cat with furious rabies is a serious menace.

Cat scratch fever is a disease entity about which little is known. Fifty percent or more of human cases follow cat scratch, but nothing is known concerning the etiological agent, how this agent affects the cat, or how it is transmitted among animals.

Among the avian populations, wild and domestic, are a number of diseases that are transmissible to man. Most important is salmonellosis, a disease caused by bacteria of the genus *Salmonella*. It has the widest distribution of any of the zoonoses, both in area range and in host range. The avians—and many mammals—are hosts to these organisms, which in humans cause food poisoning, diarrhea, enteritis, and occasionally septicemia. Next most important is psittacosis, which apparently is worldwide, especially among parakeets and parrots. The infection is common in wild birds, especially in Australia, South Africa, and parts of Central America, South America, and North America. In recent years psittacosis has been reported in turkeys as well as ducks and chickens. Turkeys sometimes develop an acute disease which may spread to man. A closely related organism causing disease also has been found in cattle, sheep, and cats.

The arthropod-borne encephalitides also have been linked to the bird population. Many authorities believe that the causative virus has its reservoir in wild birds and that mosquitoes serve as transmitters from the avian host to man and other mammals. This chain of transmission has been demonstrated in studies on the arthropod-borne encephalitides in North America.

Rats and mice are historically the most important reservoir of zoonoses. They carried plague into Europe in the Middle Ages. In many parts of the world they continue to maintain plague as a threat to civilization. Murine typhus fever has been a problem in some parts of the Western Hemisphere; it is thought to be under control, but it may break out in epidemic proportions if constant surveillance is not maintained. The rat has been described as the principal reservoir of leptospirosis, although many other animals (including the dog, as previously mentioned) are known to be sources of the disease. Illness caused by leptospira, of the rat type, *L. icterohaemorrhagiae*, is the most serious form in human beings.

Two other diseases reach human beings from rodents only. Rat bite fever is caused by *Spirella minus*, which reaches man directly through the bite of a rat. Rickettsialpox is caused by *Rickettsia akari*, an organism harbored by the mouse and transmitted to man by a mite vector.

A DISCUSSION of the zoonoses of wild animals that affect man can include every disease that has been mentioned thus far.

Probably the most important is African trypanosomiasis, or sleeping sickness. Because of this disease, an area of grazing land 4 million square miles in extent in central Africa remains economically stagnant.

Bat rabies and jungle yellow fever are the most important sylvatic zoonoses in the Western Hemisphere. Because there is little hope of eliminating them, constant efforts are necessary to prevent their spread to domestic animals or man. Rabies in other sylvatic creatures including the wolf, the fox, and the skunk is a problem of increasing importance in North America. Tularemia has its primary reservoir in wild rabbits and rodents in the United States and Canada. Rocky Mountain spotted fever most likely has sylvatic animal reservoirs. Recent studies in southeast Asia, the Middle East, and the United States indicate that leptospirosis is widely distributed in nature.

IN CLOSING, it would be amiss not to point out that the animal kingdom will continue to influence the course of civilization. The availability of food and products of animal origin are basic needs of man, as they have been since the dawn of his creation. Diseases of animals have always affected man, either directly or indirectly. Animal diseases communicable to man are a direct threat to his health; the loss of animal production immediately affects the welfare of the producer and a chain reaction may set in at that point that carries to the world markets. Seldom does a year pass that a new disease problem is not recognized among domestic animals and birds. Often these diseases are not communicable to man when first recognized but within a few years sporadic cases of similar illness in man are reported.

The constant challenge of nature to animal health oftentimes is also a challenge to man's health. For this reason, maintenance of high standards of animal health is essential to the public health of any country or continent.

JAMES H. STEELE *in 1949 became veterinary director of the Communicable Disease Center, United States Public Health Service, Department of Health, Education, and Welfare. He is a graduate of Michigan State University and holds the degrees of doctor of veterinary medicine and master of public health from Harvard University. He is a consultant to the World Health Organization as well as to many national committees and scientific associations.*

For further reading:
American Public Health Association: *Control of Communicable Diseases in Man*, 8th edition, New York. 1955.
L. F. Badger: *Rocky Mountain Spotted Fever: Susceptibility of the Dog and Sheep to the Virus*, Public Health Reports, volume 48, pages 791–795. 1933.
C. M. Haring, J. Traum, F. M. Hayes, and B. S. Henry: *Vaccination of Calves Against Tuberculosis With Calmette-Guerin Culture, BCG*, Hilgardia, volume 4, number 12, pages 307–394. 1930.
F. M. Hayes, C. M. Haring, and J. Traum: *Vaccination of Swine Against Tuberculosis With Calmette-Guerin Culture, BCG*, Hilgardia, volume 7, number 6, pages 235–261. 1932.
J. H. Steele: *Summary of Observations at the First Pan American Veterinary Congress, Lima, Peru*, Veterinary Medicine, volume 47, number 3, pages 103–105. 1952.
J. H. Steele: *The Present Status of Bovine-type Human Tuberculosis in the United States*. Proceedings of the United States Livestock Sanitary Association, 58th Annual Meeting, pages 207–211. 1954.
N. R. Stoll: *This Wormy World*. Journal of Parasitology, volume 33, number 1, pages 1–18. 1947.
United States Livestock Sanitary Special Committee: *What Is Known About Brucellosis*, United States Livestock Sanitary Association, 32 pages. 1949.
World Health Organization: *Joint WHO/ FAO Export Group on Zoonoses—Report on the First Session*, World Health Organization Technical Report Series Number 40, 47 pages, Geneva. 1951.

Parasites That Attack Animals and Man

BENJAMIN SCHWARTZ

SOME of the parasites that occur in animals also attack people.

Some have to develop in an animal or in two different animals before they can invade human beings. Man then is the definitive, or final, host. He usually acquires the parasites by eating the intermediate animal hosts or (if they are small insects) by swallowing them accidentally. For some parasites, human beings are the intermediate hosts and animals are the final hosts.

Even the few parasites that live only in man are related closely to others that live in animals. Farm animals, dogs and cats, and rats and mice contribute to man's burden of parasites. That burden tends to become lighter as our civilization advances, however, largely because the sanitary barriers that have come into existence impede the spread of parasites from parts of the world where standards of sanitation and hygiene are imperfect.

Some of the major parasites that man shares with animals are discussed here. The examples illustrate that parasites can be acquired by eating infected food of animal origin and by being in close contact with animals that harbor the kinds of pests that can be transmitted to human beings.

THE BEEF TAPEWORM derives its name from the fact that in its immature, or cystic, stage it lives in the flesh of cattle. The adult (or strobilate) tapeworm, which arises from the cystic stage, lives in the intestine of man, where it can attain a length of 40 feet or more. An infested person usually harbors only one tapeworm.

The adult tapeworm is whitish in color. It is a chain of hundreds of proglottids, or segments, which are anchored to the intestinal wall by four cup-shaped suckers on its head. A unique feature is that the head lacks the microscopic hooks that most tapeworms have. It is therefore known also as the unarmed tapeworm of man.

The immature stage, known as a bladderworm, or cysticercus, occurs mainly in the muscles, including the heart, and in other internal organs of cattle. It is grayish white. It is about one-fifth to three-fifths of an inch long and about half as wide. It has thin walls and contains a fluid into which the head of the future worm is pushed, just as the tip of a finger might be pushed into a glove.

Before the middle of the 19th century it was not known that a bladderworm was the intermediate stage of a strobilate tapeworm. Bladderworms were regarded as distinct parasites without sex organs and were therefore given scientific names of their own. The name given to the bladderworm of the beef tapeworm was *Cysticercus bovis*, which no longer has any scientific validity. Parasitologists retain that name in their writings for convenience in differentiating the bladderworm from the adult tapeworm. The valid scientific name of the unarmed, or beef, tapeworm of man in all stages of its development is *Taenia saginata*.

The life history of the beef tapeworm involves an alternation of hosts. Man, the definitive host, discharges the ripe, or gravid, segments with the excreta, or the segments may pass out independently and be discovered in the bed linen of infected individuals. Once outside the body, the gravid segment begins to disintegrate and release the eggs it contains.

A single gravid segment may contain several thousand eggs. Several segments may become gravid and be expelled almost every day for several years by one tapeworm carrier. If the segments reach pastures, barnyards, feed lots, and other places where cattle graze or feed, the animals may swallow some of the eggs and become infected with bladderworms.

Inside the body of an animal, the microscopic egg hatches, and the tiny larva bores into the intestinal wall. From there it reaches the blood stream and is carried to all parts of the body. It localizes mainly in the flesh and heart. The parasite develops rather slowly and becomes a bladderworm in about 2 to 4 months.

A person who happens to eat raw or rare beef that harbors a single live bladderworm can become infected with a tapeworm. The tapeworm head inside the bladder is already fully developed. In the stomach it becomes evaginated, or everted, and the bladder wall is digested. When it gets into the intestine, the head of the future tapeworm attaches itself to the intestinal wall and grows by producing more and more segments. The newly formed segments are the ones right below the head. New ones, as they form, push the older ones down, so that the first segment to be formed comes to occupy the lowest position in the chain that constitutes the strobilate tapeworm.

About 10 to 12 weeks after the bladderworm has been swallowed, the oldest segment becomes gravid and detached from the rest of the chain. The others follow this pattern in rapid succession. The process continues as long as the tapeworm remains in the intestine. The affected individual meanwhile passes many thousands of eggs with the detached segments nearly every day.

The tapeworm carrier who happens to live on a farm, ranch, cattle-feeding establishment, or wherever he has contact with cattle is the source of infection for them—especially if sanitary facilities are primitive. The carrier might deposit waste matter on a pasture or in a place where wind and rain can disperse it on a pasture or feed lot or wash it down to ponds and sloughs from which cattle drink.

"Beef measles" is the name applied to the condition in beef infected with these bladderworms. The economic loss from the condemnation of cattle on account of "measles" at times may be considerable, even though the percentage of infested cattle is small. About 16,500 to 27,000 beef carcasses were found annually in 1948–1954 to be infected with bladderworms out of a total annual slaughter of 12 million to 15 million head and 5.5 million to 7.5 million calves.

Infected carcasses in which the bladderworms are readily found are condemned as unfit for human food and consigned to the tank. If one dead or degenerate cyst, usually located in the heart, is discovered, the carcass is passed for food after the cyst is removed. Cattle carcasses that have a somewhat greater infestation also may be passed for food after the few visible cysts are cut away. Such carcasses, however, must be refrigerated at temperatures and for periods known to be fatal to all the parasites, or they must be thoroughly cooked at a temperature of 140° F. Such cooking also kills the parasites.

The control of "beef measles" will control the beef tapeworm in man. Detection by physicians of human carriers of tapeworm, especially those who live in rural areas, and prompt treatment to remove the parasites, however, will end the hazard of infection of cattle with bladderworms. In simpler terms: Improvement in rural areas in ways of disposing of human wastes will prevent cattle from becoming infected; that, in turn, will ultimately eliminate the carrying of tapeworms by people.

THE PORK TAPEWORM, *Taenia solium*, also lives in the human intestine. It is a long, whitish, strobilate tapeworm. It resembles the beef tapeworm in most respects, but it is usually shorter and is about 2.5 to 5 feet long. Another difference is that the pork tapeworm has a double row of tiny hooks, besides the four suckers, on its head. The pork tapeworm is also known as the armed tapeworm of man.

The cystic stage of the pork tapeworm, known for convenience only as *Cysticercus cellulosae*, is like that of the beef tapeworm. The bladderworms occur in swine, but they also can live in man. They occur in various parts of the body. They tend to localize in the muscular part of the diaphragm, the loin muscles, heart, the jaw muscles, muscles between the ribs, muscles of the hind legs and shoulders, brain, eyes, liver, lungs, and other organs.

The pork tapeworm alternates between man and the hog in its developmental cycle. Swine become infected by swallowing, with feed or water, the tapeworm eggs freed from the gravid segments passed in the excreta of a human carrier. Man, in turn, acquires the strobilate tapeworm by eating raw or incompletely cooked pork infected with the bladderworms.

Persons harboring the pork tapeworm in the intestine could get tapeworm eggs on their hands. The hands might transfer the eggs to the mouth and thus pave the way for an infection of the muscles and the heart, brain, and eyes. The pork bladderworm in the brain of man is known to produce symptoms like those of epilepsy.

Very few persons in this country harbor the pork tapeworm.

Hogs so infected also are rare in the United States, but they might harbor thousands of bladderworms in their organs and muscles. Only 11 infected swine carcasses were found by Federal inspectors in more than 57 million carcasses inspected in 1953. Only four such infected carcasses were found in 1954 in more than 50 million inspected. Federal meat inspectors condemn as unfit for human food all hog carcasses in which are bladderworms.

We can prevent bladderworms in swine and the pork tapeworm in man by not eating raw or undercooked pork and by improving rural sanitation.

THE HYDATID TAPEWORM, *Echinococcus granulosus*, lives as an adult parasite in the intestines of dogs and related wild carnivores and as a larva in man, cattle, sheep, goats, swine, horses, and wild animals. The larva localizes in the liver, lungs, spleen, kidney, brain, and other organs.

The adult tapeworm in the intestine of a dog or other carnivore is about one-eighth to one-fourth inch long and about one-eightieth inch wide. It attaches itself to the wall of the intestine by four cup-shaped suckers on its head, which also has small hooks. Behind the head and neck are two segments. The second segment contains the eggs, which start new infections.

Only rarely has the adult hydatid tapeworm been found in dogs in this country—perhaps because most dogs that have been autopsied were from pounds in cities, where they had little chance of acquiring the tapeworm. Country dogs could more easily become infected by eating offal from unsupervised slaughterhouses.

The larval stage of the hydatid tapeworm is the largest of its kind. The adult tapeworm is the smallest. The larva is several inches to almost a foot in diameter. Its size alone would make it unusually dangerous to man, because it localizes in the liver and lungs. Persons so affected require surgery.

Human beings acquire hydatids by fouling their hands in some way with the excreta of infected dogs or by picking up food or by swallowing food or water contaminated with the tapeworm eggs. Petting an infected dog is one way of contaminating the hands; dogs often roll in excreta, which may contain the eggs. The eggs hatch into larvae when they reach the human intestine. These larvae can penetrate the intestinal wall. They enter small blood vessels and so reach various organs and tissues, where they develop rather slowly and attain a diameter of about one-half inch or so after several months. Many tapeworm heads occur in a single hydatid cyst. Each head can develop into an adult tapeworm when the cyst or part of it is swallowed by a dog or other final host.

Human infections with hydatids are rare in this country but are common elsewhere, especially in Iceland, Australia, New Zealand, Argentina, and Uruguay. Campaigns to arouse the public to the danger of acquiring hydatids from dogs have been organized in some countries.

Nearly 12,000 livers from more than 50 million cattle slaughtered under Federal meat inspection and 1,133 calf livers out of 5.5 million inspected in 1937–1942 had hydatid cysts. We lack precise figures on the extent of infection of swine, but there is evidence that in some parts of the country hogs are frequently infected.

Adequate inspection could control the hydatid tapeworm. The condemnation and proper disposal of parts of affected carcasses, a practice enforced by Federal and other competent inspectors, breaks a link in the life cycle of this dangerous parasite. When inspection is lacking or is imperfect, discarded lungs and livers of affected animals might be eaten by dogs or wild carnivores and so spread the parasite.

THE FISH (OR BROAD) TAPEWORM, *Diphyllobothrium latum*, is a human parasite that spends part of its early life—the plerocercoid stage—in some species of fresh-water fish. It is rather common in man in some European countries. It has been found in man and animals in an area that extends across the Great Lakes and the upper Mississippi Basin, into Manitoba, and almost to the Rockies.

The adult tapeworm in man may attain a length of 25 feet or more. It lives also in the small intestine of dogs, cats, foxes, and other flesh-eating, warm-blooded animals.

The eggs, microscopic in size, are eliminated from the ripe segment of the tapeworm into the host's intestine. The eggs reach the outside with the excreta and continue their further development only if they get into fresh water. There they hatch. The tiny larvae develop minute appendages that propel them through the water.

The larvae continue to develop in certain copepods, or fresh-water fleas, which are the first intermediate host. Certain fresh-water fish, in which the tapeworm can reach a still further stage of development, become infected in turn by swallowing the infected copepods. The pike, the walleyed pike, the sand pike, and other lake fishes are therefore the second intermediate hosts.

Human beings, the final hosts, acquire the fish tapeworm by eating raw, nearly raw, cold-smoked, or salted fish in which are live plerocercoids. Carnivorous animals become infected by eating infected fish.

Presumably the fish tapeworm was introduced into North America by the immigrants from northern Europe, where this tapeworm is common. Eggs of the tapeworm passed with their excreta into lakes.

One infected person may discharge a million tapeworm eggs a day.

Furthermore, since dogs, cats, foxes, and other wild carnivores also are definitive hosts, links have been added to the chain that conveys this parasite from several final hosts to water fleas, with which our lakes are teeming; from there to suitable species of lake fish; and finally back to man and other mammals that eat raw fish.

OTHER TAPEWORMS living in animals also can be transmitted to man. One tapeworm from dogs and two from rats and mice are especially important because they are more likely to be found in children than adults.

THE DWARF TAPEWORM, *Hymenolepis nana*, is about 2 inches long. It occurs in the intestine of rats and mice all over the world. It is more common in warm countries. In the Southeastern States, about 10 percent of the schoolchildren whose excreta was examined for some evidence of parasitic infections were infected.

The life cycle of the dwarf tapeworm is unusual in that no intermediate host is required. Rats and mice become infected by eating feed or drinking water contaminated with the droppings of other infected rodents. The droppings contain the tapeworm eggs.

Children and adults become infected, apparently with a human strain of this parasite, by soiling their hands or contaminating their food with human excreta that contains the tapeworm eggs. Whether persons commonly acquire the tapeworm from rodents is doubtful, but almost certainly that could happen at times.

THE RAT TAPEWORM, *Hymenolepsis diminuta*, also occurs in the household rodents. It is much larger than the species we named. It also is widely distributed, but it is less common in man than the dwarf tapeworm.

Some insects, including fleas and other external parasites of rodents and some that infest cereals, can serve as the intermediate hosts. Human beings acquire the rat tapeworm by accidentally swallowing an infected intermediate host.

THE CARNIVORE TAPEWORM, *Dipylidium canimum*, occurs in the intestine of dogs, cats, wildcats, jaguars, foxes, and other carnivores. It also may occur in children and less often in adults. It is localized in the small intestine of its final hosts.

Its life cycle involves intermediate hosts, including the dog flea, the cat flea, and the human flea. The insect becomes infected while still a larva by ingesting the tapeworm eggs passed with the droppings of infected carnivores. The final host, including man, acquires the tapeworm by swallowing the infected intermediate fleas. That can easily happen when children fondle dogs or cats that harbor the tapeworms or are infested with fleas containing the intermediate stages of the parasite.

TRICHINAE (*Trichinella spiralis*) and trichinosis, the disease these roundworms cause, are gotten by people from eating the uncooked flesh of an animal that harbors the parasites. Animals become infected in the same way. Only carnivorous and omnivorous animals can transmit trichinae to man and to one another. Of the animals slaughtered for human food in the United States, none is carnivorous, and only the hog has omnivorous habits. Therefore, pork is the common source of human trichinosis. The only other source in this country is the bear, the flesh of which is eaten occasionally.

Swine become infected by eating offal or garbage containing scraps of raw infected pork or by eating infected rats, mice, or other animals that harbor trichinae. Rats, mice, and other small animals, in their turn, acquire trichinae by eating raw infected pork or other infected meat in garbage or elsewhere, or through cannibalism. Likewise dogs, cats, and wild carnivores acquire trichinae by eating the raw flesh of animals already infected. As long as trichinae exist in any animals likely to be eaten by hogs, man runs the danger of acquiring trichinosis.

The developmental cycle of trichinae is:

As the meat is digested in the stomach of a person, a hog, or other animal, the microscopic worms lodged therein are freed from the minute cysts, or sacs, in which they are enclosed. The worms then pass rapidly into the intestine, where they become localized by boring part way into its wall. They become sexually mature in about 2 days. Following mating, the worms continue to grow and attain their maximum size 4 or 5 days later, or a week or so after they have been swallowed.

The full-grown female worms are between one-eighth and one-sixth inch long. The males are half that long. The fertilized eggs are retained in the uterus, where they develop and hatch. They finally escape from it as larvae. The larvae may continue to be born for several weeks. Afterwards the adult parasites die and pass out of the intestine.

The newborn larvae, of which several hundred may be deposited by one female worm, pass into the blood stream and to all parts of the body. About 250 of these minute parasites measure an inch. They reach various tissues and organs, but they become localized mostly in the voluntary muscles or flesh by penetrating the muscle fibers. There they grow. Gradually they become surrounded by a thin capsule, or cyst, in which they remain dormant until the flesh is eaten by another animal. The completion of their life cycle therefore depends on the eating of the flesh of an infected animal by another animal.

Whether one can see the symptoms of trichinosis and whether symptoms develop at all depend on the number of trichinae that have been eaten with infected pork or other meat. If slightly infected pork is eaten in small or moderate amounts, no symptoms (or mild, vague symptoms of short duration) may be apparent. Regardless of the severity of the symptoms, however, they are due to the activities of the parasites as they grow in the intestine of a person or animal and deposit their broods of larvae, which penetrate the muscles and become encysted in them.

An affected person may become nauseated, vomit, develop a diarrhea, and suffer from abdominal pains. Sometimes those symptoms are partly or entirely absent. When the larvae are distributed throughout the body by the blood and penetrate the muscles, the affected individual may have severe muscular pain, and the muscles may become swollen, hard, and tense. Moving the eyes and the tongue and chewing, breathing, swallowing, and other muscular movements become painful. These symptoms may become more pronounced as the larvae continue to grow within the muscle fibers and become enclosed in cysts. New symptoms may appear, and the fever, which set in earlier in the course of the disease, often becomes more pronounced. Recovery from a severe attack is slow. Sometimes the affected individual may die 5 or 6 weeks after eating the infected meat.

Routine inspection of hogs will not lead to the discovery of those that harbor trichinae. In some European countries, especially in countries where people commonly eat raw pork, microscopic inspection of pork for trichinae is part of the meat-inspection procedure. Such inspection, however, cannot guarantee the detection of all infected hog carcasses. If the hog is lightly infected, the examination under the microscope of even numerous small samples of meat may fail to show any trichinae. The meat might be dangerous if large amounts of it are eaten raw or are not cooked or cured enough.

About 66 of every 10,000 hogs in the Corn Belt contain trichinae. They are so lightly infected, however, that it is doubtful that anyone would acquire a sufficient number of trichinae to get trichinosis unless he ate large amounts of raw or inadequately cooked pork. The incidence of trichinae of farm-raised hogs between 1933 and 1939 was nearly 1 percent. Early in this century it was about 1.5 percent— evidence of progress in reducing the extent of the infection in farm-raised hogs.

In garbage-fed hogs from various parts of the country, however, the incidence of trichinae in 1933-1939 was nearly 6 percent. In Massachusetts it was a little more than 10 percent. In 1949-1952, pigs from garbage-feeding establishments in Boston, New York, and Philadelphia showed an incidence of slightly more than 11 percent.

In 1954 and 1955, following the enactment by most States of legislation requiring the cooking of garbage to be fed to swine in order to prevent the spread of the disease vesicular exanthema, there were indications of a marked decline in infection with trichinae of hogs fed cooked garbage. It was still too early, however, to say whether the decline would continue and whether other possible sources of infection, such as rats and mice, also would be affected by cooking garbage.

Human trichinosis has been of considerable concern to physicians and public health workers in this country for many decades. The disease is not among the major maladies of man, but it is of considerable importance from the standpoint of human health. Trichinosis is a serious, painful, and sometimes a fatal disease of man. It is easily preventable by following the simple advice never to eat raw or incompletely cooked pork—but the fact remains trichinosis continues to occur from time to time.

From 1842, when the first case of human trichinosis was diagnosed in the United States, up to 1915, when all the known cases of the disease were summarized, the total number of recorded cases in this country was about 1,500. A search of all the reported cases in 1935 showed that the number was about 5,500. The average number of cases reported by the United States Public Health Service between 1937 and 1951 was about 350 a year. Medical authorities have assumed that not all cases of trichinosis have been correctly diagnosed and reported. Trichinosis has been confused in the past with typhoid fever, undulant fever, and other diseases.

The greatest number of trichinosis cases has been found on the Atlantic and Pacific seaboards, where the practice of feeding garbage to swine has become a sizable enterprise.

Besides cases diagnosed as such by physicians, people sometimes have had undiagnosed infections which apparently produced no symptoms during life. Since 1931, when such undiagnosed infections were reported as a result of studies made in Rochester, N. Y., on 700 persons who had died from various causes other than trichinosis, similar studies have been made in thousands of autopsies. An average of 1 of 6 persons whose muscles were examined after death by special methods showed evidence of having become infected with these worms sometime during life. Practically nothing, however, in their medical histories showed that they had ever had trichinosis.

Federal meat inspection does not guarantee that fresh pork passed as safe for human consumption is free of trichinae for the reason that there is no known practical system of inspection by which this can be done. The inspection requirements afford the consumer of ready-to-eat pork products ample protection against trichinosis, however. Among the foods that would be sources of human trichinosis without this protection are cooked hams, various classes of processed hams, frankfurters, salami, and other types of smoked sausages, as well as other pork-containing products designed to be eaten by the consumer without additional cooking. The safeguards that make those products safe include special refrigeration, special heating, or special curing. The processing, which is prescribed separately for each type of ready-to-eat product, is based on rigid, extensive experiments. Thorough cooking of fresh pork is the most effective safeguard that can be recommended to prevent trichinosis.

OTHER ROUNDWORMS of domestic animals are transmissible to man. Two are of special importance. One is a hookworm that can cause a severe skin irritation. The other is the large intestinal roundworm, which as an immature worm has migratory habits that are injurious to its host.

Certain hookworm larvae can cause a skin disease known as creeping eruption by penetrating the human skin. The principal offenders are the larvae of the hookworm known as *Ancylostoma braziliense*, a parasite of the intestine of dogs and cats.

Infection of man usually occurs on beaches where the hookworm larvae, present on sand or soil, can make direct contact with the skin. Having penetrated it, the larvae move slowly for weeks or months under the skin, form tortuous tunnels therein, irritate the tissues, and cause intense itching. If one scratches the place, the skin may become infected.

Creeping eruption is quite common in persons who visit beaches in the

South and other persons whose work brings them into contact with sand or soil containing the hookworm larvae. The larvae develop from eggs deposited on the soil or sand with the droppings of infected dogs or cats.

THE INTESTINAL ROUNDWORM, *Ascaris lumbricoides*, is a parasite of man. It is structurally and in other ways indistinguishable from a closely related species that occurs in pigs. The two parasites cannot be told apart, but each type apparently prefers its own host in which to grow to maturity. While growing up, however, the pig roundworm can also live in man, at least for a time. It invades the liver, lungs, and other organs.

Its microscopic eggs are deposited with the manure of infected pigs. The eggs develop to the infective stage in about 2 weeks. When they are swallowed by susceptible pigs or accidentally by man, the eggs hatch in the alimentary canal, and the larvae are carried by the blood to the liver, lungs, and other organs. Only those that reach the lungs can get back to the intestine—by moving up the windpipe, reaching the back of the mouth, and being swallowed a second time.

A child or an adult could swallow pig ascarid eggs by contaminating the hands with soil in which the eggs are present or by eating food or swallowing water so contaminated. Even though the parasites may not mature in the human intestine, they can do much damage while wandering as larvae through the internal organs, especially if many of them do so at the same time.

ESCAPE FROM PARASITES altogether is a goal that civilized man is attaining gradually.

Primitive man probably was beset by numerous insects and related creatures that pierced his skin to draw his blood and injected into it disabling and death-dealing microscopic parasites. He was tortured, moreover, by hookworms and other vicious marauders that anchored themselves to the lining of the small intestine. Migrating roundworms, including larvae which hardly leave an organ of the body untouched, also were part of the parasite burden he bore. He nourished huge tapeworms, which he acquired during feasts after a successful hunt. To this day internal parasites are threats to health in countries in Africa, Asia, and South America.

The devitalizing effects of internal parasites deprived primitive man of much of the energy he needed in his struggle with the forces of Nature. In fact, man's struggle against parasites undoubtedly was, and in some countries still is, an important aspect of his struggle for existence.

AS KNOWLEDGE concerning parasites and how to circumvent their attacks accumulated, especially since the middle of the 19th century, civilized man has been gradually freeing himself of this threat to health. In the United States and other advanced countries, the march of parasites has been interrupted to a large extent by sanitary walls that are being erected to impede their progress. Sanitary plumbing, meat inspection, improvements in livestock sanitation on the farm, improved standards of living, and progress in personal hygiene are among the barriers that are cutting the lifeline between parasites and their human hosts.

Much still remains to be done to sustain the barriers already constructed and to erect new ones. However strong our sanitary walls may be, they can crumble, especially in times of stress, unless they are steadily supported. We must not relax our efforts, therefore, but continue the unrelenting pressure against animal parasites transmissible to man—wherever they maintain a foothold.

BENJAMIN SCHWARTZ *became staff assistant and consultant in parasitology in the Animal Disease and Parasite Research Branch of the Agricultural Research Service in 1954. He has been engaged in parasitological research since 1915.*

PREVENTION

AND TREATMENT

OF DISEASES

basic principles

Causes of Disease

H. W. SCHOENING, BENJAMIN SCHWARTZ, E. F. KNIPLING,
AND AUBREY M. LEE

BACTERIA and viruses enter an animal's body through the skin and the organs of breathing, digestion, and sex. They may multiply, attack the tissues, and produce disease.

Or they may not: The body makes strenuous efforts to repel the invaders.

Two forces wage a ceaseless struggle—the disease-producing agent and the animal itself, the host.

If the infecting agent is to invade the tissues of a host successfully, it must have enough virulence to overcome the body defenses. It must be able also to multiply actively, thereby producing a disease process, or to survive in an inactive state, the carrier stage, until conditions are right for multiplication or until it escapes from the host and becomes infectious to other animals.

The host is protected within limits by a barrier known as immunity or resistance. Resistance is relative. It varies considerably among individual animals. In some animals it may be quite strong; in others, weak or lacking.

The infective agent is influenced greatly by its surroundings within or outside the animal host. Its invading ability is determined largely by its environment. Certain species of animals are highly resistant to certain types of infection. The resistance of cattle to glanders, a disease of horses, is an example. In the species susceptible to a specific infection, however, there is a wide variation in susceptibility and resistance among individuals.

Resistance—immunity—to a disease process may be built up in certain animals to an appreciable extent by natural contact with limited amounts of infection in the field and also by artificial procedures, such as vaccination. And to the same vaccination procedure, there is wide variation in the immunity response of individual animals.

If the infecting agent overcomes the body's defenses, the host animal acquires an infection. We say that such an animal has become sick or diseased. Although diseased animals are often seen on farms, it is difficult to state with scientific precision what disease really is.

One definition of disease is that it is the opposite of health.

Health may be defined as that state of an animal in which all of its vital processes—digestion, respiration, blood circulation, locomotion, and all other life activities—function together harmoniously. When this state prevails, the animal is properly adjusted to its surroundings.

Almost any disturbance in the finely adjusted balance that constitutes health may lead to disease. If the disturbance is severe, symptoms of the imbalance usually become evident. Rapid breathing, fever, coughing, diarrhea or constipation, listlessness, unsteady gait or other nervous manifestations, and other disturbances may be observed.

The symptoms of disease may be accompanied by certain structural changes, known as lesions, in the organs or tissues involved in the disease process. The lesions may be visible, or they may be so minute that they can be detected by a pathologist only with the aid of a microscope.

We do not know just what makes one animal more resistant to infection than another. It may be that a number of factors—hereditary, physiological, nutritional, managerial—are involved, singly or in combination.

BACTERIA, or germs, are microscopic organisms of various types and shapes. They are found everywhere in nature. Some of them can produce disease. Many are harmless or, indeed, of ac-

tual benefit because they change the composition of substances—for example, those that create the fermentation processes used in the manufacture of vinegar and the ripening of cheese.

Bacteria that can produce disease are known as pathogens, or pathogenic bacteria. Those that do not produce disease are saprophytes, or nonpathogens.

Large numbers of micro-organisms have been identified and classified as causing specific diseases or as being associated with a disease process. In this chapter we use the term "bacteria" in its broad sense to include all the various classes of plant micro-organisms that cause disease. The singular form of "bacteria" is "bacterium."

Bacteria have distinguishing features as to their growth requirements by which we can identify them.

Some bacteria can form spores in certain circumstances. As spores, they are in a resting stage, and then they are highly resistant to such adverse influences as heat and the action of disinfectants and may remain alive for years.

Some bacteria produce powerful poisons, known as soluble toxins, in the medium in which they grow. Other bacteria carry toxins within their bodies. The toxins are liberated and exert their action when the bacteria are broken up. These, known as endotoxins, are not so powerful as the soluble toxins. Diseases, such as tetanus (lockjaw) and diphtheria, are caused by bacteria that produce powerful—virulent—soluble toxins.

Certain types of bacteria produce localized inflammatory changes in tissues, such as abscesses. Depending on the virulence of the organism and the resistance of the animal, the abscesses may remain localized, or the infection may enter the blood stream and cause a serious general disturbance and sometimes death from septicemia—"blood poisoning."

FILTERABLE VIRUSES also cause diseases. A virus is an infectious agent that can pass through filters fine enough to retain bacteria.

The viruses are ultramicroscopic— that is, they cannot be seen under the ordinary high-power microscope. Among the animal diseases caused by viruses are foot-and-mouth disease, hog cholera, rabies, equine encephalomyelitis, fowlpox, and laryngotracheitis of poultry. Smallpox, measles, influenza, infantile paralysis, and mumps are examples of virus diseases of man.

Bacteria are readily grown on various types of artificial media, or substances, but the viruses require media that contain living cells. Scientists use preparations of tissues to grow certain viruses and keep them alive indefinitely through regular transfers.

They also can propagate many of the viruses in growing chicken embryos by methods developed through studies begun in 1931. Special techniques enable scientists to grow some viruses in living cells in the test tube.

Viruses in their action may attack different types of tissues, as the brain, spinal cord, skin, and blood-forming organs.

Some of the virus diseases are complicated by the action of secondary bacterial invaders. They are bacteria that may normally be present in the animal without manifesting appreciable harm, or they may be responsible for a low-grade infection that is not serious. After a virus infection, however, these organisms may become active and capable of invading the tissues to produce severe complications. A vicious circle may be established by the virus and the secondary bacterial infection—the action of one increases the virulence of the other. That sometimes happens in distemper of dogs and horses, swine influenza, and hog cholera, for example.

THE TERM "PARASITE," as we use it here, is restricted to forms of animal life that have become adapted to live on or in other animals larger than themselves.

All living agents that produce disease, including the viruses, are true parasites. Usage, however, has restricted the term "parasite" to animal organisms, which sometimes are referred to as zooparasites to differentiate them from bacteria and fungi. Bacteria and fungi are plants and sometimes are called phytoparasites. (The prefix "zoo-" implies animals; the prefix "phyto-" pertains to plants.)

Nearly all of the phyla, or major groups, of the animal kingdom contain species of parasites, but the parasites that plague man, livestock, and poultry fall into five phyla:

Protozoa, which are primitive and relatively simple animals;

Platyhelminthes, which include tapeworms and flukes;

Nemathelminthes, or roundworms;

Acanthocephala, or thorn-headed worms;

Arthropoda, in which are included ticks, mites, and insects.

PROTOZOA, or protozoans, are single-celled animals. They are nearly always microscopic in size—that is, you can see them only through a microscope.

Zoologists regard Protozoa as the lowest and probably most primitive forms of animal life. Some of the organisms are 2 to 3 microns long. (There are 25,000 microns in an inch.)

Most protozoans are free living and occur in fresh and brackish and salt water, in soil, and elsewhere where moisture is present. Others are parasitic and occur in various places in people and animals. Some parasitic protozoans are so minute that they can be seen only through a microscope of the highest power.

Many protozoans resemble closely their free-living relatives, from which they were apparently derived. Others have become so modified in structure by their parasitic life that their relationship to their free-living allies has become greatly obscured. These protozoans constitute a specialized group known as sporozoans, all of which are parasitic.

THE SPOROZOA, or sporozoans, include such disease-producing forms as the coccidia, the cause of coccidiosis of poultry, cattle, sheep, goats, swine, and wild animals. Also in this group are the sarcosporidians, which are muscle parasites of domestic animals and birds and of wild animals. The malarial parasites of man and birds, the blood-inhabiting organisms that cause tick fever and anaplasmosis in cattle, also are sporozoans.

The manner in which sporozoans produce a disease depends largely on their location in the host. The coccidia penetrate the cells of the intestinal lining, grow at their expense, and ultimately destroy them. The disappearance of even small parts of this protective, delicate layer exposes to damage the fine blood vessels of the intestinal wall. The result may be their rupture and a consequent intestinal hemorrhage, or bleeding.

The blood-inhabiting sporozoans destroy the red blood cells that they parasitize, and the host animal may become so weak that it succumbs to secondary causes.

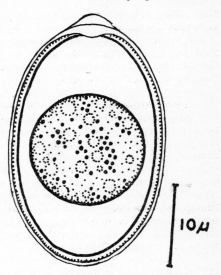

Eimeria arlongi, a sporozoan parasite of sheep. (Magnified about 2,590 times.)

FLAGELLATA, or flagellates, another major group of protozoans, get their name from the fact that they move about in water or other liquids by means of one or more whiplike appendages, known as flagella.

The parasitic flagellates include the trypanosomes, which are blood inhabiting, and cause some of the most serious diseases of man and livestock in parts of Africa and South America and elsewhere. African sleeping sickness and Chagas disease of man in South America, nagana of domestic animals in Africa, dourine of horses and mules, and related trypanosome infections of cattle and other farm animals are caused by these flagellates.

Other flagellates known as histomonads produce blackhead, a disease of chickens and turkeys. Related forms known as trichomonads cause reproductive failures in cattle. The latter parasites inhabit the reproductive sys-

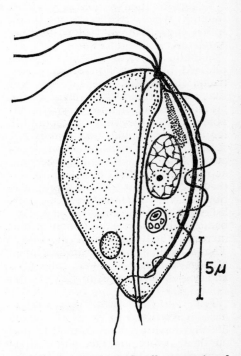

Trichomonas foetus, a flagellate parasite of cattle. (Magnified about 4,060 times.)

tem of cattle, kill the fetus in the uterus of cows, and can also completely mash it up. Other trichomonads inhabit the alimentary canal of animals and poultry, but their role as disease-producing agents has not been adequately explored.

CILIATA, or the ciliates, are another group of protozoans. They move about by means of short, vibrating processes, known as cilia, on the surface of their bodies. Parasitic ciliates occur in the intestine of swine and other domestic stock and man. Some can damage the intestinal wall. Other species occur in the lumen, or cavity, of the alimentary canal of ruminants and horses and apparently are not injurious.

THE RHIZOPODA, which include the amebae, are organisms belonging to the fourth major group of protozoan parasites. Amebae and their relatives within this group are regarded by zoologists as among the simplest of the protozoans.

Most amebae are free living, but some are parasitic. One of the latter causes amebic dysentery, a serious disease of man. Related species occur in swine and in other animals, but little is known about their effects on the health of the animals they parasitize.

The worm parasites, or helminths, of domestic animals and poultry, are visible to the unaided eye. Many are long; some of the intestinal tapeworms attain a length of 25 feet or more.

The flukes are among the smallest of the worm parasites, but some that occur in domestic stock are about 1 to 3 inches long.

Most of the roundworm parasites are small, slender, and threadlike and are commonly known as threadworms.

Some of the parasitic forms attain about the size of an ordinary lead pencil and one species may attain a length of 3 feet or more.

Worm parasites are relatively high in the scale of animal life and complex in structure. They contain muscular, nervous, excretory, and reproductive

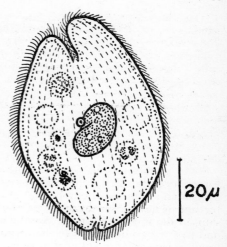

Balantidium coli, a ciliate parasite of swine. (Magnified about 1,000 times.)

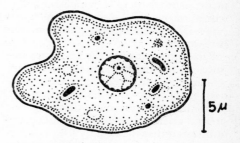

Entamoeba polecki, a rhizopod parasite of swine. (Magnified about 3,000 times.)

systems and other organs and tissues. Two of the four major worm groups, the tapeworms and thorny-heads, lack an alimentary canal and a digestive system. Flukes and roundworms have them.

The parasitic worms undergo a complex development from egg to maturity. Some of them change from one host to another during development. Most parasites require only one host and are known as monoxenous parasites. Others require 2 or 3 hosts, and are known as heteroxenous parasites.

Worms may occur in a variety of locations throughout the bodies of their hosts. One is the digestive tract.

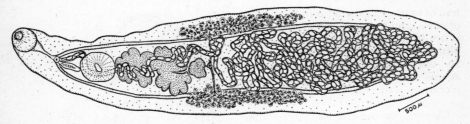

Dicrocoelium dendriticum, a trematode parasite of cattle and sheep.
(Magnified about 18 times.)

Some species inhabit the mouth. Others occur in the esophagus, stomach, small and large intestines, and the rectum. They occur also under the skin, in the muscles, in the abdominal and thoracic cavities, and in the liver, lungs, spleen, pancreas, kidneys, heart, blood vessels, brain, spinal cord, eyes, and other sense organs. In short, there is hardly an organ, a tissue, or a cavity in the animal body in which parasitic worms of one kind or another in some stage of their development have not been found.

Parasitic worms produce various injuries to the organs and the tissues in which they localize. Some species produce mechanical injuries, which result from the mere presence of the parasites on or in a tissue. The same species or others injure the host by the pressure they exert on tissues or organs or by displacing tissues as they grow on or in them. Worms also injure tissues by tearing them apart, or by pushing into them in the course of their migrations. There is evidence, moreover, that helminths elaborate and eliminate into the host's body products that are more or less toxic.

Hookworms and other roundworms suck a tuft of the host's intestinal lining into their mouth cavities and digest it slowly. They also lacerate the lining of the intestinal or stomach mucosa with their mouth parts, which have hard cutting teeth, or plates, or lancets, and abstract blood from the capillaries of the intestinal wall. The wounds so inflicted may continue to bleed after the worm has loosened its hold, presumably because a substance that prevents the blood from clotting is injected into the tiny wounds.

These and other injuries can interfere with the host's normal life processes and produce intestinal hemorrhage, anemia and debility, emaciation, and other symptoms, which may lead to death.

FOUR MAJOR GROUPS of parasitic worms affect domestic animals. Two of them, the tapeworm and flukes, belong to the phylum Platyhelminthes, or flatworms. The roundworms, or nematodes, belong to the phylum Nemathelminthes. The fourth group, known as thorn-headed, or thorny-headed, worms, constitute the phylum Acanthocephala.

FLUKES are parasitic. They are soft, somewhat flattened, leaflike worms. Some are cylindrical. Others are conical. A few are elongated.

Flukes cause disease in man and animals. The most important flukes of domestic animals in the United States are the liver flukes of cattle, sheep, and goats. They cause extensive injury to the liver and can kill sheep. Some of the most harmful flukes do not occur in the United States.

TAPEWORMS occur in all domestic animals and poultry. Some occur in livestock as adult, or strobilate, parasites attached to the wall of the intestine. Others occur in domestic stock as larvae, generally known as bladderworms, in the muscles, liver, lungs, and other organs.

Adult tapeworms of farm animals

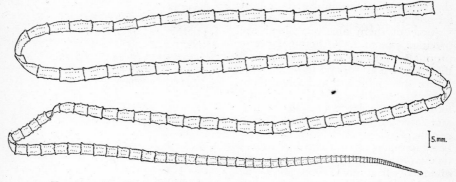

Taenia pisiformis, a cestode parasite of dogs. (Magnified about 3 times.)

and poultry are elongated, flattened, whitish, and grayish or cream colored. The body is divided into segments, or proglottids, by a series of parallel grooves. The entire chain of segments, known as the strobila, is anchored to the intestinal wall by a holdfast organ, usually called a head or a scolex. Actually, however, it is not a head in a zoological sense. It is spherical or egg shaped and it contains four muscular, cuplike structures, known as suckers, or two elongated depressions, or grooves. Most tapeworms also have microscopic hooks on the scolex.

Many stockmen and poultrymen are impressed by finding tapeworms in their animals and poultry and regard these parasites as causes of disease or unthriftiness, but comparatively little is known about the damage done by adult tapeworms.

Bladderworms, on the other hand, become embedded in various organs, including the lungs and brain, and can do much harm. The damage is brought about by interfering with the functions of the organs in which the bladderworms locate. Some bladderworms of cattle and swine are intermediate stages of human tapeworms. Their occurrence in the flesh of food animals is a cause for the condemnation of carcasses under meat inspection procedure. Bladderworms in the vital organs may cause death.

The gid bladderworm of sheep,

which occurs in the brain, produces a disease known as gid, from which the affected animals often die. This parasite does not now occur in the United States, and quarantine measures to keep it out are rigidly enforced.

NEMATODES, or roundworms, are the main disease-producing worm parasites of animals and poultry. They are long, slender, cylindrical worms, somewhat tapered at both ends. Most nematodes are free living and occur in soil, water, and other moist places. Some nematodes are parasitic on the roots of plants. Others parasitize man and animals.

The nematodes in man and livestock may be a tiny fraction of an inch in length and as slender as the finest silk thread. Other parasitic nematodes are much larger.

Nematodes occur as adults or larvae—the immature forms—in nearly all parts of the body. Each species has its preferred location. Some wander extensively as larval worms and may get into places from which they cannot extricate themselves. Their presence in such sites often produces scars and other lesions, which, under meat inspection procedure, make it necessary to condemn the affected parts. Because of their migratory habits, their ability to push into various tissues as larvae and as adults, and the biting mouth parts of some of them, the nematodes can injure their hosts seriously.

Some of them abstract blood and produce anemia. Others elaborate products that apparently are toxic to their hosts. Still others, in other ways, injure the animals that harbor them.

Among the many diseases that nematodes produce are trichinosis of man and animals; hookworm disease of people, food animals, and household pets; stomach worm disease of domestic ruminants and horses; lungworm disease of ruminants, horses, and swine; parasitic enteritis in all farm animals; nodular worm disease of sheep; heartworm disease of dogs; kidney worm disease of swine and dogs; filariasis of man, sheep, and cattle; eye injuries to cattle and dogs; and gapeworm disease of chickens and turkeys.

Anemia, a characteristic symptom produced by nematodes in the digestive tract of horses and ruminants, leads to malnutrition and wasting.

Lungworms produce a verminous bronchitis in swine, ruminants, and horses.

The lodgment of threadworms in the heart or principal blood vessels of dogs can produce severe disturbances in circulation and respiration. Invasion of the muscles by trichinae and other nematodes produces myositis, which is an inflammation of the muscles, usually accompanied by pain. The localization of bloodworm larvae in the blood vessels of horses produces blood clots, which interfere with the blood supply of certain organs and can cause death.

Many other activities of nematodes undermine the health of affected animals and often lead to emaciation and death.

THE ACANTHOCEPHALA, or thornheaded worms, are rather large, whitish, heteroxenous parasites. They have a retractile proboscis, or snout, which is armed with recurved hooks. These parasites attach themselves by means of the armed proboscis to the intestinal lining and maintain a firm hold on it.

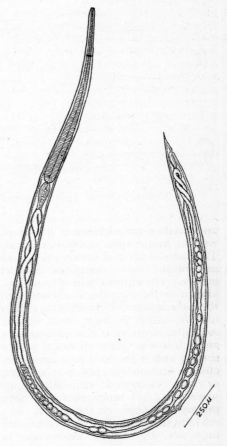

Strongyloides ransomi, a nematode parasite of swine. (Magnified about 60 times.)

Only one species of this phylum, the thorn-headed worm of swine, occurs in domestic stock.

THE PARASITIC ARTHROPODS—insects, ticks, and mites—damage animals by their feeding and by the diseases they transmit.

All of the ticks are parasitic on animals.

Most of the mites are free living or feed on plants, but several species are serious parasites on animals.

Insects are the most numerous of the arthropod group. Destructive insects are best known for the damage they do to growing plants and plant products, but insects have always plagued mankind and domestic animals. Many of the insects that affect livestock also attack man.

Several thousand species of arthropods are parasitic on animals. They are commonly referred to as external parasites, although some species, such as cattle grubs and horse bots, spend a part of their life in the body of the host. Mosquitoes, gnats, and flies feed on different species of animals. Cattle grubs, horse bots, lice, and some kinds of ticks and mites are so specialized in their mode of living that they live only on one kind of host.

External parasites affect the health of animals in one or more ways. Their mere presence may cause severe annoyance. Many kinds suck the blood of animals. Others destroy body tissues. Insects and ticks also carry important animal diseases, or they may serve as alternate hosts for internal parasites.

The bloodsucking parasites are most numerous. They include mosquitoes, gnats, flies, lice, and ticks. Some of them become so numerous they deplete the blood supply of the host. The annoyance and pain caused by mosquitoes, blackflies, horseflies, and deerflies may keep animals from feeding at a time when the need for food to replenish lost blood is most acute.

The parasites also produce a toxin—sometimes referred to as insect venom—which is injected into the host during the process of piercing the skin and sucking blood. The severe local reaction caused in people when they are bitten by insects, ticks, and mites gives some indication of damaging effects on livestock subjected to severe attack by certain bloodsucking parasites.

The larvae of cattle grubs, horse bots, and sheep bots live within the host, although the flies that produce them do not remain or feed on the animal. The presence of heavy infestation of the grubs or larvae will weaken animals, lower production, and make them susceptible to diseases.

Larvae of cattle grubs also cause losses to the leather industry by damaging the hides of cattle. The different kinds of botflies are serious pests because the animals are extremely annoyed while the flies lay their eggs or while they deposit living larvae, as does the sheep botfly. Animals react about the way you would expect if the insects were stinging the host. Actually, however, there is no pain associated with egg laying—the animals just have an instinctive fear of the fly—that is probably Nature's way of helping them avoid excessive parasitism.

The screwworm fly is about three times as large as the housefly. Eggs are deposited on wounds, and the tiny maggots that hatch feed on the flesh until they are about one-half inch long and as big around as a match. Infested wounds begin bleeding and attract more flies. Thousands of maggots may be feeding in the wound after a few days. The destruction of tissues and the loss of blood and lymph soon cause the death of the animal if it is not treated. This pest normally occurs only in the southern part of the United States, although local outbreaks occur elsewhere in the summer.

Fleeceworms are caused by flies similar to the screwworm fly. They lay eggs on soiled wool of sheep. The maggots feed on the surface of the skin and cause severe annoyance. Infestations of fleeceworms are often associated with screwworm infestations in sheep. Like the screwworm, the fleeceworms can kill infested animals unless infestations are treated promptly.

Elimination of the cattle-fever tick has solved the most important arthropod disease carrier among livestock.

There are, however, other diseases among farm animals that are transmitted by arthropods. Anaplasmosis, another important protozoan disease of cattle, may be transmitted in several ways, but ticks, horseflies, and other bloodsucking arthropods can transmit the causative agent. Equine encephalomyelitis, a virus disease of horses, is transmitted by mosquitoes, the principal vector being *Culex tarsalis*. Bluetongue, a virus disease of sheep, is car-

ried by culicoides sandflies. Leucocytozoon, a malarialike disease affecting turkeys and ducks, is transmitted
by blackflies.

NONINFECTIOUS DISEASES are the ones
that are not caused by viruses, micro-
organisms, parasites, or insects. They
are noncommunicable and are commonly found wherever livestock and
poultry are raised.

Some of them often are not considered real diseases. But that they are if
one defines "disease" correctly: In
order to have health, all organs and
systems of organs in the animal body
must function in unison. When they do
not, a disturbance in function may
develop and sickness or death may result. Such conditions are common in
livestock and poultry on all our farms.

METABOLIC DISEASES are an important group of noninfectious diseases.
Physiology has gone wrong; pathology,
or disease, has resulted.

Some of the cells have not carried on
their special function, or they have not
had normal metabolism in the building
up of their protoplasm and the elimination of their waste products. There
may have been an interference with
the production of cell secretions or the
secretion of their products into the
body fluids. Chemical substances may
be absorbed that stimulate or retard
other cells or organs. Chemical substances needed are not produced or are
produced in excess; the excess may
stimulate or retard other cells or
organs. Deficiencies or imbalance of
hormones or endocrines may result
because there is a disturbance in the
glands of internal secretion.

Metabolic diseases are so complex
that the explanation of their causes
often are only matters of theory.

Some of the important metabolic
diseases are ketosis, or acetonemia, of
cattle; lambing paralysis of ewes; milk
fever of cattle; hypoglycemia of baby
pigs; azoturia of horses; blue comb, or
pullet disease, of poultry; and some
types of sterility.

THE FEED may cause many diseases.
Overeating, particularly of unaccus-
tomed feeds, often results in such
digestive disorders as bloat, diarrhea,
scours, colic, and constipation. Some
feeds, such as green legumes, may
cause bloat in cattle, sheep, and goats.
Nutritional anemia may follow a deficiency in iron, copper, or cobalt in
the feed; rickets from a deficiency of
phosphorus, calcium, or vitamin D;
and the avitaminoses from deficiencies
of vitamins.

The feed may cause disease when an
imbalance exists in nutrient materials.
Metabolic disorders may occur at the
same time and complicate matters.

The real cause is often unknown.
Research work has been started on the
cause of some of these diseases, such as
grass tetany of cattle, wheat poisoning
of cattle, and urinary calculi, or water
belly, of cattle and sheep.

POISON IN FEED may also cause disorders and death.

Grease that contains a poisonous
chemical may get into feed when feed
mills are lubricated. Many chemicals
are used in the manufacture of
greases. No mechanical equipment
has been developed by which a feed
may be pelleted without some of the
lubricant going into some of the
pellets. This amount is usually too
small to produce ill effects in livestock, unless the chemical additive to
the grease is very poisonous. Grain
that is treated for use as seed may be
used later, instead, as feed and produce
poisoning.

Almost any chemical eaten in excess—even common salt—may cause
poisoning and varying types of disorders. New agricultural chemicals
and paints are used every year, and
some of them cause disorders if animals eat or lick them.

FLUORINE POISONING in livestock may
result from air pollution in areas surrounding industrial plants that use
products containing fluorine. Materials discharged from the factories

into the air contaminate forage, which animals may eat. The occurrence and distribution of fluorosis in livestock have coincided with the development and expansion of certain manufacturing processes, mainly in the phosphate and aluminum industries. Cement plants and enameling works may be involved to a limited extent. The fluorine in rock phosphate occurs as a natural fluoride and escapes as dust or gas; in aluminum manufacture, the fluorine is derived from the cryolite and fluorspar used as flux. In the production of cement, the fluorides are carried out mostly as dust.

The feed may cause disease in livestock when some ingredient in it has been processed by some industrially developed method. For example, the trichloroethylene method, which formerly was used in the extraction of soybean oilmeal, caused considerable disease in cattle (called Tesom disease, stockman disease, duren disease, or aplastic anemia) in 1947–1952 in the United States, in 1916 in England, and in 1923–1925 in Germany and the Netherlands.

Poisonous plants are important causes of animal sickness and losses. Hungry animals that are placed on ranges or pastures, when there is a shortage of feed, or are trailed or moved across ranges are especially likely to eat excessively of poisonous plants, and heavy losses may result.

Poisonous plants are not confined to ranges and pastures. They also grow in meadows, along irrigation ditches, and in hay fields. Some of the common ones are larkspur, lupine, waterhemlock, deathcamus, locoweeds, arrowgrass, and bracken.

Diseases may be caused by some plants that are not ordinarily poisonous but have become so: They have absorbed some chemical from the soil or have built up an excess of some substance during the process of growth. Oat hay from some soils and in some climates has contained excessive amounts of nitrate and has pro-

duced heavy death losses in livestock. In some years on some soils, Sudangrass builds up enough hydrocyanic acid so that it is quite poisonous. Woody aster growing on nonselenious soil is not poisonous, but when it grows on soil high in selenium it absorbs enough selenium to cause it to produce selenium poisoning when it is eaten.

An animal may develop an unusual susceptibility to a substance that is harmless in similar amounts to most animals of the same species. Such an animal is allergic, or hypersusceptible, to the substance. Very likely the substance is a protein—one of a group of organic nitrogenous compounds, which are widely distributed in plants and animals and form the chief constituents of the cell protoplasm.

After an animal becomes allergic to a substance, the substance will produce an unusual or exaggerated reaction, called anaphylaxis. A protein from the body cells or body fluids of one species of animals is called a foreign protein when it gets into the blood, serum, or lymph of another species. The same holds true for some of the plant proteins when they get into the blood, serum, or lymph of an animal. Thus some animals may become sensitized to a foreign protein in some plants when they eat them and later show allergic reactions.

Insecticides, herbicides, and fungicides, when accidentally eaten or improperly used, may cause sickness and death among animals. Such materials, which are used to kill, respectively, insects, plants, and fungi, seldom kill livestock if they are mixed and applied according to the manufacturers' directions.

Eating—or ingesting—pieces of wire, nails, and other metal objects by cattle is a common cause of loss of health and death. They damage the wall of the stomach and penetrate other organs.

Livestock loss is also caused by external mechanical injury.

Tumors are another important and common cause of noninfectious diseases of livestock and poultry.

These and some of the other causes of noninfectious diseases are discussed in later sections.

H. W. SCHOENING *retired in 1955 after 48 years of service in the Department of Agriculture. At that time he was assistant to the chief of the Animal Disease and Parasite Research Branch. He was chief of the Pathological Division of the former Bureau of Animal Industry for 20 years.*

BENJAMIN SCHWARTZ *has been engaged in parasitological research since 1915. He was chief of the Zoological Division of the Department's former Bureau of Animal Industry from 1936 to 1953 and professor of parasitology in the University of the Philip-*

pines from 1921 to 1923. He became staff assistant and consultant in parasitology in the Animal Disease and Parasite Research Branch of the Agricultural Research Service in 1954.

E. F. KNIPLING, *a graduate of Texas Agricultural and Mechanical College and Iowa State College, became chief of the Entomology Research Branch in 1953. He was formerly in charge of the Insects Affecting Man and Animals Section of the Entomology Research Branch. He has been with the Department of Agriculture since 1931.*

AUBREY M. LEE *is head of the Noninfectious Diseases Section of the Animal Disease and Parasite Research Branch, Agricultural Research Service. He received his degree in veterinary medicine at Kansas State College in 1922 and has been with the Department of Agriculture since 1935.*

How Diseases and Parasites Are Spread

H. W. SCHOENING, BENJAMIN SCHWARTZ, AND ARTHUR W. LINDQUIST

WHEN disease-causing bacteria and viruses establish themselves in an animal, they attack certain tissues, multiply, and set up a disease process.

The infected animal eliminates with its excreta the causative organisms, so that its surroundings become contaminated and other susceptible animals are exposed to the contagion.

The ability of the infection to survive outside the animal body until it can gain entrance to a new host largely determines its ability to spread disease.

CERTAIN BACTERIA can live for indefinite periods outside the animal body and still retain a high degree of virulence.

An example is the anthrax organism. In the final stages of anthrax, the animal's blood stream and tissues contain

large numbers of the organisms in a vegetative stage. The vegetative forms develop into spores when they become exposed to the air through the opening of the carcass or the escape of blood from the natural openings of the body. The organisms then are hard to kill. They can withstand high and low temperatures and retain their infective capacity for years. Once the soil becomes infected with anthrax spores, therefore, it may remain dangerous for susceptible animals for long periods.

Another disease-producing organism that is quite resistant to adverse influences is the germ that causes swine erysipelas. It does not go into a spore stage, but it can live in certain soils for long periods, and the suggestion has even been made that active multiplication may take place in suitable types of soil. Here again the infected animal contaminates its surroundings through its discharges.

THE VIRUS DISEASES are alike in several ways, but their mode of transmission may vary considerably, depending on the nature of the disease and the extent to which the virus has multiplied within the body of the affected animal. Infection takes place when the virus in a proper state is introduced into a susceptable animal.

Rabies, for example, is caused by a filterable virus that is found in the saliva of an affected animal and under natural conditions it is transmitted through the bite of a rabid animal, usually a dog. The disease causes degenerative changes in the brain, which cause affected animals to become aggressive and attack or bite any available object. After the virus is deposited in the tissues, usually through the injury made by the bite, it is believed to move from the site of deposit by way of the nerves. Eventually it reaches the the central nervous system—the brain and spinal cord.

Equine encephalomyelitis, which sometimes is known as sleeping sickness or blind staggers of horses, is another virus disease that attacks mainly the brain and spinal cord, although it can propagate also in other tissues, including the skin. Early in the infection the virus of equine encephalomyelitis lives for a short time in the blood stream. It then disappears from the blood and is found only in the brain and spinal cord. Nervous symptoms of the disease are noted early. It can be transmitted by the bites of a number of different species of mosquitoes and other insects. The disease is therefore considered to be spread chiefly through biting insects.

The virus of foot-and-mouth disease is an example of the viruses that affect skin membranes. Vesicles, which form in the mouth and on the soft parts of the feet, contain the infective agent. When they rupture, the virus is disseminated in the litter and on the ground, where the susceptible animals easily pick up the infection. In the early stages of the disease, the virus is found in the blood, milk, saliva, urine, and perhaps the feces. Because of the large quantities of the virus thus eliminated by affected animals and its highly infectious nature, a wide dissemination of the disease in a short time is possible.

A CARRIER ANIMAL is one that carries an infective agent within its body without showing evidence of illness. It may eliminate the infective agent from time to time and act as a source of infection to other animals; or the carrier animal itself through some adverse condition may develop a frank attack of the disease; or the infection may be carried from a carrier to a normal animal through the bite of an insect.

Certain animals that have recovered from infection with the virus of foot-and-mouth disease may retain active virus within their bodies for months or years and discharge the virus from time to time in sufficient amounts to cause the disease in susceptible animals.

In infectious anemia of horses—so-called swamp fever—a carrier stage is seen in which an apparently normal animal carries the infective agent in its blood stream for many years, perhaps during the rest of its life. It seems that this disease is transmitted mainly by biting insects.

Wild animals and birds also may be reservoirs and spreaders of diseases as, for example, foot-and-mouth disease, rinderpest, and trypanosomiasis.

FARM ANIMALS acquire parasites by grazing on contaminated pastures; by ingesting feed or hay contaminated with the manure of parasitized animals; by swallowing contaminated soil, water, insects, and other small forms of animal life that harbor infective stages of parasites; by eating the flesh or other tissues of animals that harbor infective stages of parasites; or by being bitten by infected insects and ticks.

Among the practices that contribute to the dissemination of parasites are: Bringing parasitized stock to a farm or ranch from the outside; using permanent pastures year in and year out; spreading manure on pastures; placing feed on the ground of barns, stalls, and other shelters; and allowing parasitized dogs to be near livestock.

To INSURE their perpetuation, parasites eliminate their reproductive elements in the form of eggs or larvae, which as a rule are produced in enormous numbers to compensate for the likelihood that many of them will perish before they can get into another host. Furthermore, the reproductive elements often are encased in shells and other tough membranes, which enable them to survive for a long time outside the body even when conditions are unfavorable.

Many protozoan and worm parasites of animals are transmitted through the excreta. Parasites that inhabit the digestive tract of cattle, sheep, goats, swine, horses, poultry, and wild animals are transmitted in that way.

Some protozoan parasites transmitted through the excreta of the host have a resistant form known as a cyst— a resting stage, microscopic in size, usually rounded, and enclosed in a membrane. The membrane protects the parasite from unfavorable influences after it has been eliminated from the body. Sooner or later the cyst becomes infective to other animals of the kind in which it originated. It gets into them by being ingested with grass, dry feed, or water that has become contaminated with the droppings of infected animals. Coccidia of livestock and poultry, parasitic amebas of animals and man, and the ciliates, which parasitize swine, are so transmitted.

Other protozoans are transmitted by the active stage, known as a trophozoite, which passes out of the infected host animal with the droppings. Trophozoites have to be swallowed

soon after they have been eliminated from animals, because their ability to live outside the host is sharply limited.

Trichomonads in the intestines of swine and other animals and in poultry are transmitted in that way.

WORM PARASITES of the alimentary canal, or of the lungs and other organs that have a direct or indirect connection with the alimentary canal, produce eggs, which are eliminated with the droppings.

The swine kidney worm is one of the few parasites that eliminates its eggs into the ureter, from which they are voided with the urine. Once the eggs reach the outside, regardless of how they are eliminated from the host's body, they develop and become infective as eggs, or they hatch into larvae, or the eggs have to be swallowed by intermediate hosts. Cold weather retards the development of parasite eggs, but during favorable weather the eggs develop rapidly. Those that hatch yield larvae, which undergo their transformations to the infective stage in about one week or more, depending on the temperature.

The larvae that first emerge from eggs feed almost constantly on bacteria and bits of organic matter, grow rapidly, and molt in a day or two. Before they become infective they undergo at least a partial second molt, after which they are ready to invade the kind of hosts from which they came.

During the favorable weather that prevails in most parts of the United States in late spring, summer, and early fall, the development of the egg to the infective larva takes about a week or less. The infective larvae climb upward on grass and other vegetation, especially after rains and dews when the vegetation has a film of moisture on it. The upward migration places the larvae in a situation where they are likely to be swallowed by grazing animals. In barns the larvae climb up on litter, hay, moist walls, and posts and may be eaten or licked off by animals housed therein.

Cattle, sheep, goats, horses, and swine acquire many of their internal parasites by grazing on pastures that have become contaminated with the eggs and larvae of the parasites we mentioned. Stomach worms of cattle, sheep, and goats and most of the intestinal hairworms of ruminants that produce enteritis and scouring are acquired in this manner, as are lungworms of cattle and the common lungworm of sheep.

Other parasites, however, including hookworms of farm animals and pets, intestinal threadworms of all domestic animals, kidney worms of swine, and other worm parasites can gain entrance into the host by boring into its skin. That can readily happen when an animal lies down in a pasture, barnyard, or corral that is contaminated with skin-penetrating larvae.

SOME PARASITE EGGS that develop outside the host but do not hatch there are infective as eggs when a suitable animal swallows them. Among them are the large intestinal roundworm or ascarid of cattle, horses, and swine; whipworms of cattle, sheep, goats, and swine; and intestinal roundworms or ascarids and whipworms of pet animals. The infective eggs are swallowed with contaminated feed or water in kennels, runs, yards, corrals, pastures, barns, stables, and elsewhere. The larvae hatch in the alimentary canal of the host, reach their preferred location in the digestive tract or elsewhere in the body by active migration, and develop there to maturity.

Other parasites require intermediate hosts to convey them from one animal to another. Among them are certain stomach worms of horses, mules, and swine; gullet worms of swine and ruminants; swine lungworms; sheep lungworms; intestinal tapeworms of ruminants; and other parasites of livestock, pet animals, and poultry. The eggs pass out of the host and develop into larvae only when they are eaten by certain intermediate hosts. Among the small forms of animal life that can serve as intermediate hosts are insects (particularly those that eat dung or breed in it), snails, slugs, earthworms, free-living mites, and other invertebrate creatures found in pastures, yards, corrals, barns, and other places to which animals and poultry have access. When the infective intermediate hosts are swallowed by suitable definitive hosts, either accidentally or because they are choice morsels, the parasites they contain are freed in the digestive tract of the new host, migrate to their favorite location, and develop there to maturity.

A mode of development peculiar to the liver flukes and certain other flukes involves the hatching of the egg outside the host, the eating of the larvae by snails, and finally the emergence of the transformed larvae from the snails onto vegetation. Livestock become infected by swallowing the larvae with grass, water, and sometimes even dry feed. The lancet fluke of ruminants requires a second intermediate host— a common pasture ant—before it can infect cattle and sheep.

IN ADDITION to the passive transfer of parasites by eating insects and other low forms of animal life, others are injected into the blood of their host by biting insects or other arthropods, especially ticks. Tick fever and anaplasmosis of cattle are two parasitic diseases caused by protozoans that are transmitted in this manner. Tick fever is transmitted by the bites of ticks, which transfer the causative organisms they harbor to the cattle whose blood they suck. Anaplasmosis also is transmitted in this manner and may also be transferred from cattle to cattle by horseflies during the interrupted feeding of the flies on the blood of the hosts.

Outstanding examples of the transmission of parasitic diseases by biting flies are trypanosome diseases of livestock. In Africa tsetse flies transmit trypanosomes, which they acquire while they are obtaining their blood meal from infected animals. Later the flies can transmit the trypanosomes to other suitable host animals during another blood meal. In South America trypanosomes of livestock are transmitted by other bloodsucking flies since tsetse flies do not occur there.

Many kinds of worm parasites also are transmitted by biting flies and other insects that attack their host and feed on its blood. Stableflies, for example, transmit certain stomach worms to horses. The larvae of the stomach worms, which are located near the mouth parts of the insect, are stimulated to activity during the biting process by the heat of the horse's body and enter into the skin that has been broken by the fly's bite. Various long and slender nematodes, known as filarias or filarids, which occur outside the digestive tract in practically all classes of farm animals, are transmitted by bloodsucking insects.

STILL ANOTHER METHOD of parasite transmission is through the eating of the flesh or internal organs of one animal by another. Man and animals, for example, acquire trichinae and the disease trichinosis, which trichinae produce, by eating the flesh of infected hogs or other animals. Man, dogs, and other animals acquire intestinal tapeworms by eating the flesh of animals infected with bladderworms. Hogs acquire lung flukes by eating crayfishes infected with the larval flukes.

A more unusual method of transmission is through copulation. Dourine of horses, a disease that occurs in the Western Hemisphere and is caused by trypanosomes, is transmitted in this manner. Another disease transmitted through copulation is bovine trichomoniasis, caused by trichomonads which affect the reproductive system of bovines and cause reproductive failures in cattle in the United States and other countries. The infected bull transmits the causative organisms to the cows and heifers he serves. An uninfected bull acquires these organisms by serving a cow that harbors them in the vagina.

WE NEED TO KNOW how parasites are spread from animal to animal before we can develop rational control measures. Before the existing knowledge came to light, little of practical value could be done to curtail the spread of parasites and minimize their effects. The discoveries made since 1890 or so on how parasites are transmitted by ticks, mosquitoes, and other insects make a fascinating chapter in the history of parasitology and preventive medicine. The discoveries have helped us to curb and even to eradicate some devastating parasites.

Another important discovery stemmed from the work of Arthur Looss in Egypt early in the 20th century. Looss determined that the human hookworm followed a pattern of development outside the host; that was found to be the development pattern also of some injurious nematodes in the digestive tract of farm animals. Looss determined, moreover, that hookworm larvae can enter human and canine hosts by burrowing through the skin. That, too, was later shown to be true of a number of injurious parasites of livestock.

INSECTS spread from place to place in many and devious ways. Man himself transports from farm to farm, from State to State, and even from foreign lands some destructive insect pests. Flies and ticks can be carried on commodity shipments in railroad cars, ships, trucks, airplanes, and automobiles. Lice, mites, cattle grub larvae, and some flies remain on an animal during shipments and are thus spread. Changing conditions favor establishment of new pests, such as mosquitoes in irrigated regions, when the habitat is suitable in the new areas.

The growth of livestock auctions has intensified the spread of some insect pests. Livestock may be brought many miles to an auction and within a day or two be transported an equal or greater distance to some other section. Shipping livestock to agricultural fairs occasionally hastens a reinfestation of parasites. The larvae of flies are trans-

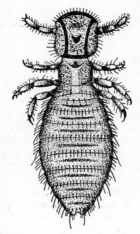

Biting sheep louse—female.

ported in the straw and in manure of trucks and railway cars. Moving livestock to new ranges or feed lots spreads many of these pests.

Animals harboring screwworm infestations are shipped from southwestern Texas to the uninfested Northern States every spring. Infestations in Northern States have become more common presumably because of more rapid methods of transporting livestock. Although the screwworm fly migrates by natural flight, the shipping of infested animals hastens spread in Texas and other Southwestern States. The screwworm was unknown in the Southeast until 1933, when it was introduced in infested cattle from Texas.

The seasonal history of cattle grubs in some localities is being altered by frequent cattle shipments. Because grubs appear earlier in the backs of cattle and persist longer than formerly, the period during which control must be conducted is extended. The heelfly, the adult of the grub, also is active for a longer period. Since 1930 the northern cattle grub, *Hypoderma bovis*, has spread from the East Coast through all of the Northern and Western States. Most of this dispersal was caused by shipment of infested cattle. The rapid spread of an insect species is exemplified by the spread of the hornfly. This insect, originally from Europe, became established in the United States about 1890. Within a decade it had spread throughout most of the United States and became one of our most important pests of cattle.

Cattle lice have been reported to attach themselves to hornflies and thus be transported to other animals.

Many insects are strong fliers and can migrate far. The black blowfly, *Phormia regina*, which produces fleeceworms in sheep, can fly at least 28 miles. The houseflies will fly at least 20 miles. Horseflies and deerflies will move several miles from their breeding places.

Lice of cattle, sheep, and goats and other animals are spread by contact of one animal with another. A clean herd can become lousy by the introduction of one infested animal. It is therefore prudent to eradicate lice on acquired animals before the animals are placed with clean livestock.

Ticks, which are wingless, spread by contact between animals. They rest on plants until a warm-blooded host passes by, and they drop on it. They also are transported by manmade shipments.

H. W. SCHOENING *retired in 1955 after 48 years of service in the Department of Agriculture. At the time of his retirement he was assistant to the chief of the Animal Disease and Parasite Research Branch. Prior to that assignment, he served as Chief of the Pathological Division of the former Bureau of Animal Industry for 20 years. He entered the Department shortly after his graduation from the School of Veterinary Medicine of the University of Pennsylvania.*

BENJAMIN SCHWARTZ *in 1954 became staff assistant and consultant in parasitology in the Animal Disease and Parasite Research Branch of the Agricultural Research Service. He has been engaged in parasitological research since 1915.*

ARTHUR W. LINDQUIST *is leader of the Insects Affecting Man and Animals Section, Entomology Research Branch. He is a graduate of Bethany College, Lindsborg, Kans., and Kansas State College. Since 1931 he has conducted and directed research on the biology of pests that affect man and livestock.*

Genetics and Disease

NELSON F. WATERS

MANY diseases and pathological disorders of domestic animals result in death or make an animal unfit for economic use. Sometimes it is difficult for the livestock owner to recognize and interpret many of the causes of death as being due to heredity or influenced by heredity.

Some persons believe that heredity has a minor role in pathology. Such reasoning is not in accordance with known facts—some genetic influence operates in all of the biological phenomena of life.

The science of genetics explains how resemblances and differences, which are found in all plant and animal organisms, are transmitted to the next generation. An understanding of the basic laws of heredity has resulted from a vast amount of experimentation with plants and animals—contributed by many workers in nearly all the sciences.

The science of plant breeding has become so exacting that strains of corn, wheat, oats, and other plants have been so bred that they will grow and thrive efficiently only in restricted climates. These same plants are bred to resist the ravages of specific diseases. Domestic animals, notably dairy and beef cattle, swine, sheep, and chickens, are monuments to man's ability to control heredity. All these things have occurred through the application of genetic laws.

Causes of livestock mortality may be divided into three groups:

Diseases caused by infectious agents such as bacteria, viruses, and rickettsiae that may infect the animal at almost any period throughout its life;

Infections by parasites that may either destroy body tissue and cause death or weaken the animal and predispose it to many infectious agents;

Abnormalities and disorders of a noninfectious nature that are inherent in the animal and are present at birth, or may develop later. Examples of such hereditary characters are achondroplasia, deformed limbs, brain hernia, cleft palate, hydrocephalus, and congenital spasm.

Many of the diseases that affect domestic animals are caused by minute parasitic forms of life, each of which has its own form of existence and is governed by the same biological laws that dictate life for the higher animals.

TO OBTAIN AN UNDERSTANDING of genetics and its relationship to pathology, we cannot confine our studies to the complex animal alone. It is necessary also to investigate the organisms responsible for diseases.

All living animals start life as one-cell structures. Within these one-cell bodies are constituents that are specific to individual species of plants or animals. Everything an animal can be from a structural and an operational standpoint is contained in this minute bit of living matter.

We are interested in the inherent capacities that are deposited in the original cell body. Some of the one-cell bodies will divide and double their number by each division until the complex animal is formed. Other cells will never advance beyond the single-cell stage.

Some of them we call bacteria. The permanent one-cell bacteria often invade and multiply in the more complex host animal. If such bacteria are disease producing, or what is termed "pathogenic," they may be harmful to their host and thus may cause any one of many of the infectious diseases with which we are familiar.

Besides the one-cell bacteria, there are even smaller units of presumably living protein matter capable of multiplying in numbers inside a host. They are quite specific in their host response. These smaller units are the viruses. Those with which we are familiar are pathogenic—or disease producing—when they invade the more complex forms of plant and animal life. Indeed, viruses are so small that they can actually invade and destroy one-cell bacteria. Viruses mostly can be seen only under an electron microscope.

Some of the lower forms of animal life, such as the coccidia, tapeworms, roundworms, flukes, and the ticks, also invade the host animal, causing disease, reducing its efficiency, and not infrequently causing death. Such internal and external parasites may act as vectors and deposit disease-producing bacteria and viruses in the animal host. All these lower forms of life likewise are regulated by the same genetic laws that regulate the higher forms.

The host animal, then, be it cattle, swine, sheep, or chicken, responds according to its genetic capacity. The lesser forms of life—bacteria, viruses, or more complex parasites—will invade and affect the host, according to their genetic capabilities. Thus we must recognize two independent variables responsible for disease—the host and the pathogen (or disease-producing agent).

A third important variable exists—environment, which may influence materially the interaction of the host and pathogen.

Any discussion of animal diseases must therefore consider not only the interrelationship of host and pathogen but also the environment that surrounds and influences all living matter.

Questions as to the relative importance of heredity and environment are ages old. Long before the Austrian Gregor Mendel provided an insight into the mechanism of inheritance, there were those who realized some of the fundamental genetic problems of breeding plants and animals. During this early period some felt that the environment was responsible for most of the variations seen in plants and animals. This difference of opinion is now history. Today's students, trained in the biological sciences, recognize heredity and environment as separate components, but often so closely interrelated that they often are difficult or impossible to separate.

When the maternal animal cell is fertilized by a male cell, it has received a quota of inheritance from its dam and a quota from its sire. Nothing genetic will be added to this animal as long as it may live. As soon as this animal is conceived, however, it becomes subject to (and influenced by) the surrounding environment established in the body of its dam. After birth the animal will be bombarded by the conditions around it.

Animals are conceived, then, with certain genetic-potential abilities. Environment can suppress or bring out the abilities, if present. But environment will never develop abilities that were not inherent in the animal.

Animals may have inherent resistance or a susceptibility to specific diseases. Only when these individuals are challenged by a disease organism do the genetic differences become apparent. The students of veterinary medicine have been too prone in animal pathology to consider the individual host *per se* without due consideration of the genetic heritage of either the host or the pathogen. The ability of the diagnostician to recognize and classify properly hereditary diseases and defects will add much to genetic knowledge and greatly assist in the ultimate eradication of heretofore incurable conditions.

It is necessary to distinguish between pathological abnormalities that are dependent alone on gene differences in the host and those caused by the genetic interaction of both host and pathogen.

OF WHAT VALUE is a knowledge of genes, viruses, and bacteria to a breeder of livestock?

The answer is that he should know and understand what the undesirable genes, viruses, and bacteria can do to his animals. From a practical viewpoint, our interest in viruses or bacteria lies in how they affect man and his animals.

First, we are interested in the pathological or disease conditions caused by infectious agents.

Second, we would like to know how these agents are transmitted from host to host.

Third, we would like to know how we may prevent the entrance of disease agents, or, after they enter, how we may prevent them from inflicting damage and possibly death.

Some of these things we know. Most of the diseases affecting domestic animals are reasonably well described as to symptoms and pathology. Some of the diseases can be controlled by antisera, antibiotics, and other prophylactic means. In only a few instances, however, do we understand the genetic nature of the pathogenic organism and its relationship to its host.

A rapid increase in studies of the viruses, especially as they pertain to heredity, has been stimulated by the action and the behavior of bacterial viruses. Here one can multiply into the millions both the bacteria and the viruses. Chemical analyses, behavior, purity, immunological reactions, virulence, the rates of multiplication, size, shape, and even photography can characterize or identify the virus. Genetic studies with both bacteria and the viruses demonstrate or exhibit all the phenomena of Mendelian heredity found in the higher organisms.

Our knowledge of genes—the determiners of inheritance—is based mostly on what they do, rather than on what they are. Their chemical nature, other than describing them as consisting mostly of desoxyribonucleic acid plus other proteins, is unknown.

A gene, as we know it, is a regulated part or segment of a chromosome structure contained within a nucleus surrounded by cytoplasm. The composite is encased in a cell wall. Because genes are capable of expressing different traits or characteristics, it seems plausible that the genes may in part differ chemically from one another.

An induced change in a chromosome or the genes of a chromosome by X-rays, ultraviolet rays, or chemicals may influence greatly the relationship of a chromosome or its genes to other chromosomes and their genes. That in turn could influence the expression of an organism. Induced changes or mutations in the less complex organisms could conceivably modify their genetic expression drastically.

There is some question whether mutations in the higher organisms, such as domestic animals, are of widespread economic importance. Circumstantial evidence suggests that the expression of the majority of genes has remained unchanged over long periods of time.

This constancy of the gene is overwhelming and past comprehension.

Every gene seems to know where it belongs and how to get there. The very nature of the constancy of the gene permits some element of predictability and allows some control in planning matings between animals.

Bacteria as living one-cell organisms should and do exhibit similar properties of cells found in other living organisms. Structurally a bacterium does not always appear to conform to the more or less conventional cell morphology of the higher animals. There is no doubt, however, that bacteria do have cell components fully comparable to those found in the more complex multicellular forms.

Nuclear material, chromosomes and genes, as well as cytoplasm with its component parts, make up the structure of bacteria. Microscopic examination of the cell content of bacteria frequently reveals what seems to be several nuclei in a single cell. Probably this multinuclear appearance is due to the fact that the nucleus divides more rapidly than the bacterial cell rather than to separate and different nuclear entities.

In certain phases in the life of a bacterium no distinct nucleus is apparent, and its specificity has been disputed in the past. The electron microscope, however, has increased vastly the range of magnification of the minute bacterial cell and permits a quite detailed study of cell morphology. The presence of a cell nucleus seems indisputable.

In cells of the higher organisms, the chromosomes and genes are paired, or diploid. In bacteria, the chromosomes and genes are single, or haploid.

Because bacteria multiply primarily by binary fission, each division theoretically consists of self-duplication. Through this method of cell division, segregation of genes would be possible, but other conventional genetic processes would be prohibited.

To fulfill the requirements of genetics, there must be some method in bacteria, akin to the sexual process, which will permit the orderly exchange of hereditary content between the individual bacteria by which new combinations of characters can be produced. It has been established that a sexlike fusion and exchange of cell material does occur in some strains of bacteria, and it may be presumed to occur with regularity in as yet untested strains.

MUTATIONS occur in bacteria. Both ultraviolet and X-ray radiations are known to induce mutations in *Escherichia coli* from sensitive (or susceptible) to resistant forms, using virus (bacteriophage) as testing material.

The sensitive bacteria will adsorb the virus in large numbers, but the resistant bacteria do not adsorb the virus. These induced mutations will breed true for this resistant factor.

Bacterial mutations showing resistance to such antibiotics as streptomycin, Aureomycin, Terramycin, and penicillin, antibiotics in general, and to some chemicals, have been demonstrated. The resistance of bacteria to one antibiotic may not mean that it is resistant to another antibiotic. This resistance to antibiotics is of great practical importance in human and in animal therapy.

The virulence of bacteria in a specific host can be altered by mutations. Likewise colonial morphology and antigenic characteristics of bacteria may be changed by the mutations. When bacteria invade a host, their virulence will depend in part on the defense mechanism the host sets up. Highly virulent forms can break down or overcome the host's defense mechanism. The bacteria that show lesser virulence can be defeated by host response. The morphology of a colony of bacteria apparently is related to the virulence of bacteria in that a higher host infection rate results with the smooth-surface forms of bacteria than from the rough or the mucoid forms.

Genetic studies in bacteria generally are in the infant stage. Most genetic investigations are based on the changes that take place in bacterial populations, rather than with single cells.

Nevertheless, studies on the population genetics of bacteria have measurably advanced our knowledge of host response to infectious diseases.

VIRUSES appear to have many of the same properties as genes. The chemical nature of animal viruses (like that of genes) consists for the most part of the nuclear protein desoxyribonucleic acid.

One of the larger viruses, vaccinia, shows a much greater and more complex chemical content.

Other viruses presumably have great diversity of chemical content. A virus may be considered as only part of a cell; viruses were termed "naked nuclei" as early as 1920. Within a virus are genes with a linear arrangement on a chromosomelike structure encased in a nucleus, but showing no cytoplasmic cell content and no cell wall.

Viruses are pathogenic, or infectious, agents that can multiply only within the living cell of the host. Other pathogenic organisms, such as protozoa and bacteria, can also multiply within the living cells of a host. These latter organisms can also live and multiply when separated from the host cells, but the virus cannot. Of necessity, therefore, one must study the pathological reactions in the affected hosts as a measurement of virus activity.

Viruses, then, have the property of existing only as separate intracellular parasitic entities, but genes are an integral part of a cell and are permanently associated with other cell components. It is not unlikely that some viruses, like genes, have existed in the same form and have had the same constancy of expression through the ages.

The constancy of a virus is useful to people in that protective serums and vaccines would be useless against a constantly changing virus. Old writings suggest the presence of smallpox virus several thousand years before Christ; it probably existed many thousands of years before that time.

Some of the most destructive diseases of mankind, such as smallpox, yellow fever, and influenza, are caused by viruses. Control of smallpox and yellow fever through immunization has resulted in a concentrated effort to understand the behavior of the virus organisms.

ALTHOUGH a knowledge of viruses has existed since about 1892, it was not until 1923 that W. M. Stanley isolated the tobacco mosaic virus. Following this initial discovery, it was established that viruses were the causative agents for many plant diseases.

Research with animal viruses, particularly those affecting domestic animals, has proceeded at a slower pace because of inherent difficulties. Work with bacterial virus diseases advanced chiefly because of the ability to culture, multiply, and identify the bacterial hosts in tremendous numbers. Viruses that are associated with bacterial hosts usually are called "bacteriophage" or "phage." These viruses invade the host cell, multiply in great numbers, and are released, through a process known as "lysis," to enter or infect other cells or become living, resting, seedlike particles that may invade susceptible cells at other periods.

Despite the difficulties in studying the habits and properties of viruses in larger animals, much has been learned about their behavior.

Viruses are quite specific in their disease-forming habits. They might have the ability in nature to exist and possibly multiply in secondary hosts, but there appear to be primary hosts that will show specific disease reactions when invaded by a specific virus.

Study has shown that certain viruses multiply freely in different parts of a developing chicken egg, which is actually a foreign host. This method of virus propagation has contributed much to our understanding of the behavior and habits of many viruses.

Tissues of other experimental animals have also proved to be useful for virus studies. Such animal tissues may be grown in the proper culture media and infected with virus bodies. Refined techniques have permitted accurate measurements and a knowledge in some instances of the destructive habits of a virus. Some viruses will not grow in cells from foreign hosts in tissue culture, but require the exact host for which they are specific.

We have said that genes under natural environmental stress may mutate and cause new genetic expressions. In the larger animals, evidence for spontaneous gene mutation is sometimes difficult to assess. Similarly, it is probable that viruses will also mutate, resulting in new expressions, but it would seem safe to assume that this rate of mutation is not high. Actually, if it were not for the ease by which tremendous numbers of viruses become available for study, the virus mutations now known would probably have been missed entirely.

Apparently many strains of viruses produce similar pathological lesions in a host, but some are much more virulent and destructive than others. The great pandemic of influenza in 1918–1919 may be interpreted as being caused by a highly virulent form or variant. Possibly it resulted from the recombination of two different virus strains, but it is not inconceivable that it was a mutant.

The evidence for mutations in viruses is rather compelling. That does not mean that prior forms cease to exist, but rather that new forms with different expressions come into being.

Change of expression in a virus, however, does not always predicate a mutation. A virus is adaptable and its virulence for a susceptible host is influenced greatly by the age and sex of the host as well as by the environmental factors, such as temperature and nutrition, which may surround both the host and the virus.

Structurally, in a virus there would appear to be some basic, threadlike chromonema which connects genes or genelike particles and which might function in a manner similar to a chromosome in the higher organisms. These genelike particles are encapsulated in a thin coat, which is believed to be left behind at the time the virus enters a host cell.

Such virus genes presumably behave similarly to genes in the higher animals. After the virus particles enter a host cell, they multiply and enter into the activity of the cell. It has not been clearly established whether the virus initiates an action or reaction in the host cell, or whether the reaction is initiated by the cell in response to the virus invasion.

Studies of the precise properties and behavior of viruses in multicellular host animals are surrounded by nearly insurmountable problems. These problems are greatly reduced if studies are conducted on the individual cell level.

For this reason, much of the recent information on virus characteristics has been gained from virus-bacterium studies. Here one may start with the resting or extracellular form of the virus and follow its behavior in bacteria. During its stay in bacterial cells, the virus multiplies or reproduces, initiates recombination and segregation of its genes, and possibly mutates to produce new forms or types. Following the active stage in the host bacterium, the virus resumes the resting stage, if there are no new host cells to conquer.

The behavior of bacteriophage (virus) in the host bacterium, *E. coli* strain B, has shown that a number of genetic types of viruses exist. The evidence is clear that mutations occur and that these virus mutations all arise from existing genetic types.

Research contributions from a number of investigators list at least seven types of virus mutants, all arising from a wild type by single mutations. The *E. coli* strain B is resistant to some of these virus types and sensitive or susceptible to others. Additional mutations may occur among some of the established types.

Evidence for gene recombination has been presented to show that when two different types of viruses infect the same bacterium, virus types will arise that differ from either of the parent types. From a number of experiments comes compelling evidence that there is a linear arrangement of genes in a virus; the suggestion that linkage and crossing over of these genes takes place may be a valid one.

Evidence for virus mutation is not confined alone to the *E. coli* group of bacteria but has also been demonstrated in the virus associated with *Salmonella typhimurium* and some other bacteria.

The knowledge gained during the past decade on virus genetics has vastly strengthened our concept of the chemical nature of genes. Continued studies in this field may break the barrier that differentiates living from inanimate matter.

WHAT IS THE SIGNIFICANCE of the similarity of action of genes and viruses? Are viruses among the simpler forms of living matter that have not yet reached the relatively complex structure of a living cell? Or are they obligate living particles that have retrogressed from some previously existing cell relationship to become wholly parasitic?

Can we correctly term viruses living particles? Presumably viruses are living entities—at least in the same sense that a plant seed is alive or that a gene is alive. Each of them is a chemical entity, endowed with something more than that possessed by one chemical or even a mixture of chemicals. Each has the ability to grow and reproduce when surrounded by the necessary environment. In addition, each of these three—virus, seed, and gene—will reproduce its specific kind.

We will have to wait for the final answer to the question, "What is a virus?"

Meanwhile we can summarize some of the activities of a virus. Viruses may be presumed to be living organisms, consisting mainly of protein molecules that are parasitic in nature and are capable of self-perpetuation and expression only in a favorable host-cell environment. They have the ability to remain constant in their expression over indefinite periods of time. Under certain conditions, some viruses are pathogenic and are responsible for extensive damage to the host cells which they invade; in other instances the course of the disease is so rapid that death occurs before cell damage is extensive. In a receptive host, some viruses may cause a specific disease reaction that presumably is dependent on the resistant or susceptible genes of the host. They are capable of remaining and multiplying in the cells of the host or an intermediate host without noticeable damage to the host for long periods of time. Viruses have genelike properties, such as specific expression, recombinability, and the ability to mutate, depending on the aid of (and possibly influenced by) the cell components, including the genes of the host which they invade.

When an animal becomes infected with a virus or a bacterium known to be pathogenic to this animal, it will eventually succumb or recover or it will show no visible effect of any kind.

If the animal recovers from the infection, it may have temporary or permanent immunity to further attacks. This type of immunity is termed "acquired immunity." Animals that show no apparent reaction to inoculation are concluded to be relatively resistant or as having a degree of "natural immunity."

In truth, both acquired and natural immunity are genetic phenomena. When an animal shows a positive reaction to a virus or bacterial attack and recovers, it means that this animal has succeeded in building up sufficient resistance by its ability to form antibodies to overcome the influence of the invasion.

The ability of the host to combat disease through the formation of antibodies has genetic implications. Without the ability to form effective antibodies, any form of vaccination or immunization of the host would be a useless procedure.

Ordinarily no antibody response following inoculation or invasion of a virus or bacterium takes place in the genetically resistant animal. However, this resistant animal may show a reaction if environmental conditions surrounding it are markedly altered. For example, a chicken generally shows no reaction to anthrax invasion, but may be killed by such an invasion if the body temperature is reduced experimentally.

How to prevent disease and how to cure disease involve two distinct concepts.

Throughout the centuries, the primary interest of man has been to increase knowledge on how a disease may be cured after it has happened. Present-day medicine has started to swing toward ways and means of removing the causes of disease. Public health activities have removed sources of infection, instituted prophylactic measures, and applied vigorous quarantine and culling procedures when advisable.

In human medicine, it has been possible through vaccination or immunization to remove almost entirely the menace of smallpox, diphtheria, scarlet fever, and typhoid fever. Recently great promise has been shown for poliomyelitis.

In animals, vaccine and immunizing agents have been introduced to protect against disease and to aid in the control of equine encephalomyelitis, rabies, canine distemper, hog cholera, brucellosis, blackleg, anthrax, fowlpox, laryngotracheitis, Newcastle disease, and many others.

Tuberculosis in animals can be controlled by eliminating infected animals through the use of the tuberculin test. Often it is more economical in animals to use rigid quarantine procedures to aid in the elimination or control of a disease or a parasite-harboring disease agent than to attempt a difficult breeding program that stresses genetic resistance. As an example, foot-and-mouth disease and tuberculosis now are held in check mainly through the elimination of infected carriers.

We have accepted more or less the belief that the resistance and susceptibility of host animals, including man, are the deciding factors in determining epidemics of disease. Certainly, host response is an important factor, but as we increase our knowledge of microorganisms, there comes a realization that these minute parasites must be credited with an important, if not equal, part in disease control.

Actually, viruses or bacteria could mutate in one step from a less virulent form to a more highly virulent form, with greater ease than could be accomplished by a genetic change from resistance to susceptibility in a complex host.

Because viruses and bacteria show genetic recombination, it is also possible that such recombinations could result in highly virulent segregates in greater frequency than would be accomplished through mutations.

GENETICS as a tool for eliminating disease and pathological abnormalities in animals holds some promise to mankind. Without any question, a careful breeding program can eliminate many of the structural disorders and defects in animals that depend solely on gene differences for expression.

Studies with experimental plants and animals have demonstrated that certain animals have a genetic resistance, or natural immunity, to specific disease. With this discovery of genetic immunity has come an equally valuable contribution in that the disease organism, bacterium or virus, also is subject to the same genetic laws as the host plant or animal.

Early plant breeders led the way in demonstrating that certain varieties of wheat are more resistant to disease than others. R. H. Biffen in 1905 demonstrated the resistance of certain varieties of wheat to mycotic stem rust; he was the first to lay the foundations for important advances in the knowledge of genetic resistance to disease. Since that time many varieties of economic plants showing genetic resistance to disease have been contributed to mankind by the scientific workers. Evidence that the same principles of genetic resistance to disease also hold for animals has been demonstrated by several investigators.

Studies at the Illinois Agricultural Experiment Station, led by E. Roberts and L. E. Card, demonstrated an innate resistance to *Salmonella pullorum* in the domestic fowl.

At the Iowa Agricultural Experiment Station, W. V. Lambert, C. W. Knox, and J. W. Gowen have contributed much to our knowledge of genetic resistance in the chicken and mouse to fowl and mouse typhoid.

F. B. Hutt and R. K. Cole of the Cornell Agricultural Experiment Station and Nelson F. Waters at the United States Regional Poultry Research Laboratory at East Lansing, Mich., have reported resistance and susceptibility of selected lines of chickens to fowl leukosis.

The application of genetics to disease control in animals presents greater problems than that found with plants.

Nevertheless this method of attack shows promise and is worthy of greater attention than it has received.

No program of disease control in either plants or animals can be complete without placing more or less equal emphasis on the study of the pathogenic organisms that cause the disease. One might say that an ounce of medical research may remove the need for a cure.

NELSON F. WATERS *is the geneticist at the United States Regional Poultry Research Laboratory at East Lansing, Mich. He has been investigating the inheritance of resistance and susceptibility to avian lymphomatosis since 1939. Earlier he was associated with Iowa State College and the University of Rhode Island. He received his graduate degrees in zoology and genetics at Harvard University. His undergraduate work was done at Connecticut University.*

Protection Against Transmissible Diseases and Parasites

B. T. SIMMS

LONG before anybody knew about germs, farmers were trying to keep diseases away from their animals. They did not know the meaning of "bacteria" and "virus," but they did know that a sick animal might spread disease. They tried to stop the spread by doing two things—just as farmers today do. One was to isolate healthy animals from animals that were sick or had been in contact with sick animals. The other was to increase the resistance of healthy animals so they would not get a disease if they were exposed.

When the number of farm animals was comparatively small and farmsteads were farther apart than now, a farmer could do much on his own farm to keep his stock healthy. But as farming and the population expanded and more and more livestock were shipped to and from markets, individual action was not enough.

Thinking people knew that group or government action was needed to stop international and regional movement of disease-spreading livestock and poultry. So quarantines to prevent the spread of some of the more serious diseases were set up—some of them many years before anybody knew what caused the disease.

Kansas and Nebraska had quarantine laws to control hog cholera 20 years before research workers in the Department of Agriculture discovered that it is caused by a virus too small to be seen with a microscope. Massachusetts set up a quarantine against pleuropneumonia of cattle long before the germ causing it was discovered. A hundred years before scientists of the Department of Agriculture discovered the blood parasite that causes cattle tick fever and proved that ticks spread the disease, North Carolina tried to stop the spread of cattle tick fever by prohibiting the movement of cattle from the eastern part of the State (which was tick-infested) to the western part (which was tick-free).

None of those quarantine measures stopped the spread of the diseases they were aimed at. Because people lacked exact knowledge of how the diseases spread, it was impossible to include the most effective preventive measures in the quarantine regulations. Neither adequate staffs nor enough funds were available to enforce the quarantines strictly enough. The significant point is that quarantines were invoked so long ago.

Long ago, also, livestock owners tried to make animals more resistant to disease by various measures. They fed them sulfur, wood ashes, or charcoal. They gave drugs that were said to act as tonics, and put pine tar in drinking troughs. Some farmers burned feathers in their barns and stables as a protective measure. None of these measures or similar ones helped much.

One factor in curbing the spread of disease before the development of the steam engine was the lack of transportation. Most livestock moved on foot and the sick animals spread disease only as far as they would walk. Two examples:

Hog cholera first appeared in the United States about 1833 in the Ohio Valley. It did not become widespread for 20 or 30 years because hogs did not go far from home. Our first outbreak of foot-and-mouth disease occurred along our northern border in 1870—in winter. Because animals and people did not move about much in cold weather, the disease spread very little and died out before spring.

Steam and internal-combustion engines changed all that. Railroads, water transportation, trucks and automobiles on good highways, and airplanes made rapid and long-distance shipments of animals commonplace. They also presented an almost unlimited possibility of spreading disease.

If our methods of preventing disease were no better than they were a hundred years ago, we might now be spending ever so much more time than we do in the elemental fight against malnutrition and hunger. But during the years that transportation was developing, science also was moving forward against the scourge of transmissible diseases.

THE FIRST big accomplishment was proving that living organisms cause

disease and that the organisms always originate from other organisms. The French veterinarian Delafond in 1863 demonstrated that the blood of sheep dead of anthrax contained microscopic organisms that would multiply if kept under suitable conditions. The German bacteriologist Koch in 1876 proved the organisms Delafond had seen and grown were the cause of anthrax in the animals and in people.

In 1869 Moritz, another French veterinarian, noticed "granulations" in chickens that had died of fowl cholera. Perroncito, an Italian veterinarian, saw and made sketches of the germs. Then the French veterinarian Toissant proved that those organisms caused the disease. He sent Pasteur, the famous French chemist, the head of a cock that had died of cholera. From it Pasteur grew the germs of cholera and produced a vaccine that would protect against it. These were epoch-making results.

Scientists now knew how to grow the germs of a disease, how to produce disease with them, and how to make from them a protective vaccine. But that was only the beginning of a program for protecting animals from transmissible diseases. Many practical questions needed answers: Where and how do germs grow in sick animals? How do they escape from such animals? How long will they live outside an animal? What will kill them? How do they enter susceptible animals? Do recovered animals continue to carry and spread germs? Each question had to be answered for each disease, because each was different from all others.

Research workers had to learn how to produce each disease studied so they could have sick animals with which to work. That in itself was quite a task.

Some examples: Scientists found out that anthrax organisms grow in practically all organs of the body. Most coccidia (the minute organisms that cause coccidiosis) multiply in the lining of the intestines only. The bacteria that cause brucellosis in cattle multiply principally in the pregnant uterus (womb) and in the udder. Anthrax germs may escape from infected animals in discharges from the nose, in urine, or in feces (dung). Coccidia are passed out mainly with the feces. Brucella organisms escape with the calf (at the time it is aborted or born), in the discharges from the uterus a few days or weeks after aborting or calving occurs, and in the milk. Anthrax bacteria can live for 50 years or more in soil even when exposed to bright sunlight and dry air. Some types of coccidia may live for many months in pastures or corrals. Brucella organisms are usually destroyed in a few days or a few weeks if they are exposed to direct sunlight and dry air.

RESEARCH WORKERS learned that animals that appear healthy may spread the organisms that cause such diseases as tuberculosis, brucellosis, glanders, fowl cholera, and coccidiosis. This discovery clarified the disappointing results that had followed attempts to eradicate disease from the infected herds and flocks by removing all animals that were showing symptoms: The carrier animals were not removed, and they continued to spread infection.

Scientists have done a great deal of research to find methods of detecting carrier animals that show no symptoms. They have given us many new methods and tests for diagnosing disease. Every cattle producer knows what tuberculin is. Every poultryman knows about the agglutination test for pullorum disease. Horse breeders do not know how to make a complement-fixation test, but they know it can be used to determine if a horse has glanders.

Active and successful research with methods of spread of disease paralleled the work with diagnostic procedures. The results of such research are discussed in another chapter (page 5).

Information and facts developed through research efforts during the last 100 years make it possible to prevent many diseases by preventing exposure. The basic principles concerned in accomplishing this consist of two steps. The first is learning where infection is. The second is prevention of any direct or indirect contact between disease-free animals and infected animals, or contaminated premises, feed, equipment, or vehicles.

The first—learning where infection is—may be accomplished in some instances by making careful and repeated examinations of the suspected animals. That, for example, is the basis of locating sheep scab infection. Trained men examine flocks and herds for symptoms and lesions—changes brought about in tissues by the disease. If they find suspicious lesions, they examine scrapings from them with a lens for scab mites. A positive diagnosis is made only when mites are found. Sometimes a combination of a physical examination and a diagnostic test is the standard diagnostic procedure. Diagnosis of foot-and-mouth disease is an example of this technique. Veterinarians examine the mouths and feet of cloven-footed animals in areas where the disease exists or is suspected. If they find suspicious cases, they may collect material and send it to a laboratory for a test. Sometimes, however, symptoms and lesions are so typical that the diagnosis is made without laboratory tests.

Sometimes one relies almost entirely on a test as the diagnostic method. Veterinarians rely on the tuberculin test rather than symptoms to diagnose tuberculosis.

The second step—preventing contact between disease-free animals and any source of infection—often is difficult. The easiest and most economical way to accomplish that is to separate all the diseased and exposed animals from healthy animals, give them a curative treatment, hold them in isolation until they are free of infection, and clean and disinfect all contaminated premises. That would eradicate disease by destroying the infectious agent at its source. It can be done with such diseases as sheep scab. Unfortunately, though, only a few diseases can be handled this way because only a few really effective treatments are known. Other methods of handling infected animals besides treatment must be resorted to in most diseases.

Sometimes the infected animals may be held in isolation and quarantine on the premises with little danger. Sometimes such procedures are unsafe. Sheep infected with lungworms may be kept on farms where lungworm-free sheep are held if they do not use the same pastures, corrals, or sheds, and if there is no drainage from them to the premises used by the lungworm-free sheep. But any attempt to hold animals infected with foot-and-mouth disease on premises with susceptible animals probably would be disastrous.

INFECTED ANIMALS are the source of all infection. They are always potentially dangerous.

Slaughter of infected animals is usually the best procedure for actually preventing exposure and spread of easily transmitted diseases like foot-and-mouth disease, which is so infectious that it is well-nigh impossible to prevent its spread if sick and healthy animals are kept on the same premises.

Slaughter is best, too, in handling diseases like Johne's disease, from which animals do not recover. Cattle with Johne's disease may live for months or years; during that time they continue to pass large numbers of germs of Johne's disease in their feces.

Slaughter of all animals affected with certain serious diseases, such as tuberculosis, is a standard procedure in the United States and several other countries. Governments usually pay indemnities for the diseased animals that are slaughtered if the owners agree to follow programs of disease prevention prescribed by the authorities.

THE CAUSATIVE AGENTS of some diseases may occur in all parts of carcasses of animals dead from those diseases.

Thus the flesh, skin, bones, blood, livers, lungs, and other parts of an animal with hog cholera, anthrax, or foot-and-mouth disease may be infected. The entire carcasses of animals that die from such diseases, or are killed because they are infected with them, should be burned, sterilized with heat, or buried deeply. If such carcasses are not disposed of properly, swine, mink, poultry, or other flesh-eating animals may become infected from eating them.

Garbage that contains uncooked meat scraps or offal is always a possible source of danger to swine or poultry that eat it.

Experiments conducted many years ago by men in the Department of Agriculture proved that hogs slaughtered a few days after exposure to hog cholera may pass the most careful inspection even though their carcasses contain the hog cholera virus. They showed, too, that the virus may live through the usual curing processes to which pork is subjected. Virus of foot-and-mouth disease may be present in carcasses of animals slaughtered in the beginning stages of the disease. Therefore countries (such as the United States) that prohibit importation of domestic ruminants and swine from countries in which foot-and-mouth disease or rinderpest exists also prohibit the importation of fresh, chilled, or frozen meat.

Premises contaminated with disease-producing agents are dangerous. Stomach worms, intestinal worms, lungworms, liver flukes, and many other parasites that cause serious diseases are picked up in contaminated barns, pens, or pastures rather than being transmitted by direct contact. Thorough cleaning and the disinfection of barns, stables, and sheds that have been exposed to any disease-producing agents are necessary.

Contaminated pastures present special problems. Spores of anthrax or blackleg organisms live indefinitely in soil. Records show some areas have remained contaminated with anthrax for 50 years or more. Viruses of hog cholera or vesicular exanthema, on the other hand, may disappear from pastures in less than a month. Eggs and larvae—the immature worms—of some of the worms that infest horses may live in pastures for 2 years or more. Plowing pastures increases the danger of anthrax but lessens the danger of parasitic infection.

PROTECTION from exposure becomes increasingly easier as the amount of infection decreases. Sheep or cattle might be raised without any infection with liver flukes on a fluke-infested farm if only an acre or less is fluke-infested. But if half or two-thirds of a farm is infested, it is hard to keep sheep or cattle free of these parasites.

Distance offers protection, too. It might be quite burdensome to prevent exposure of a herd of cattle to brucellosis if it were kept on premises surrounded by farms on which active outbreaks of the disease were occurring. It should be easy to give such protection if there were no infected animals within 5 miles and still easier if the nearest infected animal were 50 miles away. It is a sound protective procedure, then, to encourage disease eradication on a community, county, State, or national basis.

The commonest way of exposing and infecting animals in disease-free herds is by introducing infected animals into healthy herds. I can relate many instances of the appearance of such diseases as swine erysipelas, pinkeye in cattle, or Newcastle disease in poultry soon after purchased animals were added to flocks or herds. If a farmer has to add animals to a disease-free herd or flock, he should insist on official health certificates covering both the animals to be added and the herds from which they originate. The animals he buys should not be exposed in transit to infected animals or to contaminated trucks, cars, or pens. It is a wise precaution to hold newly purchased animals in separate quarters for 3 weeks or so because recently exposed animals may appear healthy and may pass all the different diagnostic tests although they are infected.

INCREASED RESISTANCE is becoming a more and more important factor in preventing transmissible diseases. It should be possible to increase resistance to some diseases by selective breeding. Plant breeders have been spectacularly successful in developing healthier varieties of wheat, oats, sugarcane, tomatoes, and many other plants by selecting partly resistant specimens and doing selective breeding from them as parent stock to get resistant strains.

But breeding farm animals for disease resistance is little beyond the early experimental stage. Large-scale attempts in this field would be both time-consuming and expensive. It seems probable that resistant strains could be developed in this way. Light breeds of chickens are more resistant to pullorum disease than are the heavy breeds. Wide variations in susceptibility to rinderpest occur among the different breeds of cattle. In the outbreak of foot-and-mouth disease in Mexico in 1946–1953, the native cattle suffered less severely from the disease than did the European breeds.

VACCINATION has been a practical method of protection against transmissible diseases since the time that Pasteur developed vaccines against fowl cholera, anthrax, and rabies more than 70 years ago.

An interesting point is that Pasteur prepared each of the vaccines by a different method. He grew the fowl cholera germ in chicken broth, killed the organisms with heat, and injected them as a vaccine. He found that anthrax germs became less virulent—capable of causing severe disease—if they were grown at high temperatures. He produced vaccine from these less virulent organisms without killing them. This type is sometimes called attenuated vaccine. Because he could not grow rabies virus outside an animal, he used dried nerve tissue of rabbits infected with rabies in preparing rabies vaccine. This is spoken of as a tissue vaccine.

Vaccines have been developed that

give good protection against many of the transmissible diseases of livestock and poultry. Among these are black-leg of cattle, tetanus, hog cholera, rinderpest, fowlpox, red water disease of cattle, Newcastle disease of poultry, bluetongue of sheep, foot-and-mouth disease, brucellosis, and encephalomyelitis in horses.

No vaccine is absolutely safe or completely effective. The anthrax spore vaccine may cause anthrax in very susceptible animals. The brucella vaccine may not protect against very severe exposure to brucella organisms. But the practical value of both products has been demonstrated in many millions of vaccinated animals.

Some vaccines give immediate and long-lasting protection. Some give immediate but short-lived protection. Some do not give satisfactory protection until 10 to 20 days after they are used. Some vaccines protect against only one type of a disease.

Here are some examples of these variations. Nearly all swine that are properly vaccinated with anticholera serum and virus are well protected against cholera immediately and usually for life. Vaccination with anti-serum alone gives immediate protection, but the protection lasts only 15 to 25 days. Crystal violet hog cholera vaccine does not give good protection until 2 to 3 weeks after it is injected. The immunity resulting from its use usually lasts until the vaccinated pigs go to market.

Foot-and-mouth disease vaccine made from Type A virus (there are several types of this virus) gives good protection against Type A foot-and-mouth diseases but does not protect against Type C or Type O virus.

Vaccination is the most practical available method of protecting animals that graze pastures and ranges contaminated with organisms of anthrax, blackleg, or red water disease. Vaccines are widely employed in protecting livestock against some of the acute insect-borne diseases, such as bluetongue of sheep. Protection of horses against encephalomyelitis (sleeping sickness) is extremely difficult if vaccines are not available because many species of birds carry the virus without showing symptoms and mosquitoes transfer the virus from birds to horses.

The use of vaccines is the most effective method for protecting animals against acute infectious diseases when epizootics appear in countries that have ineffective quarantine laws and few veterinary sanitary officers. Countries with better laws and larger veterinary staffs might attack such epizootics more vigorously with quarantine and eradication programs. (The epizootics among animals correspond to epidemics, as applied to the diseases of people.)

The use of vaccines alone does not usually result in the complete eradication of disease. More than a billion hogs have been vaccinated against hog cholera in the United States since 1915, but hog cholera has not disappeared from the country. None of the States that have depended upon vaccination alone as a control procedure has eradicated brucellosis.

On the other hand, the quarantine and elimination of infected animals to prevent exposure of disease-free animals and vaccination to increase their resistance have been successful in eliminating diseases and protecting the animal population against them. This combination eradicated the foot-and-mouth disease from Mexico and is successful against brucellosis in the United States.

PROTECTION against transmissible diseases and parasites is as important to the livestock and poultry producer as are good breeding and good feeding practices.

Accepted protective measures should be included in the day-to-day operation of the livestock and poultry farm just as are good feeding, good management, and selection of good breeding stock. This is a responsibility of the livestock or poultry producer. Veterinarians, livestock sanitary officials, and research workers with animal diseases can work with the producers, but the programs they recommend cannot succeed unless the producers carry them out.

The objective of owners and those who work with them should be complete freedom from many of the transmissible diseases and parasites in herds and flocks, in communities and counties, in States, and the entire country.

B. T. SIMMS, *director of livestock research of the Agricultural Research Service,* *is a graduate of the College of Veterinary Medicine of Alabama Polytechnic Institute. He was head of the Department of Veterinary Medicine and experiment station veterinarian at Oregon State College; director of the Auburn, Ala., Regional Animal Disease Research Laboratory of the former Bureau of Animal Industry; chief of the former Bureau of Animal Industry; and chief of the Animal Disease and Parasite Research Branch of the Department of Agriculture. His research has included work with brucellosis in cattle, liver flukes in sheep, salmon poisoning in dogs, and coccidiosis and helminth parasites in cattle.*

Feeding and Management

AUBREY M. LEE AND LLOYD A. SPINDLER

FARMERS combat diseases and parasites when they feed good diets to keep animals in good condition to maintain resistance and manage them in sanitary ways to prevent infection.

Proper feeding is important in maintaining an animal's defenses against disease and parasites. Animals in good condition generally are considered to be more resistant than animals in poor condition. This is especially true of resistance to parasites. It has never been satisfactorily demonstrated by experiments, however, that feeding alone will increase directly an animal's resistance beyond that with which nature has endowed it.

Good nutrition must therefore always be coupled with a degree of cleanliness that prevents acquisition of overwhelming numbers of parasites and germs. Good nutrition, especially if coupled with cleanliness, aids in keeping the resistance of animals at the maximum level provided by nature. It also helps the animal respond properly to immunization.

In general, the best diets are those that contain proteins, vitamins, minerals, and the other essential food elements.

Proteins are especially important, because they are necessary for growth. It is coming to be recognized that animals generally resist parasites better when they are fed diets high in proteins of various types.

Minerals, such as salt, limestone, iron, and copper, also help animals resist the effects of parasites and probably diseases. Parasites such as hookworms and stomach worms injure the lining of the intestinal tract and cause bleeding. This results in anemia. Diets rich in iron, copper, and cobalt may be of value in such cases, because they help correct anemia.

Pastures are important sources of proteins, vitamins, and minerals for livestock. Improved, heavily fertilized pastures may not always provide all the substances needed to maintain a high level of nutrition, however. Animals grazing on pastures of this kind may suffer from dietary deficiencies and have more parasites than those grazing good pastures. Consequently supplemental feeding of animals while they are on pasture is coming to be recognized as highly important from the standpoint of providing adequate amounts of proteins, vitamins, and minerals and controlling diseases, especially those caused by parasites.

Improper feeding may reduce resistance, even if the diet fed is a good one. This happens because lack of feed may lower the level of sugar in the blood in a short time—sometimes in 30 hours.

Lack of sugar in the blood may be considered to be a secondary cause of disease since it may predispose the animal to attack by the direct causes—bacteria, viruses, parasites, and fungi. Undernourished animals are ready prey to parasites. Once parasites become established, they tend to prevent the animal from making the best use of the food it eats, and it suffers from dietary deficiencies, becomes unthrifty, and is still more susceptible. A vicious cycle thus arises that takes the profit out of livestock raising.

Basic research is needed to determine the precise role of dietary deficiencies and other factors in resistance and susceptibility of livestock and poultry to parasites and transmissible diseases. Largely because of the great cost, not much proved research of that kind has been conducted.

Reports have been published showing that the resistance of experimental animals to tuberculosis is lowered when they are fed diets deficient in one or several nutritional factors. The addition of sodium citrate or sodium glutamate to the diet of mice, for example, produces a consistent and marked decrease in resistance to this disease. When mice are deprived of food for 30 hours shortly before inoculation with the germs of tuberculosis, their susceptibility is increased. Efforts have been made to modify the resistance of mice to such infections by procedures designed to alter the metabolic processes of the animals, but with little success.

It has been shown that resistance can be decreased by certain types of feeding, but it has not been proved that resistance to transmissible diseases can be increased by feeding. Claims have been made that the use of certain types of feeds will increase the resistance of animals to infectious diseases. For example, it has been stated that increasing the calcium content of the cow's ration will increase the resistance to brucellosis; the feeding of sodium bicarbonate (baking soda) will prevent shipping fever of cattle; and increasing the amount of protein in the ration of swine will increase their resistance to erysipelas. Those claims are false.

In the case of parasites, however, it has been reported that feeds fortified with antibiotics—Aureomycin, penicillin, and some others—are useful in combating, under certain conditions, the effects of cecal coccidiosis of chickens and infections of ascarids and nodular worms in swine. Such drugs as certain of the sulfonamides and nicarbazin have given good results in checking cecal coccidiosis of poultry, when administered in feed. By and large, infected animals or birds fed the fortified feeds have suffered less from the parasitism and have made better weight gains than parasitized ones on regular diets.

Poor diets or insufficient amounts of good ones are not the sole cause of dietary deficiencies, however. Gastrointestinal disorders of various kinds may interfere with proper digestion and absorption of food. Parasites often cause intestinal disorders which may interfere with digestion. This prevents the animal from utilizing to the best advantage the proteins, vitamins, and minerals, such as calcium, contained in feed and forage and which it needs to maintain health. This is especially true in the case of growing animals, since they require ample amounts of these substances for bone formation and other purposes. Some parasites, such as tapeworms and roundworms, that live in the intestine may even absorb and store up in their own bodies significant amounts of calcium and vitamin B_{12}. This robs the animal of these important substances, lowers its resistance, and makes it susceptible to disease and parasites.

Special attention should be paid to feeding and sanitation of young animals. They are the ones most susceptible to diseases and parasites. They need good feed to meet the demands of growth. Parasites and disease waste feed. Therefore the growing animal that has acquired parasites or is diseased may require more feed than the healthy one.

In summary, it may be stated that animals in good condition generally are believed to be more resistant to infection with diseases and parasites than are animals in poor condition. Proper feeding, housing, handling, and care

to maintain animals in good condition therefore are factors that assist in increasing an animal's natural resistance to disease and parasites to the highest point of which it is capable. Debilitating influences that lower the resistance, such as overwork, faulty nutrition, improper care, extreme heat and cold, and bad sanitation are predisposing factors to infection and influence the progress of disease in an infected animal.

AUBREY M. LEE *is head of the Noninfectious Diseases Section of the Animal Disease and Parasite Research Branch, Agricultural Research Service.*

LLOYD A. SPINDLER *was put in charge of the Protozoan Parasite Section, Animal Disease and Parasite Research Branch, in 1955.*

Quarantining

C. L. GOODING

FEDERAL and State laws and regulations governing the movement of livestock and poultry and their products are needed to prevent the introduction and spread of disease.

We have had such laws since May 29, 1884, when the Congress approved an act that authorized the Secretary of Agriculture to establish quarantines, cooperate with the States in the control and the eradication of animal diseases, and prevent the exportation of diseased cattle.

The laws safeguard agricultural investments in livestock and poultry that on January 1, 1956, amounted to more than 11 billion dollars.

Before we had the laws, many animal diseases were introduced into the United States from abroad. At that time the animals went mainly to local markets for slaughter, so that diseases

did not spread rapidly. But with the further development of rail and water shipping, livestock in increasing numbers began to move from one State to another, and healthy animals were exposed constantly to diseased animals.

A few States undertook to control and eradicate contagious pleuropneumonia, but the only ones that succeeded by their own efforts were Connecticut and Massachusetts. The livestock industry became concerned at the spread of disease and recommended that the Federal Government take action to prevent further losses.

The Commissioner of Agriculture in 1869 recommended to the Congress that a Veterinary Division be established to protect the Nation's livestock interests. He renewed his recommendation the following year.

Great Britain and other countries,

fearful that livestock from the United States would bring in disease, in 1879 and 1880 restricted or prohibited the importation of United States livestock.

Contagious pleuropneumonia had spread to most of the New England States and as far west as Ohio by 1883. The next year the livestock industry received Federal support in the control and eradication of disease, and the United States Bureau of Animal Industry came into existence. Other Federal legislation, notably the Acts of 1890 and 1903, have provided additional support.

INTERNATIONAL INSPECTION and quarantine measures seek to prevent livestock diseases of foreign origin from gaining entrance into the United States. Thousands of animals and millions of pounds of animal products are imported each year from all over the world.

Absolute protection against the entrance of foreign diseases through such importations probably is impossible.

Effective protection is possible, however, if our applicable laws and regulations are enforced. Public understanding and support are essential.

A number of animal diseases, some of them relatively harmless and others extremely destructive, plague many other countries but do not exist in the United States. Every effort should be made to keep them out. Our livestock population is vulnerable, and our system of moving animals from place to place might make possible an explosion of disease from a small beginning.

Two ruinous diseases are rinderpest and foot-and-mouth disease. Neither was known to be in the United States in 1955. Rinderpest has never appeared, but we have had at least 9 outbreaks of foot-and-mouth disease, 6 of them since 1900 and 1 in 1929, in California. Each time the disease was eradicated at a cost of many millions of dollars and much time and effort.

Section 306 (a) of the Tariff Act of June 17, 1930, has been of great value in keeping this country free from foot-and-mouth disease for so many years. This statute established an embargo against the importation of cattle, sheep, other domestic ruminants, and swine and against the fresh meats derived from such animals from any country declared by the Secretary of Agriculture to be infected with rinderpest or foot-and-mouth disease. Many of the major livestock-producing countries are infected with one or both of these diseases.

Animals not subject to the prohibition of section 306 (a) are potentially eligible for entry in compliance with the Department's sanitary regulations. Such regulations, promulgated under the Acts of 1890 and 1903, have been in effect for many years. From time to time it has been necessary to amend the regulations as the incidence of disease changed.

For all animals potentially eligible for entry, except equine stock, and except from Canada and some of the Northern States of Mexico, the importer or his agent must first obtain a permit from the Animal Inspection and Quarantine Branch. The Department of Agriculture thereby can weigh all essential factors relating to a proposed importation, such as disease conditions, transportation, and veterinary service in the country of origin.

It also enables the Department to specify certain conditions under which the importation may be made.

With few exceptions, animals offered for entry must be accompanied by a certificate of health issued by an official veterinarian in the country of origin showing that the animals have been in that country for at least 60 days immediately preceding shipment, that they have been inspected and found to be free from certain communicable diseases, and that they have not been exposed to such diseases.

All animals are given careful veterinary inspection upon arrival at a designated port of entry. If the examination discloses evidence of communicable disease or history of exposure to communicable disease, the animals are refused entry and are destroyed or returned to the country of origin. If they are found to be apparently healthy, they are permitted entry without further restrictions or, when subject to quarantine, are permitted to be moved into approved quarantine facilities.

Because some imported animals may be carriers of latent infections or (irrespective of certification to the contrary) may have been exposed to contagious or communicable diseases, quarantine is for a long enough time to assure freedom from disease or exposure thereto. Quarantine is considered the most important step in any importation. It stands as a bulwark between the livestock industry and diseases.

SANITARY REGULATIONS governing the importation of livestock and other cloven-hoofed animals did not include poultry before June 18, 1950.

An outbreak of Asiatic Newcastle disease in California in April of 1950, traced to an importation of game birds from China, prompted the issuance of regulations. Newcastle disease had existed in the United States for many years, but the virus strains isolated from outbreaks for the most part caused only moderate mortality. The strain isolated in the California outbreak proved to be highly lethal. The outbreak was quickly eradicated by destroying all diseased and exposed poultry and the cleanup and disinfection of infected premises.

Because of the wide variety of birds susceptible to Newcastle disease and other diseases common to poultry, the regulations broadly define poultry to include chickens, ducks, geese, swans, turkeys, pigeons, doves, pheasants, grouse, partridges, quail, guinea fowl, and peafowl, of all ages, and eggs for hatching.

An instance of the protection afforded the livestock and poultry industries through quarantine occurred in March 1954, when Newcastle disease occurred in a consignment of partridges from Spain while the birds

were in quarantine at the port of New York. All the birds were immediately destroyed, and the quarantine area was thoroughly cleaned and disinfected. The strain of virus isolated from this outbreak was shown to be highly lethal for chickens. These game birds had been intended for restocking purposes in several States. Seven different outbreaks of Newcastle disease have occurred since then in poultry quarantined at the ports of New York and Los Angeles. The disease occurred in partridges, pheasants, quail, chickens, and doves.

POSSIBLE DANGERS along the boundaries between the United States and Mexico and between the United States and Canada are typified by conditions in 1946–1954. Foot-and-mouth disease existed in Mexico for two extended periods in those 8 years, and one outbreak occurred in Canada within 50 miles of our border. To protect this country against the entrance of foot-and-mouth disease from Mexico, there was established a border patrol of 700 men, who rode back and forth constantly in jeeps, on horseback, and in airplanes. They seized and destroyed more than 3,600 stray and smuggled animals and many thousands of pounds of prohibited and restricted meats and other products during the time foot-and-mouth disease existed in Mexico.

Inspection and quarantine activities along the border between Canada and the United States were like those along the Mexican border when foot-and-mouth disease existed in Mexico. Because of relatively unrestricted commerce between Canada and the United States for many years before 1952, however, the occurrence of foot-and-mouth disease in Canada created problems, particularly as to scheduled airline flights, railroad routes that cross and recross the boundary, the use of international roads and highways, and joint ownership of land and property in both countries adjacent to the boundary. Curtailment of commerce and trade constituted large economic losses in both countries. Canada normally supplied thousands of replacement animals to dairy and breeding herds in the United States and large quantities of hay and straw for feed and bedding.

Other diseases, such as dourine and glanders in horses and splenetic and tick fever in cattle, occur in extensive areas of Mexico next to the border.

Thus a potential danger exists that those diseases will be reintroduced into the United States. Other diseases, such as tuberculosis, brucellosis, and scabies, occur in livestock in Mexico and Canada. Scrapie in sheep has appeared in Canadian flocks. Vigorous inspection and quarantine measures against them are necessary.

THE BENEFITS of animal inspection and quarantine activities to the livestock industry of the United States are shown in import figures for 1955.

That year 251,999 cattle were imported from Mexico, and 1,933 cattle were rejected for entry because of disease or exposure to disease; 18,940 head of horse stock were imported from Mexico, and 483 were rejected; 24,420 blood tests for dourine and glanders were conducted on horse stock offered for entry from Mexico; 9 were positive and 30 suspicious to the dourine test, and 18 were positive and 61 suspicious to the glanders test.

Annual imports of cattle in past years have totaled more than 525,000 head from Canada and more than 704,000 from Mexico. Livestock constantly stray over the borders, and there is the never-ending problem of smuggling. In the protection of this Nation's livestock industry, the inspection and quarantine activities in connection with international commerce and the illegal movement of livestock is a continuously increasing responsibility.

Supervision is maintained over the entry of hides and skins, wool, hair and bristles, gluestock, bones, horns and hoofs, bonemeal, tankage, and similar products, glands, oxgall and like materials, and hay and straw. Such products (except bones and bonemeal) are permitted unrestricted entry from countries not declared to be infected with rinderpest or foot-and-mouth disease.

From countries so infected, some animal byproducts are permitted entry only when consigned direct from the port of entry, under Government seal, to previously approved establishments for handling and processing in a manner designed to guard against the spread of diseases.

Because anthrax, which is known to exist in nearly every country of the world, is most likely to be introduced through the importations of bones, horns, hoofs, and bonemeal, special regulations are applicable to them.

Strict precautions also are taken in connection with the importation of restricted foreign-cured meats from the countries infected with rinderpest or foot-and-mouth disease. Even though cured meat is permitted entry under the law, it is considered a possible means of introducing the virus of rinderpest or foot-and-mouth disease. Added safeguards therefore have been set up; it is believed they remove any danger to the livestock industry. Such meats, when cured or cooked, are permitted entry subject to definitely established regulatory procedures.

Department of Agriculture employees are assigned to ports of entry to prevent the importation of prohibited animal products, supervise the landing of restricted animal products, and prevent the landing of garbage.

The regulations provide that garbage that contains prohibited meat scraps may be brought ashore only in tight containers for destruction under official supervision. In one instance, approximately 5,000 pounds of restricted or prohibited meats were confiscated from passenger baggage in order to prevent their entry into this country. Evidence showed that much of the restricted meat was destined to points throughout the United States. The possible entry of such prohibited and restricted meats is considered to be particularly dangerous because three outbreaks of foot-and-mouth disease in the United States were attributed to raw garbage, which contained meat scraps removed from foreign vessels with restricted or prohibited meats aboard and which was fed to swine.

INTERSTATE INSPECTION AND QUARANTINE measures are designed to prevent the spread of livestock diseases within the United States.

The beginning of the present system of inspection of public stockyards was an order issued on October 20, 1890. For several years Texas fever was the only disease controlled by this inspection. Inspection was extended to sheep scabies in 1897 and to cattle scabies in 1903. The scope of the work was extended by 1905 to the inspection for communicable diseases of all livestock received at public stockyards.

Authority for the Secretary of Agriculture to promulgate rules and regulations governing interstate shipments of diseased livestock was provided in the Act of February 2, 1903.

The Act of March 3, 1905, provided authority to quarantine disease-infected areas and promulgate rules and regulations governing interstate transportation of livestock from quarantined areas.

The purposes of public stockyard inspection are sixfold: To restrict the movement of diseased animals; supervise the treatment and proper disposition of the diseased animals; notify States of the origin of diseased animals received; supervise the cleaning and the disinfection of infectious stockyard facilities and transport vehicles; issue certificates for the interstate movement of animals that have been inspected and found to be apparently free of any contagious, infectious, or communicable disease; and supervise the vaccination, dipping, and testing of animals before shipment.

If the diseases that affect farm animals in the United States were allowed to spread from State to State, our livestock industry would suffer greatly. Livestock at public stockyards come from widely separated areas, and this inspection offers opportunity to examine for disease a cross section of the livestock populations of the country almost daily at a minimum cost. It is one of our greatest defenses against the spread of disease.

Of prime importance in coping with a dangerous communicable disease is early detection and prompt diagnosis. The sooner a disease is discovered and the affected animals are isolated, the fewer will be the number that become infected and exposed. Furthermore, the sooner the disease is traced back to point of origin the less likely will be the further dissemination of the disease from that locality.

The value of this service to the livestock industry would be difficult to estimate, because trained inspectors and inspection chutes, isolation quarters, dipping vats, spraying, and testing and immunizing facilities all tend to make a public stockyard one of the safest places from which to get healthy animals for breeding and feeding.

When the Act of 1884, which established the Bureau of Animal Industry, was passed, one of the main problems in disease control was domestic transportation. The use of railways was supplanting the driving of livestock to markets on foot, and the more rapid method of transportation was resulting in wider distribution of animals and their diseases. The need for official supervision in regulating the interstate movement of livestock was apparent, and public stockyards throughout the country were recognized as important points for this purpose. The number of yards maintaining inspection has continued to grow as State livestock sanitary officials, producers, and other interested groups have emphasized the importance of such protection until in 1956 inspection of livestock was conducted at 48 principal markets in 46 cities. The heavy increase in the movement of livestock to market by truck, frequently in small lots and at irregular hours, has greatly increased the inspection workload. Each year there pass through all these public markets for slaughter or other purposes between 60 million and 70 million head of livestock.

The establishment of a Federal quarantine to prevent the spread of a communicable livestock disease from one State to another is a drastic measure that is usually invoked only as a last resort. The procedure generally followed when a serious livestock disease is diagnosed is for the State involved to establish a quarantine immediately, thereby stopping the movement of diseased and exposed animals, and then proceed to eradicate the disease. If, however, it has become widespread, or there is an undue delay in disposing of the affected animals, then a Federal quarantine is resorted to in order to prevent the interstate movement of any animals from the quarantine area. It may become necessary to quarantine the whole State if the disease continues to spread.

The Secretary of Agriculture has authority to cooperate with the State concerned in drastic eradication measures, including the purchase of diseased or exposed animals and contaminated materials.

THE INTRASTATE MOVEMENT OF LIVESTOCK is controlled by State laws and regulations. Practically all States have health requirements governing the admission of animals from other States and the movement of livestock within the State.

The main losses from animal diseases, however, are in the important producing areas, and the toll is greatest among young animals, many of which never reach market. The practical course by which livestock owners may reduce such losses is to make a careful study of the probable local danger from each disease; obtain publications containing directions for dealing effectively with the danger; establish a high degree of farm sanitation; and consult a veterinarian about further methods of prevention, diagnosis, and control, including the use of biological products.

THE FIRST 28-HOUR LAW was enacted on March 3, 1873, and a somewhat stronger law, still in force, was enacted June 29, 1906. This law requires that animals in interstate commerce by rail or water shall be unloaded at stated intervals into properly equipped pens for rest, water, and feeding, or shall be fed and watered in cars if there is sufficient room for all the animals to rest.

The purpose of the 28-Hour Law is to prevent the overconfinement of animals shipped interstate by common carrier. Waybills and records maintained by carriers and others are examined daily. Apparent violations are reported at stations where Federal livestock inspectors are stationed. Inspections are also made from time to time at approximately 900 feed, water, and rest stations in 48 States to ascertain whether the facilities and equipment are maintained for the safe and humane handling of the species of animals which they were designed to accommodate. Unsatisfactory conditions found at the stations are promptly brought to the attention of the responsible railroad for corrective action.

While the 28-Hour Law was enacted primarily for humane reasons, to reduce to a minimum the cruelty incident to the transportation of livestock, it also protects the interests of owners of animals and the interests of the public by safeguarding the health and conditions of the animals and by preventing their serious injury while in transit. To have his stock reach the market in as nearly the same condition as when it leaves the farm or ranch is the object of every stockman and shipper. This can be accomplished only by giving the animals while in transit as nearly as possible the care, attention, feed, water, and rest to which they have been accustomed. If animals are confined in cars for an excessive period without feed, water, or rest, or if unloaded within the statutory time for the stipulated 5-hour rest period but into a pen too small for them to rest or even move about, or too muddy to lie down, or if the proper kind and amount of feed and water are not supplied, or if in the unloading or reloading process the animals are handled in an inhumane manner, the objective desired by the shippers and contemplated by the statute is not attained. The livestock as the result of such treatment may arrive at destination in a feverish condition, and the quality of the meat may be affected if the animals are slaughtered in that condition.

How well the 28-Hour Law has served its purpose may be judged by the fact that whereas formerly it was not uncommon for carriers to confine animals in cars for 50 to 60 hours or even more, now the carriers as a whole are endeavoring to unload them within the statutory period and to give them proper care and treatment when unloaded.

The provisions of this law, which was enacted in 1906 before motor transportation had come into general use, have been held not to apply to animals moved interstate in trucks. Several efforts have been made to have the law amended to cover this modern development in livestock transportation.

The animal quarantine laws governing the importation and the interstate movement of livestock apply only to horses, other equine stock, cattle, sheep and other ruminants, swine, poultry, related animal products, and hay and straw.

A DIGEST OF LAWS pertaining to quarantines, animal diseases, and related matters follows.

THE ACTS OF May 29, 1884, August 30, 1890, February 2, 1903, March 3, 1905, May 31, 1920, February 28, 1947, and June 16, 1948, as amended and extended (animal quarantine and related laws) (21 U. S. C. and Supp. 101–131). The purposes of these statutes are to prevent the introduction into and dissemination within the United States of contagious, infectious, or communicable diseases of animals and poultry, to extirpate such diseases, and to prevent the exportation of diseased animals and poultry. The Acts—

(a) direct the Secretary of Agriculture to give notice of the existence of contagious, infectious, or communicable diseases in any State, Territory, or the District of Columbia;

(b) prohibit thereafter the interstate movement of diseased livestock or poultry therefrom by anyone knowing them to be diseased; provided, however, that certain tuberculosis, paratuberculosis, and brucellosis reactor animals may be moved interstate for immediate slaughter under regulations prescribed by the Secretary of Agriculture;

(c) prohibit the importation of ruminants or swine which are diseased or exposed to infection within 60 days next before their exportation from the foreign country;

(d) authorize the Secretary of Agriculture to—

(1) cooperate with States, Territories, possessions, Mexico, certain organizations, and individuals in promulgating regulations and taking measures to control and eradicate animal and poultry diseases;

(2) make certain investigations as to the existence of animal and poultry diseases;

(3) provide for inspection of imported animals;

(4) prescribe the manner in which food, litter, clothing, and appliances accompanying imported animals shall be dealt with;

(5) quarantine import animals at ports designated for such purposes;

(6) cause to be slaughtered, or removed from this country, imported animals found to be infected or exposed to infection;

(7) seize, quarantine, and dispose of hay, straw, and similar material, meats, and other animal products coming from infected foreign countries or moving interstate;

(8) quarantine any State, Territory, or the District of Columbia when

he determines that animals or poultry are affected with any contagious, infectious, or communicable disease, and to give notice thereof;

(9) issue regulations permitting and governing the interstate movement of animals or poultry from such a quarantined area;

(10) provide for the inspection of animals intended for exportation and the disinfection of vessels, attendants and their clothing, and appliances involved in such exportation; and

(11) prevent the exportation of diseased livestock and poultry.

THE ACT OF March 3, 1891, as amended (46 U. S. C. 466a, b). An act to assure humane treatment and safe transportation of certain animals exported from the United States. The statute authorizes the Secretary of Agriculture to—

(a) examine vessels on which such animals are to be exported;

(b) prescribe by rule, regulation, or order the accommodations which the vessels shall provide for such animals; and

(c) direct that if the owner or master of any such vessel willfully violates any rule, regulation, or order issued under the Act, the vessel shall be prohibited from carrying such animals from any port of the United States for a period not exceeding 1 year.

THE ACT OF June 29, 1906 (28-Hour Law) (45 U. S. C. 71 et seq.). An act to prevent cruelty to animals shipped interstate and to prevent losses while in transit. The act prohibits the confining of livestock in railroad cars or vessels for longer than 28 hours without unloading for feed, water, and rest for at least 5 consecutive hours except under specified unavoidable circumstances and permits the time of confinement to be extended to 36 hours upon request of the shipper.

THE ACT OF June 30, 1906, as amended and extended (Meat Inspection Act) and the Act of July 24, 1919

(Horse Meat Act) (21 U. S. C. 71–91, 95–96, 98–99). The purpose of this legislation is to prevent the distribution in interstate or foreign commerce of meat and meat food products not fit for human food. These acts regulate the preparation of meat and meat food products of cattle, sheep, swine, goats, and horses for such commerce, and require interstate and export shipments thereof to bear marks of Federal inspection and approval. The acts also prohibit the forgery or misuse of marks or other identification devices provided under the statutes and prohibit bribery of inspectors. The Meat Inspection Act provides certain exceptions for retail butchers and dealers and for farm prepared meats and meat food products. These acts authorize the Secretary of Agriculture to—

(a) provide Federal inspection at slaughtering and similar establishments where meat or meat food products of cattle, sheep, swine, goats, or horses are prepared for interstate or foreign commerce;

(b) withdraw inspection from establishments failing to destroy condemned meat or meat food products or to maintain sanitary conditions;

(c) approve labels of meat and meat food products;

(d) cause inspection and certification of such animals and meat for export;

(e) waive, in certain cases, the requirement of export certificates imposed by law; and

(f) grant certain exemptions from inspection requirements of the Meat Inspection Act to retail butchers and dealers.

THE ACT OF March 4, 1913 (Virus-Serum-Toxin Act) (21 U. S. C. 151 et seq.). This Act—

(a) prohibits preparation or sale in places under Federal jurisdiction, interstate shipment, and importation into the United States of any worthless, contaminated, dangerous, or harmful virus, serum, toxin, or analogous product intended for use in treatment of domestic animals;

(b) requires licenses for preparation, sale, or interstate shipment of such products intended for such use;

(c) requires permits for importation of such products; and

(d) authorizes the Secretary of Agriculture, after opportunity for hearing, to suspend or revoke licenses issued under the act and to deny permits for the importation of regulated products which are worthless, contaminated, dangerous, or harmful.

THE TARIFF ACT OF 1930, section 1306 (b) and (c) (19 U. S. C. 1306 (b) and (c)). These provisions prohibit the importation of meat which is not fit for human food, and provide for the destruction of meat offered for entry and refused admission into the United States unless it is taken out of the country within the time fixed by the Secretary of Agriculture.

The Tariff Act of 1930, section 306 (a) and (c) (19 U. S. C. 1306 (a) and (c)). The purpose of these provisions is to prevent the introduction of foot-and-mouth disease or rinderpest into the United States. The section provides that when the Secretary of Agriculture determines that foot-and-mouth disease or rinderpest exists in any foreign country and gives certain notices thereof, the importation of domestic ruminants and swine, and fresh, chilled, and frozen beef, veal, mutton, lamb, and pork from such country is prohibited until the Secretary has given certain notices that such disease no longer exists in that country. The section also provides for the destruction of domestic ruminants and swine, and of all meats, offered for entry and refused admission into the United States, unless such animals or meats are taken out of the country within a time fixed by the Secretary.

The Tariff Act of 1930, section 201, paragraph 1606, as amended (19 U. S. C. 1201, par. 1606). This paragraph—

(a) permits the importation of any animal, except certain foxes, duty free, by a United States citizen specially for breeding purposes, if such animal is purebred of a recognized breed and registered in a book of record recognized by the Secretary; and

(b) authorizes the Secretary to make rules and regulations for the purpose of recognizing breeds and books of record, and determining the purity of breeding and the identity of such animals.

THE ACT OF August 24, 1935 (Anti-Hog-Cholera Serum and Hog-Cholera Marketing Agreement Act) (7 U. S. C. 851–855). This act is designed to insure the maintenance of an adequate supply of anti-hog-cholera serum and hog-cholera virus by regulating the marketing of such serum and virus in interstate and foreign commerce, and to prevent undue and excessive fluctuations, unfair methods of competition, and unfair trade practices in such marketing. The act authorizes the Secretary of Agriculture to enter into marketing agreements and to issue orders for the regulation of the marketing of serum and virus in interstate or foreign commerce after appropriate administrative proceedings, and provides for the enforcement of such agreements and orders by criminal and civil court actions.

THE AGRICULTURAL MARKETING ACT of 1946, section 203 (h) (7 U. S. C. 1622). This provision authorizes the Secretary of Agriculture to inspect, certify, and identify the class, quality, quantity, and condition of agricultural products shipped or received in interstate commerce, under such rules and regulations as the Secretary prescribes, including assessment and collection of fees to cover the cost of the service rendered.

C. L. GOODING *is chief, Animal Inspection and Quarantine Branch, Agricultural Research Service. He received the degree of doctor of veterinary medicine in 1926 from Colorado Agricultural and Mechanical College. He has been employed since by the Department of Agriculture in California and Washington, D. C.*

some methods

Treatment of Disease

B. T. SIMMS

TREATMENT, or therapy, of disease may be defined as any effort to cure disease, arrest its course, lessen its severity, or alleviate the pain and inconvenience that disease causes. It includes the administration of drugs or medicines; physical therapy, such as massage, exercise, immobilization with bandages or splints, and application of heat or cold; and any changes in methods of feeding or handling that are made to insure recovery.

Drug and physical treatments are sometimes called direct therapy; good management may be called indirect or supporting therapy.

The art of treating disease is as old as the history of man. Written records of some of the early civilizations describe some of the diseases of domestic animals and give directions for treating

them. It is an art that has never stood still. Man has constantly striven to find better methods of restoring his sick animals to good health.

The use of drugs and medicines, including biological products such as vaccines and serums, constitute the most important segment of disease treatment. Until about 70 years ago, progress in developing new and better drug treatments was rather slow because the nature of disease was not well understood and a real scientific approach to treatment therefore was impossible, and because few organized, extensive efforts to find new treatments were being made.

The improvements that were taking place were coming largely from the trial-and-error experience of practicing veterinarians. A rapid development of

71

experimental methods of studying both the normal and the sick animal began about 70 years ago. Such studies have added enormously to our knowledge of the science of disease.

We know now that many of the treatments used in the past were aimed at the results of disease rather than at disease itself. For example, we used to see animals (and people) treated for fever. Now it is generally recognized that fever may be brought on by many different causes. The skillful veterinarian of today tries to find out what is causing the fever and then treats the disease itself. Fever medicines, which were so generally used in the early years of this century, are seldom heard of now.

Experimental studies of the action of drugs have accompanied the studies of normal and sick animals. Physiologists and pharmacologists have measured and recorded the effects of a large number of drugs and medicines on animals kept under controlled conditions. We now know rather definitely what results may be expected from the use of many of the different remedies. We know, too, that many of the remedies in common use 70 years ago have little actual effect. Furthermore, some of the treatments that were formerly in rather general use are actually harmful. For example, carbolic acid (phenol), which was used to treat wounds, did so much damage to the tissues that its use actually slowed down healing.

Experimental studies have proved that the different species of animals may respond differently to the same drug. Thus dogs are put to sleep by morphine, but morphine causes cats to become restless and excited. Chloroform is a fairly safe anesthetic for the horse but a dangerous one for the hog. Dogs may be anesthetized with ether rather easily, but cows cannot be.

All these developments have given the veterinarian and the livestock owner a good foundation for a scientific approach to treatment of disease. With a fairly good understanding of what disease is and how Nature tries

to overcome it, the veterinarian directs his efforts at assisting Nature. He tries to find out why a heart is beating faster than it normally should, rather than just giving a drug that will slow it down. He looks for the reason when an animal has quit eating, instead of prescribing some medicine that is said to stimulate the appetite. What was once mainly an art has become a science and an art.

DRUGS that act on or affect organs or tissues with which they come in direct contact at the time they are used are said to exert local action.

Drugs that are absorbed into the blood stream and are distributed throughout the body before results are produced are said to be systemic or general in their effects.

Drugs and medicines may be classified according to the actions they produce in the treated animal. Many of the terms used to describe such actions are well known. Stimulant, depressant, anesthetic, blister, irritant, antiseptic, narcotic, and antibiotic need little explanation.

Probably most of the drugs used in treating domestic animals are stimulants. Examples are laxatives or purgatives, which stimulate the bowels; diuretics, which stimulate the kidneys; diaphoretics, which stimulate sweating; and expectorants, which stimulate glandular secretion.

Many drugs have more than a single action. Turpentine is a fairly effective treatment for the coughing that accompanies certain types of laryngitis or pharyngitis, but it is an irritant to the kidneys. Alcohol is a depressant if given internally, but it is a mild local stimulant when it is applied to the skin. Some of the most active of the antibiotics have harmful side reactions, so that they must be used with a great deal of caution.

A few drugs are used as direct replacements for necessary constituents of the normal body. The treatment that is perhaps the most dramatic one in the whole field of medicine—the intravenous injection of some form of soluble calcium in a cow with parturient paresis (milk fever)—is in this group. As soon as the calcium content of the circulating blood is raised significantly, the cow that is being treated usually shows some response. It is not unusual for an animal that appeared on the verge of death and that probably would have died within a few hours if left untreated to be on her feet in 10 to 15 minutes after the injection is completed. Many of the hormones are in this group, too. Spectacular effects follow the administration of thyroxin, the secretion of the thyroid gland, to animals suffering from thyroid deficiency.

ADMINISTRATION of drugs to farm animals often is a rather serious problem. Theoretically drugs can be given to livestock by any and all the routes that they can be given to human patients, such as by the mouth, by injection with a hypodermic syringe, by inhalation, or by direct application. But there are many reasons why the veterinarian cannot leave drugs for owners to give to their animals by mouth just as the physician leaves medicine for his human patients to take that way.

Perhaps the best way for the average owner to give medicine to his livestock or poultry by mouth is to mix it with feed or salt or give it in the drinking water. But this can be done only in cases in which the animal is taking feed, licking salt, or drinking. It is not very useful in the acutely and seriously sick, which neither eat nor drink. Nor can drugs which have such disagreeable flavors or odors that animals refuse to take them be given in this manner. Sometimes flavors can be disguised by mixing a little blackstrap molasses with the feed, water, or salt. The use of salt as a vehicle for giving such needed elements as iron, copper, cobalt, and iodine now is standard practice. Some worm remedies, particularly phenothiazine, are taken rather readily by sheep and somewhat less so by cattle when they are mixed with salt.

None of the farm animals, except dogs, will take bad-tasting drugs by mouth willingly. They must be given liquids as drenches, with a dose syringe, or by a direct injection into the stomach through a stomach tube. Pills, capsules, and boluses must be placed far back in the mouth if they are to be swallowed.

All of these procedures are time consuming even to a veterinarian who is trained in ways to give medicine. They are difficult and sometimes dangerous when attempted by inexperienced persons. Many horses and quite a few cattle have died from pneumonia following attempts at drenching because the medicine went into the lungs instead of into the stomach. Stomach tubes also may pass down the trachea (windpipe), and drugs given through them may cause immediate and severe reaction.

Attempts by the inexperienced to place pills, boluses, or capsules far enough back on the tongue so they will be swallowed sometimes results in the fingers or hand being bitten.

The possible harmful effect of forcing the sick animal to take medicine is often overlooked. The excitement and the struggle that goes with drenching sometimes cause more harm than the medicine does good.

Some drugs can be given rather easily by mixing them with honey and smearing the mixture on the tongue and the inside of the cheek. Many animals will swallow most of the material given in that way if the flavor of the drug is not too objectionable.

The hypodermic syringe is coming to be used more and more in the administration of drugs. Almost any medicine that will dissolve in water and is not irritating can be given this way. If care is taken to use sterile syringes and needles and to inject sterile solutions, there is little danger. It is usually neither as time consuming nor as disturbing to the treated animal as drenching.

Inhalation is a little used method of administering drugs other than general anesthetics to domestic animals, but one uses it occasionally in treating some diseases of the throat, larynx, or trachea.

Many drugs are applied directly to the organ or area to be treated. Examples are ointments, lotions, and antiseptics applied to the skin; eyewashes; douches injected directly into the uterus; and medicines injected into the udder through the teat canal. Great care must be taken in selecting drugs that are not irritating if they are to be applied directly to tender tissues, such as the eye or the uterus. Many cows have been seriously injured or killed by irritating solutions used as uterine douches.

Nearly every owner of livestock keeps on hand at least a few drugs to be used in emergencies. These should be selected with great care and perhaps after consulting a veterinarian. In general one should avoid the more powerful drugs, such as quick-acting and severe purgatives, irritating and poisonous antiseptics, and irritating lotions and ointments. Each package should be plainly labeled and should carry directions and dosage. Since many "cure-alls" fail to cure anything, a livestock owner has little reason to keep them.

Every livestock owner should have a clinical thermometer for taking temperatures of sick animals. He should learn how to use it and know the range of temperatures in normal animals.

PHYSICAL THERAPY may not be so important in treating domestic animals as it is in treating humans, but it does have a place in handling certain types of animal diseases.

Massage stimulates circulation and promotes healing of torn or injured muscles. Exercise strengthens muscles, builds up the general tone of the body, and tends to stimulate appetite. Bandages and splints are useful in supporting and protecting injured ligaments, joints, and bones. A supporting bandage or suspensory applied to an inflamed and swollen udder helps to reduce the pain. Hot packs or alternate hot and cold packs are useful in reducing pain and swelling that come from some types of acute inflammation.

Supporting therapy is usually an important (and sometimes the most important) part of treatment of sick farm animals. It should be aimed at keeping the treated animals comfortable, quiet, and free from excitement. Many owners do not realize how helpful supporting therapy may be.

The first concern of the owner should be comfortable quarters. If the sick animal is housed, the inside temperature should be moderate. If sick animals—be they horses, cattle, swine, sheep, dogs or chickens—are kept dry, protected from drafts, and given plenty of dry bedding, they may be comfortable at temperatures much too low for comfort of humans. Sometimes owners forget this point and provide artificially heated quarters that are much too warm. Very thin animals, though, or those that are not eating may need light blankets or perhaps warmer quarters if the temperature goes too low. A paddock or lot that provides shade may be more comfortable in very warm weather than a barn or stable.

Darkened quarters add to the comfort of animals with inflamed eyes. Deeply bedded stalls are good for lame animals.

Good quality feed of the kind the animal is accustomed to eating should be placed before the sick at least 2 or 3 times a day.

Water should be available at all times. Cattle and horses that have drunk only from streams or ponds may refuse to drink from a pail or tub. It may be better to put them back where they will drink from the usual source rather than to hold them until thirst drives them to accept a pail.

Sick animals should be kept quiet and free from excitement. Cattle and horses that are handled regularly may be quieted by a visit from the owner, but even gentle animals may be somewhat upset by the presence of a stranger. Sick animals that are lying down should never be made to get up just to see how they look. Animals with fever lose strength rapidly even when they are kept quiet. Exercise increases the rate of loss of strength and is harmful. A mild febrile disease may soon become serious if the sick animal is forced to exercise.

The owner or handler should pay close attention to any sick animal that is placed in strange quarters or held under unusual circumstances. Cattle or horses (and other livestock, to some extent) may become quite nervous if their usual routine is changed. Isolating them from the herd or flock is often disquieting. Every effort should be made to prevent or overcome the unrest that may come from such changes.

Sometimes placing a companion animal in an adjoining stall or paddock is a good solution to the problem. If the restlessness is marked and cannot be overcome, it may be advisable to put the sick animal back in its original pasture or quarters.

When owners of livestock realize the full importance of adequate supporting treatment of their sick animals, the results of direct therapy will be far more effective. Good animal husbandry will do much to hasten the recovery and reduce the losses from animal disease. In itself, it will effect no cures but it will give the ailing animal the best chance for recovery in response to therapy.

B. T. Simms *is the director of livestock research, Agricultural Research Service.*

Special Principles of Parasite Control

AUREL O. FOSTER

PARASITES and parasitic diseases are of a nature that sets them apart and is the basis of special principles that determine and explain the measures used to control them.

Animal parasites are a universal hazard to livestock production, although individual species are limited in distribution and intensity by a sensitive adjustment to climate (and other factors) and by the kinds of animals in which they develop.

They are abundant in numbers and kinds and are chiefly injurious because of the inapparent, unrecognized loss from subclinical parasitism. They are, then, especially dangerous because of their insidious and unspectacular effects despite the fact that they are generally better known for their ability to cause disease and death in livestock.

They are also commonly injurious to their hosts in a quantitative way. In most instances, as in the case of almost all the parasitic worms, or helminths, they do not multiply in or on affected animals. Even in protozoan and arthropod parasites (the major groups other than helminths), the individual cycles of development within the host animals are so limited, fixed, and finite that, despite multiplication in and on their hosts, the damaging effects generally are directly correlated with degree of exposure and magnitude of infection— which cannot be said exactly of exposure or infection involving bacteria, viruses, and other disease-causing organisms.

Parasitism is essentially a herd or flock disease rather than one of individual animals. Measures to control parasites are effective therefore only if applied to a whole herd or flock as though it were but a single animal.

That is clearly true of sanitation—a broad term that includes about every means of minimizing exposure short of chemicals that have specific and selective action. But it is also true of preventive medication, because the kind and extent of such medication depend on the hazards of specific parasitism. It also is true (with minor exceptions) of the use of chemotherapeutic, or curative, agents. Those agents often are unreliable in heavily parasitized animals and should therefore be used when parasitism in a flock is most responsive to control by them, but the urgency of treating all animals of a flock or herd is dictated by the fact that parasitism ordinarily is recognized first in one or a few animals when it is incubating in all the others.

Every parasite, moreover, has a relatively fixed cycle and rate of development, despite the abundance of different species, each of which has its own forms, habits, modes of life, and potentialities for causing disease and injury.

Each species therefore must fight its own battle for survival. The strongest attack must be made on the parasite's stage of development which is most vulnerable.

Immunological techniques cannot be used as a major aid to systematic control. That circumstance, more than any other, forces us to rely mainly on chemical measures of prevention and eradication.

PARASITE CONTROL is the judicious use of feasible, profitable measures to minimize the losses and the hazards of parasitism.

The term "parasite control" connotes something quite beyond "keeping parasites in check," "holding the line" against them, or "maintaining the status quo." By modern standards, eradication is the only rational goal, however remote that prospect or possibility may be.

Eradication of most parasitic infections is unfeasible in practice—if not impossible. Measures are available, nevertheless, to effect attrition, prevention, or containment of most of the injurious species. The measures are based largely on sanitation and medication, the keystones of parasite control, which, if applied strongly enough, must ultimately spell eradication. There is therefore no logical basis for compromise or adjustment in the control of parasitic diseases.

THE GOAL has been achieved in a few instances. Tick fever—a disease that caused an estimated loss of 73 million dollars in 1906—was eradicated from the United States after an unrelenting campaign against two ticks, *Boophilus annulatus* and *B. microplus*, transmitters of the microparasite of the blood, *Babesia bigemina*.

Dourine and surra of horses, trypanosome infections that occur all over the world, were eradicated by slaughtering affected horses. One can resort to that costly procedure only when the hazard is great and the number of affected animals is small. It is the one sure method of controlling diseases of whatever cause that have not yet secured a foothold in our animals. Its usefulness depends on recognition of diseases at the very beginning and on vigilance against their importation into this country.

But those cases are exceptions. Economic and other basic influences lead to compromise and indifference in many quarters where weapons of a sort are at hand for more vigorous onslaught.

We could feasibly eradicate scabies from cattle, sheep, and swine. We could eradicate lice, warbles, screwworms, sheep nose bots, horse bots, and sheep keds. Almost within reach is the control of anaplasmosis and bovine venereal trichomoniasis. It is likely that by an all-out attack we could eradicate lancet flukes and common stomach worms of sheep and cattle, stomach hairworms of cattle, and nodular worms of sheep. We could also eradicate trichinosis and hydatid disease, both a constant risk to man. That we have not ended them is a measure of the job ahead in research and education.

THE DEVELOPMENT of control measures requires a full knowledge of injuriousness, parasite-host relationships, life cycles, sources of infection and means of transmission, epizootology, bionomics, immunity, factors that augment host resistance, and geographical distribution.

To eradicate tick fever it was necessary to have many basic facts: That the microparasites in the blood of sick animals were the sole cause of the disease; these organisms were tick-borne and were transmitted by only one kind of tick; this tick was a one-host species; there were no uncontrollable reservoirs of infection; the disease was transmitted by successive generations of ticks rather than by successive stages of the same tick; the disease could not exist if the ticks were eradicated; the developmental cycle of the tick was such that successive, definitely timed treatments would destroy all ticks before they could produce a new generation; and that efficient chemical measures could be devised for destroying the ticks. All those facts and more were used in devising the simple scheme of dipping of cattle south of the quarantine zone twice a month in a prescribed arsenical solution.

That is the "life cycle approach." A concerted attack on all fronts achieves best results, but "breaking the chain at its weakest link" is the essence of every effort directed against parasites.

Nearly every species has an environmental phase outside its host, which alternates with the parasite's stages in or on the animal. The former may involve an intermediate host—for example, the cattle tick in the instance of the microparasite of cattle fever. There are one or more intermediate, reservoir, or vector hosts of many other parasites—the trypanosomes, theiler-ias, anaplasms, histomonads (blackhead organisms of turkeys and chickens), leishmanias, liver flukes and other trematodes, tapeworms, many stomach worms, filarial worms, thornheaded worms, and numerous others, including even an arthropod species, the tropical warblefly. These, like the parasite of tick fever, almost always are more subject to indirect attack by destruction of their intermediate hosts than by direct attack on the organism.

Often there is no intermediate host. In the direct cycle, the environmental phase may consist of free-living, pre-infective, and infective stages (as in gastrointestinal nematodes) or it may be the adult stage, as in flies that produce myiasis (screwworms, blowflies, cattle grubs, horse bots, the sheep nose bots, and others).

In any, there are successive host stages—preadults, adults, eggs, larvae and embryos, in the case of parasitic worms—that alternate with extra-host stages, such as the free-living pre-infective and infective larvae.

A parasite usually is more vulnerable to attack at one stage of this cycle than at another. Anthelmintics, for example, are commonly employed to destroy the adult stage of worm parasites in their hosts. Free-choice and low-level administrations of phenothiazine, however, act primarily upon the eggs and preinfective larvae of parasites outside the host, although there are also other significant actions, such as depression of the reproductive potential of female worms in their hosts.

The radiobiological attack on screwworms is an attack on the egg stage of flies on potential hosts and also on the reproductive potential of adult flies.

Infestation by the most damaging gastrointestinal roundworm parasites is transmitted by means of the feces. Measures to prevent and destroy contamination of pastures, such as light stocking, resting and rotating pastures, stock rotation, chemical disinfestation, and general sanitation, consequently are the basis of many recommendations for control.

The time and environmental conditions that a parasite needs to develop are significant. Some parasites, such as cattle grubs and swine kidney worms, take so long to complete their life cycles that marketing the host animals often interrupts the cycle. Marketing practices, then, can influence parasitism, but time factors have greater significance in defining when, how often, and at what intervals medication can best destroy the parasite. Cattle thus are dipped or sprayed twice at an interval of 10 days for scabies, and swine are treated twice at an interval of 10 weeks to combat large roundworms.

Temperature, precipitation, and the other factors of climate determine the distribution, seasonal occurrence, and abundance of many parasites. Warmth and moisture generally favor their development. Many internal worm parasites must overwinter in breeder animals because the free-living infective stages cannot survive the cold of winter on pastures. They can be destroyed by anthelmintics between grazing seasons; so it is possible to put clean animals on clean pastures in the spring.

External parasites often exhibit just the opposite pattern. Lice, for example, survive in small numbers in the summer but become abundant in the winter. It is quite easy, therefore, to eradicate them by efficient treatment of animals in early fall. These off-season treatments are the basis of many measures of systematic, preventive medication. Generally it is advantageous to drain, fill, or fence swampy areas of pastures because they propagate parasites. Irrigation of arid lands favors parasitism and thus creates special problems of control. Always, however, good control measures take advantage of environmental influences.

PARASITIC INFECTIONS usually provoke more or less immunity, yet they are not controllable by vaccines, serums, or other biologicals that are suc-cessful against some of the infectious diseases. Immunization has been practiced with uncertain success in poultry coccidiosis. The cross-immunity conferred by a comparatively benign species of Anaplasma has been utilized in some countries to protect cattle from anaplasmosis. A comparable procedure has offered some promise in controlling East Coast Fever, a disease of cattle in South Africa caused by the microparasite, *Theileria parva*. Breeding of resistant stock has been encouraged as a control measure for African bovine trypanosomiasis.

It is hard to evaluate the potential significance of factors of immunity among helminthic infections. There is no doubt that acquired immunity is a practical force. It may largely account for the unusual susceptibility of young animals to severe worm parasitism. Investigators in this country and England have demonstrated that immunity to lungworms can be transferred to calves by injections of serum and gamma globulin from actively immunized animals. Scientists in Australia have described an "anthelmintic" effect in parasitized, hypersensitive sheep that results from exposure to living infective larvae of the large stomach worms and intestinal hairworms. Such findings bolster our hope that methods of immunization shall one day be evolved. Their practical use in the control of helminthic disease still is negligible, however.

External, or arthropod, parasites offer little prospect of being amenable to control by immunizing technics. Phenomena of immunity influence the development and appraisal of control measures, however. Cattle grubs, for example, are less abundant in older animals than in yearlings. Sheep keds are more numerous on lambs than on breeder stock.

IMPROPER FEEDING and grazing, overstocking, unsanitary conditions, and inattention to illnesses in early stages favor parasitism. On the other hand, good feeding and the removal of adverse influences increase the resistance to the invasion and establishment of parasites. The factors of health often are specific as well as general. Sometimes, as with stomach-worm disease and trichostrongylosis of sheep, good diet often cures the disease.

Some investigators, indeed, do not regard clinical parasitism as a "primary" disease. They consider it secondary to and induced by one or more predisposing influences. However, the notable significance of factors that predispose to parasitism and of the benefits from remedial measures do not obscure the fact that the real battle must be waged against the offending parasites.

Antiparasitic chemicals are powerful aids to control. They are not synonymous with control or substitutes for it. Some efficient measures of parasite control do not depend for their success on the use of these agents. Examples are the sanitation system of controlling worm parasites in swine, portable pens for controlling coccidiosis and other fecal-borne infections of calves, and artificial insemination in the control of bovine trichomoniasis. Conversely, few parasites have been successfully controlled by medication alone. Chemotherapeutic and other chemical measures for destroying or otherwise attacking parasites, however, have a prominent place in parasite control programs. In the same degree that the concept of control embraces all measures aimed at the weakest links in the cycles of parasites, the concept of antiparasitic chemicals includes all agents that accomplish, or help accomplish, interruption of the cycle at stages where parasites are open to attack by them.

Accordingly, the list of antiparasitics includes the usual protozoacides, anthelmintics, insecticides, and acaricides that are commonly used to destroy adult parasites and vectors of disease and also the ovicides, larvacides, repellents, and other agents for destroying developmental stages, preventing fulfillment of the cycle, and disinfecting premises. It also includes many chemical agents that ameliorate and suppress parasitic disease or militate against the survival and propagation of parasites.

Chemical measures generally are immediate in their effects, economical, and simple. They may not be desirable if other means are adequate, but changing concepts about antiparasitic agents and their applications are a measure of progress in parasite control. Antiparasitic chemicals, above all else, must be used preventively and systematically to the fullest extent possible. The reclamation of heavily parasitized animals is not "a stitch in time." We have increasing evidence, moreover, that medication cannot be relied upon to check the outbreaks of parasitic diseases, or even to cure worm parasitism in weakened animals. Under such conditions, the veterinarian must advise vigorous measures.

People generally recognize the need for more, better, and safer antiparasitic chemicals; for sounder and wider application of programs of systematic, preventive medication; and for more imaginative and effective use of chemical agents against other than adult stages of parasites.

Yet in most instances the best applications of chemical agents can only be determined by complete knowledge of a kind that marked the campaign against tick fever. Furthermore—to repeat—the expanding knowledge of parasites and their relationship to livestock makes it clear that efficient control goes hand in hand with sanitation, good feeding and grazing, proper stocking, intelligent breeding, surveillance, and good management.

Motivation is a practical factor in the control of parasites. Without it, measures of greatest efficiency and simplicity are of little avail. Regulatory programs with legal backing are the exception. In short, to be feasible, parasite control measures must return a profit to the producer. More than anything else, the increased recognition of the magnitude of preventable loss from parasites is the chief stimulus to an awakened interest.

AUREL O. FOSTER *is head of the Parasite Treatment Section, Animal Disease and Parasite Research Branch, Agricultural Research Service. He was trained as a parasitologist in the Johns Hopkins University School of Hygiene and Public Health. He received the degree of doctor of science from that institution in 1933. He taught in Baltimore and conducted research in Panama before entering the Department in 1939.*

Chemotherapeutic Agents for Internal Parasites

AUREL O. FOSTER

CHEMICALS are our oldest weapons for combating the parasitic infections. They are also the most practicable and powerful weapons in modern use.

The Ebers Papyrus—the oldest medical document, dating from about 1550 B. C.—mentions the use of pomegranate against intestinal worms. Pomegranate is listed for the same purpose in a late edition of the *United States Dispensatory*, an official document, which gives "original information about new drugs and current data about drugs already in use." Both volumes also mention castor oil as a purgative.

Pomegranate is listed because of longevity, not because of newness or because of uses that we can recommend. Castor oil is still without a peer in its line.

But specific treatments ordinarily are products of the times and for the times. None of the treatments currently in wide use against internal parasites was known two decades ago. There is the probability and the hope, therefore, that we shall have many new and better ones a decade or two hence.

Methods of using drugs against parasites also change. The effects of new approaches and viewpoints are fully as significant as new drugs. Today, in consequence of a better understanding of the nature and gravity of parasitism, the strictly curative use of antiparasitic chemicals is becoming rare. Emphasis is on prevention rather than cure, and the concept of parasite control embraces all feasible steps that minimize economic losses from parasites.

A corollary viewpoint is that antiparasitic chemicals may attack any vulnerable stage of a parasite and are best and most efficiently employed as adjuncts to other control measures rather than as substitutes for them: However necessary and useful these agents are for treating heavily infested animals, they are used most profitably in proved programs of systematic, preventive medication. We see this at its highest development in the extensive use of free-choice and low-level systems of medication to control the gastrointestinal parasites of cattle, sheep, and horses, and in programs of continuous and intermittent medication for controlling coccidiosis and blackhead of chickens and turkeys.

Chemotherapeutic agents, or chemicals used in treatment or control of parasitic infestations and infectious diseases, ordinarily come into use only after critical evaluation from standpoints of safety and efficiency. Nevertheless, the most widely used drugs are those about which we are constantly learning most. Phenothiazine, for example, has been in wide and increasing use throughout the world for more than 15 years, yet the scientific literature now contains more accounts of research and experience with it than with all other anthelmintics combined. In the last analysis, then, treatments, like the language, are made by use.

PHENOTHIAZINE is a synthetic organic compound prepared by the union of diphenylamine and sulfur in the presence of iodine as a catalyst. It has well established applications in horses, cattle, sheep, goats, swine, and poultry. Against many of the damaging gastrointestinal roundworms, it is the most effective treatment—and for some species the only known treatment.

Phenothiazine evolved in three periods: The discovery of its application as a standard anthelmintic (1938–1940); standardization and development of methods of using the drug to achieve effective control of parasites (1941–1948); and its greatly increased use (from 1948 on) in cattle, particularly free-choice and low-level systems of preventive medication of beef animals and dairy calves. The third stage marks an awakening to the importance of parasitism in cattle and a recognition of the benefit that may be derived from controlling subclinical parasitism in cattle and other livestock.

Despite the extensive use and study of phenothiazine and despite the well-marked stages in its evolution, many problems remain unsolved. They have grown in importance. Among them are:

The mechanism of action of phenothiazine against parasites;

Subjective factors that influence its therapeutic efficiency, such as diet and condition of animals requiring treatment;

Physical factors, such as the relationship of particle size to therapeutic efficiency of the chemical and to low-level and free-choice use of it;

The versatility and mode of action of programs of systematic, preventive medication;

The applicability of these programs to parasite control in dairy cattle and goats;

The economic benefits of periodic medication and of low-level and free-choice methods of administration for the control of subclinical parasitism;

The significance of catalytic iodine in commercial products;

The net longtime effects of low-level and free-choice medication; and

The evolution and occurrence of phenothiazine-resistant strains of parasites.

New problems arise, but sound usage of the chemical depends largely on solving the old problems.

Of the remarkable anthelmintics that have been developed—carbon tetrachloride in 1921, tetrachloroethylene in 1925, and hexachloroethane, sodium fluoride, lead arsenate, toluene, and many others in later years—phenothiazine must be ranked as outstanding. It combines a unique range of application, a high degree of efficiency, an unusual margin of safety, an ease and versatility of administration, and a variation and range of antiparasitic actions not found in any other anthelmintic.

But phenothiazine has some disadvantages. It is comparatively expensive. Therapeutic doses are very bulky. A few animals, especially horses and swine, are rather susceptible to intoxication by it. Treated animals eliminate breakdown products as a red dye, in the urine and feces, which is sometimes alarming, although harmless. The dye temporarily stains the wool of treated sheep, which are animals in which the drug has great overall usefulness. The dye also discolors the milk of dairy animals. Finally, the drug is deficient in desired efficacy against some important parasites, such as the trichostrongyles of sheep and several gastrointestinal nematodes of cattle. These considerations make it clear that there is a place for an even better drug.

SODIUM FLUORIDE is a very efficient chemotherapeutic agent for removing large roundworms from swine. As developed in 1945 and later, the administration of the chemical (technical grade, tinted) in dry, ground feed at a concentration of 1 percent for 1 day is a safe treatment for growing pigs.

The treatment removes immature and mature parasites and is more effective than ascaricides that formerly were available. Because the roundworms take about 10 weeks to mature in pigs, effective chemotherapeutic attack on it requires strategic dosing at intervals just short of 10 weeks. For systematic control, therefore, pigs should be treated when they are about 8 weeks old, or at weaning time, and again at about 16 weeks.

The treatment is not safe unless properly administered—sodium fluoride is poisonous. Some pigs have been killed by incorrect dosage and by adding the chemical to slops, garbage, milk, water, and wet feed. Properly administered, the treatment has natural safeguards. Its taste is unpleasant, and it irritates the stomach—factors that prevent excess consumption of medicated feed and cause reflex vomiting if too much is taken in.

Sodium fluoride has other disadvantages. It presents the hazard of poisoning not only to pigs but to users, children, and pets. Transient diarrhea and vomiting occur in some pigs, even when the drug is properly administered. Feed intake by pigs is reduced for a day or two at the time of medication. Ingestion of fluorine-containing compounds, such as sodium fluoride, results in a cumulative deposition of insoluble fluorides in the animal body, but the amounts that accrue in edible portions of pork from proper use of the treatment in question are too small to constitute a hazard to consumers.

Because of disadvantages of the treatment, researchers have looked to other chemicals, including cadmium salts and piperazine derivatives, as possible substitutes.

CADMIUM SALTS, the oxide and the anthranilate, showed promise of superseding sodium fluoride as treatments to remove large roundworms from swine. Cadmium oxide was first marketed in 1953. Cadmium anthranilate was marketed in 1954. Both salts are administered in feed for 3 consecutive days, the former at a concentration of 0.015 percent and the latter at 0.044 percent.

These compounds are as effective and simple as the sodium fluoride treatment; and they are also safer and more palatable, although they present the similar problem of potential residues in tissues. Our limited data, however, suggest that the residues are not dangerous to consumers. Nevertheless, it is recommended that treated animals not be slaughtered within 30 days. Retreatment is not recommended for hogs intended for food for people.

Cadmium treatments are more expensive than the sodium fluoride treatment, but, despite their excellence and popularity, seem destined to be surpassed by chemicals, such as the piperazines, which have become prominent in the experimental field.

PIPERAZINE COMPOUNDS were first investigated for antiparasitic action by a commercial company in the United States. A useful treatment was developed in 1947 for Bancroft's filariasis of man, a troublesome worm infection among soldiers in the South Pacific.

The drug, designated as diethylcarbamazine, has shown value as an ascaricide in dogs and cats and has been described as a treatment for cerebrospinal filariasis (*Setaria cervi*) in sheep, goats, and horses and for dermal filariasis (*Elaeophora schneideri*) in sheep. It has been used also against heartworms, esophageal worms, and threadworms of dogs.

After diethylcarbamazine was introduced, investigators in France and England turned to simpler piperazine derivatives, such as the hexahydrate, the citrate, and the adipate. Following studies on mice, piperazine citrate came into use in 1953 as a treatment for human pinworm infection. It and related salts were found to be effective also against the large roundworm. Against these parasites of men, piperazine has become established as the treatment of choice. It is also effective against large roundworms in dogs and cats and partially active against one species of hookworms.

Piperazines, notably piperazine adipate, are promising anthelmintics for horses, cattle, swine, and chickens. Piperazine is essentially nontoxic in effective doses (about 0.1 to 0.2 gram of a salt, or 50 milligrams of the base, per pound of body weight). It is easily administered and contains no metallic or other noxious ingredients. It seems to cause no side effects.

The status of piperazines in veterinary medicine, including the proprietaries known as Safersan and Parvex, could not be defined exactly in 1956, but they seemed destined for prominent and profitable use.

TOLUENE, or methylbenzene, has antiparasitic action in horses, swine, chickens, dogs, and cats. It was first tested in 1926, but the preliminary trials led to the wrong conclusion that the chemical was ineffective. After retesting, the chemical was described in 1947 as an efficient drug for removing large roundworms and hookworms from dogs. Doses of about 0.1 cubic centimeter per pound of body weight are about 97 percent effective against roundworms and 87 percent against hookworms. (There are approximately 30 cc. in a fluid ounce.) Toluene has become the accepted, standard treatment against those common parasites of dogs.

Limited studies with swine and chickens have not established a superiority of toluene over newer treatments, but in horses the results suggest that toluene may be a suitable and long-awaited replacement of carbon disulfide, which has been the drug of choice against large roundworms and stomach bots. The use of toluene for this purpose was in the experimental stage in 1956, but tests have indicated that it is safe and effective, although optimum dosages had not been determined and the number of trials has been too small to warrant recommendations.

METALLIC ARSENATES are effective for removing the common broad tapeworm from cattle, sheep, and goats. A question is which of several active compounds is best in safety, efficacy, simplicity, and cost.

Workers in the Department of Agriculture determined in 1940 that lead arsenate could remove tapeworms from chickens. The chemical was too toxic for use in poultry, but the result was noteworthy because poultry tapeworms were then regarded as resistant to drug action.

Lead arsenate was tried against tapeworms in lambs at the State College of Washington. Doses of one-half gram of the chemical (acid, spray-grade) were given to 555 lambs. The tests were not designed to give critical information on the efficacy of the chemical, but the doses did cause the expulsion of large numbers of tapeworms without hurting the lambs.

A veterinarian in Texas reported in 1944 his experience in treating 1,158 lambs, 2,072 kids, 131 calves, and 4 cows. The treatments seemed to be well tolerated and efficient.

Studies conducted by the Department of Agriculture and the South Dakota Agricultural Experiment Station in 1947 established the efficacy at about 92 percent, a figure that, in the light of later experience, might have been conservative.

Despite the favorable experience with lead arsenate and its status as the standard tapeworm treatment for ruminants, the undesirability of its lead component was recognized from the beginning. A few trials with arsenates of calcium, cobalt, copper, and iron have indicated that lead is unnecessary for effective teniacidal, or tapeworm-killing, action. Presumably, therefore, more complete data will show that dosage depends on the arsenic content of the compound and that some other arsenate is as efficient as lead arsenate. We have indications that some metallic arsenates have effective action also against stomach worms.

SULFONAMIDES and certain newer chemical agents have been beneficial in controlling coccidiosis, a kind of "intestinal malaria" that affects all classes of our domestic animals except horses. In rabbits, besides intestinal infection, the disease often produces severe involvement of the liver.

Coccidiosis is a general term for a number of related diseases, all caused by protozoan organisms known as coccidia but differing in their occurrence, pathobiology, treatment, and control.

In calves, kids, lambs, and rabbits, sulfamethazine effectively arrests the disease in individual animals and checks an outbreak. Many other drugs of its class, however, have been used with variable and uncertain success.

Among them are sulfaquinoxaline (which appears, however, to lack efficacy against one of the injurious bovine species, *Eimeria bovis*), sulfamerazine, sulfadiazine, phthalylsulfathiazole, succinylsulfathiazole, and sulfapyrazine.

Many sulfonamides are reliable agents also in controlling poultry coccidiosis. Sulfamethazine is one of the best. Other drugs, however, such as Nicarbazin, furazolidone, nitrofurazone, nitrophenide, 3-nitro-4-hydroxyphenylarsonic acid, and 2,2'-methylene-*bis* (4-chlorophenol), have all come into competitive prominence since 1944. Certain antibiotics, such as chlortetracycline and chloramphenicol, may be superior to sulfonamides in treating coccidiosis in dogs and cats.

We are not able to assert positively which of the aforementioned drugs is superior for preventing a specific kind of coccidiosis or arresting its course. None of them was used before 1944, and some questions about them have remained unanswered in the subsequent swift march of events.

Indeed, as a measure of the progress that has been made in the chemical control of coccidial diseases, it should be noted that no drug possessing anticoccidial efficacy was known before 1936, when research workers at the University of Wisconsin showed that elemental sulfur helped to prevent the development of cecal coccidiosis in chicks. Other early developments, to which the Department of Agriculture contributed, included sulfanilamide in 1939, sulfaguanidine in 1941, and sodium borate in 1944, none of which came into wide use although, like sulfur, they were noteworthy precursors of better drugs.

ANTIBIOTICS have no established applications in the control of livestock parasites, but they are of special pertinence because of their potentialities.

Chlortetracycline (Aureomycin) and oxytetracycline (Terramycin) exhibit suppressive and sometimes curative action in bovine anaplasmosis. The former is said also to influence the course of piroplasmosis, or tick fever, in horses and cats and has been described as an efficient treatment in dog coccidiosis.

Some antibiotics at times have appeared to reduce the mortality from cecal coccidiosis of poultry. Some have shown specific action on amebic infection in man and animals, pinworms of man and mice, and large roundworms of cats.

Many other antibiotics, besides those we have named, also influence certain protozoan and helminthic infections of man, laboratory animals, dogs, and cats. They include puromycin, erythromycin, tetracycline, chloramphenicol, bacitracin, carbomycin, fumagilin, trichocidin, neomycin, penicillin, streptomycin, streptocin, octidione, and progidiosin.

Because some antibiotics have proved active in certain parasitic infections, there appears to be good prospect that this rapidly growing and meagerly tested class of chemotherapeutic agents (there are already some 4,000 known antibiotics!) will some day provide efficient treatments for some of the parasitic diseases of livestock and poultry.

Antibiotics are especially useful for combating bacterial infections that commonly occur in animals suffering from parasitic diseases.

Certain chemotherapeutic agents of comparatively recent introduction have received prompt verification and acceptance. A few have been mentioned. Others of note include 2-amino-5-nitrothiazole (Enheptin) for controlling blackhead, hexamitiasis, and trichomoniasis of poultry; quinacrine hydrochloride, for curing giardiasis and removing tapeworms of dogs, man, and certain other host animals; acriflavine, soluble iodides, and hydrogen peroxide as treatments of a sort

for bovine venereal trichomoniasis; antimony potassium tartrate (tartar emetic), for dermal filariasis of sheep; emetine hydrochloride, a promising drug against certain lungworms (Protostrongylus and Muellerius) of sheep; thiacetarsamide, for heartworm infection of dogs; Anthelin, against canine tapeworms; Phthalofyne, against canine whipworms; and di-N-butyl tin dilaurate, for the removal of some species of tapeworms from chickens.

These and many other agents are examples of the developments that are rapidly taking place. The job ahead is a challenging one, however, because present treatments fall far short of the ideal, and no chemotherapeutic agents are yet available for use against the majority of helminthic species and many of the protozoan species that cause loss and damage in livestock.

AUREL O. FOSTER *is head, Parasite Treatment Section, Animal Disease and Parasite Research Branch, Agricultural Research Service.*

Chemotherapeutic Agents for External Parasites

E. F. KNIPLING

INSECTICIDES employed for many years to control ticks, mites, lice, and other arthropod parasites affecting animals were chiefly dips, sprays, or dusts containing arsenicals, nicotine, sulfur, cresols, rotenone, or pyrethrum.

To them have been added a long list of synthetic organic chemicals, which provide more effective materials than those formerly used to control certain external parasites and make it possible to control a wider range of species.

These newer insecticides, including

DDT, methoxychlor, toxaphene, BHC, lindane, and chlordane, have come into prominence for controlling many pests. But we still rely heavily on pyrethrum and rotenone, which have been used for many years and are of proved safety.

A major concern in the development of new chemotherapeutic agents for external parasites is that they be safe. We must be certain that the materials will not harm the animal. It is equally imperative that their use will not lead to the appearance of harmful residues in the meat or milk products derived from the livestock.

The chemicals employed most extensively for the control of the more important external parasites of livestock are discussed here.

ROTENONE is the active constituent in ground roots of plants. Sold commercially as cube or derris, these plant products are low in hazard to animals and man and are effective against several livestock pests.

Rotenone insecticides are still the only approved materials for controlling the ox warble or cattle grubs. The insecticide is employed as a dust, wash, or in high-pressure sprayers for destroying the grubs in the backs of the hosts.

Rotenone also is used extensively for controlling lice on cattle and fleas and ticks on pets.

PYRETHRUM, another plant product, has an outstanding record for its safety and desirable insecticidal properties. It possesses unusually rapid paralytic action against insects, a property not present in any of the newer chlorinated hydrocarbon insecticides, like DDT. Cost has been the chief drawback to the more extensive use of pyrethrum for controlling some livestock pests.

That objection has been overcome in part by the development of compounds, called synergists, which, when combined with pyrethrum, increase its efficiency to a marked degree. Sesame oil concentrate, piperonyl butoxide, sulfoxide, and *n*-propyl isomer are the common synergists for pyrethrum.

Pyrethrum is used against livestock pests chiefly as a spray for controlling the hornflies, stableflies, horseflies, and deerflies on dairy animals and also as dusts, dips, or washes to control fleas and lice on pet animals.

After years of research, the Department of Agriculture succeeded in synthesizing allethrin, a compound similar to pyrethrum in chemical properties and in insecticidal properties.

DDT, the first of a series of new chlorinated hydrocarbon insecticides, has proved invaluable to the livestock grower. A white, crystalline, odorless compound, it controls a wider range of external parasites than any previously known chemical. DDT, when properly formulated, may be used as a dust, emulsion spray, or as a spray or dip prepared from wettable powder concentrates. It can also be sprayed in an oil solution.

DDT has a low order of acute toxicity to animals, but is readily absorbed and stores in animal tissues and excreted in milk. The avoidance of residues is, therefore, the chief concern in the safe use of DDT. The insecticide is not recommended for use in dairy barns or on dairy cows for controlling livestock pests.

DDT is employed on livestock, other than dairy animals, for controlling hornflies, the sheep ked, lice, and fleas. In combination with lindane or BHC, it is also used against ticks. DDT alone, at the 0.5 percent concentration usually employed on livestock, is not effective against engorged ticks, but it will protect animals against reinfestation with other stages of the parasites. BHC or lindane, on the other hand, kills all stages of ticks readily but the residual action in protecting animals is short. A combination of the two materials is, therefore, desirable.

For a number of years DDT gave good control of houseflies, but the flies became resistant to the insecticide and it is no longer a dependable control agent for them.

METHOXYCHLOR is closely related chemically to DDT and will control a number of the same external parasites. It is of a lower order of acute and chronic toxicity to animals. Because it has little tendency to store in animal tissues or to appear in milk, it is used on dairy cows and beef cattle to control flies and lice.

TOXAPHENE, another chlorinated hydrocarbon insecticide, is excellent for controlling livestock pests. It is used as sprays and dips prepared from emulsifiable or wettable powder concentrates.

Toxaphene compares favorably with DDT for the control of hornflies on cattle, the sheep ked, and all of the various kinds of lice that attack livestock. At a concentration of 0.5 percent, toxaphene will destroy all stages of the ticks and provide protection against reinfestation comparable to that obtained with DDT.

BHC AND LINDANE are two grades of a chemical that contain the gamma isomer of benzene hexachloride, the active principle of a highly effective material for controlling a wide variety of livestock pests. The commercial product, known as BHC, contains 12 to 40 percent of the gamma isomer. Lindane consists of more than 99 percent of the gamma isomer.

The gamma isomer of benzene hexachloride is used for controlling lice on livestock, the sheep ked, several kinds of mange mites on livestock, poultry mites, lice, and fleas. It is employed in sprays or dips at concentrations ranging 0.025 to 0.075 percent. It is effective against all stages of ticks at a concentration as low as 0.025 percent gamma isomer, although it lacks the desired residual action. It is employed therefore in combination with DDT for controlling different kinds of ticks.

Lindane, in a special preparation known as EQ-335, also is used to prevent screwworm infestations when applied to wounds and to kill maggots present in wounds.

CHLORDANE has had somewhat limited use against livestock insects because its chronic toxicity to livestock and the hazard of insecticide residues in meat and milk products from treated animals have not been adequately studied. It is about as effective as DDT, BHC, and toxaphene. It is especially effective against lice on livestock and the sheep ked. It is recommended as 0.5 percent sprays for single applications for louse control and for sheep keds.

Chlordane is also used for the control of lice, ticks, and fleas on dogs and of mange mites on swine.

OTHER NEW INSECTICIDES have been under study. Among the materials of special interest are dieldrin, aldrin, heptachlor, perthane, strobane, malathion, Bayer L 13/59, and chlorothion. Further research on them will be needed to establish their safety.

Some of the chemicals will destroy external parasites such as the cattle grubs, screwworms, lice, and blood-sucking flies when injected into the host or when administered orally. Several chlorinated hydrocarbon insecticides, including lindane, aldrin, and dieldrin, and certain phosphate insecticides, including diazinon, Bayer L 13/59, and chlorothion, destroy such pests when administered internally.

RESEARCH WORKERS have been trying to formulate a systemic insecticide, which destroys all of the grubs in cattle with a single injection or feeding. The most effective materials under investigation in 1956 killed the grub larvae only during the time that they are in the back of the host, and two or more treatments were necessary in order to destroy all of the parasites. A safe, economical, and effective material, which will kill the grubs in any part of the host, has been the objective of investigators. Such material would make it practical to control or eliminate the cattle grubs.

Before any systemic insecticides can be recommended for controlling external parasites, much fundamental and applied research has to be done to determine how to use them effectively and without harm to the animals. This promising method of controlling external parasites, therefore, must be regarded a challenge for future research workers. This new approach offers such great advantages over conventional methods that scientists are devoting more and more effort to it.

E. F. KNIPLING, *a graduate of Texas Agricultural and Mechanical College and Iowa State College, is chief of the Entomology Research Branch, Agricultural Research Service. During the Second World War, Dr. Knipling was in charge of the* Department's laboratory at Orlando, Fla. *The laboratory was awarded the Distinguished Service Award of the Department of Agriculture in 1947. The Army awarded Dr. Knipling the Medal for Merit and the United States Typhus Commission Medal.*

Veterinary Biological Products

OREN E. HERL AND LEIGH T. GILTNER

TO LOUIS PASTEUR mankind will always be in debt for his momentous work with biological products, which hold first place among medical accomplishments in preventing and treating infectious disease in man and animals.

The noted French chemist and biologist in 1881 published results of his first successful experiment in immunizing sheep against anthrax, an acute infectious disease that is caused by the anthrax bacillus and can attack all mammals, including cattle, sheep, and man.

Pasteur administered vaccine to the sheep. After a definite waiting period, the vaccinated animals were subjected to an infective culture of the anthrax organisms. Pasteur and his skeptical opponents waited to see what would happen. To the surprise of the doubters, the vaccinates remained well, but most of the controls, the unvaccinated animals that were kept for comparison and checking, died.

Following his first experiment, Pasteur began to study immunization against rabies. He reasoned that if he followed a pattern of preparation for rabies vaccine like the one he used for anthrax he should get similar results. He was disappointed, however. The new vaccine failed to stimulate immunity. The vaccinated animals, as well as the unvaccinated controls, con-

tracted the disease when rabies virus was injected into them.

The reason was this: In the first instance, with sheep and anthrax, Pasteur was working with a bacterial organism. In the second, he was working with a virus. Later, however, he developed the famous Pasteur treatment for rabies.

Since the great Pasteur's time, scientists have been working eagerly to develop ways to immunize animals against disease-producing micro-organisms and viruses.

Three groups of disease-producing agents—bacteria, viruses, and rickettsiae—include most of the infective pathogens (disease-producing agents) that plague man and animals.

The bacterial organisms, such as anthrax and tubercle bacilli, can be seen under a microscope that magnifies a few hundred diameters.

Viruses, such as of hog cholera and rabies, may be seen only with the aid of an electron microscope, which gives a magnification of many thousands of diameters.

The rickettsiae are smaller than bacteria but larger than viruses; heartwater disease (*Rickettsia ruminantium*) in ruminants is an example.

Nature has given animals an immunizing mechanism whereby they may acquire immunity or resistance against such infective agents. The agents stimulate body tissues to produce protective substances, called antibodies, against the disease.

Scientific work to learn more about the antibodies and to make further use of them made slow progress at first.

It was a tremendous, unexplored field—as unprobed but as challenging as atomic energy was in 1945 and outer space was in 1956. Then, to help the scientists, came better microscopes and laboratory equipment and a wider exchange of research findings through scientific journals and conferences, which summarize research work already performed, eliminate duplicate work, and stimulate new ideas and new products.

WHEN THE VIRUS-SERUM-TOXIN law went into effect in 1913, only a dozen or so veterinary biological products were being produced in the United States. Most of them were bacterins—inactivated bacteria.

The law provided for a licensing system to control the production and distribution of viruses, serums, toxins, and similar products intended for the treatment of domestic animals. It provided that no worthless, contaminated, dangerous, or harmful product may be produced and distributed in interstate trade.

Before the law was enacted, immunization of swine against hog cholera had been developed by Marion Dorset and his coworkers in the Department of Agriculture. Within 2 or 3 years, about 80 firms or individuals had applied for licenses for different products. Following this first rush for licenses and the establishment of a system of inspection for the products under the Office of Virus-Serum Control, progress was more orderly. In another 3 or 4 years, many of the less responsible producers had given up their licenses and gone out of production. Other, more progressive ones, met requirements, and over the years the number of licensed firms remained much the same.

On January 1, 1956, 70 firms held more than a thousand United States veterinary licenses covering more than 115 different products.

A GREAT CHANGE occurred in 1945, when the development of live-virus and modified live-virus vaccines took on new impetus. More vaccines and somewhat fewer serums and bacterins were produced. Serum production dropped from 70 million doses in 1950 to 50 million doses in 1955. Bacterin production dropped in doses from 84 million in 1950 to 75 million in 1955. Vaccines went up from 158 million doses in 1945 to 1,500 million doses in 1955. The greatest increases were in vaccines for Newcastle disease and infectious bronchitis for poultry, hog-cholera vaccine for swine, and bluetongue vaccine for sheep. Despite the trend toward the use of live-virus products, the continued demand for certain virus vaccines, such as rabies vaccine (phenol killed) and hog-cholera vaccine (killed-virus), remained.

Poultry immunization was improved when methods using sprays, dusts, and drinking water were developed for mass vaccination against Newcastle disease and infectious bronchitis. The methods were authorized in 1954. They make unnecessary the handling of each bird individually—in fact, the chicks treat themselves when they breathe the spray or dust or drink the water containing the vaccine. Also unnecessary, when they are used, is the employment of vaccinating crews, who go from farm to farm and who may carry disease from one flock to another. The new methods enable one person to vaccinate thousands of birds in an hour. Costs are greatly reduced, and results are good if the user follows strictly the manufacturer's directions.

Veterinary biological products may be classified generally as antiserums, antitoxins, bacterins, mixed bacterins, diagnostics, diagnostic antigens, and vaccines and viruses.

The production procedures for antiserums and antitoxins are much alike.

For antiserum, the producing animals are injected with appropriate amounts of an antigen to stimulate the tissues to create antibodies. In the production of anti-hog-cholera serum, the hog-cholera virus is the antigen and is produced from the blood of pigs that become sick from inoculation with hog-cholera virus.

In the instance of tetanus antitoxin, the tetanus toxin is the antigen (antibody stimulating substance). It is produced as a byproduct by growing the tetanus organism on artificial liquid media. After the production animals for these types of products are injected with adequate quantities of the appropriate antigen and enough time (which varies with the product as much as 10 days to 3 months) is allowed for the injected animals to develop sizable quantities of antibodies, bleedings are collected from the production animals and are processed into antiserums and antitoxins, respectively.

The antiserums and antitoxins contain large amounts of antibodies. They are used to give immediate, brief protection, which may last 2 to 6 weeks. They have curative value when given in large doses. Antiserums may be used simultaneously with viruses or vaccines in certain instances to stimulate a more lasting immunity. The use of antitoxins simultaneously with toxins or toxoids (detoxified toxin) is not a common practice in veterinary medicine, however.

Bacterins and mixed bacterins are produced from bacterial organisms grown on artificial media, such as nutrient agar or broth preparations. After incubation, the growth is harvested. It is inactivated by chemicals or other means, standardized to contain a required number of organisms, and put into containers.

Bacterins may contain 1, 2, or 3 different organisms designed to stimulate immunity in animals against specific disease conditions. They are referred to as named bacterins. Mixed bacterins are prepared from four or more bacterial organisms using much the same procedure as outlined for the named bacterins. Since it has not been demonstrated that this type of product possesses antigenic value for any specific disease, the recommendations for use have been restricted to a phrase like, "for use in the prevention of conditions attributed to the organism used in producing the product."

Diagnostics and diagnostic antigens are used for the detection and diagnosis of diseases. They are produced in much the same way as bacterins. They are designed and developed to detect specific disease conditions.

Some diagnostics, such as tuberculin and mallein, when injected or appropriately applied to an animal infected with either tuberculosis or glanders, will cause a reaction indicating the infection.

Diagnostic antigens are used for making serological tests for the detection of disease in the laboratory or in the field in some instances on samples of blood collected from the suspected animals. Certain reactions indicate positive infection. Negative reactions indicate no infection.

Eighteen different diagnostics and diagnostic antigens were produced in 1955. They are a valuable weapon in the hands of the Federal and State agencies in the control and eradication of disease. By the use of tuberculin in an eradication program which began a few decades ago, tuberculosis in cattle was reduced from 5 percent infection in the beginning to less than 0.011 percent infection in 1952. That figure had remained practically unchanged through 1955.

Vaccines and viruses embrace a large number of important biological products, which are becoming increasingly more in demand for use in the prevention and control of diseases in livestock and poultry. More than fifty forms of vaccines or viruses were being produced on January 1, 1956. They vary greatly as to origin, composition, combination, virulence, (relative infectiveness), attenuation (made less virulent), and modification. Thus different methods of preparation as well as special techniques and methods of application are sometimes necessary. Fowlpox and fowl-laryngotracheitis vaccines, for example, are processed from the natural viruses that cause those diseases. Yet by administration of the pox vaccine by the wing-web puncture method and the laryngotracheitis vaccine by brushing it on the membranes of the vent, immunity is established without the danger of causing disease.

Other vaccines or viruses may be prepared from biological agents that have been attenuated or modified to the extent that they are safe for use yet stimulate a satisfactory immunity.

Vaccines are produced essentially from virus agents, although they may be of bacterial origin in some instances. In general there are three types: Killed-virus vaccine, live-virus vaccine, and modified live-virus vaccine.

The preparation of killed-virus vaccines entails the injection of a virus or bacterial agents into a susceptible production animal. The agents usually are virulent (infective) and cause the disease. At the height of infection, the animal is sacrificed, and selected tissues are harvested and processed into a vaccine. This type of product usually is inactivated with an agent, such as formalin. Such vaccines cannot multiply when injected. Killed-virus rabies vaccine is an example.

The preparation of the live-virus vaccines entails the use of a mild, live-virus agent inoculated into a medium, such as the developing chick embryo. When these agents are inoculated into the embryonated egg, the virus grows in the cells and fluids of the embryonic tissues. Following the incubation and growth, the eggs are opened, and the infected cells, tissues, and fluids are harvested and processed into a vaccine. An example is live-virus, B_1 strain, Newcastle disease vaccine.

The preparation of a modified live-virus vaccine entails the repeated passage of a viral agent in an unnatural host to the point where it loses its infective power but retains its ability to stimulate immunity. The use of the principle of modification of live viruses

in the preparation of vaccines has been increasing rapidly, particularly since 1950, when rabies vaccine, modified live-virus, chick-embryo origin, was first licensed. Four similar products have been licensed since then for distribution; namely, hog-cholera vaccine; canine-distemper vaccine; distemper vaccine—mink; and the blue-tongue vaccine. Those vaccines, except hog-cholera vaccine, were modified by repeated passage in chicken embryos. The number of egg passages required for modification varies with the product. Other methods of modification of viruses, besides egg passage, include repeated passage through an unnatural host (hog-cholera virus through rabbits), growth in an unnatural environment at unusually high or low temperatures, and growth in the presence of mild chemical agents.

Three different forms of modification and production of a vaccine are exemplified in modified live-virus, hog-cholera vaccine, of swine origin, rabbit origin, and tissue culture origin. The vaccine of swine origin is produced from hog-cholera virus, modified by repeated passages through rabbits, but the material used in producing the vaccine is collected from susceptible swine inoculated with the rabbit-passage inoculum. The vaccine of rabbit origin is produced from hog-cholera virus, modified by repeated passage through rabbits; the finished vaccine is prepared from affected rabbit tissues. The vaccine of tissue culture origin is produced from hog-cholera virus modified by the repeated passages and growth on artificial media and fortified with bone marrow from susceptible swine.

With the discovery of modified live-virus vaccines came several important techniques of production, such as desiccation (freeze drying), whereby they are prepared and distributed in dried form which, before use in the field, must be reconstituted to a liquid state by the addition of a diluent. The desiccation of these vaccines adds greatly to their stability. Stabilization of vaccines is a process whereby adjuvants are added during production for the purpose of helping to maintain and lengthen the viability—live state—of the virus vaccine. These live-virus vaccines must contain living virus and be capable of multiplication when injected to accomplish their intended purpose.

THE REQUIREMENTS for a licensee to manufacture biological products depend somewhat on the biologic involved. Any product to be eligible for interstate shipment must be produced under a United States veterinary license issued by the Secretary of Agriculture. A license may be issued after all the requirements of the law and regulations promulgated thereunder have been met. These include appropriate laboratory facilities and equipment; trained personnel; an outline method of production and testing; information and research data; citation of literature of published work; proposed trade labels and circular material; cultures of the organism used; and samples of the finished product. All this material is given thorough study by experienced personnel; the cultures are examined and the product is tested for purity, safety, and potency, when necessary, to evaluate the product.

If the application is for an entirely new product, with a new principle of immunization involved, or the nature of the product is such as to warrant assembling additional evidence on the safety and efficacy of the product, field tests on larger numbers of animals, as directed by the Biological Products Licensing Section of the Animal Inspection and Quarantine Branch of the Department of Agriculture, are required of the applicant. After all the information is made available and the results of the laboratory and field tests are reported and tabulated, final consideration is given to the application.

A license may be issued by the Secretary of Agriculture through the Animal Inspection and Quarantine Branch

when it is found that requirements have been met and it is determined that the product is pure, safe, and efficacious and will serve the purpose under field conditions for which it is intended. Once a license is issued, it remains in effect until terminated for cause or at the request of the manufacturer without prejudice.

VETERINARY BIOLOGICAL PRODUCTS, before release for use, are required to be tested satisfactorily by licensees for sterility, purity, safety, and potency. The sterility test involves basically the inoculation of a small amount of the product on artificial media in glass. The inoculated media are incubated at a temperature that promotes growth of contaminating organisms, if present. After a period of incubation, the materials are examined under the microscope and otherwise to determine the presence or absence of contaminants. For many products, it is required that the cultures be sterile (no growth); in others, some organisms may be present, provided safety tests prove that they are nonpathogenic (not disease producing) and harmless. We expect that techniques and procedures will be developed to the point that all the products may be produced free of bacterial contaminants.

The safety test provides for the injection of the product into laboratory animals, such as mice, guinea pigs, rabbits, pigeons, and sometimes large animals. The animals are observed over a period of time to make sure that they do not develop symptoms or become sick and die from the product injected. The safety test is designed to demonstrate the absence of toxins or disease-producing organisms.

Potency tests of many types are required for veterinary biological products. One of the more common is known as the vaccination-challenge test. An example is the one required by regulation for the modified live-virus, hog-cholera vaccines as follows: Of 14 susceptible pigs selected for the test, 10 are vaccinated with 2 cubic centimeters of the vaccine and 4 are held untreated as controls. After at least 7 days, all 14 pigs are challenged by injecting each with 2 cc. of virulent hog-cholera virus. For a satisfactory test, 3 of the 4 controls must sicken with hog cholera between the 4-7 days, and 9 of the 10 vaccinates must remain well through the 14-day holding period.

Various other controls have been established over the years to insure that products have merit, are efficacious, and are safe. After a license is issued, if it is for anti-hog-cholera serum or hog-cholera virus, a Government resident inspector is assigned to the establishment. He gives general inspection and supervision to operations involved in the production and testing of the products. If the license issued is for a product other than hog-cholera serum or hog-cholera virus, a veterinary inspector assigned to the area in which the establishment is located makes periodic inspections. He checks on the sanitation of the establishments and its techniques, determines whether the outline method of production and testing is followed, analyzes procedures and records, observes tests, collects samples for check testing, and makes whatever other inspections are needed.

Minimum standards for testing a number of products have been adopted. They provide for greater uniformity in evaluating products before and after licensing and before release for market. They do not prevent competition but encourage licensees to improve and market products above a minimum standard.

IT MUST BE REMEMBERED that immunity is relative and the degree may vary from mild resistance to solid protection against severe challenge. Veterinary biological products are designed to give ample protection under ordinary exposure and yet be cheap enough for the livestock owner to make full use of them.

Cautions and directions for use are important and should be followed strictly. Only persons having special training and knowledge of animal diseases and experienced in the use of biological products should attempt the immunization of pets, livestock, and poultry.

ONLY HEALTHY animals should be vaccinated, unless an emergency exists and then only on the advice of a veterinarian. Unthrifty animals or those heavily parasitized are poor vaccination risks.

Persons who handle and use biological products should read carefully all information on labels and direction circulars before making any injections; keep the products stored under refrigeration; handle them in accordance with directions; use products produced under a United States veterinary license; keep records of vaccination, including the serial number of the product; follow instructions for restoration of desiccated products; and carry out precisely the recommendations of the manufacturer.

OREN E. HERL, D. V. M., *heads the Biological Products Licensing Section of the Animal Inspection and Quarantine Branch, Agricultural Research Service. He is a graduate of Ohio State University.*

LEIGH T. GILTNER, D. V. M., *before his retirement in 1954, was a consultant for the Pathological Division of the former Bureau of Animal Industry. He received degrees from Cornell University and the George Washington University. He died on November 17, 1955.*

For further reading about insecticides:
Bureau of Entomology and Plant Quarantine: *Fly Control on Dairy Cattle and in Dairy Barns,* U. S. Department of Agriculture Leaflet 283, 12 pages. 1950.
Bureau of Entomology and Plant Quarantine and Extension Service: *Horn Flies, Enemies of Cattle,* U. S. Department of Agriculture Leaflet 270, 4 pages. 1950.
E. F. Knipling: *The New Insecticides for Controlling External Parasites of Livestock,* U. S. Department of Agriculture, Bureau of Entomology and Plant Quarantine publication E–762, second revision, 27 pages. 1951.
W. S. McGregor, R. D. Radeleff, and R. C. Bushland: *Some Phosphorous Compounds as Systemic Insecticides Against Cattle Grubs,* Journal of Economic Entomology, volume 47, number 3, pages 465–467. 1954.

Antibiotics

L. MEYER JONES

ANTIBIOTICS are produced during the normal growth of many types of threadlike, soil-inhabiting micro-organisms. Antibiotics inhibit the growth of bacteria that compete with the soil micro-organisms for the available foodstuffs.

Antibiotics have been isolated and purified for use to control disease-producing bacteria. Several hundred antibiotics have been isolated from various sources. Penicillin, dihydrostreptomycin (streptomycin), chloramphenicol, chlortetracycline, oxytetracycline, tetracycline, erythromycin, bacitracin, and neomycin are among the best known antibiotics.

The chemical and physical characteristics of antibiotics must be known and respected in order to use them with good results. The common antibiotics are light-colored, comparatively unstable, and moisture-absorbent powders.

The antibiotics are stable indefinitely as dry powders in evacuated containers. When exposed to the air, the powders and their water solutions largely decompose within 24 hours. Exceptions are tetracycline, which remains potent for 2 to 3 weeks in solution, and chloramphenicol, which resists boiling and wide variations in acidity.

The exact mode of action of antibiotics against bacteria is still unknown. Considerable evidence indicates that the antibiotics interfere with various steps in cellular metabolism vital to bacterial growth. The antibacterial activity of antibiotics is highest during the period of greatest bacterial multiplication. When present in adequate concentration, antibiotics kill bacteria, but lower concentrations only inhibit the growing organisms. Old cultures of bacteria beyond the stage of rapid growth show less response.

The administration of antibiotics to animals for the control of disease is ordinarily by intramuscular or occasionally intravenous injection. Antibiotics are invariably administered by injection in herbivorous animals because oral administration for the treatment of disease suppresses the important cellulose-splitting and vitamin-synthesizing bacteria normally present in the digestive tract.

The antibiotics can be administered orally in the nonherbivorous animals, such as the dog, cat, and nonruminating calf, but intramuscular injection seems to be more successful because it provides better absorption of the drug with no opportunity for disturbing the digestion.

Most antibiotics are absorbed readily following injection into the tissue.

The simple antibiotic salts are absorbed to produce a maximum blood concentration within 30 minutes for penicillin and about 60 minutes for other antibiotics, such as dihydrostreptomycin and the tetracyclines (Aureomycin, Terramycin, tetracycline).

Slowly absorbed preparations of some antibiotics are available, so that the period of effective treatment following injection is much prolonged; that is, a therapeutic dose of one penicillin preparation is absorbed continuously for 3 days, whereas another is absorbed for nearly 3 weeks in smaller daily amounts.

When it is given orally in nonherbivorous animals, penicillin must be protected with an alkali against destruction by the secretion of the stomach. Even when protected, five times the intramuscular dose of penicillin must be administered orally to obtain equivalent blood levels. Erythromycin, which may be employed instead of penicillin, need not be given in excessive dosage, because it is absorbed adequately following oral administration. The tetracycline antibiotics and chloramphenicol are absorbed readily from the digestive tract. Only about 10 percent of an oral dose of streptomycin is absorbed into the blood stream. The rest of the dose remains in the digestive tract, where it inhibits many kinds of bacteria. Neomycin is also poorly absorbed and produces a high concentration in the feces.

Most antibiotics are distributed readily through the body (except the central nervous system) in concentrations adequate for the treatment of either systemic or local infections. Antibiotics diffuse into the central nervous system with difficulty, but excessively high concentrations in the blood stream promote diffusion also into the nerve tissues. Chloramphenicol is superior to other antibiotics for treatment of infections of the central nervous system because it diffuses into the cerebrospinal fluid in a concentration approaching 75 percent of that found in the blood.

The blood level of an antibiotic is determined primarily by the balance between the rate of absorption and the rate of excretion. Antibacterial levels of antibiotics persist in the tissues beyond the disappearance of the antibiotics in detectable levels from the blood stream.

Antibiotics absorbed into the blood are excreted primarily through the kidneys. Detectable amounts may be eliminated in other secretions of the body, particularly the bile. Antibiotics that are not absorbed from the digestive tract following administration by mouth are eliminated in the feces.

One of the greatest difficulties in the early use of penicillin arose from the rapid elimination of the antibiotic by the kidneys. It was unwise to delay the excretion of penicillin by altering the function of the kidneys, so the activity of a therapeutic dose of penicillin was prolonged by delaying its absorption following intramuscular injection.

Dihydrostreptomycin, chloramphe-nicol, and the tetracycline antibiotics are not excreted by the kidneys as rapidly as penicillin and are active in the tissues in antibacterial concentration for periods up to 24 hours. Chloramphenicol is split into excretion products by the liver. A small amount of chloramphenicol plus large amounts of the split products are eliminated in the urine and in the bile. High concentrations of chloramphenicol, streptomycin, neomycin, and bacitracin are found in the feces following oral administration.

THE TOXICITY of antibiotics to an individual animal is generally low when it is properly employed. The relatively low toxic activity combined with relatively high antibacterial activity has made the antibiotics one of the most important groups of therapeutic drugs now available to combat infectious disease organisms.

Allergic reactions of an animal to penicillin or other antibiotics must be noted and further administration halted. When streptomycin is administered for a long time at high dosage, degeneration of the auditory nerve and the organ of equilibrium may occur.

With the recognition of the tendency for bacterial pathogens to become streptomycin-resistant during prolonged therapy, the duration of treatment has been markedly decreased; therefore, the probability that neurotoxicity will develop in animals during streptomycin therapy appears remote.

The toxicity from the tetracycline antibiotics is seldom serious except following the administration of an excessive dosage, which suppresses bacteria needed in the normal digestive processes.

Contrary to the experience in human medicine, toxic reactions to chloramphenicol have not been serious in animals. Blood-cell abnormalities have been noted in dogs and birds receiving chloramphenicol, however. Several antibiotics have been infused into the udder of the cow without causing signs of undue irritation or other toxicity.

Not all antibiotics are free from toxcity however. The polymyxins, for example, have considerable renal toxicity, which definitely limits their use.

A disturbing and increasingly dangerous practice of giving antibiotics promiscuously for almost any and all kinds of sickness has become increasingly common in recent years when many antibiotics became generally available.

Some susceptible strains of disease-producing bacteria, especially staphylococci, may develop a total resistance because the antibiotics are improperly used. It has become apparent that when an antibiotic is used promiscuously in any given community or hospital, resistant strains of staphylococcic bacteria can be found in a significant portion of the animal or human population.

The appearance of a disease germ during antibiotic treatment may be a major tragedy for a patient, but it will have little significance for other animals if the patient is properly isolated. Resistant germs, if they are to assume great significance, must be spread from a sick animal to other susceptible animals. Therefore the population of antibiotic-resistant disease germs in a herd or flock is directly proportional to the number of carrier animals and susceptible animals and to the frequency and intimacy of contact between the two groups.

Many persons have relied too much on antibiotics to control diseases. Under such circumstances it is natural that there should be concurrent laxness of hygiene and management of animal patients. Before we can take full advantage of antibiotic therapy, there must be renewed emphasis on isolation of the sick animal, with feeding and management measures that decrease the transmission of antibiotic-resistant organisms from patient to patient and from carrier to patient.

Antibiotics must be used cautiously, or their value will be lost. On the other hand, no patient should be deprived of the benefit of antibiotic therapy solely because of fear of inducing resistance in the disease germ.

L. MEYER JONES *is professor of veterinary pharmacology in Iowa State College. He formerly was a fellow of the Research Council of the American Veterinary Medical Association and a Fulbright lecturer in pharmacology in Tierärztliche Hochschule in Vienna.*

The Sulfa Drugs

L. MEYER JONES

THE SULFONAMIDES were discovered in 1935. They have been as important in controlling bacterial diseases in animals as in man.

Despite the subsequent introduction of the more effective and less toxic antibiotics, the sulfonamides continue to be widely used in the treatment of certain animal diseases because many domestic animals individually are of low economic value and must be treated as members of a herd or flock. Mass treatment in most instances involves giving the drug in water or ground feed. The sulfonamides possess greater physical and chemical stability than do the antibiotics and are more adaptable to mass treatment in the control of diseases in animals.

The sulfonamides are produced by

chemical synthesis, and are stable white powders, which may be mixed in animal feeds or compressed readily into tablets for administration by mouth. They are sparingly soluble in water and in the fluids of the body. The low solubility sometimes leads to difficulty in eliminating the drug in the urine.

Sulfanilamide was the first of the sulfa drugs to be synthesized. It was followed by sulfapyridine, sulfathiazole, sulfadiazine, sulfamerazine, and sulfamethazine. Other sulfonamides—phthalylsulfathiazole and phthalylsulfacetamide—have been synthesized for slow release in the digestive tract to control infections. Sulfasoxizole is admirably adapted to treatment of urinary infections because of a broad antibacterial activity and a high solubility in the urinary system.

The sulfonamides inhibit bacterial multiplication during the growth phase. A therapeutic dose of sulfonamide does not kill the micro-organisms but prevents further bacterial multiplication until the body defenses can destroy the invading organisms. Early treatment of an infected animal is therefore necessary if the sulfas are to be effective.

The sulfonamides have little value in treating prolonged sickness, because the body defenses already have been exhausted by the chronic infection and cannot dispose of the invading disease germs. Prolonged use of sulfonamides in a chronic infection tends to make the disease germs more resistant to the drugs.

The sulfonamides must be administered at regular intervals throughout the 24 hours for greatest effectiveness. The objective in sulfonamide therapy is to maintain an antibacterial concentration of sulfonamide continuously in all tissues of the body where the disease germs might multiply.

The sulfonamides are excreted primarily by way of the urine. Large amounts of the poorly absorbed sulfonamides are excreted in the feces. They are excreted also in milk and in bile in concentrations approaching that of the blood stream.

Chronic toxicity from sulfonamides is more important than acute toxicity. The most significant form is kidney toxicity, which occurs after several days of therapy because the kidneys fail to excrete the sulfonamides properly.

The sulfonamides have a low solubility in the body fluids. After filtering out of the blood into the urinary fluid of the kidney, the sulfonamides normally are concentrated five times or more through the reabsorption of water from the filtrate by the kidneys. The sulfonamides may exceed their solubility and precipitate in the urinary system. The tendency for crystallization to occur is increased by the normal reabsorption of the alkali ions by the kidneys, which lowers the acidity of the urine and the solubility of the sulfas.

The needlelike crystals of a precipitated sulfonamide puncture and tear the lining of the kidneys. The crystals may become numerous enough to conglomerate and to form stones, which obstruct the urinary tract. After the obstruction, waste products that normally are eliminated in the urine accumulate in the body. The accumulation of wastes is progressive until it leads to the death of the animal.

Other toxic reactions are noted. In poultry, for example, sulfanilamide causes a hen to lay eggs with soft shells or without shells. Other sulfonamides may not interfere with the formation of shells but will lower egg laying. Large amounts of sulfonamides cause a marked interference with the structure and the function of the nerves to the legs so that walking becomes difficult or impossible. The continuous use of sulfonamides at therapeutic levels suppresses the bacteria in the digestive tract that the animal needs to synthesize certain nutrients.

Sulfonamides may be prescribed for any generalizing disease that is caused by a susceptible organism, if there is no impairment of kidney function that handicaps excretion.

Virus infections are not susceptible to sulfonamides, although secondary bacterial invaders may be.

Water must be available at all times to the patient receiving sulfonamide. If necessary, forced intake of water is indicated to insure a nearly normal consumption. Water is the vehicle for excreting sulfonamides, which will precipitate and block the kidney if there is too little fluid.

Signs of sulfonamide toxicity, especially bloody and frequent urination, must be recognized promptly and the treatment stopped immediately.

Sulfonamides should be administered no longer than absolutely necessary.

The maximum period is 4 days. The dose should be decreased soon after the patient shows improvement. Therapy should be stopped 24 to 36 hours after the patient appears vigorous or after the 4-day maximum.

L. MEYER JONES, *professor of veterinary pharmacology in Iowa State College, holds degrees of doctor of veterinary medicine from Iowa State College and doctor of philosophy from the University of Minnesota. He is author of a textbook,* Veterinary Pharmacology and Therapeutics.

Disinfection

W. L. MALLMANN

A FARMER can do much for the health of his animals by keeping his barns and sheds absolutely clean.

The initial step in sanitation is to know (and to have workers who know) what proper cleaning is, why it is important, and how to do it.

Disinfection—destroying the disease germs—is possible only after thorough cleaning. Disinfectants spread over unclean surfaces kill only the microorganisms on the surface; the embedded organisms are untouched; the disinfectant is wasted.

Effective cleaning begins with the removal of all gross waste, such as manure and bedding. Then the surfaces are scrubbed with brushes and a good detergent solution until they are visibly clean. The surfaces then can be flushed with clean water and a disinfectant applied.

Any good alkaline detergent in warm water is satisfactory, but lye (caustic soda) alone may be used. Because lye is very caustic, rubber boots should be worn and the solution should be handled carefully lest it come in con-

tact with the skin. The surfaces should be treated with the alkaline solution and allowed to react for a few minutes before brushing. The surfaces should be thoroughly flushed with clean water to remove all traces of the detergent.

Lye tends to destroy most microorganisms; it kills as it cleans. It corrodes metals and so cannot be used as a general cleaner.

The value of good cleaning before disinfection was shown in a test made in a meatpacking plant. On a badly contaminated concrete wall, 28 million bacteria were counted per 2-inch square. A section of the wall was sprayed with a good germicidal solution. The bacterial population was reduced to 11 million, which demonstrated the disinfectant had failed. Another section was washed with an alkaline detergent solution. Before rinsing, the bacterial count was 380,000. After rinsing with clean water, the count was 53,000. The wash operation removed the visible soil and 99.8 percent of the bacteria. The same disinfecting solution applied to the clean-washed and rinsed surface reduced the population from 53,000 per 2-inch square to 100. The wall that had been washed-rinsed and sanitized was properly treated, but the wall that had been sanitized only was still unclean and had many bacteria.

In another experiment to demonstrate the ineffectiveness of a sanitizer on an unclean surface, two milking machines were carefully cleaned. Each day one was rinsed with an ineffective sanitizer and the other with an acceptable sanitizer. Both machines were rinsed with cold water after each milking and stored for the next milking without washing. For the first 4 days there were very few bacteria in the milk from either machine. From the fifth day on, the number of bacteria increased in the milk from both machines, but more rapidly in the machine treated with the ineffective sanitizer. The accumulating milk soil in both machines began to interfere with the sanitizing action, however— proof that disinfection was impossible when the surfaces of a milking machine had not been cleaned of all milk soil.

THE DISINFECTION PROCESS is a chemical reaction between the disinfectant and the micro-organisms. The disinfectant has to touch the organism.

If the organism is embedded in organic soil, no contact is made and no disinfection results. All soil that contains embedded organisms therefore should be removed from surfaces by cleaning. Thus only the exposed organisms are left on the clean surfaces and the disinfectant can reach them.

Some disinfectants come in contact with the organisms readily. Others need the addition of other chemicals to obtain rapid contact. These agents are called wetting agents, because they cause the water to wet the soil and the organisms more rapidly than water alone. The wetting agents such as soap tend to improve contact with the organisms, and they also serve as detergents to aid in the removal of any organic soil from the surface of the organism. Thus the disinfecting agent is given penetrating power.

Because soaps may react with the disinfectant and reduce its activity, the cleaning operation should precede the disinfection process. Only the products that are called detergent-sanitizers should be used as combination cleaners and sanitizers.

Some disinfectants, such as the quaternary ammonium compounds, (sometimes called "quats") are wetting agents. They exhibit some detergency, which aids in better contact with organisms. Compatible wetting agents have been added to these compounds to increase the detergency-sanitizer effect. They are used to clean and disinfect dairy utensils.

Disinfectants work best when they and the surfaces to be disinfected are warm. Phenol in a concentration of 1:90 kills the typhoid bacillus in 5 minutes at 68° F., but a weaker concentration of 1:60 kills it at 100°. The difference at lower temperatures is greater. A 1:70 solution of phenol kills staphylococcus in 100 minutes at a temperature of 50° but at 68° the killing time is 20 minutes.

Lye is one of the few disinfectants that is only slightly affected by temperature. A 2-percent lye solution can be used at 32° without little reduction in germicidal efficiency. Disinfection should not be done when the temperature is below 32°.

THE ACIDITY OR ALKALINITY of the disinfectant or the thing to be disinfected should be considered in the selection of the disinfectant. For example, a hypochlorite solution is active in slightly acid solution and inactive in alkaline solution. But quaternary ammonium compounds generally are more active in alkaline solution than in acid solutions.

In a series of tests, a quaternary ammonium compound was tested at pH values of 5 (acid), 7 (neutral) and 9 (alkaline) in a 1:1,000 dilution. A culture of *Micrococcus pyogenes* var.

aureus was used and the percentage of kill was determined after exposures of 1 minute. The kills were 55.6 percent, 96.2 percent, and 100 percent when the pH was 5, 7, and 9, respectively.

Only in the alkaline solution was complete kill obtained in 1 minute. If the solution had been allowed to act for a longer period, kill would have occurred in the acid (pH 5) solution. If the concentration had been increased materially, kill would have occurred in the acid solution in 1 minute. One can use large amounts of most disinfectants and get satisfactory results at varying pH values if the disinfectant is not excessively acid or alkaline.

MOST ORGANIC-TYPE DISINFECTANTS —like the cresols—react slowly even when present in large amounts. The fastest acting disinfectants known are the halogens, such as the hypochlorites.

In the absence of organic matter, 1 part per million (p. p. m.) of free chlorine at 6 pH killed 100,000 cells of *Escherichia coli* in 15 seconds. The cresols and their derivatives are much slower. Where contact periods of three or more minutes occur, the cresols do an equally good job in proper concentration.

THE CONCENTRATION of the disinfectant also is important. In general, the greater the concentration is, the shorter is the time of kill. An example is the action of mercuric chloride ($HgCl_2$) on *Salmonella paratyphi*. The times taken for disinfection (in minutes) were 1.5, 7, 10, 13, 65, and 230 when the solution was, respectively, 1, 0.50, 0.10, 0.05, 0.01, and 0.005 parts of $HgCl_2$ per 1,000 parts of water. Thus, diluting the mercuric chloride solution 50 percent lowers its germicidal activity about 50 percent. Diluting a phenol solution 50 percent, however, lowers the germicidal activity approximately 64 times.

Disinfectants should always be used in proper concentrations. The user should follow recommended dilutions closely unless he knows how dilution will affect the compound he is using.

THE PRESENCE OF ORGANIC MATTER in the disinfecting solution or on the surfaces to be disinfected may reduce germicidal activity to a point where no disinfection results. The organic matter may cover the organism so the disinfectant cannot reach the organism; it may neutralize the disinfecting action by combining with the disinfectant; or it may serve as an adsorbing surface to reduce the amount of active disinfectant present.

The table below shows the effect of organic matter on several disinfectants by adding varying amounts of horse serum.

The figures indicate that the quaternary ammonium compound and the 2-chloro-4 phenyl phenol are reduced markedly in germicidal activity by organic matter. The comparative values of the compounds should be measured on their effectiveness in the presence of 10 percent of organic matter.

Percentage of organic matter	Quaternary ammonium compound	*Killing Dilutions*		
		2-chloro-4 phenyl phenol	Ortho phenyl phenol
0	22, 000	13, 500	2, 400
1	....	9, 000	....
2	16, 000	....	....
3	....	7, 500	2, 200
4	9, 200	....	....
5	....	6, 000	2, 100
6	7, 400	....	....
7.5	....	4, 500	2, 000
8	5, 800	....	....
10	5, 200	4, 000	1, 900

The relationship would be—

Quaternary ammonium compound	5,000
2-chloro-4 phenyl phenol	4,000
Ortho phenyl phenol	2,000

Hard waters interfere with some disinfectants because of the presence of calcium, magnesium, or iron. The cresol preparations are affected because the calcium and magnesium precipitate the soap and thus upset the proper ratio between the cresols and the soap in the disinfectant preparation. Quaternary ammonium compounds are reduced materially in activity by calcium, magnesium, and iron.

Disinfectants that are sold in interstate trade are checked for germicidal activity by Government agencies. The methods of testing, however, are done under ideal conditions for action and do not consider the various factors that may cause the product to be ineffective. The user has to use the compound in a proper manner.

MANY TYPES of chemicals have germicidal values, but varying physical and chemical properties make many of them suitable for only specialized uses. For example, only a few compounds will destroy the organism responsible for tuberculosis. If a need arises to destroy those organisms, only the cresylic-type compounds, such as cresol, should be used.

The cresylic compounds are good disinfectants for general use. Because the cresols and cresol derivatives are relatively insoluble in water, they are emulsified in a mixture of soap and alkali. The compounds are stable and mix readily with water.

Many of these preparations have a phenol coefficient of 5—meaning that by a laboratory test they are 5 times more germicidal than phenol. The recommended dilution of phenol is 5 percent; hence a product with a phenol coefficient of 5 would be used in a 1-percent concentration.

The cresylic compounds, used in proper concentrations, destroy all bacteria except spore-forming bacteria—they can be used for disinfections for nearly all bacterial and virus diseases.

The virus diseases are best controlled by strict cleanliness. The cresylic disinfectants have strong odors, which milk takes up readily. They are relatively nontoxic, and no special precautions are necessary in handling them. They are especially good for disinfecting floors and walls and may be applied by flushing over the surfaces or by spraying.

Caustic soda, or lye (sodium hydroxide), in a 2-percent solution is a good disinfectant. It is effective against most common disease-causing bacteria except the tubercle bacillus.

When lye is used, the surfaces should be scraped and brushed to remove gross soil, a warm 2-percent solution of lye should be applied, and the surface should be scrubbed with stiff brushes. The surfaces should be flushed with clean water until no soil remains. Because lye corrodes metal and irritates the skin, one should be cautious when he uses it.

The hypochlorites are excellent disinfectants. They are widely used. Sodium hypochlorite and calcium hypochlorite are equally effective. Sodium hypochlorite is sold in liquid concentrations of 3 to 5 percent. The hypochlorite bleaches sold in the grocery stores generally are 5-percent solutions. The calcium hypochlorites are sold in powder form and range in concentrations from 15 to 70 percent.

The hypochlorites are commonly used on milking machines and other dairy equipment. They kill bacteria rapidly on clean surfaces.

The hypochlorites should be used in concentrations of 50 p. p. m. or more; 200 p. p. m. is used generally to insure a safety factor.

The sodium salts are preferable for dairy equipment because they do not leave waterstone, or milkstone, on the surfaces. Calcium salts are apt to cause more of the waterstone to be deposited. The calcium hypochlorites can be used for flushing the walls and floors.

The hypochlorites are cheap. A gallon jug of laundry bleach will make 250 gallons of 200-p. p. m. hypochlorite solution. The hypochlorites are nonirritating but are slightly corrosive for tinned utensils.

The iodophores depend on the free iodine for germicidal activity. These compounds can be used to disinfect dairy utensils but are too expensive for use as general disinfectants for floor, walls, and other large surfaces.

The iodine-bearing compounds are like hypochlorites in action but, unlike chlorine, they destroy the tubercle bacillus. Active iodine colors the solution yellow. A colorless solution means that too little of the iodophore has been used—a handy index of germicidal strength that helps the user know when the germicidal power of a solution is too low.

The quaternary ammonium compounds act fast. They are wetting agents in themselves and so have some detergency value and penetrating power. They are odorless, nonirritating, and noncorrosive in use dilutions. They are also good deodorants. They should be used in concentrations of 200 p. p. m. (1:5,000) and applied only to properly cleaned surfaces. Hard waters, particularly those containing iron, slow down the speed of kill.

Alkyl dimethyl benzyl ammonium chloride, a quaternary ammonium compound, has little germicidal activity in water with a hardness of 310 p. p. m. in 10 minutes, but at the end of 90 minutes it has a nearly complete kill. In distilled water, complete kill occurs in 10 minutes.

The quaternary ammonium compounds are used for disinfecting dairy and restaurant utensils. They can be used for flushing floors and walls. They are effective in concentrations of 200 p. p. m. against most of the disease-producing bacteria and viruses.

W. L. MALLMANN *has been a professor in the department of microbiology and public health in Michigan State University since 1918. He holds the degree of doctor of philosophy in bacteriology from the University of Chicago.*

For further reading:

W. L. Mallmann, and E. S. Churchill: *The Control of Microorganisms in Food Storage Rooms*, Refrigerating Engineering, volume 51, number 6, pages 523–528, 1946.

W. L. Mallmann, Frank Peabody, and Don Muentener: *The Influence of Accumulated Soil on Bacterial Populations of Milking Machines*, Soap and Sanitary Chemicals, volume 29, number 11, pages 132, 137–139, 1953.

F. W. Tilley: *An Experimental Study of the Influence of Temperature on the Bactericidal Activities of Alcohols and Phenols*, Journal of Bacteriology, volume 43, number 4, pages 521–525.

United States Livestock Sanitary Association: *Health Requirements Governing Admission of Livestock*, United States Livestock Sanitary Association Circular 1, 178 pages, United States Livestock Sanitary Association, Trenton, N. J., 1954.

several species
of animals

Urinary Calculi

N. R. ELLIS

URINARY calculi is a disorder of the kidney and the urinary tract in which stones, or calculi, form and often block the secretion of urine. It is thought to be due to nutritional or metabolic disturbance. It is also called urolithiasis and water belly.

Cattle, sheep, and mink are the main classes of animals of economic importance that are affected. Swine seldom develop calculi. Horses, cats, dogs, and the laboratory rat are among the other animals that do.

The disorder has a counterpart, kidney stones, in human beings.

Medication, surgery, and changes in the rations are employed in treatment. No effective general remedies or dietary treatments can be relied upon for general relief or prevention of calculi. Some special treatments suited to par-ticular types of cases are used to good advantage, however.

Deaths of affected animals frequently run rather high. The economic loss, especially to individual farmers and ranchers, may be serious.

Cattle and sheep are affected on the range and in the feed lot. Bulls, steers, rams, and wethers are the principal victims.

A great variety of feeds and other environmental conditions are associated with the disorder. It is not surprising therefore that the development of water belly to a great extent is unpredictable. Sometimes only one animal out of a large herd may be affected, but sometimes a fairly high proportion may be affected, with death losses likewise high.

Several causes have been suggested.

Among them are inherent characteristics of certain specific feeds; deficiency of vitamins A and D; imbalance of mineral elements, such as calcium, phosphorus, magnesium, and others; high silica content of feeds; and the urine colloid system.

Various investigators have reported trouble that seemed to be associated with certain feeds. Sorghum feeds, both grain and fodder, have been blamed. Such reports have come from Nebraska and Texas and other States in the Great Plains. From Australia have come reports of trouble on pastures of subclover. Farmers in the more arid districts, where the oat fodder along with grain were important feeds, have reported trouble. Wheat bran has been blamed in this country. Alfalfa hay, corn, barley, and beet tops generally have not caused difficulty.

Vitamin A deficiency has been suspected as responsible for calculi formation. Laboratory tests on rats have shown that certain diets lacking carotene or vitamin A may produce calculi.

Apparently calcified bits of kidney tissue formed when vitamin A is deficient serve as focal points for calculi formation. In cattle and sheep, however, there is little evidence of any association of vitamin A or carotene intake with occurrence of water belly.

Studies on the balance or ratio of the several mineral elements, such as calcium, phosphorus, and magnesium, with regard to influences on calculi formation have yielded some interesting but conflicting results. Analyses of calculus stones have shown a varied composition. Some consist largely of calcium carbonate; others, of ammonium magnesium phosphate or mixtures of calcium and magnesium phosphates, with varying amounts of nitrogenous material and other mineral salts.

Research at the Texas Agricultural Experiment Station disclosed a high incidence of calculi in steers fed grain sorghum heads and demonstrated that high magnesium levels encouraged formation of stones. To a less extent, the addition of calcium carbonate caused accumulations of granular material in the bladders of the steers. On a typical ration of milo grain, cottonseed meal, cottonseed hulls, and sorghum silage, the use of bonemeal and dilute phosphoric acid generally have prevented serious calculi trouble.

C. E. Lindley and his associates at the Washington Agricultural Experiment Station, however, found that potassium phosphate, one of several supplements tested in sheep, caused greatest increase in numbers of cases. Other investigators have reported that magnesium supplementation failed to aggravate the trouble.

The relationships of mineral intake and excretion to the alkalinity-acidity balance in the urine has been suspected as a factor in formation of calculi. Up to 1955, there was insufficient evidence to judge whether the amount of calculi and the alkalinity of the urine actually were related.

Ammonium chloride has been tried as a means of reducing the alkalinity. It has proved fairly effective in feeding mink and so has become a practical means of keeping down calculi in mink. Apparently it is less effective in ruminants than in nonruminants.

The presence of silica in varying amounts in the stones collected from cattle and sheep has emphasized the possible importance of silica as a factor. Stones obtained from range animals may show silica to be the predominant element. Even in the feed lot, the focal points for formation of the larger stones may be the minute silicate particles. There also is considerable variation in the silica content of the feeds used in rations. Accordingly silica, along with calcium, phosphorus, and magnesium, needs to be considered as involved.

The state of suspension of colloidal as well as crystalloidal matter in the urine has claimed considerable attention. It has been suggested that the enzyme hyaluronidase, which can disperse the colloidal matter in a finely divided state, should be effective in holding down calculi formation. The enzyme has been used with some success as an aid in voiding or eliminating stones.

N. R. ELLIS *became chief of the Animal*

and Poultry Husbandry Research Branch, Agricultural Research Service, in 1955. He has been with the Department of Agriculture since 1920 and has conducted researches in a wide range of nutrition and meat problems of swine, cattle, poultry, and other stock.

Tumors

C. L. DAVIS AND W. T. SHALKOP

ANIMALS may be subject to different types of tumors, which can be said to have essentially the same cellular makeup, grow and spread in much the same way, and follow a similar clinical pattern as tumors in man.

Practically all the body tissues and organs in animals are susceptible to the formation of tumors, which may be benign or malignant. The term "cancer" has come by usage to designate any malignant tumor that may endanger life, whereas "benign" or "noncancerous" means "innocent" in that the life of the individual is not necessarily threatened.

Some differences exist. In food-producing animals the rare occurrence of cancer of the stomach, colon, mammary gland (breast), and prostate are in sharp contrast to the frequency in which those organs are affected in human beings.

Primary cancer of the lung, which is considered to be rather common in man, is seldom seen in animals. Tumors in the bovine lung are much less frequent than malignant growths elsewhere in the body, principally from cancer of the eye or uterus. Tumors in animals, as in man, become more prevalent with increasing age.

THE MOST COMMON SITE of cancerous involvement in cattle is the eye or its appendages. As the lesions become

larger, they are exposed to trauma, and secondary infection produces an ulcerating, foul-smelling lesion. During the fly season, the affected eye is often infested with maggots. A tumor that is incompletely removed in the early stages will grow and spread to the adjacent bony structures and eventually reach the lymph stream.

Secondary growths in the lymph glands of the head and in the lung may soon follow. Occasionally the liver and other organs may also become involved. Animals in the advanced stage of the disease will eventually die or are likely to be condemned for human use if they are sent in for slaughter before death ensues. In cattle showing only a small, localized eye tumor at slaughter, only the head may be unfit for food purposes.

THE SPECIFIC CAUSE of cancer of the eye or eyelids, like other malignant tumors, is not known. Several theories have been expressed. One opinion is that it is an hereditary predisposition, particularly in the Hereford breed, because the disease prevails in the cattle-raising sections of the country, the Western and the Southwestern States, where the Hereford breed predominates. Perhaps certain strains are more susceptible than others. Whether this greater occurrence of cancer eye in Herefords is more apparent than real is problematic. In slaughtering establishments where eye tumors are most commonly found, however, about 90 percent of the cattle so affected are of the Hereford breed. The majority of Herefords affected with this tumor, particularly of the eyelids, have no pigmented skin about the eye, but the disease may occasionally arise in those with pigmented skin.

The relative frequency with which cancer eye and other tumors appear in cattle was reported in 1933 after a survey of animals coming to slaughter in federally inspected abattoirs in Denver, Colo. In 3 months, 213 cattle were found with cancer eye among 32,499 slaughtered (0.65 percent); 203 (95.3 percent) were in the Hereford breed; and 10 (4.7 percent) involved other breeds. Cancer eye has been observed as well in the Holstein, Guernsey, Jersey, and the Shorthorn breeds. Cancer eye in sheep has also been reported.

THE COMMON WART (infectious papilloma) of the skin occurs in animals and is more prevalent in cattle. The condition also has been reported in goats. Calves and yearlings seem to be more susceptible than older cattle. In the younger animals, the warts usually appear on various parts of the head and on the sides of the neck and the shoulder but may spread to other parts of the body. Warts in cows customarily affect the udder and teats. Severe cases may sap the strength and stunt the growth of young cattle. More important is the damage to the hides in areas of the skin containing the warts.

After tanning, the hides so affected have rough and weak spots and frequently contain numerous pits or holes, which impart a moth-eaten appearance to the finished leather. The hide consequently is of less value.

COMMON WARTS in cattle are infectious and are caused by a virus. They have been produced experimentally in the laboratory. Infection is believed to take place under natural conditions when injured skin comes in contact with infectious material. Segregation of affected animals is recommended, followed by cleaning and disinfecting all stables, pens, chutes, and rubbing posts where they have been. Particular care should be taken in milking cows with warts on their udders and teats to prevent spread of the warts from animal to animal.

A wart vaccine is used for immunization, prevention of the disease, and treatment of affected animals. It is said that a single injection of the vaccine under the skin will result in rapid regression of the warts in most cases.

THE ADRENAL GLANDS of cattle and sheep are more apt to contain tumors than any of the other internal body organs. Adrenal tumors are usually unilateral, but both glands may be involved. They may be benign or malignant. They often grow to considerable size. The growths usually remain localized, although sometimes they spread to the lung by way of the blood stream.

The uterus of the cow is involved with malignant growth oftener than was once supposed. Observations made in the Animal Disease Research Laboratory in Denver in 1953 and 1954 indicate that cancer of the bovine uterus can no longer be considered a rare tumor. In fact, the uterus can now be classed as one of the body organs most frequently affected with malignancy. Cancer of the uterus is not easily diagnosed in the cow, however, and is probably not recognized until the animal comes to slaughter. It seems reasonable to assume that when the uterus is involved with a malignant growth, a breeding problem, if not sterility, may result.

THE PRIMARY SITE of tumorous growth occurs occasionally in other body organs of cattle in the following relative order of frequency: Liver, gallbladder, ovary, kidney, and heart.

Lymph glands, bone, cartilage, and muscle also may be sites of tumor formation. The most important is the malignant lymphoma arising from lymphoid tissue, particularly the lymph glands. It often is found throughout the carcass in slaughtered animals of all ages and breeds. Nearly all body organs and the tissues at one time or another have been affected with a malignant lymphoma. It is among the commonest type of malignant tumor in slaughtered cattle, sheep, and hogs for which there is total condemnation of the carcass. Many animals die of the disease before coming to slaughter.

Tumors of the peripheral nervous system that are referred to as "Schwannomas" have their origin from certain connective tissue cells (Schwann's cell) in the enveloping membrane of nerves. A report made in 1953 of a series of 24 cases of this type of tumor in cattle coming to slaughter listed the Schwannoma as one of the more usual bovine tumors. The tumors may involve several nerves in different parts of the body simultaneously. The heart, brachial plexus, and intercostal nerves are the most common locations of the tumors. They are primarily benign, but not always so.

They are uncommon in other food-producing animals.

Tumors in swine are seen less frequently, probably because hogs are slaughtered at a comparatively early age. Aside from the occurrence of malignant lymphoma and melanotic pigmented tumors of the skin, only one other tumor need be mentioned here. That is a primary tumor of the kidney called embryonal nephroma. It is the commonest tumor of swine. It is of interest also because of its similarity to a malignant, often fatal tumor of the kidney (Wilm's tumor) that sometimes occurs in children. The tumor in swine, however, is recognized only at the time of slaughter. It may grow to considerable size, with complete destruction of the involved kidney, and may spread to other organs of the body. Both kidneys are sometimes involved at the same time.

The estimated loss from tumors in slaughtered cattle, sheep, and swine was nearly 2 million dollars in 1949. At that time, only about 65 percent of all meat-producing animals were slaughtered under Federal inspection (80 percent in 1954). Assuming that the condemnations for tumors were in equal proportions among the 35 percent slaughtered in nonfederally inspected establishments, another million dollars could be added to the annual loss from tumors in slaughtered animals.

The annual loss attributable to this disease on farms and ranches would be difficult to assess. No statistics are available; there is no method of reporting them. But there is no doubt that many die each year of cancer in one form or another.

C. L. Davis *became director of the Animal Disease Research Laboratory at Denver, Colo., in 1947. He received his degree in veterinary medicine at Colorado Agricultural and Mechanical College in 1921 and has been with the Department of Agriculture since 1922.*

W. T. Shalkop *joined the Department of Agriculture in 1946. He was employed in the Tuberculosis Eradication Division and Meat Inspection Division before joining the Washington laboratory of the Animal Disease and Parasite Research Branch as a veterinary pathologist. He received his degree in veterinary medicine from Texas Agricultural and Mechanical College in 1942.*

For further reading:
G. T. Creech: *Etiology of Common Warts in Cattle,* Journal of Agricultural Research, volume 39, number 10, pages 723–737. 1929.
C. L. Davis, R. B. Leeper, and J. E. Shelton: *Neoplasms Encountered in Federally Inspected Establishments in Denver, Colorado,* Journal of the American Veterinary Medical Association, volume 83, pages 229–237. 1933.
A. W. Monlux and C. L. Davis: *Multiple Schwannomas of Cattle,* American Journal of Veterinary Research, volume 14, number 53, pages 499–509. 1953.
Paul E. Steiner and John S. Bengston: *Research and Economic Aspects of Tumors in Food-Producing Animals,* Cancer, volume 4, number 5, pages 1113–1124. 1951.

Bloat in Ruminants

ROBERT W. DOUGHERTY

BLOAT, a digestive disorder of ruminants, is the distention of the stomach with gas. The swelling is limited mainly to the first two compartments of the stomach—the rumen (or paunch) and reticulum (or honeycomb).

The occurrence of bloat has increased remarkably since 1930, perhaps a reflection of changes in management and feeding practices, a great increase in acreage of legumes, and other factors.

Bloat is a major disease of cattle and sheep. It is hard to assess the actual numerical or monetary losses for two reasons. Postmortem gaseous distention of the full ruminant stomach usually occurs following death from other causes and sometimes the death may be attributed wrongly to bloat. The most serious loss from bloat to many dairymen and cattlemen is the loss in milk production and the slower gains in weight that usually follow recovery from severe bloat, but such losses are not easily estimated. Nevertheless we have some estimates that in the United States bloat costs dairymen and producers of beef cattle and sheep about 40 to 45 million dollars a year.

One must also take into account the great losses that occur because of sudden changes that have to be made in management practices, such as the abrupt cessation of the pasturing of lush and productive legume pastures after the loss of a few animals.

GENERAL CLASSIFICATIONS of bloat describe it as acute (of short duration) and chronic (of long duration); as mild, moderate, and severe; as frothy or foamy and nonfrothy; and in other ways. Those classifications are inadequate in one way or another. Some animals that never have had serious trouble may suddenly bloat and die. Others may bloat mildly; that is, after

no more than a mild distention of the rumen and with no apparent distress or aftereffects, they may bloat severely and die. Some cattle in Mississippi bloated mildly more than 100 times before serious or fatal bloat occurred; they were grazing Ladino clover pastures off and on and showed mild distention of the rumen almost every day.

The classification of bloat into mild, moderate, and severe forms reflects a person's own variable and inexact interpretations. Sometimes an animal may not appear to be greatly distended and yet may actually be close to death. Other animals may seem to be greatly distended but in no particular distress. Body conformation, thickness of the body wall, and muscle tone may have a pronounced influence on the apparent distention of the rumen and even the feel of the distended left side of bloated animals.

We have little data on the actual pressures in the paunches of severely bloated cattle or sheep. Investigators in California devised an instrument that, pressed against the area at the top part of the left flank where the distention is usually most evident, can measure indirectly the pressures in the rumen. Differences in the ways in which the instrument is applied make the data of only relative value.

The most accurate and direct methods of obtaining existing pressures in the paunch available in 1956 were rather hard on the animal and were of practical use on only a few animals for experimental purposes.

Critical pressures vary in different animals of the same breed and species. In man, accurate, indirect methods of measuring blood pressure are in use, but it is impossible to set up definite pressure standards for differentiating between high or low blood pressure and the normal values that can be applied for all individuals.

The classification of bloat into "frothy" and "nonfrothy," or free-gas types, is probably a matter of degree. Some cases may have a large pocket or a number of pockets of gas in various parts of the rumen; in other cases most of the material in the paunch may be a frothy or foamy mass. It is unlikely that there is an absolute absence of free gas (gas pockets) in any case of bloat. The amount of gas so retained may be relatively small, however.

The extent of frothing becomes serious because of its possible effects on eructation, or belching. The rumen gases are formed from bacterial fermentation of food material in the paunch. The retention of the gases largely in millions of small bubbles throughout the feed in the paunch probably would lower the efficiency of the animal's belching mechanism.

BLOAT generally is believed to be due to some dysfunction of the eructating mechanism. If the belching mechanism is working normally, the animal can eructate more gas than can be expected to form in the rumen under normal feeding conditions. Because our knowledge of the physiology of normal eructation is incomplete, we can list the causes of bloat only as theories.

Theories for the cause of bloat may be classified in general as physical, biochemical, and hereditary and as connected with soil fertility and the climate.

The physical theories suggest there is too much dense feed, or excessive formation of gas, altered surface tension, or physical deficiency. The biochemical theories have to do with the presence of hydrogen cyanide, flavones, saponins, and allergies.

Scientists at Iowa State College noted that alfalfa forms a more compact mass than bluegrass when treated in the same way. They also observed that grazing cows may eat 50 to 100 pounds of succulent feed before resting. This material, remaining in a compact mass,

would weight the stomach down and make the cardia (the esophageal opening into the stomach) less capable of opening. The fermenting mass of freshly eaten food would be buoyed up by the gas of fermentation and would also make belching more difficult. As the pressure increases, the tendency for the cardia to be blocked would be still greater.

Excessive gas formation once was a widely accepted theory. It is true that, pound for pound, there may be considerable difference in the rate of gas formation from different feeds. But investigators generally have come to believe that an animal that can belch normally has no difficulty in eructating all the gas formed in its stomach.

The surface tension theory holds that bloat is caused by any material that will alter surface tension so that the gas of fermentation will be entrapped in countless bubbles throughout the feed mass in the rumen.

Saponins—substances found in highest concentrations in some of the legumes—are most apt to cause bloat. Eight saponins have been isolated from alfalfa. We have no good quantitative method for determining the amounts of saponins in various plants. Saponins do have an effect on surface tension, but in this respect the part they have in causing bloat is moot. Either saponins or something else does influence surface tension so that the gas of fermentation does not rise freely to the top of the rumen.

Research in the Animal and Poultry Husbandry Research Branch at Beltsville, Md., the Western Utilization Research Branch at Albany, Calif., and at Cornell University has thrown new light on the saponins. The saponins were found to be extremely toxic. The investigators induced bloating and death by feeding or by injecting relatively large amounts of alfalfa saponins into the blood stream. When the internal organs were examined after death, lesions were found that are not usually seen in animals dying from ordinary bloat. This could be a matter

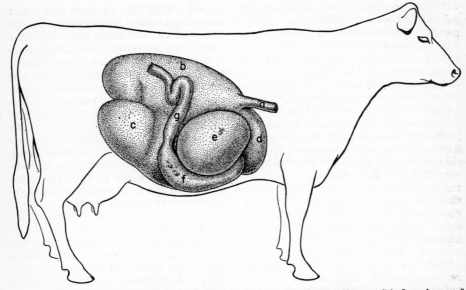

The approximate position of the stomach of the cow: (a) Esophagus; (b) dorsal sac of rumen; (c) ventral sac of rumen; (d) reticulum; (e) omasum; (f) abdomasum; (g) duodenum.

of dosage or lack of purification of the alfalfa saponin extracts. The findings may eventually be of great importance, but so far they must be regarded as tentative. Alfalfa probably contains no more of the saponins than other legumes. It was the first plant to undergo such extraction. There may be marked differences between what happens to legumes in the extraction processes and the changes that occur in the digestive tract of ruminants.

The amount and kind of saliva may have an influence on surface tension and foam formation. Succulent leafy feed, such as that of legume pastures, stimulates a minimum secretion of saliva. The presence of coarse feed in the rumen reflexly stimulates the salivary glands to increase greatly their output. Copious amounts of saliva apparently prevent the gas of fermentation from accumulating as foam in the food mass, and therefore it rises to the top where it can be easily eructated. Cattle on lush legume pastures spend little time ruminating;

it is assumed that most of the total amount of saliva is secreted during rumination.

Research workers at the University of California investigated aspects of physical deficiency and came to the belief that the belching mechanism is stimulated in the same manner as the rumination mechanism—that is, by the scratching of the wall of the rumen and reticulum by coarse material in the feed. Thus they agree with scientists in South Africa that coarse material in the feed has a direct or indirect influence on belching. The two groups of investigators differ as to whether coarse feed stimulates belching by directly stimulating the mechanism or whether the feed affects belching indirectly by stimulating an increased rate of salivary secretion.

HYDROGEN CYANIDE, a highly toxic poison that occurs in certain plants, was thought by some to be a primary cause of bloat. Experimental work has disproved that theory. Experimental feeding of hydrogen cyanide does not inhibit belching, at least when gas is pumped into the rumen of the animals. Some varieties of birdsfoot trefoil may contain 19 times as much cyanide as Ladino clover; trefoil causes little or no bloat, but Ladino clover has probably caused as much bloat as any other legume.

Flavones in legume juice are active substances that have a paralyzing effect on rabbit gut (a smooth muscle similar in structure to the muscle of the rumen wall), according to investigators in England. They theorized that flavones might influence the belching mechanism, but we have no direct evidence. Safe grass juice contains small amounts of flavones.

THE THEORY that an allergy might be responsible for bloat was offered by veterinarians in Ireland, who noted a high incidence of bloat following the second dose of trichomonal antigen, a vaccine. The first, or sensitizing, dose had been received 7 to 10 days previously, about the proper spacing for an allergic response. This is an interesting theory and may eventually open up new fields for the study of allergic reactions originating from the digestive tract. It is, however, no more than a theory.

SOME THEORIES are chiefly biochemical in nature. One is that certain toxins that might inhibit belching are absorbed from the rumen. Another, developed in Germany, is that the high phosphatase content of rumen ingesta and the rich phosphate content of bloat-producing plants are responsible for an increased rate of gas production in the bloating animals.

The theories are interesting to research workers but of little practical value to farmers in 1956, but some of them may eventually prove to be very important in the prevention and treatment of bloat.

Heredity is listed as a possible cause of bloat only on limited experimental evidence. A number of bloating steers

were sired by one bull. In a limited number of experiments with identical twins, members of the same set showed a tendency to bloat. The importance of heredity as a factor in bloat cannot be ignored. Even if the tendency is inherited, however, it is unlikely that bloating will occur unless aggravated by other factors.

There is some indication that bloat rarely occurs on certain types of soil. Climatic and weather conditions must be involved also, but until the definite substances are found in plants that are responsible for bloat, little can be definitely said regarding the effect of soil fertility and weather.

HOW DOES BLOAT CAUSE DEATH? We do not know exactly. Some researchers assign a physical basis—that is, the increased pressure in the rumen interferes with blood flow and respiration and the animal actually dies of suffocation. Others think that absorption of certain gases from the rumen and possibly other toxic substances might be responsible. It is possible that increased pressure may increase the rate of absorption of certain substances that ordinarily might be detoxified or excreted as fast as they were absorbed. Investigations at the New York State Veterinary College at Cornell University indicate that the effects of increased pressures in the rumen may be responsible for a complex set of symptoms.

TREATMENT with turpentine and phenol preparations or coal tar derivatives, commonly used in the treatment of bloat, did not reduce the amount of gas formed. The benefits of such treatments were due to their surface tension—defoaming—action. A number of American scientists have reported on methyl silicone, another defoaming agent, as an effective treatment in bloat. Such defoaming agents appear to act by changing the surface tension of liquids. Studies in New Zealand indicated that antifoaming agents never failed to protect animals from bloat and to relieve the bloated ones. This should not be interpreted as meaning that all bloat is due to frothing and that antifoaming agents are the complete solution to the bloat problem.

The New Zealand research workers discovered that paraffin, silicones, peanut oil, soybean oil, and turpentine, all of which are surface-active agents, would successfully relieve and prevent bloat. Here, again, it must be remembered that conditions may be different in different parts of the world and that further experimental work will be necessary under the existing conditions in various parts of this country.

It is doubtful even in "frothy" bloat that defoaming agents would be effective in the critical stages of bloat.

In the acute cases, time is of utmost importance so that an emergency rumenotomy would probably be the only effective method of treatment.

In cases that are not critical, the stomach tube method of relieving gas pressure is always worth a trial. In the "frothy" type, however, it may be disappointing, because it is difficult to locate the possible existing gas pockets before the tube, or trocar, becomes clogged.

Extensive work is being done on more effective and efficient defoaming agents. It will be necessary to study the effect of these agents on the rumen bacteria and protozoa and their direct effect on the treated animals. There is little experimental evidence that physical methods or drugs now in use are effective in stimulating belching. It is difficult to evaluate clinical data, as a high percentage of bloated animals recover without treatment.

PREVENTION OF BLOAT should be the primary aim of investigations. When enough basic knowledge is available as to the cause of bloat, it should be possible through feeding and management practices and animal and plant breeding programs to reduce the incidence greatly. If plants are the primary cause and if their chemical and physical characteristics that cause

bloat are known, it may be possible to change those characteristics.

Certain feeding practices may offer considerable relief in areas where bloat is a serious problem. There is some evidence that pure legume pastures are more dangerous than pastures that are 50 percent legume plants or less. Weather and other conditions may make it difficult to maintain such ratios.

Bloat occurs occasionally in the feed lot; with the use of fresh, field-chopped legumes, the number of cases may increase. Some feeders control this type of bloat by mixing coarse, nonlegume feed or straw with the roughage. One large feeder puts a bale of straw to every 3 or 4 bales of alfalfa hay through the chopper (dry hay) and believes that it greatly reduces bloat.

Technicians in California reduced the incidence of bloat by feeding Sudangrass to animals before they were turned on the pastures each day.

Experimental work has started in England on the spraying of harmless defoaming agents on bloat-producing pastures.

Investigators in Wisconsin found some evidence that common household detergents may be effective in preventing bloat.

FEW DEFINITE recommendations can be made other than the use of mixed pastures and the feeding of coarse nonlegume roughages daily before turning on pastures or supplying it to animals on legume pastures. In dry-lot feeding, the inclusion of straw or other nonlegume hay with legume roughage may help to prevent bloat.

Studies of the physical, chemical, and pharmacological characteristics of saponins have been undertaken by scientists of the Department of Agriculture at Beltsville, Md., and Albany, Calif.

The innervation of anatomical structures involved in belching is being studied at the University of Minnesota. Men at the University of Wisconsin began studies of the effect of detergents on foaming and other physical characteristics involved as possible causes of bloat.

The physiology of belching and the place of rumen bacteria in bloat are studied at Cornell University and the University of Maryland.

ROBERT W. DOUGHERTY *is professor of physiology in the New York State Veterinary College, Cornell University. He has done extensive research with rumen physiology and bloat. He has published many papers on problems connected with the digestive and reproductive tracts of cattle and sheep.*

Chemical Poisoning

WAYNE BINNS

ARSENIC poisoning in livestock may be caused by arsenic trioxide (white arsenic), paris green, sodium arsenite, and sodium arsenate. Arsenic has been a common cause of accidental and criminal poisoning of animals because it often is used to kill insects, parasites, weeds, and rodents and as a tonic for animals.

Arsenic compounds usually are palatable to animals, especially when they are hungry for salt. Many cattle and sheep have died from eating arsenic-treated plants, grasshopper bait, or discarded arsenic residues. The toxic dose of arsenic depends on the species of animals, the type of arsenical compound, its physical state, and the method of administration.

ARSENIC POISONING may be acute or chronic, depending on the amount consumed.

In acute poisoning, a form frequently encountered, the symptoms may include intense abdominal pain, salivation, a diffuse diarrhea, depression, weakness, incoordination, and posterior paralysis, and a subnormal temperature. These symptoms terminate in convulsions and death within a few hours, or the animals may linger for 3 or 4 days. Some eventually recover.

The chronic form of arsenic poisoning in animals is hard to diagnose because the symptoms may be obscure and much like the symptoms of other diseases. Some of the common symptoms are loss of flesh; a bright-red coloration of the mucous membranes; digestive disturbance, with slight to marked diarrhea, irregular pulse, and depression.

Animals poisoned with arsenic usually have taken such large amounts that treatment is of no value.

FLUORINE is an active chemical element. It is widely distributed in the soil, rocks, water, and plants. It combines with other elements to form fluorides.

The main naturally occurring fluorine compounds, which are used for commercial purposes, are fluorspar, cryolite, and apatite (rock phosphate).

Chronic fluorosis results from the ingestion of small amounts of fluoride for a long time. It occurs in livestock from the use of mineral mixtures containing rock phosphate, water high in fluorine, and from contaminated forage grown near industrial plants that emit fluorides into the atmosphere. It is possible that surface contamination of growing plants with dust from soil high in fluorides may cause chronic fluorosis in animals subsisting entirely on such forage.

All classes of livestock may be affected by excess amounts of fluorides. Considerable variation exists among the different species in the levels of intake required to produce symptoms of chronic fluorosis. Cattle are the most susceptible, followed by sheep, swine, horses, and poultry.

The severity of the lesions caused by fluorine poisoning depends on the form of fluoride consumed, the nutritional quality of the feed, age and species of the animals, the level and the period of fluorine intake, and such other factors as reproduction and lactation.

Feeding experiments show that cattle may ingest about 1 to 2 milligrams per kilogram (2.2 pounds) of body weight or approximately 30 to 60 parts per million (p. p. m.) of fluorides in the total ration without harmful effects if they are in good state of nutrition. An excessive amount of fluorine interferes with the normal calcification of the bones and teeth.

The symptoms of chronic dental fluorosis appear during the periods of formation and eruption of the permanent teeth. The incisor teeth lose their ivorylike appearance. They may show definite crossmarkings and become dull and chalklike. Excessive wearing of the teeth, staining, and slight pitting or excessive erosion of the enamel, with exposure of the dentine (which becomes brown or black) occur. In severe cases, the joints may become enlarged and the shaft of the long bones may thicken and show slight roughness or prominent areas of outward enlargement, with intermittent lameness.

If excessive amounts of fluorides are not ingested until after all permanent teeth have erupted (in cattle, at the age of 4 to 5 years), the teeth will not show the characteristic lesions of dental fluorosis, but eventually some animals may show slight thickening of long bones, lameness, and loss of flesh.

Such changes as diarrhea, long toes, and reproductive disturbance are not specific symptoms of chronic fluorosis in cattle and have not been observed to be related to the level of fluorine intake.

Diarrhea, sudden loss of appetite, rapid loss of flesh, slight to marked inflammation of stomach and intestines, and, in some animals, a lowering of the blood calcium are often characteristic of acute fluoride poisoning.

The fluorine content of normal bones varies greatly and may reach a level of 1,200 p. p. m. or more on fat-free, dry basis. A fluorine content of more than 4,500 p. p. m. may occur in bones that show lesions of fluorosis.

I know of no substance that can be given to animals on a high fluorine diet to overcome completely the poisoning effects. Liberal amounts of calcium and phosphorus or aluminum compounds in the feed, however, reduce somewhat the toxic effects. Those compounds combine with the fluorine in the digestive tract and prevent to some extent its accumulation in the bones and teeth.

Prevention of chronic fluorosis depends entirely on eliminating any excessive fluoride intake by selecting feeds and mineral supplements that are low in fluorine.

LEAD POISONING occurs oftenest in cattle and calves, but all animals are susceptible. The lead compounds usually involved in livestock poisoning are lead oxide, red oxide of lead, lead acetate, white lead, and lead arsenate.

Animals may get lead by chewing or licking lead-painted objects, paint-lined feeding buckets or troughs, discarded paint containers, lead storage batteries, and discarded painting materials, such as old brushes and drop cloths. Allowing stock to graze in orchards that were sprayed shortly before with lead compounds may be dangerous.

Many lead compounds are described as insoluble or slightly soluble in water, but they may be readily soluble in the digestive juices in the stomach and intestinal tract of animals.

Lead is a cumulative poison in the body, and toxic effects may result when the total amount of small daily doses equals that of a single toxic dose.

Symptoms of acute lead poisoning are in two groups.

First, inflammation of the lining of the stomach and intestines resulting from the corrosive action of the lead on the mucous membranes, complete loss of appetite, diarrhea with a strong fetid odor, grinding of teeth, and salivation.

Second, symptoms arising from the toxic effect of the lead on the nervous system. Affected animals may walk in circles and run into objects because of blindness. Cattle often bellow, as if terrified, with a marked change in the voice, or they may stand with heads pressed against the wall or manger.

In chronic lead poisoning there may be a loss of weight, depression, staggering gait, and constipation alternating with diarrhea. Horses may show swelling of the knees, blue line on the gums, gradual paralysis of the hind legs, and a peculiar roaring when they inhale.

Epsom salts may be effective as an antidote to change the soluble lead in the stomach and intestines into a less soluble form so as to reduce further absorption of the poison.

MOLYBDENUM POISONING may occur in cattle and sheep that graze in areas where molybdenum is present in the soil in excessive amounts and is taken up by forage plants.

Small amounts of the element appear to be beneficial in the growth of nitrogen-fixing bacteria found in the roots of leguminous plants. When excessive amounts are present in the soil, however, alfalfa and the clovers generally take up much greater quantities of molybdenum than the grasses in the same area and are responsible for most of the poisoning that occurs.

Poisoning has been produced experimentally by feeding calves 2 to 3.5 milligrams per pound of body weight of sodium molybdate. The presence of excess molybdenum in the animal's body apparently interferes with copper metabolism, and the condition produced is sometimes referred to as complicated copper deficiency.

Animals vary considerably in susceptibility to molybdenum poisoning. Young cattle are more susceptible than older animals, and dairy cattle seem to be more susceptible than beef cattle and sheep. Horses and swine appear to be resistant.

When the molybdenum content of forage is approximately 10 p. p. m., it may take 1 to 7 months of continuous feeding to produce the disease, while symptoms of molybdenum poisoning may appear 24 hours to a week after cattle are put on spring pastures, the forage of which contains 20 to 100 p. p. m. of molybdenum.

The clinical symptoms of chronic molybdenum poisoning are profuse diarrhea, with the feces containing gas bubbles, emaciation, swollen vulva, marked anemia, general weakness and stiffness, fading of the hair coat, and occasionally death from severe and prolonged diarrhea.

If the molybdenum content of the ration does not exceed 15 to 20 p. p. m., the diarrhea may be controlled to a considerable extent by using, during the grazing season, a salt mixture containing 0.5 pound to 1 pound of copper sulfate to 100 pounds of salt. The action of the copper sulfate on molybdenum poisoning is not yet definitely known, except that it may relieve the deficiency of copper created by the excess molybdenum.

NITRATE POISONING in animals may be produced by a number of plants, some of which are oat hay (mainly the leaves); redroot (*Amaranthus retroflexus*); Russian-thistle (*Salsola kalitenufolia*); white ragweed (*Franseria discolor*); and variegated thistle (*Silybum mariamum*). Beet tops also have been found to be high in nitrate after the beets had been sprayed with a very low concentration of 2,4-D.

Nitrate fertilizer is quite palatable, especially to cattle, and may cause nitrate poisoning when animals can get at it while it is in storage.

The experimental feeding of potassium nitrate has shown that the minimum lethal dose is approximately 25 grams (0.8 ounce) per hundred pounds of animal weight.

The nitrate level in plants depends largely on the amount of nitrate in the soil, although other unidentified factors are present. When the nitrate content exceeds 2-percent dry weight of the plants, such forage is dangerous to feed and may cause poisoning.

While nitrate poisoning results from the ingestion of excess amounts of nitrate, the active toxicant appears to be the highly toxic nitrite that has been formed by the reduction of the nitrate to nitrite probably by bacterial or enzymatic action within the digestive tract of the animal.

When the nitrites are absorbed into the blood stream, they change the oxyhemoglobin to methemoglobin; the red blood cells cannot then carry oxygen to the tissues.

Cattle, sheep, and horses are susceptible, but poisoning occurs most frequently in cattle.

The symptoms of nitrate poisoning include staggering gait, muscular tremors, blue coloration of mucous membranes, rapid and labored breathing, marked dilation of pupils, and coma. Death results from asphyxiation.

The object in treatment is to convert the methemoglobin in the blood back to oxyhemoglobin so the red blood cells can release oxygen to the tissues.

The injection intravenously of 4 milligrams of methylene blue per pound of body weight, given in a 4-percent solution with distilled water, is effective if given early and the methemoglobinemia is not greater than 70 percent. Repeated injections of this solution may be necessary until the material containing the nitrate has been eliminated from the digestive tract. The administration of a large volume of mineral oil through a stomach tube may help reduce the absorption of the nitrites and aid in elimination.

SALT POISONING may occur in livestock from the excessive consumption of sodium chloride, or common salt, which is an essential food substance and harmless when properly used.

The normal consumption of salt by cattle on range and pasture is 1 to 2.5 pounds a month. For sheep the amount generally is estimated on the basis of 0.5 pound a month per ewe. Lambs in dry lots may consume about 0.6 pound of salt a month. Salt always should be available to livestock.

Cattle may consume up to 1 pound of salt daily without harmful effects if fresh water is available at all times. Natural waters that contain up to 1 percent of salt generally are considered satisfactory as a water supply for cattle.

Range cattlemen have been using salt in a mixture with feed concentrates in an effort to control the intake of protein or grain supplements that are fed from a self-feeder. This type of feeding usually has been satisfactory, although the amount of salt consumed by the animals greatly exceeds their requirements. Losses may occur with this system of feeding on ranges where the water supply is limited or when the salt and protein supplement mixtures are fed at too great a distance from the water supply.

Salt poisoning has occurred when animals were deprived of salt for a long time and then allowed free access to an abundant supply.

Hogs have been poisoned by drinking brine or by eating garbage that contained brine pickle.

Symptoms first noticed in salt poisoning are hypersensitivity to touch, loss of appetite, marked redness and dryness of mucous membranes of the mouth, and loss of coordination. Paralysis and death may follow.

The autopsy usually shows a distention of the rumen, slight congestion of the mucous membrane of the stomach, and marked edema along the lining of the first portion of the small intestines.

To prevent salt poisoning, it is important to give animals enough salt and a liberal supply of water if salt-protein supplements are used.

Treatment of salt poisoning usually

is ineffective, but sometimes in the early stages it helps to give a large volume of water through a stomach tube, and after that a large dose of mineral oil.

SELENIUM POISONING in animals is caused by the ingestion of plants that have absorbed selenium from the soils. Many areas of seleniferous soils that were derived from cretaceous formations have been found in the Western States, principally in the region from the Rocky Mountains to South Dakota and Kansas.

Chronic selenium poisoning results when an animal ingests feed containing low levels of selenium (10 to 40 p. p. m.) for a few weeks to several months.

Alkali disease was the name usually applied to chronic selenium poisoning before the cause was recognized. Symptoms of selenium poisoning are loss of hair from the mane and tail of horses, from the switch of cattle, and from the body of hogs. Rough horns, long and deformed hoofs, and later sloughing of the hoofs occur in all affected animals.

Affected animals may be sterile or may be slow breeders.

The hatchability of chicken eggs is greatly reduced. The chicks that are hatched have a wiry, greasy down; they are weak and live only a short time. Unhatched eggs usually contain deformed embryos.

Acute selenium poisoning may cause death within a few hours to 2 or 3 days if the animals have ingested forage containing 200 p. p. m. or more of selenium.

The only practical means of preventing selenium poisoning in livestock is to avoid the use of seleniferous forage and grain. The feeding of a ration high in protein is reported to give some protection to sheep and laboratory animals against the toxic effects of selenium.

WAYNE BINNS *in 1954 joined the Department of Agriculture as a veterinarian in charge of studies of livestock poisoning by plants.*

For further reading:

Ruth Allcroft and K. L. Blaxter: *Lead as a Nutritional Hazard to Farm Livestock. V. The Toxicity of Lead to Cattle and Sheep and an Evaluation of the Lead Hazard under Farm Conditions,* Journal of Comparative Pathology and Therapeutics, volume 60, number 3, pages 209-218, 1950.

K. L. Blaxter: *Lead as a Nutritional Hazard to Farm Livestock. II. The absorption and Excretion of Lead by Sheep and Rabbits,* Journal of Comparative Pathology and Therapeutics, volume 60, number 2, pages 140-159, 1950.

K. L. Blaxter: *Lead as a Nutritional Hazard to Farm Livestock. III. Factors Influencing the Distribution of Lead in the Tissues,* Journal of Comparative Pathology and Therapeutics, volume 60, number 3, pages 177-189, 1950.

W. B. Bradley, H. F. Eppson, and O. A. Beath: *Livestock Poisoning by Oat Hay and Other Plants Containing Nitrate,* Wyoming Agricultural Experiment Station Bulletin 241, 20 pages, 1940.

J. W. Britton and H. Goss: *Chronic Molybdenum Poisoning in Cattle,* Journal of American Veterinary Medical Association, volume 108, number 828, pages 176-178, 1946.

C. L. Comar, L. Singer, and G. K. Davis: *Molybdenum Metabolism and Interrelationships with Copper and Phosphorus,* Journal of Biological Chemistry, volume 180, page 913, 1949.

C. S. Hobbs, R. P. Moorman, Jr., J. M. Griffith, J. L. West, C. M. Merriman, S. L. Hansard, and C. C. Chamberlain: *Fluorosis in Cattle and Sheep,* Tennessee Agricultural Experiment Station Bulletin 235, 163 pages, 1954.

Louis W. Holm, Louis F. Johnson, and Joanne K. Critchlow: *Experimental Poisoning of Cattle and Sheep with Dynamite,* Cornell Veterinarian, volume 42, number 1, pages 91-96.

L. Meyer Jones: *Veterinary Pharmacology and Therapeutics,* 850 pages, Ames, Iowa, Iowa State College Press, 1954.

A. T. Kinsley: *Arsenical Poisoning,* Veterinary Medicine, volume 24, number 10, page 445, 1929.

John W. Kenrick, John Tucker, S. Anderson People: *Nitrate Poisoning in Cattle Due to Ingestion of Variegated Thistle, Silybum marianum,* Journal of American Veterinary Medical Association, volume 126, number 934, pages 53-56, 1955.

E. E. Maas: *Arsenic Content in Urine from Cattle Dipped in Arsenical Solutions,* Journal of the American Veterinary Medical Association, volume 110, number 841, pages 249-250, 1947.

W. T. Miller and H. W. Schoening: *Toxicity of Selenium Fed to Swine in the Form of Sodium Selenite,* Journal of Agricultural Research, volume 56, number 11, pages 831-842, 1938.

W. T. Miller and K. T. Williams: *Minimum Lethal Dose of Selenium, As Sodium Selenite, for Horses, Mules, Cattle, and Swine,* Journal of Agricultural Research, volume 60, number 3, pages 163-173, 1940.

Poisonous Plants

WARD T. HUFFMAN, EDWARD A. MORAN, AND WAYNE BINNS

PLANTS that poison livestock can grow anyplace, but they are a serious problem mainly in the western grazing areas where overgrazing has impaired or destroyed the good but less sturdy forage plants.

The poisonous plants usually grow among forage plants and so are available to grazing animals. Only a few are agreeable to the taste, however, and animals avoid the toxic plants unless there is a shortage of feed and better vegetation.

Overgrazing is a major factor in livestock losses from poisonous plants. Overgrazing has increased in some sections because moisture deficiencies have reduced the growth of forage. Hungry animals feed on whatever is available.

Sometimes harmful plants are harvested with the hay and their seeds become mixed with grain. Then animals can hardly separate the good feed from the bad. Livestock owners have considerable control over conditions conducive to poisoning by plants.

Some plants contain acute poisons and produce visible symptoms or death soon after they are eaten. Others may be eaten for some time before any noticeable effects are apparent. Most poisonous plants may be eaten for a considerable time with little or no ill effects.

IT IS NOT EASY to control poisonous plants in pastures and on the range. Plowing and cultivation usually eradicate them, but in some areas, such as the western grazing lands, these methods are not feasible because of expense, the time they take, and the amount of benefit. Sometimes the plants are pulled up, grubbed out, or killed with herbicides, but that is slow and expensive even under favorable conditions.

Many poisonous plants are distributed so widely over grazing areas of limited value in the Western States that the cost of eradication would be much greater than the benefits. A more practical procedure is to remove the toxic plants from limited areas, including trails and watering places. The method of eradication used would depend on the character and growth habits of the species, the other plants with which the toxic plants grow, and the type of soil.

When eradication is impractical, a system of range and pasture management can be worked out to permit the use of the forage crops without excessive livestock losses. That is largely a matter of wise control of grazing.

Poisonous plants often are the first to start growth in the spring and may harm livestock if too early grazing is practiced. If pastures and ranges are stocked to full capacity in normal years and the number of livestock is not reduced in drought years, the usual forage can be supplemented with other roughage or feed in order to avoid injury to the existing vegetation and losses of animals from the poisonous plants.

Another aspect of control is that one species of animals may avoid certain plants, or one species may not be injured by plants that poison another species. Losses then may be avoided by permitting only the animals least affected to graze them.

Some examples: Horses seldom eat cyanogenetic plants—plants that can produce hydrocyanic acid—in toxic amounts, but cattle and sheep frequently do eat such plants and are poisoned by them. Pastures that contain cyanogenetic plants should be used by horses in preference to cattle and sheep. Horses are more frequently poisoned by ragworts or groundsels, which are species of *Senecio*, than are cattle or sheep, and sheep are less susceptible to their poisoning than are cattle. Pastures containing ragworts should be used by sheep in preference to cattle or horses. Cattle often are poisoned on larkspur. Sheep, however, can consume large amounts of larkspur without being poisoned but with apparent benefit. Only under abnormal conditions are sheep ever poisoned by larkspur on the range. Horses never eat enough of the larkspur to produce any ill effects. Pastures containing larkspur should be used by sheep and horses but not by cattle.

Another aspect: Some plants, such as the sorghums, become toxic under certain conditions. Sorghum in the mature stage does not contain any appreciable amount of potential hydrocyanic acid, but the young plants, or suckers (young branches from the roots), of mature sorghum may contain very much potential hydrocyanic acid. Arrowgrass grown on water-covered or very wet soil is far less poisonous than arrowgrass that continues to grow on soil that has dried after the water has receded. Oil meal made from immature flaxseed is more apt to be poisonous than oil meal made from thoroughly ripe flaxseed.

TREATMENT OF ANIMALS poisoned by plants usually is unsatisfactory and useless, because most of the damage may have been done by the time the poisoning is discovered.

Certain feeds or medicines that have some preventive value are described later in connection with plants that contain selenium. Good care and a symptomatic treatment (treatment that will reduce symptoms) will save some poisoned animals. The outcome in each case depends largely on the amount of toxic material that has been eaten and assimilated. Treatment usually is directed toward eliminating any of the toxic substance that still remains in the digestive tract. In chronic poisoning, recovery may follow a change of feed, especially if green feed is available; good care, with plenty of water and the right kind of feed, will do much to hasten recovery. (Later we suggest treatments for three types of poisoning.)

It is well to know something of the chemistry of the poisonous elements, especially those in the compounds that are physiologically active. Knowing whether the substance is an alkaloid, a glucoside, or something else makes it possible to determine by laboratory examination whether a sample of the plant is potentially deadly and to detect the poison in the tissues of animals so that a diagnosis can be made in obscure or doubtful cases.

ALKALOIDS are substances that are like the alkalies. An alkaloid turns red litmus paper blue, reacts with an acid to form a salt, and has some other properties that solutions of the alkali metals have, such as soda or potash.

The alkaloids are organic substances that contain nitrogen. Some of the alkaloids are quite stable and may be detected by a chemist in the plant tissues or the tissues of poisoned animals.

It is important for the farmer or student to know that certain groups or families of plants, such as the legume, lily, buttercup, potato, and some other families, are more likely to contain alkaloids than some other groups.

Some of the groups do not so metabolize their nitrogen as to yield alkaloids. The large and important mint family seldom contains any alkaloidal plants. The aster, or composite, family is another nonalkaloidal group, although there is an outstanding exception in the ragworts, or groundsels, of that family. The grasses are not characteristically alkaloid bearing, although darnel yields loliine, which is a true base.

A well-known alkaloid is strychnine, which is obtained from poisonnut (*Strychnos* species), a member of the logania family, whose members are mostly tropical plants. Morphine is an alkaloid that can be separated from the drug opium (an extract from certain kinds of poppy). Other well-known alkaloids are atropine, nicotine, and solanine, from the potato family; aconitine and several alkaloids of the larkspur group, from the buttercup family; zygadinine and colchicine, from the lily family; and physostigmine, lupinine, and other lupine alkaloids, from the legume, or pea, family. Names of alkaloids usually end in "-ine."

Alkaloids occur in many stock-poisoning plants. Among them are the larkspurs, lupines, deathcamas, groundsels, Dutchmans-breeches and other plants of the Dutchmans-breeches family, poison-hemlock, wildtobaccos, crotalarias, and African-rue.

Larkspurs seem to attract cattle because of the pleasant acidity of their leaves, which is refreshing in hot weather. They are one of the few poisonous plants that are palatable. The larkspur alkaloids are complex.

Delphinium barbeyi, one of the tall larkspurs, and *D. menziesi,* a low species, are the main poisonous species, although most of the species of *Delphinium* are dangerous, especially when the plants are small or when they are available in quantities. *D. occidentale,* a tall and comparatively nontoxic larkspur, resembles *D. barbeyi* and often is mistaken for it. *D. occidentale* contains about 1 percent of an alkaloid.

A treatment recommended for cattle poisoned by larkspur during drives and roundups is a subcutaneous injection of a mixture of 1 grain of physostigmine salicylate (also called eserine), 2 grains of pilocarpine hydrochloride, and one-half grain of strychnine sulfate, thoroughly dissolved in sterile water. This formula applies to an animal weighing 500 to 600 pounds. For a larger steer or cow of 1,000 pounds or more, the dose should be twice that amount. The medicine relieves constipation and stimulates respiration. The materials can be obtained from a druggist.

LUPINES, also known as bluebonnets and by other local names, belong to the legume family. Some species are harmless, at least at some stages of growth, and are excellent feed for grazing animals. Others are dangerous at certain times. Some are toxic at any stage of growth.

The alkaloids in lupines have the peculiarity that slight alterations in the molecular structure may convert the toxic alkaloid into a comparatively nonpoisonous substance, and vice versa. The alterations may take place in the plants and may account for the variations in the toxicity of the growing plants.

Reports from Germany in the 1860's attributed great losses to the yellow lupine (*Lupinus luteus*) and other lupines. Actually, however, the losses were due to molds. In this country losses from lupines have been due to alkaloidal poisoning.

Deathcamas (species of *Zigadenus*) are another group of alkaloid-containing plants. They are grasslike and not conspicuous until they bloom. They are also known as the poison sego, mystery-grass, lobelia, soap plant, alkaligrass, waterlily, squirrel food, wild onion, and hog's potato.

Species of *Senecios,* or groundsels, have caused a number of losses in livestock in Texas and other States.

Among the other alkaloidal plants there are many in the fumitory, or Dutchmans-breeches, family (*Fumariaceae*). Two examples are fitweed (*Corydalis caseana*) and Dutchmans-breeches (*Dicentra cucullaria,* sometimes called *Bikukulla cucullaria*). In the carrot family is poisonhemlock or spotted hemlock (*Conium maculatum*). One member of the potato, or nightshade, family is wildtobacco (*Nicotiana attenuata*). A member of the legume family is crotalaria or rattlebox (*Crotalaria sagittalis*). A member of the caltrop family is *Peganum harmala.*

GLUCOSIDES contain various sugars that are combined in the molecule and can be split out by acids and then detected by chemical reagents. The breaking apart of a glucoside molecule is a complicated technical process.

The definition of a glucoside in a medical dictionary may be helpful: "Chemically a glucoside may be defined as a carbohydrate compound formed by a union of a sugar with a non-sugar accompanied by the elimination of water." A chemist refers to the non-sugar as an aglycone. It can be seen there is some comparison between the structure of a glucoside and the structure of a salt, but the organic components of a glucoside are more confusing than what we consider the simple inorganic components of a salt.

Flax contains the glucoside linamarin, which, when hydrolized (water added), yields acetone (a ketone), glucose (a sugar), and hydrocyanic acid (the poisonous principle).

In a similar way cherry seeds, or pits, contain the glucoside amygdalin, which, when hydrolized, yields benzaldehyde (an aldehyde), glucose, and hydrocyanic acid.

Esculin is a phenolic glucoside from the horsechestnut. Dhurrin is a cyanogenetic glucoside from sorghum. Githagin is a glucoside called a saponin from corncockle. The characteristic ending of names of glucosides is "-in."

A chemist often can readily detect a glucoside or its aglycone, either or both of which may be poisonous. The plants that owe their poisonous properties to such substances are many and diverse. Some form soapy solutions with water and therefore have been called saponins. Others are called cyanogenetic glucosides because they develop hydrocyanic acid, or prussic acid, in certain circumstances. Others are outside these two categories.

The cyanogenetic glucosides have been responsible for large losses of livestock in many sections of the United States. Many plants have cyanogenetic characteristics, but usually only a few are dangerous to livestock.

The more important of the cyanogenetic plants include wild chokecherry (*Prunus virginiana, P. virginiana* var. *melanocarpa*, and *P. virginiana* var.

demissa); sorghum (*Sorghum vulgare*); Sudangrass (*Sorghum vulgare* var. *sudanense*); Johnsongrass (*Sorghum halepense*); flax (*Linum usitatissimum*); and arrowgrass (*Triglochin maritima* and *T. palustris*).

Wild chokecherry and other wild-cherries are always a potential danger in spring and early summer for animals that are unusually hungry, but like most poisonous plants they may be eaten in small amounts without causing injury. The leaves of the wild-cherries contain prunasin, a glucoside. In the seeds this is associated with another cyanogenetic glucoside, amygdalin, which also occurs in bitter almonds and in peach kernels.

The sorghums—*Sorghum vulgare*, Johnsongrass, and Sudangrass—have a cyanogenetic glucoside known as dhurrin. Sorghums grown under ordinary conditions are considered good feed, but when the normal growth has been interrupted by drought, frost, trampling, or other causes, hydrocyanic acid may develop to a point where the plants become toxic.

The amount of hydrocyanic acid that the sorghums can develop varies considerably according to conditions and varieties. Young and second-growth plants can develop larger amounts than older plants. The amount of hydrocyanic acid diminishes more or less regularly as the plant matures. When the seed heads are well formed, the plants generally cannot cause fatal poisoning. A possibility always exists that young suckers or branches or second-growth plants grow in the field as some plants are maturing; poisoning may result if livestock are allowed access to them. The stubble that sprouts after harvest is high in hydrocyanic acid.

Arrowgrass growing where there is plenty of water is only slightly toxic, but under drought conditions it may become toxic.

When cyanogenetic plants are made into hay, most of the hydrocyanic acid supposedly volatilizes or evaporates. One has to be careful, however, for occasionally the hay may retain enough acid to make it dangerous, especially for hungry animals that may overeat.

Wild flax and wild lima beans contain a cyanogenetic glucoside known as linamarin or phaseolunatin. Wild lima beans, imported into France as feed for cavalry horses during the First World War, caused several outbreaks of poisoning. Cultivated lima beans usually are not dangerous in the United States, because they contain little or no hydrocyanic acid. One or two cases of supposed hydrocyanic acid poisoning in cattle as a result of feeding ensilage made from lima beans have been reported.

A number of factors influence the absorption of hydrocyanic acid from plants in the digestive tract, but the rate at which such plants are eaten and the amount of food already in the stomach are probably the most important.

Hydrocyanic acid acts so rapidly that there is little chance for remedial treatment. If the victim can be reached in time, however, a combination of sodium thiosulfate and sodium nitrite injected into the lining of the abdomen or into the veins is effective against doses of hydrocyanic acid up to three minimum lethal doses. (It is considered that the minimum lethal dose of hydrocyanic acid is 1 milligram per pound of animal—a 100-pound animal may be killed with 100 mg. of HCN.)

Poisoning by cyanogenetic plants may cause rapid respiration, depression, stupor, convulsions, cyanosis of the mucous membranes (which causes them to turn blue), and paralysis. Death may follow in a few minutes or several hours.

When one animal in a group pasturing on plants that might be dangerous shows symptoms of poisoning, the others should be removed promptly from the pasture.

THE SAPONIN-CONTAINING plants include some that are highly dangerous.

The seeds of corncockle (*Agrostemma githago*), a troublesome weed, contain a mixture of saponins. The seeds some-times get into wheat and make it dangerous to feed to poultry and livestock.

Rubberweeds, both the bitter rubberweed, or bitter actinea (*Hymenoxys odorata*), an annual in the Southwest, and Colorado rubberweed, or pingue (*H. richardsoni*), a perennial of the Rocky Mountain area, contain saponins. Both rubberweeds are poisonous to stock. Sheep especially have been poisoned by them.

The nightshade group, particularly the genus *Solanum*, may have a saponin (solanine) that contains basic nitrogen and so acts also as an alkaloid. Solanine occurs in sprouted white potatoes (which belong to the nightshade family) and has at times caused poisoning of persons who have eaten the tubers. The toxic effects of bullnettle (*Solanum carolinense*) and bittersweet (*S. dulcamara*)—and, somewhat doubtfully, of black nightshade (*S. nigrum*)—are attributed to solanine.

RESINOIDS, a large group of somewhat indefinite substances, occur in some plants. One of the most common is andromedotoxin, a poison, in ericaceous plants. A complex substance, it is considered the active principle in some of the rhododendrons and azaleas and possibly the laurels. We have no precise knowledge of the peculiar structure of the molecule involved in the toxic action. Waterhemlock (*Cicuta vagans*), an extremely poisonous plant, contains a poisonous resinoid.

Milkweeds (*Asclepias* species) contain resinoids. Little is known about the chemistry of the milkweeds, but some investigators have concluded that a resinous substance extracted from milkweeds produced typical cases of range poisoning when fed to animals. They did, however, find other substances of a slightly toxic nature.

Among the species that have been studied are *Asclepias subverticillata*, the whorled milkweed of the Southwest; *A. eriocarpa*, the broadleaf (wooly-pod) milkweed of California; *A. fascicularis*, the whorled milkweed of the Western States; and *A. pumila* and *A. verticillata* var. *geyeri*, the whorled milkweeds of the Central and Eastern States. The toxicity of the different species varies greatly and ranges approximately in the order in which we list them.

Losses from the whorled milkweed (*A. subverticillata*) of the Southwest can be severe. Once, near Hotchkiss, Colo., 400 sheep died within 24 hours after feeding on the plant. In 1917 a loss of 736 sheep out of a band of 1,000 near Cortez, Colo., was traced to the same species. Next to waterhemlock, this whorled milkweed has been considered the most toxic plant in the United States, but another species of milkweed, *A. labriformis*, is much worse. The toxicity of *A. labriformis* is highest during the early part of the growing season, when about 1 ounce of its green leaves can kill a sheep weighing 100 pounds. The lethal amount for cattle is even less in proportion to weight.

The plant loses some of its toxicity at maturity, but the dry leaves retain enough of the toxic substance to cause heavy losses of livestock in winter and early spring.

Apparently *A. labriformis* grows only in eastern Utah, mostly in sandy places and along watercourses. This species, like other poisonous milkweeds, is not palatable. Animals eat it only when they have no other feed. On overgrazed ranges and trails it is a hazard at all times.

We know of no remedy for milkweed poisoning. If losses are to be avoided, hungry animals must be kept away from places in which poisonous milkweeds grow or the plants should be eradicated.

The symptoms of milkweed poisoning are uneasiness; some lack of muscular coordination; rapid, shallow, noisy respiration due to edema (swellings filled with fluid) of the lungs; spasms; and considerable struggling. Death may result from respiratory failure. The kidneys usually are affected more than the other organs.

OXALIC ACID occurs in sorrels, docks, halogeton (*Halogeton glomeratus*), grease-wood (*Sarcobatus vermiculatus*), and other plants. The oxalic content of the dried leaves and fine stems of greasewood may exceed 10 percent in late summer and early fall. Halogeton may contain 18 to 20 percent.

Cattle and sheep are susceptible to poisoning by greasewood and halogeton. Most of the losses have occurred in bands of hungry sheep that have been grazed in places where these plants predominate and desirable forage is scarce. Animals may eat small amounts of the plants daily over a long period of time without apparent injury. A sheep that eats them slowly all day with other forage may safely consume twice the amount that would be toxic if eaten in an hour without other forage. The animals can eliminate the oxalates fairly rapidly and thus prevent the accumulations of toxic levels within the body. With good management of ranges and livestock, especially during trailing and following shipping, losses from poisoning by greasewood and halogeton can be kept down.

Books giving antidotes to poisons recommend either chalk (which is mostly carbonate of lime or calcium carbonate), or limewater as an antidote for oxalic acid poisoning. The lime forms an insoluble compound (salt of lime) called oxalate of lime (calcium oxalate). When formed in the intestines, the compound would be eliminated as an insoluble compound with the feces instead of being absorbed into the blood stream as might be the case if it were either oxalic acid or oxalates (salts) of other elements prevalent in most foods and vegetation, such as sodium (forms oxalate of soda called sodium oxalate) and potassium (forms oxalate of potassium called potassium oxalate). Both are water-soluble salts of oxalic acid.

In one experiment, however, with a sheep poisoned on halogeton, we gave the animal some chemically pure calcium carbonate as an antidote. It did not prove so effective as in another experiment, when the antidote we gave was the leaves of alfalfa hay. Possibly the lime in the alfalfa hay was more soluble and consequently more reactive with the oxalic acid (to form an insoluble salt) than was the lime in the calcium carbonate.

Tremetol produces a disease known as trembles in livestock and milksickness in people. Tremetol, an oily alcohol, can be isolated from white snakeroot (*Eupatorium rugosum*), which grows in the Eastern States, and from rayless goldenrod or jimmyweed (*Aplopappus heterophyllus*), which grows in the Southwestern States.

Cases of trembles or milksickness have been reported in Virginia, North Carolina, South Carolina, Georgia, Maryland, Missouri, and Michigan, where white snakeroot grows, and in Texas, New Mexico, and Arizona, where rayless goldenrod grows.

Milksickness has been caused by milk and by butter made from milk of cows that had fed on tremetol-containing plants. The isolation of tremetol and the production of trembles by feeding poisoned butter to sheep completed the chain of evidence linking the plants to milksickness in human beings.

NITRATE POISONING in animals has been reported to be caused by animals eating oat hay, Russian-thistle (*Salsola pestifer*), tarweed (*Amsinckia intermedia*), redroot pigweed (*Amaranthus retroflexus*), puncturevine (*Tribulus terrestris*), beet tops (*Beta vulgaris*), white ragweed (*Fraseria discolor*), variegated thistle (*Silybum marianum*), and many others.

SELENIUM is a nonmetallic element. Chemically it resembles sulfur, however, the physiological action of selenium is different from that of sulfur.

Selenium-bearing plants sometimes cause considerable damage. Some plants known as indicator plants, which seem to require selenium in the soil for their growth, such as princesplume (*Stanleya* species), woody aster (*Xylorrhiza parryi*), and some species of *Astragalus*, contain considerable selenium and poison the animals that eat

them in large quantities. Some crop plants and others tolerate selenium in the soil and may absorb selenium and metabolize it in their tissues in quantities that would make them poisonous to livestock if eaten in sufficient quantity.

Experimental work with laboratory animals indicates the resistance of animals to selenium poisoning is increased by a high-protein diet.

Research workers in Wyoming learned that increasing the protein and vitamin A intake of sheep improves the quality of the diet to the extent that the poisonous effects of selenium are lessened. If the selenium intake was reduced or stopped and a high protein diet was continued, the animals recovered from selenium poisoning within a short time and the selenium was completely eliminated in about 30 days. If the protein content of the diet was low, however, the recovery was slow or the animals died. It was found also that iodine increases the susceptibility of animals to selenium poisoning. The recommendation was made that in places where selenium occurs, salt that contains no iodine should be used.

Arsenic compounds, especially compounds with sodium, tend to protect animals against the toxic action of selenium. In one experiment, a group of steers that were given 25 parts per million of arsenic in the salt made better gains and sold for higher prices than others.

Selenium poisoning is mentioned in another chapter (p. 117).

Some compounds of molybdenum (a heavy metal that belongs to the chromium group), are soluble and may be absorbed by plants so as to make them harmful to stock that eat them. We discuss these compounds under the term "molybdenum."

A discussion of molybdenum poisoning appears in a previous chapter (p. 115).

English stockmen have known for a long time that certain pastures, which they called "teart," were harmful to stock. The teartness was especially prevalent in Somerset, and they became known as the "teart pastures of Somerset." The outstanding symptom of cattle grazing teart pastures was scouring, or diarrhea. Affected animals also might show emaciation, anemia, stiffening or enlargement of the joints, dry skin, and loss of coat color or hair. Black tended to become gray, red became tan, and white became a light tan. This discoloration was first noticed around the eyes and the ears. Young, growing cattle were more susceptible to the teartness of pastures than old cattle.

Several possibilities were mentioned to explain the disease, but the real cause of the trouble was shown in 1938 to be an excess of molybdenum in the vegetation. Studies were started later in Europe, Australia, the islands of the Pacific, and the United States.

The first recorded molybdenosis (a condition of stock effected by excess molybdenum in their feed) in the United States was from an area of the San Joaquin Valley of California by J. W. Britton and H. Goss less than 10 years after the discovery in England.

According to the early reports on molybdenosis, any pasture whose vegetation contained 20 p. p. m. (parts per million) of molybdenum or more was a dangerous one. Recent studies show that a certain amount of molybdenum in the vegetation or in the soil is not the only factor to be considered as the cause of the disease or the toxicity of the pastures. The acidity of the soil, the species of plants, the stage of growth of the plants, the part of the plant eaten, the amount of molybdenum in the soil, the condition of the animals and the character of any supplementary food they eat all contribute to the poisoning of livestock.

Generally speaking, dry hay from a high-molybdenum area is less likely to cause scouring than green, succulent pastures in the same area. Some alfalfa hay occasionally has caused severe symptoms of molybdenum, but hay usually loses its toxicity with storage. Legumes in general absorb more molybdenum than nonlegumes. The greatest concentration is found in most instances in the blades of the leaves and in the actively growing parts of the plant. That fact may account for the beneficial effect of feeding roughages to reduce excessive scouring to which cattle are subject when they graze succulent leguminous pastures.

Molybdenum is widely distributed in the soils of many places in the United States. Most of the reports of trouble that we have had have come from San Joaquin Valley, although the molybdenum in the troublesome soils there is not always high. It may range from 1.5 to 10 p. p. m., and most of it is soluble. The high solubility of those soils is due mainly to their alkaline reaction, for water soluble molybdenum has been greatly reduced by acidification. In this respect molybdenum behaves as selenium does, and the opposite of manganese, boron, zinc, and copper. Soils that are overlimed become alkaline and may produce toxic vegetation even in humid regions if the soil contains enough molybdenum.

The toxicity of molybdenum to animals seems to be due at least partly to an imbalance of nutrients or minerals in the animals' system. Research in Australia revealed that the symptoms of animals with excess molybdenum resemble the symptoms of a disease known as peat scours, which affects animals pastured on peat soil and occurs in animals that have a deficiency of copper. Symptoms of copper deficiency and molybdenosis are relieved by giving animals soluble compounds of copper.

Investigators in England considered that teartness or molybdenosis was a disease only of cattle. Early investigators in the United States recognized that sheep also may be affected. It is now known that, although it is primarily a disease of ruminants and that field cases of reported molybdenum poisoning seem to be confined to cattle and sheep, horses, swine, poultry, and laboratory animals may be poisoned if they get too much molybdenum. Nonruminant animals are relatively immune to poisoning, however.

LOCOWEEDS, copperweed, paperflower, horsebrush, bracken fern, and eupatorium are examples of plants that contain unknown and miscellaneous poisons.

The locoweeds (species of *Astragalus* and *Oxytropis*) were so important that at one time the term "locoed" was used synonymously with "poisoned," especially in the Western States.

The locoweeds have been analyzed extensively in the past 80 years. White loco (*Oxytropis lamberti*) was studied by James F. Couch, who found that the active principle belongs to none of the recognized groups of poisonous compounds but appears to be a new type.

Some members of the genus *Astragalus* are nontoxic. Others produce poisoning but not the true locoism. Examples of the first group include the red locoweed (*A. drummondii*) and *A. tenellus*. In the second group is *A. tetrapterus*. Nothing is known about their chemistry.

Another group of the genus is poisonous not because of any constituent normally produced by the plant itself but because of selenium, which the plants may take up from the soil in the form of a compound and accumulate in dangerous quantities.

Copperweed (*Oxytenia acerosa*) grows over much of the Colorado Basin along streams and seepage areas where the soil is strongly alkaline. Copperweed only recently was proved to be poisonous. It affects cattle and sheep. The plant increases in toxicity as it reaches maturity. Poisoning usually occurs in the fall when the cattle are being driven down from the summer ranges over trails that are overgrazed and contain little or no desirable forage. Enough copperweed, which ordinarily is quite unpalatable, may be eaten then to cause poisoning. Less than one-half pound of green leaves to 100 pounds of animal weight is lethal for cattle.

Most animals that show severe symptoms die. Losses may be prevented by providing suitable feed along the trails and on the ranges so that animals are not compelled to eat the toxic plants.

In copperweed poisoning, the liver seems to be affected first and the kidneys later. The symptoms usually are marked depression, weakness, and coma. Death follows without much struggling.

Occasionally an animal shows considerable nervousness and excitement. Frequently animals are found dead in the morning without having shown symptoms the previous evening.

Greenstem paperflower (*Psilostrophe sparsiflora*) has become a problem of sheepmen in northern Arizona. It has been spreading over a wider area, so that it is becoming increasingly difficult to utilize the range. Two other species of *Psilostrophe* in Texas have caused losses of sheep.

The paperflower grows in semiarid regions that are used largely as intermediate and winter ranges. Overgrazing may have been responsible for its spread. Very likely cattle do not eat enough of it on the range to be poisoned because the paperflower is not palatable. In places where the forage consists largely of plants low in palatability, it is necessary to move the sheep to uninfested areas as soon as loss starts in order to prevent further losses. Some deaths occur even then after the animals are moved.

Because *P. sparsiflora* is abundant over a rather wide region, eradication, even if it could be accomplished, would not be economically practicable, and the control of sheep losses in the region must depend on improvement in range conditions. That is, the range area should be widened so there would be larger grazing area for each sheep.

In paperflower poisoning, the kidneys appear to be affected primarily. Poisoning is usually the result of feeding for several days on the plant. Consequently the symptons may develop rather slowly. The principal symptoms are loss of appetite, depression, and weakness. Death follows a week or more of partial coma.

Horsebrush is the name of two related plants. One is called littleleaf horsebrush, spring rabbitbrush, or coal oil brush (*Tetradymia glabrata*) and has been known for many years as a cause of heavy losses of sheep. It is common in dry areas of western Utah, Nevada, eastern California, southern Oregon, and southwestern Idaho.

Spineless horsebrush (*T. canescens*) is poisonous to sheep, but rather large amounts are necessary to produce poisoning. It grows to a limited extent in the same areas as those occupied by littleleaf horsebrush. It is found in greater abundance at the higher elevations and extends through central Utah to southwestern Wyoming, southwestern Montana, eastern and southern Idaho, eastern Oregon, eastern Washington, eastern California, and northern New Mexico.

The most toxic stage of both plants is during their active growth period—April and May for littleleaf horsebrush and May and June and early July for spineless horsebrush.

In sheep the horsebrushes cause a disease known as bighead or swellhead. Bighead is essentially a range disease and has been prevalent in many areas of the intermountain region since the early days of the sheep industry. It probably has caused a greater financial loss to the sheep owners in the affected areas than any other disease. Bighead apparently has two separate stages—first, a toxic condition produced by the plants and affecting primarily the liver; second, a swelling, or edema, which affects principally the head. This edema affects only animals with white or light-colored skins and is the result of sensitiveness to light. Either white sheep or black sheep may be affected by the toxic substance in the plants, but the pigment in the skin of black animals protects them from the effects of the light rays, so that photosensitivity does not occur. The same is true of sheep kept in total darkness after eating *Tetradymia*. The exact nature of the substance causing photosensitization and the manner in which it gets into the circulation near the body surface are not known definitely.

The areas where bighead occurs correspond with the distribution of the species of *Tetradymia*, but although the plants are the main cause of bighead, other factors are involved in the occurrence of the disease. The kind and character of the feed on which the sheep subsist at the time they eat the plants are probably the most important factors in producing the edema or photosensitization. Horsebrushes are among the first to begin growth in the spring and usually are well leaved out by the time sheep start on the trails to the shearing corrals and summer ranges. Most of the bighead outbreaks occur at that time.

Since plants are not palatable and are seldom eaten in toxic amounts when good forage is available, sheep may graze normally in an area where *Tetradymia* is abundant with a very little danger of bighead, but a hungry herd that is being trailed through the same area may develop the disease.

Stormy weather also is apt to change the feeding habits of animals to the extent that unpalatable or poisonous plants will be eaten. Early spring use of ranges before the forage plants are well started may cause sheep to eat *Tetradymia* in sufficient amounts to produce bighead.

Bighead usually appears quite suddenly in a band. Many animals may become affected within a few hours, although symptoms usually appear 16 to 24 hours after the plants are eaten.

Prevention of range bighead depends on a knowledge of the distribution of the *Tetradymia* plants. Avoiding *Tetradymia* areas on the ranges or trails when sheep are hungry will eliminate the greatest danger.

BRACKEN (*Pteridium aquilinum*) may be poisonous to both horses and cattle and may cause rather severe losses.

Several species of ferns have been suspected of being poisonous to livestock. Because of their low palatability, bracken are seldom eaten when other forage is available. Therefore they are not considered of much importance.

The bracken fern occurs in many parts of the United States, especially in moist places and in meadows.

Most of the cases of bracken poisoning in horses have been caused by ferns that were cut and cured in meadow hay. Poisoning in cattle usually is the result of grazing on the green plants when other forage is scarce. Hay containing ferns is more dangerous in winter if it is the only feed. Poisoning from green plants usually occurs during the latter part of the grazing season until frost.

Bracken poisoning does not usually occur until after the animals have been feeding on ferns for 3 or 4 weeks, unless the feed consists very largely of these plants. When large daily amounts are consumed, the symptoms may appear earlier and be more acute than when the ration contains less of the toxic material.

The toxic substances in the ferns apparently have a cumulative effect, so that a period of time must elapse before symptoms become noticeable. The course of the disease and the severity of the symptoms largely depend on the amount of the plants consumed daily, although there is some variation in the individual susceptibility of different animals.

The symptoms of bracken poisoning in horses may be emaciation, weakness, staggering, nervousness, and constipation. The temperature may remain nearly normal, although the pulse rate is usually higher. The disease may extend over a week or more. The appetite may remain fairly good for some time after symptoms appear.

The symptoms in cattle are usually more acute and may include a high temperature, rapid loss of flesh, salivation, hemorrhage from the nostrils, small hemorrhagic spots (petechiae) in the membranes of the eyes, nostrils, and mouth, and a bloody diarrhea.

The symptoms of fern poisoning may vary, but when such a condition is suspected and it is known that the plants are being eaten, a change to other feed should be made.

The mortality rate of animals showing symptoms of bracken poisoning is usually high. Some benefit may be derived from treatment of the symptoms, such as a diet of readily available soft, nutritious food to relieve exertion, constipation, and irritation of the hemorrhagic intestine, but no specific cure is known. Prevention is the best way to control the disease.

LIMESTONE DISEASE of southern New Mexico and southeastern Arizona, which has resulted in heavy losses of cattle over a period of years, is probably caused by Wrights eupatorium (*Eupatorium wrightii*). The nature of its toxic substance has not been determined. Unlike white snakeroot (*E. rugosum*), a related and highly toxic species of the East Central States, Wrights eupatorium does not contain tremetol.

Toxicity is confined principally to the leaves, and the margin between a nontoxic and a lethal dose is very narrow. Poisoned animals are usually found dead on the range, having died during the night while lying in a normal position without any signs of having struggled. The plant is as toxic during the summer as later, but apparently it is not eaten until fall; the losses start about the time of the first heavy frosts and continue for a month or longer. In experimental feeding, sheep were found to be as susceptible as cattle to the poisonous effects of the plant, but the reported losses have all been among cattle.

Wrights eupatorium is found mainly in limestone outcroppings on ridges and slopes of foothills and lower mountains. These areas may occupy only a small portion of a pasture and, if fenced off, the remainder of the pasture would be safe for cattle. If additional fencing is not feasible, the cattle should be moved to other pastures shortly before the first of October.

TALL FESCUE (*Festuca arundinaceae*) has received attention lately as a possible cattle-poisoning plant. We have not been able to learn what is its poisonous principle.

Tall fescue, a coarse, reedlike grass, is a prominent grass crop in some swampy areas of New Zealand. In areas where this fescue grew, some cattle in the fescue pastures became affected with a condition in which lameness sometimes developed within 14 days after they first ate the fescue. One or both hind limbs were involved. Heat, swelling, and pain occurred in the affected limb. Later the pain and the swelling subsided, but drying and hardening of the skin and of the extremity of the leg or foot set in. An indented line formed in the hide of the leg, which separated the lower part of the leg and foot, which was cold and apparently dead from the normal skin above. The warm and cold places usually were sharply separated at this point. Sometimes the extremity of the limb was shed.

Such a description is like a description of poisoning of cattle by the black, hard, hornshaped sclerotia (horny mass of fungus tissue) that form the resting stage in the growth of the ergot fungus. Because ergot sclerotia commonly replace some of the seeds of many grasses on which they grow (they often replace rye grains in the head), it was thought it was ergot of the tall fescue that was causing the trouble in New Zealand.

That assumption was readily made from the similarity of symptoms of ergot and fescue poisoning. The ergot sclerotia forms only in the seed heads of a grass which it infects. Study and observation led to the discovery that the cattle-foot condition occurred in places where there were no seed heads of fescue and that consequently the poisoning from fescue could not be as a result of the ergot.

The first published report we have on the effect of fescue is one by I. J. Cunningham, of Wallaceville, New Zealand, in the New Zealand Journal of Agriculture, November 1948, page 519. Dr. Cunningham reported in the Australian Veterinary Journal, February 1949, that the fescue grass under consideration should be classed as a toxic plant and not as a plant that acquired toxicity through infestation by ergot.

After they received the reports from New Zealand and Australia, research workers in the United States undertook to determine whether some trouble in the United States that had been attributed to the ergot actually might have been caused by fescue.

LAMENESS IN CATTLE that had been eating fescue had been reported at various times by cattlemen in western Colorado. They believed it was due to ergot poisoning, foot rot, or frozen feet, but after the reports came from New Zealand, the disease was associated with fescue.

Festuca arundinaceae is often referred to as tall fescue, but other common names for it are alta fescue, king fescue, giant fescue, ditchbank fescue, and reed fescue. A. A. Goodman, extension veterinarian of the Colorado Agricultural and Mechanical College, in an early report of the trouble in Colorado expressed the opinion that other more palatable species of fescue grasses, which are recommended for pasture grass mixture, do not carry the toxic substance which was reported to be in the coarse tall fescue.

Dr. T. J. Stearns, a practicing veterinarian in Louisville, Ky., in an article in the Journal of the American Veterinary Medical Association, May 1953, page 388, reported a similar ailment among cattle grazing fescue 31, a smaller more palatable variety. He wrote: "It would seem that most fescue species of grasses contain the toxic substance, and under certain climatic conditions will cause trouble."

Other references to fescue foot or

fescue lameness, as the disease is often called, have come from Tennessee, Alabama, California, and Texas. Research workers in Colorado, Kentucky, and Tennessee began experiments in an effort to determine the causative agent and develop a corrective treatment.

A report from the Tennessee Agricultural Experiment Station said that cattle have recovered when removed from fescue to other pastures, sometimes slowly and after loss of considerable weight. Some of the recovered animals were returned to the fescue pastures without recurrence of toxicity symptoms or any further untoward effects.

The report stated, "Based on the lack of complaints from farmers and Extension people, many fescue pastures may not be toxic." Because of the large number of pastures of tall fescue on which cattle graze and the small number of cases reported, the percentage of toxic pastures may be small. It is likely that toxicity in certain pastures does not persist from year to year.

Most of the cases of toxicity from tall fescue have been in localities where because of ecological factors the coarse, persistent plants were nearly in pure stands.

The danger of toxicity probably can be reduced considerably by providing a variety of feed rather than depending on fescue as the only feed. Tall fescue, even though the palatability is low and the danger of poisoning from it has to be considered, serves a purpose because of its hardiness, persistence, and tolerance of swampy conditions.

If vigilance and careful observation is made for initial symptoms and the cattle are removed promptly from pastures, possibly tall fescue has a useful place under certain conditions as an economic plant for cattlemen.

WARD T. HUFFMAN, *a veterinarian in the Animal Disease and Parasite Research Branch, Agricultural Research Service, since 1908, was in charge of the investigations of* livestock poisoning by plants from 1938 until his retirement in 1955.

EDWARD A. MORAN, *an animal physiologist in Noninfectious Diseases Section of the Animal Disease and Parasite Research Branch, has been studying stock poisoning plant problems as an employee of the Department of Agriculture since 1929. Until 1951 his field quarters were in Utah during the summer. He is a graduate of the New York State College of Agriculture at Cornell University.*

WAYNE BINNS *holds degrees from Iowa State College and Cornell University. He was a member of the veterinary science department of the Utah State Agricultural College from 1940 to 1942 and head of the department from 1946 to 1954. He joined the Agricultural Research Service as a veterinarian in charge of studies of livestock poisoning by plants in 1954 with headquarters in Logan, Utah.*

For further reading:

J. W. Britton and H. Goss: *Chronic Molybdenum Poisoning in Cattle.* American Veterinary Medical Association Journal, volume 108, number 828, pages 176–178. 1946.

A. B. Clawson: *A Preliminary Report on the Poisonous Effects of Bitter Rubber Weed (Actinea odorate) on Sheep,* Journal of Agricultural Research, volume 43, number 8, pages 693–701. 1931.

A. B. Clawson, James F. Couch, and H. Bunyea: *The Toxicity of Sodium Cyanide and the Efficiency of Nitrite. Thiosulphate Combination as a Remedy for Poisoned Animals,* Washington Academy of Science Journal, volume 25, pages 357–361. 1935.

James F. Couch, Reinhold R. Briese, and J. H. Martin: *Hydrocyanic Acid Content of Sorghum Varieties,* Journal of Washington Academy of Science, volume 29, pages 146–161. 1939.

M. W. Emmel: *The Toxic Principle of the Tung Tree,* Florida Agricultural Experiment Station Bulletin 431, 35 pages. 1947.

C. E. Fleming, M. R. Miller, and L. R. Vawter: *The Fitweed (Capnoides caseana) A Poisonous Range Plant of the Northern Sierra Nevada Mountains,* Nevada Agricultural Experiment Station Bulletin 121, 29 pages.

W. J. Pistor, J. C. Nesbitt, and B. P. Cardon: *The Influence of High Salt Intake on the Physiology of Ruminants,* Proceedings Book, American Veterinary Medical Association, Eighty-Seventh Annual Meeting. 1950.

W. E. Rand and H. J. Schmidt: *The Effect Upon Cattle of Arizona Waters of High Fluoride Content,* American Journal of Veterinary Research, volume 13, number 46, pages 50–61. 1952.

Toxicity of Insecticides

R. D. RADELEFF, G. T. WOODARD, AND R. C. BUSHLAND

MANY insecticides are highly poisonous to animals and must be handled carefully. When they are used according to the recommendations and instructions of the Department of Agriculture, the State agricultural experiment stations, and the manufacturers, however, there is little danger to livestock.

There are many basic insecticides and a variety of commercial preparations of each, so that there are thousands of different brands and mixtures. For our purpose it is best to discuss the toxicity of the basic compounds because the dosage and its effects do not vary a great deal with the formulation.

PETROLEUM OILS that are used as insecticides and in insecticide preparations are harmless when they are applied in small amounts to the skin.

But in large amounts (4 ounces or more per animal) they cause blistering, excessive salivation, difficult breathing, loss of appetite, depression, and perhaps death in cattle, horses, sheep, and goats.

The effect of the oils usually is observed the first few days after they are applied and may continue for some time. Many instances of poisoning of livestock have been attributed to the insecticide dissolved in the oil because of the failure to recognize the dangers associated with the oil itself.

Straight oil solutions of insecticides therefore are never recommended for use on livestock except as mist sprays applied at rates not exceeding 2 ounces per cow and as saturants for devices commonly called backrubbers, used to deposit a thin film of solution. Even this rate of application, if continued for a long time, may produce a scruffy thickening of the skin that is unsightly, if not actually harmful. Used crankcase oils should not be employed, because they may contain lead or additives, which might cause trouble.

Manufacturers of emulsifiable concentrates intended for use on livestock must arrange their formulas so that recommended amounts of the products will not lead to excessive doses of the oils. The stockman should use only the recommended dosages lest he increase the dosage of oil to a toxic level, although he may be using a safe amount of the dissolved insecticide.

SOLVENTS are used in most liquid preparations of insecticides. They may be natural or synthetic products.

The solvent may or may not be toxic, but the possibility that it is toxic should be considered when losses of animals occur following treatment. Although solvents influence the speed of absorption of insecticides into the body, the total absorption is essentially the same, regardless of the solvent.

Certain solvents, notably xylene and toluene, cause itching and burning for a short time after application in the hot sunshine, even though used in small amounts. If the concentration is high (6 percent), the animal may become dizzy or may even be anesthetized. If still higher (25 percent), it may die.

Each manufacturer is responsible for making certain that the solvents he uses are not toxic in the amounts recommended.

INSECTICIDES PRODUCED FROM PLANTS are generally safe for use on livestock. They are neither acutely toxic nor stored within the animal sufficiently to create a hazard to people. Pyrethrum and rotenone are notable examples of safety.

An exception is nicotine, which, in the form of nicotine sulfate, is used chiefly to control scabies. Because nicotine sulfate has been most commonly used by skilled regulatory officials who have a reliable test for the strength of the dip, poisoning as a result of dipping has been uncommon. Animals poisoned by nicotine sulfate show tremors, nausea, and disturbed respiration; finally they become unconscious and may die.

Some plant products are irritants and cause discomfort when they are applied to animals, but rarely is an animal killed by an insecticide derived from plants.

SULFUR and lime-sulfur have been used as insecticides on animals. Sulfur, used externally, is almost completely harmless to livestock.

Lime-sulfur, which is actually a complex of sulfides, may cause itching, a general discomfort, and blistering. Rarely does it kill an animal.

ARSENIC, as used in cattle dips, is extremely poisonous. The many losses in deaths and in injuries to livestock as a result of burning and blistering after dipping amply prove its toxic nature.

Poisoning by arsenical dips is not always the result of excessive concentration in the dip. Even a normally safe dosage may produce burning or death if the animals are treated in wet weather, or are overheated, or are handled too much after treatment.

Because arsenical dips are primarily solutions of arsenic in water and an accurate test is available, losses have been less than if the dipping solutions could not be easily checked.

The many arsenical compounds used in treating field crops may be poisonous to livestock that eat them. Poisoning has resulted from dusts that drift across fields into pastures, from arsenical compounds remaining in containers carelessly left on premises occupied by livestock, and occasionally from dip emptied on unprotected pasture. Some animals seem to crave arsenic and will seek out the spots contaminated with it.

Arsenic is absorbed through the unbroken skin and stored in various tissues of the body.

Acute arsenical poisoning usually causes death in 1 or 2 days from the time of treatment. Less acute poisoning may cause blistering, cracking, and peeling of the skin, profuse diarrhea (possibly with some free blood), rapid emaciation, a poor appetite, and obvious pain. Death may not occur until many days after exposure. In animals that die from arsenical poisoning, the intestinal tract is inflamed, the liver and other organs may be swollen, and the lungs may be dark and heavy with blood.

THE SYNTHETIC ORGANIC INSECTICIDES have some factors in common.

All are absorbed through the unbroken body surfaces regardless of the way in which they are applied to the surfaces. The popular preparations for use on animals are the emulsifiable concentrates and the wettable powders, which require dilution with water, and dusts composed of the insecticides diluted with clay or other inert material.

The toxic effects are exerted after absorption from the skin or digestive system. In most (if not all) cases, normal functioning of the nervous system is impaired. It is possible for some of these compounds to produce irritation of the skin and of the lining of the digestive tract, but only rarely do they do so.

At equal concentrations of insecticide, less will be absorbed from dry powders than from the emulsifiable or wettable formulations, but there is no difference in the amount absorbed from emulsifiable or wettable formulations.

Young animals, generally speaking, are more easily poisoned than the older ones. At all ages there is a wide variation in individual susceptibility.

In some cases the physical condition of the animal determines the toxicity of insecticides.

We have observed no difference in toxicity between emulsions and suspensions given orally. In giving insecticides to laboratory animals, some scientists have observed wide differences in toxicity according to the physical state of the compounds. Scientists of the Department of Agriculture have observed differences in the DDT content of milk from dairy cattle as a result of using various solutions and solids.

When emulsifiable materials are used, the emulsion particles gradually increase in size by uniting with one another (the concentration of insecticide in the emulsion remaining uniform), and the amount of insecticide deposited on animal hair increases. This is a characteristic of emulsions used for many years by entomologists to obtain heavy deposits of chemicals on plants by means of emulsions containing large particles, often called quick-breaking emulsions. The first animals dipped in emulsions containing large particles receive the highest dose. This behavior of emulsions explains some of the losses of animals that have occurred after dipping in emulsions known to be safe when applied as fresh dips or sprays.

The increased deposition will occur from any emulsion, but is of greatest importance in dipping because in dipping the animals pass through hundreds or thousands of gallons of emulsion while traversing a vat and may extract the larger particles of that many gallons.

In spraying there is a limited exposure to the emulsion, generally not exceeding 2 gallons, governed by the operator's judgment of when the animal has been thoroughly wetted. The sprayed animal is not exposed to more than the total insecticide contained in those 2 gallons. When the emulsion is allowed to "cream," or partly separate in the sprayer, thereby increasing the insecticide content of one part of the total volume at the expense of the other part, and insufficient agitation follows this "creaming," some animals receive a reduced dose while others may receive a toxic dose.

Because of the influence of size of particles on toxicity, it is not enough to have a method of determining accurately the concentration of insecticide in a dip or spray. Some knowledge must also be had of the size of the emulsion particles and of the uniformity of the emulsion.

Manufacturers of insecticide formulations are aware of these effects and have taken steps to provide emulsifiable concentrates that form emulsions that remain stable for a long time. Nevertheless, constant care is needed to see that the emulsion is of proper stability and consistency before spraying or dipping is begun.

DDT is a relatively safe insecticide. All livestock can tolerate single applications of 8 percent DDT. Ten applications of 2 percent DDT or 36 applications of 0.5 percent DDT at 2-week intervals failed to produce clinical changes in cattle.

Cattle, horses, sheep, goats, and hogs tolerated 8 treatments with 1.5 percent DDT at 4-day intervals.

DDT is safe for dogs. It must be used sparingly on cats, as they may be poisoned by relatively small amounts.

Chickens may be poisoned by dips containing 1 percent of DDT, but dusts containing 5 percent are safe.

Given orally in single doses, DDT will poison young calves at 250 and above but not at 100 milligrams per kilogram (mg./kg.).

(The abbreviation "mg./kg." stands for the phrase "milligram per kilogram." As used here, mg./kg. designates the weight of chemical in milligrams given for each kilogram the animal weighs. One thousand milligrams make a gram; one thousand grams a kilogram. There are 28.35 grams in an ounce, and a kilogram is equal to 2.2 pounds. An animal weighing 440 pounds also weighs 200 kilograms. If that animal were given 100 mg./kg., then $100 \times 200 = 20,000$ milligrams, or 20 grams, is the dose. That dose would then be slightly less than two-thirds of an ounce for the animal. The metric system, using the gram as a unit, is much easier to use in calculating and reporting dosages since decimal fractions are the only ones encountered.)

Sheep were poisoned and recovered from doses of 500 and 1,000 mg./kg. Mature hens were poisoned by five daily doses of 100 mg./kg., as indicated by loss of weight, but there were no other symptoms.

A lactating Jersey cow was given 100 mg./kg. of DDT daily for 23 days. The first 16 doses produced no evidence of toxic disturbance. The last seven doses caused her to lose weight rapidly.

Research workers at the Oklahoma Agricultural Experiment Station sprayed dairy cows with 5.0-percent suspensions of DDT daily for 14 days without producing symptoms of poisoning. The same dosage was attempted, using emulsions, but skin injury resulted from the solvents and the spraying had to be discontinued.

Research workers of the Department of Agriculture at Beltsville fed three dairy cows 100 mg./kg. of DDT daily for 6 days, then increased the dose of two of the cows to 150 mg./kg. daily for 6 days and then to 200 mg./kg. for 6 days. The third cow received the 100 mg./kg. dose for the three 6-day periods. All three cows showed nervous disturbances during the first week, but all survived the treatment. A fourth cow was given 200 mg./kg. of DDT daily for 6 days and survived, although she was severely affected.

The same workers fed sheep 100 mg./kg. daily for 6 days, followed by 150 mg./kg. for 6 days and 200 mg./kg. for the third 6-day period. The sheep showed no evidence of poisoning other than a loss of weight. Individual sheep were given 500, 1,000, 1,500, or 2,000 mg./kg. of DDT as a single dose. The sheep receiving 2,000 mg./kg., the only one affected, showed slight nervous disturbances.

The men also fed horses DDT. One horse was given 200 mg./kg. daily for 6 days and did not show symptoms other than loss of weight. A second horse was given 100 mg./kg. daily for 6 days, then 150 mg./kg. daily for 6 days and 200 mg./kg. for the third 6-day period. The horse lost weight but showed no other evidence of poisoning.

A. S. Telford and Paul D. Harwood, of the Hess and Clark Laboratory, administered 150 grams of DDT to a horse weighing 1,405 pounds (234 mg./kg.) without producing symptoms of poisoning.

Scientists of the Public Health Service fed DDT to goats and found that single doses of 500 and 1,000 mg./kg. produced definite poisoning, followed by recovery, and concluded that the minimum lethal dose was in excess of 1,000 mg./kg. Of 4 goats given 1,000 mg./kg. daily, 2 were sacrificed in a moribund state after 6 doses; 1 died after 9 doses; and the fourth died after 11 doses. The investigators concluded that the susceptibility of goats to DDT poisoning partly depended on the amount of body fat, because the goats in best condition survived the greater number of doses.

Howard Welch, of the Montana Agricultural Experiment Station, produced poisoning in cattle with DDT at 500 mg./kg., followed by recovery. Sheep showed slight symptoms after a single dose of 500 mg./kg. and definite symptoms, with recovery, at 1,000 and 2,000 mg./kg. One sheep given 4.5 grams of DDT daily (100 mg./kg.) was poisoned after 10 doses.

OF TECHNICAL BENZENE HEXACHLORIDE only the gamma isomer is useful against pests of livestock.

The gamma isomer may be separated from the other isomers of technical benzene hexachloride and a purified product obtained, which is composed of 99 percent or more of the gamma isomer. This purified product is known as lindane.

Adult cattle and horses can withstand single treatments of sprays or dips containing 0.25 percent gamma isomer, which is 5 to 8 times the recommended concentrations. Sheep, goats, and hogs can withstand 0.5 percent.

The gamma isomer must be used with caution on young calves, 0.05 percent having produced poisoning. No deaths or poisonings resulted from the use of 0.03-percent sprays or dips on thousands of calves.

Emaciated animals—those in extremely poor condition—particularly the emaciated nursing ewes, are more sensitive to poisoning than are well-nourished animals. Dips containing as little as 0.03 percent of gamma isomer have poisoned ewes that were emaciated and nursing.

The gamma isomer of benzene hexachloride has little danger as a chronic toxicant. The use of 0.25 percent in suspensions on range cattle resulted in no clinical disturbances, although the dose was repeated 10 times at 2-week intervals.

Technicians of the Department of Agriculture reported on an accidental spraying of 240 adult dairy animals with a 0.3-percent lindane suspension used for spraying barn walls. Of 11 cows poisoned, 5 died.

Benzene hexachloride is safe for dogs and cats at 0.5 percent gamma isomer in dry dusts. It should not be used excessively on cats.

If benzene hexachloride is used to spray poultry houses, care should be taken to avoid wetting the birds, as they are easily poisoned. Dusts containing 1 percent lindane are safe for direct application to chickens.

The minimum toxic oral dose for dairy calves appeared to be between 2.5 and 5 mg./kg. of gamma isomer. The lower dose produced no intoxication, but the higher dose caused death.

The minimum toxic dose for yearling Hereford cattle appeared to be between 10 and 25 mg./kg. The lower dose produced no symptoms, but the higher dose was lethal.

Cattle were fed 100 parts per million of lindane in their feed for 112 days without apparent harmful effect. Sheep tolerated single doses of 10 mg./kg. of lindane. Sheep were poisoned by 25, 50, and 75 mg./kg., and were killed by a dose of 100 mg./kg.

Of six sheep given 25 mg./kg. of lindane orally once a week for 6 weeks, all were affected by at least one of the doses, but none was affected by all six doses. One sheep was given 5 mg./kg. of the gamma isomer of BHC (from 12 percent gamma isomer technical BHC) 4 days a week until 22 such doses had been given, without producing symptoms of poisoning. Two daily doses of 50 mg./kg. were then given. They caused poisoning and death. A second sheep was given 50 mg./kg. of BHC (6 mg./kg. gamma isomer) 4 days a week for 15 doses without producing poisoning, but the 16th dose initiated symptoms of poisoning and the 17th caused death.

Dairy cows at Beltsville were fed 6.22 mg./kg. of crystalline lindane daily for 110 days without showing symptoms of poisoning.

In Montana, Howard Welch gave cattle 125 mg./kg. of BHC (12.5 mg./kg. gamma isomer) without producing symptoms. He also gave sheep 750, 1,000, and 2,000 mg./kg. of BHC (10 percent gamma). They were poisoned but did not die. One of his sheep was given 2.25 grams of BHC daily. It showed symptoms on the 20th day, but survived 60 such daily doses.

CHLORDANE is a reasonably safe insecticide. Changes have been made in its manufacture to make it less toxic.

All livestock, except baby calves, lambs, and kids, tolerated at least three applications of 1.5 percent chlordane produced before 1953. Lambs and kids were poisoned by three such applications, but all others tolerated eight treatments, even when applied at 4-day intervals. Three of 10 cattle, however, were poisoned and died after three applications of 2 percent of older chlordane applied at 2-week intervals.

With currently produced chlordane, 8 cattle were treated 12 times at 2-week intervals with 2.0-percent sprays without evidence of any harm.

Young dairy calves have been killed by 2.0-percent sprays.

Chickens tolerated 5-percent dusts.

The newer chlordane has not been used in our dips and sprays on horses, hogs, sheep, or goats, but its toxicity for them would be expected to be less than we observed with the old material.

Emaciation and lactation will increase the susceptibility of sheep to chlordane poisoning. Ewes may be poisoned by 1.0-percent dips of chlordane, although their lambs may be unaffected by the same dipping.

The newer chlordane, given by mouth in single doses, produced poisoning of dairy calves at 25 mg./kg. and higher, and sheep were poisoned by 50 mg./kg. doses and higher. Adult cattle were not poisoned by 75 mg./kg. Mature hens were poisoned (as indicated by loss of weight) by five daily doses, each of 25 mg./kg.

Scientists at the Montana Agricultural Experiment Station found the minimum toxic dose of chlordane for cattle to be 91 mg./kg. and the minimum lethal dose to be 129 mg./kg. when given in the form of a grasshopper bait. Dr. Welch administered 50 mg./kg. of chlordane to cattle with no harmful effects, but sheep were poisoned by 500 mg./kg. and killed by 1,000 and 2,000 mg./kg. One sheep was given 3.5 grams of chlordane (approximately 100 mg./kg.) and was poisoned by the dose.

The symptoms of chlordane poisoning observed by the scientists in Montana are similar to those given in this chapter and those previously observed by scientists at Kerrville, Tex.

TOXAPHENE, as an acute toxicant, is most dangerous for the young calf. Concentrations of 1.0 percent toxaphene have killed very young calves. Adult cattle, sheep, goats, horses, and hogs withstood 2.0-percent concentrations. Chickens were unharmed by 5-percent dusts but were poisoned by 0.1-percent emulsions.

We have no indication that toxaphene is chronically toxic to farm animals when it is used at recommended strengths. Cattle treated 10 times at 2-week intervals with 2.0-percent sprays displayed no clinical disturbances.

No toxic effects were noted when cattle, sheep, goats, horses, and hogs were treated eight times at 4-day intervals with 1.5 percent toxaphene.

Emaciation and lactation apparently may increase the susceptibility of ewes to poisoning by toxaphene. Under such conditions, ewes were poisoned by dips containing 1.0 percent of toxaphene. Their lambs could be poisoned by the same dip.

The minimum toxic oral dose for baby calves appears to be about 5 mg./kg.; for cattle, between 10 and 25 mg./kg.; for sheep, 25 mg./kg.; and for goats, approximately the same.

One adult sheep was given 50 mg./kg. of toxaphene orally in a xylene emulsion 4 days a week. The eighth dose initiated symptoms of poisoning. The 14th dose produced death—an indication of the wide variation in susceptibility of individual animals.

Research workers at the Montana Agricultural Experiment Station found that the minimum toxic dose of toxaphene for cattle was 35 mg./kg., while deaths occurred at 144 mg./kg., when it was given in the form of a bait for grasshoppers.

STROBANE produced occasional poisoning of dairy calves at 1.5 percent but not at 1.0 percent. Adult cattle were moderately affected by 6-percent sprays.

Sheep were poisoned by 3-percent dips but not by 2-percent dips.

Weaned pigs were not affected by 6-percent sprays.

Chickens were poisoned by dips containing 0.05 percent or more of Strobane, but 0.025-percent emulsions of Strobane were tolerated, as were 5-percent dusts.

Administered orally, the minimum toxic dose of Strobane is 10 mg./kg. for dairy calves, between 10 and 25 for cattle, 50 for sheep, 10 for chickens, and 50 for weaned pigs.

Adult cattle were unharmed by six sprayings with 2.0 percent or 12 sprayings of 0.5 percent Strobane, applied at intervals of 2 weeks.

DIELDRIN was toxic to week-old calves at 0.25-percent concentration, to cattle at 2.0 percent, and to sheep and goats at 3.0 percent. Hogs were unharmed by 4.0-percent sprays.

Dieldrin is not so safe when used repeatedly. Cattle sprayed three times at 2-week intervals with 0.5 percent material showed clinical symptoms of poisoning.

The minimum toxic dose of dieldrin for calves is between 5 and 10 mg./kg. Mature cattle were killed by 25 mg./kg.

The minimum toxic dose for pigs was between 25 and 50 mg./kg.

For horses, 25 mg./kg. was definitely toxic.

For sheep, 15 mg./kg. was toxic, while 10 was not.

ALDRIN, applied as a spray to calves, seems to have a minimum toxic concentration of 0.25 percent or slightly less. Given by mouth, the minimum toxic dose is 5 mg./kg. for young calves and between 10 and 25 mg./kg. for cattle.

The minimum toxic dose for sheep appears to be 10 to 15 mg./kg.

In experiments at Kansas State College, small amounts of aldrin were fed to cattle and sheep and produced symptoms of poisoning as follows: Cattle were killed by 10 daily doses of 1.9 mg./kg. of aldrin, by 21 daily doses of 0.84 mg./kg., and by 33 daily doses of 0.686 mg./kg. In a second series, a heifer was given 4 mg./kg. daily; she developed symptoms on the 7th day and died on the 21st day. A second heifer received 2 mg./kg. daily; she developed symptoms after 29 doses, recovered, and survived a total of 64 doses. Heifers fed 1.0 or 0.5 mg./kg. daily for 64 days were unaffected.

In the same series of studies, one ewe died after receiving 20 daily doses of aldrin at 0.414 mg./kg. One ewe receiving 6 mg./kg. daily lost her appetite after 15 doses and died after 28 doses.

HEPTACHLOR seems to have a minimum toxic concentration for young calves of from 0.25 to 0.5 percent.

Cattle were not harmed by spraying six times at 2-week intervals with 0.5 percent heptachlor.

Lambs appear to be resistant to as much as 4.0-percent concentrations, but a minimum toxic dose has not been established.

The minimum toxic oral dose for calves appeared to be between 15 and 25 mg./kg., for sheep between 25 and 50 mg./kg.

TDE, LIKE DDT, is relatively nontoxic. All livestock tolerate single sprays of 8-percent concentration or eight applications at 1.5 percent.

Chickens are not harmed by 5-percent dusts.

Dairy calves were poisoned by oral doses of 250 mg./kg., but not by 100. Sheep tolerated 1,000 mg./kg.

METHOXYCHLOR is one of the least toxic of the chlorinated hydrocarbon insecticides we have studied. As with DDT and TDE, we have been unable to induce poisoning of calves, cattle, sheep, goats, hogs, or horses by external applications of methoxychlor.

Chickens were not harmed by 5-percent dusts.

Oral doses of 500 mg./kg. of methoxychlor produce only mild symptoms in calves. We gave one sheep oral doses of an emulsion of methoxychlor 4 days each week, each dose being 50 mg./kg., until a total of 21 such doses had been given without producing symptoms. Two doses, each of 250 mg./kg., and one dose of 500 mg./kg. were then given, and no symptoms appeared.

Dr. Welch did not induce poisoning in cattle by a single dose of 500 mg./kg. of methoxychlor. Sheep given 1,000 and 2,000 mg./kg. were unaffected. One sheep failed to show symptoms after 60 daily doses of 4.5 grams of methoxychlor.

PERTHANE, also known as Q–137, has been applied to dairy calves as an

8-percent suspension without producing symptoms of poisoning. We believe that its toxicity is similar to that of DDT, TDE, and methoxychlor as one of the safest of the chlorinated hydrocarbon insecticides.

DILAN is also known as CS–708. Of the three calves we treated in 1953 with 8-percent suspensions, none showed symptons of poisoning.

THE CHLORINATED HYDROCARBONS outwardly show their effect on an animal by various nervous disturbances. No two animals poisoned by a given insecticide will show exactly the same chain of symptoms, yet the symptoms are enough alike to enable one to identify them.

The following symptoms apply for all chlorinated hydrocarbon insecticides except DDT, TDE, and methoxychlor. Symptoms of poisoning may appear in as little as 15 minutes and usually within 24 hours after exposure.

An affected animal will generally first become excitable and more alert to its surroundings. Twitches of various muscles follow, usually beginning at the head and moving back along the body. The twitches may increase in intensity until there are spasms and finally convulsions.

The animal may also assume abnormal attitudes, such as standing with the head between the forelegs and under the body or in a sternal position with the hind legs in a standing position.

There may be persistent chewing movements. Occasionally the animal attacks any moving object. Usually there is profuse salivation, dyspnea (difficult breathing), rolling of the eyes, dribbling of urine, and bawling. The body temperature often reaches 114°–116° F.

Some animals show none of these active symptoms. Instead, they become depressed and unaware of their surroundings. Others are alternately depressed and excited.

Severity of symptoms is no index of the likelihood of death or survival.

Death may occur in less than an hour—or several weeks after exposure. Most cases run their course within 72 hours.

THE DISCUSSION that follows pertains to DDT, TDE, and methoxychlor.

In this type of poisoning, the animals first show restlessness and are excitable and hypersensitive, much as are the animals poisoned by the other chlorinated hydrocarbons.

Fasciculations (twitches) of the facial muscles then appear; they are rapid, particularly in the eyelids, and approach the character of tremors. The muscular twitches are more rapid than with the more toxic compounds and are not so violent.

Tremors then appear in other muscles of the body and finally involve all the muscles at once. The tremors become stronger and finally cause the animal to shake violently. Such seizures may be provoked almost at will by sudden noises or movements. Dyspnea occurs with such attacks. The animal is depressed and stiff after each seizure.

Tremors are absent or barely noticeable in the milder cases of poisoning. The animal walks with the pasterns extended stiffly and with short, choppy steps.

This is followed by a period of apparent laminitis, or founder, when the animal walks as though all feet were extremely sore. The reflexes then are slow, and the animal loses weight rapidly.

FINDINGS at necropsy are variable and are never diagnostic of poisoning by the chlorinated hydrocarbon insecticides. Usually there is cyanosis (blue-colored skin and membranes) and congestion of various organs.

Small hemorrhages may be found, most frequently on the heart. The lungs may be congested, heavy, and dark in color, suggesting the early stages of pneumonia. Often an excess of fluid occurs in and around the brain and spinal cord.

If the animal was affected over a longer period, the carcass may be thin and lacking in moisture, and the liver and kidneys may show abnormalities.

Microscopic lesions in animals dying quickly are few, other than those indicated at postmortem examination. In prolonged cases, there are fatty changes in the liver and kidney and some degeneration in those organs and in the brain. Otherwise, only few significant changes can be seen.

No specific antidotes are known for poisoning by chlorinated hydrocarbons.

Attention should be given first to control of convulsions or depression, as the case may be, then to removing the poison by washing, purging, or gastric lavage, according to the exposure.

The more rapidly the absorption can be stopped the greater the chances of recovery.

The patient should be provided with comfortable quarters and good feed. Then it should be left alone as much as possible.

Organic phosphorus insecticides have in common the element phosphorus and a degree of activity against esters of choline. Otherwise they differ widely from one another in chemical makeup and toxicity.

Because they are good insecticides and are useful against many insects that have developed resistance to chlorinated hydrocarbon insecticides, they will be used extensively.

Poisoning from parathion may be expected in young dairy calves sprayed with concentrations as low as 0.01 percent, whether the parathion is applied as an emulsion or as a suspension.

A single dose of 0.5 mg./kg. produced poisoning of young calves. For cattle, the toxic dose was 50 mg./kg.—100 times that for calves. Two doses of 25 mg./kg. had an equal effect, but 71 doses of 20 mg./kg. each were tolerated by a Hereford heifer.

Sheep were poisoned by 20 mg./kg.

but not by 10 mg./kg. Sheep were not affected by 48 doses, each 5 mg./kg., but one was moderately affected after 29 doses at 10 mg./kg.

Chickens were poisoned by five daily doses, each 1 mg./kg.

Because of the edema and congestion that occasionally develop during the course of parathion poisoning, secondary pneumonia may occur.

EPN is roughly equivalent in acute toxicity to gamma benzene hexachloride. It has produced poisoning at concentrations of 0.05 percent when applied to dairy calves.

Administered orally in single doses, EPN produced poisoning in dairy calves at 1.0 mg./kg. and in sheep at 20 mg./kg. Cattle were not poisoned by 10 mg./kg.

The minimum toxic concentration of malathion to young dairy calves was 1.0 percent. Adult cattle tolerated 16 weekly sprays of 0.5 percent of malathion. Dairy cows tolerated single 1.0-percent sprays.

Chickens were not harmed by 1-percent dusts.

Turkeys were not harmed by 5.0-percent emulsions or 25-percent dusts.

The minimum toxic oral dose for baby calves is between 10 and 20 mg./kg., and for sheep between 50 and 100 mg./kg.

Chickens were poisoned by single 200 mg./kg. doses.

Diazinon was toxic to dairy calves at 0.1-percent concentration in sprays.

The minimum toxic oral dose for baby calves was 1.0 mg./kg. For sheep it was 30 mg./kg. For adult cattle the minimum toxic dose was between 10 and 25 mg./kg., 25 having produced severe symptoms. Chickens were not harmed by 1-percent dusts.

Three doses, each 20 mg./kg., produced severe symptoms in sheep. Two doses, each 10 mg./kg., produced severe symptoms in cattle.

For chickens, 2 doses, each 2 mg./kg., were lethal.

A SUMMARY OF THE MINIMUM TOXIC AND MAXIMUM NONTOXIC CONCENTRATIONS OF INSECTICIDES APPLIED AS SPRAYS OR DIPS TO LIVESTOCK

Chemical	Animal	Age	Maximum nontoxic dose tested (percent)	Minimum toxic dose found (percent)
Aldrin	Calves	1–2 weeks	0.1	0.25
	Lambs	3 weeks		4.0
	Kids	....do....		4.0
BHC, gamma isomer (normal animals, see text).	Calves	1–2 weeks	.025	.05
	....do....	6–8 months	.15	
	Cattle	Adult	.1	.25
	Lambs	6 weeks	1.0	
	Sheep	Adult	1.0	
	Pigs	3 months	1.0	
	Horses	Adult	.15	
Chlordane (normal animals, see text).	Calves	1–2 weeks	1.0	2.0
	Cattle	Adult	2.0	
	Lambs	3 weeks	1.0	2.0
	Sheep	Adult	3.0	4.0
	Goats	....do....	3.0	4.0
	Horses	....do....	1.5	
Dieldrin	Calves	1–2 weeks	.1	.25
	Cattle	Adult	1.0	2.0
	Lambs	2 weeks	2.0	3.0
	Sheep	Adult		4.0
	Pigs	8 weeks	4.0	
	Goats	Adult		4.0
	Horses	....do....	1.0	
Heptachlor	Calves	1–2 weeks	.25	.5
	Cattle	1 year	.5	
	Lambs	3 weeks	4.0	
Strobane	Pigs	2–3 months	6.0	
	Calves	1–2 weeks	1.0	1.5
	Cattle	1 year	2.0	6.0
	Sheep	....do....	2.0	3.0
Toxaphene (normal animals, see text).	Calves	1–2 weeks	.5	1.0
	Cattle	Adult	2.0	4.0
	Lambs	6 weeks	4.0	
	Sheep	Adult	1.5	4.0.
	Kids	6 weeks	4.0	
	Goats	Adult	1.5	4.0
	Hogs	....do....	4.0	
	Horses	....do....	1.5	
Bayer 21/199	Calves	1–2 weeks	.2	.5
Diazinon	....do....	....do....	.05	.1
EPN	....do....	....do....	.025	.05
Malathion	....do....	....do....	.5	1.0
Parathion	....do....	....do....		.01
	Sheep	1–2 years		1.0
	Goats	....do....	.1	1.0

DDT, TDE, methoxychlor, Dilan, and Perthane were nontoxic to baby calves at 8.0-percent concentration.

Bayer compound L13/59, also known as Dipterex, has been sprayed on dairy calves and adult cattle at 1-percent concentration without producing symptoms of poisoning.

The minimum toxic oral dose for young dairy calves was between 5 and 10 mg./kg., for cattle between 50 and 100 mg./kg.

Two doses, each of 50 mg./kg., at 48-hour intervals produced severe symptoms of poisoning in cattle.

Single doses of 50 mg./kg. produced poisoning in chickens.

CHLORTHION SPRAYS at 0.5-percent concentration were tolerated by adult cattle.

A SUMMARY OF THE MINIMUM TOXIC AND MAXIMUM NONTOXIC SINGLE DOSES OF VARIOUS INSECTICIDES ADMINISTERED ORALLY TO LIVESTOCK

Chemical	Animal	Age	Maximum nontoxic dose tested (mg./kg.)	Minimum toxic dose found (mg./kg.)
Aldrin	Calves	1–2 weeks	2.5	5.0
	Cattle	1 year	10	25
	Sheep	1–2 years	10	15
BHC, gamma isomer	Calves	1–2 weeks	2.5	5.0
	Sheep	1–2 years	10	25
	Cattle	1 year	10	25
Chlordane	Calves	1–2 weeks	10	25
	Sheep	4–5 years	35	50
	Cattle	1 year	75	....
DDT	Calves	1–2 weeks	100	250
	Sheep	4–5 years	....	500
Dieldrin	Calves	1–2 weeks	5	10
	Cattle	1 year	10	25
	Pigs	3 weeks	25	50
	Horse	....	....	25
	Sheep	1 year	10	15
Heptachlor	Calves	1–2 weeks	15	25
	Sheep	4–5 years	25	50
Methoxychlor	Calves	1–2 weeks	250	500
	Sheep	4–5 years	1,000	....
Strobane	Calves	1–2 weeks	5	10
	Sheep	1–2 years	25	50
	Cattle	.....do	10	25
	Pigs	2–3 months	25	50
Toxaphene	Calves	1–2 weeks	2.5	5.0
	Sheep	4–5 years	10	25
	Goats	.....do	......	50
	Cattle	1 year	10	25
TDE	Calves	1–2 weeks	100	250
	Sheep	4–5 years	1,000	....
Bayer L 13/59	Calves	1–2 weeks	5	10
	Cattle	1 year	50	75
	Sheep	.....do	75	....
Chlorthion	Calves	1–2 weeks	50	100
	Cattle	1 year	....	50
Diazinon	Calves	1–2 weeks	.5	1.0
	Cattle	1 year	10	25
	Sheep	3–4 years	20	30
EPN	Calves	1–2 weeks	.5	1.0
	Cattle	1 year	10	....
	Sheep	1–2 years	10	20
Malathion	Calves	1–2 weeks	10	20
	Sheep	1–2 years	50	100
Parathion	Calves	1–2 weeks	.25	.5
	Cattle	1 year	25	50
	Sheep	1–2 years	10	20

The minimum toxic oral dose of Chlorthion for both dairy calves and adult cattle was between 50 and 100 mg./kg. Adult cattle were severely poisoned by 2 doses, each of 50 mg./kg., given 48 hours apart.

BAYER COMPOUND 21/199 was toxic for young calves at 0.5-percent concentration in sprays.

Adult cattle were not poisoned by 0.5-percent sprays. One yearling Hereford heifer given 50 mg./kg. of compound 21/199 died of poisoning; a similar heifer given 25 mg./kg. was unaffected.

SYMPTOMS OF POISONING by organic phosphorus compounds studied in our experiments (parathion, EPN, malathion, Bayer L 13/59, Chlorthion, and Bayer 21/199) are so similar from compound to compound that we could find no real differences. The symptoms are those associated with interference in the activity of the enzyme that destroys esters of choline.

Poisoned animals generally first show excessive salivation. The flow is abundant, and the consistency of the saliva approaches that of water. The animal then usually encounters respiratory difficulty and breathes with the mouth open and with greatly exaggerated respiratory movements. As the respiratory effort increases, the animal walks stifflegged and wanders about restlessly. Rippling spasms of all body muscles are present. Eventually exhaustion forces the animal to lie down. As death approaches, there are rasping sounds from the lungs and the animal grunts softly with each breath. Death appears to occur by respiratory failure. With the very high doses convulsions have been seen.

THE LESIONS found at necropsy in acute poisoning by cholinesterase-inhibiting insecticides are never outstanding and never sufficient to prove these compounds as the cause. In many cases the necropsy findings are entirely negative.

In cases that show lesions, there may be hemorrhages of varying sizes on the heart, lungs, stomach, or intestines. The lungs may be congested, edematous, and heavy, Frothy exudate is often present in the bronchi and trachea.

When the animal is affected over a long period, pneumonia may occur. In our experience several cases have suggested pneumonia by the symptoms, but the lungs were perfectly clear at necropsy.

ATROPINE is a specific antidote for poisoning by this group of compounds. It may be given by a veterinarian subcutaneously, intramuscularly, or intravenously.

In our studies of the treatment of poisoning of sheep and cattle, we have had remarkable success in using the intravenous and subcutaneous routes together, giving approximately one-fourth of the total dose intravenously and the remainder either subcutaneously or intramuscularly.

For poisoned cattle, at least 45 milligrams of atropine sulfate should be given for each 100 pounds of weight. Higher doses must be given if the animal has been severely poisoned.

An initial dose of 1 milligram for each pound of weight should be given to sheep.

Regardless of the initial dose given, additional doses must be given in most cases to keep the animal under the influence of the atropine, usually for at least 24 hours.

The specific treatment must be followed by removal of the remaining insecticide by washing or purging or other indicated methods.

R. D. RADELEFF *became veterinarian in charge of the Kerrville, Tex., laboratory of the Animal Disease and Parasite Research Branch in 1949. He is a graduate of Schreiner Institute and of the Agricultural and Mechanical College of Texas.*

G. T. WOODARD *was made the assistant veterinarian of the Kerrville laboratory in 1952. He is a graduate of the Agricultural and Mechanical College of Texas. He has assisted in the Kerrville studies since 1952.*

R. C. BUSHLAND *became entomologist in charge of the Kerrville laboratory of the Entomology Research Branch in 1951. He is a graduate of South Dakota State College and received his doctorate from Kansas State College. Most of his work, since he joined the Department of Agriculture in 1935, has been with insecticides.*

For further reading:
R. D. Radeleff, George T. Woodard, W. J. Nickerson, and R. C. Bushland: *The Acute Toxicity of Chlorinated Hydrocarbon and Organic Phosphorus Insecticides to Livestock*, U. S. Department of Agriculture Technical Bulletin 1122, 46 pages. 1955.
Ray E. Ely, L. A. Moore and R. H. Carter: *The Effect of Various Dosage Levels of Crystalline Lindane on the Concentration of Lindane in Cow's Milk*, Journal of Dairy Science, volume 35, pages 733–737. 1952.

Pesticide Residues in Animal Products

ROSCOE H. CARTER, H. V. CLABORN, G. T. WOODARD, AND RAY E. ELY

ANIMAL products intended for food may become contaminated with pesticide chemicals in a number of ways.

DDT and other chlorinated materials are used to control insects on such forage crops as alfalfa, clover, and grass and on peas, beans, corn, and similar crops, of which a part is used as animal feed. Some pest killers, used at recommended dosages and in accordance with good agricultural practices, leave enough residue on forage crops so that some is stored in the animal or excreted in milk if the forage is fed to livestock. Pastures or grain that have had pesticide treatments also may be a source of contamination of animal products.

DDT—the common name for the commercial product dichloro-diphenyl-trichloroethane—has been found in milk samples from cows stabled in barns sprayed with it, even though the cows were outside when the spraying was done. Enough DDT was picked up from feed troughs, water fountains, and other sources to cause excretion in the milk. Some other pesticides, sprayed directly on the animals, have been excreted in the milk.

Some of the pesticides used in spraying and dipping cattle, sheep, goats, and swine are stored in the animals' bodies. Some materials have caused serious disturbances and even fatalities. Others have little apparent effect. Most of the pesticides used for insect control are soluble in the fat and are stored in the fatty tissues of the animal. Three to four months are required before some of the chemicals are entirely eliminated.

Public Law 518 provides for the establishment of tolerances for pesticide chemicals in or on raw agricultural commodities. The term "pesticide chemical" means any substance which alone, in chemical combination, or in formulation with one or more other substances is an economic poison within the meaning of the Federal Insecticide, Fungicide, and Rodenticide Act. Raw agricultural commodities include fresh fruits and vegetables, grains, nuts, eggs, raw milk, meats, and similar agricultural produce. It does not include foods that have been processed, fabricated, or manufactured by cooking, freezing, dehydrating, or milling.

Detecting and estimating pesticide residues in the biological materials by chemical analysis are complicated procedures. General methods, such as the determination of the organic chlorine content, are used sometimes to determine residues. Specific and spectrophotometric methods are available for certain pesticide chemicals.

The procedures generally require an extraction of the biological product with an organic solvent, such as Skellysolve B or benzene. These extracts contain fat, glycerides, and other constituents. Because some pesticide materials are stable toward acids and some are stable toward alkali treatments, procedures using those reagents have been developed to break up the glycerides without decomposition of the pesticide. Chromatographic procedures have also been developed to aid in the separation of the pesticide residue from fats, waxes, coloring matter, and such materials.

Methods of analysis capable of detecting minute amounts have been developed so that it is possible to determine residues considerably less than 0.1 part per million (p. p. m.) for some pesticides.

Bioassay procedures capable of determining residues less than 0.1 p.p.m.

of some materials have also been developed. They are useful in detecting toxic residues of metabolic products that are not detectable by the specific method for the original toxicant.

EXPERIMENTS in which dairy cows were fed forage that had been treated with insecticides during the growing season and other tests in which the cows were given oil solutions of the insecticides in capsules are briefly described. The insecticides included DDT, BHC (the common name for the technical product benzene hexachloride), lindane, methoxychlor, chlordane, toxaphane, aldrin, dieldrin, heptachlor, and endrin.

Growing alfalfa was sprayed with the insecticides at dosages recommended for insect control. After an interval of 3 to 10 days the crop was cut, field cured, baled, and stored in barns 6 to 8 months until used as feed. Normal, healthy milking cows, generally four to each test, were fed the hay with a supplemental grain ration. The amounts consumed daily and the milk production were recorded.

The tests were generally continued 40 to 90 days, or until it was thought that equilibrium had been established between intake and excretion of the insecticide. After this phase, the cows were given oil solutions of the insecticides in capsules at varying levels of intake considerably above the levels of intake as residue. Milk samples were taken every tenth day for chemical analysis. Since the chlorinated insecticides are fat-soluble and are present only in the butterfat portion of milk, butterfat determinations were made on all samples and the results calculated and adjusted to a uniform butterfat (FCM) content of 4 percent. Composite samples of the hay representing every 10 days of feeding were analyzed for residue. Milk samples were collected in most instances for some time after insecticide intake had been discontinued to obtain information on the persistence of the materials in the animals.

Alfalfa hay that had been treated with 2.4 pounds of DDT on an acre resulted in milk production containing a maximum of 10.1 p. p. m. of DDT; 0.6 pounds of DDT resulted in 0.9 p. p. m. of DDT in the milk.

A comparative study of the effects of dosage level and various methods of administration on the concentration of DDT in milk indicated that increasing intakes of DDT as a residue on hay or in oil solution gave progressive increases in the DDT concentration in the milk in a straight-line relation. This straight line had a greater slope for intake as residue over intake in oil solution.

DDT in oil solution and alfalfa containing various amounts of DDT residue was fed to dairy calves. DDT intake varied from 0.07 to 2.9 milligrams per kilogram of body weight, or 2.2 to 106 p. p. m. of the dry matter consumed. The storage of DDT in the body and kidney fat ranged from 2 to 345 p. p. m., and the concentration was proportional to the DDT intake.

Residues of methoxychlor on alfalfa ranging from 16 to 109 p. p. m. did not result in detectable amounts in the milk. Crystalline methoxychlor administered orally as a 10-percent solution in soybean oil in daily dosages equivalent to 2,000 p. p. m. of the feed consumed, or approximately 19 mg. per kg. of body weight, resulted in detectable amounts of methoxychlor in the milk.

Four cows were fed hay containing approximately 0.4 p. p. m. of lindane for 100 days and four cows received hay containing approximately 2.6 p. p. m. of lindane for 60 days. The concentrations of lindane in the milk of these cows ranged from 0.13 to 0.27 p. p. m.

Two lots of alfalfa hay, which had been treated with toxaphene emulsion at the rate of 1.5 pounds per acre, were fed to two sets of three cows each for 150 and 100 days. The average insecticide residue on the two lots of hay was 81.8 and 31.8 p. p. m., equivalent to an average daily intake of 1.4 mg. and 0.5 mg. per kg. of body weight, respectively. The average toxaphene content of the milk from the two sets of cows was 0.5 and 0.1 p. p. m., respectively. Increased dosages of toxaphene in soybean oil solution resulted in increased excretion in the milk.

Two lots of alfalfa hay, which had been treated with chlordane emulsion at the rates of 1 and 2 pounds per acre, were fed to two sets of three cows each for 150 and 100 days, respectively. The average chlordane residue on the two lots of hay was 20.4 and 20.8 p. p. m., equivalent to an average daily intake of 0.39 and 0.37 mg. per kg. of body weight, respectively. The average chlordane content of the milk from the two sets of cows was 0.2 and 0 p. p. m., respectively. Increased dosages of chlordane in soybean oil solution resulted in increased excretion in the milk.

Alfalfa hay that had been sprayed with aldrin at the rate of 3.9 ounces per acre was fed to four milk cows for 48 days. The average aldrin content of the hay was 6.6 to 7.1 p. p. m., equivalent to an average daily aldrin intake of 0.10 to 0.15 mg. per kg. of body weight. No aldrin was detected in the milk samples from the hay feeding tests or from increased dosages in soybean oil solution below a daily intake of 0.8 mg. per kg. of body weight.

Two fields of alfalfa were sprayed with dieldrin at the rate of 3.5 ounces and 7.0 ounces per acre and the hay was fed to normal milking cows for 54 and 52 days, respectively. The average dieldrin content of the milk from the cows on the two batches of hay was 0.8 p. p. m. and 1.8 p. p. m., respectively. A daily intake of 50 to 1,000 mg. of dieldrin in soybean oil solution daily for 40 to 50 days resulted in an average dieldrin content in the milk ranging from 1.7 to 13.1 p. p. m.

Alfalfa hay that had been sprayed with 3.8 ounces and 8 ounces of heptachlor contained average residues of 1.2 and 5 p. p. m., respectively. The first lot of hay was fed to four cows for 54 days; following that, the second lot was fed to the same cows for 52 days. The average daily heptachlor intake was 0.03 mg. per kg. of body weight

when feeding the hay sprayed with 3.8 ounces per acre; from 0.10 to 0.13 mg. per kg. of body weight from the 8-ounce treatment. After the hay feeding tests, the cows were given increased dosages of heptachlor in a soybean oil solution. No heptachlor was detected in the milk of the cows fed the treated hay or given the oil solutions.

A metabolic product, heptachlorepoxide, was detected in the milk from cows receiving heptachlor at dosages of more than 1.3 mg. per kg. of body weight.

Two lots of alfalfa hay, which had been treated with 2.7 ounces and 6.6 ounces of endrin per acre, were fed to two sets of four cows each for 48 and 44 days, respectively. The average endrin content of the milk was approximately 0.1 p. p. m.—which is below the sensitivity of the method of analysis. When a soybean oil solution of endrin was fed by capsule, an intake of 500 mg., or approximately 1.4 mg. per kg. of body weight, was required before definite indications of excretion in the milk were noted.

Milk samples from cows grazed in pastures that had been treated with DDT and dieldrin contained small amounts of these insecticides.

Samples of fat from swine that had grazed in pastures treated with insecticides contained small amounts of the insecticide. When meat containing DDT residue was fed to pigs, the DDT accumulated in the fat of the pigs.

Dairy cows were sprayed with 0.5-percent concentrations of DDT, methoxychlor, dieldrin, Dilan, Perthane, and malathion to determine the amounts of insecticides excreted in milk and the duration of milk contamination caused by spraying. This concentration for all the insecticides tested (except dieldrin) is used against the hornfly.

The cows used were grade Jerseys in full lactation. They were sprayed all over. Two quarts of spray were used for each. They were milked by machine and samples were taken before spraying and at various intervals after spraying. Care was taken at all times to avoid mechanical contamination of the milk.

In milk samples taken 2 days after spraying, 2.8 p. p. m. of DDT was found. This amount gradually dropped to 0.6 p. p. m. in 21 days. The amount of dieldrin found was approximately twice that of DDT. The maximum contamination from Dilan was one-fourth and from methoxychlor and Perthane one-seventh that of DDT. Less than 0.1 p. p. m. of malathion was found in milk samples taken 5 hours after spraying with emulsion sprays. Only traces were present in the milk 24 hours after spraying. All subsequent samples were free of contamination. Malathion suspensions caused slightly higher residues than emulsions.

STUDIES have been made on the storage of insecticides in the fat of beef cattle following ingestion of feed artificially contaminated with the insecticides to simulate residues on hay and forage crops. The first tests were made at concentrations thought likely to exceed field contamination. If insecticide storage seemed excessive, further experiments were made at progressively lower dosages until minimum field residues were studied. The first studies covered feeding periods of 4 weeks. Later the feeding time was extended to 8 weeks and finally to 16 weeks, which was the feeding period used in most of these studies.

The test animals, cattle and sheep, were maintained under the supervision of the cooperating veterinarians, who were responsible for all details of the feeding and the collection of the fat samples. Each feeding was weighed and the insecticide added in acetone solution to the feed at the time of weighing. The feed consisted of ground corn and oats, cottonseed meal, and chopped alfalfa hay.

Fat samples were taken by omentectomy before starting the feeding, at 4-week intervals during the feeding time and at intervals after the feeding of the insecticides ceased to determine the duration of contamination.

The insecticides studied include aldrin, BHC, chlordane, DDT, dieldrin, endrin, heptachlor, methoxychlor, and toxaphene. Some of the materials were fed at several dosage levels.

Methoxychlor showed less tendency to be stored in the body fat than any of the insecticides studied. There was no detectable accumulation of methoxychlor in the fat after feeding 25 p. p. m. in all items of the diet for 16 weeks.

Technical aldrin, dieldrin, endrin, and heptachlor fed at dosages of 2.5 p. p. m. for 16 weeks were stored in the fat at rates of 5.2, 14.3, 0.8, and 0.2 p. p. m., respectively, in cattle, and 4.5, 10.5, 1.4, and 2.1 p. p. m. in sheep.

Toxaphene fed at 25 p. p. m. for 16 weeks resulted in the storage of 12 p. p. m. in the fat of cattle and 8 p. p. m. in the fat of sheep.

Dieldrin resulted in the greatest storage of any of the insecticides studied. A dosage of the 1.0 p. p. m. in the diet for 16 weeks resulted in a storage of 2.2 p. p. m. in the fat of both cattle and sheep.

DDT residues on corn plants that had been treated for control of European corn borer averaged 23 p. p. m. when beef cattle were placed in the field. After 2 months on the stover range, the DDT content of their fat was 4.1 to 5.8 p. p. m. Three months after discontinuance of feeding on the contaminated forage, DDT was not detected in the fat.

Thus the insecticides can be arranged in the approximate order of their tendency toward storage as follows: Dieldrin, aldrin, BHC, DDT, endrin, chlordane, heptachlor, toxaphene, and methoxychlor. The insecticides having the greatest tendency toward storage in the fat were also the ones most slowly eliminated from the fat after feeding of the insecticides ceased.

Studies were made on the storage of insecticides in the fat of beef cattle resulting from spray treatments with practical concentrations of DDT, methoxychlor, lindane, chlordane, gamma chlordane, heptachlor, toxaphene, malathion, and TDE (the common name for the technical product dichlorodiphenyl-dichloroethane).

The storage of insecticides in the fat of beef cattle 3 weeks after a single spray treatment with 0.5 percent DDT, TDE, and methoxychlor was 11.2, 11.0, and 2.8 p. p. m., respectively. The residue of methoxychlor had been eliminated 8 weeks later, but small residues of DDT and TDE were still present in the fat 27 weeks after spraying. Six repeated spray applications with these insecticides at 3-week intervals resulted in storage in the fat in the following amounts: DDT, 35 p. p. m.; TDE, 28 p. p. m.; and methoxychlor, 2.4 p. p. m. Detectable residues of DDT and TDE were still present 36 weeks after the last spraying had been made.

Detectable amounts of lindane were not found in fat of cattle sprayed six times at 3-week intervals with 0.03 percent lindane. A method sensitive to 2.5 p. p. m. was used.

There was no detectable storage in the fat of cattle sprayed 16 times at weekly intervals with 0.5 percent malathion. The fat samples were taken 2 weeks after the last spraying and were analyzed by a method that was sensitive to ±0.5 p. p. m.

Samples of fat taken from cattle 2 weeks after the last of six spray treatments at 2-week intervals with 0.5 percent heptachlor, chlordane, and gamma chlordane contained residues of 19, 21, and 24 p. p. m., respectively. The residues had dropped to 2, 4, and 0.3 p. p. m. 14 weeks later.

When cattle were sprayed 12 times at 2-week intervals with 0.5 percent toxaphene, analysis for organically bound chlorine indicated 14 p. p. m. of the insecticide to be present in the fat. The method used for this experiment was sensitive to only ±4.0 p. p. m., however.

In conclusion, then, recommendations for the application of insecticides to forage crops and to farm animals must take into consideration the possibility that the chemicals may contaminate milk and meat products.

ROSCOE H. CARTER, *a chemist in the Entomology Research Branch, Agricultural Research Service, is a graduate of Morningside College and the State University of Iowa. He has been employed by the Department of Agriculture since 1927 in insecticide investigations.*

H. V. CLABORN *is chemist in charge of Pesticide Chemicals Research Section of Entomology Research Branch at Kerrville, Tex. Since entering the Department of Agriculture in 1927, he has worked in the Bureau of Chemistry and Soils, Bureau of Entomology and Plant Quarantine, the research laboratories of the Bureau of Dairy Industry, and the Food and Drug Administration.*

G. T. WOODARD *is assistant veterinarian in charge of the Animal Disease and Parasite Research Section at Kerrville, Tex. He is a graduate of the Texas Agricultural and Mechanical College. Since 1952 he has been engaged in work on the problems of insecticide toxicology.*

RAY E. ELY *is animal nutritionist in the Experiment Stations Division of the Department of Agriculture. He is a graduate of Michigan State College and the University of Missouri. Formerly he was employed by the Nutrition and Physiology Section of the Dairy Husbandry Research Branch at Beltsville.*

For further reading:
R. C. Bushland, H. V. Claborn, H. F. Beckman, R. D. Radeleff, and R. W. Wells: *Contamination of Meat and Milk by Chlorinated Hydrocarbon Insecticides Used for Livestock Pest Control,* Journal of Economic Entomology, volume 43, pages 649–652. 1950.
R. H. Carter, Paul E. Hubanks, F. W. Poos, L. A. Moore, and Ray E. Ely: *The Toxaphene and Chlordane Content of Milk from Cows Receiving These Materials in Their Feed,* Journal of Dairy Science, volume 36, pages 1172–1177. 1953.
H. V. Claborn, H. F. Beckman, and R. W. Wells: *Contamination of Milk From DDT Sprays Applied to Dairy Barns,* Journal of Economic Entomology, volume 43, pages 723–724. 1950; *Excretion of DDT and TDE in Milk From Cows Treated With These Insecticides,* Journal of

Economic Entomology, volume 43, pages 850–852. 1950.

H. V. Claborn, J. W. Bowers, R. W. Wells, R. D. Radeleff, and W. J. Nickerson: *Meat Contamination From Pesticides*, Agricultural Chemistry, volume 8, number 8, pages 37–39, 110, 121. 1953.

Ray E. Ely, L. A. Moore, R. H. Carter, H. D. Mann, and F. W. Poos: *The Effect of Dosage Level and Various Methods of Administration on the Concentration of DDT in Milk*, Journal of Dairy Science, volume 35, pages 266–271. 1952; *Excretion of Dieldrin in the Milk of Cows Fed Dieldrin Sprayed Forage and Technical Dieldrin*, Journal of Dairy Science, volume 37, pages 1461–1465. 1954.

Ray E. Ely, L. A. Moore, P. E. Hubanks, R. H. Carter, and F. W. Poos: *Results of Feeding Methoxychlor Sprayed Forage and Crystalline Methoxychlor to Dairy Cows*, Journal of Dairy Science, volume 36, pages 309–314. 1953; *Studies of Feeding Aldrin to Dairy Cows*, Journal of Dairy Science, volume 37, pages 294–298. 1954.

Ray E. Ely, P. C. Underwood, L. A. Moore, H. D. Mann, and R. H. Carter: *Observations on Lindane Poisoning in Dairy Animals*, Journal of the American Veterinary Medical Association, volume 123, pages 448–449. 1953.

H. D. Mann, R. H. Carter, and Ray E. Ely: *The DDT Content of Milk Products*, Journal of Milk and Food Technology, volume 13, pages 340–341. 1950.

W. S. McGregor, R. D. Radeleff, H. V. Claborn, and R. C. Bushland: *Dieldrin, Aldrin and Lindane–Systemic Insecticides–Against Livestock Pests*, Agricultural Chemistry, volume 10, number 1, pages 34–36, 123. 1955.

R. D. Radeleff, H. V. Claborn, R. W. Wells, and W. J. Nickerson: *Effects on Beef Cattle of Prolonged Treatment With a DDT Spray*, Veterinary Medicine, volume 47, pages 94–96. 1952.

J. B. Shepherd, L. A. Moore, R. H. Carter, and F. W. Poos: *The Effect of Feeding Alfalfa Hay Containing DDT Residue on the DDT Content of Cow's Milk*, Journal of Dairy Science, volume 32, pages 549–555. 1949.

Liver Flukes of Cattle and Sheep

EMMETT W. PRICE

MANY species of flukes infest the livers of warm-blooded animals.

All liver flukes are hermaphroditic; that is, the male and female reproductive organs occur in one individual. Usually mating is unnecessary to insure their perpetuation.

Because all liver flukes of domestic animals must have one or more intermediate hosts for completion of their life cycles, it is hard to develop control measures that apply to all species.

Four well-known species attack cattle, sheep, and other domestic livestock. They are the common liver fluke, the giant liver fluke, the large American fluke, and the lancet fluke.

The liver flukes cause extensive losses. The Department of Agriculture estimated that the annual loss was 3.5 million dollars in cattle and 4.5 million dollars in sheep between 1942 and 1952. The figures represented mostly condemnations of livers at slaughter and did not include unthriftiness, lack of condition, the poor use of feed, and special care, which are hard to measure.

THE COMMON LIVER FLUKE, *Fasciola hepatica*, is widely distributed.

The adult fluke in the bile ducts is flat and leaflike. The anterior end is conical and is set off from the rest of the body. The parasite is about an inch long in sheep and a little larger in cattle. It apparently is long lived. Viable, egg-producing worms were recovered at the Agricultural Research Center from a sheep that had been experimentally infected and kept for 11 years under conditions that precluded reinfection.

F. hepatica occurs most abundantly in the United States in Florida, Louisiana, Texas, California, Oregon, Washington, Nevada, Idaho, Utah, and Montana. It has also been found in Arizona, New Mexico, Colorado, Arkansas, Wyoming, Michigan, Wisconsin, Alabama, and Missouri. We do not know why it has not become established in the Eastern States, other than Florida, because conditions seem favorable there for their propagation.

The principal hosts for the common liver fluke are cattle, sheep, and goats. It has been found also in swine and deer. Infected rabbits and hares are encountered often in some parts of the country, particularly in the gulf coast region of Texas, and complicate attempts to control the parasite.

The life history of *F. hepatica* has been known since 1882, when Rudolph Leuckart in Germany and A. P. W. Thomas in England independently discovered that the snail *Lymnaea truncatula* was the intermediate host in those countries. Since that time about 14 lymnaeid snails have been shown to be vectors of the parasite throughout the world.

In the United States the snails serving as intermediate hosts are *Fossaria bulimoides*, *F. cubensis*, *F. ferruginea*, *F. modicella*, *Pseudosuccinea columella*, *Lymnaea traskii*, and *Stagnicola bulimoides techella*. Some of those snails have somewhat restricted ranges, but their combined distribution makes it possible for the liver fluke to become established in every State.

The common liver fluke deposits its eggs in the bile ducts in enormous numbers. They pass out of the host in the droppings. The eggs embryonate when they reach water and hatch in 2 to 6 weeks, depending on temperature.

The liberated larva, or miracidium, is ciliated and swims about in the water until it comes in contact with a suitable snail, into which it bores. Then it changes into a form known as a sporocyst. From then on its form changes a number of times, finally becoming what is known as a redia. Large numbers of minute stages, shaped like minute tadpoles and known as cercariae, are produced in the redia. These eventually escape from the snail, swim about, and become encysted on grass or other vegetation or under the surface of the water. Development within the snail takes 50 to 80 days.

When the encysted cercariae, or metacercariae, are taken into the body of cattle, sheep, or other hosts, they encyst in the small intestine, penetrate its walls, and reach the abdominal cavity. There they wander about, penetrate the capsule of the liver, and eventually reach the bile ducts, where they mature in about 3 months.

The most obvious injury to cattle is to the liver, where the parasites cause irritation of the bile ducts, enlargement and thickening of the walls, and fibrosis of the liver tissue. The lumen of the bile ducts is heavily encrusted with deposits of calcium phosphate. Such livers are unfit for human use. Systemic disturbances—resulting in loss of condition, digestive disorders, anemia, and other symptoms of parasitism—are reported in cattle, particularly in the Gulf Coast States. Whether this condition is due entirely to the flukes is questionable, as similar effects are reported to be rare in cattle in Oregon and other Northwestern States.

Sheep are particularly susceptible. Sheep cannot be raised profitably in many places without a regular system of medication. The livers of infested sheep have thickened bile ducts, but the encrustations with calcium, characteristic in cattle livers, are absent. Sheep heavily infested with young flukes may die without showing symptoms. Sheep with chronic infestations tire easily and appear dull, weak, and anemic.

A further complication to sheep raising in flukey areas in some Western States is "black disease"—infectious necrotic hepatitis, a condition caused by the bacterium *Clostridium novyi*. The organism does not seem to cause disease in normal animals. In sheep, whose livers are extensively damaged by the wanderings of the young flukes, however, it becomes active and liberates toxins, which cause rapid death. The inside of the pelts of infected sheep is dark or black, and the carcass has a peculiar, sweetish odor.

THE GIANT LIVER FLUKE, *Fasciola gigantica*, is like *F. hepatica* in form and structure, but it is much longer and its ends are less pointed. It is the common liver fluke of India, other southern Asian countries, and Africa. It is also the common fluke of cattle in Hawaii. We have had some inconclusive reports of its occurrence in cattle in the gulf coast area.

The life cycle of *Fasicola gigantica* resembles that of *F. hepatica*. Its snail intermediate hosts are *Lymnaea natalensis* and *Physopsis africana* in Africa, *L. acuminata* in India, and *Fossaria ollula* in Hawaii.

The giant liver fluke also injures the livers of cattle and causes general systemic disturbance similar to those reported for flukey cattle in Texas and other Gulf Coast States.

THE LARGE AMERICAN FLUKE, *Fascioloides magna*, was first discovered in 1875 in deer in Italy, where it was believed to have been introduced through importations of American elk. Other ruminants in Europe are known to harbor the parasite, but its widespread distribution and variety of hosts on this continent leave little doubt as to its American origin. The parasite is fleshy and leaflike. It may be 3 inches long when it is fully extended.

This fluke occurs in Texas, Louisiana, Arkansas, Wisconsin, Michigan, Colorado, Illinois, Iowa, Idaho, Oklahoma, New York, Montana, and North Dakota. It has been found in British Columbia, Alberta, and Ontario.

Its definitive hosts in North America are cattle, sheep, goats, several species of deer, bison, and elk. It also has been found in horses.

Its life history resembles that of *F. hepatica*. The snail intermediate hosts all belong to the family *Lymnaeidae* and are *Stagnicola bulimoides techella*, *Fossaria modicella*, *F. modicella rustica*, and *Pseudosuccinea columella* in the United States, and *S. palustris nuttalliana* and *F. parva* in Canada.

The young flukes, which gain access to the liver in the same way as do those of *F. hepatica*, wander through the liver tissue and form extensive channels. Finally they come to rest as a result of the host's tissue reaction. They become surrounded by connective tissue and complete their sexual development within these cysts.

The cysts in cattle are thick-walled and have no access to the bile ducts. Therefore the eggs of the parasites cannot escape, and the life cycle is not completed. In deer and related mammals and in sheep and goats, the cyst wall is thin, the bile ducts are open, and the eggs and other material from the cysts flow freely into them and escape from the body in a normal manner. Consequently it is generally believed that cattle and closely related ruminants are not important in the spread of infection.

Infested cattle sometimes show symptoms of liver fluke disease in areas where *F. magna* is common. Sheep and goats are particularly susceptible to the effects of *F. magna*, and deaths are frequent. On postmortem examination, the livers show dark-red cysts, about the size of a walnut. If they are superficial, they are somewhat elevated above the surface of the liver. The liver substance, particularly in sheep and goats, often shows tracks or burrows filled with blood and pigment as a result of the migration of the flukes. Adhesions of the viscera, especially near the liver, are commonly seen; the liver, adjacent lymph nodes, and omentum show streaks and patches of black pigment, a condition that does not occur in other infestations of liver flukes.

THE LANCET FLUKE, *Dicrocoelium dendriticum*, is the smallest of the liver flukes that infest livestock. It rarely is more than one-half inch long. It has pointed ends and so has the shape of a lancet. The body is thin and semitransparent, except for the middle part of the posterior half, which contains the uterus filled with small, brownish eggs. Its small size and transparency make it difficult to detect on casual inspection of the opened bile ducts.

The lancet fluke is widely distributed in Europe, the Near East, and some other parts of the Eastern Hemisphere. It was first definitely established to be present in North America in 1930, when cases in sheep were found in Nova Scotia.

The infection was first found in the United States in 1940, when eight infested cattle from New York were found during the course of Federal meat inspection at Newark, N. J. The parasite since has been reported in sheep, cattle, goats, deer, woodchucks, and rabbits in 11 counties in central New York. Two cases have been found in Massachusetts and one in northern Pennsylvania. We have had unconfirmed reports of one case in North Dakota and another in Arkansas.

The lancet fluke requires two intermediate hosts, one a snail and the other an ant.

The first intermediate host is a land snail—*Zebrina detrita, Torquilla frumentum, Helicella ericetorum*, and *H. candidula* in Europe, and *Cionella lubrica* in America. *C. lubrica* is minute and occurs widely in the United States, Canada, and parts of Mexico.

The second intermediate host in America is a common and widely distributed species of black ant, *Formica fusca*. The second intermediate host in other parts of the world is unknown.

Eggs of *D. dendriticum* are passed in the droppings of cattle and sheep or other mammalian hosts and are eaten by the snails. The miracidia hatch from the eggs in the snail's intestine, migrate to the middle digestive gland, and are transformed into sporocysts. The sporocysts, which are saclike bodies, give rise to a second generation of sporocysts, which are tubular and have a birth pore. Long-tailed stylet cercariae develop within this generation of sporocysts. The cercariae eventually escape from the snails, and large numbers of them become cemented together by the secretions of their large glands. These masses, or slime balls, adhere to grass in the course of the snail's migrations and are eaten by ants. Ants containing the young flukes, or metacercariae, are eaten by cattle or other host animals while grazing, and the young flukes finally reach the bile ducts, where they mature.

Lancet flukes in cattle seem to cause little injury, aside from slight enlargements of the bile ducts. In sheep, however, there is a pronounced cirrhosis of the liver, as shown by scarring of the organ and thickening of the bile ducts, thickening of the inner lining of the ducts, and adjacent fibrosis. The damage to the liver increases in proportion to the age of the infection and the number of flukes present. Infested livers are unfit for food. Infested sheep do not gain normally. Extremely heavy infestations cause death.

THE CONTROL OF LIVER FLUKES of livestock is a complex problem. More information on its various aspects is needed before any great success can be expected. Possible eradication of the snail intermediate hosts, treatment for the removal of the parasites from infested animals, keeping livestock off infested pastures, and the control of wild animal vectors must all be taken into account.

Drainage of the places where snails live would be a logical beginning, because the three fasciolinid flukes I have discussed have water or amphibious snails as vectors. Such drainage, however, cannot be done economically in some sections. In Texas, for example, the coastal prairie, which is essentially a continuous habitat, is 250 to 330 miles long, 20 to 80 miles wide, and 0 to 100 feet in elevation; to drain any but small places there would be extremely costly, or impossible. Some ranchers in Florida prefer to maintain the water table 4 inches below the ground surface to get good grass for grazing; extensive drainage under those conditions would be impracticable. In some of the Western States, moreover, irrigation is necessary for crops and livestock. Except for small, swampy areas caused by seepages from the irrigation canals, drainage would tend to defeat the purpose of irrigation and return the land to an arid condition.

An effective and inexpensive way to destroy lymnaeid snails is to use chemical poisons. Asa C. Chandler, after a long search for a chemical that could be used on a large scale and was cheap, soluble in water, destructive to snails, and nontoxic to man and animals, reported in 1920 that copper sulfate met those specifications. He found that copper sulfate in dilutions of 1:100,000 would kill *Fossaria bulimoides* in 8 hours and in 1:1,000,000 in 24 hours. Subsequent investigators demonstrated the practicability of the chemical under various conditions, and it is now used extensively against snails in different parts of the world.

The concentration of copper sulfate and methods of application depend on the type of habitat and the amount and kind of vegetation. Sprays containing 0.5 percent of the chemical applied at the rate of about 140 gallons to the acre will destroy snails on damp pastures with heavy vegetation.

Dusting with a mixture 1 part of powdered copper sulfate to 4 to 8 parts of a carrier, such as sand, China clay, or land plaster, is satisfactory for treating swampy land over which spraying equipment cannot be taken. Dusting is also useful in treating small swampy areas, well overflows, and places around drinking troughs and the margins of pools. Dusting of large areas, as in the coastal prairie of Texas, by the use of airplanes might be effective, but it would be expensive. Copper sulfate will not kill the eggs of snails, and new generations will reappear soon after the treatment of pastures. Therefore it is most effective when it is used in connection with drainage in killing snails in ditches and in small areas not adequately drained. Copper sulfate is likewise useful in treating streams, but the promiscuous use of the chemical in streams is not advocated because it kills fish and other aquatic life.

Another way is to fence cattle out of land known to be infested. The fences should be placed far enough back from the infested area to keep animals away from herbage contaminated with infective metacercariae. Hay from the areas should not be fed to livestock unless it has been thoroughly dried and stacked for at least 18 months.

Medical treatment of fluke-infested animals is a valuable, if not an essential, adjunct to any program of control. Of several medicaments that will kill the mature flukes in the bile ducts, the most promising so far are carbon tetrachloride for sheep and hexachloroethane for cattle. Carbon tetrachloride is frequently toxic to cattle and should not be given to them. No treatments so far discovered are entirely satisfactory, because they do not destroy the young flukes in the liver tissue and because the animals must be treated at least twice a year in order to destroy the maximum number of flukes as they mature in the bile ducts.

Wild animal vectors complicate the task of controlling flukes in livestock. Deer, hosts for the large American fluke, contaminate ranges and pastures and so transmit the parasite to cattle, sheep, and goats. Many or all of the snails that are intermediate hosts for the parasite also are hosts of the common liver fluke. Hares and rabbits commonly are infested with *F. hepatica* and maintain infestation on pastures. To control or eradicate them is impossible.

CONTROL OR ERADICATION of the lancet fluke is even harder. There are no control methods for snails and ants, its two intermediate hosts. We know of no medical treatment that removes the flukes from infested animals.

As for other liver flukes, control is complicated by the occurrence of the parasite in wild animals. Since the parasite in North America is restricted to a relatively small area in New York, Massachusetts, and Pennsylvania, and perhaps a smaller area in Canada, it is important that steps be devised to eradicate the fluke before it becomes widespread. Quarantine, slaughter of infested animals, keeping noninfested animals off infective pastures until the infection dies out, and extermination of deer and the other mammal vectors are possible—but remote—measures.

EMMETT W. PRICE *is head of the Helminth Parasite Section, Animal Disease and Parasite Research Branch, Agricultural Research Service. He joined the United States Department of Agriculture in 1926 and from 1936 to 1953 was assistant chief of the former Zoological Division of the Bureau of Animal Industry. He has written many articles dealing with helminth parasites. He has degrees in veterinary medicine and philosophy from the George Washington University.*

Tapeworms and Bladderworms

DALE A. PORTER AND KENNETH C. KATES

DOMESTIC ruminants in the United States may harbor three species of adult tapeworms and five species of bladderworms, or larval tapeworms.

These larval tapeworms develop to maturity in certain nonruminant hosts, such as dogs and related animals and man.

Adult tapeworms of ruminants are flat, ribbonlike, segmented parasites up to several yards long and three-fourths inch wide. They are attached to the lining of the small intestine by a small head, or scolex, which has four suckers without hooks. The segmented body, or strobila, consists of hundreds of segments, or proglottids.

Two species, *Moniezia expansa* and *M. benedeni*, commonly occur in the small intestines of domestic ruminants and some of the wild ruminants in the United States. Both parasitize cattle, sheep, and goats, but *M. benedeni* is the species usually found in cattle and *M. expansa* is the one usually found in sheep.

Of all the parasites of ruminants, these tapeworms are the best known to farmers because of their large size and because ripe segments can be seen

easily in fresh manure. Their mode of transmission was unknown until 1937. Dr. H. W. Stunkard, of New York University, then discovered that small mites, known as oribatid or beetle mites, were the intermediate hosts of *M. expansa*. Parasitologists in the Soviet Union have since determined that *M. benedeni* also is transmitted by oribatid mites.

When microscopic tapeworm eggs, or the segments containing eggs, are voided on pasture with the droppings of infected ruminants, each egg already contains an oncosphere, or small tapeworm larva. Oribatid mites eat the tapeworm eggs with their food. Inside the mite the oncosphere penetrates to the body cavity and develops into the next larval stage, known as a cysticercoid, in about 2 months. Large numbers of oribatid mites live in the humus layer of soil and migrate onto forage plants, especially in the early morning, when the grass is moist with dew.

Ruminants swallow infected mites while grazing on contaminated pastures. In their digestive tracts the cysticercoids escape from the mites.

The young head of the tapeworm attaches itself to the lining of the small intestine, and from it grows the long strobila. These tapeworms become mature in about 35 days. Thereafter segments and eggs are discharged with the droppings.

The effect of these tapeworms on ruminants is still unsettled. Because of the simplicity of making a diagnosis and the large size of these worms, they have been often held responsible for outbreaks of disease and losses of stock when other parasites, or other disease-producing agents, may have been the causes. Diarrhea, emaciation, convulsions, and death have been ascribed to tapeworm infections in calves, lambs, and kids and to adult animals as well. Convincing proof that these parasites were primarily responsible usually has been lacking.

Investigations with tapeworm infections uncomplicated by other agents of disease have been carried out only with *M. expansa* in lambs. The results showed that this parasite produced at most only minor effects of doubtful significance to the health of the animals involved.

Control of these two tapeworms can be achieved through medication to remove them from their hosts. Spray grade of lead arsenate, administered in doses of one-half gram for lambs and kids, 1 gram for adult sheep and goats, and up to 2 grams for calves and cattle, is safe and effective treatment for removing the worms.

Infected mites may live a year or longer on pasture, and there is no practical method of destroying them over a large area.

ANOTHER TAPEWORM, *Thysanosoma actinioides*, commonly known as the fringed tapeworm because of a fringed rear border of its segments, occurs primarily in range sheep in the Western States. It occurs infrequently in cattle and goats and is not uncommon in various wild ruminants, such as deer, elk, moose, and antelope. It is shorter than the moniezias. It is often found in

the main bile ducts of the liver as well as in the small intestine.

A high percentage of western range lambs at slaughter have fringed tapeworms in their livers. It has been estimated that more than 2 million sheep livers, worth more than half a million dollars, are condemned annually by meat inspectors because of this parasite.

Its life history is unknown. An intermediate host is probably involved. Many attempts at direct transmission have been unsuccessful. Perhaps small insects or other small invertebrate animals act as intermediate hosts.

The economic importance of the fringed tapeworm is due primarily to its effect on the bile ducts of the liver, which become enlarged and inflamed and make the liver unfit for human food. Sheep in most instances suffer only slight ill effects from the fringed tapeworm.

Efforts to control the fringed tapeworm must be largely limited to development of treatments for their removal from sheep until the life history of the parasite is known. Several chemicals have been tried, but none has proved to be entirely satisfactory.

THE BLADDERWORMS that parasitize cattle, sheep, and goats are *Cysticercus bovis*, which occurs in the adult stage (*Taenia saginata*) in man, *Echinococcus granulosus, Coenurus cerebralis, Cysticercus tenuicollis*, and *Cysticercus ovis*, which occur as adults in dogs and related canines. Ruminants serve therefore as their intermediate hosts.

The bladderworms are larval tapeworms with a small scolex, or head, inverted into a small, membranous, bladderlike sac, or cyst, which contains fluid. The scolex of the larva is similar to (but smaller than) that of the adult.

Sometimes, as with the gid bladderworm (Coenurus) and also the hydatid worm (Echinococcus), many immature tapeworm heads, or miniature bladderworms, develop within a cyst derived from a single tapeworm egg.

The life histories are much the same. Dogs harbor the adult tapeworms after eating the cysts in dead animals left unburied on the range or in offal from cattle or sheep slaughtered on the farm or at unsupervised slaughterhouses, where there is improper disposal of viscera and diseased parts of carcasses. Infection of man occurs through eating the bladderworm in raw or incompletely cooked beef.

After the proper host swallows the bladderworm, the tapeworm head or heads, as the case may be, push out from the bladder, attach to the intestinal lining, and develop to maturity. Adult tapeworms produce large numbers of eggs, which leave the host in the feces.

THE RUMINANT host acquires bladderworms by eating tapeworm eggs eliminated in the feces of dogs or man on pastures or in such places as would otherwise contaminate food and water. Once the eggs are swallowed, larvae hatch from them in the digestive tract. These active organisms then penetrate the intestinal wall and are carried by means of the circulating blood and their own movements to various locations in the body, where development into bladderworms is completed.

The hydatid worm, the gid bladderworm, and the thin-necked bladderworm locate in the internal organs of ruminants.

The hydatid cyst may reach a diameter of 6 inches and is found in sheep, goats, swine, and cattle. It has been reported in deer, moose, caribou, other animals, and man. The parasite locates in or on the liver, lungs, and heart and sometimes in the brain.

The gid bladderworm, *Coenurus cerebralis*, is found in sheep and goats and rarely in cattle, and is the larval stage of a tapeworm (*Multiceps multiceps*) of dogs and other canines. Once in the blood stream, the young parasite may be carried to various parts of the body. Those that reach the brain complete their full development and may attain the size of a hen's egg or larger. The damage due to migration and growth of the parasite in the brain results in muscu-lar incoordination and in a circling, stumbling gait—the animal is "giddy" and the "gid" is said to reflect that condition.

THE THIN-NECKED BLADDERWORM, *Cysticercus tenuicollis*, is the larval stage of a tapeworm of dogs and other canine animals and is known as *Taenia hydatigena*. It is about an inch in diameter. It is found in the liver or in the body cavity attached to the mesenteries, or omenta, which are membranes attached to the internal organs. The parasite migrates within the liver. When invasion is massive, the liver surface has ridges or serpentine markings along the paths taken by the parasites. Sheep are more commonly parasitized than cattle.

Two other species of bladderworms occur in the muscles and are responsible for a condition termed "measles." The larval form, *Cysticercus bovis*, which precedes the tapeworm, *Taenia saginata* of man, is found in cattle. These parasites occur as small, spherical or elliptical bladders, one-fifth to three-fifths inch long and one-eighth to one-third of an inch wide. They may occur throughout the muscles of the body, but they are most commonly found in the muscles of the heart, neck, tongue, and diaphragm.

The bladderworm, *Cysticercus ovis*, is responsible for sheep measles. It is the larval stage of a tapeworm known as *Taenia ovis*, which occurs in dogs. They occur as small, oval cysts about one-third inch long and one-sixth of an inch wide in locations similar to those of *C. bovis*.

The effect of bladderworms on the ruminant host depends on the number of parasites and the parts of the body invaded. Destruction of tissues, because of invasion and migration of large numbers of worms, makes the host visibly ill and it may die, but such cases are uncommon.

MILD INFECTION with the various bladderworms produces no appreciable effect on the host, unless the hydatid worm reaches sufficient size to crowd vital organs or to be ruptured. As a matter of fact, infections of bladder-worms usually go undiagnosed, except for the gid parasite, which develops in the brain. Their presence in the brain causes progressive nervous disorder or paralysis, which leads to the death of sheep or their ultimate destruction as unprofitable to the owner.

The significant loss from the bladder-worms is encountered when inspectors condemn grossly infected carcasses or parts of carcasses containing parasites as being unfit for food. Such disposition is made because of the appearance of the meat and (in the case of beef measles) because of the danger of transmitting tapeworms to man.

THE CONTROL OF BLADDERWORMS of cattle, sheep, and goats depends largely on measures taken to break the parasites' life cycles.

Refuse from slaughtering, dead animals, and other sources of parasitized meat should be burned, buried, or otherwise made inaccessible to dogs or other canine species.

Farm dogs that might have access to infective meat should be kept free of tapeworms through medicinal treatment by a veterinarian. The remedies most widely used are arecoline hydrobromide, Nemural, Anthelin, and Diphenthane-70. The last three are proprietaries. Only the first one mentioned is satisfactory for removing the hydatid tapeworm. All are dangerous in untrained hands. Stray dogs may be kept out of pastures by proper fencing or other measures.

The cysticerus (*C. bovis*) of the human tapeworm can be kept from cattle by disposal of human feces in such a manner as not to contaminate the food and water.

TAPEWORMS AND BLADDERWORMS in sheep and cattle contribute a share in loss of meat production alone that is conservatively estimated at 667,000 dollars annually. But regardless of whether or not individual species are of major or minor economic importance, it is desirable and good practice to control all such pests.

DALE A. PORTER *is director of the Regional Animal Disease Research Laboratory, Animal Disease and Parasite Research Branch, in Auburn, Ala. He has been associated as a parasitologist with the Department of Agriculture since 1935 and is the author of several papers on parasites of swine and cattle. Dr. Porter is a graduate of Kalamazoo College, Kansas State College, and the Johns Hopkins University.*

KENNETH C. KATES *is parasitologist in charge of investigations on helminth parasites of sheep and goats in the Helminth Parasite Section, Animal Disease and Parasite Research Branch, Beltsville, Md. He holds degrees from Columbia and Duke Universities and has specialized on parasites of domestic animals since 1938.*

For further reading:

G. Dikmans: *Internal Parasites of Cattle*, U. S. Department of Agriculture Circular 614, 39 pages. 1942.

G. Dikmans, J. T. Lucker, and A. O. Foster: *Parasites and Parasitic Diseases of Sheep*, U. S. Department of Agriculture Farmers' Bulletin 1330 (revised), 49 pages. 1955.

M. F. Hansen, A. C. Todd, G. W. Kelley, and M. Cawein: *Effects of a Pure Infection of the Tapeworm, Moniezia expansa, on Lambs*, Kentucky Agricultural Experiment Station Bulletin 556, 11 pages. 1950.

K. C. Kates and C. E. Runkel: *Observations on Oribatid Mite Vectors of Moniezia expansa on Pastures, With a Report of Several New Vectors From the United States*, Proceedings of the Helminthological Society of Washington, volume 15, pages 19–33. 1948.

T. B. Magath: *The Importance of Sylvatic Hydatid Disease*, Journal of the American Veterinary Medical Association, volume 125, pages 411–414. 1954.

D. A. Porter: *On the Occurrence of Tapeworms, Moniezia expansa and Moniezia benedeni, in Cattle and Sheep*, Proceedings of the Heminthological Society of Washington, volume 20, pages 93–94. 1953.

G. C. Shelton: *Reexamination of Some Aspects of the Hydatid Tapeworm, Echinococcus granulosus (Batsch 1786)*, North American Veterinarian, volume 34, pages 487–490. 1953.

H. W. Stunkard: *The Development of Moniezia expansa in the Intermediate Host*, Parasitology, volume 30, pages 491–501. 1938.

R. A. Wardle and J. A. McLeod: *The Zoology of Tapeworms*, 780 pages, North Central Publishing Co., St. Paul, Minn. 1952.

Ticks That Affect Domestic Animals and Poultry

ALLEN McINTOSH AND WILLIAM C. McDUFFIE

TICKS are among our commonest parasites.

They are blood feeders and transmit disease-producing organisms to man and domestic animals. In man, several tickborne diseases are known in the United States, including Rocky Mountain spotted fever, tularemia, relapsing fever, Colorado tick fever, and tick paralysis. In domestic animals, babesiosis, anaplasmosis, tularemia, and avian spirochetosis are tickborne.

An appraisal in 1954 of the estimated annual losses by ticks to cattle was nearly 14 million dollars. The estimate was made after the eradication of tick fever in the United States; previously cattle fever caused estimated losses of 40 million dollars each year.

Not all ticks are known to transmit disease-producing organisms. They may cause injury by secondary infections of the wounds produced during feeding, by injection of toxic substances, and by extraction of blood.

Death may occur in both domestic and wild animals when the ticks are numerous. Sir Arnold Theiler, in the Union of South Africa, in 1909 reported a case in which a horse died from acute anemia, caused by the blue ticks, *Boophilus decoloratus*. Fourteen pounds of engorged ticks were collected from the horse in 3 days—and that was only about half the ticks present.

In range animals and certain wild mammals, especially moose and elk, death may result from heavy infestations of the winter tick, *Dermacentor albipicus*. They are particularly bad in late winter and early spring when feed is short.

Ticks are parasitic arthropods of the class Arachnida, order Acarina, super-family Ixodoidea. There are two families, Argasidae and Ixodidae. They are usually larger than mites, to which they are related. Ticks range in body length from 1.2 millimeters (unengorged females of *Ixodes soricis*) to 28 millimeters (engorged females of *Amblyomma varium*, the largest tick known).

Ticks occur on toads, lizards, snakes, turtles, birds, and mammals. Most of the species are not host specific, but are found on a large variety of animals. In number of valid species, ticks are less numerous than the insects or the mites. The total number of ticks probably does not exceed 450 species—but that does not mean that ticks are not abundant.

Some species are noted for their great fecundity. C. B. Phillip, of the Rocky Mountain Laboratory at Hamilton, Mont., has recorded more than 18,000 eggs laid in one batch by a single specimen of one of our common ticks, *Amblyomma maculatum*. Some species (argasids) lay only a few eggs but are able to survive long periods of fasting.

Ticks must have a meal of blood if they are to produce eggs, and some can wait 9 or 10 years for it.

Ticks occur in all parts of the world, except in the extreme frigid zones.

Some species are restricted in their distribution by lack of suitable hosts; others, by climatic requirements. Two common species, the brown dog tick and the fowl tick, have become established in most of the tropical and temperate areas of the world.

Some species in their development may require three hosts. Some may require only one host. The three-host ticks drop from the animal to molt after each stage has become fully engorged; each metamorphosis, from larvae to nymphs and from nymphs to adults, takes place off the host. The engorged larvae and nymphs of the one-host ticks do not drop but remain attached to the host; they spend their quiescent periods, or metamorphoses, on the same animal.

THE LIFE HISTORY of a tick involves four stages—egg, larva or "seed tick," nymph, and adult.

Eggs are not deposited until the engorged tick has left the host. The preoviposition (pre-egglaying) period in many instances is 5 to 14 days—perhaps shorter in warm weather and a month or more in cool weather. Some ticks (the fowl tick, for example) lay a few hundred eggs, return to the host for another blood meal, and then lay more eggs; they repeat the process for several feedings. Most ticks, however, lay but a single batch of eggs and die when oviposition is completed. Oviposition usually lasts 1 to 2 weeks if the weather is warm.

The incubation period for the eggs of several of the common ticks is about 10 days to 3 weeks, but some may take 3 months.

The six-legged larva, or "seed tick," must find a suitable host when it hatches if the life cycle is to be continued. The period of larval engorgement may be 2 days for some species and 2 to 3 weeks for others. Thereafter they remain attached, if they are one-host species, or drop off, if they are of the three-host kind. After a quiescent period, which may last 10 days to several weeks, larval metamorphosis is completed.

The eight-legged nymph finds a new host, or at least a new place of attachment, if it is of the one-host variety. The engorgement period for nymphs is like that of the larvae, but the quiescent period is longer. The nymphs may vary in size. The smaller ones become males and the larger ones become females.

After the nymphs have engorged, a few days to several months may elapse before they transform into adults. The final molt having been completed, the

adults search for new hosts or (in the case of the species that molt on the host) the female reattaches and the male goes searching for a mate. Most species mate on the host.

Many individuals in each of the developmental stages—larvae, nymphs, and adults—die without finding suitable hosts. Many of the species, however, can survive long periods of fasting. Larvae of the brown dog tick, an ixodid, has been known to live 253 days; the nymphs, 2 to 6 months; and adults, up to 596 days. This ability to survive without a blood meal makes the pest difficult to control.

Some argasids, or leather ticks, may have even longer periods of fasting. Gorden E. Davis, of the Rocky Mountain Laboratory, kept a specimen of *Ornithodoros turicata* for 9 years without a blood meal and for 3.5 years more after one feeding.

TAXONOMICALLY, ticks are divided into two family groups:

1. The scutate, or shield ticks, family Ixodidae. They are characterized by a dorsal scutum, which covers the anterior part of the body in the female and immature stages and completely covers the body in the adult males.

2. The nonscutate ticks, of the family Argasidae, which lack a scutum and have a leathery integument.

SIXTEEN SPECIES OF ARGASIDS are known in the United States. Four, *Ornithodoros talaje*, *O. turicata*, *O. hermsi*, and *O. parkeri*, are known vectors of relapsing fever spirochetes.

The fowl tick, *Argas persicus*, is a vector of avian spirochetosis (rare in the United States) and also is believed to be the cause of fowl paralysis. It causes considerable losses. Heavy attacks may cause death. The hosts include most species of domestic fowls, particularly chickens, and several species of wild birds, including some game species, quails, turkeys, and doves. The fowl tick is most prevalent in Florida and the Southwestern States. And it occurs also in Mexico, Central

America, South America, and many other countries.

The spinose ear tick, *Ornithodoros* (*Otobius*) *megnini*, is troublesome to livestock. It is not known to be a vector of any disease-producing organism, although the infectious agent of Q-fever has been reported from it. The immature stages are found deep in the ears of the host. Cattle, sheep, goats, and horses are the common hosts. It also attacks mules, asses, hogs, cats, dogs, and a number of wild mammals. Most records of this tick have come from animals in the Southwestern States and Mexico. It is found also in Central America and South America and in parts of South Africa.

The spinose ear tick is unique in that the adults never feed. The nymphs engorge until they reach adult size, drop to the ground, and seek a place to molt. After molting, the adults mate and the females lay their eggs.

Great losses are attributed to this tick. The annual loss in the United States for sheep alone has been estimated at 1.3 million dollars.

The pajaroello tick, *Ornithodoros coriaceus*, has been taken from cattle and deer. It attacks man, particularly cattlemen, readily. Its venomous "bite" is painful. It is not known to be a disease vector. It occurs in California and the Pacific coast region of Mexico.

Two additional species of argasids, *Ornithodoros turicata* and *O. talaje*, occasionally attack domestic animals. The former attacks pigs, cattle, and horses. The latter attacks dogs, cats, and chickens. Both species are vectors of spirochetes that cause relapsing fever. Both occur in Florida and several Southwestern States and Mexico.

THE FAMILY Ixodidae is represented in the United States by 50 species comprising five genera: *Ixodes*, *Dermacentor*, *Ambylomma*, *Haemaphysalis*, and *Rhipicephalus*. Two additional species belonging to a sixth genus, *Boophilus*, *B. annulatus* and *B. microplus*, once were present in this country.

Many species of the genus *Ixodes* occur in America, but only three are common on domestic animals. The black-legged tick, *Ixodes scapularis*, and the California black-legged tick, *Ixodes pacificus*, are common on cattle and horses in the Southeastern States and on the Pacific coast, respectively.

Ixodes cookei occurs on cattle, sheep, dogs, cats, and people in the Eastern States. Wild mammals are its chief hosts.

The *Ixodes* are not known to be disease vectors, but *I. pacificus* is a suspected vector of *Pasteurella tularensis*. Experiments have indicated that *I. scapularis* may transmit anaplasmosis. *Ixodes* have long mouth parts, which often are broken off in the tissue of the host when the ticks are removed.

Nine species of the genus *Dermacentor* occur in the United States. Six are common parasites of domestic animals. Three of the species attack man. Two or more species are present in most States. In this group of ticks we find the vectors of the dreaded Rocky Mountain spotted fever, tularemia, and Colorado tick fever and the cause of tick paralysis.

Three species of the genus *Dermacentor*—*D. albipictus*, *D. nigrolineatus*, *D. nitens*—are one-host ticks. The immature stages remain attached to the host and molt on it. The others leave the host to molt, and the second host may be quite different from the first one.

The American dog tick, *Dermacentor variabilis*, is a pest of dogs and man. In the adult stage it also occurs on most domestic animals and many wild animals. Small mammals are the hosts of the immature stages. It transmits two diseases of man, spotted fever and tularemia. It also may produce tick paralysis and carry bovine anaplasmosis. The species is found in all of the States east of the Rocky Mountains and in California and Oregon.

The Rocky Mountain spotted fever tick, *Dermacentor venustus*, often referred to as *D. andersoni*, probably is the worst transmitter of disease. It is a vector of Rocky Mountain spotted fever, tularemia, Colorado tick fever, American Q-fever, and (in experiments) encephalomyelitis and anaplasmosis. It also can produce tick paralysis in man and mammals. When it is abundant, it may produce anemia when its feeding causes rapid loss of blood. Most domestic animals, man, and numerous wild mammals are its hosts.

C. B. Phillip and William L. Jellison of Hamilton, Mont., and H. F. Wilkins of Helena, Mont., reported in 1935 an unusual case of an epizootic tickborne tularemia in a band of 1,320 sheep near Ringling, Mont. The epizootic occurred during April and May 1934. The sheep were heavily infested with adults of *Dermacentor venustus*. There were then more ground squirrels and jackrabbits there than in several previous years; the rodents had aided in the increase in the number of ticks that later attacked the sheep. Ground squirrels are hosts for the immature stages. Rabbits may serve as hosts for the immature and adult stages. About 40 percent of the sheep in the flock were affected, and 200 died before the disease subsided.

The Rocky Mountain tick occurs in Montana, Wyoming, Colorado, Utah, Nevada, and Idaho; parts of Washington, Oregon, and California; western North Dakota, South Dakota, and Nebraska; northern New Mexico; and northern Arizona.

The Pacific coast tick, *Dermacentor occidentalis*, which occurs in Oregon and California, has been taken from the cow, horse, sheep, dog, man, and many other mammals. We have evidence that it can transmit Rocky Mountain spotted fever, tularemia, and anaplasmosis.

The winter tick, *Dermacentor albipictus*, is found often on range stock in numbers sufficient to cause losses through weakened condition or death of the host. Cattle, horses, moose, and elk are the common hosts. Its greatest abundance is in Canada and our Northern States from Maine to Oregon. It also has been found in several Western States. The species is a one-host tick. It does its greatest damage to

stock in the late winter and early spring, when the adult female becomes fully engorged. It is not a proved vector of disease, but it has been suspected of transmitting a disease of moose in Minnesota.

The brown winter tick, *Dermacentor nigrolineatus*, is a close relative of *D. albipictus*. Some authorities regard the two as variations of the same species. *D. nigrolineatus* has been found on deer in New York, and ticks typical of this species were taken from deer on Prudence Island, R. I., in late October of 1954. In the Southern States, the brown winter tick is commonly found on horses, mules, cattle, and deer. It does not occur as far north as *D. albipictus;* the two species, however, do overlap in certain areas, and probably interbreed, giving rise to hybrids that are difficult to place in either species.

The tropical horse tick, *Dermacentor nitens*, is principally a parasite of horses and related animals. Specimens have been collected from goats, sheep, and cattle. Deer may serve also as a host. This tick is usually confined to the ears, where it remains for its two molts. The inside of the ear is often inflamed and packed with various developmental stages of the tick, cast-off skins, and tick feces, which create a nauseating odor. Screwworm infestation may follow the inflammation. The tropical horse tick is limited in the United States to the southern tip of Texas. The species is abundant in the West Indies, the eastern coast of Mexico, and several Latin American countries.

The genus *Amblyomma* is represented in the United States by six species. Three of them are economically important, for they attack man and most of the domestic animals. Many wild mammals, reptiles, and birds are hosts for some of the species. These are three-host ticks. The long mouth parts usually are imbedded deeply in the host and often break off when the tick is removed. The three most common species can transmit disease.

The lone star tick, *A. americanum*, commonly occurs in the larval, nymphal, and adult stages on man, cattle, horses, dogs, goats, and hogs. Many wild mammals and several kinds of birds, including wild turkeys, are hosts for the immature stages. The distribution area includes the coastal States from New Jersey to Texas and several inland States, including Oklahoma, Arkansas, Missouri, Tennessee, and Kentucky, and the southern parts of several adjoining States. It also occurs in Central America and South America. The lone star tick is capable of transmitting the causative organisms of Rocky Mountain spotted fever, tularemia, and American Q-fever.

The cajenne tick, *Amblyomma cajennense*, is an annoying pest of man and most domestic animals. It is found also on a few wild animals. All stages, often in large numbers, attach themselves to the hosts. The range of distribution includes North America, Central America, and South America. In the United States it is believed to occur only in 12 southern counties of Texas. It has been reported to be a carrier of spotted fever in Brazil.

The gulf coast tick, *Amblyomma maculatum*, in the adult stage is most common on sheep, mules, horses, cattle, dogs, and goats. It also has been taken from man and a number of wild mammals. The immature stages have been reported from more than 20 species of birds. Huge numbers have been found on the meadow lark and other ground-frequenting birds. Its range includes North America, Central America, and South America. In the United States it is most numerous in a 100-mile-wide coastal strip from South Carolina to Texas. It has been ranked second to the cattle fever tick, *Boophilus annulatus*, in losses it causes.

The favorite place of attachment is the inner surface of the outer ear, in which they cause swelling, scabbing, and cracking of the skin. The screwworm fly, attracted to the wounds, deposits its eggs on the lesions. Serious complications occur as the fly larvae develop. The supporting cartilage of the ear is often destroyed, so that the

ear droops, a common occurrence among mules. Severe cases may destroy the entire ear in just a few days. Death may occur if animals are left untreated.

R. R. Parker and coworkers of the Rocky Mountain Laboratory reported a pathogenic rickettsial organism from specimens of the gulf coast tick in Texas, Mississippi, and Georgia. The disease, as produced in guinea pigs, has been named "maculatum disease." Some of the ticks sent to Dr. Parker in August 1938 were taken from a flock of sick sheep near Ludowici, Ga. The owner of the flock reported that some of the sheep had died.

The genus *Haemaphysalis* is represented in the United States by two species, a rabbit tick and a bird tick. Neither is found commonly on man or domestic mammals. The members of the genus are three-host ticks.

The bird tick, *Haemaphysalis chordeilis*, occasionally is reported as a parasite of game birds and other ground-inhabiting species. Young turkeys in Vermont have been reported as having been killed by it. The type host was a night hawk taken in Massachusetts. The bird tick has also been reported from several other States and British Columbia, Alberta, Saskatchewan, Manitoba, and Ontario in Canada.

The rabbit tick, *Haemaphysalis leporispalustris*, is a parasite of rabbits and hares and several species of ground-frequenting birds. It may occur in enormous numbers. Several thousand have been found on a single animal. It seldom is found on man or domestic animals, but it is of considerable importance as a factor in the natural maintenance of two diseases, Rocky Mountain spotted fever and tularemia. The rabbit tick is found in the Western Hemisphere from southern Alaska to Brazil.

The genus *Rhipicephalus* has many species, most of which are confined to Africa. A single species, the brown dog tick, is found in the United States and several other countries.

The brown dog tick, *Rhipicephalus*

sanguineus, is found principally on dogs. It occasionally attacks people who are in close association with infested dogs.

Numerous other animals, wild and domestic, have been reported as hosts in some other countries. The tick was first reported in the United States in 1907 in Texas. It was reported in Key West, in Florida, in 1913. It had been found in Texas, Florida, Louisiana, Mississippi, New York, Pennsylvania, and in Ohio by 1931—R. A. Cooley, of the Rocky Mountain Laboratory, in 1946 listed 34 States. He believes this tick is probably the most widely distributed species in the world, as it is present in nearly all countries between 40° N. and 40° S. This dog tick is a three-host tick, but the dog serves as host for each of the three stages. It breaks no records as an egg layer—it deposits an average of 2,500 eggs—but it can rapidly cover a dog.

The engorged female drops from the dog and then seeks a protected crack or crevice of the kennel or other quarters to deposit her batch of eggs. Hatching takes place in 20 to 30 days.

If a dog is available, the six-legged larvae may complete their engorgement in 3 to 6 days. The engorged larvae drop from the dog and they, too, seek a protected place for a nap of 9 or 10 days. On awakening, the tick—now in the nymphal stage—has 8 legs and an appetite. If it finds a dog, the nymph can satisfy its appetite in 4 to 9 days, after which it drops and sleeps 11 to 15 days or up to 2 months if the weather is cool.

After completion of nymphal metamorphosis, the newly emerged male and female adults go searching for a dog. Mated females have been known to engorge fully in 6 days. Unmated females have been observed only partially engorged after having been attached 40 to 50 days.

The brown dog tick transmits several diseases. *Babesia canis*, the causative organism for malignant jaundice, common in dogs in France, Africa, and other places, has been reported from Florida. *Hepatozoon canis*, the cause of canine anemia, although not known to occur in America, is transmitted by this tick. *Trypanosoma cruzi* has been experimentally transmitted to dogs. The brown dog tick also is a potential vector of Rocky Mountain spotted fever and tularemia.

The genus *Boophilus*, which probably has only four valid species, occurs mostly on cattle in tropical and subtropical regions. The species are one-host ticks; the various stages do not drop to molt. Two species occur in North America. The members of this genus are notorious as vectors of cattle fevers.

The cattle fever tick, *Boophilus annulatus*, was found on deer in Florida in 1821. Cattle are the most common hosts. Other hosts include horses, mules, goats, sheep, deer, and buffalo. It is the vector of Texas cattle fever. The original area covered by the tick in the United States included all or parts of California, Oklahoma, Texas, Missouri, Arkansas, Louisiana, Kentucky, Tennessee, Mississippi, Alabama, Virginia, North Carolina, South Carolina, Georgia, and Florida.

The tropical cattle tick, *Boophilus microplus*, is a close relative of the cattle fever tick and may indeed be only a variety of that species. The host is similar, and both species are vectors of cattle fever and anaplasmosis. It occurs in North America, Central America, South America, Australia, parts of Africa and Asia, the East Indies, and the Philippine Islands. Before it was eradicated in the United States, it was known to occur in about 30 counties in central Florida and in at least 3 counties in the southern tip of Texas.

The Congress appropriated funds in 1906 to eradicate the cattle fever tick. That was the beginning of an extensive program, which did not cease until both species of cattle ticks were eradicated. In 1954, eradication had been completed in all 15 States, with the exception of a narrow zone along the Texas-Mexico border, where reinfestation occurs from time to time because the adjacent area in Mexico is heavily infested.

TICKS that affect livestock and poultry can be controlled with several of the new insecticides. Most widely used for the purpose are toxaphene, DDT, and lindane (the essentially pure gamma isomer of BHC). Chlordane is also effective but is not used extensively to combat ticks. These insecticides have largely supplanted rotenone, nicotine, arsenic, and other materials that were in general use until about 1945. The standard arsenical dip containing 0.19 percent arsenious oxide is still used, however, against the cattle fever tick.

Insecticides may be used in two ways to control ticks that affect livestock.

The most common procedure is to apply them directly to infested animals. Applications may be made as dusts or sprays or by dipping. Such treatments provide effective control of the ticks on animals and minimize reinfestation for 2 to 6 weeks, depending on the species.

The second way is to apply the insecticides to infested premises or natural habitats. Sprays or dusts may be used. Treatment of premises is essential to control the fowl tick and brown dog tick and is also useful against other species that may infest farm buildings. Thorough treatment of premises will control existing tick populations and minimize reinfestation for a month or more, depending on the species and the season of the year.

Treatment of natural habitats of ticks—pastures, brushy areas, and fence rows—is desirable to prevent the infestation of animals. Such treatments are practicable on small areas or if the ticks are confined to a particular environment. They are not practical for large areas of pasture or woodlands.

TOXAPHENE is the insecticide of choice to control ticks on livestock. It is available in emulsifiable concentrates and wettable powder, both of which are suitable for use in sprays or dipping vats. Sprays and dips should contain 0.5 percent of toxaphene. This concentration will kill all stages of flat or unfed ticks and all the engorged stages, except possibly a few adults. The residue of insecticide on animals will minimize reinfestation by three-host ticks for about 2 weeks and by the one-host ticks for a month or more.

DDT is highly effective against flat or unfed stages of ticks and also will keep down reinfestation for 2 weeks or a month. It is not effective against engorged ticks. Generally, therefore, it is used with lindane, which is highly effective against engorged ticks but has little residual effect. The combination sprays or dips containing 0.5 percent of DDT and 0.025 percent of lindane or the gamma isomer of BHC will provide the same immediate and residual effectiveness as those containing 0.5 percent of toxaphene. DDT and lindane are available as wettable powders and emulsifiable concentrates. Ready-mixed DDT-lindane or DDT-BHC wettable powders are made by several companies.

SPRAYING is the most widely used method of applying insecticides to livestock to control ticks. Hand-pressure sprayers, of a capacity of 2 or 3 gallons, may be used to treat small herds. For large groups it is best to use a power sprayer equipped with a mechanical agitator to maintain equal distribution of the insecticide in the spray. Power sprayers should be operated at a pressure of 100 to 400 pounds to the square inch. Treatment should be thorough so as to insure complete wetting of the hair and penetration of the spray to the skin. Treatments can be made at pressures lower than 100 pounds, but more time and care are required for thorough coverage.

The amount of spray to apply varies in different sections of the country and according to the size and type of animal. In the Southern States, for example, less than 1 gallon may be enough for a beef cow of average size, but in the Northern States, where cattle have thicker, longer hair, 2 gallons or more may be needed for thorough wetting.

In any event, the spray should be applied in whatever amount is necessary to wet thoroughly all parts of animals. This procedure should be followed in spraying for the control of all ticks that attach to the animal's skin, including the lone star tick, the gulf coast tick, and the winter tick. From a regulatory standpoint, however, spraying may not be adequate in eradication programs such as are conducted against the cattle fever tick.

Sprays for the spinose ear tick need be applied only to the head and neck and inside the ears. The sprays should be applied at low pressures inside the ear so as not to injure the ear and annoy the animal unduly. From 1 to 2 pints is enough for a cow of average size. Single treatments with any of the recommended sprays will eliminate existing infestation and minimize reinfestation for a month or more.

Several special formulations have been developed as ear treatments to control the spinose ear tick. One of the most satisfactory and widely used formulations is a mixture of 5 percent of BHC (15 percent gamma isomer), 10 percent of xylene, and 85 percent of pure pine oil. It is applied inside the ears with a common spring-bottom oiler. Light applications kill existing infestations and prevent reinfestation for a month or longer under average conditions.

Tick treatments are most effective if applied when the animals are restrained. Individual animals may be held with a halter or tied to a post. Large groups, especially range animals, should be placed in chutes. Small crowding pens also may be used, but the proper treatment of animals under such conditions is more difficult than in chutes and more hazardous for the operator.

DIPPING is the most practical means of treating large herds of livestock to control ticks. The animals are forced through a chute into the vat and must swim through the dip to the opposite side. They are completely submerged momentarily and are in the dip long enough to assure complete wetting. The animals usually emerge into a small pen, where they are allowed to drain for several minutes. The pen is so built that the excess drip drains back into the vat. Several hundred goats or sheep and 50 to 100 head of cattle can be treated in an hour in a vat of average size—one that has a capacity of 2,000 gallons.

The vat should be thoroughly cleaned before it is used. A measured amount of water should then be run into it and the amount of concentrate added to give the recommended concentration of insecticide. The concentrate—wettable powder or emulsifiable—should be slowly and evenly distributed along the full length of the vat. Mixing should begin as soon as the concentrate is introduced and be continued for several minutes after all has been added. Mixing may be accomplished with large paddles or by dragging a bucket on a rope back and forth through the vat.

Dipping should begin as soon as mixing is complete. Because the dipping of animals gradually reduces the amount of dip, it is usually necessary to add water and insecticide after each dipping operation. The old and new material should be thoroughly mixed before dipping is started again.

The effectiveness and safety of dipping operations depends largely on the use of properly formulated insecticide concentrates. The material should disperse spontaneously and uniformly in any type of water and remain in perfect dispersion during dipping operations, and it should redisperse readily even after standing for several weeks. In short, stability should be such that the dip can be used throughout an entire season. All vats should be drained, thoroughly cleaned, and recharged after each season's use, or at least twice a year if it is in more or less continuous use.

Toxaphene and DDT–BHC wettable powder and toxaphene emulsifiable concentrates that will fulfill the performance requirements for use in vats are available commercially. Instructions for their use are given on the containers. The user must see that the material is used as recommended and performs properly in his vat. He should take special care that the dip never contains more than 0.5 percent of toxaphene or 0.5 percent of DDT plus 0.03 percent of lindane. Higher concentrations may result in the death of livestock. He should take equal care to see that the amount of insecticide does not fall much below the recommended level because low concentrations will not kill engorged ticks.

How often to dip depends on the species of tick. Dipping is necessary every 2 or 3 weeks to control three-host species, especially during the season of greatest abundance, spring and summer. Usually it is only necessary to dip at monthly intervals to control one-host ticks.

The main exception to the 1-month interval involves the cattle fever tick. Because the cattle fever tick transmits a disease that can kill cattle in a short time, dipping programs in the United States used to be designed for eradication, rather than for immediate control. The cattle fever tick has been eradicated from the United States, and the only infestations are on animals shipped in from countries infested with it. The treatments are made at 14- to 18-day intervals to kill all engorged females and thereby end their chance to reproduce. This dipping schedule may have to be maintained for a year or more to achieve eradication. Localized infestations of the cattle fever tick can be eradicated by keeping livestock out of the area for about a year. Existing tick populations will usually starve and die within a year. As a rule, however, stockmen are unwilling or unable to lose the benefits of pastures for so long a time.

NYMPHAL AND ADULT FOWL TICKS congregate in cracks and crevices, behind loose boards, under the bark of trees, and in similar hiding places in or near poultry houses. They thrive best in loosely constructed poultry houses, but they may also abound in tight henhouses, particularly if proper sanitation is not maintained. The combination of proper construction and regular, thorough cleaning of litter from poultry houses therefore is essential in preventing or minimizing infestations.

Established fowl-tick infestations can be controlled by spraying the poultry houses and outdoor roosts with insecticides. The sprays should be applied to all roosts and throughout the interior of the houses. Applications should be made at a pressure to insure thorough coverage of outer surfaces and penetration of all hiding places. Small power sprayers are best, but satisfactory results can also be had with 2- or 3-gallon, compressed-air sprayers, operated by hand.

DDT, toxaphene, and lindane are approved for use in controlling fowl ticks in poultry houses. Toxaphene and lindane should be used at a concentration of 0.5 percent and DDT at 5 percent. Wettable-powder suspensions, emulsions, or oil solutions can be used, but emulsions are generally preferred because of the ease of preparation from emulsifiable concentrates. The individual applying the spray must judge for himself the amount needed, keeping in mind thorough coverage of exposed surfaces as well as complete penetration of all likely hiding places. Several treatments may be required to control heavy infestations. As a rule, however, a thorough treatment about every 6 months will maintain control of these pests in properly constructed poultry houses.

Control of the fowl tick is especially difficult in poorly constructed shelters and in trees, barns, and sheds or under houses where fowls roost indiscriminately. Then it is necessary to spray more thoroughly and more frequently than if the fowls are properly housed and confined to a limited area. It is therefore strongly recommended that growers provide well-constructed shelters and follow approved procedures for rearing and handling their fowls. This practice will greatly reduce the possibility of tick infestation and will make it easy to maintain control with a minimum of spraying.

ALLEN MCINTOSH *is in charge of identifications of helminths and miscellaneous parasites in the Helminth Parasite Section, Animal Disease and Parasite Research Branch, Agricultural Research Service, at Beltsville, Md. He has degrees in zoology and parasitology from Mississippi Agricultural and Mechanical College and the University of Minnesota. Since entering the former Bureau of Animal Industry in 1929, he has been engaged in research on helminths and miscellaneous parasites and has published extensively in these fields.*

WILLIAM C. MCDUFFIE *is assistant leader of the Insects Affecting Man and Animals Section, Entomology Research Branch. He is a graduate of Mississippi Agricultural and Mechanical College and since 1931 has conducted and directed research on a variety of insect pests of man and animals.*

For further reading:
N. G. Cobbett: *DDT and DDT Combined With Benzene Hexachloride for the Control and Eradication of Boöphilus annulatus*, American Journal of Veterinary Research, volume 9, number 32, pages 270–276. 1948.

James A. Deer: *Control of Ticks Infesting Cattle*, Texas Agricultural and Mechanical College L–136, 2 pages. 1951.

W. P. Ellenberger and Robert M. Chapin: *Cattle-Fever Ticks and Methods of Eradication*, U. S. Department of Agriculture Farmers' Bulletin 1057, slightly revised, 27 pages. 1940.

H. E. Kemper: *The Spinose Ear Tick and Methods of Treating Infested Animals*, U. S. Department of Agriculture Farmers' Bulletin 980, 10 pp. 1947.

E. F. Knipling: *The New Insecticides for Controlling External Parasites of Livestock*, U. S. Department of Agriculture, Bureau of Entomology and Plant Quarantine publication E–762, second revision, 27 pages. 1951.

George F. Knowlton and Wayne Binns: *Spinose Ear Tick Control*, Utah State Agricultural College Extension Bulletin 240, 2 pages. 1951.

United States Department of Agriculture: *Insecticides for Use in Livestock Dipping Vats*, E–880, 16 pages. 1954; *New Sprays for Ticks on Livestock*, EC–10, 8 pages. 1950; *The Fowl Tick—How To Control It*, Leaflet 382. 1955; *Wood Ticks—How To Control Them in Infested Areas*, Leaflet 387. 1955.

Flies That Affect Livestock

E. F. KNIPLING AND WILLIAM C. McDUFFIE

FLIES affect livestock in two ways—by biting them and sucking their blood and by transmitting diseases.

The hornfly, stablefly, and a hundred or more kinds of horseflies and deerflies that flourish in the United States are a constant worry to cattle and to other livestock during the fly season. The horseflies and deerflies are doubly important because they also transmit certain diseases directly or by inoculation from one animal to another.

The common housefly, which occurs wherever livestock are raised, is a nonbiter, but it is capable of mechanically spreading filth and disease organisms, and it serves as an intermediate host of certain internal parasites.

We did not fully realize the losses caused by flies until control measures were developed. Then we could compare the productivity of the animals treated for hornfly control with that of untreated animals. Tests conducted by the Department of Agriculture in 1945 in cooperation with several Midwestern States showed that beef cattle subjected to heavy attacks of hornflies gained an average of 50 pounds less during the fly season than did cattle treated with insecticides. Research at the University of Illinois in 1947 showed that dairy cows protected from hornflies produced 10 to 20 percent more milk than unprotected cows.

The stablefly and the horseflies and deerflies generally are less abundant than the hornfly; severe attacks by them are more restricted in area, or they are present during shorter periods. They are more severe biters, however, and when they are present in large numbers can cause more worry than the hornfly. Horseflies in moderate numbers may lower the butterfat production of dairy cows as much as 20 percent.

THE HORNFLY is primarily a pest of cattle. It breeds only in cattle droppings. It entered this country from Europe in the 19th century.

The adult is about one-half as large as the housefly. As far as we know, they are not vectors of any cattle diseases, but hundreds or thousands of the insects may be on the animals and their constant attack prevents the animals from feeding properly, so that they lose weight and fall off in milk production. Before any suitable control measures were developed, hornflies caused annual losses to stockmen estimated at 150 million dollars. The losses have been greatly reduced since DDT, methoxychlor, toxaphene, and TDE were discovered.

Freshly laid eggs of the hornfly hatch in less than 24 hours. The larvae mature and pupate in 5 to 10 days, depending on the temperature. Flies may emerge from the pupae in 3 to 7 days and begin laying eggs a few days later.

Adult hornflies can be controlled with most of the insecticides now generally available. As the adults stay on the cattle almost continuously—leaving only briefly to deposit eggs on fresh droppings—applications of some of the newer, long-lasting insecticides provide effective control for 2 to 4 weeks. Repeated treatment of cattle at those intervals during the hornfly

season will keep populations at a low level.

Spraying is the best method of applying the insecticides for the control of hornflies on cattle. The amount of spray to apply depends on the size of the animal and the thoroughness of the treatment. One or two quarts is enough to treat the backs of cattle, where the adult flies prefer to rest and feed.

Treatment of the entire animal takes 2 to 4 quarts or more, depending on the type of animals treated. A thorough treatment designed to control lice or ticks as well as hornflies is often necessary or desirable.

The small hand-pressure or knapsack types of sprayers of 2- or 3-gallon capacity are satisfactory for treating small herds of dairy or beef cattle. Power sprayers are more practical for large herds. Power sprayers should be equipped with agitators to keep large volumes of spray well mixed during spraying operations.

Methoxychlor is the preferred insecticide for the control of hornflies on dairy cattle. Unlike other chlorinated hydrocarbon insecticides, it is not excreted to any extent in milk. Methoxychlor is usually used at a concentration of 0.5 percent, especially if sprays are applied to the entire animal. Higher concentrations of 1.5 percent or more are used in some sections of the country, but proportionately less spray is applied. Either emulsifiable or wettable powder concentrates of methoxychlor may be used to prepare sprays. Treatments with this insecticide are effective about 3 weeks. Methoxychlor may also be used as a dust. About one heaping tablespoon of the 50-percent wettable powder concentrate should be applied evenly on the back of the animal—with a shaker can or by hand.

Synergized pyrethrum sprays are also suitable and effective. The finished spray should contain from 0.025 to 0.1 percent of pyrethrins and from 0.25 to 1.0 percent of a pyrethrum synergist. These concentrations may be obtained by diluting a synergized pyrethrum concentrate containing 1 percent of pyrethrins and 10 percent of activator. The finished spray should be applied at the rate of about 2 quarts per animal with hand or power equipment.

The pyrethrum sprays are effective against the hornfly only about 3 to 7 days. The treatment is therefore less effective than methoxychlor, but has the advantage of providing better protection against stableflies, horseflies, and deerflies.

DDT, toxaphene, and TDE may be used for controlling hornflies on beef, but they are not recommended on dairy cattle because they may cause excessive insecticide residues in milk. Methoxychlor, which is recommended for use on dairy cows, may also be applied to beef cattle. The four insecticides are all used at a concentration of 0.5 percent; the sprays are prepared from either emulsifiable or wettable powder concentrates. Treatments will usually be required at intervals of 3 or 4 weeks.

Community cooperation in treating all cattle will reduce the number of hornflies in an area to a point where less frequent treatments are required.

Self-treatment devices are used sometimes for cattle. One of these, developed at the South Dakota Agricultural Experiment Station, is a rubbing device consisting of a post wrapped with insecticide-treated burlap sacks or a cable similarly wrapped and stretched between two posts. The cable—a chain or several strands of wire—is stretched from the top of a 4-foot post to an anchor at ground level 15 to 20 feet away. It is effective when cattle rub their backs and sides against the burlap. It should be placed near watering and feeding places or where animals rest, so cattle will rub against it to relieve irritation from biting flies and lice. For dairy cattle, the sacks should be treated with a 5-percent methoxychlor oil solution. For beef or dairy cattle, 5-percent oil solutions of DDT, methoxychlor, toxaphene, or TDE may be used. About 1 gallon of oil solution is required to treat 15 or 20 feet of burlap sacks.

The sacks should be re-treated every 3 to 5 weeks.

Another self-treatment device is the automatic or treadle-type sprayer developed at the Illinois Agricultural Experiment Station. It consists of a narrow chute equipped with a spray unit, which is set in operation as the animal walks through it. The treadle sprayers are usually installed in the gateway between pastures and watering or feeding places so that the cattle must pass through them. Since the cattle go back and forth once or twice daily, the units are designed to dispense only 2 to 4 milligrams of insecticide per animal. This amount is ample only for immediate control, and almost daily applications are necessary to keep hornflies under control.

Synergized pyrethrins or methoxychlor oil solutions are satisfactory for use in treadle sprayers for hornflies on dairy cattle. They and DDT, toxaphene, or TDE may be used on beef or dry dairy cattle.

THE STABLEFLY has piercing mouth parts like those of the hornfly, but it is about twice as large. It is like the non-biting housefly in looks and size and often breeds in the same situations. Unlike the hornfly, the stablefly stays on an animal only long enough to engorge with blood. Stableflies during warm weather may feed several times a day. After feeding, the adult rests on nearby walls, trees, or other objects while digesting the blood meal. The stablefly is known as the dogfly in some parts of the country.

Stableflies feed readily on man or any type of livestock. They are most troublesome and damaging to cattle and horses. The legs and lower parts of animals are the preferred sites for feeding. A relatively small number of stableflies can cause severe annoyance to cattle.

The preferred breeding sites of the stablefly on livestock farms are wet straw, manure, and decaying vegetable matter. Eggs hatch in 1 to 3 days. The larvae develop to maturity and pupate in 11 to 30 days. Maturation of the pupae and emergence of adults may take 6 to 20 days, depending on the temperature. The life cycle may be completed in about 3 weeks in summer. High populations of the stablefly and consequent serious damage to livestock often occur in Midwestern States and along coastal areas, where the insect often breeds in great numbers in seaweeds. Severe local outbreaks of the stablefly also occur in peanut-growing areas, where they breed in peanut litter.

The stablefly can be controlled by proper sanitation so as to prevent the accumulation of breeding material, by spraying barns and the other resting places, and by treating animals with insecticides.

The greatest returns for the effort often can be had by preventing the accumulation of plant waste and manure, the insect's favorite breeding places. Manure should not be allowed to accumulate but should be spread at least two times a week. Plant material, such as hay, peanut litter, citrus pulp, celery waste, and other vegetable products, should not be permitted to accumulate, especially during rainy periods. Where extensive waste products accumulate, it may be necessary to organize community control programs to cope with the problem and arrange to dispose of breeding material or to apply appropriate insecticides to the waste materials to keep the flies from breeding.

Good barnyard sanitation and the application of insecticides to livestock barns, corral fences, trunks of trees, or similar places where the flies like to rest will usually reduce the problem of stableflies on individual farms.

DDT is the best all-round insecticide for the purpose. It is not recommended for use in dairy barns, but methoxychlor, which is almost as effective, can be used. One should apply the DDT or methoxychlor as emulsion or wettable powder sprays. For the emulsion, one should dilute the concentrate with water so that the spray contains 5 percent of the insecticide. It should be applied at the rate of 1 gallon for each 1,000 square feet of surface. A power spray rig is most practical to use, but a hand sprayer can be used for small areas. The wettable powder spray is usually mixed so that the spray contains 2.5 percent of the insecticide. A stronger mix may clog the spray nozzle. From 1 to 2 gallons of spray should be applied for each 1,000 square feet of surface.

Chlordane spray mixed to contain 2 percent chlordane may also be used around livestock buildings instead of DDT in places other than inside of the dairy barns. Lindane is also recommended for use inside of dairy barns instead of methoxychlor; 0.3 to 1.0 percent of lindane should be used in the spray. These two insecticides are not so long lasting, however, as DDT or methoxychlor.

For treating livestock, synergized pyrethrum formulation is the most effective. A water spray of the type recommended against hornflies—mixed to contain 0.1 percent of pyrethrins and applied at the rate of 1 to 2 quarts per animal—will protect cattle for several days. Oil-base cattle sprays containing pyrethrum, allethrin, or organic thiocyanates, applied to dairy cows as a light mist at each milking, will give good protection from stableflies. Oil sprays of this kind should never be used so that the animal's skin will be wet with oil, because excessive oil can severely burn or cause death of the animal. From 1 to 2 ounces misted on animals at each treatment slightly moistens the hair but will not wet the skin.

Emulsion or suspensions containing from 0.5 to 1.0 percent of methoxychlor, sprayed at the rate of 1 to 2 quarts per animal, will help control stableflies, but these treatments are less effective than pyrethrum sprays.

Because of the short security against stableflies obtained with available insecticides, sprays seldom are considered practical for treating beef animals. The automatic treadle sprayers that apply pyrethrum mists will reduce stableflies and thus give added benefit when used against hornflies.

HORSEFLIES AND DEERFLIES usually occur only spasmodically. In many parts of the country they might be severe for weeks, but in most sections during the summer only a few horseflies are present to annoy livestock. These insects may be not much larger than the housefly, but some species are an inch or more long. They breed mostly in water or in mud near water, although several kinds breed in relatively dry areas.

They are vicious biters. They cut a small slit in the hide of animals with their lancelike mouth parts and suck the blood. Often the blood oozes out of the bites after the fly is through feeding. The horseflies and deerflies can spread anaplasmosis, anthrax, and tularemia.

Satisfactory methods of controlling horseflies and deerflies have not been developed. There are so many kinds and their breeding habits vary so much that no practical method has been found for controlling the insects in the breeding places. The adults vary in their ability to resist insecticides and repellents that are applied to animals.

The livestock sprays used on dairy cows for stableflies give some protection to dairy cattle or horses from horseflies and deerflies, but they are seldom practical for use on range cattle. The automatic treadle sprayer provides good protection against horseflies and deerflies in some localities.

THE HOUSEFLY does not bite livestock, and therefore many stockmen are prone to believe—wrongly—that it is less important than biting flies.

The housefly is the product of filth and poor sanitation. It breeds abundantly in manure, garbage, and decaying vegetable matter on farms and in cities. Female flies may deposit as many as 2,500 eggs during their life span of 2 to 4 weeks. Eggs hatch in 10 to 24 hours. The larvae mature and pupate in 4 to 10 days. The pupae mature and adults emerge in 3 to 6 days. The newly emerged adults are sexually mature in a day or two and begin laying eggs. Thus the biological potential of the housefly is even greater than that of the hornfly and stablefly, and continuous efforts are therefore necessary to keep it under control.

The control of houseflies is difficult because they breed in so many places. No single method provides satisfactory control in a given situation; methods effective in one situation may be impractical or inadequate in another. Consequently the first step in control is to survey the area, learn where the flies are breeding, determine the relationship between abundance of flies and sanitation, and observe the distribution and resting habits of adult flies in various situations. Then the farmer can select the procedures most likely to remedy his problem.

Good sanitation is necessary. Prompt disposal or storage of manure and other breeding places are essential.

Wastes that cannot be disposed of promptly should be piled compactly on the ground or in pits.

Proper location and construction of barns and feeding pens will reduce materially the effort required to maintain a high standard of sanitation.

Barns and pens should be located on the highest available ground so that neither rain nor subsurface water will collect and create conditions favorable for fly breeding. Good drainage of premises is essential and is easier on high than on low ground.

Concrete floors in barns—especially dairy barns—are essential to good sanitation. Properly designed concrete floors improve drainage and make cleaning easier. Dirt floors in barns, stables, or sheds are difficult to keep sanitary and dry. If they are cleaned weekly and kept hard packed and dry, however, fly breeding will be minimized. Similar procedures are necessary to minimize fly breeding in feeding lots. Where the soil is moist or the drainage poor, 4 to 6 inches of gravel on feed lots will create a fairly hard surface in which few flies will breed, provided wastes are raked up and disposed of regularly.

Applications of insecticides as space or residual treatments inside barns and animal sheds and residual treatments on favored outdoor resting places are a necessary adjunct to sanitation in controlling the housefly. Sprays containing pyrethrins, allethrin, or organic thiocyanates are available for use as space sprays. Residual treatments will provide effective control of the adult houseflies, provided breeding is kept down and the adults are not resistant to the insecticides used.

Where resistance is not a factor, DDT is the preferred insecticide, but chlordane, lindane, or methoxychlor also are effective. Only methoxychlor or lindane should be used in dairy barns or milk rooms. Wettable powders of these insecticides are preferred for residual treatments, but emulsions or oil solutions may also be used. The concentrations and methods of applying residual treatments for the control of houseflies are similar to those described for the control of stableflies.

Poison baits are the most effective means of controlling houseflies that have become resistant to DDT and other chlorinated hydrocarbon insecticides. The baits may be granular or liquid formations, but all consist of an organic phosphorus insecticide and a food that attracts the insects.

Available insecticides for use in baits are malathion, Diazinon, and Bayer L 13/59 (Dipterex). The most satisfactory food attractants are granulated sugar, molasses, corn sirup, honey, and malt. A number of baits are available commercially. It is recommended that the user purchase ready-prepared preparations, but the farmer can purchase the ingredients and prepare his own if he desires.

Liquid baits are usually mixed to contain 0.1 percent insecticide and 10 percent attractant in a water solution. Either an emulsifiable concentrate or wettable powder of the insecticide may be used in the preparation. Liquid bait formulations perform best when applied on clean, hard surfaces. Dirt or heavily littered surfaces quickly absorb the liquid bait, thereby reducing its attractiveness and effectiveness. Good control of flies can be obtained under such conditions, however, by increasing the rate and frequency of application or by using a higher concentration of attractant. Baits containing 50 percent or more of sirup are not so readily absorbed and usually remain on the surface in sufficient volume for flies to ingest a lethal amount.

The usual rate of application of liquid baits in clean, hard-floored (concrete) barns is 1 gallon to 1,000 square feet. Where surfaces are absorbent or littered, larger amounts may be necessary to provide control. The usual amount will suffice for control, however, if applied to burlap sacks or strips of tin, wood, or paper placed in areas where flies congregate around the infested premises. Applications may be made with an ordinary garden sprinkling can or with a 2-gallon, hand-pressure sprayer. If a sprayer is used, it should be equipped with a coarse spray nozzle or have the whirl plate removed so that the bait will be emitted in coarse drops or streamers.

Several types of dry granular baits give effective control of houseflies under a variety of conditions. The most widely used formulation consists of dry sugar with 1 percent or 2 percent of malathion, Bayer L 13/59, or Diazinon. The user who prepares his own bait should mix the necessary amount of a wettable powder concentrate with granular sugar. Dry sugar baits are especially well suited for use in barns and sheds with dry, hard-surfaced floors. They are not recommended for use on damp surfaces because the sugar dissolves and loses its effectiveness in a short time.

The most satisfactory dry baits for use on damp surfaces and outdoors are prepared with inert granular materials such as cornmeal, grits, sand, or crushed oyster shell. These materials are coated with a mixture of insecticide and attractant, usually powdered sugar. The finished bait consists of 88 percent of inert material, 10 percent of powdered sugar, and 2 percent of an organic phosphorus insecticide. Such baits, ready for use, are available commercially.

Dry baits should be applied with a shaker-type dispenser wherever flies are congregating and feeding. The flies are attracted to and feed on the dry bait, and some of them begin dying in a few minutes, so that a high degree of control is usually apparent within an hour after application. About one-fourth pound of dry sugar bait or 1 pound of granular bait is enough to control a fly population of average size in a barn or poultry house having 2,500–5,000 square feet of floor area. Heavier applications may be required for control outdoors or when large numbers of flies are in barns.

E. F. KNIPLING, *a graduate of Texas Agricultural and Mechanical College and Iowa State College, became chief of the Entomology Research Branch, Agricultural Research Service, in 1954. He was formerly in charge of the Insects Affecting Man and Animals Section of the Entomology Research Branch. He has been with the Department of Agriculture since 1931. During this period he was active on research on insects affecting livestock and man.*

W. C. McDUFFIE *is assistant leader of the Insects Affecting Man and Animals Section, Entomology Research Branch. He is a graduate of Mississippi Agricultural and Mechanical College and since 1931 has conducted and directed research on a variety of insect pests of man and animals. From 1951 to 1954 he was in charge of the Department's laboratory in Orlando, Fla.*

Screwworms That Attack Livestock

GAINES W. EDDY AND R. C. BUSHLAND

THE SCREWWORM, *Callitroga hominivorax*, is an obligatory parasite of warm-blooded animals. Animals infested with it usually die unless they are treated promptly. It can be controlled by good management and prompt treatment with an insecticide.

The screwworm fly is bluish or bluish green and is about twice the size of the housefly. It lays its eggs on all kinds of wounds but prefers fresh abrasions—wire cuts, nail scratches, boils, brand marks, shear cuts, and sores caused by tick bites, by needle grass on the legs and face of sheep and goats, and by prickly pear in the mouths and other parts of the body. The navel of newborn animals is especially vulnerable.

The screwworm fly lays shiny white eggs in masses that contain about 200 eggs. The eggs are glued to each other and are placed on the edge of the wound, usually on a dry part of the skin. The masses of white eggs, arranged in neat rows, are unlike the eggs of other blowflies, which are yellowish and laid at random in uneven masses. Eggs of screwworms hatch in 12 to 24 hours, and the tiny maggots feed as a colony in the living flesh.

They feed with their heads down. The tail, or blunt end, usually is exposed for breathing. During development they have a pinkish color, which is very noticeable by the fourth day. The pigmented air tubes, or tracheal trunks, which open at the blunt end of the body, are also noticeable then.

These show as two almost straight black lines. They and the pinkish color identify them from larvae of other blowflies. Wounds infested with screwworms smell bad. There is considerable drainage of brownish-red fluid, which stains the hair below the wound.

Larvae complete their growth in 5 to 7 days and drop to the ground, where they burrow into the soil and pupate. The pupal stage lasts 7 to 10 days in warm weather but may last several weeks when the weather is cool. Flies emerge from the puparia in the soil, work their way to the surface, where they crawl up on vegetation, and expand their wings within a few minutes.

For the first few days of adult life, the flies visit animals to feed on wound fluids. They also take water, nectar, and plant juices. The insects mate when they are 2 days old. The females, when they are 5 or 6 days old, seek out wounded animals on which to lay their eggs. The eggs usually are deposited in one mass. The average life span probably is only about 3 weeks but may be as long as 65 days.

The distribution of the screwworm fly in the United States in winter is confined normally to the southern part of California, Arizona, New Mexico, and Texas, and most of Florida. The flies breed the year around in tropical and subtropical North America and South America. The fly occurs only in the Western Hemisphere.

The flies migrate in spring and summer at a rate of about 5 miles a day. The limits of winter survival determine the areas or States infested one year or another. The southeastern areas usually infested by fall include all of Florida, the southern tip of South Carolina, the southern half of Georgia, and the southeastern part of Alabama. Occasionally the flies move into Mississippi and northward into Kentucky and Virginia. Outbreaks have occurred in New Jersey. In the Southwest, the flies migrate out of Texas into Oklahoma, Kansas, Missouri, Arkansas, and occasionally Mississippi.

The infestations in California, Arizona, and New Mexico are usually local and cover only the southern parts. Severe outbreaks have occurred in many of the Northern States; they usually are costly, because many stockmen in those areas are not familiar with screwworms and by the time expert advice is available the flies have spread over a large area.

Because many animals, especially cattle, move across the country today by rail and truck, outbreaks are likely unless all animals from infested areas are checked closely. Many of the outbreaks in the Northern States have been traced to the shipment of infested animals.

SCREWWORMS cost the livestock industry an estimated 20 million dollars a year in deaths of cattle, permanent injury, and poor weight gains.

Another loss lies in the constant watch necessary to find and treat infested animals. Animals with screwworms tend to stray from the herd or flock and hide in underbrush to escape the flies. Sheep and goats hide under old buildings or in caves. Stockmen may spend the equivalent of several months each year looking for screwworm cases and treating them.

In some years the loss of game animals, especially deer in Florida and Texas, is great. When the fly season comes early and the fawn season is late, a heavy toll of the fawns and their mothers can be expected. Deer are one of the favorite hosts of certain ticks in Florida and Texas, and the sores the ticks cause are also favorite spots for screwworms to lay their eggs.

CONTROL OF SCREWWORMS consists of good ranch practices and the use of an approved remedy.

Corrals, fences, and gates should be kept in good repair so that livestock do not suffer snags and cuts from them.

Dogs used in working stock should not be allowed to bite animals.

Necessary surgery, branding, earmarking, and birth of young should be scheduled for the winter months, when screwworm activity is at its lowest.

Livestock need special watching during the fly season. Because animals are killed so quickly by screwworms, every animal should be seen at least once a week. In brushy country, cowboys need to ride the pastures early in the morning and late in the afternoon to find wormy animals grazing and watering when flies are least annoying.

In places where sheep and goats are pastured, brush should be controlled so that infested animals can be found easily.

Several chemicals can be used to kill the maggots.

Chloroform is an old remedy. It kills maggots quickly, but it irritates the wounds. Benzol is less damaging to tissues, but deep wounds must be plugged with cotton, soaked with benzol, to assure kill of the larvae. Since neither benzol nor chloroform protects wounds against reinfestation, pine oil was used as a repellent dressing. However, such treatments are no longer recommended.

Much better than those treatments is Smear 62, which was developed in 1941. Smear 62 contains 35 percent of benzol, which kills the larvae; 35 percent of diphenylamine, which protects wounds; 10 percent of turkey red oil, a wetting agent; and 20 percent of lampblack, a thickening agent.

EQ–335 was recommended in 1950. The figure "335" stand for the concentrations of the two main active ingredients, lindane (3 percent) and pine oil (35 percent). The formula contains lindane, 3 percent by weight; pine oil, 35 percent; mineral oil, 40-44 percent; emulsifier, 8-12 percent; and silica aerogel, 8-12 percent. The mineral oil is used mostly as a filler and the silica aerogel as a thickening agent. The emulsifier makes the compound mix more easily with wound fluids and with water.

EQ–335 is better than Smear 62 in that it does not stain, it is not highly volatile, it is more effective against fleeceworms and other blowflies, and it is considerably more toxic to the screwworm fly. This last point is important, because the flies may visit wounds to feed even before they are old enough to lay eggs.

In treating screwworm cases, the main idea is to get plenty of material in the wound and a good dressing around the outer edges.

Deep pockets need special attention, because larvae in them often escape being killed. As the flies lay their eggs around or on the outer edges of the wound, a good coating of material will protect the wound against reinfestation and kill many of the flies that visit the wound to feed or to lay eggs.

In sheep and goats, the area below the infestation, which is usually covered with exudate, should be given a light application as a preventive against attack by fleeceworms.

EQ–335 is best applied with a 1-inch varnish brush. The wounds should be treated at 7-day intervals or so until they are completely healed. Large, bleeding wounds, especially in cattle, may require two treatments during the first week, although one or two treatments may be enough to protect the wound until it is healed.

A NEW METHOD of screwworm control—that of releasing laboratory-reared sterilized flies—has been studied in the hope that it might eradicate screwworms from the Southeastern States, where screwworms were introduced in a shipment of infested cattle in 1933 and where infestation normally is isolated from the midwestern screwflies, which overwinter in Texas. If the screwworms that overwinter in Florida could be eradicated, the Southeast would again be free of screwworms. Proper inspection should prevent reintroduction through shipment of infested animals.

Keeping flies from breeding in domestic animals alone is not enough to eradicate screwworms because too many flies breed in wild animals. Therefore, Dr. E. F. Knipling, of the Department of Agriculture, proposed that research be conducted to determine the feasibility of control through the release of sterilized insects.

Screwworms are easily reared in the laboratory on a medium containing blood, water, ground meat, and a little formaldehyde. The laboratory-reared flies can be made incapable of reproducing by exposing the pupae to gamma rays from radioactive cobalt.

Laboratory experiments at Kerrville, Tex., field tests in Florida during 1950–1953, and an eradication experiment on the Island of Curaçao in 1954 were successful. Sterile males competed with the normal males for mates. Wild females, once mated to a sterile male, do not mate a second time and so cannot reproduce.

Curaçao was heavily infested with screwworms until sterile flies were released there. Each week 400 sterile males and 400 sterile females to a square mile were released. The screwworms were eradicated within a few months.

Research began in 1955 to adapt procedures that worked on Curaçao to conditions over the area of 50,000 square miles in Florida where screwworms ordinarily survive the winter. The eradication procedure seems limited to the Southeast. It would not be worthwhile to try to eradicate screwworms from the Southwest, because they would be replaced soon by flies migrating north from Mexico.

Although the control of screwworms through the release of sterilized insects has received considerable attention, research also has been conducted on the feasibility of other methods. Research on materials that attract the flies has shown a great deal of promise.

Gaines W. Eddy *is an entomologist in the Department of Agriculture. He has conducted research on various insects affecting man and animals since entering Government service in 1942. In 1954 he was put in charge of the Corvallis, Oreg., laboratory of the Entomology Research Branch.*

R. C. Bushland *entered Government service in 1935 as an entomologist in the Dallas, Tex., laboratory of the Department of Agriculture. Since that time he has done research on various livestock insect problems in the Southern States. Dr. Bushland made major contributions in work to control the human body louse, which is a carrier of typhus fever. That research saved thousands of lives during the Second World War. Dr. Bushland has been in charge of the Entomology Research Branch's laboratory at Kerrville, Tex., since 1952.*

Fleeceworms

GAINES W. EDDY AND R. C. BUSHLAND

SEVERAL kinds of maggots may attack the fleece of sheep and goats, infest old wounds, or be primary invaders of fresh wounds of animals.

The black blowfly (*Phormia regina*), the secondary screwworm fly (*Callitroga macellaria*), and the green-bottle fly (*Phaenicia sericata*) are the main species. They usually breed in large numbers in carrion.

The black blowfly is blackish green and about the size of the screwworm fly. It lays 50 to 100 or more yellowish eggs in a heap, quite different from the neat, white mass deposited by the screwworm.

The egg masses of all three blowflies look much alike. In infestations on sheep and goats they usually are deposited on soiled fleece. The larvae are creamy white. The larvae do not usually feed as a colony, but may do so, especially in wounds of dehorned cattle. The life cycle takes about 2 weeks.

The black blowfly occurs in many parts of the world and in almost every State in the United States. It likes the cool weather of spring and fall. In midwinter and hot summer it becomes scarce.

Most of the infestations in sheep occur during the early spring when the wool gets soiled by feces, urine, or rain.

Usually only one or two animals in a group become infested at the same time, but an entire flock may be attacked when conditions are right. The flies also lay eggs on old wounds or wounds that are infested with screwworms. The wool below the wounds infested with the screwworms is usually soiled or covered with matter and is attractive to the black blowfly.

THE SECONDARY SCREWWORM FLY resembles the screwworm fly in general appearance and color but is slightly smaller.

The eggs of the secondary screwworm fly are yellowish and are deposited in loosely cemented masses that contain few to several hundred eggs. The larvae are grayish. The life cycle is completed in about 10 days.

The secondary screwworm fly has been found in most of the States. It seldom becomes abundant in the North, but breeds the year around in Texas, Florida, and Arizona, and probably in southern California. Usually the black blowfly has just about disappeared by the time the secondary screwworm fly becomes abundant.

Livestock losses attributed to the secondary screwworm fly probably equal those caused by the black blowfly, because the fly is usually present in greater numbers and during the period when the screwworm fly occurs. It is most important in the areas where the screwworm fly abounds. It not only acts as a secondary invader by getting into wounds infested with screwworms; it also has the bad habit of leaving the wounds and infesting the fleece of sheep and goats. In such cases the death of the animal is almost certain unless the larvae are killed. The second-

ary screwworm fly is also a primary invader of fresh wounds.

THE GREEN-BOTTLE FLY is metallic green. It is about as large as the secondary screwworm fly. The pale-yellow eggs ordinarily hatch in less than 24 hours. They are laid on or around wounds and on the soiled fleece of sheep and goats. The larvae are deep cream in color with a slight purplish or pinkish tinge. Eggs develop into adults usually in less than 2 weeks.

The green-bottle fly has been found in almost every State. It is more prevalent in the South than in the North.

In importance to the stockman, the green-bottle fly does not rank with the other blowflies. Although the fly normally lives on dead or decaying matter, it may turn parasitic and attack livestock, especially sheep. Many cases in Texas, New Mexico, and Arizona are caused by the green-bottle fly. In Arizona it is especially bad. It may attack newborn lambs even before they are dry. It is active throughout the year in many parts of the South.

THE CONTROL of fleeceworms is difficult under many conditions, but good ranch practices and the use of an approved insecticide can cut livestock losses sharply.

The stockman's aim is to reduce the number of cases. Sheep should be sheared, if possible, before the flies become numerous. If that cannot be done, the animals should be watched closely for signs of infestations. Tagging, or shearing the wool from the crotch area, is used as a preventative measure by many ranchers, especially in the Southwest.

Insecticide sprays applied to the crotch and the tail prevent attack by fleeceworms.

Toxaphene is highly effective. Benzene hexachloride and chlordane are very good as preventives. Other chlorinated insecticides, such as DDT and TDE, are less effective.

Toxaphene is best applied as a 2-percent spray to the tail and the crotch area. The animals should be treated early in the season or before the flies become too active. A single spraying should carry the animals through the critical period.

A green-bottle blowfly, a closely related species, has caused heavy damage to sheep in Australia. Best results have been obtained there with benzene hexachloride at 0.5–1.0 percent (gamma isomer) and DDT at 1.0 percent.

Infestations of fleeceworms can be effectively controlled with the screwworm preparation, EQ–335. For use against fleeceworms, the material is diluted 1 part to 9 parts of water. The infested area and about 3 inches outside the infestation should be encircled with the material. If the infested area is not too large, a very light dressing of the material in the undiluted form works well. It should be used with care, because the lindane in it (3 percent) is highly toxic to animals. It is not necessary to remove the fleece when EQ–335 is used.

GAINES W. EDDY, *a graduate of Oklahoma Agricultural and Mechanical College, heads the Department's laboratory in Corvallis, Oreg. He has done extensive research on the control of lice, mites, and other arthropods that affect the health of man.*

R. C. BUSHLAND *became head of the Kerrville, Tex., laboratory of the Entomology Research Branch in 1952. He is a graduate of South Dakota State College and Kansas State College.*

Mosquitoes on Livestock and Man

ARTHUR W. LINDQUIST AND WILLIAM C. McDUFFIE

WE THINK of mosquitoes primarily as scourges of mankind. They cause discomfort and irritation. They may keep us from developing industrial, agricultural, and recreational areas.

They may transmit appalling diseases—filariasis, yellow fever, encephalitis, and malaria.

Mosquitoes also attack livestock. They can transmit encephalomyelitis, anaplasmosis, swamp fever, fowlpox, and other diseases to animals. Mosquitoes irritate cattle and cause them to mill around, stamp, and swing their heads in efforts to fight off the insects.

That and loss of blood from bites cause losses in weight and milk production. Livestock have been killed by swarms of mosquitoes.

About 145 species of mosquitoes exist in the United States. Some are localized and of little economic importance. Others are widespread.

The species vary in their habits, but all have a common characteristic—the larvae develop only in water. But not all species breed in all types of water.

Some prefer fresh water and cannot tolerate alkaline, highly acid, or polluted water. Others prefer brackish water in salt marshes or in tree holes.

Some develop in fresh, alkaline, or polluted water. Larvae do not breed in rapidly flowing streams, canals, or irrigation ditches, but they may be present in quiet backwaters of streams or in vegetation-choked channels.

To CONTROL mosquitoes, one has to know the places where larvae are breeding and the adult habits.

Some of the main breeding areas and species are:

Temporary rain pools: *Aedes atlanticus, A. vexans, A. infirmatus, A. canadensis, Psorophora confinnis.*

Flooded areas: *A. sticticus, A. vexans, A. dorsalis.*

Irrigated pastures: *A. nigromaculis, A. dorsalis, Culex tarsalis.*

Salt marshes: *A. sollicitans, A. taeniorhynchus, A. squamiger.*

Standing water around houses: *A. aegypti, C. quinquefasciatus, C. pipiens.*

All mosquitoes have four stages in their life development—eggs, larvae, pupae, and adults. Most of the mosquitoes of the *Aedes* group lay their eggs on the ground after the water has receded.

Culex and *Culiseta* lay their eggs in rafts on the surface of the water.

Anopheles lay theirs singly on the water surface.

Aedes and *Psorophora* species overwinter in the egg stage (except *A. varipalpus*, which overwinters either as eggs or larvae).

Anopheles and *Culex* mosquitoes generally overwinter as adults and can be found in such protected places as cellars, caves, culverts, and buildings.

Mansonia overwinter as larvae attached to roots of aquatic plants.

Some species fly 10 to 15 miles or more from the point of origin. *Culex, Culiseta,* and *Anopheles* seldom fly more than a mile or two.

The number of generations of mosquitoes varies with the species and the type of climate—the *Culex* and *Anopheles* and many of the *Aedes* have several generations each year. Other *Aedes,* such as the snow-water species, usually have only one generation a year.

YOU CAN END the annoyance of mosquitoes by directly controlling larvae and adults or by applying protective treatments to animals.

Direct control means filling or draining the breeding places or applying chemicals to larval breeding sites or areas infected by adults. Since mosquitoes may fly some distance, community action in eliminating breeding areas and applying insecticides offers the best method of control. Lacking that, protective applications of insecticides and repellents to animals must be made.

If a control program is to be successful, surveys must be made to determine where mosquitoes are breeding and what species are involved. To locate mosquito larvae, a search must be made in every water area in the locality—ponds, ditches, swamps, overflows, seepages, and containers such as wells, cisterns, cans, jars, and discarded auto tires. An ordinary water dipper may be used for taking water samples. Ten to twenty dips near the edges of a pond are usually necessary. A close examination of the water in the dipper will reveal the wrigglers (larvae).

IRRIGATED PASTURES and meadows frequently produce myriads of mosquitoes when water is allowed to stand on the land for 5 to 8 days. Irrigation in the United States has created serious new mosquito problems.

To curtail the breeding of mosquitoes in pastures, the land must be prepared properly for irrigation and for the removal of excess water. Water should be used only as needed. Overirrigation should be avoided. Animals should be taken from pasture when the soil is wet. Trampling of the soil by farm animals reduces the penetration of water into the earth and forms small depressions, which hold water long enough to produce mosquitoes. The stock should graze fields in rotation. Those practices reduce mosquito breeding and increase crop production. Groups of farmers can do much to control mosquitoes by following the proper irrigation and pasturing practices.

On the farm and in suburban areas, septic tanks and cesspools may produce hordes of mosquitoes. Drains from septic tanks should lead to a properly constructed drainage field, where the fluid will enter into the soil. Cesspools should be tightly covered.

Dairy drains may be sources of mosquitoes. The liquid can be applied to fields, and collected water can be pumped into the irrigation system. Keeping weeds from growing in the dairy drain pond also reduces mosquito breeding.

Water tanks are another source. The tramping of livestock around the tanks makes soil impervious, and the imprints of hoofs hold water, in which larvae might breed. Overflow of the tanks usually can be prevented. An adequate pavement of concrete or gravel around the water trough or tanks is desirable. The mosquitoes are likely to breed in tanks that are not cleaned of leaves and soil.

Streams may stop flowing during dry seasons and leave stagnant pools. Backwater impoundments also develop. Those situations may breed mosquitoes. Ditching sometimes will remove the water. It is wise to remove vegetation from the shoreline so as to encourage wave action and movement of minnows.

Mosquitoes also develop in vast numbers in marshes, swamps, overflows, and tidal flats, especially along coastal areas. Ditching, diking, filling, and leveling and clearing—which are costly operations and require coordinated efforts of many groups of people, especially if the areas are extensive—eliminate standing water.

INSECTICIDES can be applied against larvae or adults.

The destruction of larvae usually is most effective and cheapest. The insecticides must be applied to the water areas where the larvae are found before the larvae become mature and emerge as adults. The water must be examined often for the presence of larvae. Spraying must be done as soon as they are found. Spraying should be repeated whenever one finds that larvae are present.

DDT is widely used. TDE, lindane, toxaphene, chlordane, heptachlor, and dieldrin also are effective. These materials are applied at a rate of 0.1 to 0.5 pound per acre of water surface.

Insecticides can be applied as emulsions, oil solutions, or dusts. Emulsion concentrates contain the technical insecticide, an organic solvent, and an emulsifier. They are diluted with water or oil to obtain the desired strength of toxicant, usually 1 percent, for application with ground equipment. Oil solution concentrates should be diluted with fuel or diesel oil to 1 percent. About 10 quarts of the 1-percent DDT spray are applied per acre. Dusts usually are not so effective or practical as the solutions or emulsions, but they can be used in some places.

LARVICIDES can be applied to small areas up to several acres with a garden-type sprayer holding 3 or 4 gallons. Motor-driven, paint-type air sprayers, which produce an atomized spray, can be used in many places.

Power equipment, like orchard-type sprayers, mist blowers, and the heat-generated aerosol machines, is necessary for the larger control operations. Such machines are expensive and so big that they cannot be used in some places, but frequently the insecticide can be drifted for several hundred feet over mosquito-breeding water.

Airplanes are used to disperse some insecticides over large areas. Community action is usually required because the expense may be too great for one person.

IF IT IS IMPRACTICAL to control the larvae, efforts must be devoted to control the adult mosquitoes. One way to do that is to make a heavy residual application of insecticide in and around buildings, the woodlands, grass areas, and various resting places of mosquitoes. Applications of 2 to 3 pounds of DDT or related insecticide to the acre will leave a residue that will continue to kill mosquitoes for 1 to 4 weeks. Individual property owners can obtain some relief by treating their premises, but best results are obtained when large areas are treated.

Another method is to kill the adults on the wing in buildings or outdoor areas with a fine mist spray, or aerosol, which are called "space sprays." They should be applied in the early morning or late evening when wind conditions are favorable for dissemination over the desired area. Treatments must be repeated frequently, as mosquitoes usually reinfest the area within a short time. The amount of insecticide used is much less than for residual application—usually only 2 quarts of 5 percent DDT (0.2 pound) to the acre. Pyrethrum or allethrin sprays fortified with activators are effective but are expensive for use outside.

REPELLENTS AND INSECTICIDE SPRAYS may be applied to livestock to protect them against mosquitoes, but none of the available preparations remains fully effective on an animal for more than a few hours or 1 or 2 days at most. Frequent respraying is therefore necessary—a practical procedure for small herds of dairy cattle, but not for range cattle.

Walkthrough, treadle-type sprayers permit cattle to spray themselves. The devices are set up so cattle walk through them on the way to the barn or to water. A treadle on which the animals walk activates the sprayer, which delivers a mist of insecticide over them. The sprayers are useful with dairy herds and small beef herds, but the animals must be trained to use them.

The best insecticide for use in treadle sprayers is a concentrated solution containing 1 percent of pyrethrins or allethrin plus 10 percent of synergist. Some preparations include also about 1 percent of methoxychlor and solvents, which have some insecticidal action. These materials may be applied daily with hand-operated mist sprayers. The treatments discourage biting and stun or kill the mosquitoes that land on an animal. Frequent applications are necessary.

CATTLE CAN BE SPRAYED while in the barn with oil solutions of pyrethrum or allethrin insecticides. About an ounce of spray is misted over each animal with a hand-operated or power sprayer. Permanent mist sprayers, which have several nozzles, are installed in some barns. The spray kills mosquitoes and flies in the barn, and some of it settles on the cattle. Heat-generated fog machines are sometimes used in the barns to treat cattle. They are also useful outside to drift insecticides over cattle bunched together.

ARTHUR W. LINDQUIST *is leader of the Insects Affecting Man and Animals Section, Entomology Research Branch, Agricultural Research Service. He is a graduate of Bethany College and Kansas State College. Since 1931 he has conducted and directed research on the biology and control of hornflies, tabanids, screwworms, blowflies, cattle grubs, mosquitoes, and other pests affecting man and livestock.*

WILLIAM C. McDUFFIE *is assistant leader of the Insects Affecting Man and Animals Section, Entomology Research Branch, Agricultural Research Service. He is a graduate of Mississippi Agricultural and Mechanical College. Since 1931 he has conducted and directed research on a variety of insect pests of man and animals.*

For further reading:

American Mosquito Control Association: *The Use of Aircraft in the Control of Mosquitoes,* American Mosquito Control Association Bulletin, number 1, 46 pages. 1948; *Ground Equipment and Insecticides for Mosquito Control,* American Mosquito Control Association Bulletin, number 2, 116 pages. 1952.

Stanley F. Bailey, Richard M. Bohart, and L. J. Booher: *Mosquito Control on the Farm,* California Agricultural Experiment Station Circular 439, 28 pages. 1954.

W. V. King, G. H. Bradley, and T. E. McNeel: *The Mosquitoes of the Southeastern States.* U. S. Department of Agriculture Miscellaneous Publication 336, 96 pages. 1944.

H. H. Stage, C. M. Gjullin, and W. W. Yates: *Mosquitoes of the Northwestern States.* U. S. Department of Agriculture Handbook 46, 95 pages. 1952.

W. W. Yates, A. W. Lindquist, and Don C. Mote: *Suggestions for Mosquito Control in Oregon,* Oregon Agricultural Experiment Station Bulletin 507, 12 pages. 1951.

L. A. Moore, R. H. Carter, and F. W. Poos: *Insecticide Studies With Dairy Cattle,* Journal of Milk and Food Technology, volume 12, pages 103–104. 1949.

R. D. Radeleff, R. C. Bushland, and H. V. Claborn: *Toxicity to Livestock,* U. S. D. A. Yearbook of Agriculture 1952, *Insects,* pages 276–283. 1952.

R. D. Radeleff, H. V. Claborn, H. F. Beckman, R. W. Wells, and R. C. Bushland: *Toxaphene Residues in Fat of Sprayed Cattle,* Veterinary Medicine, volume 46, pages 305–308. 1951.

Biting Gnats

ARTHUR W. LINDQUIST AND WILLIAM C. McDUFFIE

THE MANY species of biting gnats that affect livestock may be classified in two major groups, *Simulium* and *Culicoides*.

The *Simulium*, or blackflies, are small, hump-backed, and dark-colored insects, commonly known as buffalo or turkey gnats.

The *Culicoides* are much smaller and usually are gray or black and have spots on the wings. They are known as punkies, no-see-ums, and sandflies.

The gnats in these groups are smaller than mosquitoes. Stockmen usually do not see the gnats, especially the night biters.

Blackflies suck blood from livestock and poultry, and so irritate them, interfere with their feeding, and sometimes kill them. In outbreaks such as occur in the Mississippi Valley, thousands of head of livestock have been killed by these vicious biters.

Some blackflies carry diseases and protozoan parasites of turkeys and ducks. In some countries they transmit filarial worms, which affect the eyes and cause blindness in people and animals. Blackflies transmit a similar filarial disease in cattle in Australia.

At least 80 different species of blackflies occur in the United States. They breed most abundantly in swift streams. They also are found in slowly moving streams and irrigation canals. The larvae and pupae are attached to stones, vegetation, and other objects in streams. Only one generation occurs a year in northern climates, but some species may produce several broods a year in the Southern States.

The larvae can be controlled by applying DDT or TDE to the water where the larvae breed. An oil solution of DDT, applied at a rate of about 0.2 part per million of water flowing by a certain point for 30 minutes will destroy larvae for several thousand feet downstream. After the waterflow is calculated, the insecticide solution is dripped or sprayed on the water for about 30 minutes. All streams within 5 miles of the places to be protected should be treated.

Airplanes can be used to disperse insecticides over large areas in which are many streams. The spray is usually applied in strips of 100 to 300 feet across streams at intervals of one-fourth to one-half mile. About 0.1 pound of DDT per acre of water sprayed is satisfactory for strip spraying. The flow of the water will give adequate dispersion of the insecticide between strips and destroy the larvae throughout the stream.

Water emulsions of DDT are more toxic to fish and other aquatic life than oil solutions. Care should be taken therefore to apply them only in dosages that will not harm aquatic life.

Control of adult blackflies with insecticides has been successful in some localities but not in others. DDT oil sprays applied by aircraft or from the ground by fog machines or mist blowers have given good control in some places. Enough spray should be used to give 0.2 pound of DDT on an acre.

In places where it is impossible to destroy larvae in their breeding places, the farmer can protect his livestock by spraying them. Synergized pyrethrum formulations are best for this purpose but must be applied to the animals daily. This can be done with hand or power sprayers. Automatic or treadle-type sprayers also may be used.

Culicoides, or sandflies, are pests of man and animals over most of the country. About 60 species are known. They are vicious biters, cause severe irritation and discomfort, and transmit diseases.

At least one of the species transmits bluetongue, a virus disease of sheep that was discovered in Texas in 1948. It was apparently introduced in some unknown way from Africa several years earlier but had not been recognized as a new disease. Bluetongue has been prevalent in Texas, New Mexico, Arizona, California, and Utah.

Some species of sandflies breed in the mud or moist soil around the margins of streams, ponds, sloughs, and watering tanks. Some are found in holes in trees. Several species breed in vast numbers in the salt marshes along the Atlantic coast. The larvae are thread-like and move by a whipping motion through ooze or water.

Larval breeding places can be destroyed by draining and filling. Since these measures are seldom practical, insecticides are usually applied to breeding areas to control the larvae. Control of these tiny pests over large areas requires organized effort and considerable money. Excellent control of the larvae in mangrove swamps along the Florida coast has been obtained with soil applications of 1 to 2 pounds an acre of lindane, chlordane, heptachlor, and dieldrin.

Sandflies can enter dwellings and livestock shelters through ordinary 16-mesh screens, which exclude mosquitoes and flies. Painting lindane or chlordane on window and door screens is helpful.

The livestock owner can protect his animals from sandflies by frequent application of pyrethrum insecticides.

Insect repellents are effective for protection of people against sandflies. They should be applied to the hands, face, and clothing.

ARTHUR W. LINDQUIST *is leader of the Insects Affecting Man and Animals Section, Entomology Research Branch, and is a graduate of Bethany College and Kansas State College.*

WILLIAM C. McDUFFIE, *assistant leader of the Insects Affecting Man and Animals Section of Entomology Research Branch, is a graduate of Mississippi Agricultural and Mechanical College.*

Vesicular Stomatitis—V. S.

W. C. PATTERSON AND L. O. MOTT

VESICULAR stomatitis is a damaging disease, but its special importance derives from the fact that its clinical picture is like that of foot-and-mouth disease.

Vesicular stomatitis (V. S.) is characterized chiefly by the formation of vesicles, or blisters, in the mouth of cattle and horses and on the snout and feet of swine. One can tell it from foot-and-mouth disease only after inoculations or laboratory tests.

Vesicular stomatitis as a disease of horses and mules was initially reported in South Africa in 1897. The disease had probably occurred among horses used in the Civil War, but the first established report in the United States was in 1916, when horses with V. S. were seen in the Denver stockyards. That year the disease spread through remount stations across the Great Plains to Chicago and Virginia.

Cattle in Richmond, Ind., were diagnosed as having vesicular stomatitis in 1925. The organism that caused it was preserved and now is known as vesicular stomatitis Indiana type. The next year a serious outbreak of vesicular stomatitis in New Jersey was diagnosed as being caused by an organism that was immunologically different from the one isolated in Indiana. It was identified as vesicular stomatitis New Jersey type. All later outbreaks have been found to be of one of these two types.

Severe outbreaks occurred in Texas and Louisiana in 1941, and in Colorado in 1942, 1943, and 1944. The Indiana-type organism was isolated from the 1942 outbreak in Colorado. That type has not been diagnosed in the United States since then.

An outbreak in California in 1945 had additional importance because a second vesicular disease (vesicular exanthema) was present in that State at the same time. Small, sporadic outbreaks in cattle occurred the following years. In 1949 V. S. swept across the United States from Mexico to Canada and from the Rockies to the Appalachians. Large numbers of animals were involved in the Southeastern States, the upper Mississippi Valley, and the Rocky Mountain States.

No vesicular stomatitis was reported in the United States in 1950 or 1951. Vesicular stomatitis was diagnosed in Georgia in 1952; in Georgia, New Jersey, Oklahoma, North Carolina, Virginia, Maryland, and West Virginia in 1953; in Florida, Louisiana, North Carolina, and Georgia in 1954; and in Georgia, Louisiana, North Carolina, and South Carolina in 1955.

An outbreak of V. S. occurred in swine in a hog cholera serum plant in Missouri in 1943. Fifty percent of 1,500 swine were involved. It was diagnosed as of the New Jersey type. This was the first time that V. S. had been diagnosed officially in swine. It is still not known how the virus got into the plant.

The first natural outbreak of V. S. in swine on a farm was diagnosed by Department of Agriculture veterinarians in Georgia in May 1952. V. S. in swine was diagnosed in Georgia and North Carolina in 1953; in Florida, Louisiana, and North Carolina in 1954; and in Georgia, Louisiana, North Carolina, and South Carolina in 1955. Those outbreaks occurred in May, June, July, and August. Information collected from veterinarians, livestock owners, and game wardens during the 1952 outbreak in Georgia indicates that V. S. may have occurred in swine there for at least 15 years.

THE CAUSE of vesicular stomatitis is a virus that is concentrated in the blisters and the blister coverings formed during the course of the disease. The virus is also found in the blood during the fever stage of the disease and for a short period afterwards.

The virus, as seen under an electron microscope, is rod shaped, about 0.000008 inch long, and about one-fourth as wide—125,000 of the organisms would measure 1 inch.

The virus remains active for several days at body temperature (98.6° F.). Infectivity is retained for several months in the refrigerator at 42° to 46° F. The virus retains its infectivity for years when it is frozen at −94°. It is affected considerably by caustic chemicals like acids, lye, and lime, which can make the virus noninfectious if they are used in the proper strength. Sunlight and ultraviolet light rapidly destroy the virus. A temperature of 130° destroys its viability in 15 minutes.

One of the two types of virus (Indiana and New Jersey) does not immunize against the other type, and an animal recovering from one type might suffer a fresh attack of the disease by the other type. Animals immune to either type of V. S. have not been found to demonstrate any immunity to foot-and-mouth disease or vesicular exanthema.

During the past 25 years V. S. has been mainly a disease of cattle. Early reports were that it was found primarily in horses. Since 1952, the number of infected swine has increased. It is believed that many outbreaks in swine go undiagnosed each year. Only since the great outbreak of vesicular exanthema in 1952 has a close check on all suspicious swine been made.

The disease occurs seldom in sheep and goats. The infection has been reported in deer and dogs. Mice, rats, guinea pigs, chinchillas, hamsters, ferrets, chickens, and chicken embryos are rather easily infected. Man also is somewhat susceptible to the disease. According to R. P. Hanson and his coworkers at the University of Wisconsin, the disease appears to be confined entirely to persons who come in close contact with it in their work.

The disease is not usually found in cattle and horses less than 1 year old. Only one 6-month-old animal was reported in the 1949 outbreak in Wisconsin, which involved 11,380 head of cattle. V. S. has been reported in suckling pigs.

The first symptoms usually noted in cattle and horses are salivation and a softening and tearing off of the mucous membrane of the tongue, lips, hard palate, and gums. A sick animal shows an acute temperature rise 2 to 5 days after exposure. Temperatures in cattle rise to 105° F., but are seldom observed in the field because this stage of the disease has passed before the farmer is aware of an abnormal condition in his cattle.

In cows and horses there is a patchy reddening of the oral mucous membranes, especially the tongue. Small areas start swelling. The swellings develop into vesicles, which may be as small as a dime or as big as a dollar.

The vesicles often join together to form large vesicles. The fully developed vesicle contains a clear, straw-colored fluid, which has a high virus content. The vesicles usually rupture in a few hours and therefore are not often seen in the field.

A raw undersurface, red with gray-white fragments, is seen after the rupture of the vesicles. The virus disappears in a few days. Severely infected animals may lose the outer tissue layers from the entire tongue. The lesions in horses are chiefly on the upper surface of the tongue but may be seen on the inner surface of the lip and at the angles of the mouth. The lesions in cows are mainly on the tongue, but they spread to the lips, gums, hard palate, muzzle, and the nostrils.

A great amount of stringy saliva is formed when the lesions develop, and moving the jaws causes pain. Cattle make a smacking sound. Horses grind their teeth. Often there is a thick nasal discharge. The animal loses appetite and usually is depressed. Sometimes in cattle there are lesions on the teats, between the toes, and directly above one hoof. Secondary infection may lead to swelling and lameness.

THE FIRST SYMPTOMS IN PIGS are lameness and vesicles on the snout.

Vesicles also form on the lips and occasionally on the tongue, between the toes, and above the hoofs. These lesions look exactly like those of vesicular exanthema and foot-and-mouth disease. The animal may have a body temperature ranging from 104° to 107°—usually 2 to 5 days after exposure. The temperature drops when the vesicles break. Some—but not all—go off feed. Animals with severe lesions on their feet may be unable to get to the feeding troughs.

Severely affected swine will show hairless areas on their knees from knuckling over because of the soreness of the feet. Lesions on the mammary glands of nursing sows have been reported. The vesicles usually appear first on the nipple and then spread to the teat and the mammary gland itself. The lips and the tongues of the suckling pigs may be affected.

Vesicles develop in the pig as they do in horses and cows. Vesicles develop within a day or two and fill with clear fluid. They usually rupture and leave red, raw areas. Shreds of tissue adhere to the margin of the lesions. The feet may be so severely affected that a loosening of the hoof occurs.

A PROMPT and exact differential diagnosis of vesicular stomatitis is imperative—the disease is contagious and causes considerable alarm because of its close resemblance to foot-and-mouth disease. A mistaken diagnosis would lead to unnecessary and serious economic disturbances and to the spread of one of the most dreaded and easily communicated diseases.

Whenever a vesicular disease appears, therefore, State livestock officials impose local quarantines so as to prevent its spread. State and Federal veterinarians make primary investigations. If their findings warrant, a specially trained Federal veterinarian is sent to the infected premises to make a differential diagnosis, which involves the inoculation of a series of normal test animals.

Procedures followed in making a differential diagnosis are described in the next chapter.

The reactions of the test animals give a basis for differentiating the three vesicular diseases. Material is submitted to a laboratory for confirmation and typing of the virus by serological methods. If the infection is old and infectious material cannot be had for the inoculations, samples of serum from recovering animals are collected and tested. The initial outbreak of an unknown vesicular condition in any State or area is always diagnosed by animal inoculations.

IMMUNITY is important in the control and diagnosis of vesicular stomatitis. Some animals may be reinfected experimentally as early as 30 days after recovery from the disease. Usually a good immunity is retained up to the fifth or sixth month after infection, and then a rapid drop in immunity takes place. An infection thus may pass through a given area one summer and repeat itself the next year because many animals would have lost their immunity.

It is highly significant that veterinarians occasionally find immune test animals when they make differential diagnoses. It is an indication that large numbers of undiagnosed cases of V. S. occur each year.

Antibodies can be detected in the serum of recovered animals by serological tests. Complement-fixing antibodies are highest 2 to 5 weeks after infection and have disappeared in most cases at 3 to 6 months. Neutralizing antibodies are detectable for much longer periods than complement-fixing antibodies. Significant numbers of neutralizing antibodies may be detected 2 years after an infection. The amount of these different antibodies found in convalescent serums may help determine the time at which an animal was previously infected.

THE DISEASE IS SPREAD with difficulty by indirect contact but easily by direct contact. The period in which active virus is shed does not extend past the fifth or sixth day after the formation of vesicles. The natural method of spread is unknown. Biting insects have been held responsible, because V. S. appears in the summer and disappears shortly after the first killing frost.

Workers at the University of Wisconsin have reported that the disease has been transmitted by biting insects in the laboratory. Several species of mosquitoes and horseflies carried the virus 1 to 3 days. The disease has been transmitted by aerosol inoculations in swine.

Vesicular stomatitis seems to spread from a reservoir of infection in the Southeastern States or Mexico. Very likely it is spread by an arthropod from this source of infection each year. The outbreaks of V. S. in 1952, 1953, 1954, and 1955 started in Georgia, Florida, or Louisiana.

THE TREATMENT of V. S. consists in removing infected animals from healthy ones and keeping them isolated until they recover. Healing usually is complete in 2 to 3 weeks. Complications are rare. There is a quick return of appetite and milk production.

Rigid sanitary precautions are needed to prevent spread of the disease. All contaminated premises and equipment should be disinfected. Spraying with a 2-percent solution of lye (sodium hydroxide) is effective.

Medication or undue handling of affected parts should not be attempted until after the disease has been diagnosed. Handling the infected tissues increases the chance of spread of the disease. Treating will not alter the course of the disease and will tend to make diagnosis more difficult. Of primary importance in the treatment and control is the isolation of affected animals and the maintenance of strict quarantine for 3 weeks after the lesions have disappeared.

A prompt differential diagnosis of any vesicular condition is imperative. Any suspicious condition should be reported immediately to the nearest local, State, or Federal veterinarian.

W. C. PATTERSON *is a veterinarian*

employed by the Animal Disease and Parasite Research Branch of the Agricultural Research Service, where he is the project leader on vesicular diseases. He received a bachelor's degree from the Pennsylvania State University and the degree of doctor of veterinary medicine from the University of Pennsylvania.

L. O. MOTT *is a veterinarian in charge of the Viral and Rickettsial Diseases Section of the Animal Disease and Parasite Research Branch. He received the D. V. M. degree from Kansas State College, where he served 2 years on the veterinary faculty. Dr. Mott has been in the Department of Agriculture service since 1934. He has engaged in research work on periodic ophthalmia, equine encephalomyelitis, equine infectious anemia, anaplasmosis, hog cholera, foot-and-mouth disease, V. S., and vesicular exanthema.*

Foot-and-Mouth Disease

M. S. SHAHAN AND J. TRAUM

FOOT-AND-MOUTH disease has become one of the most dreaded of the animal diseases.

Also known as FMD and aphthous fever, it occurs and generally is considered enzootic, or frequently epizootic, in most of the major livestock producing countries of the world, except those in North America, Central America, Australia, and New Zealand.

In Australia it last occurred in 1872.

Africa, Asia, Europe, and South America have not been free from it for decades.

The United States has experienced nine outbreaks of FMD, the first in 1870 and the latest in 1929. In all but two instances, the disease was eradicated and quarantines were removed within a few months. In outbreaks that began in 1914 and 1924, 20 months of ceaseless effort were required before it

was considered safe to remove all restrictions from all the involved areas.

The first diagnosis of the disease in Canada was in February 1952. Because of the diligent efforts of Canadian officials, that country was placed on the list of countries free from the infection by the United States Department of Agriculture on March 1, 1953.

The presence of FMD in Mexico was established in 1946, and that country was not declared free until September 1952, after nearly 1 million animals had been slaughtered and 60 million vaccinations had been applied. The infection was again discovered in May 1953, and restrictions against the importation of cattle, swine, sheep, and goats from Mexico into the United States were not lifted again until December 31, 1954.

Susceptibility to natural infection

with this acute and highly contagious disease is primarily and almost exclusively limited to cloven-footed animals, domestic and wild. Cattle, hogs, sheep, and goats are most frequently affected in the order mentioned. This order of susceptibility to the disease does not, however, always prevail. Deer were seriously affected in an outbreak in 1924–1925 in California.

Dogs and cats, especially young ones, are slightly susceptible to artificial infection. Rats have been experimentally infected, and rare cases of natural infection of rats have been reported in England. Rabbits have been infected artificially. The European hedgehog may be readily infected experimentally with FMD, and natural infections in hedgehogs have been observed in England. Attempts to infect horses experimentally have failed. Guinea pigs have been used extensively in FMD research since the early 1920's. The disease produced experimentally in this species is a prototype of the disease in cattle, but infection is not acquired by contact.

Research workers at the Pirbright Institute in England discovered that suckling white mice are highly susceptible to intra-abdominal injections of the virus, which causes spastic paralysis and inflammation of the muscles. Embryonated chicken eggs, although generally regarded as nonsusceptible, have nevertheless been reported as susceptible to some strains of the virus passed intermittently through guinea pigs and incubated eggs, or from 1-day-old chicks to incubated eggs.

Generally speaking, all animals of susceptible species in a given herd develop infection in time, but in some circumstances the rate of incidence is considerably less than 100 percent. Inapparent infections have been reported in some outbreaks. Although they show no clinical evidence of the disease at the time, such animals are subsequently immune.

People are rarely infected with FMD even though they are repeatedly exposed to the disease in many countries. Few authenticated cases of human infection have been reported.

THE DISEASE MANIFESTS ITSELF by the formation of vesicles, or blisters, on the mucous membrane covering the various parts of the mouth, including the tongue, lips, gums, dental pad, and the palate.

Often vesicles also are found on the skin between and above the claws of the feet, and occasionally on the dew claws, muzzle, and nostrils of cattle.

Vesicles may be present on the teats and udder of milking or nursing cows. The lesions may be located at any one, several, or most of these places. The blisters usually rupture within a day or two, leaving a raw, eroded surface. The erosions heal rather rapidly as a rule, but at times they become secondarily infected by various bacteria. The feet and the udder are especially prone to such complications.

In swine the lesions are practically the same as in cattle, but they appear more frequently on the snout or feet.

In sheep, goats, and deer, the lesions are most often observed on the feet, but that may be because the small vesicles in the mouth may be overlooked.

These pathological changes in the tissues produce a series of other symptoms—an increase in body temperature, loss of appetite, lassitude, and profuse slobbering. Because chewing may be painful, the animal may eat less or not at all, and therefore loses condition and weight. The animal usually becomes lame. Milk flow usually drops or stops. Abortion, mastitis, and sterility may occur.

Mostly the mortality in adult animals is less than 5 percent but is somewhat higher in calves and other young animals. In some outbreaks, however, mortality has reached 50 percent of the animals affected. In such instances, sudden deaths may follow severe inflammation and degeneration of the heart muscle, with or without the usual symptoms.

THE INCUBATION PERIOD following

natural exposure varies from 2 days to a week but may be longer, depending on the particular strain of virus and the nature and extent of exposure to infection. Experimentally inoculated animals commonly develop lesions within 24 to 48 hours, but the lesions may be delayed a week or more.

In recovered animals there is residual damage, which may not be obvious for some time but which affects the general well-being and productivity of the animals. Recovered animals, especially cows, frequently are destroyed or sent to market at a sacrifice rather than retained in the hope that they will regain normal productivity.

THE VIRUS of FMD is one of the smallest viruses that cause disease in animals. Its size has been estimated to be between 8 and 12 millimicrons— that is, 3 million to 2 million measure 1 inch.

By field and laboratory observations and tests, at least six types of FMD virus have been found. These are designated as A, O, C, SAT–1, SAT–2, and SAT–3. The last three types have thus far been reported only from Africa. The others have been found in various parts of the world.

Each of the six types produces a disease picture that cannot be differentiated by the symptoms and lesions from the disease produced by the other five types. An animal that has recovered from an attack of FMD is immune for several months to 2 years to another exposure of the same type of virus, but it can be infected readily with any of the other five types. The six types thus are immunologically distinct, as well as serologically different, as reflected in tests with serum of such animals.

The virus is present in the fluid and coverings of the vesicles. It may be found in the blood and in various organs, tissues, secretions, and excretions, and therefore in the urine and milk in the initial, feverish stage of the infection.

The conditions under which materials harboring the virus are found in and outside living animals or in the slaughtered animals determine its viability and infectivity.

In the living animal, the virus in the vesicle coverings and fluid, in other parts involved in the vesicles, and in most of the body tissues and organs usually loses its infectivity within 5 to 7 days after the lesions appear. Certain parts, such as the skin, hair, and loose parts and crevices in the hoofs, however, sometimes carry infective virus for some time.

It is also generally believed that the virus loses its activity in a short time within the body and that animals in the later stages of the disease are relatively less dangerous.

Many investigators and livestock sanitary officials believe nevertheless that virus may remain alive on parts of the animal not reached by the circulating blood, that virus carriers exist, and that such animals may harbor the virus for a long time after recovery. The percentage of carriers, however, is believed to be very small.

The field evidence presented to support this view is strong. Instances are reported in which the disease occurred in clean herds shortly after the addition of animals that had previously been affected, other possible sources of infection having been excluded. Animals have been held responsible for causing outbreaks of the disease more than a year after they recovered from it.

In the slaughtered animal, the formation of acid in the normal process of rigor mortis—stiffening of muscles after death—in muscle tissue rapidly inactivates the virus that may be in the muscles and other parts reached by the acid. Quick freezing, however, suspends acid formation, and such muscle may retain its infectivity until thawed. Lymph nodes, liver, kidney, bone marrow, rumen, other organs, and residual blood are not affected by the changes attending rigor mortis and, depending on circumstances, may retain infective virus for weeks. They, like the muscle tissue that has not undergone rigor mortis, may retain infective virus indefinitely when frozen.

Varying conditions affect viability of the virus outside the animal body. Virus exposed to direct sunlight is readily destroyed. But virus in tissue fragments or even on contaminated materials, such as hair, feed, and stable equipment, may remain infective for weeks under average stable and farm conditions.

That the virus does not always perish rapidly outside the animal body is strongly indicated by the fact that FMD sometimes has appeared on premises during the gradual restocking that usually is started under the eradication policy in this country 30 to 90 days after slaughter of affected and contact animals and disinfection of the premises. In one instance in California the virus persisted on such premises for 345 days. In the control and eradication of the outbreaks of FMD it is advisable, therefore, to regard the virus as relatively resistant to physical and other influences.

The viability of FMD virus in milk and milk products depends in general on the degree and rate of acid formation and on the temperatures involved in the processing of the various products. The virus is destroyed by heat, and standard pasteurization temperatures generally are considered adequate for its inactivation.

When kept in an incubator at about 37° C. (98.6° F.), the virus loses infectivity within 48 hours. At average room temperature, 18° to 20° C. (64° to 68° F.), it remains viable somewhat longer (2 to 3 weeks). At ordinary refrigeration temperatures, 4° to 7° C. (39° to 45° F.), it usually remains infective for many months, especially when properly buffered. When rapidly dried under vacuum at low temperatures, −50° to −70° C. (−58° to −94° F.), the virus remains viable for several years.

THE EFFECTS OF VARIOUS CHEMICALS on the virus of FMD have received considerable attention. Generally speaking, most chemicals for various reasons have been proved unsatisfactory for practical use as disinfectants.

An exception to this general rule is sodium hydroxide (caustic soda, lye). A 1-percent solution destroys the virus within 1 minute. In practice, a 2-percent solution is generally used. If less than 1-percent is employed, longer exposures are required.

Sodium carbonate in 5-percent solution has proved satisfactory where speed of action is not urgent.

Many new virucidal (virus-destroying) preparations have been put on the market, but their efficacy against FMD and other vesicular viruses has not been determined.

THE SPREAD OF FMD is primarily by and from the infected animal itself. Experimental evidence indicates that infected animals spread the virus most actively in the earlier stages of the disease. They may do so even before any lesions can be seen. The virus is contained in the fluid and the coverings of the vesicles and in the blood during the early, febrile stage of the disease; at that time the saliva, urine, milk, and probably other secretions and excretions are also infectious. The active virus leaving the infected animal contaminates the animal's surroundings and it can be carried mechanically by people, horses, and dogs or other not generally susceptible species, or on litter, feed, stable equipment, vehicles, and other objects and products—milk, creamery products, serums and other biological products, garbage, barns, pens, pastures, stockyards, saleyards, railway cars, and trucks. Susceptible animals can become infected when they come in contact directly or indirectly with contaminated material. People can spread the disease by contaminated hands or clothing. Under conditions favoring persistence of the virus outside the animal body, the danger of spreading infection is considerable.

FMD apparently is not transmitted by insect vectors. There has been no evidence in the United States that birds are an important factor in the spread of the disease. People, dogs, cats, farm animals, and vehicles that may act directly or indirectly as mechanical carriers of the virus are subject to close control in quarantine areas.

ALL INITIAL or primary outbreaks in the United States before 1902 were attributed to importations of animals from infected countries. The source of the 1902 outbreak was traced to a case near the docks in Chelsea, Mass.; the infection may have been introduced through contaminated shipments of hay, straw, halters, ropes, hides, hair, or wool from overseas. There was some evidence, however, that the disease may have been introduced through importation of vaccinia virus (smallpox vaccine) contaminated with FMD virus, as was true in the 1908 epizootic.

There were definite indications that the 1914 outbreak, first discovered near Niles, Mich., started in hogs fed trimmings and offal from a packinghouse that handled foreign meats. The outbreaks in 1924 and 1929 in California are considered to have started in hogs fed raw garbage from vessels carrying meat stores obtained in countries where FMD was enzootic. The source of the infection in the Texas outbreaks of 1924–1925 is unknown.

British reports attribute primary outbreaks in England in 1938–1953 to feeding swill (garbage), or contact with imported meats and bones other than swill, or infected serum. Circumstantial evidence indicates that migrations of starlings from the continent of Europe to the British Isles may have been contributory. Of the 540 primary outbreaks during the period, 214 were attributed to swill and 36 other points of primary infection were in herds with possible contact with swill.

DIAGNOSIS of typical cases showing the clinical lesions and symptoms described in cattle, hogs, sheep, goats, or other cloven-footed animals should not give the trained observer any difficulty were it not that two other vesicular diseases in the United States produce lesions and symptoms that cannot be differentiated from foot-and-mouth disease or from each other except by animal inoculations or serologic and other laboratory tests. One of them is vesicular stomatitis (VS), which affects cattle, swine, and horses. The other is vesicular exanthema (VE), which affects hogs only.

Diagnosis may be made in the field or in the laboratory, or both. In the field it is usually accomplished by different methods of inoculation of horses, cattle, and swine. If other species, such as sheep or goats, are involved in the outbreak, they are included. Veterinarians trained in these diagnostic procedures are available in all parts of the United States, and anyone suspecting the existence of a vesicular disease should report immediately to State or Federal livestock sanitary officials or to the local veterinarian.

In basing differential diagnosis on animal inoculations, the diagnostician bears in mind: (1) That the horse is not susceptible to FMD but is susceptible to VS and it is only slightly or irregularly susceptible to VE; horses naturally infected with VE have not been reported; (2) that cattle are susceptible to FMD and VS but not to VE; and (3) that swine are susceptible to all three diseases, and only swine have been naturally or experimentally infected with VE, except as noted in point 1.

These field procedures should be left to specially trained diagnosticians who in turn may require assistance from the laboratory. In the laboratory, animal inoculation tests, serum neutralization, and complement-fixation tests may be performed for confirmation of field tests or primary diagnosis.

In addition to VS and VE, such other diseases as rinderpest, mucosal disease, bluetongue, cowpox, and contagious ecthyma in sheep are suggestive of FMD at times.

PREVENTION of FMD in the United States, with its largely self-sufficient production of livestock and its relative geographic isolation, is maintained most effectively by close control of the importation of animals, animal products, and other agricultural products, such as hay and straw.

A Federal act passed in 1930 prohibits importation into the United States of cattle, swine, sheep, or goats, or fresh, chilled, or frozen meats from these species from all countries except those known to be free of the disease. Other products considered to be potentially dangerous, such as hides, bones, animal casings, and glands, are permitted entry only under prescribed conditions. Some products may be imported only for processing under supervision at designated, officially licensed establishments. Hay or straw from infected countries may not enter the United States, even when used as packing material for merchandise of nonagricultural origin. Garbage from ships or aircraft from foreign countries not on the United States FMD-free list also is prohibited, as are certain biological and therapeutic products of animal origin. In short, every practical means is applied to keep this plague out.

Other countries less fortunately situated than the United States are exposed repeatedly to the disease from adjoining infected countries. Especially exposed are the countries that permit importations of animals or animal products from infected areas. Only the most rigorous quarantines will prevent spread of the disease, but such action alone almost never suffices to contain the infection. Vaccination is practiced in many countries. To be effective, though, vaccine must be universally and conscientiously applied every 6 months or oftener, and other control measures must be taken.

CONTROL AND ERADICATION METHODS vary. In many countries, the reporting of such diseases as FMD is mandatory, and failure to do so is punishable by fine or imprisonment. Every livestockman and veterinarian and others as well are held responsible for reporting immediately any illness in livestock suspected as FMD. In the United States, such reports are made to the State or Federal animal disease control officials.

Prompt and effective quarantines, the immediate establishment of inspection procedures to check all possible contact herds, quick disposal of infected and exposed animals, and thorough cleaning and disinfection of the affected premises are the chief means of combating the disease.

There used to be only two important methods of control of FMD—isolation, quarantine, and disinfection, and those plus slaughter and burial of infected and exposed animals. The first method was supplemented in some European countries in the 1920's by the use of hyperimmune serum or convalescent serum from recovered animals. In most European countries there is legal authority for slaughter of infected and exposed animals if the authorities consider slaughter to be economically and otherwise practical and effective in each circumstance. Slaughter, however, has been used seldom in countries subjected to epizootics, and many countries have come to depend largely on FMD vaccines to control the disease.

THE STAMPING-OUT—or slaughter—method of eradication has been used in the United States beginning with the 1902 outbreak of FMD. Great Britain, Eire, Northern Ireland, Norway, and Canada also rely upon the slaughter method.

After a 2-year study in the British Isles and other countries, the Departmental Committee on Foot-and-Mouth Disease, appointed by the Minister of Agriculture and Fisheries of Great Britain, stated in its report: "In the circumstances of today, and of the immediate future so far as they are foreseeable, any idea that it would be possible to do away with stamping-out by making the whole susceptible animal population—or even all cattle—immune by vaccination is in the realm of fantasy. In present circumstances stamping-out must continue to be the policy in Great Britain."

Other countries—Belgium, France, Italy, West Germany, Spain, and most of the South American countries—depend largely on vaccination. Denmark, Finland, the Netherlands, Sweden, and Switzerland make use of stamping-out methods as well as vaccination when it is considered feasible. Restrictions, quarantines, and sanitary measures are employed to varying extent in all countries.

The stamping-out method consists of:

1. A complete isolation of infected premises, with prohibition of traffic therefrom pending disposal of animals, disinfection, and testing.

2. Prompt slaughter and proper disposal of animals infected with or exposed to foot-and-mouth disease, thus removing at once the greatest source of active virus and avoiding the possibility of carriers.

Slaughter and burial or cremation are done as soon as possible after the establishment of a diagnosis. Early discovery and diagnosis are paramount in prompt eradication of the disease.

Indemnities contributed to by the Federal and State Governments are paid to owners of animals or property destroyed in the course of eradicating FMD.

3. Thorough cleaning and disinfection of the premises and of materials possibly contaminated with virus.

This removes and destroys the greater part of whatever virus may remain active after proper burial or burning of slaughtered animals. These procedures are carried out under direct official supervision, in accordance with standard instructions for employees engaged in eradication of FMD.

4. Testing of premises following an appropriate interval of time after disinfection.

Test animals, including cattle and hogs, are placed to feed and graze and otherwise come in contact with all parts of the premises and objects that might have been contaminated with FMD virus. Hogs are especially desirable because of their rooting habits. Occurrence of the disease in test animals reveals any virus that may have survived cleaning and disinfecting procedures.

The effectiveness of these procedures is shown by the records on some 5,000 premises cleaned and disinfected in outbreaks since 1902: There were only two instances in the California outbreak of 1924–1925 and 14 cases in the interstate 1914–1916 outbreak where infection developed in test animals after cleaning and disinfection—in all, only 0.3 percent. The places were detected by the test animals before complete restocking had been permitted.

5. Quarantines, which are essential. Authority for quarantines rests primarily with the officials of the State, although affected areas or entire States may be put under quarantine by the Federal Government. The area surrounding infected premises within a distance of 5 to 50 miles—or more, depending on circumstances—should be quarantined immediately. All contact premises should be inspected as soon as possible and infection eliminated.

The extent of quarantines is increased or decreased in accordance with prevailing conditions.

6. Inspections, which are systematized and coordinated among Federal, State, and local authorities.

TREATMENT only alleviates the symptoms of the disease. It does not prevent spread of infection. Indeed, the repeated handling of animals in trying to treat them interferes with attempts to eradicate the disease. Treatment has no place in the stamping-out program.

Immunity for 6 months to 2 years follows recovery from natural or artificially induced FMD. The immunity is type-specific—that is, to 1 of the 6 types of virus—and may be influenced by variations of the virus within the specific types.

VACCINATION is an important tool for control in many countries where the disease is enzootic.

The most commonly used vaccine is the one developed by S. Schmidt of Denmark and O. Waldmann of Germany just before the Second World War. It consists essentially of FMD virus adsorbed on aluminum hydroxide and inactivated by formalin and incubation.

Variations of the Schmidt-Waldmann vaccine have been used in different countries. Generally the virus for the vaccine is derived from the tongue epithelium of artificially inoculated cattle. H. S. Frenkel of the Netherlands has developed techniques for propagation of the virus in tongue epithelium from normal slaughter cattle.

Anybody who uses vaccine has to know which type of virus is the prevalent one in the outbreak. The vaccines must be critically tested to prove that they do not produce the disease and do protect against it.

Opportunities were exceptionally good in Mexico for producing, testing, and observing effects of aluminum-hydroxide-adsorbed, formalin-treated vaccines produced with virus from inoculated cattle. The resistance induced by vaccines is known from experience in Mexico to depreciate rapidly after 4 months.

There is some evidence that hogs and sheep are not satisfactorily immunized with vaccine made with virus of bovine origin.

Import regulations are formulated and administered by the Animal Inspection and Quarantine Branch of the United States Department of Agriculture, under authority of section 306 (a) of the Tariff Act of 1930 and the acts of 1890 and 1903. The regulations are subject to revision from time to time as conditions change.

THE POLICY OF THE Department of Agriculture is to continue its vigilance to prevent the introduction of FMD and to combat it vigorously by the stamping-out, or slaughter, method of eradication if it should occur here.

The disease was conquered in the outbreaks of 1902, 1908, 1924 and 1925 (Texas), and 1929, each of which involved no more than a few thousand animals. It was also stamped out in the more severe and extensive epizootic of 1914–1916 and the outbreak of 1924–1925 in California.

In the 1914–1916 epizootic, foot-and-mouth disease occurred in 22 States and the District of Columbia. It invaded the large Union Stockyards of Chicago. In the outbreak, 77,240 cattle, 85,092 swine, 9,767 sheep, and 123 goats were destroyed. There has been no recurrence or new infection in the 22 States.

In the 1924–1925 outbreak in California, 58,791 cattle, 21,195 swine, 28,382 sheep, and 1,391 goats were slaughtered. Among them were many cattle and sheep grazing on the range. The infection spread to deer in the Stanislaus National Forest, and it was necessary to destroy 22,214 deer, of which 2,279 showed lesions of foot-and-mouth disease, but it was possible to keep the outbreak from other States and to eradicate it in California. The later, much milder occurrence of foot-and-mouth disease in California in 1929 was not linked with the 1924 outbreak.

The stamping-out procedures followed in all the outbreaks have been supported by the United States Livestock Sanitary Association, which comprises the animal disease control officials and producers of the various States and livestock and agricultural organizations generally.

In Mexico, the disease got a foothold before adequate eradication measures were started. It was limited to central Mexico, but it became so widespread there that eradication by slaughter threatened to upset the Mexican economy. Cattle are used in Mexico as work animals, and the agriculture of the country might have been damaged if more and more animals had continued to be exposed, infected, and slaughtered. Vaccination was added to the eradication measures in an effort to reduce the rapid spread of infection. At the same time, slaughter of all infected and exposed animals was continued wherever infection appeared. As of December 31, 1954, the cost to the United States of the Mexican-United States campaign of eradication in Mexico and the protective measures taken in the United States was about 130 million dollars.

RESEARCH ON FMD has interested the United States Department of Agriculture for many years. During the 1924 outbreaks in California and Texas, people recognized the need for more technical information on the disease. The Department therefore established a Foot-and-Mouth Disease Commission, which carried on research in Europe in 1925 and 1926. At that time experimentation with the virus of FMD was prohibited in the United States, which had no safe and suitable facilities available for research on the problem.

In 1947, following the outbreak in Mexico, the Department's Foot-and-Mouth Disease Advisory Committee recommended that further research be initiated at once in cooperation with European laboratories to help the Mexico-United States Commission for Eradication of Foot-and-Mouth Disease and to strengthen protection against the disease in the United States. The cooperation that was started in 1948 with laboratories in Denmark, England, and the Netherlands has been continued.

The committee and the Department also recommended that research facilities be constructed in the United States as soon as possible. In 1948 the Congress authorized establishment of a special laboratory for the purpose (Public Law 496, 80th Cong.). The law required that the laboratory and related facilities for the research be established on a coastal island. Research was authorized on FMD and such other animal diseases as, in the opinion of the Secretary of Agriculture, might constitute a threat to the livestock industry of the country.

In 1952, THE CONGRESS appropriated 10 million dollars for building a laboratory. Plum Island, N. Y., the site of the Army's Fort Terry, was selected as the location. The entire island was transferred to the Department of Agriculture in 1954, and limited research was started in existing facilities that had been rehabilitated and adapted for safe experimentation. A new, more complete laboratory has been built.

Research at the Plum Island Animal Disease Laboratory will be devoted primarily to investigations of foot-and-mouth disease, but if need arises attention may be given to diagnosis and research on other foreign plagues. Its program includes investigation of diagnostic procedures, modes of transmission, susceptibility of various species, virus propagation and destruction, and other phases important to more complete knowledge of preventive means, including the immunization procedures and fundamental studies of the virus.

M. S. SHAHAN *was appointed director of the Plum Island Animal Disease Laboratory of the Department of Agriculture in 1952. He was graduated from Colorado Agricultural and Mechanical College in 1924. He has been with the Department since 1926.*

J. TRAUM *is chief scientist of the Plum Island Animal Disease Laboratory, with which he became associated in 1952 after more than 40 years of research on animal diseases in the Department of Agriculture and at the University of California.*

For further reading:
Bureau of Animal Industry: *Foot-and-Mouth Disease*, U. S. Department of Agriculture Farmers' Bulletin 666 (revised). 1952.

Great Britain Ministry of Agriculture and Fisheries Foot-and-Mouth Disease Committee: *Report of the Departmental Committee on Foot-and-Mouth Disease, 1952–1954*, Ministry of Agriculture and Fisheries, H. M. S. Stationery Office, London, 151 pages. 1954.

J. R. Mohler and Jacob Traum: *Foot-and-Mouth Disease*, U. S. D. A. Yearbook of Agriculture, *Keeping Livestock Healthy*, pages 263–275. 1942.

Rabies

H. W. SCHOENING

RABIES, or hydrophobia, is caused by a filterable virus—a type of infective agent that can pass through certain filters that retain ordinary bacteria and cannot be seen through ordinary microscopes. The virus is found in the saliva of affected animals. The disease is produced by the bite of a rabid animal or by contact with the saliva of a rabid animal. The bite makes a wound in which the virus in the saliva is deposited.

The disease is primarily one of the dog, although many species, including people, are susceptible to infection.

Rabies has been reported in the cat, cow, horse, mule, sheep, goat, hog, wolf, fox, coyote, hyena, skunk, monkey, deer, antelope, camel, bear, elk, polecat, squirrel, hare, rabbit, rat, mouse, jackal, badger, marmot, woodchuck, porcupine, weasel, hedgehog, mongoose, gopher, raccoon, the owl, hawk, chicken, pigeon, stork, and several species of bats.

When rabies is once controlled in dogs its importance from an economic or public-health standpoint will be greatly reduced. When a disease becomes established in a wild species, however, a serious situation develops, and strenuous efforts must be made to control it in the species affected.

Rabies in foxes became rather widespread after 1945 in certain States, and considerable livestock losses occurred when rabid foxes attacked farm animals, particularly cattle.

The number of cases of rabies in all species between 1938 and 1955 was 146,627—a staggering total. The financial loss to the country runs into large figures and the constant hazards to human beings and animals call for strong national action to control and eventually eradicate the disease.

The period of incubation—the time between exposure to infection and the first appearance of symptoms of the disease—may be as short as 2 weeks or as long as many months. Most cases develop within 3 months.

All animals or persons bitten do not develop the disease. The proportion of persons who contract the disease after being bitten by rabid dogs and who were not treated has been estimated at 15 percent.

From 35 to 45 percent of the dogs, 40 percent of the horses, 36 percent of the hogs, and 25 to 30 percent of the cattle bitten by rabid animals contract the disease. Whether an individual animal contracts the disease depends in part on the location and size of the wound, the amount of bleeding produced, and other conditions. In general, the nearer the bite is to the central nervous system and the deeper the wound, the greater is the danger of infection. If the hemorrhage resulting from the bite is profuse, the possibility exists that the virus will be washed out of the wound. Also, exact information is not available on whether the virus of rabies is constantly present in the saliva of a rabid animal and whether it varies in both quantity and virulence.

After it is deposited in the wound, the virus remains latent for an extremely variable period, which depends on the size, location, and depth of the wound and the amount of virulent saliva introduced. The virus follows the course of the nerves to the spinal cord and along the spinal cord to the brain before the symptoms appear. The period between the bite and the appearance of the first symptom may be 14 to 285 days.

The bite of a dog may be infectious at least 3 days before the dog manifests symptoms of rabies. In one case in the

Pasteur Institute at Athens, Greece, infection was found to be present in the saliva 8 days before the dog showed signs of the disease.

A dog can transmit rabies through a bite only if it is rabid. A normal dog cannot transmit the disease. Rabid foxes and other wildlife, through their attacks upon animals, have been responsible for outbreaks of rabies.

A FEW INSTANCES of finding rabies virus in the milk or udder tissue of lactating animals have been reported. Research workers in different parts of the world have investigated the subject at various times, but most have failed to find the virus in milk or udder tissue.

Scientists in the Department of Agriculture conducted some experiments on this point in 1934. They inoculated the virus of rabies into the tongues of two milking cows. Samples of milk were taken at frequent intervals, and milk from the udder tissues was collected at death. Samples were inoculated into the brains of rabbits. The results were negative. A calf and four pigs were fed the milk taken daily from the two cows from the time of exposure to the virus to the time of death from rabies. The mucous membrane of the mouth of two of the pigs and the calf was scarified to make minute wounds, but in no case did the animals show any harmful effects from the consumption of the milk. Rabies virus in the form of a brain emulsion also was added to milk and fed to four hogs. Abrasions were produced mechanically on the mucous surfaces of the mouths of the animals. In no case did the animals show any evidence of rabies. It appears, therefore, from the information available, that although the virus of rabies at times may be found in milk, such chances are remote.

From a practical standpoint, there seems to be little danger in consuming milk from even a rabid animal. Milk secretion usually is considerably diminished at the clinical appearance of the disease, so that it is quite unlikely that the animal's milk has been consumed after symptoms have appeared. Nevertheless, the milk from a rabid or suspected cow should be condemned as unfit for consumption.

The same position should be taken with regard to the meat from a rabid or suspected animal. The disposition of farm animals that have been exposed to the bites of a rabid dog but do not show signs of the disease also presents a problem. The International Rabies Conference in Paris in 1927 made the following recommendation on this point: "Animals bitten by rabid animals, whether treated or not after the bite, should not be butchered between the eighth day and, at the very least, the end of the third month following the bite."

IN DOGS the first symptom of rabies may be a change in behavior. The animal may become restless and excitable. A friendly dog may become irritable and snappy, and a dog that ordinarily is less amiable may become friendly. Later it may have a tendency to wander and may disappear for a day or two, returning exhausted and considerably emaciated. The dog may seek dark corners and hide. At times the bark might change in tone.

Later on the dog develops partial paralysis and has difficulty in drinking, although it may make efforts to lap water. It staggers around until complete paralysis sets in. Because the virus attacks the brain and spinal cord and sets up degenerative changes, the symptoms—excitability, convulsions, and paralysis—can be correlated with changes in the central nervous system. The inability to swallow results from paralysis of the muscles of the throat.

The term "hydrophobia" means fear of water, but its application to the disease in dogs appears to be a misnomer, because affected dogs show no fear of water. The use of the term probably has its origin in the fact that affected dogs and human beings have been observed to develop convulsions through their unsuccessful efforts to drink. Even the mere thought of drinking on the part of human beings has been responsible for convulsions, and a dread of water or drinking becomes established in many patients.

In the furious form of the disease, the animal is aggressive. It snaps at objects placed before it and will attack dogs and people. It may attack the bars of a cage with such vigor as to break its teeth. The dog's tendency to roam, its restlessness, and its inclination to bite spread the disease widely.

Rabies may take a number of forms, and the symptoms I described are those of a typical case. Many animals affected with rabies do not exhibit these symptoms. The symptoms may be more or less masked and may perhaps be manifested eventually only by paralysis.

Paralytic symptoms are the outstanding feature in the dumb form of rabies. The dog is not vicious. It has no tendency to bite or roam. It is not excitable. In fact, it may be the opposite.

The outstanding clinical feature of dumb rabies is paralysis of the lower jaw, or dropped jaw. The animal's mouth stays open an inch or more. It can be closed with the hands, but the dog cannot close its own jaw.

Many times this is mistakenly thought to be due to a bone in the throat, and many persons have exposed themselves to the virus by examining the mouth and throat for a bone. Usually a dog with a bone stuck in its mouth or throat makes repeated efforts with its paws or otherwise to remove the bone, but in dumb rabies the animal makes no motion about the head with its paws. An animal with a dropped jaw should be viewed with suspicion. No examination should be made of the throat. The animal should be taken immediately to a veterinarian for diagnosis.

Also in the dumb form of rabies the animal shows evidence of paralysis of the hindquarters and forequarters within a few days. It eventually becomes completely paralyzed and dies.

The course of the disease in both the furious and the dumb forms is usually short, and the animal dies in 3 to 7 days.

CATS that have rabies generally hide under the furniture or in a dark corner. There they may die unobserved in a day or two. As a rule, however, the disease in cats implies danger for human beings. The rabid cat becomes bellicose. From its dark corner it may suddenly attack animals or persons, especially children, jumping up to the face and inflicting severe wounds with its teeth and claws. In the violence of this attack it frequently bites itself.

The rabid cat nearly loses its voice and is able only to mew hoarsely.

Later it loses its appetite, has difficulty in swallowing, becomes emaciated, and succumbs within several days with symptoms of paralysis.

CATTLE are susceptible to both furious and dumb rabies. The former is the more common. A sharp distinction cannot always be drawn between the two, however, as the furious type usually merges into the dumb type because of the paralysis that always appears before death. In typical cases of dumb rabies, the paralysis occurs at the beginning of the attack and remains until the animal dies.

The first signs are loss of appetite, stopping of the secretion of milk, great restlessness, anxiety, manifestations of fear, and a change in disposition. There follows in a day or two a stage of excitation or madness, which is indicated by increasing restlessness; loud bellowing, with a peculiar change in the sound of the voice; violent butting with the head and pawing the ground; and an insane tendency to attack other animals, although the desire to bite is not so marked in cattle as in dogs.

About the fourth day the animal usually becomes quieter, and the walk is stiff, unsteady, and swaying—the final paralysis is coming on. Loss of flesh is rapid. Even during the short course of the disease, the animal becomes extremely emaciated. The temperature usually remains about normal or even subnormal. Finally there is complete paralysis of the hindquarters, the animal is unable to rise, and (except for irregular convulsive movements) lies in a comatose condition. It dies usually 4 to 6 days after the first symptoms appear.

The rabid fox, through its attack on cattle, has been responsible for heavy losses in cattle in some areas. In 1953 there were 1,033 cases of rabies in foxes and 1,028 cases in 1954.

THE VAMPIRE BAT (*Desmodus rotundus murinus* or *Desmodus rufus*) has been responsible for the spread of rabies to cattle and human beings in parts of Mexico, Central America, and South America, to the warm parts of which the vampire bat is indigenous.

The vampire bat feeds on the blood of animals and man, and an infected bat so transmits rabies. Reports have indicated that in Mexico the vampire bat is moving northward and eastward from the western mountain areas and has been reported in Chihuahua, within 100 miles of the United States border. A survey in southern California in 1952 by the Pan American Sanitary Bureau revealed evidence of the presence of the vampire bat in that area.

Rabies has been found in several insect- and fruit-eating varieties of bats in the United States. Some persons have been attacked by these bats, which, on laboratory examination, were found to be affected with rabies. The first bat found to be affected with rabies was in Florida. It was a Florida Yellow bat (*Dasypterus florindanus*) and was killed while attacking a boy in Tampa in June 1953. In September 1953, a bat, which was found to be rabid, attacked a woman near Carlisle, Pa. Its species could not be determined because the carcass had been destroyed. Rabid insect- or fruit-eating bats have since been reported in Texas and Montana. Just where the infection in

these bats originated is not known, but the findings indicate that a new problem may be facing those concerned with the control of rabies in the United States.

MANY SPECIES of wild animals are susceptible to rabies.

Severe outbreaks of rabies among wild animals, especially coyotes, appeared in Oregon, California, Nevada, and Idaho in 1950. A rabid coyote bit and caused the loss of 27 steers in one feed lot. Serious outbreaks have been reported since that time.

Outbreaks of rabies in foxes occurred in Maine in 1934, in Massachusetts in 1935, and in 1940 in Georgia, South Carolina, and Alabama. The origin of that infection is not known, but of 291 fox heads examined in Georgia, 30.2 percent were affected with rabies. At least 90 head of livestock were reported to have developed the disease from exposure to rabid foxes, and the antirabic treatment was given 17 persons who were exposed.

In 1954 the red fox and the gray fox were to blame for outbreaks along the Appalachian range from New York to Florida and westward across the Southern States to eastern Texas.

Skunks and civet cats have been responsible for outbreaks in Iowa, Missouri, Minnesota, Nebraska, South Dakota, and North Dakota.

The first step in the control of rabies in wildlife is to reduce the number of wild animals in an area, particularly the affected species, by such means as trapping and poisoning. Effective cooperation of Federal, State, and local agencies and the public is essential.

DIAGNOSIS is important. One has to establish the presence or absence of rabies infection in dogs that have bitten people or animals so that proper measures can be taken.

Because the diagnosis of the disease can be based on both clinical and laboratory examinations, it is essential that the dog be kept under observation by a veterinarian.

As rabies is a fatal disease and an affected animal dies in a short time, its brain can be examined in the laboratory for the presence of specific changes, which are indicated by the presence of Negri bodies in certain parts. These bodies, named after their discoverer, an Italian scientist, are found on microscopic examination in certain of the brain cells and are considered to be a result of the action of rabies virus on the brain cell. The bodies are specific in the diagnosis of rabies, but sometimes they are few in number, particularly if the animals have been destroyed in the early stages of the disease. It is advisable therefore to allow the disease to progress to its termination or to a well-advanced stage so that the laboratory diagnosis can be conclusive.

The diagnosis of rabies also can be established by animal inoculation tests in the laboratory. Mice generally are used for the purpose. The brain material from the suspected rabid animal is injected under ether anesthesia into the brain of the test animal.

Dogs suspected of having rabies or dogs that have bitten people should be held in strict quarantine in suitable strong, tight, escapeproof quarters for 2 weeks in order that a correct diagnosis may be made. If a rabid dog is not properly confined, it may work its way out and disappear and die later at a distant point without having been identified. That would complicate the handling of a case of a person bitten by the dog. The fact that the dog had escaped would in itself be some indication that it might have been rabid, but, without proof, an uncertain situation develops.

On postmortem examination, no constant or definite lesions are observed. The alterations are slight, variable, and almost absent at times, so that (unless there is a definite history of characteristic symptoms) a positive diagnosis cannot be made without recourse to microscopic examination or animal inoculations with material from the brain of the suspected animal.

The most suggestive indication of rabies is the presence in the stomach of unusual articles, such as stones, wood, earth, cloth, iron, and feathers. Frequently the stomach is empty of food but is distended with material of this kind. The mucous membrane of the stomach frequently is inflamed. A marked reddening of the folds of the stomach, with or without erosions, is noticed sometimes. The covering of the brain and spinal cord and the mucous lining of the mouth, throat, and respiratory tract also might be inflamed.

The feet of rabid dogs may be sore and bruised, denoting extensive travel during the period of roving.

The heart and the surrounding membrane are often inflamed, but these and similar lesions are more frequently due to the condition of the animal before dying than to any specific alteration. The carcass undergoes rapid decomposition.

The Department of Agriculture has collected data on the incidence of rabies since 1938 by means of a questionnaire to State officials.

The data are summarized in the following paragraphs, but it is probable that there were more cases of the disease in the United States than were reported.

The information received by the Department of Agriculture showed that the 146,627 cases of rabies in the United States between 1938 and 1955 were distributed as follows: Dogs, 113,484; cattle, 10,793; horses, 557; sheep, 679; swine, 854; cats, 6,514; goats, 152; people, 429; miscellaneous, 13,165. The incidence of rabies was greatest in 1946 (10,872 cases) and lowest in 1940 (7,238 cases). Eight human cases were reported in 1954 and 47 in 1938. In 1954 there were 4,083 cases and in 1944 there were 9,067 cases among dogs.

Figures for the States showed 86,390 cases in 1945–1954, inclusive. The totals for the 10 years were: Alabama, 5,126; Arizona, 407; Arkansas, 1,549; California, 2,282; Colorado, 185; Connecticut, 4; Delaware, 11; District of Columbia, 120; Florida, 1,748; Georgia, 4,554; Idaho, 37; Illinois, 2,925; Indiana, 4,847; Iowa, 2,140; Kansas, 429; Kentucky, 5,689; Louisiana, 3,837; Maine, 3; Maryland, 218; Massachusetts, 4; Michigan, 1,949; Minnesota, 879; Mississippi, 2,268; Missouri, 1,922; Montana, 15; Nebraska, 271; Nevada, 0; New Hampshire, 1; New Jersey, 606; New Mexico, 145; New York State, 6,408; New York City, 197; North Carolina, 2,748; North Dakota, 249; Ohio, 4,423; Oklahoma, 1,284; Oregon, 3; Pennsylvania, 2,546; Rhode Island, 2; South Carolina, 2,382; South Dakota, 536; Tennessee, 5,015; Texas, 11,712; Utah, 66; Vermont, 0; Virginia 2,254; Washington, 26; West Virginia, 2,051; Wisconsin, 309; and Wyoming, 8.

In 36 States in 1953 there were 8,837 cases. Cases reported in other countries in 1953 included Algeria, 323; Ceylon, 428; Spain, 201; France, 1; Italy, 350; and Japan, 4.

A report on the prevalence of rabies in various countries of the world was made in 1954 by the International Office of Epizootics.

Belgium, Denmark, France, Great Britain, Ireland, Luxembourg, Norway, the Netherlands, Portugal, Sweden, Switzerland, Australia, and New Zealand were free of rabies in 1952. Rabies existed in Mexico, Central America, South America, and most of the countries of Asia and Africa.

Outbreaks of rabies in dogs continually occur in certain sections of the United States. In some of the outbreaks, vigorous steps are taken to bring the disease under control and to eradicate it. In other areas little is done to reach that goal, primarily because of lack of organization and funds. As long as rabies exists to any appreciable extent in the dog population in any locality, areas that are free of the disease are menaced. Not only does a rabid dog travel far; very likely dogs

in the incubative stage of the disease are transported in automobiles, and so may spread the disease from an infected area to a distant clean one. Energetic measures will bring rabies under control and lead to its eradication in an area, but it can be introduced readily again from an infected locality.

THE SOLUTION of the rabies problem in the United States lies in an effort to control it on a national basis. The control of rabies is within the authority of the States. The authority often is divided between the State livestock sanitary service and the State health service. The Public Health Service and the Fish and Wildlife Service are empowered to engage in a rabies control program. A third Federal agency interested in the problem, the Department of Agriculture, is not empowered to engage in such a control program in dogs because its authority is limited by law to the control of the disease in livestock, and it has been ruled that dogs are not considered to be livestock. In the event rabies becomes a serious disease threat to livestock, the Department of Agriculture has the authority to participate in a program for the protection of livestock.

At a conference in Philadelphia in 1947 under the auspices of the Special Committee on Rabies of the American Veterinary Medical Association, representatives of the American Public Health Association, the American Medical Association, the Public Health Service, the Department of Agriculture, the United States Livestock Sanitary Association, the American Animal Hospital Association, and the American Veterinary Medical Association agreed on the following principles in connection with any rabies control program that might be undertaken on a national basis:

Rabies in the United States is of sufficient importance to make it desirable that the Federal Government participate in means for its control through cooperation with the several

States. Rabies in man is generally a disease reportable to local and State health authority. Rabies in lower animals should be specifically a reportable disease to be reported to public health or other responsible State health or livestock sanitary authority. It should be reported by States, and the place of the occurrence should be specified. Through a central Federal agency, the consolidated information should be assembled, analyzed, and distributed to all States, agencies, and individuals having responsibility in a rabies-control program. Prime consideration should be given to adequate diagnostic facilities, the control of animals capable of transmitting the disease, and mass immunization of susceptible animals, particularly dogs.

The conference also recommended that the Department of Agriculture, the Public Health Service, and the Fish and Wildlife Service coordinate efforts for the control of rabies on a national scale.

Measures necessary for the effective control of rabies in dogs include strict licensing of all dogs, impounding and destroying stray dogs, destroying rabid or suspected rabid dogs and definitely diagnosing the disease in them, destroying dogs known to be bitten by rabid animals, quarantining and destroying dogs that have been in contact with rabid animals, enforcing strict general quarantine measures over a sufficiently wide area, and vaccinating all dogs—mass immunization.

A definite diagnosis in a rabid animal and tracing its movements are of particular importance—one has to know the dogs and other animals with which it came in contact and whether any of them were bitten, for each one then would be a potential spreader of rabies. The bitten dogs should be destroyed. Dogs that have been in contact with a rabid animal but have no history of being bitten should be kept in quarantine for 3 months to 6 months. Such action will shorten the duration of a rabies outbreak. An effective organization, with sufficient funds and personnel, is necessary to do that. Such efforts would put us ahead of the disease instead of behind it, as has been the case all too often in outbreaks in this country: Getting ahead of a disease is a cardinal precept in control.

Also important is the use of prophylactic vaccination of dogs—so-called mass immunization. When that procedure was introduced in the United States in about 1930, some persons questioned its efficacy and safety. But since then the value and safety of the vaccines have been established by laboratory findings and through their extensive use.

Two types of vaccine are employed for dogs.

One is of the phenol-killed type; it has been used extensively with excellent results for a number of years. The immunity it produces lasts in most animals for a little more than a year and in some animals for several years.

The other vaccine, of the so-called avian type, is a modified live virus produced in the embryonated chicken egg. It has had an extensive use in the United States and elsewhere. All reports indicate that it is safe and effective. It gives a high degree of protection in dogs shown experimentally to be as long as 3 years. Vaccination, to be a successful control measure, must be carried out on a large scale in a sufficiently wide area. It has been estimated if at least 70 percent of dogs in a region are vaccinated the full beneficial effects of such vaccination will be realized.

IF ALL those measures are put energetically into practice, rabies can be brought under control in a given area in several months or less.

The annual or periodic vaccination of dogs, even after the disease has been eradicated in an area, is desirable. The danger always exists of the introduction of the disease from an infected area under present conditions. Periodic vaccination of all dogs keeps immunity high and constant, and aids in preventing the disease from establishing itself in an area.

Outbreaks of rabies among wildlife usually occur in areas where the various species have reached a high density of population. The procedures then include the reduction of the numbers of animals in the area through trapping, shooting, gassing dens, and poisoning. Those procedures should be handled by trained specialists and should be undertaken in cooperation with the Fish and Wildlife Service and the corresponding agencies in the States. As in the control of rabies in dogs, the public should be informed about the need for the program.

Once rabies has been eradicated or at least controlled on a national basis, a quarantine of 6 months of all dogs imported into the United States from countries where the disease is prevalent would be of great value.

H. W. SCHOENING *was assistant chief of the Animal Disease and Parasite Research Branch, Agricultural Research Service, before he retired on April 30, 1955.*

Brucellosis

C. A. MANTHEI, A. K. KUTTLER, AND E. R. GOODE, JR.

BRUCELLOSIS is an infectious, widespread, and costly disease that mainly affects cattle, swine, and goats. It may affect other species of domestic and wild animals and can be transmitted to people.

Brucellosis is caused by bacteria of the genus *Brucella*, which includes three principal species: *Brucella melitensis, Brucella abortus,* and *Brucella suis.*

Br. melitensis, the first of the three species to be identified, was reported by David Bruce of England in 1887 on the Island of Malta and is the main cause of brucellosis in goats. *Br. abortus,* discovered by Bernard Bang of Denmark in 1897, is the principal cause of brucellosis in cattle. *Br. suis,* isolated by Jacob Traum of the United States in 1914, is primarily responsible for the disease in swine.

Although each of the three species of *Brucella* is relatively specific for individual species of animal, all can produce infection in other species and people. Brucellosis therefore must be considered as a single problem and not as three individual control problems.

Brucellosis of cattle was formerly known as Bang's disease and infectious abortion. It is prevalent in every cattle-raising country of the world.

The most frequent cause of brucellosis of cattle is *Br. abortus,* but *Br. suis* and *Br. melitensis* occasionally may infect cattle.

Brucellosis commonly is transmitted from infected animals and a contaminated environment to susceptible cattle by close association. Infection is believed to take place mainly through the alimentary tract.

Aborted fetuses, placental membranes, placental fluids, and the vaginal discharge that persists for several weeks after an animal has aborted teem with virulent *Brucella.* Cows may lick those materials and the genital organs of other cows and so are exposed to the infective agent.

Exposure to infection also takes place by ingestion of contaminated grass, dry roughage, and water. *Brucella* also may enter through the skin and the mucous membranes of the body openings, such as the eyes and nostrils.

All our evidence indicates that the disease is not transmitted directly from infected bulls to cows by natural service. It has been transmitted to susceptible females, however, by the intrauterine method of artificial insemination with *Brucella*-contaminated semen from an infected bull. Transmission has not been successful by the intracervical method of artificial insemination with semen from the same infected bull. Probably the greatest potential danger of spreading infection by bulls is by contaminating the surroundings with semen and urine or the discharge of infectious semen from the vagina of cows soon after breeding.

The course of brucellosis is related to the susceptibility of the individual and the number and virulence of *Br. abortus* organisms that gain entrance to the body. The incubation period—the time organisms enter the body until manifestations of the disease appear—may be 7 days to 7 months or longer.

Cattle generally are resistant to *Br. abortus* before reaching sexual maturity and become increasingly susceptible as they approach breeding age. Pregnant cattle usually are highly susceptible to infection. The disease is more progressive and severe in them than in nonpregnant females. Sexually mature bulls usually are more resistant to infection than cows and sexually mature heifers.

A factor, other than natural immunity, that also could be responsible for the lower incidence of brucellosis in males than in females is management. Because most dairy bulls and many beef bulls are maintained separately from the herd, their exposure to infection is lessened.

If an animal is susceptible and adequate numbers of virulent *Br. abortus* enter the body, a progressive infection takes place. The organisms are taken up by the blood and carried to the various tissues and organs, where multiplication occurs. The udder, uterus, testicles, seminal vesicles, lymph glands, and spleen are affected oftenest.

The first manifestation of infection usually is development of *Brucella* antibodies in the blood stream. The one antibody most commonly recognized is called an agglutinin and is measured by the blood serum agglutination test, which is used for establishing the brucellosis status of cattle.

The predominant symptoms of brucellosis in pregnant females are abortions, birth of weak calves, retained placentas, and vaginal discharge, often followed by temporary or permanent infertility. Milk production is reduced approximately 25 percent because of the alteration of the normal lactation period by abortions and delayed conceptions.

Symptoms are generally absent in mature females that are infected while open. Cattle infected by intrauterine insemination with infectious semen, however, show a pattern of repeat breeding similar to that observed in other venereal diseases—vibriosis and trichomoniasis. In either case udder infection occurs frequently.

Infected bulls may or may not show clinical evidence of brucellosis. The most apparent symptoms are enlargement of one or both testicles, loss of sexual desire, and infertility. There is usually involvement of one or more accessory genital organs, but that can be determined only by rectal examination.

If an animal is relatively resistant to brucellosis, or the number and virulence of the invading organism are low, or several of these factors are present, the infection may not develop or it may be temporary or become localized in some part of the body without clinical manifestations.

Br. abortus infection that becomes localized, particularly in the udder and supramammary lymph glands, has a tendency to persist for the productive life of most cattle.

Infection of cattle with *Br. suis* is infrequent. This infection is usually temporary, but when it becomes permanently established, it localizes most frequently in the udder and adjacent lymph glands, but clinical symptoms usually are absent.

The prevalence and significance of

Br. melitensis infection in cattle in this country are not clearly defined. Results of limited studies indicate that it is a relatively benign disease in cattle, causing localized udder and uterine infection with an occasional abortion.

RELIABLE AND PRACTICAL diagnostic procedures are essential for the successful control of diseases. The principal procedures employed for the diagnosis of brucellosis of cattle are the tube and plate seroagglutination tests and the milk-ring test. Herd history and clinical symptoms are used as supplemental evidence.

Isolation of *Brucella* from the animal is the most accurate diagnostic procedure, but it has limited practical value in the field. All diagnostic tests have definite limitations of accuracy and practicability, but the limitations can be held to a minimum by standardizing the *Brucella* antigens, reference serums, equipment, techniques, and interpretations.

Studies were begun in 1938 by the Bureau of Animal Industry to standardize the tube and plate seroagglutination tests at the request of the United States Livestock Sanitary Association, an organization made up of all segments of the livestock industry. The studies included selection of a highly antigenic strain of *Br. abortus*, development of procedures for the selection and maintenance of smooth colony forms, production of adequate quantities of organisms, and development of standard methods and equipment for preparing antigens with a constant sensitivity.

The first standard *Brucella* tube and plate antigens were made available in 1940 for the diagnosis of brucellosis in livestock. This was followed by adoption of standard equipment in all State-Federal testing laboratories. Procedures were then inaugurated to standardize the interpretation of the tests. Reference serum samples, along with both tube and plate antigens, were submitted annually or semi-

annually to each official testing laboratory in this country. Results of tests in each laboratory are returned to the central antigen laboratory at Beltsville, Md., for compilation and evaluation. From 1948 to 1955, 91.88 percent of the tube-test and 91.07 percent of the plate-test interpretations agreed with the standard interpretation. Furthermore, there was 99.12 percent agreement between the tube and the plate test.

The tube and plate seroagglutination tests are the most practical, accurate methods of diagnosing brucellosis in the individual animal. Both are used principally to measure the concentration of *Brucella* agglutinins in blood serum but may also be used to detect the same antibody in milk whey and semen plasma.

Specific agglutinins are produced in the body of animals by exposure to *Brucella*. As the disease progresses, the concentration of *Brucella* agglutinins increases. The concentration of agglutinins is measured by mixing increasing dilutions of serum with a standard amount of *Brucella* antigen (suspension of *Brucella* cells). When agglutinins are present, they cause the *Brucella* cells to clump and settle out of suspension. Complete agglutination (clumping) in the 1:100 dilution of serum is considered evidence of infection in nonvaccinated cattle more than 6 months of age.

Recent studies have brought about the official adoption of a new interpretation of the tube and plate seroagglutination tests for brucellosis in officially calf-vaccinated cattle 30 months of age or older. This new interpretation allows the diagnostic titer to be one dilution higher in officially calf-vaccinated than in nonvaccinated cattle. Therefore, complete agglutination in the 1:200 dilution of serum is now considered evidence of infection in calf-vaccinated cattle 30 months of age or older.

Comparisons of interpretations of the seroagglutination tests for brucellosis in nonvaccinated and calf-vaccinated cattle are presented on the next page.

FOR NONVACCINATED CATTLE

Dilutions			
1:50	*1:100*	*1:200*	*Diagnosis*
— 1	—	—	Negative.
I 2	—	—	Suspect.
+ 3	—	—	Do.
+	I	—	Do.
+	+ or higher	—	Positive.

FOR CALF-VACCINATED CATTLE

Dilutions			
1:50	*1:100*	*1:200*	*Diagnosis*
+	—	—	Negative.
+	I	—	Suspect.
+	+	—	Do.
+	+	I	Do.
+	+	+ or higher	Reactor.

1 — : No agglutination.
2 I: Incomplete agglutination.
3 + : Complete agglutination.

With the standard antigens, techniques, and interpretations, two principal factors limit the accuracy of the tube and plate seroagglutination tests. One is mechanical errors by the operators. The other is the character of the disease itself. *Brucella* agglutinins are either absent or below the diagnostic level in the early stages of the disease and in an occasional animal which has limited localized infection or is in the process of recovering from infection. Infected bulls occasionally have a serum agglutinin titer below the diagnostic level but most of them have a diagnostic agglutinin titer in the semen.

The milk-ring test is the latest of the diagnostic procedures to be adopted for the brucellosis control program. The antigen laboratory of the Animal Disease and Parasite Research Branch at Beltsville, Md., started producing and distributing milk-ring antigen for official testing in 1949. Progress has been made in developing a standard antigen, procedures for collection and preservation of milk and cream samples, standard test procedures, and uniform interpretation of results. The principal purpose of the milk-ring test is to locate brucellosis-infected herds and thereby to save manpower, time, and materials.

Can samples of milk and cream are usually collected at milk depots and creameries. The milk and cream samples are taken to testing laboratories where portions of each are mixed with the milk-ring antigen. If any milk or cream samples from a herd show a positive reaction, blood samples are collected from all the cattle in the herd and the serum is tested by the tube or plate agglutination test.

The milk-ring antigen is purposely standardized high in sensitivity so that only a minimum number of infected herds are missed by the test. Consequently a certain proportion of brucellosis-free herds is classified as suspicious. Failure to identify a limited number of infected herds with the milk-ring test may happen because bulls, sexually mature heifers, and dry cows are not represented in any one milk collection. The efficiency of the milk-ring test, which is generally conducted every 4 or 6 months, increases with each successive test.

All diagnostic antigens used for official testing of animals for brucellosis are produced and distributed by the Brucella Antigen Laboratory, Animal Disease and Parasite Research Branch, Beltsville.

None of the diagnostic tests available in 1956 was capable of accurately differentiating between serum agglutinin titers caused by virulent *Br. abortus* and those caused by Strain 19 vaccine. Progress has been made in differentiating between specific agglutinins (those produced by *Brucella*) and nonspecific agglutinins (those not caused by *Brucella*) found in the blood and milk of cattle. If the procedures can be standardized, they will be of considerable aid in correctly classifying animals with questionable agglutinin reactions.

Vaccination of cattle against brucellosis is for the sole purpose of producing a level of immunity that will protect the majority of animals against average field exposure to infection.

Any other use of the present official vaccine is not supported by research.

Strain 19 is the only officially recognized vaccine in this country. This strain is a member of the species *Br. abortus*, and has the unique properties of low pathogenicity and relatively high immunogenicity, which have remained stable since 1930. All available evidence shows that immunity follows the rapid, complete recovery of cattle from a low-grade infection produced by Strain 19. Furthermore, the disease is not transmitted from vaccinated to susceptible nonvaccinated animals by contact. This type of immunization is analogous to smallpox immunization in human beings.

The desirable characteristics of Strain 19 are maintained by careful selection of specific colony forms that have been found to be suitable for the production of vaccine. Growth requirements and culturing procedures also are kept as constant as possible.

New seed cultures of Strain 19 are selected every 3 or 4 months and supplied to biological companies in this country and to many foreign countries for production of the vaccine. Each lot of vaccine produced in this country is tested in the vaccine control laboratory at Beltsville for number of living *Brucella*, purity, and characteristics of the *Brucella* colonies. Established standards must be met before any lot of vaccine is released for use.

Tests are conducted at intervals to determine the keeping qualities of vaccines maintained under recommended storage conditions. This is the basis for establishing the length of time a product can be sold.

Strain 19 vaccine is available either as a liquid or dried product. The dried product is more stable than the liquid one under average environmental conditions. However, one should always keep in mind that gross mishandling of the dried vaccine kills the Strain 19 organisms and so makes the vaccine useless. The cattle owner should insist on the use of vaccine that has been properly handled.

Immunity produced with Strain 19 vaccine against brucellosis in cattle is generally accepted as being relative and not absolute. The degree of immunity induced is related directly to the response of the individual to the vaccine, and that may vary considerably among animals. Most of the evidence provided by field studies and research indicates that immunity produced by calf vaccination with Strain 19 does not decrease with an increase in age of the animal—it remains serviceable throughout the productive life of the average cow. Experimental results also show that any increase in immunity resulting from revaccination is temporary and does not persist long enough to be of any practical value.

One of the chief problems concerns the proper age at which to vaccinate cattle with Strain 19. Accumulated evidence supports 6 to 8 months as the most desirable age for vaccinating heifer calves. Cattle vaccinated at that age develop an immunity equal to that produced in cattle vaccinated at older ages. Furthermore, their vaccinal titers recede faster and to a lower level than those in cattle vaccinated at a later age.

Of a group of 88 cattle vaccinated between 6 to 8 months of age, only about 5 percent had persistent, diagnostic seroagglutinin titers at 30 months of age, compared to approximately 55 percent of 73 vaccinated between 12 and 15 months of age. These comparisons are based on the new interpretation of the seroagglutination test for vaccinated cattle. The only conclusion that can be drawn from the evidence is that overage vaccination does not accomplish increased immunity and materially hinders a sound control and eradication program.

We have incomplete information as to the advisability of vaccinating calves between 4 and 6 months old. An advantage of this procedure is that most of the animals lose their vaccinal titers rather rapidly, but vaccination of animals in this age group should proceed with caution until more definite information is developed on the degree of immunity produced. Finally, there is the practical aspect concerning vaccination ages that is closely related to management practices—hence the present tolerance of vaccination ages of 4 to 12 months for beef cattle and 4 to 8 months for dairy cattle.

Generally vaccination of bull calves with Strain 19 vaccine is not recommended. The reasons are that bulls are relatively resistant to brucellosis; many are maintained separately from other cattle, and so have less chance of exposure to infection; and vaccinal titers tend to persist.

Other points to be considered are dosage and method of administering Strain 19 vaccine. Some pertinent facts should be kept in mind. The most important requisites for successful vaccination is that the organisms in Strain 19 vaccine must be viable. The minimum number of live organisms required to produce a serviceable immunity in a mixed group of heifer calves, vaccinated at 6 to 8 months of age, is unknown. No controlled experiments have been conducted to determine the degree and duration of immunity produced in calves of this age with doses of Strain 19 vaccine smaller than 5 ml. Consequently, most of the information is on the 5-ml. dose administered subcutaneously, which has provided a serviceable immunity in the majority of animals against average exposure to infection. The 5-ml. dose of Strain 19 represents approximately 50 billion organisms, or 10 billion per milliliter. However, sexually mature heifers have been initially vaccinated with doses as small as 0.25 ml., which have produced a satisfactory immunity for at least the first pregnancy. These smaller doses have been administered intradermally, intracaudally, and subcutaneously with approximately the same results.

Many advantages have been claimed for intradermal method of vaccination with the smaller dose of Strain 19, but most of them have not been substantiated by controlled experiments. One of the claims is that intradermally vaccinated animals lose their agglutinin titers more rapidly and a greater number return to a negative status than with the 5-ml. dose administered subcutaneously. That is true only in calves vaccinated between 4 and 8 months of age and not in animals vaccinated as yearlings or older. Intradermal vaccination cannot be justified, therefore, on this basis with the adoption of the new interpretation of the seroagglutination test for officially calf-vaccinated cattle; furthermore, there is no statistically sound information on the degree of the immunity produced in cattle vaccinated at 4 to 8 months of age by this method. The small dose, regardless of method of vaccination, has no immunological or diagnostic advantage over the 5-ml. dose administered subcutaneously to cattle over 8 months of age. It is not true that the intradermal injection of Strain 19 vaccine into pregnant cows is less likely to cause abortions and a drop in milk production than subcutaneous injection.

Another consideration is persistence of local reaction at the site of inoculation. A proper intradermal inoculation with Strain 19 vaccine is always followed by central necrosis and sloughing, regardless of the injection site. Complete healing usually takes 2 to 4 weeks.

If subcutaneous inoculation is made at the upper one-third of the lateral surface of the shoulder, the swelling is usually diffuse and completely disappears within 7 days. Intracaudal vaccination is followed by swelling in the tip of the tail. The amount of necrosis and sloughing at the site of injection varies considerably.

Several factors recommend the subcutaneous vaccination with a 5-ml. dose of Strain 19 vaccine. If the vaccine is not handled according to recommended procedures, the number of viable organisms will be lower. Consequently, the 5-ml. dose provides added insurance that the animals will receive an adequate number of live organisms to produce a serviceable immunity than with the smaller doses of vaccine.

The cost of a 5-ml. dose of Strain 19 vaccine is not prohibitive and is only a minor part in the total expense of raising a heifer to maturity. Most important, it is the only vaccinal dose of Strain 19 that is supported by a reasonable amount of research.

Before leaving the subject of Strain 19 vaccination, we should also point out its limitations. Strain 19, being a living product, is vulnerable to adverse environmental conditions, which make necessary great care and added facilities and cost in handling to prevent loss in viability. Maximum viability must be maintained to insure maximum benefits. Even with maximum viability, the degree of protection induced with Strain 19 vaccine varies with the individual. Therefore it is extremely important to use precautionary measures for prevention of mass exposure to infection, which may overwhelm the immunity in vaccinated animals.

Treatment of brucellosis in cattle has not been successful. Practically all of the antibiotics and the newer drugs have been tried. Some of them have a tendency to depress the infection temporarily. After treatment is stopped, infection usually returns to its normal course. Many alleged cures have gained considerable prominence by being used in herds when symptoms are normally subsiding. Another consideration is the cost, which is prohibitive for the average animal.

Brucellosis in cattle can be prevented only by employing the basic principles of sanitation or good herd management or vaccination or any combination of them that may be necessary.

Sanitation does not mean only the use of disinfectants. It means cleanliness—thorough washing and scrubbing of footwear, equipment, and barns, with an ample amount of water, which tends to dilute contamination to a subinfective level. Disinfectants have their greatest value when applied to surfaces relatively free of filth.

Good herd management involves employing routine management practices that help to prevent the spread of infection into and within a herd of cattle. Aborting cows and cows with retained placentas should be isolated from the remainder of the herd at least until vaginal discharge has ceased.

It is much safer to raise herd replacements, but if that is impractical, cattle should be purchased from *Brucella*-free herds. If that cannot be done, replacements should be negative to the seroagglutination test at the time of purchase and 30 days later before being added to the herd.

The use of community pastures, which may harbor infected animals, should be avoided. Breeding cattle in the neighborhood to the herd bull always involves traffic of cattle of unknown health status to and from the farm. If herd replacements are raised on the farm, heifers should be vaccinated at the recommended age. If herd replacements are purchased, it is safer to obtain properly vaccinated than nonvaccinated cattle.

Regardless of their vaccination status, every effort should be made to purchase animals from a *Brucella*-free source.

Before 1934, control of bovine brucellosis was limited mainly to individual herds. In 1934 a nationwide program for the control and eradication of brucellosis of cattle was begun under the direction of the Department of Agriculture in cooperation with State livestock sanitary officials. Vaccination of calves with Strain 19 vaccine became part of the official program in 1940. In order to conduct such a program successfully, it was necessary to develop methods and rules, which were continuously revised until 1947 when they were made uniform. Only minor changes have been made as needed since then.

Important features of the uniform methods and rules are:

1. Individual herd plans:

Plan A. Test and slaughter with or without calf vaccination.

Plan B. Test, calf vaccination, temporary retention of reactors until they can be disposed of for slaughter without excessive loss to the owner under provisions of the law.

Plan C. Calf vaccination without test of any part of the herd.

Plan D. Adult vaccination, only when approval is received in writing from State and Federal cooperating agencies before the time of vaccination, which should be confined to herds where there is evidence of rapid spread of virulent infection indicating the need for emergency measures, and only after the owner has been informed in writing that the vaccinating of his adult animals may not prevent the spread of infection.

2. Compulsory area testing when 75 percent or more of the livestock owners holding 95 percent or more of the cattle in a given area sign up under any one or a combination of the four plans.

3. Service to owner shall be made available without expense to him except for the handling of his cattle.

4. Permanent identification of all reactors with a letter "B" brand on the left jaw.

5. Identification of the vaccinated animals.

6. Movement of cattle: No female cattle or breeding bulls over 6 months of age shall be moved after an announced date, except in compliance with State laws and regulations.

During the early years of the campaign, the infection was above 6.0 percent, as determined on the basis of cattle tested. By 1941 the infection had been reduced to 2.4 percent. The Second World War interrupted the program, and by 1947 the infection had risen to approximately 5 percent. By 1955 the percentage of infection had again been reduced to 2.4 percent, and three States were declared modified certified brucellosis-free.

At the 1956 rate of infection, it was

estimated that the livestock industry suffered a loss of 45 million dollars a year because of brucellosis—46 million dollars a year less than in 1947.

BRUCELLOSIS OF SWINE, formerly called contagious abortion in swine, is a chronic infectious disease. It is prevalent in most sections of the United States and other countries of the Western Hemisphere and in some countries of Europe and Asia.

The principal cause of brucellosis in swine is *Br. suis*, but *Br. abortus* and *Br. melitensis* may cause the disease in swine.

Transmission of infection in swine is through the alimentary tract, skin, mucous membranes, and the genital tract.

Br. suis infection is readily transmitted to susceptible sows from infected boars at the time of natural service because the sow's genital tract is such that contaminated semen can gravitate into the uterus and because boars ejaculate a large amount of semen, which favors severe exposure.

The course of brucellosis in swine is rather variable but in general is shorter than in cattle. Sows and boars of all ages are equally susceptible to *Br. suis*, but infection usually lasts a shorter time in suckling pigs less than 6 weeks old.

Blood serum agglutinin titers do not reach so high a level and tend to recede more rapidly in swine than in cattle. Many sows have early abortions, which are unobserved if infection occurs at the time of service. Abortions may occur at all stages of pregnancy. Birth of stillborn or weak pigs is common.

Infected boars may show enlargement of one or both testicles. One or more of the accessory genital organs may be affected. Temporary or permanent infertility frequently follows infection of the genital organs in both sexes.

Lameness and posterior paralysis are noticeable in some herds.

Localization of infection is found more frequently in the lymph glands and genital organs. Genital infections in sexually mature boars usually persist throughout their reproductive life.

The duration of genital infection varies considerably in sows, which have a greater tendency toward recovery than boars. Persistent udder infection is uncommon in most sows.

Suckling pigs more than 6 weeks old and weanling pigs become infected, but many of them tend to recover from the disease before sexual maturity.

Natural infection of swine with *Br. abortus* does occur, but clinical symptoms usually are absent.

Br. melitensis likewise infects swine. It is generally considered a benign infection, but marked symptoms and severe losses have been observed in some herds. Probably the greatest significance of these two infections in swine is their potential source of exposure to cattle, goats, and people.

Widely used and practical methods of diagnosing swine brucellosis are the tube and plate seroagglutination tests. The same antigens, procedures, and equipment used for testing cattle are used for testing swine.

Both the tube and plate tests are reliable for diagnosing the disease in a herd of swine but have some limitations for use in the individual animal. *Brucella* agglutinins frequently do not develop to the diagnostic level of 1:100 in some infected swine or recede rapidly below it. Most infected herds, however, have some animals with blood serum agglutinin titers of 1:100 or higher. It is not uncommon to find a few swine with titers less than 1:100 in some noninfected herds; they are considered nonspecific. Therefore the fact that we find specific seroagglutinin titers in some infected swine and nonspecific seroagglutinin titers in some noninfected swine at the same low levels makes a complete herd test extremely important in making an accurate interpretation of the seroagglutination tests on individual animals.

Considerable research has been undertaken to develop means of differentiating between nonspecific and specific *Brucella* agglutinins found in the blood of swine.

Immunization of swine against *Br. suis* infection has not been successful with vaccines prepared from several modified strains of *Br. suis*, as well as *Br. abortus* Strain 19. Strain 19 does not produce a serviceable immunity against *Br. suis* infection in swine.

None of the *Br. suis* strains so far employed as immunizing agents has had the combined characteristics of safety, stability, and immunogenicity necessary for a reliable vaccine. The self-limiting character of swine brucellosis and prolific nature of swine make the need for a vaccine in a control of the disease questionable.

Treatment is not generally successful for brucellosis in swine. Some antibiotics, combination of antibiotics, or combination of antibiotics and sulfonamides tend to lessen the severity of the disease and degree of localization, but most of them will not bring about a high percentage of complete cures. Consideration also must be given to the economic soundness of any proposed treatment.

Prevention of brucellosis of swine is essentially the same as that of cattle, with two main exceptions: No satisfactory vaccine has been developed against brucellosis of swine, and particular care must be used in purchasing boars.

Because boars are one of the major means of spreading the disease, they should be purchased from herds free of *Brucella*. If that cannot be done, boars should be negative to the seroagglutination test at the time of purchase and 30 days later before being put in service.

A program for the control and eradication of brucellosis in swine was recommended in 1949 after 10 years of research in State and Federal institutions. It is a voluntary program. Its principles have been adopted by a number of States.

The basic procedures are:

A. Plans of control:

Plan 1. This plan is recommended for infected commercial herds.

1. Market the entire herd for slaughter.

2. Clean and disinfect houses and equipment. Hog lots should remain idle for 90 days if possible.

3. Replace with stock from certified brucellosis-free herds.

4. Following two consecutive negative tests 30 to 90 days apart, the herd is eligible for certification.

Plan 2. This plan is recommended for use in purebred infected herds where it is desirable to retain valuable blood lines.

1. Separate pigs from sows at 56 days of age or younger.

2. Market infected herd as soon as practicable.

3. Test the gilts to be used for the following breeding season about 30 days before breeding. Save only the gilts that are negative. Breed only to negative boars.

4. Retest the gilts after farrowing and before removing them from individual farrowing pens. Only pigs from negative sows should be selected for breeding gilts.

5. If a herd is not clean at this time, the process is repeated another year. As soon as the entire herd can pass two negative tests between 30 and 90 days apart, it becomes eligible for certification.

Plan 3. This plan is not generally recommended but has been found useful in small herds in which only a few reactors are found and no clinical symptoms of brucellosis have been noted.

1. Remove reactors from farm.

2. Retest herd at 30-day intervals and remove reactors.

3. Two clean tests, between 30 and 90 days apart, qualify the herd for certification.

4. If the herd is not readily freed of infection, abandon this plan in favor of Plan 1 or Plan 2.

B. Certification of swine herds as brucellosis free.

Certification is made on the basis of two negative tests on the entire herd 30 to 90 days apart. This includes all animals 6 months or older, with no agglutination tests positive 1:100 or higher.

This certification is valid for 12 months. Recertification is made annually by the passing of a single negative test on the entire herd.

These procedures have proved to be practical as demonstrated by the establishment of an increasing number of certified herds in States where hogs are raised.

BRUCELLOSIS OF GOATS, also called contagious abortion and Malta fever, was the first of the *Brucella* infections to be recognized as a specific disease of animals. It is prevalent in most sections of the world where goats are raised. It occurs in parts of the Southwestern and Rocky Mountain States.

The cause is *Br. melitensis*. Natural infection with either *Br. abortus* or *Br. suis* has not been demonstrated. Goats can be infected experimentally with *Br. abortus*, but goat husbandry practices do not generally favor exposure to *Br. abortus* or *Br. suis*.

Brucellosis in goats is transmitted as it is in cattle, but we have no information on its spread by artificial insemination.

The course of the disease in goats is influenced somewhat by age, sex, status of pregnancy, susceptibility of the individual, and the degree and virulence of *Br. melitensis*.

Most goats develop a diagnostic blood serum agglutination titer shortly after acquiring infections, but a significant number have a rapid recession of titers below the 1:100 level at the time of a demonstrable bacteremia. *Br. melitensis* can be demonstrated intermittently in the blood and urine of a considerable number of naturally infected goats for a relatively long time.

Abortions and stillborn or weak kids are the most significant clinical symptoms of the disease. A vaginal discharge, in which are large numbers of *Brucella*, usually persists for 2 to 3 weeks following abortions. Lameness, mastitis, loss of weight, rough hair coat, and infertility have been observed.

Br. melitensis has a tendency to localize in the udder and the lymph glands and may persist for the productive life of some animals. The causative agent can usually be isolated from organs and glands of the body at the time of autopsy, if there is a persistent, high seroagglutinin titer. However, animals with very limited localized infection or no demonstrable infection that is indicative of recovery from the disease usually have relatively low seroagglutinin titers. Kids nursing infected does usually develop seroagglutinin titers, which recede rapidly after weaning. Most of these kids are susceptible to *Br. melitensis* at their first breeding season. They will remain free of the disease if maintained in a *Brucella*-free environment following weaning.

The diagnosis of brucellosis of goats with the tube and plate seroagglutination tests has been practical in this country. Materials and methods of the tests are identical to those used for diagnosing brucellosis of cattle and swine except for a modification of the interpretation of infected flocks.

Considerable success has been attained in eradicating the disease from goat herds by classifying as infected all animals that show seroagglutinin titers of 1:25. The seroagglutination tests have been successful in lowering the incidence of infection and in eradicating the disease from goat herds in large areas.

Vaccination of goats against *Brucella melitensis* infection in this country has been limited. We have had a few reports of vaccinating goats with Strain 19 vaccine but had no proof of its efficiency. Limited research on the use of modified strains of *Br. melitensis* for immunizing goats has not been encouraging. Vaccination studies in goats and sheep have been conducted by Paul Renoux of France in Tunisia in cooperation with the World Health Organization and Food and Agriculture Organization in an effort to find a reliable immunizing agent.

Efforts to treat goats affected with brucellosis have been limited. Treatment depends on economic considerations.

Prevention of brucellosis of goats is the same as that of cattle, except that no satisfactory vaccine has been developed against the disease in goats.

The control and eradication program of brucellosis of goats is essentially one of testing for agglutinins in the blood serum and the slaughtering of infected animals. The disease usually can be eradicated from a herd in a short time by regular routine testing.

Extensive testing of goats for brucellosis has been conducted in Colorado. The highest incidence there was about 8 percent, found during the first year. Repeated testing and removal of reacting animals reduced the incidence in 3 years to about 1.5 percent.

BRUCELLOSIS OF OTHER SPECIES OF ANIMALS is important from the standpoint of potential reservoirs of infection for cattle, swine, and goats.

Brucella melitensis infection in milking sheep is similar to that in goats. It is particularly prevalent in countries bordering the Mediterranean and in Asia Minor. Mutton breeds of sheep are relatively resistant to *Br. melitensis* and *Br. abortus* infections. When these infections occur they are usually self-limiting. There are no reports on natural infection of goats with *Br. suis*.

A *Brucella*-like organism was isolated from sheep in New Zealand. This disease is characterized by infertility of the rams and abortions in ewes.

Brucellosis of horses is characterized by infection of the bursae at the poll and withers. Swellings in these areas are called poll evil and fistula of the withers. *Br. abortus* and *Br. suis* have been isolated from these affected areas.

At the time these areas are discharging pus and serous fluid, horses can be a serious source of infection for cattle and swine.

Dogs and chickens may have brucellosis, but the disease is self-limiting.

American bison and water buffalo are susceptible to *Br. abortus* and develop a progressive form of the disease. There is also serological evidence that deer have brucellosis.

Br. suis has been found in the wild hare of Europe.

BRUCELLOSIS is a significant public health problem, particularly in people whose occupations bring them in contact with infected animals and Brucella organisms or those that consume unpasteurized milk and milk products such as the farm families.

Human beings are susceptible to all three species of *Brucella* and acquire an infection by contact with infected animals or by consuming improperly cooked animal products and unpasteurized milk and milk products contaminated with *Brucella* organisms.

Brucellosis is most prevalent in the owners of livestock, the veterinarians, employees at the slaughterhouses and rendering plants, and laboratory workers. Pasteurization of milk has helped prevent brucellosis in a large segment of our population. Complete elimination of brucellosis in people, however, can be accomplished only by eradicating the disease in all our animals.

C. A. MANTHEI, *head of the Bacterial and Mycotic Diseases Section of the Animal Disease and Parasite Research Branch at Beltsville, has been engaged in animal disease research since 1938. He is a native of Wisconsin and received the degree of doctor of veterinary medicine from Michigan State University in 1935.*

A. K. KUTTLER *is chief of the Brucellosis Eradication Section of the Animal Disease Eradication Branch. He has been engaged in such work since 1917. He is a native of Kansas and received the degree of doctor of veterinary medicine from San Francisco Veterinary College in 1917.*

E. R. GOODE, JR., *project leader of brucellosis investigations at the Animal Disease and Parasite Research Branch, received his degree of doctor of veterinary medicine from Alabama Polytechnic Institute in 1945. He has been engaged in research on animal diseases since 1948.*

Tuberculosis and Its Eradication

HOWARD W. JOHNSON AND ALBERT F. RANNEY

ROBERT KOCH discovered in 1882 the Mycobacterium—the bacterium, or bacillus—that causes tuberculosis. Thus the great German bacteriologist proved that tuberculosis is a specific, infectious disease, and he ended fears and uncertainties about it that men had had since the time of Moses.

As a country practitioner in Posen, he made many microscopic studies of bacteria. He devised a method of staining bacteria with aniline dyes and ways to grow colonies of bacteria. In 1890 he developed tuberculin—a sterile liquid that contains the growth products of the tubercle bacillus—as a test for tuberculosis. That discovery brought him a Nobel prize and marked the beginning of widespread efforts to end bovine tuberculosis, the type that attacks cattle.

The next big step in the conquest of tuberculosis was the discovery that human tubercle bacteria are not the same as bovine tubercle bacteria. That discovery was made by Theobald Smith, a pathologist in the Department of Agriculture whose other notable contributions included the discovery of the parasite that causes Texas cattle fever and its transmission by the cattle tick.

There followed some of the most fruitful scientific investigations that modern medicine has witnessed. The investigations gave us the definite knowledge of the nature of the disease that made it possible to eliminate tuberculosis from infected herds and to keep it out of healthy herds. They brought out a number of basic facts:

Practically every species of animals can be affected by tuberculosis. The disease in each species is similar in character and always ends in a slow wasting of the body tissues.

There are three types of tubercle bacillus. The kind found in man cannot produce progressive disease in many animals. The tubercle bacillus in cattle is different from the human type, although it can infect people. The third type exists in poultry. The three kinds of tubercle bacillus were classed as the human, bovine, and avian (bird) types.

THE TUBERCLE BACILLUS is a rod-shaped organism. It is 1.5 to 4 microns long—6,000 to 16,000 of them laid end to end measure 1 inch. The bacillus has a waxy capsule, which cannot be readily penetrated by the various stains used in bacteriological studies to render the organisms visible.

Because micro-organisms of the genus *Mycobacterium* are acidfast, they are hard to stain. Once they are stained, however, the stain cannot be removed by acid treatment, as it can from most other germs. Thus, if the micro-organisms in a sample are stained with a red dye and then treated with acid and counterstained with a blue dye, the tubercle bacilli will show red, but the other organisms, which are not acidfast, show blue.

THE TUBERCLE BACILLUS grows very slowly on culture media, which are foods for growing bacteria artificially. Bacteria are grown on media in order that they may be studied and closely related species may be differentiated. On the first culture of tubercle bacillus, it may be 1 month and sometimes 2 months before a colony of germs grows enough to be seen by the unaided eye.

Most other organisms show colony growth in 24 to 48 hours.

The three types of tubercle bacilli—human, bovine, and avian—produce colony growths different from one another on a culture medium. The growth of the human type appears thick and wrinkled. The bovine type looks sparse, rough, and dry. The avian type is heavy, smooth, moist, and glistening.

Tubercle bacilli usually enter the body by way of the mouth in contaminated food or water. Sometimes they are breathed directly into the lungs.

An animal spreads the bacilli when the tuberculous excretion from its lungs reaches the mouth and is washed into the water trough when it drinks. Then it subjects other cattle using the trough to the most dangerous kind of exposure. When they swallow the tuberculous sputum, the tubercle bacilli in it are passed unchanged through the intestines, and their dung is extremely infectious. Stagnant pools into which cows drop their manure thus offer means by which the disease may be spread, as tubercle bacilli in such pools may remain alive for a year or longer. Small streams may likewise become contaminated with tubercle bacilli. Around hayracks, dung may become mixed with particles of hay. One feeding of milk from a dam with tuberculosis localized in the udder may make it possible for a calf to pick up the disease.

TUBERCULOSIS exists in many forms according to the part of the body in which the organism becomes localized.

Human beings may have lupus, or tuberculosis of the skin; scrofula, or tuberculosis of the lymph nodes; bone and joint tuberculosis; tuberculosis of the linings of the brain, or tuberculous meningitis; and so on.

In animals, the organs most commonly affected are the lungs. In most species it is tuberculosis of the lungs on which depends the spread of the disease, from man to man or animal to animal.

In poultry, the liver and spleen are most commonly affected. Tuberculosis is spread from the birds' droppings.

The udder of cows may become infected when the disease is chronic, and large numbers of tubercle bacilli may be given off in the milk.

All organs and sections of the body have specialized glands, called lymph nodes, which filter out bacteria from the lymph stream and thus hinder the spread of infection to another part of the body. The lymph nodes are often the site of the first localization of tubercle bacilli. The nodes in the throat and neck have the first opportunity to become infected; next the mesenteric nodes, which drain the intestines; and next the lungs and their adjacent lymph nodes. Tubercles in other sections of the body are usually the result of the spread of infection from a primary center, or focus.

WHEN TUBERCLE BACILLI lodge in any part of the body, certain blood cells are attracted to the site and attempt to ingest them. The waxy capsule of the bacillus makes it resistant to destruction. Other blood cells congregate around the area and form a protective wall against the spread of the bacilli. Thus a tubercle, or morbid nodule, is formed. If the wall, or encapsulation, becomes dense on all sides, the tubercle remains stationary and is called an arrested lesion. Calcium salts may be deposited in the tubercle and transform it into a gritty, or calcified, lesion. If the lesion is very small, it might even be absorbed.

If the tubercle bacilli are not checked, the tubercle enlarges on the outside, developing into what is known as a proliferative, or spreading, lesion. Bacilli may escape from this mass and cause the formation of new tubercles, either adjacent to the old tubercle or remote from it. During the growth of a tubercle in the lungs, a terminal branch of a bronchus, or air channel, may be surrounded. The poisons secreted by the bacilli tend to soften the inner parts of the tubercle, and they may be expelled into a bronchus, thence to the trachea, and then coughed up. A tubercle thus broken down is known as an exudative type of lesion.

Tubercles vary in number and kind in different individuals, according to the resistance offered. After localization of tubercle bacilli in the body, the resultant tubercle may disappear completely in a few weeks or months or it may cause the fulminative type of the disease, which spreads rapidly and results in death in a few weeks or months.

Usually the tubercle remains in the body as a walled-off, or encapsulated, tumor, and it may remain as such for the life of the host. At any time, however, such a tubercle may become active because of lowered resistance and be a focus for the spread of the disease to other parts of the body.

The time between the exposure to tubercle bacilli and the development of a tubercle is the period of incubation. The period varies in length. In the first place, tubercle bacilli multiply very slowly in the animal body, and infection develops only when the germs have multiplied to a certain number in the spot where the tubercle is formed. Depending on various conditions, it may be one to several months before the disease can be detected by the tuberculin test (to be explained later). When tubercle bacilli once gain a foothold, the disease is usually slowly progressive. It may be months or years before the general physical condition becomes noticeably impaired.

TUBERCULOSIS may be suspected when an animal shows a gradual loss of weight and condition. A chronic cough develops in cattle affected with tuberculosis of the lungs. It is remarkable, however, that cattle that appear to be in prime condition may be grossly tuberculous and may be spreading the disease.

Poultry may be suspected of being tuberculous when some of the flock show lameness, thinness, especially in the breast muscles, and paleness of combs and wattles.

In swine the disease may not be suspected because most of the animals are marketed during their first or second year of life and because the disease only rarely spreads from hog to hog. It is in older animals that the condition usually becomes apparent by a gradual loss in weight and condition or by enlargement of joints.

SOME SPECIES OF ANIMALS are susceptible to infection with only one type of the tubercle bacillus. Others may be susceptible to two types. Still others may be susceptible to all three.

Cattle are the chief hosts and likewise the chief disseminators of the bovine tubercle bacillus. Only rarely are they known to develop lesions or visible tubercles as a result of exposure to infected poultry or a tuberculous human being.

Horses and mules are resistant to all three types.

Chickens are susceptible only to the avian tubercle bacillus.

Sheep and goats as a rule are resistant to tuberculosis. A few flocks of goats and, rarely, a sheep or two have been found to be infected with the bovine organism. A few sheep that have been in close contact with infected poultry have shown lesions caused by the avian organism.

Swine may be infected by all three types of the tubercle bacillus. The bovine type causes the severest disease, but in the United States probably nine-tenths of the tuberculous lesions in swine are caused by the avian organism. Lesions in swine caused by the human tubercle bacillus are not of the progressive type and usually remain localized in lymph nodes of the head or intestine. The feeding habits of swine provide for ample exposure to all three types: To the bovine type in cattle-feeding lots where the swine eat cow dung; to the avian type on farms where there are tuberculous chickens, which may soil the ground, or where

the farmer may throw his dead chickens to the hogs; and to the human type from uncooked garbage or from the sputum of a tuberculous attendant.

Dogs may become infected with human tuberculosis, the usual source of exposure being a tuberculous owner, but they are only slightly susceptible to bovine tuberculosis.

Cats are more susceptible to the bovine tubercle bacillus than to the human type. Tuberculosis in cats is usually a result of their being fed contaminated cow's milk.

Domesticated rabbits are susceptible to the bovine and avian types, but are resistant to the human type. Guinea pigs are susceptible to both bovine and human tubercle bacilli, but not to avian. The rabbit and guinea pig thus are useful to the investigator in determining the type of infection in various tuberculous specimens submitted for examination.

MAN IS SUSCEPTIBLE to the human type of tubercle bacillus. He is slightly susceptible to the bovine type. He is very resistant to the avian type. Human tuberculosis continues to be one of the leading death-causing diseases, although great strides have been made by public health agencies, medical commissions, and the other interested groups in preventing exposure, detecting early cases, and hospitalizing affected persons.

The dangerous person is one who has an open lung lesion. By spitting and coughing openly, a careless individual so affected may spread thousands of tubercle bacilli daily as possible sources of infection to others.

Coughing expels hundreds of tiny droplets. And they may contain tubercle bacilli, which may be inhaled by other persons or may fall on food to be eaten. Drinking cups and eating utensils may be sources of exposure unless properly sterilized.

Although man is much more resistant to the bovine tubercle bacillus than to the human type, if exposure is severe enough and repeated often enough, tuberculosis may be produced in human beings by the bovine organism in every form that is produced by the human type.

Children, especially infants, are much less resistant to bovine tuberculosis than adults. Before 1917, when programs for eradication of bovine tuberculosis were inaugurated, vital statistics of States showed that hundreds of children died annually of tuberculous meningitis and miliary (rapidly developing) tuberculosis contracted from cow's milk. Many others became affected with scrofula and tuberculosis of bones and joints.

Unpasteurized milk of tuberculous cows is practically the only source of the bovine type of infection in children. The bovine tuberculosis eradication program has markedly reduced tuberculosis in livestock and has saved hundreds of children from this disease, which kills and cripples.

Fewer than 100 cases of tuberculosis in man reputed to be caused by the avian type of tubercle bacillus have been reported from all over the world. Apparently, therefore, man can resist this type of infection, or sufficient exposure to produce the disease is lacking. We do not eat raw poultry meat. Eggs from tuberculous hens sometimes contain tubercle bacilli, but as a rule diseased hens lay few or no eggs. Furthermore, eggs are usually cooked, so that few virulent tubercle bacilli are thus eaten. Poultry tuberculosis is prevalent in some sections of the United States, however, and the possibility that repeated exposure might cause disease in persons handling such flocks should be a further reason why an owner should take steps to eradicate the disease from his poultry.

DIAGNOSIS of tuberculosis is made by the tuberculin test. The body becomes sensitized, or allergic, to the infecting germs of many infectious diseases and to the products of the germs. That phenomenon is very marked in tuberculosis and is the basis of diagnosis. It is done in this way: Tubercle ba-

cilli are grown in a broth medium. The broth, sterilized by flowing steam, is filtered from the tubercle bacilli. After concentrating the broth, phenol and glycerine are added. The product is tuberculin.

If tuberculin is injected into an animal having tuberculosis, a reaction to the substance takes place. The injection of tuberculin subcutaneously (under the skin) is followed within a few hours by a rise in temperature, or fever, which gradually subsides. Injection made intradermally (into the skin) causes a reddened swelling at the site of injection 24 to 72 hours later. If tuberculin is dropped on the eye (applied ophthalmically), a milky discharge from the eye appears within a few hours. The degree of infection has no relation to the extent of the reaction, for a lesion of tuberculosis so small that it can hardly be seen with the naked eye may develop a sensitization to tuberculin as marked as that caused by a lesion a hundred times larger.

From the standpoint of efficiency and simplicity of application, the intradermic test, using the caudal fold area (loose skin at the tail head), is preferred for routine testing. The skin in the cervical area (side of neck), which is about three times more sensitive to tuberculin than the caudal fold, is frequently used in herds known to be infected, especially those in which infected animals are found on repeated tests.

Diagnosis may be made also by animal inoculation or culture of diseased tissues, and in people by X-ray photographs.

PREVENTION AND CONTROL of bovine tuberculosis involves several practices.

Of outstanding importance is the Federal-State program, which was started in 1917. Cattle are tested with tuberculin, infected animals are killed, and indemnity is paid for animals slaughtered. More details concerning this successful program are given later. First, let us emphasize some preventive measures.

Cattle should be admitted to a herd only if they are negative to the tuberculin test, and they should preferably be obtained from a herd accredited to be free from tuberculosis.

Feeding hogs and calves separated milk that is bought from creameries is undesirable unless the milk is pasteurized (heated to 145° F. for 30 minutes) or heated for a few minutes at the boiling point and then cooled before being fed.

Small, slow-flowing streams which pass through or drain an infected farm are a hazard to livestock having access to such a stream lower down. Such a stream should be fenced off.

Grazing on community pastures should be avoided unless all the cattle have been tested and found to be negative to the tuberculin test.

Cattle may be exposed to tuberculosis at fairs, sales, and unloading places unless all contact cattle and premises used are free from infection. Such cattle should be tested about 3 months after arrival on home premises.

Tuberculosis in people may be arrested by treatment and complete rest, but in domestic animals a comparable procedure is not effective. Since practically all tuberculosis in domestic animals may be traced to cattle and poultry, freeing all livestock from the disease is a matter of eradicating tuberculosis from cattle and poultry.

When tuberculous cattle are removed as a result of a positive tuberculin test, the infected premises should be carefully cleaned and disinfected. It is especially important to remove manure. Direct sunlight kills tubercle bacilli within a few minutes, but germs covered with manure or soil may remain alive for weeks.

In the campaign started in 1917 to eradicate bovine tuberculosis in the United States, the main course of action was the testing of all dairy and breeding cattle. In 1940, 23 years after the program began, all 3,071 counties in the country and Puerto Rico and the Virgin Islands were officially declared to be modified accredited areas—that is, bovine tuberculosis among the cattle in them had been reduced to less than 0.5 percent. The disease was found to be present to some extent in all States. The greatest incidence was in areas furnishing milk to the larger cities, particularly in the northern half of the country. The disease was detected in 40 to 80 percent of the cattle in some of the badly infected areas; in a few instances, the incidence of infection approached 100 percent of the cattle in the locality.

Of the cattle slaughtered on regular kill in 1917 in establishments maintaining Federal meat inspection, 49,214 carcasses, or 0.53 percent, were condemned or sterilized on account of tuberculosis. In 1954 this number was reduced to 441, or 0.002 percent.

The death rate of persons from tuberculosis was 150 per 100,000 population in 1918. The rate was approximately 15 per 100,000 population in 1952. The eradication of bovine tuberculosis must be recognized as a factor in this improved condition.

Between the time the campaign was started and January 1, 1955, about 364 million tuberculin tests and retests were made. About 4 million tuberculous animals were discovered by the tests. The cost to the Federal and the State Governments was about 310 million dollars. If no effort had been made to control or eradicate tuberculosis and the incidence of the disease had remained the same as it was in 1917, approximately 98,000 carcasses—instead of 441—would have been condemned or sterilized in 1954.

It was calculated in 1954 that at least 150 million dollars is saved each year as a result of reducing the incidence of bovine tuberculosis.

The success in reducing bovine tuberculosis to a low point, however, calls for a word of warning. Because tuberculosis among cattle is at a low point, all cattle must be regarded as highly susceptible to the disease. Further protection of the livestock industry therefore depends largely on maintaining and keeping up our efforts to

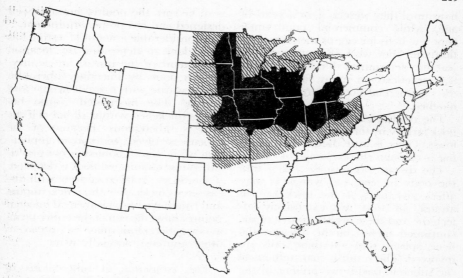

The darkened section shows the general area with the highest concentration of avian tuberculosis in 1956. The incidence of the disease declines with the distance away from the heavily shaded area.

bring about eventual eradication. If we do not do so, the disease could easily spread rapidly from any remaining centers of infection.

State and Federal meat inspectors furnish those in charge of tuberculosis eradication work with reports of cases where tuberculosis is found in carcasses of cattle and swine on regular kill. The information in these reports is used as an aid in locating infected herds.

Since 1951 increased emphasis has been given to this phase of tuberculosis eradication. Some highly infected herds have been uncovered through the tracing to the herds of origin animals that showed lesions of tuberculosis on regular kill. During 1954, 15 percent of the total reactors found were in herds where the infection was located by tracing tuberculous carcasses. It is expected that this record will be surpassed as meat inspection is increased and methods of tracing animals are improved.

The cooperation of meat inspectors, packers, cattle dealers, operators of livestock auction markets, commission firms, veterinarians and others closely associated with the handling of livestock is imperative in locating centers of infection by this means.

TUBERCULOSIS IN POULTRY was first recognized in the United States about 1900. It was not known to be distributed widely until about 1920, when veterinarians assigned to eradicating tuberculosis in cattle found many diseased flocks on the farms they visited in their routine work of testing cattle. A survey was started to determine the extent of the disease. It was found to exist to an alarming degree in the Corn Belt. Little was found in the Eastern States and on the west coast.

A further study disclosed that the average farm flocks often were heavily infected and the large commercial flocks were comparatively free from the disease. Investigators found that on most of the farms where tuberculous chickens were discovered, it was the practice to keep a large number of the hens until they were 2, 3, or 4 years of age, while commercial poultrymen kept few hens for egg or meat production after they were 18 months old. It was also determined that hen hatching was practiced on many farms, while the commercial flocks were incubator hatched.

The disease is spread from flock to flock largely by the exchange of infected fowls. There is little danger of spreading it through the exchange of eggs.

The disease organism is taken into the body in feed and water. It may affect any part of the fowl, but in almost all that are extensively affected—and these are the source of the continued spread of the disease—the liver, spleen, and intestinal walls are involved. The result is that millions of the tubercle bacilli are present in the excretions. As flocks of chickens usually range over a comparatively small area, the yards and runways, especially near the poultry house, become contaminated.

No medicinal remedy is effective. In the management of a flock such as is maintained on the average midwestern farm for meat and egg production, it is advisable to follow a plan of raising a new flock on clean grounds and disposing of the old birds at the end of the laying season or when they are about 18 months old. Because tuberculosis is only slowly progressive, most hens will not have become spreaders if they are disposed of when they are 12 to 18 months old. The disease may thus be materially reduced and even eradicated by this method of control.

Because the tubercle bacillus may remain alive and virulent in a moist and dark protected place for as long as 2 years, sanitation is important in control and eradication. The poultry house should be thoroughly cleaned and disinfected and, if practical, moved to a new location. Where that is not possible, the runway should be used only a year; then it should be plowed up and planted to some crop before it is used again for chickens.

Another way to combat tuberculosis is to be sure the poultry house is well designed and has proper equipment.

A considerable amount of testing has been done to determine the location and extent of the disease in poultry. This is done by injecting tuberculin into a wattle with a small needle and syringe. The inoculated wattle becomes thickened within 48 hours if the bird is tuberculous. Because of the expense involved, widespread application of the test in poultry is not practical. When an infected flock is detected, it should be replaced entirely with disease-free chicks after the chickenhouse and runs have been cleaned. If infected poultry have the run of the entire farm, avian tuberculosis may be spread to other animals, especially swine.

THE INCIDENCE of tuberculosis in swine, found by Federal meat inspectors, becomes a little more favorable year to year. Carcasses in which tuberculosis was detected by Federal meat inspection were 3.9 percent of the total kill in 1954, compared to 15.2 percent in 1924. The decrease has been gradual since 1945. The campaign to eradicate tuberculosis in cattle has helped to reduce the losses from tuberculosis in swine.

Tuberculosis in swine is not spread from animal to animal unless—as happens seldom—the udder of the sow is infected. The control and eradication of the disease in swine therefore depend on eradicating tuberculosis in the cattle and poultry.

Sanitation should be practiced. Feed lots should be rotated at least once a year. Tuberculin tests with avian and mammalian tuberculins may be used in purebred breeding herds to determine which animals are diseased. The reactors should be slaughtered under veterinary supervision.

HOWARD W. JOHNSON *received his degree of doctor of veterinary medicine from Michigan State University in 1932. He was assistant bacteriologist there for 4 years and was a member of the staff of the State veterinarian in Wisconsin from 1934 to 1936.*

He joined the Bureau of Animal Industry of the Department in 1936 as junior veterinarian and became the chief of the Animal Disease and Parasite Research Branch in 1956.

ALBERT F. RANNEY *was appointed chief of the Tuberculosis Eradication Section, Animal Disease Eradication Branch, in* 1954. He received his degree of doctor of veterinary medicine from New York State Veterinary College at Cornell University in 1932 and his master's degree from Cornell Graduate School in 1934. In 1933 he joined the Department of Agriculture. He has devoted a major part of his efforts to the study of tuberculosis and brucellosis.

Paratuberculosis (Johne's Disease)

AUBREY B. LARSEN AND HOWARD W. JOHNSON

JOHNE'S disease (paratuberculosis) was diagnosed for the first time in the United States in 1908 and since has been reported in almost every State.

The yearly death loss from the disease may vary from 2 to 10 percent of the animals in the herd. Usually only 1 or 2 animals are sick at one time.

The period of incubation is usually a year or longer. Animals may remain infected for years without showing any outward signs of the disease. Symptoms are usually seen in animals 2 to 6 years old. Calving, with a subsequent heavy milk production, tends to lower the resistance of cows, so that they often develop symptoms of the disease at any time during the year. Symptoms are more likely to develop during periods when the herd is consuming feeds with a laxative effect, such as lush pastures, however. Change in environment, such as that resulting from transfer through sale, also seems to be a factor.

TYPICAL SYMPTOMS include a persistent diarrhea. The excretion has a fetid odor. Straining is not observed. The diarrhea responds only temporarily or not at all to usual treatments for such conditions. A rapid loss of flesh accompanies the diarrhea. Occasionally a gradual loss of weight may precede the diarrhea by a month or more.

An infected animal develops an unthrifty appearance. It has a rough hair coat, which does not shed with the change of season. The skin loses its normal texture, becomes dry, and adheres tightly to the body. The appetite remains normal in the early stages. The milk flow drops or stops entirely. The diseased animal maintains a normal body temperature, but it continues to scour and waste away until it becomes extremely thin.

Temporary improvement is not uncommon—the animal may gain weight and appear to be on the road to recovery, only to start scouring again and eventually die. A complete recovery from an advanced stage of the disease is rare.

Symptoms similar to those observed in Johne's disease sometimes attend such conditions as coccidiosis, malnutrition, winter dysentery, pyelonephritis (a type of kidney infection), abscessed liver, and parasitism. A thorough examination of the animal and the husbandry practiced on the premises often is necessary before one can make a diagnosis.

The causative organism is a short, plump, acid-fast bacillus. When it is stained with a suitable dye, such as carbol fuchsin, the color cannot be removed from the bacillus by the action of acids diluted in alcohol. It is therefore described as "acidfast."

The bacillus is found in typical clumps in stained smears prepared from the intestinal mucosa or adjacent lymph glands of diseased animals. It occurs in greatest numbers in the region of the ileocaecal valve, which connects the large and small intestines, although the habitat may extend from the rectum to the upper part of the small intestine. Microscopic studies of stained pathological sections show the bacillus to be both inside and outside of the cells in the tissues.

The causative organism is excreted with the feces and will live outside the animal's body for a year or even longer. It is not killed by disinfectants containing chlorine as the active ingredient or by lye solutions. The bacillus is killed by a 3-percent solution of cresylic acid disinfectant or a 1-percent solution of sodium orthophenylphenate.

The disease cannot be established in small animals in the laboratory. It is hard to isolate the bacillus and cultivate it on artificial media. Primary isolation is accomplished by adding to the medium an essential growth factor found in *Mycobacterium phlei* (timothy hay bacillus).

A diagnosis of Johne's disease should be confirmed if possible by demonstrating the causative bacillus, *M. paratuberculosis*, in stained preparations (prepared from either small bits of the intestinal mucosa picked off the wall of the rectum or from droppings) and by obtaining a positive reaction to a skin test with johnin.

The diagnostic agent—johnin—is prepared from *M. paratuberculosis* bacilli that have been adapted to grow on liquid media. To prepare johnin, the bacilli are incubated at 38° C. until satisfactory growth has been obtained. The bacilli are then killed by steam sterilization and discarded after filtering. The medium is concentrated; chemicals are added; it is refiltered; and the finished product is tested for sterility and potency.

Animals showing clinical evidence of Johne's disease usually die, so a postmortem examination should be conducted to confirm the diagnosis. Except for extreme emaciation of the carcass, little evidence of the disease is observed grossly. The small intestine may feel soft and thick to the touch and the adjacent lymph glands may be swollen. The ileocaecal valve is often inflamed and larger than normal. The intestinal mucosa may be thrown up in irregular reddened folds several times its normal thickness. However, lesions alone should not be relied upon, and, before reaching a diagnosis, the causative bacillus should be demonstrated microscopically in smears or pathological sections prepared from the lesions.

TREATMENT OF CLINICAL Johne's disease has not been successful, probably because it is a chronic disease often diagnosed only in the terminal stage. Such agents as streptomycin, viomycin, $4:4'$ diamino sulfone, isonicotinic acid hydrazide, and others that have been found useful in the treatment of other diseases caused by acid-fast bacilli have been tried without success in the treatment of Johne's disease. Vaccines have also been tried, but the methods of vaccination now available sometimes cause vaccinated animals to react positively to the tuberculin test.

Since medicinal treatment cannot be used successfully to treat the disease, one must depend on other measures for keeping it under control. When Johne's disease is diagnosed in a herd for the first time, johnin tests should be conducted on all animals in the herd to determine the extent of the infection.

To conduct the johnin test, 0.2 cubic centimeter of johnin is injected in the skin of either the neck or the caudal fold. The injection site is examined 48 hours later for evidence of a reaction. An increase of 3 millimeters over the original skin thickness indicates a positive reaction.

If the number of reactors to the test is not large, they (and all animals showing clinical evidence of the disease) should be removed at once and slaughtered.

If a large number of reactors is disclosed on the initial test, disposing of them at once may be too heavy a loss to the owner. He may decide to take immediate steps to eliminate only the animals that show clinical symptoms of the disease and to dispose of the remaining reactors by slaughter as rapidly as young animals can be raised for replacement. This procedure involves a risk, as reacting animals may spread the disease even though they show no symptoms. Breeding stock should not be sold as long as reacting animals remain in the herd.

Because the disease is spread by the droppings of infected animals, precautions must be taken to keep susceptible animals from swallowing contaminated manure and from being exposed to drainage from the manure.

As calves are more easily infected with Johne's disease than older animals, it is important to raise calves in quarters that have not been contaminated by infected animals. Calves should be removed from their dams within 12 hours after birth, placed in clean quarters, and cared for by attendants whose footgear is cleaned and disinfected each time they enter the quarters. Separate feeding and cleaning equipment should be provided for the calf-rearing quarters. The equipment should never be exchanged with that used in caring for mature animals. All feeding and watering equipment used for mature cattle should be so constructed that fecal contamination of feed and water is prevented. Equipment used in cleaning out stables should never be exchanged with equipment used in feed rooms and alleys. Foot baths containing suitable disinfectants should be placed at the entrances to feed alleys and feedrooms. Attendants should disinfect footwear in these containers.

Immediately after the removal of infected animals, the premises should be disinfected. A disinfectant approved by the Department of Agriculture, such as a 1-percent solution of sodium orthophenylphenate, should be applied to all mangers, pens, troughs, walls, and floors. Stagnant water holes should be fenced off or drained. All lots used by infected animals should have all manure and a thin layer of topsoil removed and fences arranged so that all parts of the lot are exposed to direct sunlight at some period of the day. Johnin tests should be conducted periodically on all animals in the herd. If negative results are obtained on three successive tests at intervals of 6 months and no clinical symptoms have been observed, the herd is considered free of the disease.

SHEEP AND GOATS sometimes contract Johne's disease. As in cattle, the disease is diagnosed from symptoms and by demonstrating the acid-fast bacillus in the droppings or intestinal lining. It is difficult to control the disease in sheep and goats, and the entire flock sometimes is slaughtered and replaced with healthy animals.

The Department of Agriculture has started research to find methods that we hope will eventually eliminate the disease. One result of the research was the development of methods of growing the bacillus in large amounts in the laboratory. These cultures are used in preparing various products that have been used experimentally as diagnostic and immunizing agents.

AUBREY B. LARSEN, *a bacteriologist in the Animal Disease and Parasite Research Branch, is a native of Wisconsin. He holds the degree of doctor of veterinary medicine from Michigan State University. He has been with the Department since 1940.*

HOWARD W. JOHNSON, *a veterinarian in the Animal Disease and Parasite Research Branch, is a native of Michigan. He holds three degrees, including that of doctor of veterinary medicine, from Michigan State University. He has been employed by the Department of Agriculture since 1929.*

Vibriosis of Cattle

A. H. FRANK

VIBRIO FETUS is an infection of the reproductive organs of cattle. It causes infertility and abortion.

The causative organism, *Vibrio fetus*, is transmitted at the time of coitus. Most infected bulls will remain carriers indefinitely unless they are treated successfully. Some chronic carrier cows retain infection throughout pregnancy and after calving. One case in a herd can be enough to perpetuate the disease and infect clean bulls.

The clinical findings and breeding records of a herd are helpful, but one cannot rely on them to diagnose vibriosis or to differentiate it from trichomoniasis and other conditions that cause infertility in cattle. The clinician must use laboratory methods for a diagnosis.

An infected bull might be considered a poor breeder because of his high number of services to settle a cow. Otherwise no clinical abnormalities are observed. His semen may appear to be of normal quality. The prepuce is considered to be the common site of infection.

When *Vibrio fetus* enters a herd, cows of all ages are susceptible. While 15 to 45 percent may conceive at first mating, other animals repeatedly return to service and conception may be delayed 3 to 6 months. In other herds, conception may be delayed 12 months or longer. A delayed oestrous cycle of 25 to 60 days, or perhaps more than 100 days, may follow the first service to an infected bull, but a delayed interval might follow any service. Later in the course of the disease, the fertility of cows which have already encountered the infection will be fairly satisfactory. Only the cows that have not been served previously by an infected bull and the heifers present a problem. Difficulties from each succeeding group of heifers may continue as long as an infected bull is used for service.

Some cows that conceive at first service or at a later mating remain infected for an indefinite period during gestation. Abortion, when it occurs, is generally during early pregnancy, but it rarely exceeds 3 to 5 percent of the cases. Cows that abort usually recover spontaneously and conceive when they are bred again.

Information from breeding records may indicate whether infection is present in a herd. If it is not possible or desirable to obtain samples from all individuals in a herd, the records may be used to select bulls with low fertility rates and the repeat-breeder cows, which should be examined.

SEVERAL PROCEDURES may be used to diagnose vibriosis. The cultural isolation of the causative organism from the reproductive tracts of cattle is the only reliable method to detect infected individuals. In this procedure, however, *V. fetus*, which is the pathogenic type of *Vibrio*, must be differentiated from a nonpathogenic type of *Vibrio* commonly found in the genitals of cattle.

Three methods may be used to isolate the organism from bulls: Breeding suspected bulls to virgin heifers, followed by culturing the vaginal mucus (mucus from cervicovaginal juncture) 10 to 30 days after service; culturing semen collected in the artificial vagina; and culturing samples from the prepuce.

Cultural isolation from cows may be used to diagnose infection in individual cases or to study the extent of infection in a herd. The organism is found most frequently in mucus from the cervicovaginal juncture. It is also occasionally isolated from uterine samples.

When abortion occurs in infected herds *V. fetus* may be isolated from both the fetus and the afterbirth. It has been isolated from all parts of the fetus, but contents of the abomasum and rumen are generally collected for microscopical demonstration and cultural isolation.

For cultural isolation of *Vibrio*, care should be taken to obtain samples free from contamination, and specimens of all types should be sent to the laboratory as soon as possible.

THE BLOOD AGGLUTINATION TEST is of limited value in both males and females. For diagnostic purposes it is much inferior to the vaginal mucus agglutination test.

The vaginal mucus agglutination test may be used for a herd diagnosis. Mucus may be collected by any method that provides clean samples and does not involve the risk of transmission of infection from cow to cow. The main methods employed are the use of either tampons or glass or metal tubes. The appearance of vaginal agglutinins generally occurs about 5 weeks after infection. The titer becomes lowered in chronic cases and may disappear eventually. Specimens taken during oestrous usually give negative results, although the tests may be positive at other times in the oestrous cycle.

IN PREVENTION AND CONTROL several alternatives are available for combating vibriosis in cattle.

If facilities are available, a clean herd made up of virgin heifers and sexually immature bulls may be separated from the infected herd and maintained as a clean unit. It can be kept clean by adding only known vibriosis-free animals. While establishing a clean herd, the infected animals may be maintained in a separate unit, which may breed satisfactorily after the cows become immune from an attack of vibriosis.

Artificial insemination may be used in infected herds. Semen should be obtained from bulls free of *Vibrio fetus*.

Semen treated with antibiotics from known infected bulls, however, has been used to restore the conception rate to a satisfactory level. The best way to treat the semen to prevent any possible spread of *V. fetus* has not been established. Satisfactory results have been obtained by diluting semen to 1 to 30 or more and warming the diluter containing the antibiotics to the temperature of the semen (near body temperature) for its addition. After mixing, the diluted semen was cooled to storage temperature, at which it was held for at least 5 hours before use.

ANY TREATMENT for vibriosis should be considered as experimental—there are no established medicaments or procedures, but cows and bulls have been treated successfully.

It is seldom practical to treat cows, because most individuals recover spontaneously. On followup examinations of treated cases, the infection may be missed. Cows thought to be cured therefore can reinfect bulls bred to them. It is much more practical to use either artificial insemination on infected cows or to breed them to infected herd sires until it becomes possible to dispose of them.

It is more practical to treat bulls, but the procedure is laborious and expensive and should be confined to valuable individuals. Infected animals may be detected by cultural isolation of the organism (by methods described earlier). The tests also may be used to determine the success or failure of the treatment. Semen for artificial insemination may be collected from males during the process of treatment and the testing period following treatment.

A. H. FRANK, *project leader of investigations of vibriosis in animals at the Animal Disease and Parasite Research Branch, Agricultural Research Service, in Beltsville, has been engaged in research on animal diseases since 1936. He is a native of Missouri and received his degree of doctor of veterinary medicine from Michigan State University in 1934.*

Leptospirosis

G. B. VAN NESS AND C. A. MANTHEI

LEPTOSPIROSIS was first described as a disease of man. Leptospira, which cause it, once were considered the cause of yellow fever, because jaundice occurs in both diseases. When mosquito-transmitted virus was found to be the cause of yellow fever, interest in Leptospira declined. Leptospirosis is a problem where carriers of the infection are found. The chance of spreading the disease is increased if animals have access to contaminated water.

Leptospira differ from other causes of infectious disease. They are parasites that have no surface covering.

They have freely moving ends with no flagella. They move by a corkscrew motion of the ends of the cell. They have been confused with true viruses because of their resistance to bacterial stains, failure to grow on the standard laboratory media, filterability, and growth in embryonated eggs. Leptospira can be readily demonstrated by using Giemsa's stain and silver preparations or by outlining the organisms with india ink. The motility of Leptospira as seen through the dark-field microscope is the most reliable means of differentiating them from protoplasmic strands and other artifacts.

Leptospira are separated into serotypes by serological tests, because size, biochemical activity, and the nutrient requirements are not reliable means of identification. Detailed studies are necessary to identify them. Because specific antiserums and known serotypes must be maintained in the laboratory for comparison, laboratory centers primarily interested in leptospirosis have been set up.

The extent of leptospirosis and the number of animal species affected in the United States are not known. Leptospira are found most commonly in rodents, from which infection can spread to man or domestic animals.

Weil's disease in man is due to Leptospira carried by the Norway rat. Harvest fever, ricefield fever, and mud fever are other leptospiral infections transmitted from mice and moles to man. Dogs may become infected from rodents, particularly rats, and cattle in the United States have antibodies in their blood for *Leptospira sejroe*, an organism found in field mice.

Two serotypes commonly produce infection in domestic animals in this country. *L. canicola* occurs in dogs and can be transmitted to man and cattle. *L. pomona* is found in swine and cattle, and infection may occur in horses and men. Carriers disseminate Leptospira through the urine. Animals can become infected by splashed urine and by eating and drinking contaminated feed and water. The Leptospira usually gain entrance to the body through abrasions of the skin and the mucous membranes of the mouth, nose, and eyes.

IN CATTLE, leptospirosis can vary from a mild to a severe infection, which may be followed by death. Fever and loss of appetite may last for several days and usually do not recur, although infection is still present. Discoloration of the urine with blood may vary from a mild pink to deep red or almost black. Anemia may occur as a result of loss of blood. Milk production drops or ceases. The milk becomes yellowish and like colostrum and may be tinged with blood. The udder may become flaccid or hardened, but not inflamed. The return to normal production may take several weeks.

Abortions may occur at any stage of pregnancy, but they usually occur in the last one-third. Full-term calves may be dead or weak. The afterbirth and the umbilical cord are often enlarged and edematous. Stunting of young animals, unthriftiness, and debility are symptoms of chronic leptospirosis.

The most frequent cause of bovine leptospirosis is *L. pomona,* but two other serotypes have been associated with the disease of cattle in this country.

IN SWINE, leptospirosis is not a new problem. Early investigators encountered an organism like Leptospira in their study of hog cholera, which is caused by a virus. Leptospirosis, however, was first reported in the United States in 1952.

Symptoms in hogs may vary from mild icterus and slow gains in weight to pronounced nervous and digestive disturbances. Poor appetite, fever, frequent urination, mild conjunctivitis, weakness of the hind legs, stiffness, and drowsiness occur in varying degrees in infected herds. Leptospirosis may be responsible for serious losses from abortions and death of newborn pigs. Icterus and anemia may lead to condemnation of slaughtered hogs. The most common cause of the disease in swine is *L. pomona.*

IN SHEEP AND GOATS, leptospirosis resembles leptospirosis in cows.

Information regarding the disease of these animals in the United States is limited, but the development of jaundice should suggest the presence of leptospirosis.

CANINE INFECTION is widespread. Many cases are accompanied by visible disease. Muscular stiffness, thirst, vomiting, dehydration, weakness, and constipation or bloody diarrhea are seen.

Most cases develop uremic symptoms, with a foul or an ammoniacal breath, icterus, tucked-in abdomen, and arched back.

Infected dogs may shed large numbers of Leptospira in the urine.

IN THE HORSE, general symptoms of leptospirosis may be lacking, but an eye condition may be a prominent feature. It has been suggested that the condition called periodic ophthalmia in horses is due entirely to leptospirosis.

The eyes are frequently affected in leptospirosis. The mucous lining of the eyelid and the white of the eyeball are reddened, and the blood vessels are enlarged. The eyeball itself can become involved. The anterior chamber of the eye can be the site of leptospiral multiplication. Hemorrhage may occur from weakened blood vessels. More permanent injury may develop.

DIAGNOSIS of leptospirosis is made by isolating the organism or by the testing of serum for the presence of antibodies produced by the infection. A definite diagnosis can be made only by demonstration of the causative organism. It is hard to do that because only a few Leptospira usually are found in the blood and because of the difficulty of separating Leptospira from the contaminating organisms in the urine. After death, Leptospira tend to be destroyed by decomposition of tissue. Most isolations are made from susceptible laboratory animals that have been injected with tissue from suspected cases.

A tentative diagnosis can be made with the serological tests on two or more serum samples, taken periodically from the time of onset of disease. To make the tests, it is desirable to have a stock-culture collection of known Leptospira. Thirty or more serotypes are now recognized, and new ones may be found.

Workers with leptospirosis in livestock in the United States must consider the possibility of infection with at least these five serotypes: *Leptospira pomona, L. icterohaemorrhagiae, L. grippotyphosa, L. canicola,* and *L. sejroe.*

THE AGGLUTINATION-LYSIS TEST generally is considered the standard test for the detection of leptospirosis. Its chief advantage is that the serotype involved usually can be identified. When live cultures of Leptospira are mixed with dilutions of serum from animals affected with a similar serotype, they are clumped together and lysed, so that the mixture is freed of organisms. Even very high dilutions of sera of recovered animals may have this property, and it can persist for several years after the infection occurred. The test is read by the use of the dark-field microscope. Some of the clumps of organisms are large enough to be seen with the unaided eye. The number of organisms must be sufficient to make the reading of the test relatively easy. Experience in interpretation is necessary, as Leptospira have the peculiar property of tangling themselves into masses, brought about by changes not associated with infection. Agglutinated Leptospira lose their individual cellular identity before lysis and become granular masses. Because living organisms are employed, care must be taken by laboratory workers to prevent exposure of themselves and others.

The complement-fixation test is a reliable means of detecting leptospiral infections employing Leptospira that have been washed and killed, egg-propagated Leptospira, or Leptospira cultures that have been sonic vibrated. The complement-fixation reaction may not persist so long as the agglutination-lysis reaction. The complement-fixation test is also less specific in identifying the serotype causing the infection.

Plate and tube macroscopic agglutination tests, which make use of killed Leptospira, have been described by several investigators. The main advantages of these tests are the safety (as compared with the live antigens used in the agglutination-lysis test) and the greater serotype specificity over that of the complement-fixation test.

Also, they have the most practical application under average diagnostic laboratory conditions. The greatest disadvantage is production of amounts of uniform antigens economically.

Most efforts to treat animals affected with leptospirosis have been for the purpose of alleviating symptoms. Various antibiotics have been employed,

and of these Terramycin and dihydro-streptomycin appear to be of value in reducing urinary discharge of organisms.

Vaccination for leptospirosis was in the experimental stage in 1956. The experimental results have been promising, but the natural course of the disease in outbreaks is frequently followed by a disappearance of symptoms without the use of any corrective measures.

Control of leptospirosis is hampered by a lack of fundamental knowledge of the disease. For example, any successful program must depend on a source of Leptospira-free replacements and identification of the carrier animals. Because Leptospira transfer readily in large, closely confined herds, isolation into small units has a tendency to reduce the chance of spread. Damp, low ground and slow streams and ponds favor spread of the infection.

The application of serological tests on a herd basis, repeated at regular intervals, will indicate the extent of infection in the herd. Practical segregation and sanitary measures for the individual farm should be applied when indicated. The idea that all the animals exposed to infection become immune is a dangerous one, because it does not take into account that some become carriers of the causative agent.

The meaning of leptospirosis to the health of the community cannot be disregarded. Persons who have contact with infected animals and contaminated materials may contract the disease. Streams draining from infected premises may carry the organisms for several miles and be a potential source of infection.

G. B. Van Ness *has been engaged in research on animal diseases in the Animal Disease and Parasite Research Branch, at Beltsville, Md., since 1953.*

C. A. Manthei *became head of the Bacterial and Mycotic Diseases Section of the Animal Disease and Parasite Research Branch in 1954. He has been engaged in animal disease research since 1938.*

Anthrax

C. D. STEIN AND G. B. VAN NESS

ANTHRAX, or splenic fever, is an acute, infectious, febrile disease that has a rapidly fatal course. Sometimes it is referred to as charbon and milzbrand in animals, and as a malignant pustule and the woolsorter's disease in people.

Anthrax is one of the oldest and most destructive diseases of livestock. Outbreaks that took many animal and human lives are recorded by many medieval and modern writers. The disease has been associated closely with early discoveries that lead to the development of the modern sciences of bacteriology and immunology. It was the first infectious disease of animals in which the causative agent was definitely demonstrated to be a specific micro-organism and the first disease against which a bacterial vaccine was found to be an effective and practical means of prophylaxis.

The specific cause of anthrax is *Bacillus anthracis*, a Gram-positive, nonmotile, spore-forming, rectangular-shaped bacterium of relatively large size. The growing bacilli are usually arranged in chain formation in animal tissue or cultures, but they may occur singly or in pairs. When properly stained, the bacilli in blood and tissue smears of animals dead of the disease usually reveal a distinct capsule.

The organisms are highly virulent. When they gain access to the animal body, they multiply rapidly, invade the blood stream, and produce a rapidly fatal blood infection (septicemia). In the presence of oxygen, sufficient moisture, and a favorable temperature, the bacilli develop spores of remarkable tenacity. It is generally believed that spores do not form in the unopened carcass, but sporulation occurs readily when organisms are discharged from the body of an infected animal or when the carcass is opened for autopsy.

Anthrax spores are highly resistant to heat, low temperatures, chemical disinfectants, and prolonged drying. They may retain their viability for many years in the soil, in water, on hides, and on any contaminated objects held in storage.

On some marshy or bottom land or in soils that contain decomposed vegetable or animal matter, the organisms survive for long periods. In anthrax districts where the soil is known to be seriously infected, the disease may occur in epizootic form among livestock on pasture, especially during late summer and early fall, when grazing is closer because of scanty pasturage and when flies are numerous. Anthrax tends to be seasonal, but sporadic outbreaks may occur anywhere at any time.

ANTHRAX OCCURS in all parts of the world. Districts where repeated anthrax outbreaks occur exist in southern Europe, parts of Africa, Australia, Asia, and North and South America.

Large recognized areas of infection exist in South Dakota, Nebraska, Arkansas, Mississippi, Louisiana, Texas, and California, and small areas exist in a number of other States. Anthrax has been recognized as a disease of livestock in the United States for more than 60 years. There were 3,447 outbreaks in 39 States, with losses of 17,604 head of livestock, between 1945 and 1955.

Anthrax is spread from one country to another mainly through infected animals and the interchange of infected objects closely associated with animal life, such as hides, hair, wool, bonemeal, meat scraps, fertilizer, and forage.

When anthrax is once established in an area, it may spread to adjoining localities and even to distant points by contamination of soil, drinking water, and pasture plants with discharges of diseased animals; by dogs, cats, coyotes, and other carnivora that have fed on infected carcasses; by carrion-eating birds, especially buzzards; by flies and possibly other types of insects; by streams contaminated with surface drainage from anthrax-infected soil and tannery wastes; and by mixed feeds containing contaminated bonemeal, meat scraps, and other animal proteins.

All animals are susceptible to anthrax in some degree. Cattle, horses, sheep, and goats are most commonly affected. Man and swine possess a greater natural resistance to the disease. Dogs, cats, and wild animals of prey, as well as birds, frogs, and toads may become infected under certain conditions. Mice, guinea pigs, and rabbits, which are commonly used in the laboratory diagnosis of anthrax, are highly susceptible, but rats have considerable resistance.

Infection in cattle, horses, mules, sheep, and goats is usually the result of grazing on infected pastureland. Infection may also be caused by contaminated fodder or artificial feedstuffs, such as bonemeal, blood meal, oilcake, and tankage; by drinking from contaminated pools; or by the bites of contaminated flies. Swine, dogs, cats, mink, and wild animals held in captivity usually acquire the infection from consumption of infected meat. Widespread outbreaks in herds of swine in the Midwest in 1952 were traced to mixed feeds containing contaminated bonemeal.

THE SYMPTOMS OF ANTHRAX vary according to the species of animals and the acuteness of the attack. The average period of incubation—that is, the period of time elapsing between exposure to infection and the appearance of the first symptoms—under natural conditions is not known definitely, but experimental evidence indicates it may vary from 24 hours to 5 days or much longer.

The disease may occur in a peracute, acute, subacute, or chronic form.

The peracute form, most common in cattle, sheep, and goats, occurs at the beginning of an outbreak and is characterized by its sudden onset and rapidly fatal course. Victims present a picture of cerebral apoplexy—sudden staggering, difficult breathing, trembling, collapse, a few convulsive movements, and death. Death may occur without any noticeable illness.

In the acute and subacute forms, most common in cattle, horses, and sheep, there is first a rise in body temperature and a period of excitement, followed by depression, stupor, spasm, respiratory or cardiac distress, staggering convulsion, and death. During the course of the disease, the body temperature may reach 107° F. Rumination ceases, the milk secretion of milking cows is materially reduced, and pregnant animals may abort. Bloody discharges may emanate from the natural body openings. Swellings may appear in different parts of the body.

Horses may show fever, chills, severe colic, loss of appetite, extreme depression, muscular weakness, a bloody diarrhea, and swellings in the region of the neck, sternum, lower abdomen, and external genitals. The acute form usually terminates in death in a day or two. The subacute form may result in death in 3 to 5 days or longer—or recovery.

A cutaneous, or localized, form of anthrax characterized by swellings in various parts of the body may occur in cattle and horses when anthrax organisms lodge in wounds or abrasions of the skin. This form of the disease may occur following bites by infected flies or in highly susceptible animals following vaccination.

Chronic anthrax, with local lesions confined to the tongue and throat, occurs mostly in swine but is observed occasionally in cattle, horses, and dogs.

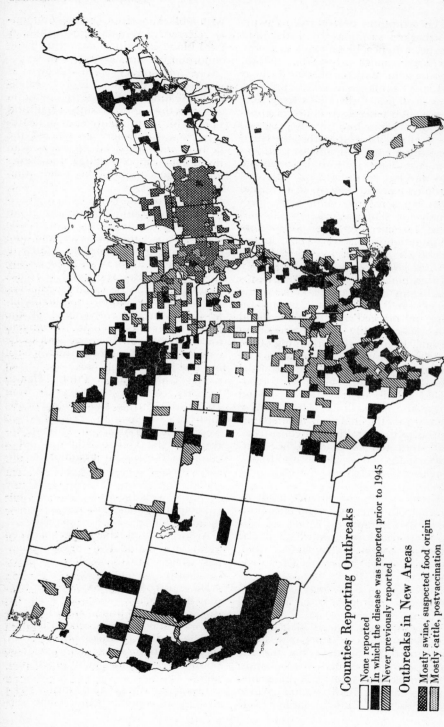

Counties Reporting Outbreaks

None reported
In which the disease was reported prior to 1945
Never previously reported

Outbreaks in New Areas

Mostly swine, suspected food origin
Mostly cattle, postvaccination

Outbreaks of anthrax in livestock in 1945–55—based on reports of State livestock sanitary officials and Federal veterinarians in charge. A total of 3,447 outbreaks in 714 counties in 39 States was reported.

The symptoms of anthrax in swine are marked swellings of throat and tongue. Often a blood-stained, frothy discharge comes from the mouth.

Some swine may die of acute anthrax without having shown any previous signs of illness. Others in a herd may have a high temperature, loss of appetite, depression, and rapidly progressing swelling about the throat, which sometimes causes death by suffocation. A comparatively large percentage may develop the disease in a mild and chronic form and may make a gradual recovery; some of them, when presented for slaughter as normal animals, however, on the postmortem examination may show some evidence of chronic anthrax infection in the cervical lymph glands and tonsils.

In animals dead of anthrax there is usually an oozing of blood from the nostrils and anus, rapid decomposition, and marked bloating. The blood fails to clot readily and is darker than normal. Rigor mortis (stiffening of the muscles) is frequently absent or incomplete. Hemorrhages beneath the skin are common. Clear or blood-tinged gelatinous exudates are found at the site of swellings. The spleen is usually greatly enlarged. The splenic pulp is soft or semifluid in consistency and dark red to black. The liver, kidneys, and lymph glands are usually congested and enlarged.

ANTHRAX IN MAN is acquired by skinning, butchering, or making postmortem examinations of infected carcasses (agricultural anthrax), or by handling contaminated hides, wool, hair, or other material (industrial anthrax).

In man the disease may occur as a cutaneous, pulmonary, or intestinal infection.

The cutaneous form, which is most prevalent, occurs as a primary, localized infection of the skin, usually on exposed parts, such as the hands, arms, neck, and face. The lesion first appears as a small pimple, which rapidly develops into a large vesicle with a black, necrotic center, commonly referred to as malignant pustule. A fatal blood infection may result if the condition becomes generalized.

The pulmonary form (known as woolsorter's disease) affects principally the lungs and is due to inhalation of spores during processing of hair and wool. This form usually ends in death.

In countries where people eat the flesh of animals dead of disease, an intestinal form of anthrax sometimes follows the consumption of contaminated meat.

Prompt diagnosis and early treatment are of utmost importance in combating the disease in man. While specific antiserum, arsenicals, and sulfa drugs have given excellent results in treatment of anthrax in man during the past 20 years, the trend in recent years appears to be toward penicillin, which has been found to be highly effective. More recently some of the newer antibiotics, such as Aureomycin and Terramycin, have proved to be extremely effective in the treatment of a limited number of cases.

The United States Public Health Reports, covering the 10 years from 1945 through 1954, show a total of 483 anthrax cases in man, most of which were of industrial origin. Human anthrax in the United States is not a common disease, but it cannot be considered rare.

DIAGNOSIS is based on history, clinical symptoms, and laboratory examination. Only the last is conclusive.

Anthrax should be suspected when animals die suddenly on or near premises where the disease has appeared previously.

Diagnosis based on clinical symptoms may be difficult, especially when the disease occurs in a new area. Peracute anthrax may be confused with other conditions that produce sudden death, such as lightning stroke, sunstroke, lead poisoning, and other acute, fatal maladies.

Less acute cases may be mistaken for malignant edema, hemorrhagic septicemia, the tick fever, anaplasmosis, blackleg, and sweetclover poisoning in cattle; and for purpura hemorrhagica, acute swamp fever, and colic in horses; and for malignant edema and acute hog colera in swine.

A tentative diagnosis based on clinical symptoms should always be confirmed by a laboratory examination.

When anthrax is suspected, it is not advisable to make a postmortem examination, because opening or skinning the carcass may result in spreading the disease and transmitting the infection to the operator. If a postmortem examination is necessary, the operator should use rubber gloves, rubber boots, and effective disinfectants to avoid infecting himself and the premises.

Specimens for laboratory examination should be obtained a short time following death, since specimens from carcasses showing evidence of decomposition are unsuitable for laboratory examination.

Good specimens for sending to the laboratory for examination are blood smears on clean glass slides and sterile cotton swabs, gauze, or blotting paper saturated with a sample of blood collected aseptically from a superficial blood vessel and allowed to air-dry. Specimens should be placed in clean containers labeled "suspected anthrax" and sent to the laboratory in a sealed metal mailing tube. When anthrax in swine is suspected, specimens of the cervical lymph nodes packed in borax should be submitted for examination, because anthrax organisms rarely occur in the blood stream of swine.

Laboratory examination for anthrax includes, first, a microscopic examination of blood smears properly stained for the presence of encapsulated bacilli having the characteristics of *B. anthracis;* second, culture tests on solid media for characteristic anthrax colonies showing no hemolysis; and, third, regardless of whether the microscopic and cultural tests are negative or positive, inoculation tests on guinea pigs or mice. If the injected material contains virulent anthrax organisms, the laboratory animal dies usually within 72 hours, and shows characteristic lesions of anthrax.

ANNUAL VACCINATION of livestock in anthrax districts well in advance of the anthrax season is the most effective method of prevention. Vaccination of exposed animals in an infected herd will reduce losses and help control the outbreak.

Vaccination is not completely effective, however, and an occasional loss from anthrax in a vaccinated herd does not constitute grounds for questioning the value of the vaccine that was used nor does it justify hasty revaccination of the herd.

The immunizing agents used in the United States in 1956 for vaccinating animals against anthrax were of two types—sterile products (anthrax antiserum and anthrax bacterin) and the living-spore vaccines, which consist of suspensions of living anthrax spores of different degrees of attenuation suspended in a solution of normal saline in combination with glycerine. Spore vaccines are designated as being of No. 1, No. 2, No. 3, or No. 4 strength, according to their degree of virulence.

Anthrax antiserum is of value as a preventive and as a therapeutic agent. It produces rapid immunity of short duration. Anthrax bacterin produces an active immunity of low degree but of longer duration than anthrax antiserum. Long experience, however, has shown that living-spore vaccines produce a higher degree of immunity than do bacterins.

Satisfactory results have been obtained with spore vaccines given subcutaneously by the single-, double-, or triple-injection method, but in known anthrax areas exceptionally good results are obtained with single-injection, intradermal spore vaccine of selected virulence, which produces a rapid, durable immunity with little or no reaction and is especially useful for immunizing exposed animals in an infected herd. In this method of vaccination, the spore vaccine is injected directly into the skin (intracutaneously) and not under the skin (subcutaneously), the usual method used in other forms of vaccination.

A new type of spore vaccine of low virulence, prepared from an uncapsulated variant strain of *B. anthracis* and developed at the Onderstepoort Veterinary Research Laboratory, Pretoria, Union of South Africa, has been used with excellent results in South Africa, England, India, and in other countries. A spore vaccine of this type is produced and distributed in the United States.

The simultaneous administration of antianthrax serum and spore vaccine (No. 2, 3, or 4) is likewise an effective method of immunization and is the method preferred by many veterinarians for vaccinating exposed animals during an actual outbreak.

The use of spore vaccines requires considerable discretion, and immunization should be carried out in accordance with recommendations of the livestock sanitary officials.

In administering and handling spore vaccines, the recommendations of the manufacturer should be followed carefully. Ordinarily it is inadvisable to use anthrax spore vaccines on premises where the disease has not existed previously unless danger from exposure is imminent. When spore vaccines are used, due care should be taken by the operator to prevent contamination of the surroundings and infecting himself.

Vaccination in anthrax areas with the proper type of immunizing agent usually affords protection for a season—but not more than a year—and should be repeated annually. In some endemic areas that have a long anthrax season, a booster dose of vaccine is administered 4 to 6 months after the date of the first vaccination.

TREATMENT OF ANTHRAX CASES showing advanced symptoms is of little value, but animals showing temperature reactions and other early symptoms may recover under prompt treatment.

For many years antianthrax serum was most commonly used for the treatment of anthrax in animals. In recent years, however, penicillin and other antibiotics, such as Terramycin, which have proved to be effective in the treatment of the disease in animals, are being used widely instead of specific antiserum.

Although the Department of Agriculture has conducted no experiments to determine the merits of antibiotics, such as penicillin and Terramycin, in the treatment of anthrax, clinical reports from veterinarians in the field indicate that these preparations may have considerable therapeutic value if properly administered during the early stages of the disease. Treatment of affected animals with any of the above-mentioned preparations should be under veterinary supervision.

THE FOLLOWING CONTROL MEASURES will assist in checking the disease and preventing its spread: (1) A strict quarantine of the infected premises, rigidly enforced to prevent the movement of livestock from or into the infected area; (2) prompt disposal of dead animals by complete cremation or deep burial under a layer of quicklime; (3) destruction of manure, bedding, and other contaminated material by burning; (4) isolation of visibly sick animals and immediate treatment with antianthrax serum, penicillin, or Terramycin; (5) vaccination of the apparently well but exposed animals with the immunizing agents recommended by the livestock sanitary officials; (6) change of pastures if practicable; (7) cleaning and disinfecting with a 5-percent lye solution of contaminated stables and sterilization of all milking equipment if the outbreak occurs in a dairy herd; (8) control of flies and maintenance of good sanitation; (9) due precaution to prevent spreading the infection through rats, dogs, cats, swine, chickens, buzzards, and crows feeding on the carcasses of animals dead of anthrax, or by skinning the carcass or removing it to a rendering plant.

Federal and State responsibilities in connection with the anthrax problem are carried out as follows: Actual handling of outbreaks of anthrax in each State is performed by the State livestock sanitary officials. The Department of Agriculture furnishes the diagnosticians, technical assistance, and advice when requested by State officials and carries on research on the disease.

Federal regulations to prevent the introduction of anthrax infection into the United States through importation of certain animal products are also enforced.

The regulations governing the importation of bonemeal for use in animal feeds or fertilizer are enforced by the Department of Agriculture. Regulations pertaining to the admission of hair and bristles intended for use in manufacturing shaving brushes are enforced by the United States Public Health Service.

From standpoints of economics and public health, anthrax is a serious disease against which every means of suppression needs to be exerted. The problem of control is a common cause to which every livestock owner should contribute. All persons concerned should cooperate to the fullest extent with the local veterinarian and the livestock sanitary and the public health officials who are charged with the responsibility of controlling the disease.

C. D. Stein, *a graduate of the University of Pennsylvania, is a veterinarian in the Animal Disease and Parasite Research Branch of the Agricultural Research Service. He has been with the Department of Agriculture since 1911, having served in three divisions of the former Bureau of Animal Industry. For many years he has contributed important researches on anthrax, equine infectious anemia, and other infectious diseases of livestock.*

G. B. VAN NESS, *a graduate of Kansas State College, is a veterinarian in the Animal Disease and Parasite Research Branch. He was a member of the research staffs of agricultural experiment stations in Washington, Arkansas, and Florida before joining the Department of Agriculture in 1953.*

Malignant Edema

C. D. STEIN

MALIGNANT edema is a wound infection that usually is quickly fatal. It is marked by painful gangrenous swellings and severely toxic symptoms.

It is caused by a spore-forming, rod-shaped germ, *Clostridium septicum*. The organism resembles the germ that causes blackleg; both grow only in the absence of oxygen. Therefore the infection usually enters the body through wounds caused by puncture or laceration. The infection develops in the injured tissue.

The germs are widely scattered in the top layers of soil. Animals kept in dusty, unsanitary surroundings may get the disease following hypodermic injections, surgical operations, parturition, and accidental wounds.

Horses, cattle, and sheep are most susceptible. Swine, dogs, and cats are rarely affected.

In horses, which are most susceptible, the infection frequently follows punctures caused by nails, splinters, and such. In sheep, it may follow castration, docking, and shearing. It often occurs in cattle in areas where blackleg infection exists; sometimes it appears with blackleg and the two diseases are often confused. In man it produces a type of gas gangrene following war wounds.

A disease of sheep, known as braxy or bradshot, which occurs in Norway, Scotland, the Faroe Islands, and Iceland, apparently is caused by the malignant edema organism, but the infection is believed to enter the body through the digestive tract instead of through external wounds.

Malignant edema can be transmitted to rabbits, guinea pigs, white rats, mice, and pigeons under experimental conditions.

The first symptoms of malignant edema usually appear 12 to 36 hours after the infection enters the body. There are hot, painful swellings at the points of infection, high fever, loss of appetite, a drop in milk secretion, severe depression, difficult breathing, and convulsions before death. Most affected animals die 1 or 2 days after the symptoms appear.

The clinical diagnosis of malignant edema usually is difficult because it may be mistaken for blackleg, anthrax, hemorrhagic septicemia, or other types of gas edema.

Laboratory tests are the only conclusive method of distinguishing malignant edema from similar types of infection. The following points of difference between malignant edema and blackleg may be of some help in making a tentative diagnosis: Malignant edema affects cattle of all ages. It generally starts from a wound. The gangrenous swellings appear at the point of injury. The swellings, which develop rapidly, are usually extensive and doughy; they pit when they are pressed and discharge a reddish, gelatinelike substance mixed with gas bubbles when they are opened.

Blackleg affects young animals. It is rare in animals more than 2 years old. It occurs from minute, invisible puncture wounds. The swellings appear mostly over the muscles of the hind or front quarters, and emit a crackling sound on pressure. They discharge a frothy, dark-red exudate, with an odor like that of rancid butter, when they are incised.

MEDICAL TREATMENT of an established case of malignant edema that shows advanced symptoms is of little or no value. Such antibiotics as penicillin, Aureomycin, and Terramycin may have some therapeutic value if administered during the early stages of the disease. They should be used only under the supervision of a veterinarian.

Vaccination is an effective way to prevent malignant edema in animals exposed to it. In districts where the soil is believed to be heavily contaminated with its spores, animals should be vaccinated shortly before being placed on pastures.

An immunizing agent known as *Clostridium septicum bacterin*, prepared from the causative organism, is used for vaccinating. In some districts where blackleg infection also exists in the soil, cattle and sheep are vaccinated with a bivalent bacterin, *Clostridium chauvoeisepticus bacterin*, which protects the vaccinated animals against both infections.

The danger of exposure can be greatly reduced by giving prompt and proper attention to punctures and penetrating wounds; by sterilizing surgical instruments; by observing strict aseptic surgical procedures; and by housing animals during parturition in clean, dust-free quarters.

Because malignant edema can be transmitted to man, persons handling suspected cases should wear rubber gloves and rubber boots. They should use effective disinfectants to avoid infecting themselves and the premises.

CONTROL MEASURES for checking outbreaks of the disease and preventing its spread to other premises include: Isolation of all animals showing symptoms of the disease; vaccination of apparently well but exposed animals and, if feasible, immediate removal to a new pasture; prompt disposal of the carcasses of dead animals by complete burning or deep burial in quicklime; burning manure, bedding, and other contaminated material; thorough cleansing of contaminated stables, followed by disinfection with a 5-percent solution of lye; and restrictions against skinning dead animals, feeding the carcasses to other animals on the farm, and removing the carcasses from the premises to a rendering plant.

C. D. STEIN, *a graduate of the University of Pennsylvania, is a veterinarian in the Animal Disease and Parasite Research Branch of the Agricultural Research Service. He has been with the Department of Agriculture since 1911. For many years he has done research on anthrax, equine infectious anemia, and other infectious diseases of livestock.*

Tetanus

C. D. STEIN

TETANUS, commonly called lockjaw, is a wound infection disease that is usually accompanied by a fatal toxemia. The toxemia causes contractions of the voluntary muscles, mainly those of the face, neck, body, legs, and tail. Spasms are the result of steady and prolonged contractions of the affected muscles.

Tetanus is caused by a rod-shaped germ, *Clostridium tetani,* which produces an extremely potent toxin. The germs form highly resistant, large terminal spores, which give the organism a peculiar drumstick appearance. The tetanus germs and spores remain localized at the place of the wound where they enter the body. They multiply and produce the powerful toxin. The poison is absorbed and carried by the blood to all parts of the body. It acts directly on the nervous system. It is so potent that a mere prick with a hypodermic needle contaminated with it may be enough to cause symptoms of tetanus in people.

C. tetani, like the germs that cause blackleg and malignant edema, thrive in the absence of air. They become especially active and dangerous when they are implanted in injured tissue from which the air is excluded. Deep punctured or lacerated wounds contaminated with foreign material or soil—such as may result from nail or splinter punctures, fractured bones, gunshot wounds, castration, and harness and saddle galls—therefore are more apt to produce tetanus than superficial open wounds.

The disease occurs all over the world. It is most common in old farming areas, especially in sections where truck gardens, heavily manured land, and swamps are contaminated with tetanus germs. The organisms or their spores are scattered in the top layers of soil and in street dust and hay. They often are in manure.

The disease is common in people and horses. It may attack other warm-blooded animals.

Horses, mules, and asses, which are highly susceptible, may contract the disease from any type of wound but most frequently from wounds of the feet.

In sheep, which are rather susceptible, the infection sometimes occurs after castration, docking, and shearing; in the umbilical (navel) cord of lambs during birth; or in ewes during parturition. Cows may get infection following parturition and calves after castration.

Cases are observed occasionally in swine, dogs, and cats.

Poultry is highly resistant.

SYMPTOMS appear in most cases in 1 to 2 weeks after the germs enter the body. Sometimes—depending on the type of primary injury, the character of the healing process, and the degree of infection—the symptoms may not appear for several weeks. Very young animals may develop symptoms in less than a week.

The first signs of the disease usually are manifested about the head. Chewing is difficult at first, and swallowing is slow and awkward. Spasms spread rapidly from one group of muscles to another and make them rigid. Eating may become impossible when the muscles used in chewing are affected and the jaws are "locked."

The nictitating membrane (the inner, or third, eyelid between the lower eyelid and the eyeball proper) protrudes up on the surface of the eyeball. This is noticeable especially in the horse.

The legs are spread and stiffened, giving a straddling gait and the appearance of a sawhorse. The tail is elevated and stiff. The ears are held rigidly erect. Constipation commonly occurs. The breathing is rapid and forced. The heart action may or may not be quickened. Usually there is little or no fever except in the severe cases and then just before death.

The muscles may tend to relax at intervals, but they contract instantly, like a spring, at the slightest noise, a ray of light, or a touch. Death is usually due to exhaustion or nonfunction of the vital organs. Pneumonia, which results from the inhalation of water, saliva, feed, or improperly administered medicines, is a frequent complication.

Death usually comes 7 or 10 days after the first symptoms appear. Mortality is 55 to 90 percent, depending on the individuals, the species of animal, and severity of the infection. Animals that recover often are sick a month.

Tetanus is not hard to diagnose because its symptoms are unusual. Rigidity of the muscles is one of the most constant and typical symptoms. No typical lesions are found on postmortem examination, but microscopic examination of stained smears made from deep portions of wounds may reveal the typical drumstick-shaped organisms of tetanus.

PREVENTION of tetanus depends first on cleanliness. Cleanliness in all operations includes strict aseptic surgical procedures and the use of sterile surgical instruments.

Animals should be housed during parturition and following surgery in clean, dust-free quarters.

Prompt and proper attention should be given to deep wounds—the removal of dirt and other foreign material, proper drainage with surgery, and irrigation of the wound with suitable medicaments, such as hydrogen peroxide.

Stables, corrals, paddocks, or pastures used by horses and other livestock should be kept free of sharp objects which are apt to cause injuries.

In known tetanus districts, routine preventive immunization of animals against tetanus and immediate treatment of injured animals with tetanus antitoxin following wounds will materially reduce the chances of infection.

THE PREVENTIVE immunizing agents against tetanus are of two types, tetanus antitoxin and tetanus toxoid.

Tetanus antitoxin is produced from the blood serum of horses. It is standardized as to potency, so that a given amount neutralizes a specific amount of toxin. Injected into susceptible animals, it confers a passive or temporary immunity against the disease. As a preventive, it should be injected immediately following an injury and not after symptoms occur.

The tetanus toxoid is prepared by

treating the toxin with formalin to inactivate its toxicity. The refined formalized toxoid, which has largely replaced antitoxin for immunization, especially in man, confers an active immunity against the toxin in about 2 weeks after its injection. The immunity lasts about a year and can be increased by booster injections. The use of tetanus toxoid in animals and man has become a routine practice in some areas where tetanus is prevalent.

The prevalence of tetanus in animals and man has decreased because of improved methods of wound treatment, better hygiene, and preventive vaccination with tetanus toxoid. The incidence of tetanus in troops during the First World War was greatly reduced by better treatment of battle wounds and administration of tetanus antitoxin. Its incidence in the Second World War was negligible, because immunization of all the troops with tetanus toxoid was a routine measure.

TREATMENT of an established case of tetanus in an animal that shows well-marked symptoms has little value.

Chances for recovery are improved if treatment is started early. It is first essential to open the wound through which the infection entered, if it can be located, to provide adequate drainage and to keep it open by irrigation with a suitable antiseptic.

Confinement of affected animals in clean, cool, quiet, darkened quarters is advantageous.

If tetanus antitoxin is indicated, it should be given in large, repeated doses. Sedatives of various types are commonly employed to produce relaxation of the muscles. Artificial feeding may be required.

Veterinarians have reported that the administration of penicillin, alone or as an adjunct to antitoxin, has given good results in the treatment of some cases that show early symptoms of tetanus.

When attempts are made to treat a case of tetanus, the procedure should be carried out under the supervision of a veterinarian.

C. D. STEIN, *a graduate of the University of Pennsylvania, is a veterinarian in the Animal Disease and Parasite Research Branch of the Agricultural Research Service. He has been with the Department of Agriculture since 1911, during which time his research has contributed fundamental information for a better understanding of anthrax, equine infectious anemia, and other infectious diseases of livestock.*

Listeriosis

H. E. BIESTER AND L. H. SCHWARTE

LISTERIOSIS, an infectious disease, is caused by a bacterial organism that affects animals and people.

Three British scientists first recovered the organism from laboratory rabbits and guinea pigs in 1926. They named it *Bacterium monocytogenes*. Later a similar organism was isolated from some rodents in South Africa. Various names have been used for the organism—*Bacterium monocytogenes*, *Listerella hepatolytica*, *L. monocytogenes*, *Corynebacterium parvulum*, and *Bacillus monocytogenes*. It has been designated as *Listeria monocytogenes* since 1948. The disease formerly was known as listerellosis.

Various investigators have found

the infection in sheep, cattle, swine, foxes, chickens, and man. Increasing numbers of cases of listeriosis have been reported from many States since 1936.

Generalized gross changes are observed in children, chickens, and rodents, but those changes usually are absent in infected cattle, sheep, and swine. Listeriosis causes changes in the cells of the nervous system. The changes are much like those associated with some virus infections. The organism has been recovered primarily from the central nervous system, but some investigators have found Listeria in other organs.

Listeriosis in sheep often reaches epidemic proportions. An outbreak in large flocks, particularly large feeder units, may cause heavy losses. Losses of 200 to 500 in feeder flocks of 3,000 sheep have occurred. Fewer than 2 percent of the animals with definite clinical symptoms recover. Losses on the range are seldom extensive.

The exact mode of transmission under field conditions is not well understood. The infection may be spread by contact and through contaminated feed and water.

The suspension of operations on an infected area for 6 months or more after thorough cleaning and disinfection is advisable in order to prevent recurrence of the disease.

The first indication of listeriosis in lambs may be a loss of appetite and a temperature up to 106° F. The infected animals appear depressed and weak. They are inclined to tremble and lean against objects. Incoordination of various degrees is frequently observed. Lambs may have a tendency to throw their heads back. Others show unilateral involvement, so that the head turns to one side. The disease usually runs a rapid course. Some infected animals lie on their sides and their legs move, as if trying to run. Convulsions may occur. The corneas of the eyes may appear grayish toward the termination of the disease. Breathing becomes faster. Sometimes strands of mucus, from the mucosa of the turbinates, exude from the nose and mouth.

Examination of an infected animal usually discloses no definite pathologic changes in the viscera. The liver and kidneys may be swollen and grayish brown. Slight congestion or inflammation of the meninges and occasionally petechial hemorrhages may be observed in the brain tissue.

Microscopic examination of parts of the central nervous system may show focal areas of concentrations of white blood cells in the brain tissue and vast accumulations of monocytic cells around the walls of the blood vessels. Degeneration is not unusual in the areas of cellular infiltration. The organism is seldom isolated from the blood stream, liver, spleen, or kidney of infected sheep in the advanced stage of the disease.

Routine culture methods of brain tissue often fail to secure positive results in infected animals. More satisfactory results are obtained when composite samples taken from various parts of the brain and cord are triturated in a mortar and shaken for 15 minutes or when the composite samples are thoroughly processed in a Waring blender to break up the infected foci. The bacterial organisms are then uniformly distributed in the emulsion of brain tissue and can be transferred and grown on culture media. General characteristics of this organism are: Small rods 0.4 to 0.5 by 0.5 to 2.0 microns; Gram - positive, flagellated, aerobic, catalase positive; acid but no gas from glucose and a few additional carbohydrates; easy growth on ordinary culture media. The organism is not acid-fast. This brief summary differentiates this bacterial species from others that have similar size and shape.

Listeria infection in swine has been reported in a small number of droves in the Corn Belt. The disease has been found in suckling pigs and larger animals of 150 pounds or more. Mature stock is seldom affected.

The early symptoms include restlessness, less appetite, periodic thirst, increased temperature reaction in most cases, and more and more nervousness. The larger animals develop definite central nervous disturbances. Some individuals drag their hind legs or show various degrees of incoordination; the forelegs move in a stilted gait. The suckling pigs develop a progressive central nervous involvement, including spasms and paralysis, which often ends in death. Some cases recover despite severe clinical symptoms. The highest mortality occurs in the young pigs.

The disease occurs usually in large droves. It is believed to be spread by contact and by exposure to infected feed, water, buildings, and equipment.

Gross pathologic changes in the visceral organs are usually vague or absent. Congestion or inflammatory reactions in the meninges may be observed. Congestion of the cerebral blood vessels or a few petechial hemorrhages may or may not be present.

Microscopically, focal areas of monocytic infiltration or infiltration by these cells about the blood vessels is characteristic of listeriosis. Degenerative changes may be observed in some focal areas of the brain and cord with the appearance of increasing numbers of polymorphonuclear leukocytes which is accompanied by necrosis. Swine apparently are more resistant to this disease than sheep. The disease does not spread so rapidly or extensively in swine under field conditions. The progressive clinical symptoms are less severe and the percentage of recovery is much greater, especially in swine 70 pounds or more in weight.

LISTERIA INFECTION IN CATTLE has been reported in herds throughout the United States for more than a quarter of a century. Most of the outbreaks have been sporadic and have involved only a few animals, but up to 20 percent of animals in larger beef and dairy herds may be affected.

The first indications of infection in cattle are restlessness and loss of appetite. A rise in temperature from 104° to 106° usually is recorded in the early stages. Symptoms of a central nervous disturbance usually follow. Complete paralysis and a subnormal temperature may occur just before death. Other animals become nervous and walk in circles for several days without taking food or water. Apparently their vision is poor, and they will walk into objects. Some of the animals improve, slowly regain their appetite, and eventually recover. Others are depressed, lose their appetite, and show progressive incoordination and paralysis, which precede death.

Careful examination following death shows no specific gross lesions in the heart, liver, lungs, spleen, or lymph nodes. The eyes are clear. Usually a digestive disturbance is not evident. Examination of the brain shows only a slight congestion with a few small pinpoint hemorrhages in the brain and brain stem. There might be a slight softening or degeneration in the brain stem and spinal cord.

Under the microscope, one can find in cattle the same type of infiltrations around the blood vessels and in focal areas of the central nerve tissue as are commonly observed in infected sheep and swine. Animals that have recovered from severe infections retain the microscopic lesions in the brain tissue for a long time. Organisms were not isolated from the recovered cases.

LISTERIOSIS IN CHICKENS and other birds has been reported in different parts of the world, especially in Europe and North America. The clinical-symptoms in birds are vague or absent.

Apparently few specific symptoms are noted in infected chickens. Often adult birds die suddenly. A slow degeneration or wasting occurs in young, naturally infected chickens. Mortality among birds varies from a few individuals in sporadic cases up to 50 or 60 percent over a period of 4 or 6 weeks in more severe outbreaks.

Listeriosis has caused more than 25 percent loss of canaries maintained in aviaries. Avian listeriosis invariably causes a septicemia, especially in chickens. The commonest lesions are the massive infiltration and necrosis of the heart muscle. Diffuse and focal areas of necrosis in the myocardium occur and involve the entire structure. Little normal tissue can be seen in some cases. Pericarditis also is accompanied by considerable accumulation of fluid in the pericardial cavity. Generalized edema may occur, with enlargement of the liver and spleen. Necrotic foci in the liver and various degrees of enteritis with or without fibrinous exudate have been recorded.

The diagnosis is made by isolation of the bacterial organism on culture media. This organism is usually confined to the central nervous system in our domesticated mammals but can readily be isolated from the abdominal organs and from the heart blood of birds. Listeria can be easily grown on most of the common media, but blood agar is probably the medium of choice.

LITTLE SUCCESS has been reported for treatment of listeriosis. Most of the drugs and antibiotics have not proved satisfactory or practical. Vaccination has been ineffective.

The control of listeriosis, especially avian listeriosis, seems to be accomplished most effectively by a program of rigid sanitation, plus frequent inspection and elimination of any infected or undesirable birds.

Some observers have associated the incidence of listeriosis with the feeding of silage, but in many of the outbreaks we studied the animals were not fed silage.

Carl Olson, Jr., and his associates at the University of Nebraska reported in 1953 that the continuous feeding of silage did not clearly influence the development of listeriosis in sheep, nor did the previous feeding of silage reduce the resistance of sheep to the disease.

Listeriosis may be considered an insidious disease. The body may harbor the organisms for a long period before the disease appears in clinical form.

Some of the characteristics of *Listeria* resemble those of *Erysipelothrix*. G. S. Wilson and A. A. Miles, of the University of London, in 1946 placed *Listeria* in the genus *Erysipelothrix*.

When the organism is recovered only from the central nervous system in the final stage of listeriosis, there is evidence of a previous bacteremia. The kidneys, spleen, and liver of such cases frequently show focal and perivascular infiltrations of monocytes, but Listeria are not recovered from these organs in the late stages of the disease.

H. E. BIESTER *received his training in the University of Pennsylvania. He became associate director of the Veterinary Medical Research Institute of Iowa State College in 1944. For more than 30 years he has investigated swine enteritis, coccidiosis, equine encephalomyelitis, moldy corn intoxication, trichiniasis, hog cholera, listeriosis, and other diseases of domestic animals.*

L. H. SCHWARTE *became associated with the Veterinary Medical Research Institute of Iowa State College in 1930. He was trained in Cornell University and Iowa State College, and has engaged in investigations of virus diseases, neurotropic infections, and swine diseases.*

DISEASES
AND PARASITES
AFFECTING

cattle

Milk Fever

W. J. GIBBONS

MILK FEVER is a disease of high-producing dairy cows.

It is marked by paralysis, inability to rise, and partial or total loss of consciousness in cows that have recently calved. It occasionally affects cows during calving but occurs oftenest in the first few days after calving or when the cow is coming into full production. It occurs after the first lactation and is not common in 3-year-olds. Most cases occur in cows 4 to 8 years old. The condition may return at subsequent calvings in good cows.

Milk fever is also called parturient pariesis and parturient hypocalcemia. The condition is produced by a rapid lowering of the calcium, or lime, in the blood—hence the name "hypocalcemia." The name "milk fever" is a misnomer, as there is no fever. The temperature is normal or subnormal.

Milk fever used to cause collapse and rapid death in as many as 90 percent of the affected dairy cows. Now, thanks to more complete knowledge about the disease and modern methods of treatment, only a small percentage of dairy cattle die of uncomplicated milk fever.

A major advance in our knowledge came in 1925, when H. Dryere and J. R. Greig, of England, concluded from their extensive research that milk fever was linked to an acute deficiency of calcium in the blood and that the injection of calcium into the blood effected a cure.

Other research revealed that there is also a decrease in phosphates and sometimes magnesium. Usually there is an increase of blood sugar.

Earlier investigators had cured milk

243

fever by inflating the udder with air, but they could not explain why. The cure, it was learned later, had a mechanical basis. The new milk, or colostrum, is rich in calcium. Udder distention prevents further draining of calcium from the blood and the calcium already in the udder is reabsorbed. The body of the cow is able to restore the calcium level in the blood in 3 to 5 hours, and recovery takes place.

Research on the cause of milk fever has continued because of two circumstances. Rarely does a cow fail to show response to calcium therapy and die if there are no complications. Most research has been directed to a study of relapsing milk fever cases and the prevention of the disease. As the parathyroid gland is closely connected with calcium metabolism, it has been postulated that this internal gland becomes disturbed to provide the basic cause of the breakdown of the mechanism of calcium metabolism. The theory has not been completely substantiated, but we have some evidence that the basic cause may be associated with the parathyroid gland.

MOST CASES of milk fever occur within 72 hours after calving.

Odd cases that occur a long time before calving or several weeks afterwards are apt to be complicated infections or other conditions that resemble milk fever. A positive diagnosis can only be made by laboratory tests. Occasional conditions may arise in which blood calcium drops; they may respond to calcium treatment.

The owner may not notice or recognize the earlier stages of milk fever. Dullness and reluctance to move may appear a few hours or—more commonly—24 and 48 hours after calving. The first symptoms sometimes include excitement and tetany or spasms of the hind legs.

The early symptoms pass off quickly. Then paralysis begins to affect the hind legs. The cow staggers and finally goes down. She becomes unconscious and her head and neck are kinked laterally or turned back along the side. The pulse may be fast. She may groan and breathe heavily. Bloating occurs quickly if she becomes stretched out.

Many cases of milk fever are complicated by metritis (infection of the womb); pneumonia, caused by inhaling stomach contents; acetonemia; paralysis of the nerves of the hind legs; and sometimes dislocations and fractures.

VARIOUS WAYS TO PREVENT milk fever have been suggested. None has had much success.

Delayed or partial milking may help for some cows but may be ineffective in high producers and may predispose to mastitis.

Giving calcium immediately after calving may have some merit with cows that have had milk fever. As soon as the lack of calcium was discovered as producing the symptoms of milk fever, the feeding of lime in various forms during the dry period was tried as a means of prevention. The results were nil.

J. M. Boda and H. H. Cole, of the University of California College of Agriculture, conducted more than 3 years of field trials on the prevention of milk fever. They accepted the theory that a disturbance of the parathyroid was the basic cause of milk fever. They began with several assumptions: If the cow were on a diet adequate in calcium during the dry period, very little calcium would be needed during the precalving period, when calcium metabolism (regulated by the parathyroid gland) became dormant. When the cow calves, the demand for calcium becomes enormous and, if the parathyroid gland is out of condition, calcium metabolism breaks down, calcium becomes deficient in the blood, and milk fever results. Then, they theorized, the parathyroid of a cow placed on a low-calcium diet during the dry period would be in good shape to meet the increased calcium demands after freshening because the parathyroid had been active to maintain calcium due to low intake.

They proposed the following formula for use during the dry period (in pounds): Ground barley, 800; rolled barley, 600; wheat bran, 500; cottonseed meal, 100; monosodium phosphate, 40; and salt, 10. Each cow should receive 8 pounds a day for 6 weeks before freshening plus 8 pounds of oat hay or poor hay.

In several herds where the incidence of milk fever was very high, feeding of the low-calcium diet reduced the number of cases from 30 to 3 percent. Production was not reduced noticeably.

Research conducted by J. W. Hibbs and H. D. Pounden, of the Ohio Agricultural Experiment Station, showed that the addition of vitamin D to the diet of the cow 5 days before calving reduces the incidence of milk fever.

THE COW down with milk fever should be kept up on her sternum and not allowed to get out flat. Pneumonia caused by bloating and inhalation can be prevented by keeping the cow upright. The cow should be placed in a well-bedded stall to avoid injury. If she is in the pasture, she should be watched so that she does not roll or struggle into ditches or over embankments.

Air inflation of the udder will cure milk fever, but the danger of mastitis is so great that the practice has been abandoned except in dire emergency. It should be done with great care and strict antisepsis.

The procedure preferred by veterinarians is the intravenous injection of calcium gluconate in a 20-percent solution. Because acetonemia, or a lack of sugar in the blood, often accompanies milk fever, dextrose is added to the calcium solution. Calcium injections should be made slowly to avoid heart block, which is dangerous. Immediately after treatment the cow brightens up and usually makes a good recovery in 1 to 2 hours.

Relapsing cases may need one or more additional treatments. The cause of relapses has yet to be solved. Some authorities believe the addition of phosphates and magnesium to the calcium solution prevents relapses. When treatments fail, very likely the diagnosis was wrong or complications developed.

W. J. GIBBONS *is professor of medicine and infectious diseases in the Alabama Polytechnic Institute, in which he formerly was professor of large-animal surgery and medicine. For more than 20 years he was an instructor and professor in the New York State Veterinary College.*

Bovine Mastitis

R. W. BROWN, JR.

MASTITIS means inflammation of the udder. It results principally from infection with micro-organisms.

Many kinds of bacteria and some yeasts can produce mastitis. The streptococci (mainly *Streptococcus agalactiae, S. dysgalactiae,* and *S. uberis*) and the staphylococci (*Micrococcus pyogenes*) are the chief causative agents, but mastitis due to the bacteria *Escherichia coli, Aerobacter aerogenes,* and *Pseudomonas aeruginosa* has been occurring with greater frequency.

Other organisms, such as *Pasteurella multocida,* yeasts, and acid-fast bacilli, also have caused outbreaks of mastitis, which have involved a large proportion of the cows in different herds. Another organism that usually causes sporadic cases, particularly in the dry cows rather than in lactating cows, is *Corynebacterium pyogenes.*

The udder also can become infected with bacteria that cause tuberculosis, brucellosis, and scarlet fever or streptococcic sore throat in man. Most of the varieties of bacteria found in mastitis, however, are harmless to the consumer. When milk is pasteurized properly, practically all danger is eliminated.

The bacteria that cause mastitis are usually carried from diseased cows to the teats of healthy cows on the hands of milkers or in the teat cups of milking machines during milking. Bacteria also can be spread by flies or by contact with contaminated bedding or floors.

Injury to the teat opening and teat canal and the improper use of teat tubes and dilators also are responsible for some udder infections.

The teat canal is of considerable importance in preventing infection and should be protected from injury as much as possible. Once the bacteria enter the opening in the teat, they may pass up the teat canal and establish themselves in the milk cistern or lower part of the quarter. From that point they spread to other parts of the gland.

Mastitis exists in two forms— acute and chronic.

Acute mastitis is readily detectable and is the form most familiar to the cattle owner. The affected quarter is hot, tense, hard, and tender. Milk secretion is largely or entirely suspended. The milk may be watery, straw-colored, or blood-tinged and may contain few or many clots. A general systemic disturbance, such as depression, fever, and loss of appetite, may be present. In acute mastitis, the organisms have invaded and inflamed much of the involved quarter.

Chronic mastitis is not readily recognized. That is because a general balance exists between the infecting organisms and the udder, with the result that few observable symptoms develop, although damage to the secretory tissue does occur.

Inflammation like that of the acute form also develops in chronic infections of the udder, except that it usually involves only very small areas of secretory tissue at any one time. Consequently the gland is not swollen and the milk appears normal, but the inflammation changes the composition of the milk. The milk does not contain the usual amounts of butterfat or milk sugar, but the number of leucocytes, the salt content, and the products resulting from inflammation and bacterial activity increase. Even those changes will not be found if the areas of inflammation involved are microscopic—yet the gland is infected and may be a constant source of infection to other cows.

Sometimes during a chronic infection, flareups occur. They may develop into acute mastitis or they may be milder and cause little or no swelling of the gland, but will change the milk so that it has flakes or clots and a watery or unusual appearance.

The milder symptoms are often called subacute mastitis and may disappear after several milkings, although the quarter remains infected.

As a result of the inflammation, the cells that secrete milk become inactive and may be replaced by nonsecreting fibrous or scar tissue.

When large areas of secretory tissue are destroyed, as in acute mastitis, the quarter becomes atrophied and hard. The changes are gradual in chronic mastitis. The hard areas, circumscribed or diffuse, usually are formed first near the milk cistern. The quarter gradually loses its soft, pliable quality. In advanced cases it becomes hardened throughout, and the secretory tissue is lost almost entirely.

The change in the character of the udder tissue causes a drop in milk production and shortened lactation periods. How long it takes for the change to occur in chronically infected quarters varies according to the virulence of the invading bacteria, the cow's natural resistance, and the number of acute or subacute attacks. Sometimes the animal passes through several lactation periods before the disease manifests itself, but many cows become useless in a short time.

THE CONTROL OF MASTITIS in any herd in which mastitis has become a problem is best attained by adopting a control program that includes an accurate diagnosis, adequate sanitary and management practices, proper treatment, and close cooperation between the dairyman and veterinarian.

The importance of management and veterinary service in the control of *Streptococcus agalactiae* mastitis was shown in a study conducted by the New York State Mastitis Control Program. In herds that had good management and adequate veterinary service, 71 percent made good progress in controlling mastitis, but in herds with poor management and inadequate veterinary service, only 19 percent made good progress.

EARLY DETECTION and treatment of infected udders are necessary if one is to control the spread of infection. Acute attacks are diagnosed readily by clinical symptoms, but the chronic form presents some difficulty.

A combination of cultural and microscopic examination of quarter samples of milk is the best way to diagnose chronic udder infections. They are laboratory procedures that require milk samples drawn into sterile tubes or vials and trained persons to run them. All milk samples must be obtained as aseptically as possible. That means that the organisms that occur outside the udder on the skin and in the manure, dust, or bedding must be kept out of the sterile tube as the milk is withdrawn from the teat. Therefore, before the milk samples are obtained, the udder and teats should be washed and the teat openings thoroughly cleaned with a piece of cotton soaked

with alcohol or some other nonirritating disinfectant. Any conditions that favor the raising of dust in the barn at the time of sampling should be prevented.

SIMPLER TESTS can be used on the farm. They depend on the physical and chemical changes in milk produced by mastitis. Anybody who uses them should understand that abnormal changes do not appear regularly in the milk of all cows with chronic mastitis and that the type of organism infecting the udder cannot be determined. A positive test in most instances indicates an infected quarter. But a negative test does not indicate that the quarter is not infected.

The simplest test uses the strip cup. Several streams of milk are drawn from a quarter into a cup covered by a fine-mesh wire screen or into a pan with black plastic or metal plates. The appearance of clots and flakes or watery or off-colored milk usually is evidence of mastitis. The test is limited because only infected udders that show gross changes in the milk can be detected. The strip cup should be used before each milking or at least once a day.

The second test is the bromthymol-blue test. It is carried out by adding specific amounts of milk and dye solution in a test tube or by drawing a small amount of milk onto blotters impregnated with dye solution. Blotters and kits that contain test tubes, dye solution, and directions possibly may be purchased from farmers' cooperatives, feedstores, drugstores, or mail-order companies that sell farm equipment. The color resulting from the mixture of milk and dye depends on the degree of acidity or alkalinity of the milk. Milk from healthy quarters is slightly acid and gives a yellowish-green shade. In exceptional cases, a bright yellow or acid reaction may be observed. Milk from quarters affected with mastitis is predominantly green, because the milk is more alkaline. The more alkaline the milk, the darker the shade of green becomes.

This test discloses a somewhat larger number of diseased animals at any one time than the strip cup, but it should be used primarily to determine the relative amount of mastitis in a herd. The test, under most circumstances, will detect only about 33 to 50 percent of the infected quarters.

Another method for determining abnormal milk is the modified Whiteside test. It is simple and is more accurate than the other tests mentioned. It is used for individual cows. On an experimental basis it has been found useful for testing composite milk samples at a creamery to determine the herds from which mastitis milk is being delivered. To perform the test, 2 drops of a 4-percent solution of sodium hydroxide are added to 5 drops of fresh milk on a glass plate. If the milk has been refrigerated, only one drop of sodium hydroxide is used. The mixture is stirred with a glass rod for 20 seconds and then examined. Normal milk shows little or no change. Abnormal milk shows varying changes from a slight precipitate to a thick, sticky mass.

Neither the bromthymol-blue nor Whiteside tests should be used during the first several weeks of lactation or when the cow is almost dry, because false-positive reactions may occur.

VARIOUS MANAGEMENT practices help control mastitis in a herd. Milking procedures and injury to the teats and udder have received the greatest attention as predisposing causes of mastitis, and most control programs emphasize measures to control them.

Because the act of milking provides a constant source of contact between infected and healthy udders, all cows with infected udders should be milked last.

To minimize the spread of disease-producing organisms from cow to cow, separate cloths soaked in a solution of chlorine (250 to 400 parts of chlorine per million parts of water) or quaternary ammonium compounds (a 1:5000 dilution of the active compound or that recommended by the manufacturer for sterilizing dairy equipment) should be used to wipe the teats and udder of each cow before milking. Between milkings the cloths should be washed, boiled, and dried. The teat cups of the milking machine should be submerged in water and then in a solution of a quaternary ammonium compound or chlorine between each cow. The water and disinfectant solution should be changed often.

After the cow is milked, each teat should be immersed in a small amount of the disinfectant solution. That removes from the end of the teat the drop of milk, which tends to attract flies or contaminate the bedding.

The milking machine should be thoroughly cleaned and disinfected between milkings and always kept in good repair. The manufacturer's instructions concerning the rate of pulsations and inches of vacuum must be followed. Teat-cup liners that are dirty or in poor repair, wornout or improperly regulated pulsators, too high or too low vacuum caused by plugged lines, leaky stall cocks, and faulty regulators lower the efficiency of the machine and often cause injury to the teats—thus predisposing the udder to mastitis.

Cows should be handled properly to stimulate the letdown of milk before the milking machine is applied. Complete removal of all milk is also important, particularly for infected cows. After the cow is milked out, the machine should be removed immediately, because teats exposed to the action of milking machines when milk is not flowing through them may be injured.

Other measures that help reduce injuries to the udder and teats are properly constructed stalls, which allow adequate space for each cow; stall partitions, to prevent cows from treading on one another's teats; and a well-bedded, dry floor. Mud holes, high doorsills, and similar obstructions should be removed.

Feeding, age, and heredity may also influence the incidence of udder infections and clinical mastitis in a herd, but their influence on any immediate problem of mastitis is hard to determine.

PEOPLE HAVE THOUGHT that feeding might stimulate or inhibit mastitic conditions. There is no evidence that any particular feed predisposes the udder to infection. The feeding of high-protein rations or a major change in feeding, as when cows are first turned out to pasture, may result in an increased number of flareups in cows with infected udders. Therefore it is wise to follow regular feeding schedules; use balanced rations, with good and adequate roughage; and avoid all sudden changes in feed.

The number of the udder infections increases with age, when no attempt is made to eradicate the disease from a herd. Some scientists consider that the increased susceptibility to streptococcal infection is independent of environmental conditions and probably results from some change occurring in the cow's udder. Others attribute the increased incidence of mastitis to injury, degree of exposure to infection, and how open or unobstructed the teat canal is.

Heredity may have some bearing on mastitis. Some bovine families are more susceptible than others. Inheritance may determine the shape and structure of the teats, the potency of the bacteriostatic substance in the milk, and the conformation of the udder. Large, pendulous udders are more prone to injury and consequently to infection. Breeding cows for good udder conformation and attachment may reduce the hazard of teat injury and mastitis.

THE TREATMENT of mastitis with drugs gives best results when used in conjunction with proper diagnosis, sanitation, and management, and not as a substitute for them.

When only flareups (clinical cases), of mastitis are treated, treatment may give temporary relief to the treated cows, but will do little to solve the problem in the herd. To get maximum results from treatment, all infected cows should be treated at one time to reduce the chances of reinfection.

Before treatment, therefore, a bacteriological examination should be made of the milk from all cows in the herd. It is well to have two or more bacteriological examinations made of the milk after the first treatment or series of treatments so that one can find out which cows did not respond favorably and discover which should be re-treated or eliminated.

One should bear in mind always that cows that have been freed from udder infection may become reinfected if the infection remains in the herd or the organisms normally exist in the barn and pasture.

Cows with severely diseased udders, as evidenced by hardening of the udder tissue, are poor risks for treatment. They do not respond readily to drug therapy. Seldom are they economical producers even if the infection is eliminated. Such cows should be detected by a veterinarian at the time the milk samples are obtained and before any treatment is used.

THE MAIN THERAPEUTIC agents for treating mastitis are the sulfonamides, nitrofurazone, and the antibiotics, such as tyrothricin, penicillin, streptomycin, Aureomycin, Terramycin, tetracycline, neomycin, bacitracin, polymyxin, and Chloromycetin.

Because no one drug is effective against all the different organisms associated with mastitis, combinations of antibiotics and sulfonamides are used. The combinations show antibacterial activity against more types of organisms than if only one antibiotic is used, and in some cases increase the activity of some of the antibiotics against certain species of bacteria. For instance, when penicillin and streptomycin are combined, smaller amounts of each are needed to show antibacterial activity against staphylococci than if either is used alone.

To obtain best results in treatment, an adequate concentration of the drug must be maintained in the udder for a period of time. Best results are usually obtained when the drugs are administered once or twice daily over a period of 2 to 4 days, depending upon the causative agent and the nature of the case. Most staphylococcal infections must be treated longer than streptococcal infections. Clinical cases must be treated longer than cases not showing symptoms to produce a cure.

Many of the antibiotics are available in various vehicles, such as ointments and water-in-oil emulsions, that are designed for infusion into the udder. The vehicles aid in maintaining an adequate therapeutic level of the antibiotic in the udder for about 24 to 48 hours after 1 injection. Because antibiotics can persist for several days in the udder, the milk from the treated cows should not be marketed during the period of treatment or for at least 72 hours after the last treatment. The antibiotics interfere with the growth of the bacteria necessary for the production of cheese.

The drugs are administered by infusion into the infected quarter through the teat canal. First, though, the teat must be washed thoroughly and the teat orifice cleansed with a pledget of cotton wetted with alcohol.

Because drugs do not cure all infections caused by some of the bacteria and yeasts, the danger exists of introducing these resistant micro-organisms into the udders while treating for another type of organism and of allowing a more severe form of mastitis to develop. Faulty technique in preparing the teat for injection and contamination of the instruments, drug, or vehicle may be to blame.

In treating acute mastitis, it is desirable to have the drugs administered intravenously or intramuscularly, in addition to infusing them into the udder.

Frequent milking of the quarter and application of icepacks at the beginning of the attack often are helpful in preventing excessive swelling until veterinary treatment can be obtained. After the cow no longer shows marked symptoms, the application of hot packs to the udder, along with gentle massage, may hasten recovery.

R. W. BROWN, JR., *project leader of Mastitis Investigations at the Animal Disease and Parasite Research Branch, Agricultural Research Service, Beltsville, Md., has been engaged in animal disease research since 1947. He has been with the Department of Agriculture since 1951. He is a native of Pennsylvania and received his degree of doctor of veterinary medicine from the University of Pennsylvania in 1945.*

Ketosis in Cattle

JOSEPH A. DYE AND ROBERT W. DOUGHERTY

KETOSIS in dairy cattle is not a specific disease but a metabolic disorder. It is an imbalance between the nutritive intake and the nutritive requirements of the animal.

The lack of balance is indicated by several associated disturbances: Low blood glucose levels (hypoglycemia); depletion of liver glycogen (glucose stores); mobilization of body proteins, as amino acids, to the liver for new production of glucose (gluconeogenesis); mobilization of storage fat; fatty infiltration of the liver; increased production of ketone bodies; increased ketone bodies in the blood and urine; loss of body weight (emaciation); lower milk production; and dehydration.

One may compare ketosis to a bank account. At the beginning one may assume that the account is in balance and the reserve is big enough to draw on in an emergency. If the income falls below the expenditures and if the emergency is prolonged or is severe, however, the condition may become serious.

THAT GENERAL REASONING may be applied to the high-producing dairy cow, which is metabolically a delicately balanced milk-producing "machine."

At the time of calving and onset of lactation, the animal's nutritive and metabolic requirements are increased about 100 percent—partly because of the loss of sugar, protein, and fat in the milk and partly because of the increased metabolic work associated with the production and secretion of milk.

For every 20 pounds of milk produced, approximately 1 pound of glucose, 0.8 pound of fat, and 0.7 pound of protein are withdrawn from the animal. Those withdrawals are from the animal's available resources. If the dietary intake is adequate, the animal remains normal. If the diet is too poor to maintain approximately normal levels of blood glucose and liver glycogen, an imbalance in metabolism develops.

This upset is indicated by the existing anorexia (loss of appetite), hypoglycemia, and depletion of liver glycogen. In response to these disturbances, compensatory metabolic adjustments are initiated and tend to correct the imbalance.

The adjustments are triggered primarily by the hypoglycemia via specific physiological mechanisms. Some of the mechanisms are nervous in character. Others are linked to hormone actions. The hormones include primarily ACTH and possibly growth hormone of the anterior pituitary gland and hormones produced by the adrenal cortex such as cortisone and 17-hydroxycorticosterone.

The important physiological effects are an increased mobilization of depot fat and fatty infiltration of the liver and an increased mobilization of amino acids from body protein to the liver, in which some are converted to glucose and glycogen. Fatty infiltration of the liver tends to produce a temporary increase in ketogenesis (the production of ketone bodies). Glucose or glycogen tends to prevent it.

Small doses of these hormones of the adrenal cortex may cause a temporary increase in ketogenesis, but as the glucose production by the liver is sufficiently increased, ketogenesis is checked. Glucose acts to prevent ketogenesis from fatty acids by the liver by maintaining a small supply of "oxalacetate," which has to combine with fatty acid fragments if they are to be oxidized. If fatty-acid oxidation in the liver is blocked by a deficiency of oxalacetate, the metabolism of fatty acids is incomplete and ketogenesis may occur.

A SECOND FACTOR that may lead to the development of ketosis in dairy cattle is the unique nature of rumen digestion. The microbial fermentation of carbohydrates in the rumen leads to the production of large amounts of the lower fatty acids. A high percentage of them is ketogenic, and about 20 percent—propionic acid—can be converted to glucose by the animal body.

The true dietary intake of carbohydrate, compared to that of carnivores, therefore is relatively small, and the intake of potential formers of ketone bodies is large. If, however, the blood glucose and liver glycogen levels can be maintained, both glucose and fatty acids are oxidized and ketosis does not occur.

On the contrary, when the blood glucose is low, the carbohydrate stores in the liver tend to become depleted in an attempt to maintain the level of blood glucose and, in turn, the carbohydrate requirements of other tissues. Ketogenesis and ketosis tend to develop under those conditions. An abnormal amount of ketone bodies in the blood, body fluids, and tissues characterizes ketosis.

The liver is the principal organ in which ketone bodies are produced. They are normal intermediary metabolites, associated chiefly with the metabolism of fatty acids under conditions of relative deficiency of the carbohydrates. The intensity of the ketosis is directly related to the level of the deficiency.

Ketone bodies cannot be metabolized further by the liver but are passed into the blood and to the other tissues, where they can be oxidized. Ketosis develops only when the rate of ketone body production (ketogenesis) exceeds that at which they are utilized. There is no inability of the tissues, other than the liver, to oxidize either glucose or ketone bodies under those conditions. Although the concentration of ketone bodies in the blood is high, only a fraction of those produced is excreted by the kidneys, the mammary glands, and expired air.

KETOGENESIS and ketosis are not due to an initial or absolute deficiency in the hormonal secretory capacity of the anterior pituitary or adrenal cortex—in fact, such deficiencies would make ketogenesis nearly impossible.

Because of the increased metabolic requirements of the animal under the stress of high milk production, starvation, disease, and other single or multiple conditions, the anterior pituitary and adrenal cortex and various available body resources are mobilized to meet the immediate metabolic requirements. The resources include the mobilization of depot fat and muscle proteins as amino acids. The former is associated with fatty infiltration of the liver. The latter leads to an increased conversion of amino acids to glucose in the liver and an increased urinary nitrogen excretion. Both lead to emaciation of the animal.

Under those conditions, a relative anterior pituitary or an adrenal cortex secretory deficiency, or both, usually develops.

The hormonal mechanism for stimulation of the adrenal cortex by a specific hormone (ACTH) from the anterior pituitary may induce an enlargement and increase in number of cells of the adrenal cortex. Within wide limits, this is a physiological process; if it were followed by cellular degeneration or complete exhaustion, however, the results might be fatal. That occurs rarely.

VARIOUS CLINICAL CLASSIFICATIONS of bovine ketosis have been used.

Lactation ketosis includes cases that suffer from a simple imbalance between the nutritive intake and the nutritive requirements to maintain the increased demands of the lactating animal. This type occurs most frequently 14 to 28 days after parturition, but may occur as early as the seventh day and as late as 40 to 70 days after calving. The cases often are classified as uncomplicated, primary, and digestive ketosis, which occur in most countries where ketosis is prevalent. The terms "small-farm acetonemia" (in which the nutrition may be inadequate) and "estate acetonemia" (in herds apparently in good nutrition, but in which the acetonemia is frequently severe) are used in the British Isles.

Complicated or secondary ketosis may occur in varying intensities in lactating or nonlactating cattle—even in steers—and include cases in which the metabolic disturbance is precipitated or aggravated by infections, exposure, foreign bodies (hardware) in the rumen or reticulum (traumatic gastritis), peritonitis, mastitis, cystic ovaries, vaginitis, displacement of the abomasum, indigestion, and starvation. The treatment and correction of the complicating factor or factors in such cases is imperative if the animal is to recover.

DIGESTIVE KETOSIS INCLUDES the cases we listed that do not develop the so-called nervous symptoms.

In nervous ketosis the animals usually are reported to be excited and show signs of neuromuscular incoordination. They keep looking around and are disturbed if someone enters the stall. The condition is occasionally described as a semiconscious state and one indicating a depression of the cortical nerve centers of the brain. The manner of walking of the animal is often staggering, swaying, and more or less paretic and listless. Other symptoms are frequent licking of the stanchion walls, sucking, biting, salivating, and hyperesthesia of the skin. Those disturbances probably are due to a progressive depression of the higher nerve centers in the brain, which in turn progressively releases the subcortical centers in the brain stem.

Nervous symptoms of ketosis have been produced in fasting pregnant ewes by relatively severe hypoglycemias and in normal ewes and cows by the intravenous administration of isopropanol (an alcohol). Isopropanol is present in appreciable amounts in rumen liquor, blood, and milk of ketotic ruminants. The isopropanol concentration is greatest in the rumen, and is believed to be formed from acetone by the ruminal micro-organisms. The combined effects of hypoglycemia and isopropanol may act in an additive or synergistic manner to produce the effects. Similar effects occur in various species of animals under incomplete anesthesia and in intoxicated persons.

KETOSIS IN CATTLE occurs in practically every country in which dairying is practiced. Only a few cases occur in some regions, but in others its incidence may be 15 percent or more.

It develops primarily in high-producing dairy cows and seldom in low-producing cows, steers, or bulls, except those suffering prolonged starvation and protracted diseases. In many areas the number of recognized cases of ketosis has increased greatly since 1940. The first described case of ketosis in cattle in the United States is reported to have been in 1929.

Ketosis may occur in dairy cattle of all ages, but is more prevalent during the years of greatest milk production—after the second, third, and later lactation periods.

A million cases of ketosis occurred in 1950 among the 24,577,000 milking cows in the United States, an incidence of approximately 4 percent.

Mortality from ketosis in dairy cattle is low, ranging from 1 to 5 percent. Lactation ketosis is rarely fatal even if untreated—not more than 1 or 2 percent. Reports for "estate ketosis" indicate a somewhat higher death rate.

Statistics from the ambulatory clinic of the New York State Veterinary College for the year that ended July 1, 1950, showed only 6 deaths out of 284 treated cases, a little more than 2 percent. Appreciably greater financial losses from ketosis in dairy cattle arise from the associated drop in milk production and removal of animals from the milking line to be slaughtered prematurely.

UNDER CONDITIONS of ketogenesis, the primary metabolic defect in the liver (the principal organ of ketone body production) is a deficiency of oxalacetate. This metabolite must be present so as to combine with the two-carbon fragments of fatty acids and other ketogenic substances in order that they may be oxidized to carbon dioxide and water. In its absence, the fragments are converted to acetoacetic acid, beta-hydroxybutyric acid, and also acetone—the well-known ketone bodies. The main metabolic sources of oxalacetate are from carbohydrate and glycogenic amino acids.

PREVENTION of ketosis in dairy cows is the ultimate objective. We know of no perfect preventive regime, but the following suggestions may help:

Be alert to recognize conditions of infections, disease, injury, exposure, or disturbance that might subject the animals to unnecessary stress.

The diet should contain enough of the right kind of nutrients for maintenance and lactation.

A marked decrease in the intake of feed just before calving is not advised.

Stimulate the appetite by suitable rations. The addition of molasses or glucose to the ration frequently increases its palatability, stimulates the appetite, and increases feed intake. The reliability of the practice of feeding molasses or sugar to augment the blood sugar and liver glycogen has been questioned.

Feed an adequate quantity of high-quality hay and roughage.

Assure the maintenance of a proper balance between roughage and grain.

After calving, it is desirable to bring the cow up to maximal grain feeding as rapidly as seems justifiable.

The metabolic requirements of protein for the lactating cow should be met. The glucogenic amino acid content of the dietary protein is important.

The silage, especially if it is grass silage, should be checked for its content of butyric acid, which, if high in concentration, would tend to increase the incidence of ketosis.

Increase the facilities for comfort, ample pasture, exercise, and ventilation for the animals.

SEVERAL PRACTICES have been used successfully in treating ketosis in dairy cattle.

The administration of glucose, preferably by the continuous infusion method or by repeated intravenous injections of 50-percent glucose solutions at relatively short intervals of 2 or 3 hours until the animal responds, has given excellent results. Unless frequently repeated injections are made, the liver glycogen is neither increased appreciably nor is maintained for a sufficient time to correct the oxalacetate deficiency. The amount of oxalacetate required is not large at any given time, but these small amounts must be maintained if ketosis is to be cured.

Intravenous injections of fructose in the same manner and for the same purpose as that of glucose are also satisfactory. Some investigators have reported fructose to be more effective than glucose for alleviating ketosis. These two sugars are metabolized similarly in the animal body, but fructose metabolism is independent of the action of insulin, while glucose is not. The specific identity of these sugars is lost in the metabolic pathways.

Propionic acid, as sodium propionate, gives good results when administered with the feed or by drench. This acid is a normal end product of ruminal digestion and when absorbed can be converted to glucose by the liver. The intravenous administration of solutions of glucogenic amino acids or solutions of glucose and glucogenic amino acids combined (Aminosol) by methods similar to those for glucose also gives good results.

Gloconate or lactate may be used in the same way.

Similar to sodium propionate, glycerol or propyline glycol is satisfactory when administered orally in the feed or by drench.

Frequently lactation ketosis in high-producing dairy cows can be successfully treated by an increase in feed alone, especially the grain ration.

The feed intake of cows just before calving should not be limited, as some dairymen do with the aim of checking edema.

Any existing complicating disease, condition stress, or disturbance afflicting the animal must first be treated and corrected if the usual method of treating the accompanying ketosis is to be effective.

ACTH (adrenocorticotrophic hormone of the anterior pituitary) and the so-called glucocorticoid hormones of the adrenal cortex have been administered with good results. ACTH has no direct effect on carbohydrate, protein, or fat metabolism and ketogenesis; it acts by stimulating an increased output of adrenal cortex hormones. The specific corticoadrenal hormones involved are cortisone, 17-hydroxycorticosterone (compound F), and corticosterone. Their specific responses are the mobilization of amino acids from body protein and fatty acids from depot fat to the liver. The interaction of growth hormone of the anterior pituitary and corticoadrenal hormones is necessary for body fat mobilization. As we stated earlier, the primary functions of these hormones are to mobilize the body resources to meet the metabolic needs of the animal body. They thus serve as a compensatory mechanism.

Ketosis, with or without complications, increases the metabolic requirements roughly proportionately to the magnitude of the combined stresses associated with lactation and other disturbances.

Because of the increased requirements, the animal's own pituitary and adrenal mechanisms have been brought into increased functional activity, but the mechanisms may be unable to cope with the physiological needs. A relative pituitary or corticoadrenal insufficiency then exists. Supplementary administrations of commercial corticoadrenal or ACTH hormones are indicated and have been found to be good.

Functional exhaustion of the anterior pituitary or of the adrenal cortex has not been satisfactorily demonstrated. That the latter is not exhausted or degenerated is indicated by the fact that ACTH is effective when administered. Furthermore, exhaustion of the pituitary would tend to eliminate ketosis.

Experiments have demonstrated that ketosis is produced by an increased output of hormones of the pituitary and adrenal cortices and not by a deficiency of one of both of these systems. Ketosis can be experimentally terminated by removal of the pituitary or the adrenal cortices.

JOSEPH A. DYE *received the degree of doctor of philosophy at Cornell University in 1925 and since has been a member of the teaching and research staff of Cornell. Since 1940 he has been associated with the Department of Physiology, New York State Veterinary College. His publications include some 50 scientific papers in the fields of endocrinology, hormone action, intermediary metabolism, and the physiological basis of ketosis in dogs, sheep, and cattle.*

ROBERT W. DOUGHERTY *was trained in animal husbandry at Iowa State College and in veterinary medicine at Ohio State University. He was on the staff of the Department of Veterinary Medicine at Oregon State College for 5 years. From 1942 to 1946 he served in the Army and was physiologist in the Chemical Warfare Service and was the veterinary officer in an Army medical laboratory in the Philippine campaign. Later he was chairman of the Division of Veterinary Science at the State College of Washington, School of Veterinary Medicine. In 1948 he joined the staff of the Department of Physiology, New York State Veterinary College, at Cornell University.*

Shipping Fever

W. A. AITKEN

BOVINE shipping fever is an infectious respiratory disease. It is somewhat comparable clinically to influenza in man, but it has a longer incubation period and is primarily a disease of the lungs.

It has been a major disease of cattle for at least half a century. In some years it probably has caused the death of more young cattle than any disease.

Yet, because its primary cause has not been determined, it has never been given a fully satisfactory name.

Shipping fever, or the shipping-fever complex, usually is associated with the shipping of animals. It often spreads to exposed native stock, and it seems to occur occasionally in unexposed, unmoved cattle. At one time it was called stockyard disease because the animals so frequently had passed through stockyards.

It also has been called "hemorrhagic septicemia," but that name seems to have little justification because it does not indicate the cause or the primary characteristics of the disease. Hemorrhages are rather common, but septicemia—infection in the blood stream—is present only in the later stages, if at all. Furthermore, for many years the name "hemorrhagic septicemia" has been used, then abandoned, for such a variety of diseases that it has become confusing. When the true cause of shipping fever is established, a more appropriate name may be applied.

Shipping fever occurs in all parts of the United States. It may affect cattle of any age or type. A few or most of the animals in a herd may be affected. It is particularly prevalent in feeder cattle just after they have been moved from the range or from their home environment to the feed lot. Thus it is most commonly encountered in the Corn Belt and the other grain-raising areas, where most of the country's cattle are fed.

It may occur in any season, but most cases are in the fall, when most of the movement occurs. The crowded feeder cattle traffic lanes apparently become quite contaminated, thus increasing the exposure of the animals to all infections. Stockyards, sales barns and other yards, railroad cars, trucks and other vehicles, and private feeder yards become contaminated. It is possible that healthy-looking or recovered animals may carry and spread the infection.

Stress conditions are major predisposing factors for shipping fever, especially the excitement, exhaustion, and changes of feed and water that attend the shipping of animals. Irritation of the respiratory mucous membrane by dust stirred up during movement, overcrowding, long periods without feed and water, and weather changes also frequently are predisposing factors.

Calves weaned just before being shipped seem to be most susceptible, probably because they are more excitable and because they experience more marked feed changes than older cattle. Resistance increases with the age of the animals.

Good physical condition seems to afford little protection against incurring shipping fever, but it undoubtedly is a factor in avoiding complications and serious losses. Poorly nourished and highly parasitized animals usually are more seriously affected and less responsive to treatment. Deficiencies, particularly of vitamin A, could also be expected to reduce the resistance of the animals against respiratory infection.

Many authorities once believed that the bipolar bacillus, or Pasteurella organism, was the primary cause of the disease. (Before 1887 that organism was called the "bacterium septicemiae hemorrhagicum," hence the obsolete name—hemorrhagic septicemia.) Certain strains of Pasteurella frequently are recovered from animals dead of shipping fever, but the general opinion is that they are secondary invaders that merely complicate the infection.

Pasteurella germs commonly are found on the mucous membranes of the respiratory tract of healthy cattle and of other animals, in many sections of the world. They vary in their ability to cause disease. Presumably, most of them do so only when the resistance of the animal is lowered.

Many strains of the organism seem to be unable to cause disease.

In a study of shipping fever in Ontario in 1954, G. R. Carter recovered *Pasteurella hemolytica* from the lungs of 15 of 26 affected animals, *P. multocida* from the lungs of 10, and pleuropneumonialike organisms from 1. Inoculation of normal calves with cultures or with suspensions made from the infected lungs failed to reproduce the disease even when the suspension was injected directly into both lungs. That would seem to indicate that the true causative agent no longer was present in the tissues. Dr. Carter later isolated *P. hemolytica* from nasal swabs of 27 of 33 affected animals and the pleuropneumonialike organism from 16 of the 33.

J. L. Palotay in 1953 reported on studies of shipping fever in a large feed lot in Colorado. Pasteurella were found in the lungs of about 40 percent of the animals that died and in the spleen and other organs of fewer than 7 percent. *Escherichiae coli* were found in the lungs of 46 percent. *Cornybacterium pyogenes*, an organism that has been considered an important complicating infective agent in shipping fever, was not found. No Pasteurella or other infective organisms were discovered in the blood stream of 430 clinical cases in Colorado or in 7 cases in Ontario—an indication that shipping fever is not a septicemia.

Some research workers have suspected that a virus is the primary infective agent in shipping fever, but the suspicion has not been confirmed. The virus theory would seem to be challenged by the fact that animals in the early stages of the diseases usually respond markedly to treatment with certain drugs, whereas most viruses that produce disease are not affected by any drugs. Some viruses, such as the one that causes psittacosis of birds and man, however, are killed by some antibiotics. It is possible also that in shipping fever a virus could cause only a mild disease but one that predisposes the animal to complicating infections. The variations in these complicating infections could account for the apparent difference in response of animals with shipping fever to the same drug when used in different geographical areas.

If the disease were caused by a single micro-organism, then the response to a certain treatment should be constant.

The symptoms of shipping fever usually appear within 10 days after the animals arrive at their destinations, which often is 5 to 14 days after the date of first possible exposure.

The first and most diagnostic signs are a tired appearance, a reduced appetite, obvious chilling, and a soft cough. The temperature at this stage is usually 105° F., or higher. Similar temperatures are frequent in animals in the groups before they reveal any symptoms.

The affected animals soon become depressed and gaunt. Their breathing rate is somewhat increased. They may have a watery discharge from the nose and eyes and a dirty, encrusted muzzle. Diarrhea may occur, but usually only if the animals have been carelessly fed or have a complicating infection, such as coccidiosis.

Some years the disease will follow a mild course, and many cases will recover in a few days without treatment unless pneumonia develops. Other animals, unless treated, may linger one to several weeks. When they do recover, they are apt to be unthrifty.

In other years, especially since 1950, the disease has been more prevalent and more severe. Many affected animals have died in 24 hours. Only the increased alertness of the attendants and the improved methods of treatment have prevented tremendous losses in these years.

The swellings under the skin of the throat and dewlap, which were commonly reported at one time, seem to be observed less often in recent years. A commoner occurrence, especially in animals that require prolonged treatment, is a nearly total loss of appetite plus constipation. That probably is the result of changed conditions for the micro-organisms of the rumen, which are so important in digestion. Those organisms may be affected adversely by the prolonged use of drugs or possibly by the lack of eating and by the fever. Such animals usually respond to transplants of rumen content (cud) from healthy animals.

Overtreatment with the sulfonamide drugs may also cause serious damage to the kidneys and result in a lingering illness, without fever, and in death.

THE LESIONS found on postmortem examination are confined chiefly to the respiratory organs. The character of the changes and the extent of involvement of other organs depend on the length of the illness and on the complicating infections.

In the most complete study made in many years, W. R. Graham in 1953 reported on 57 cattle that had died out of hundreds affected with shipping fever in Colorado feed lots. He found pneumonia present in 55, or 96.5 percent, of the fatal cases. The other two animals had a severe congestion of parts of the lungs.

He observed that shipping fever begins with a severe congestion of the lung, followed by hemorrhage and the outpouring of fibrinous exudate into the aleveoli (the air spaces of the lung) and a severe inflammation of the tract leading to the lungs. Abscesses or gangrene were present in some lungs.

Subcutaneous edema (dropsy) was found in 10 percent of the fatal cases. An inflammation of the serous membrane lining the thoracic cavity was found in most of them, and the mucous membrane of the stomach and intestine was inflamed in many.

In the later stages of the disease, bacteria apparently had invaded the blood stream in a few, producing a septicemia, which was indicated by small hemorrhages on various organs. The hemorrhages most frequently were found in the subcutaneous tissues, in the thymus gland, on the heart, and occasionally on the kidneys. The brain was congested in 22 percent of these animals, and it contained actual hemorrhages in about 10 percent.

Inclusion bodies in the tissue cells, the cell changes that indicate a virus infection, were not found.

A diagnosis of shipping fever is indicated when a respiratory illness, accompanied by a high temperature, occurs in cattle that have been shipped within about 10 days.

Cattle with pneumonia or with leptospirosis, anthrax, blackleg, certain intoxications, or even a mild digestive disorder may sometimes show similar symptoms before other symptoms more characteristic of those diseases develop. In all except the respiratory diseases, however, the characteristic coughing is usually absent.

Blood tests, animal inoculations, or tissue cultures may be required to differentiate some of these diseases. There is no definite laboratory test for shipping fever.

A respiratory disease called infectious rhinotracheitis, which has occurred in Western States since about 1954, might be confused with shipping fever. It is caused by a virus. It appeared in California as a rather mild disease of dairy cattle and in Colorado as a more severe disease of feeder cattle. They developed necrotic lesions in the nose and trachea, but most of them recovered. This disease is not associated with shipping.

Other new diseases which might be confused with shipping fever in their early stages are called virus diarrhea and mucosal disease. Each is much less responsive to treatment than shipping fever is.

Many cases of leptospirosis, a bacterial infection, also could be confused with shipping fever. Cattle with the most common form of uncomplicated leptospirosis usually have a mild, chronic illness. They often have a poor appetite, a tired appearance, signs of jaundice, and an increased heart rate, but their temperatures seldom are much above normal. They usually show no signs of respiratory involvement. They also show little or no response to treatment. Cattle that are affected apparently simultaneously with both leptospirosis and shipping fever often develop a rapidly fatal pneumonia.

Because of the serious nature of several of the diseases I mentioned, the diagnosis, treatment, and methods of control should be promptly delegated to a veterinarian.

For many years attempts to prevent shipping fever were confined chiefly to the use of various vaccines and a serum. They were produced by using various strains of Pasteurella organisms alone or in combination with other organisms that were believed to be involved. The products still have many advocates, but controlled experiments indicate they have little, if any, value and there is much field evidence of their inefficiency.

W. A. Moynihan experimented with 9,410 feeder cattle being shipped from western to eastern Canada in 1954. Some were given stock bacterin 10 to 42 days before shipment. Some were given stock serum 1 to 4 days before. About a third received no treatment. About 5 percent were sick on arrival, and 78 died of shipping fever. There was no significant difference between the serum-treated and control groups. Although the losses were about one-half as great in the bacterin-treated group, they had been shipped earlier when less infection was evident.

J. P. Scott and H. Farley in 1932 reported a study of many thousands of feeder cattle that had been vaccinated with either the Pasteurella bacterin or aggressin before they were shipped to feed lots from the Kansas City market. When compared to similarly handled cattle that were given no vaccine, the losses were greater in the vaccinated than in the nonvaccinated group, although the difference was small.

Undoubtedly the opportunity for increasing the animals' resistance would be greater if the bacterin (aggressins have been abandoned) were given about 10 days before shipping and greater yet if the vaccination was repeated at about 10-day intervals before exposure. There are field instances, however, where these procedures have also failed. Bacterins given after the animals arrive at the feed lot may actually be harmful.

After extensive experiments, Dr. Palotay in 1953 and D. L. Thomas, O. G. Bentley, N. B. King, and E. W. Klosterman in 1955 reported that shipping fever was as common and severe in animals that received the recommended dosage of the serum as in the untreated controls.

Treatment with antibiotics or other effective drugs, if given a few days after the animals arrive at the feed lots or at the first sign of the disease, has reduced the number of cases developing in some serious outbreaks.

When properly timed, they would seem to be more beneficial than bacterins or serums. Furthermore, they avoid the risk of the anaphylactic shock or "serum reactions," which occasionally follow the use of bacterins or serums.

Until effective drugs became available, about 1940, the treatment of shipping fever was usually a discouraging procedure. Sodium bicarbonate, because it was inexpensive and possibly beneficial, had been commonly added to the drinking water. An experiment by Dr. Thomas and associates in 1953 indicated that giving sodium bicarbonate, sodium acetate, or sodium propionate in the drinking water of cattle after they arrived at the feed lot was of no value in preventing the disease.

Suggestions for reducing the losses associated with the long distance shipment of animals are given in Leaflet 38, *Maintaining the Health of Livestock in Transit*, of the Department of Agriculture. The following procedures are recommended:

"Avoid hard driving and allow ample time for rest before loading.

"Avoid overcrowding cattle in the cars. . . . In very severe weather in northern latitudes, it may be well to line the sidewalls of the car with heavy paper, especially if the cattle are young or unthrifty.

"Feeder cattle on arrival [at the destination] should be given a fill of dry roughage such as timothy hay, or prairie hay . . . . After having access to this roughage a few hours, they should have water, but not all they will drink. By the end of the first day, give free access to dry roughage and water."

It is important that the animals be handled as little and as quietly as possible for a day or two before shipment, during shipping, and for at least 2 weeks after shipment. Above all, no operations, such as dehorning or castrating, should be done then.

After shipment, range cattle should be allowed to rest quietly where they have access to a good windbreak and a dry place to lie. Well-bedded, open sheds are preferred. Serious losses have occurred after cattle have been crowded into closed buildings overnight or during a storm. If any sick animals are present, the others have little chance of avoiding the infection.

For the first few days, the feed should be similar to what the animals have been eating. A nutritious ration to sustain the resistance of the animals is essential, but any changes, particularly to richer feed, should be made gradually. A little grain, preferably oats, may be fed but no animal should get more than its share. The amount then can be increased gradually. Large feeding establishments control grain feeding effectively by having it thoroughly mixed with chopped roughage.

Recently shipped cattle should be kept apart from other cattle, particularly from common watering tanks. The tanks should be cleaned often to reduce the possible spread of infec-

tions. At the first signs of illness the herd should be inspected 2 or 3 times daily. Sick animals should be isolated in dry, draftless quarters, where they will be undisturbed except when being treated. They should be reexamined and possibly re-treated at least once daily. When they recover, their feed should be increased gradually to avoid a digestive upset when they are returned to the feed lot.

Animals that die should be removed promptly and before they are opened for postmortem examination.

The stables, feed bunks, and tanks that may have been contaminated should be thoroughly cleaned and disinfected as soon as the animals recover or are removed, and should then be exposed to the air and sun as much as possible until they are used again.

To avoid losses from shipping fever in cattle, the chief reliance should be centered on buying healthy animals, avoiding infected yards and vehicles, preventing stress factors, and providing prompt treatment for the herd at the first sign of infection.

W. A. AITKEN *is editor of the Journal of the American Veterinary Medical Association. He was on the faculty of the Division of Veterinary Medicine at Iowa State College for several years and from 1931 to 1952 was in general practice in Iowa.*

Grass Tetany and Wheat-Pasture Poisoning

R. E. DAVIS AND H. R. CROOKSHANK

IN THE WINTER wheat grazing area, particularly the Texas and Oklahoma Panhandles, a condition known locally as wheat-pasture poisoning sometimes develops when cattle graze

on the growing wheat. The condition is worse when growth is lush and moisture is plentiful.

The first symptoms are unusual excitement, incoordination, and loss of appetite. Viciousness, staggering, and falling come later. Nervousness becomes more apparent with muscular twitching, particularly in the extremities. The animal may grind its teeth and salivate profusely. The third eyelid will protrude or flicker, as in tetanus.

General tetanic contractions of the muscles follow until the animal nears a state of prostration. A sudden noise—or merely touching the animal—causes a reflex response.

THE NEXT SYMPTOMS are a labored breathing and pounding of the heart. A comatose condition follows. Convulsions, with periods of relaxation, occur before the animal dies. The animal usually becomes comatose 6 to 10 hours or so after the onset of the initial symptoms.

The chance of recovery is slight if treatment is not started before coma.

The symptoms are almost identical with those of highly fatal grass tetany, which occurs in a number of States and usually occurs when young, fast-growing pasture grass is grazed.

Because grass tetany and wheat-pasture poisoning appear to be the same except for the type of pasture, we consider them together.

THE MOST COMMONLY used treatment is the intravenous or intraperitoneal injections of a solution of calcium gluconate. Several solutions have been used experimentally, but calcium gluconate, with or without fortification, seems to be best. The solution should contain not less than 17 percent of calcium gluconate. It may be fortified with magnesium or phosphorus or both. Calcium gluconate solutions with added magnesium and phosphorus seem to speed recovery and lessen the need for a second injection. Some preparations of calcium gluconate also contain glucose (dextrose), but the glucose does not appear to have any appreciable effect on treatment or recovery.

The dosage, whether given intravenously or intraperitoneally, should be 500 milliliters of calcium gluconate.

Intravenous injection should be given slowly. At least 20 to 30 minutes should be allowed for treatment. Intraperitoneal injection may be given more rapidly.

If treatment is given during the first few hours after the development of the symptoms, recovery is usually fairly rapid and uneventful. The chance of recovery is slight if treatment is delayed 8 to 12 hours. No type of treatment has been found that will be successful in cases when treatment is delayed. The removal of the cow from wheat pasture for a few days appears to speed complete recovery. It is unusual for an animal to have a second attack after recovery from the initial attack.

SIXTY CASES of wheat-pasture poisoning were studied at the Pan Tech Field Laboratory near Amarillo, Tex. None of the cases was complicated by other conditions, and it was possible to obtain a complete history of each case.

All were cows at least 2 years old and pregnant or with a calf at the side. The time of the attacks varied from the fifth month of pregnancy to 6 or 7 months after calving. The length of time on wheat varied from 1 week to 6 months. Most cases occurred between 60 and 150 days on winter-wheat pasture. Seventy-nine percent of the cases occurred in cows with a calf under 60 days of age. In 17 percent of the cases, the disease occurred within 1 week after calving; in 24 percent, between 1 and 2 weeks; in 11 percent, between 15 and 29 days; and in 27 percent, between 30 and 60 days. Seven percent of the cases occurred during the last 3 months of gestation. The remaining 14 percent had calves more than 60 days old.

Many reported cases of wheat-pasture poisoning in calves, steers, and dry cows were investigated, but the only cases observed occurred under the conditions we outlined. Beef, dairy, and crossbred cows have had the disease.

The use of salt, minerals, cottonseed meal, dry feeds, silage, or various combinations of these supplements has been suggested as a preventive measure. An analysis of 41 cases of poisoning in the Panhandle region during the 1953-1954 grazing season, however, showed that supplements or combinations of them had little effect on the incidence of the disease.

Only 3 of the 41 cows had not received supplemental feed. All the others had received salt, mineral mixtures, cottonseed meal, dry feed, or silage, or a combination of them. Included among the dry feeds were sorghum bundles, grain, hay, and stalks. The diluting effect of some of the supplements apparently delayed the onset of the disease but did not prevent it.

The analysis disclosed also that a number of other maladies have been confused with wheat-pasture poisoning. Many investigations were made of what were thought to be cases in calves, steers, and dry cows. The most common condition confused with wheat-pasture poisoning is spinose ear tick infestation, in which there was incoordination much like that in wheat-pasture poisoning.

Black disease, or *Clostridium novyi* infection, supposedly confined to sheep, has accounted for many deaths of both yearling and mature cattle that grazed wheat. The diagnosis was confirmed by bacterial cultures and inoculation.

OTHER CONDITIONS that have been mistaken for wheat-pasture poisoning are: Acetonemia in mature cows, prussic acid poisoning from feeding bundles or grazing nearby stalk fields, pneumonia and shipping fever, milk fever in dairy breeds of cattle, "water belly" (urinary calculi) in young steers, and contagious abortion in cows—all of which were grazing wheat. These conditions and others often are confused with wheat-pasture poisoning when sickness and losses occur during the grazing season.

The chemical composition of the serums from afflicted cows was compared with that of cows that were grazing wheat but did not show any symptoms of wheat-pasture poisoning.

The total calcium level was depressed well below the normal level, and the diffusible calcium dropped to near the tetany level, which is about 2.5 milligrams per 100 milliliters of serum. The magnesium level was depressed markedly. The level of potassium was increased slightly. The total serum protein level was raised. This increase was due to an increase in the globulin fraction. Hence, albumin globulin ration was decreased. The values found in this study were in general agreement with those of other workers.

Research workers in the Netherlands have suggested that the cause of grass tetany in dairy cows is intestinal autointoxication. There is a similarity of the symptoms of grass tetany to the condition produced by administration of histamine; that is, intestinal disorder, acetonemia and hypoglycemia, dehydration, disturbances in the mineral and acid-base balance, hypomagnesemia, hypocalcemia, and frequently hypophosphatemia.

It is estimated that grass tetany affects 1 out of every 100 dairy cows in the Netherlands and that 1 of every 7 affected cows succumbs. In most cases, the dietary intake of magnesium is sufficient. Most cases occur within 1 or 2 weeks after the animals are put out to pasture. It requires more than 2 weeks on magnesium-deficient rations to reduce the absolute values of blood magnesium in dairy cows.

There appears to be a definite difference in time required for the development of symptoms of grass tetany and wheat-pasture poisoning.

R. E. DAVIS *was put in charge of cattle nutrition investigations of the Beef Cattle Research Section of the Animal and Poultry Husbandry Research Branch, Agricultural Research Service, in 1955. He has been engaged in animal nutrition research for the Department since 1931.*

H. R. CROOKSHANK *is animal nutritionist with the Beef Cattle Research Section. He has been with the Department of Agriculture since 1949 and has conducted research in the field of nutrition of cattle and sheep.*

Blackleg

C. D. STEIN

BLACKLEG is known also as black quarter, quarter ill, and symptomatic anthrax. It is an acute, infectious disease that affects mainly young cattle and sometimes sheep.

Blackleg occurs in nearly all sections of the United States and the world. It is more prevalent and causes greatest losses in cattle-raising and cattle-feeding areas in the Central West and Far West. Most cattlemen in the districts where the soil is heavily infested with the blackleg organism are familiar with this rapidly fatal disease.

Most susceptible to blackleg are cattle 6 to 18 months old. Suckling calves under 4 months and cattle past 2 years are rarely attacked. Cattle of improved breeding and fat, thrifty calves and yearlings usually develop the disease first. Common stock and thin, scrubby, or stunted calves seldom become infected. Sheep, goats, and hogs may contract the disease occasionally. Man, horses, dogs, cats, and fowl appear to be immune. Guinea pigs, which are used in laboratory diagnostic tests, are highly susceptible.

Spring and the fall are the seasons most favorable for the development of blackleg, but outbreaks may occur at any time of the year. The infection in some areas appears to be more prevalent on wet bottom land than in hilly areas, but it may occur on any type of terrain.

THE CAUSE of blackleg is a rod-shaped, gas-producing micro-organism, *Clostridium chauvoei* (blackleg bacilli). It forms spores, which are very resistant to destruction by heat, cold, drying, and disinfectants. The spores survive in the soil of a pasture and retain their ability to germinate and produce the disease for many years.

The blackleg germ is one of the an- aerobic bacteria, which grow only in the absence of oxygen. Minute puncture wounds that exclude the air therefore favor the development of blackleg.

HOW THE INFECTION enters the body tissues is not definitely known. It is generally believed that animals usually acquire the disease when food, water, and soil contaminated with the blackleg germs gain entrance to the body through small punctures of the mucous membrane of the digestive tract or skin. Penetrating wounds of this nature may be produced by thorns, briers, stubble, burs, and barbed wire. The organism may also gain entrance to the membranes of the mouth during eruption of the teeth.

Because the infection in sheep usually occurs through new wounds, the site of blackleg infection in freshly docked lambs frequently occurs in the tailhead or hip and in the area of skin cuts in freshly sheared animals.

The infection is not directly communicable from affected to healthy animals by mere contact.

BLACKLEG is marked by high fever (105° to 107° F.) and the formation of gaseous swellings under the skin, especially on the hind quarter or shoulder, and also on the neck, chest, flank, rump, or other parts of the body. The swellings usually cause stiffness or lameness and sometimes complete paralysis of the affected part.

The swellings at first are small, hot, and painful. They grow in size and later become cold and painless. In sheep the skin over the swellings has a purplish cast. Other general symptoms, such as loss of appetite, suspension of rumination, rapid breathing, and great depression develops as the disease progresses. The temperature falls, and violent convulsions may occur just before death. Some animals recover, but most affected animals die in 12 to 36 hours after the first symptoms appear. The onset of the disease is so sudden that in new outbreaks the first animals to be affected usually are found dead in the pasture without showing any previous symptoms.

DIAGNOSIS is based on history, clinical symptoms, postmortem examination, and the laboratory examination of specimens from suspected cases.

Blackleg infection should be suspected when calves and yearlings in known blackleg districts die suddenly, showing gassy swelling of the muscles while on pasture, or when sheep develop symptoms after shearing or docking.

Further evidence of blackleg are found if the carcass is examined a few hours after death. It will usually show rapid and excessive bloating, which causes the legs on the upper side of the carcass to extend out straight and which forces a bloody-colored foam to escape from the natural body openings. One or more gaseous swellings located on the region of the hip, shoulder, neck, jaw, brisket, or loin may be observed. They emit a crackling sound on pressure.

If the swellings are lanced, a frothy, dark-red fluid with a characteristic sweetish-sour, rancid odor like that of butyric acid is discharged. Long, deep cuts made in the affected muscles at the site of the swellings expose tissues that are blackened and streaked with dark-red areas, in marked contrast to the unaffected muscle tissue—hence the name "blackleg." The body lymph glands draining the affected areas may be enlarged and inflamed. The body cavities may contain a bloody exudate, but the internal organs usually show little or no alterations.

But in contrast to anthrax, which is sometimes confused with blackleg, the spleen is not enlarged, and the coagulability and color of the blood are normal.

Since blackleg may be mistaken for malignant edema, anthrax, hemorrhagic septicemia, sweetclover poisoning, and other abnormal conditions, a laboratory examination should be made of tissue specimens from suspected cases if any doubt exists as to exact nature of the trouble.

MEDICAL TREATMENT is of little value in an established case of blackleg with advanced symptoms. Veterinarians have reported that antibiotics, such as Aureomycin, Terramycin, and penicillin, have given good results in the treatment of cases showing early symptoms of the disease.

The incidence of infection in sheep can be greatly reduced by observing cleanliness in all routine operations and keeping the animals in uninfected pastures.

VACCINATION is the only effective and reliable means known for protecting animals against blackleg. Before the first vaccine was developed in 1883 in France, it has been estimated that 20 percent of the calves in badly infected districts died of blackleg. The vaccine has since been greatly improved. Some of the older types of vaccines in the form of powder, pills, filtrate, and aggressin have remained in use, but blackleg bacterin, a highly effective immunizing agent, is the product used most extensively now.

Between 1897 to 1922, the Department of Agriculture prepared and distributed about 47 million doses of powdered vaccine. Losses from blackleg were reduced from 10 percent to less than 0.5 percent in those 25 years. In compliance with an act of Congress, the free distribution of the vaccine was discontinued on July 1, 1922.

Blackleg bacterin and other types of vaccine, used in accordance with directions, usually produce in 10 or 12 days a high degree of immunity, which lasts 9 to 12 months or longer. As some young calves may not develop and retain lasting immunity, all animals younger than 4 months when vaccinated in the spring should be revaccinated in the fall to insure protection during the fall and winter. Some cattle owners in badly infected areas follow the practice of vaccinating every 6 months all animals between the ages of 2 and 10 months.

A product known as antiblackleg serum is sometimes used for immunizing valuable calves exposed in outbreaks. This product immediately increases the animal's resistance to blackleg, but the type of immunity it confers ceases after about 2 weeks.

In some blackleg districts where the soil is also believed to be infected with the organism that causes malignant edema infection in animals, a bivalent or mixed bacterin containing both organisms and known as *Clostridium chauvoei-septicus* bacterin has been used for the prevention of both blackleg and malignant edema.

RECOGNIZED CONTROL measures in outbreaks of blackleg include:

The isolation and treatment of all animals showing early symptoms of the disease;

The vaccination of apparently well but exposed animals and, if feasible, their immediate removal to a new pasture on higher ground;

The prompt disposition of dead animals by complete burning or deep burial in quicklime;

The destruction of manure, bedding, and other contaminated material by burning;

The cleaning and disinfection of contaminated stables; and

The rigid enforcement of restrictions against skinning dead animals, feeding the carcass to other animals on the farm, and removing the carcass from the premises to a rendering plant.

When a suspected outbreak of blackleg occurs, a veterinarian or the State livestock sanitary official should be promptly notified.

C. D. STEIN, *a graduate of the University of Pennsylvania, is a veterinarian in the Animal Disease and Parasite Research Branch of the Agricultural Research Service. He has been with the Department of Agriculture since 1911, having served in three divisions of the former Bureau of Animal Industry. For many years he has done research on anthrax, equine infectious anemia, and other infectious diseases of livestock.*

Actinomycosis and Actinobacillosis

A. W. MONLUX AND C. L. DAVIS

MANY swellings or growths found in the tissues of the head and throat of cattle are diagnosed as either actinomycosis or actinobacillosis. The two infections were regarded as a single disease until the 1930's.

Investigators finally proved that an infection designated as actinobacillosis is found in the softer tissues (lymph nodes, tongue, lungs, and the deeper layers of the skin) and is amenable to treatment. It is caused by the micro-organism, *Actinobacillus lignieresi*, which lives only in the presence of oxygen.

Research groups also established that actinomycosis generally is localized in bone (usually the maxilla and mandible, or jaws) and that recurrence of the infection often follows therapy. An anaerobic micro-organism, *Actinomyces bovis*, which is more closely related to fungi than to true bacteria, produces these lesions involving the jaws.

Veterinarians now use the sulfonamides, antibiotics, iodides, and surgery to treat both diseases. Healing of the lesions of actinobacillosis usually can be expected after proper therapy. Reports indicate that streptomycin has produced more rapid clinical improvement in cases of actinomycosis than one would expect with iodide medication. However, substantiated claims of permanent cures of an actinomycotic infection with this antibiotic have not appeared in the veterinary reports.

NO METHOD OF IMMUNIZATION for either infection has been devised.

Veterinarians report epizootics of actinobacillosis among young feeder cattle on individual farms and ranches, particularly in the Western States.

The records of the Meat Inspection Branch indicate that observed infections of actinobacillosis and actinomycosis in cattle are tabulated together in their inspection procedures. They represent a cause for condemnation in cattle that exceeds any other individual condemnation for any disease or condition. During the fiscal year that ended June 30, 1953, the two diseases were reported to occur in 200,645 cattle and calves out of 21,231,784 slaughtered. Parts (usually the head) of the carcasses were condemned; 807 entire carcasses were considered unfit for food for people.

ACTINOMYCOSIS, commonly known as "lumpy jaw" or "big jaw," usually involves the bones of the head, particularly the lower jaw. Actinomycotic infections of the softer tissues occur in cattle but are rare.

Large, pus-filled tracts or cavities (abscesses) form when the infection spreads through the bone. Connective and other body reparative tissues in and near the bone grow abundantly in an attempt to wall off the abscess. By the time the infection has extended from the bone to the soft tissue and skin to establish a fistula or drain for the lesion, the involved parts of the jaws may be enlarged 2 or 3 times.

Fistulas from abscesses of the bones of the head sometimes extend inward and discharge into the pharynx or mouth. The palate and gums next to the bones often are swollen and inflamed. The teeth may loosen.

Small, hard, yellowish granules, called "sulfur granules" or "rosettes," are present as tiny grains in the pus from abscesses of both actinomycosis and actinobacillosis. They are barely visible to the unaided eye.

All the granules look alike when viewed under a microscope. Many small, clublike bodies are arranged around a colony of micro-organisms, like the petals of a flower. This microscopic resemblance to a rose is responsible for the designation of the granules as "rosettes." The actinomycotic rosettes are usually 2 or 3 times larger than those of actinobacillosis.

An accepted diagnostic procedure is to crush large numbers of washed granules on a slide and stain the prepared slide with a Gram stain. Gram-positive micro-organisms, which may be seen either as short rods, filaments, or branching forms, are identifiable microscopically in typical cases of actinomycosis. The actinobacillosis micro-organisms can also be demonstrated by a similar treatment of its rosettes and is characteristically a short, Gram-negative bacillus.

Bacteriologic cultural studies of the lesions can be made as a supplemental and conclusive diagnostic procedure for each disease. Results of such examinations are never available for several days or weeks. Experienced diagnosticians usually can predict accurately which specific micro-organism will be isolated in bacteriologic studies by the microscopic examination of the stained smears of crushed rosettes.

ACTINOBACILLOSIS of the head and neck region often can be recognized easily in a herd of cattle, as there may be swellings under the skin, which can be moved with the fingers and may be as big as a walnut or an egg, or even larger. A livestock owner who inspects his cattle every week generally notes a progressive increase in the size of the growths.

One or more lymph nodes of the neck may be abscessed. These growths usually are more firm and located deeper in the soft tissues. Sometimes "chains" of enlarged lymph nodes can be palpated as the infection spreads down the neck. Firmness of both the subcutaneous and lymph nodes lesions is also related to the amount of connective tissue deposited in and around them and invariably increases as the growths become older.

These older, fibrotic growths may become partially calcified. The abscessed enlargements of the subcutis often break through the skin, discharging pus. The most common manifestation of the disease in slaughtered cattle are abscesses of variable sizes in the cervical (neck) lymph nodes, which one may not be able to detect in the live animal.

The tongue may be affected, but less often than the lymph node and subcutaneous tissues. Abscesses and ulcers may occur in or near the groove on the upper surface of the tongue. When the tongue is extensively involved, a marked increase in the fibrous tissue of the organ (fibrosis) results. The tongue then becomes increasingly hard and immobile and may protrude from the mouth—hence the term "wooden tongue." The animal will have great difficulty in eating and drinking.

An infection with actinobacillosis may produce a polyp, or pendulous type of growth, in the pharynx, larynx, or upper respiratory tract. Interference with swallowing and breathing is sometimes very noticeable in such cases. The growth often can be removed by surgery.

Besides the head and neck, actinobacillosis has been reported in almost every organ and tissue in cattle. Lung, liver, kidney, spleen, brain, mammary gland, testis, salivary gland, forestomach, intestine, and lymph node and subcutaneous tissue (other than that of the head and neck) are some of the sites where the infection has been found.

Cases with extensive lesions on the internal lining of the body cavities (pleura, peritoneum) are quite spectacular to see and have been the subject of several published reports.

The occurrence of actinobacillosis varies in different sections of the United States, but generally it seems to be 5 or 6 times as prevalent in cattle as actinomycosis.

Natural infections with actinobacillosis are also found in sheep, swine, deer, and other wild animals, but not so often as in cattle. Laboratory animals, including rats, mice, guinea pigs, and rabbits, are difficult to infect by the inoculation of cultures of *Actinobacillus lignieresi*.

Few cases of actinobacillosis in man have been reported. Actinomycosis, on the other hand, has been found in man, mostly among young and middle-aged males. Actinomycosis is also diagnosed in swine, sheep, horses, dogs, and many species of wild animals.

A SIGNIFICANT DISCOVERY, first reported in 1905, was that micro-organisms identical to *Actinomyces bovis* were present in the tonsils, teeth, and mouth in man as a part of the normal bacterial flora. Scientists subsequently have substantiated the findings and have noted that lesions of actinomycosis could be produced in cattle and hogs by the inoculation of cultures isolated from human tonsils.

There is a need for thorough investigations of the bacterial flora of the tonsils and mouth cavity of cattle. D. J. Davis, in a study in 1923 at the University of Illinois, made a bacteriologic investigation of the micro-organisms which could be recovered from a group of supposedly normal and representative human, bovine and swine tonsils. He found *Actinomyces bovis* in the human and swine tonsils but not in the bovine. His work provided a logical explanation for the high incidence of actinomycosis of the udder in sows. The infection is now thought to enter from the mouths of suckling pigs through wounds made by their teeth.

Abrasions or lacerations in the oral cavity in cattle are believed to be the primary portal of entry for infections of actinomycosis and actinobacillosis. Dry, harsh, rough feeds may cause injuries to the mouth. Particles of hay or grain, especially the barbed awns of barley and bearded grasses, often are found in the oral lesions and sometimes are covered with a growth of either *A. bovis* or *A. lignieresi*. In such cases, the vegetable particles probably acted as a foreign body about which the organisms grew. Neither of the two microorganisms has ever been reported on such material except when it has been incorporated into abscesses in the living animal.

Teething may be the explanation for the more frequent occurrence of both infections in young cattle. Lacerations, swelling of the gums, and the trapping and decay of foodstuffs in the oral cavity accompany the eruption of the permanent teeth during the first 3 years of life of the domestic bovine animal.

PREVENTIVE MEASURES that can be adopted to reduce actinomycosis and actinobacillosis infections have been limited to the application of basic concepts of animal sanitation. The only proved transfer of infection from one animal to another is by the inoculation of diseased tissues or cultures.

Animals of all species affected with either disease should not be permitted to remain in pastures or feed lots with healthy cattle. This will prevent pus from open lesions from contaminating food, water, bedding, or cuts and abrasions in noninfected animals.

A. W. MONLUX *is head of the Department of Veterinary Pathology in the Veterinary School at Oklahoma Agricultural and Mechanical College. He was graduated in veterinary medicine from Iowa State College in 1942 and later received advanced degrees at Iowa State College and the George Washington University.*

C. L. DAVIS *became director of the Animal Disease Research Laboratory in 1947. He was engaged in tuberculosis eradication and meat inspection before assignment to the laboratory. He was graduated in veterinary medicine from Colorado Agricultural and Mechanical College in 1921.*

Anaplasmosis of Cattle

JOHN C. LOTZE, DANIEL W. GATES, AND T. O. ROBY

ANAPLASMOSIS, sometimes called gall sickness, is a disease of cattle that is marked by anemia and fever and microscopic parasites in the red blood cells.

It is infectious and transmissible. It occurs the world over and is especially troublesome in the warmer regions.

The causative agent, *Anaplasma marginale*, apparently belongs to the Protozoa, a group of minute, one-celled

animals that includes such organisms as the causative agents of coccidiosis and malaria.

The first account of the disease now known as anaplasmosis is contained in the famous report by Theobald Smith and Fred L. Kilborne on the cause and method of transmission of so-called Texas or southern cattle fever, published in 1893 (Bulletin No. 1, Bureau of Animal Industry). In this report are detailed accounts of anaplasmosis and another disease, piroplasmosis or tick fever.

Anaplasmosis was encountered frequently by Smith and Kilborne, and the question arose as to whether they were dealing with two different diseases. They found, however, that the course and events in the diseases were similar. They concluded that anaplasmosis was a type of piroplasmosis in which some unknown factor interfered with the normal development of the parasites. They concluded that Texas fever was transmitted by the cattle tick, *Boophilus annulatus;* it is assumed that they were referring to both types of Texas fever, which would include anaplasmosis. Primarily because the cattle tick was found to transmit Texas fever, preparations were made and a campaign to eradicate the cattle tick was begun in 1906.

Arnold Theiler, an investigator of animal diseases in Africa, presented good evidence in 1910 to show that Smith and Kilborne had been dealing with two separate diseases, piroplasmosis or tick fever, and another, which he named anaplasmosis.

K. F. Meyer recognized anaplasmosis in 1913 from experimental infections that he brought about in cattle in the United States.

Anaplasmosis was given no further special attention in the United States, however, until 1926, when P. B. Darlington reported that it was a troublesome disease in southeastern Kansas and that he failed to find cattle ticks on the affected animals. For the first time, therefore, the cattle industry was alerted to the fact that the eradication of the cattle tick was not eliminating anaplasmosis. Subsequently the disease was reported from areas outside the original boundaries of Texas fever. The Federal Government and several States thereupon began investigations to determine how anaplasmosis might be controlled and eliminated.

Economic losses from anaplasmosis in the United States probably amount to millions of dollars each year. The disease is most prevalent in the southern part of the country where piroplasmosis or tick fever was formerly coexistent with it, and it occurs sporadically though not infrequently in other areas. It is encountered usually in the warm months from June to November, especially in the late summer or early fall. Cases occur occasionally in winter.

Anaplasmosis is most severe in mature cattle. As many as 50 percent of the affected animals have died in some outbreaks. The disease is usually mild in calves and may therefore be unnoticed.

The parasites apparently destroy or cause the red blood cells of the infected animal to be destroyed. Here follow various degrees of anemia and weakness, which interfere with the animal's normal physiologic processes. In cases of long standing, bile pigments accumulate in the various tissues. It is not known whether the parasites produce toxins. Evidence that some kind of poisonous material is present is provided by the fact that a pint or more of blood from clinical cases produces symptoms of shock and sometimes even death when injected into the blood stream of a noninfected animal.

Little is known concerning the parasites that cause bovine anaplasmosis. Except when infections are started by experimental inoculation of extremely large amounts of blood containing parasitized red blood cells, 2 to 4 weeks or more elapse from the time of inoculation to the time that anaplasma are first observed in the blood of a newly infected animal.

During this prepatent period—the period before the parasites can be found in the blood—nothing is known as to where the organisms are located or what they may be doing. They may not produce any noticeable effects on the host during this period.

The parasites that occur in red blood cells range in size from about 0.2 to 0.9 micron. (An inch contains 25,000 microns.) During the course of the disease, the parasites apparently enter the red blood cells and increase in size and undergo a type of division characteristic of certain Protozoa. The largest are each divided into eight small, spherical bodies. The smaller parasites are each composed of a single mass of living material.

After the parasites first appear in the blood, the population increases for about 7 to 13 days and then starts to decrease. After it has declined for about the same number of days, it may increase for a few days and then drop again. The population of the parasites may fluctuate in this manner for months. Finally no more red blood cells are parasitized, as far as can be determined with the microscope. They may reappear in small numbers in the red blood cells at some distant and unpredictable time, however.

The anaplasms occur in their greatest numbers in the first parasitic attack. This is the only time when the damage may be severe enough to produce visible symptoms of anaplasmosis and sometimes death. Usually one or two parasites are found in mild infections in a single red blood cell; in severe infections, six or seven may be in a single cell. After a red blood cell becomes parasitized, it disappears in 3 or 4 days from the circulating blood.

Symptoms of anaplasmosis vary greatly in severity and duration, depending on the severity of the anemia and its duration. With the exception of fever, which may occur even before parasites are found in the red blood cells, the onset of symptoms occurs at about the time (or within a few days) the peak of the infection is reached and anemia is worst. Symptoms gradually disappear when the red blood cell count improves noticeably, and the anemia subsides.

Symptoms may be as severe in animals that will recover as in those that will die from the disease. The principal symptoms are sudden loss of condition, increased pulse and breathing, and paleness of mucous membranes. As the disease progresses, there is drooling from the mouth, a discharge of thick mucus from the nostrils, progressive weakness, and cessation of rumination and defecation.

The severity and duration of the disease varies greatly. Sometimes the disease may be subclinical—so mild that it is unlikely to attract attention. This form is found most frequently in younger cattle. Calves may become stunted or unthrifty because of it.

In other cases the disease may run a severe course. More than half of the red blood cells may be parasitized at one time. The animal may die within about 24 hours after symptoms first appear. This peracute form occurs in some of the older, mature cattle, especially dairy cattle.

In still other cases, the disease may run a longer course. A variable number of red blood cells is parasitized at the peak of the infection. Symptoms may vary in intensity. Death or quick recovery may follow. This acute form occurs in cattle of all ages.

In some animals the disease may last a week or more and end in death or the beginning of a slow recovery. This chronic form occurs in some animals about 3 years old or older. Its long duration is due primarily to their inability to regenerate red blood cells fast enough.

A postmortem examination of animals that have died of anaplasmosis shows the blood to be thin. Small hemorrhagic spots usually appear on the outer surface of the heart and sometimes throughout the viscera. The gall bladder is filled with thick bile. The liver has a yellowish discoloration. The spleen is enlarged, and its contents have the appearance of blackberry jam. The flesh of an animal that has died shortly after the onset of symptoms may appear normal. An animal that has died after a lengthy siege of anaplasmosis may be greatly reduced in flesh, and the fat and viscera have a yellowish discoloration.

No specific medicinal treatment for anaplasmosis is available.

Two antibiotics, oxytetracycline and chlortetracycline, suppress the multiplication of the parasites and can rid carrier animals of infection. The drugs do not stimulate the formation of red blood cells and therefore do not show marked beneficial effects when used for treatment of clinical cases. It is reported, however, that mortalities are reduced and recovery is more rapid following treatment with them.

Blood transfusions are beneficial in the chronic form of the disease and may be useful in many cases in the acute form. To be effective, 2 to 3 gallons or more of whole blood must be injected into the sick animal. The blood can be transfused or transferred directly from one animal to another, or it can be let into vessels containing an anticoagulant, such as sodium citrate, and then administered. Blood from carrier animals as well as blood from uninfected cattle can be used. As much as 1 gallon of whole blood can be removed from a large animal without risk of injury.

Sick animals should be isolated from uninfected animals, protected from biting insects by the use of sprays, and kept in the shade. They should be provided with fresh water and a succulent or green feed.

IMMUNITY in anaplasmosis is similar to that in some protozoan diseases, in that once an infection is acquired it is usually carried for a long time—in most cases of anaplasmosis, for the life of the host. All cattle are receptive to anaplasmosis, regardless of their age, and once they lose the infection they become receptive to infection again. Reinoculation of an animal carrying the infection has no appreciable effect on it, however.

Efforts have been made to produce a vaccine that would protect an uninfected animal against anaplasmosis without infecting it, but the results have not been satisfactory.

It is the practice in some countries to "premunize," or artificially immunize, cattle against anaplasmosis before they have had the opportunity of acquiring the infection naturally. The cattle are inoculated with infected blood and allowed to go through the throes of the disease under conditions favorable for the survival of the affected animals. Some are inoculated in calfhood or at a time when the disease is likely to run a mild course. A strain of the parasite that affects the animal less severely than the regular strains of the parasites was found in Africa in 1911. It has been maintained and used in infecting cattle to protect them from the ravages of the injurious form. This strain sometimes is called *Anaplasma centrale* and sometimes *Anaplasma marginale* var. *centrale*.

THE MANNER in which anaplasmosis is spread under natural conditions is mostly an unsolved problem. We have reports that some calves born of infected mothers became infected before birth, but we have no information as to the part these prenatal infections may play in the spread of the disease.

The causative agent does not occur in the feces or urine of infected animals. The disease is not contracted through contact with an infected animal. The parasites are present in the blood of all infected animals, even when they cannot be found by blood examinations, as is the case at most times in carrier animals of long standing.

It is remarkable how readily the disease is transmitted to uninfected animals by such operations as dehorning when proper precautions are not taken to clean the instruments each time they are used on a different animal. Even such small instruments as bleeding needles or needles used in vaccinations can transfer the disease from an infected to an uninfected animal unless they are sterilized each time they are used.

Experiments have shown that blood-sucking insects, such as mosquitoes and horseflies, can readily transmit the disease from clinical cases when the insects are allowed to feed for a few minutes on an infected animal and then are quickly transferred to an uninfected one and allowed to finish feeding on it. The parasites may reappear in small numbers in the blood of a carrier animal as long as 11 months after the animal was first inoculated. Horseflies feeding on the animal at that time and then on a clean animal can transmit the disease to it.

Experimental studies with various ticks remaining in the United States after the eradication of the cattle tick have incriminated seven species of them as possible vectors of anaplasmosis in this country. They are the fowl tick, *Argas persicus;* the American dog tick, *Dermacentor variabilis;* the Rocky Mountain spotted fever tick, *Dermacentor (andersoni) venustus;* the Pacific coast tick, *Dermacentor occidentalis;* the winter tick, *Dermacentor albipictus;* the brown dog tick, *Rhipecephalus sanguineus;* and the black-legged tick, *Ixodes scapularis.*

Unlike experimental transmissions by insects of anaplasmosis, which involves the quick transfer of infective material from the source animal to the susceptible one, tick transmission involves the survival of the infective material in the ticks for days or even months. During this time it is possible that multiplication of the causative agent takes place.

In some experimental transmissions, ticks in one stage of development were removed from an infected animal and some time later were placed on susceptible animals. In some cases, ticks in one stage of development were allowed to engorge on an infected animal and then were allowed to undergo further development or moulting before they were placed on the susceptible animals. In the case of certain ticks, for example, *Boophilus annulatus* and *Dermacentor (andersoni) venustus*, transmission of anaplasmosis was accomplished by allowing the adults to feed on infected animals and then allowing the progeny of these ticks to feed on susceptible animals; in the latter cases, the tick eggs contained the causative agent of anaplasmosis. About 15 species of ticks from various parts of the world can transmit anaplasmosis under certain conditions. One or more of them may be an important reservoir of the causative agent of anaplasmosis under natural conditions.

CARRIER ANIMALS are suspected as being the reservoir and source of infective material responsible for new outbreaks of the disease. Attempts have been made consequently to find a suitable method of detecting them so that they may be eliminated from herds. As a result, a diagnostic test based on the principle of complement fixation has been perfected.

The test has been used in field surveys to determine the prevalence of anaplasmosis in cattle in various parts of the United States. It has revealed that there are more infected cattle in some places than was at first suspected. Plans were made to use the test in a program designed to control anaplasmosis in the Hawaiian Islands for the first time on a large scale.

The outlook for the control of anaplasmosis in the United States is encouraging. After years of effort, drugs capable of destroying the parasites have been found, blood transfusions have been a valuable aid in treating sick animals, a complement-fixation test of high efficacy is available for detecting carrier animals, and certain ticks and biting insects have been shown to be capable of transmitting anaplasmosis under certain experimental conditions. It appears, therefore, that tools are now available for the beginning of a concerted drive against this disease.

It is possible that eradication of the carrier animals may eliminate anaplasmosis. It should be remembered, however, that ticks might act as reservoir hosts of the parasite. In combating this disease, care should be taken to clean properly all surgical instruments, bleeding needles, vaccinating needles, and dehorning instruments after each use. Animals known to be infected should be isolated, sprayed with fly repellent in the warmer months, and should either be sent to slaughter or treated to destroy the carrier state.

JOHN C. LOTZE *is a parasitologist in the Animal Disease and Parasite Research Branch and has been doing research on protozoan diseases of livestock at the Agricultural Research Center, Beltsville, since 1938. He has conducted investigations particularly on anaplasmosis of cattle and coccidiosis of sheep and goats. Dr. Lotze is a graduate of Miami University and Ohio State University.*

DANIEL W. GATES *is a veterinarian in the Viral and Rickettsial Disease Section of the Animal Disease and Parasite Branch of the Agricultural Research Service. Following*

graduation from the University of Pennsylvania in 1925, he was employed by the Pennsylvania Bureau of Animal Industry. He received the degree of master of science from Cornell University in 1933 and served as zoo veterinarian for the Staten Island Zoological Society for a number of years.

T. O. ROBY *is a veterinarian in the Animal Disease and Parasite Research Branch, and is working principally on the complement fixation test for anaplasmosis. He has degrees form Michigan State University and Auburn Polytechnic Institute. Before joining the Department of Agriculture in 1952, Dr. Roby was a practitioner for 2 years, was in the Veterinary Corps of the United States Army for 3 years, and worked as a virologist at I. E. du Pont de Nemours Co. for 5 years.*

Hyperkeratosis

AUBREY M. LEE

A NEW and strange disease of cattle was first seen and reported by Dr. Peter Olafson, of the New York State Veterinary College, in 1941. It was called hyperkeratosis, or X-disease— "X" being a symbol for the unknown and "hyperkeratosis" indicating the increased amount of keratin, or horny material, that develops on skin of the neck, shoulders, and withers in chronic cases.

This ailment was reported in 10 States in 1946. A year later it was known to exist in 27 States. Officials of the Department of Agriculture and of Southeastern States in 1948 investigated 26 affected herds in 20 counties in Alabama, Florida, Georgia, Tennessee, and Virginia. They found an average loss of 4,200 dollars per herd.

The disease was causing an estimated loss of 2 million to 4 million dollars a year by 1949. Deaths were highest—up to 80 percent—in calves

less than 6 months old. About 50 to 60 percent of older calves died. The mortality in adult cattle was 10 to 35 percent.

In Texas the disease was diagnosed in 53 counties by 1950. In Wisconsin in June 1952 we had reports of 1,085 cases among cattle on 268 premises; an estimated 10,000 calves died in the winter of 1952. In Illinois 33 herds were affected. Tennessee reported more than 3,000 cattle had died or had to be slaughtered before 1952 because of the hyperkeratosis. About 20,000 animals were affected in Texas and 5,000 in Oklahoma in the winter of 1952–1953.

The disease then had been diagnosed and reported in 35 States, and in 4 more States it had been suspected in a herd or two. No new cases of hyperkeratosis of cattle were reported to the Department of Agriculture in 1954 or 1955—an indication that it had been eradicated or reduced to the extent that it was no longer important to the livestock industry.

SYMPTOMS usually start with listlessness, depression, excessive secretion of tears, drooling of saliva and a watery discharge from the nose, and loss of flesh. A rapid drop in blood plasma vitamin A often to very low levels may occur.

Often there also develops loss of condition, emaciation, a variable appetite, intermittent diarrhea, and a dry, scurfy skin. Raised areas, or wartlike lesions, often are found on the floor of the mouth and on the dental pad, hard palate, lips, tongue, gums, and the inside of the cheeks. They have been found also on the muzzle, the margins of the nostrils, and the lining of the esophagus.

If the animal survives those systemic effects and does not die from secondary bacterial infection, pneumonia, or inflammation of the intestines, the typical skin hyperkeratosis develops slowly. Then there develops gradually an accumulation of hard, keratinous material, which makes the skin thick, inelastic, and wrinkled. The deep fissures and bold folds formed in the skin become so hard that they are not reducible by stretching with the hands. The skin feels more like a hide than a skin. Hair on the affected skin gets thin or disappears entirely. The sides of the neck, shoulders, and withers are affected most commonly. Skin on the inner surface of the thigh, the udder, and scrotum, the convex surface of the ear, the dewlap, and the sides also may be affected. Almost all the skin of the body and sometimes the skin of the legs may be affected in extreme chronic cases.

A few herds, free of brucellosis but severely affected with bovine hyperkeratosis, have had abortions and stillborn calves and greatly reduced milk secretion. In some experimentally produced cases of hyperkeratosis in pregnant cows, abortion took place and milk flow dropped markedly. The extreme lowering of blood plasma vitamin A in hyperkeratosis could predispose to secondary bacterial infections, such as abscess formation, and inflammations of some of the internal organs.

The symptoms vary according to the amount of the toxic or poisonous substance the animal eats or touches and the duration of the exposure. The concentration of the toxic substance in the feed or in the compound that the animal comes in contact with will also cause variations in some symptoms. Other factors, such as age, individual differences, rations, and the material in which the toxic principle is suspended, may determine which symptoms are shown and which form the disease takes.

Research workers applied known hyperkeratosis-producing substances in diluted form locally to the skin of cattle. Little or none of the general systemic effects were produced, but a typical definite hyperkeratosis of the skin developed. The scientists found, however, that the systemic effects developed if the material were fed or given internally and that the skin hyperkeratosis developed from this internal administration, although usually it took 6 weeks to 2 months or longer. Calves died with the acute—rapid—form of the disease before skin changes appeared.

THE INTERNAL changes or lesions in the internal organs that are most characteristic of hyperkeratosis are swellings on the inside lining of the gall bladder, gall duct, and the large bile ducts. Characteristic changes of the small bile ducts of the liver commonly occur. The pancreas, liver, kidneys, and reproductive organs may be affected. The intestines, may become inflamed, and the inside lining of the fourth, or true, stomach, especially near the intestinal opening, may have reddened areas, flat erosions, and small ulcers.

SCIENTISTS in 18 States in 1949–1953 undertook research in a cooperative project with the Department of Agriculture to find the cause of hyperkeratosis. They had to start from scratch. They had only a few theories to begin with.

They had to study practically the whole environment of the affected cattle—soils, plant life, fertilizers, bacterial flora of the rumen, livestock feeds, viruses.

Drs. A. G. Johnson and W. O. Robinson, of the Department of Agriculture, established that soil, plants, and fertilizers were not factors.

Dr. W. O. Gibbons, of Alabama Polytechnic Institute, did extensive survey work and proved that DDT did not cause the disease.

Dr. William Sippel, of the Georgia Coastal Plain Experiment Station, Dr. Dennis Sikes, of the University of Tennessee, and Dr. Hubert Schmidt, of the Texas Agricultural and Mechanical College, demonstrated that the disease was not caused by a virus and was not infectious. They also proved that road oils and American wood preservatives did not cause it.

Dr. Carl Olson, Jr., of the University of Nebraska, in 1950 produced hyperkeratosis experimentally in cattle with a pelleted feed that had been suspected because of being connected with an outbreak.

Dr. Peter Olafson, of Cornell University, produced it by feeding a particular lot of suspected breadcrumbs from the slicers in a commercial bakery which were being fed to cattle and found the toxic substance was eliminated in the milk.

Dr. R. C. Miller and Dr. A. L. Bortree, of Pennsylvania State University, induced the disease by feeding a certain cutting of timothy hay that had been fed to cattle on a farm where the disease had caused heavy losses.

All the experiments were made under rigid controls, so there was no question but that each particular lot of the three products contained something that caused or brought on the disease.

Dr. H. W. Schoening, of the Department of Agriculture, at a conference in Europe in May 1950 learned of a disease condition in cattle produced experimentally at the Hannover Veterinary College in Germany. It seemed to be like the bovine hyperkeratosis in the United States. In Germany the condition had been caused by a particular tank carlot of a commercial wood preservative. Some of the wood from a barn at Hannover and some of the preservative with which it had been treated 2 years previously were taken to Cornell University and Pennsylvania State University for study.

Dr. William Hansel, Dr. Olafson, and Dr. Kenneth McEntee, of Cornell University, and Drs. Bortree and Miller produced hyperkeratosis with both the wood preservative and the wood in April 1951. They found the disease produced was the same as existed on farms in this country and as had been produced experimentally with pellets, breadcrumbs, and timothy hay.

Drs. Olafson, Hansel, and McEntee began studies of the place of vitamin A in hyperkeratosis produced experimentally by breadcrumbs and by the German wood preservative. They found that the blood plasma vitamin A was lower than had previously been produced experimentally—as low as 3 and 4 micrograms per 100 milliliters. Dr. Miller and Dr. P. H. Phillips, of the University of Wisconsin, later confirmed the finding, which was of value in studies in nutrition and in the research program to determine if a suspected causative agent should be studied further.

Cattle will eat grease from machinery and grease cans. Dr. Wilson B. Bell, of Virginia Polytechnic Institute, found in 1951 that a lubricant or grease recovered from a farm on which the disease had occurred and a similar product purchased on the market produced hyperkeratosis. With the cooperation and help of the company that made it, he fed this serial number of grease minus its various chemical additives.

Soon afterwards he found the item in the grease that made it produce hyperkeratosis was highly chlorinated naphthalene. Dr. Sikes, at the University of Tennessee, at the same time was feeding several chemicals used in greases and also found that highly chlorinated naphthalene produced hyperkeratosis.

N. R. Ellis, R. E. Davis, and Ivan Lindahl, of the Department of Agriculture at Beltsville, Md., investigated a feed mill of the kind that is commonly used in this country. The directions for operating it called for the use of grease every 2 hours of operation. The grease lubricated the bearings of the rollers that force the feed against the die plate. The end of the shaft is in contact with loose feed, and provision is made that the grease will work out from the bearing in order that feed and dirt will not get into the bearings. The workers concluded that the grease used as replacement every 2 hours went into the pellets.

The men at Cornell University started working on the breadcrumbs in an effort to find the chemical as soon as they proved the breadcrumbs would produce hyperkeratosis. The test itself had to be developed and perfected. It required expensive equipment and much time. They developed a testing method and identified highly chlorinated naphthalene as the contaminant in the breadcrumbs and also in the German wood preservative. They later cooperated and worked closely with several industries concerned in the production of pellets that were causing hyperkeratosis in Texas. One large corporation bought expensive special equipment and set a large staff of chemists to work on the problem. Highly chlorinated naphthalene was found and identified in the pellets and in the grease used to lubricate the pellet machines. Dr. Roger P. Link and Dr. E. F. Reber, of the University of Illinois, later identified this chemical in pellets that produced hyperkeratosis in Illinois.

Dr. Bell prepared a good livestock feed. He pelleted one-half of it in a machine greased with a lubricant that did not contain highly chlorinated naphthalene. For the other half the pellet machine was lubricated with a grease that contained 3 percent of highly chlorinated naphthalene. The pellets made when the machine was greased with the lubricant that did not contain highly chlorinated naphthalene were not toxic to the calves to which they were fed. The pellets made when the machine was lubricated with a grease which contained highly chlorinated naphthalene produced hyperkeratosis in calves. The first pellets made following the lubrication were highly toxic, but the ones made just before lubrication were only slightly toxic.

Oil companies and feed manufacturers, warned of the danger, did what they could to keep the damaging additive away from livestock and livestock feeds.

AUBREY M. LEE *became head of the Noninfectious Diseases Section of the Animal Disease and Parasite Research Branch, Agricultural Research Service, in 1952. He received a degree in veterinary medicine at Kansas State College in 1922 and master of science in 1930 at Ohio State University. He joined the Department of Agriculture in 1935. He has served with the Brucellosis and Tuberculosis Eradication Division and with the Pathological Division.*

For further reading:
Wilson B. Bell: *Further Studies on the Production of Bovine Hyperkeratosis by the Administration of a Lubricant,* Virginia Journal of Science (new series), volume 3, pages 169–177. 1952.
Wilson B. Bell: *The Relative Toxicity of the Chlorinated Naphthalenes in Experimentally Produced Bovine Hyperkeratosis (X-Disease),* Veterinary Medicine, volume 48, pages 135–140. 1953.
W. Hansel, P. Olafson, and Kenneth McEntee: *Bovine Hyperkeratosis Studies on a German Wood Preservative,* Cornell Veterinarian, volume 43, pages 311–324. 1953.
W. Hansel, P. Olafson, and K. McEntee: *The Isolation and Identification of the Causative Agent of Bovine Hyperkeratosis (X-Disease) From a Processed Wheat Concentrate,* Cornell Veterinarian, volume 45, pages 94–101. 1955.

Trichomoniasis of the Reproductive Tract

DATUS M. HAMMOND, PAUL R. FITZGERALD, AND
J. LeGRANDE SHUPE

ONE OF THE SERIOUS reproductive troubles in cattle, trichomoniasis, is transmitted by bulls. It causes temporary infertility in females and occasionally abortion. The disease is widespread.

Trichomoniasis is due to a microscopic, one-celled animal, *Tritrichomonas (Trichomonas) foetus.* It occurs in both dairy and beef cattle. In dairy herds, losses result from reduced milk production, reduced calf crop, interference with the breeding programs, and the necessity of treating or slaughtering infected bulls and some infected females. The losses are similar in beef herds except, of course, for those relating to milk production.

TRICHOMONADS, the causal organisms, occur in the sheath of bulls. Rarely are they in the deeper parts of the reproductive tract. Once a bull is infected he usually (but not always) retains the infection for the rest of his life.

The infected bull deposits the trichomonads in the vagina of the heifer or cow. Trichomonads usually multiply in the vagina until about 3 weeks after the service that initiated the infection.

Frequently a heifer returns to heat (oestrus) at about that time or within the following 10 days. After oestrus, trichomonads partly or completely disappear from the vagina. Several days before the next oestrus they are again present in larger numbers; after oestrus, another decrease in numbers or complete disappearance occurs. This pattern continues until the end of the infection, usually 3 to 4 months after its beginning.

Trichomonads enter the uterus from the vagina, perhaps before the fertilized egg enters it or soon thereafter.

Trichomonads in the uterus usually cause death of the fertilized egg or of the later stages in its development as embryo or fetus.

If pregnancy is interrupted in its earlier stages, the fertilized egg or embryo disintegrates and, except for a possible delay in oestrus, there is no indication that a pregnancy has occurred. If pregnancy is interrupted at a later stage, the dead fetus usually is discharged. That may not be noticed, however, because abortions caused by trichomoniasis usually occur relatively early in pregnancy. Occasionally in infected females pregnancies are not interrupted.

Sometimes the infection in the uterus persists longer than the usual 3 to 4 months. Pus frequently accumulates in the uterus in such cases, a condition called pyometra. The pus, which contains numerous trichomonads, may be discharged at intervals or may continue to accumulate in the uterus for several months. It is typical that the heifer or cow does not come in heat and appears to be pregnant. The occurrence of pyometra is associated with interruption of pregnancy without abortion and without regression (waning) of the corpus luteum. These cases usually require treatment by a veterinarian.

A heifer or cow that has recovered from an infection may be resistant to a second infection. If she is bred to an infected bull, she may not become infected or may develop only a slight infection that will not interfere with pregnancy. This resistance, however, varies considerably in degree and duration among different females. Reinfections are more likely to be associated with recognizable abortions, pyometras, and uninterrupted preg-

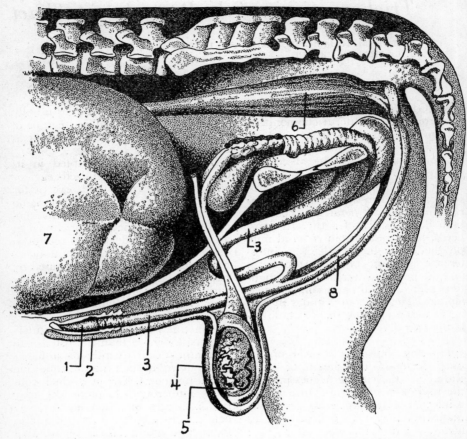

The reproductive system of the bull: (1) Glans penis; (2) prepuce; (3) penis; (4) scrotum; (5) testes; (6) rectum; (7) stomach; (8) retractor muscle.

nancies than are the original infections.

Studies made by Department of Agriculture scientists at Beltsville and analyzed by David E. Bartlett showed that 70 percent of 29 original infections and 21 reinfections resulted in apparent early interruption of pregnancy, with little or no disturbance of the estrual cycle. Pyometra occurred in 10 percent of the cases, abortion in 4 percent, and normal pregnancies in 12 percent.

M. Vandeplassche and coworkers at the Veterinary Medical School at Ghent, Belgium, found, however, that trichomonads did not enter the uterus

from the vagina until 25 or more days after service and that interruption of pregnancy usually occurred 2 months or more after service. Differences in strains of trichomonads may be a factor in such apparent differences in the course of infection.

SYMPTOMS include slight reddening and swelling of the vulva and walls of the vagina. The discharge from the vagina is somewhat greater in quantity and more watery than usual. Some degree of irregularity in heat periods may occur.

Some investigators have reported that infected bulls show inflammation of the penis and lining of the sheath, but others have stated that little or no inflammation occurs.

None of the symptoms in males or females is distinctive or consistent enough to have practical value in diagnosis.

TRANSMISSION is nearly always by breeding. Heifers and cows become infected by being bred to an infected bull. Bulls become infected by breeding infected females. Herds usually become infected by introduction into the herd of infected females or an infected bull or by intercourse between animals within the herd and infected animals outside of the herd.

Ninety to 100 percent of heifers and cows that have not developed resistance to infection as a result of previous infection become infected when bred to an infected bull. Some bulls have a natural resistance to infection, but infected bulls usually do not develop resistance.

Heifers and cows sometimes become infected in ways other than by breeding, but there is no evidence to indicate that this is of any practical importance.

Species of trichomonads living in other domestic animals are able to multiply in the vagina or uterus of the cow if experimentally introduced into those organs. Such experiments have been done with trichomonads cultured from the nose, stomach, and cecum of pigs.

Presence of the trichomonads in some cases was associated with apparent failure of the heifer to settle or with interruption of pregnancy when the trichomonads were inoculated into the uterus of a pregnant heifer.

These findings indicate the importance of obtaining more information about the relations of *T. foetus* to other trichomonads of domestic animals.

ARTIFICIAL INSEMINATION may be a means of transmitting trichomoniasis. Trichomonads can survive at least as long as sperm at the temperatures and in the diluting agents used for storing semen. The antibiotics, such as penicillin and streptomycin, and sulfa drugs that are frequently added to the diluting agent have no apparent effect on the trichomonads at the concentrations used.

Infected bulls have been found in a relatively high proportion of artificial insemination centers examined. Dr. Bartlett and his coworkers at the University of Minnesota found that 23 of 168 bulls in 5 artificial insemination organizations were infected. Infected bulls also have been found in artificial insemination centers in several other States.

Observations of scientists at the University of Minnesota and the Utah State Agricultural College indicate that the rate of transmission of trichomoniasis by artificial insemination is low. The investigators at Ghent, however, found that the rate of transmission was not much lower in artificial insemination than in natural breeding.

The spread by artificial insemination probably occurs often enough to be a serious problem. In order to prevent such transmission, each bull used in an artificial insemination center should be examined at the time he is brought into the center and at intervals of 6 months or a year thereafter. When infected bulls are discovered, they should be eliminated from further use unless successfully treated.

DIAGNOSIS involves finding trichomonads in suspected animals. Trichomoniasis may be suspected in herds in which more than the normal number of services are required to settle heifers and cows. In addition, early abortions and cases of pyometra may occur but perhaps are not noticed. Trichomoniasis is more likely to be present if natural service is used than if artificial insemination is employed.

The breeding record of a herd suspected of having trichomoniasis should be examined carefully to determine which animals are most likely to give positive results. If one or more bulls

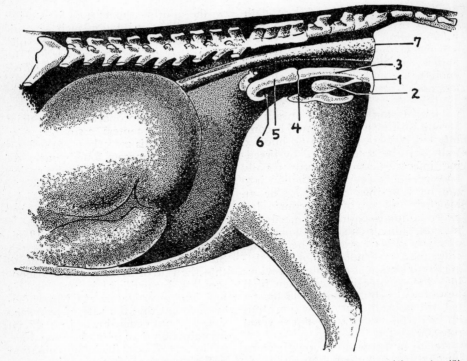

The reproductive system of the cow: (1) Vulva; (2) bladder; (3) vagina; (4) cervix; (5) uterus; (6) ovary; (7) anus.

have been used and are available, it is best to examine them first. It is usually easier to find trichomonads, if present, in bulls than in heifers and cows, because trichomonads are always present in the sheath of an infected bull.

The organisms are present in the vagina of females in demonstrable numbers only during a relatively small part of the time the infection is present. Trichomonads are more likely to be found in females 2 weeks or a month after they have been bred. Females bred more than a month earlier are best examined at oestrus or just before. Occasionally an infection may be discovered by finding trichomonads in an aborted fetus or in the fluids associated with it.

AN EXAMINATION of a bull involves collection of a sample of fluid from the sheath. One of several ways of doing that is the douche method. A weak salt solution (saline) is injected into the sheath with a pipet and a rubber bulb. The penis is massaged so that material from its surface, where the concentrations of trichomonads are highest, is included in the sample. The fluid is then allowed to drain from the sheath into a container and is centrifuged to concentrate the cellular material. The material is examined microscopically for trichomonads which can be distinguished from other similar organisms by the presence of an undulating membrane.

If no trichomonads are found, a part of the material is inoculated into a culture medium, in which trichomonads may multiply sufficiently to be found easily under the microscope after about 3 days of incubation at 102.2°F. Addition of penicillin and streptomycin to the medium inhibits the growth of bacteria, making conditions more favorable for trichomonads. Several kinds of media can be used. Good results have been obtained with a beef-extract medium. About 81 percent of 272 douche samples from 3 infected bulls were positive as determined by immediate examination, and an additional 8 percent of positive samples were detected by the culture method.

In another method, a pipet about 21 inches long is introduced into the sheath of the bull. Fluid from the surface of the penis and rear part of the sheath is sucked into the pipet with the aid of a rubber bulb. The recovered material is examined by the same method used in the douche method. The pipet method is somewhat simpler and faster and is therefore more practical for use in the field when large numbers of animals must be examined.

There is variation in concentration of trichomonads in preputial (sheath) samples at different times in a bull and among different bulls. Simultaneous infection in the sheath with certain bacteria may be associated with relatively low concentrations of trichomonads. It is advisable to repeat the examination of a bull before deciding that trichomonads are absent.

A breeding test may be used as a check on other methods of diagnosis or if special circumstances exist. A virgin heifer is bred to the bull suspected of having the infection, and the heifer is examined 12 to 19 days later. The bull is considered to be free of the infection if no trichomonads are found, but the test is not final.

Heifers or cows are examined by collecting a sample of fluid from the vagina with the aid of a pipet and bulb similar to that used for the bull, but with a sideward opening at the end opposite the bulb. Sterile saline solution is injected into the forward region of the vagina; then fluid from this region is sucked into the pipet. The fluid collected is examined for trichomonads in a way similar to that used for the samples from bulls.

Methods of diagnosis other than those depending on the detection of trichomonads in the reproductive system involve reactions of the body or of its fluids to the trichomonads. Probably the most important of these methods is one in which vaginal mucus from a suspected heifer or cow is tested to see if it will cause agglutination of trichomonads. A positive result indicates that the female or the herd is infected or has been infected, but the test must be confirmed by demonstration of trichomonads in the herd bull or in other animals in the herd.

Other methods that have been investigated include agglutination or precipitin tests of the blood or serum and tests involving skin reactions.

TREATMENT is much more important for bulls than for females, because an infection in females usually disappears without treatment within a few months, but an infection in the bull does not.

The main type of treatment is the application of curative agents to the penis and the internal surface of the sheath. The two methods that have been most thoroughly tried were developed by R. Abelein at the University of Munich and by Emil Hess at the University of Zurich.

In Abelein's method, as modified by Dr. Vandeplassche, Dr. Bartlett, and others, the bull is treated in a standing position. An anesthetic is injected into the region near the tail head to cause anesthesia of the penis and the muscle that pulls it backward. The penis and lining of the sheath are exposed. They are washed with soap and massaged thoroughly with bovoflavin salve.

Then a solution, trypaflavine, is injected into the opening of the penis. The treatment is repeated in 10 days or 2 weeks. This method has been successful in approximately 90 percent of the animals treated.

Dr. Vandeplassche learned that preliminary washing with warm trypaflavine solution instead of soap improves the percentage of success, so that 90 percent of infected bulls were cured with a single treatment. An acriflavine salve also is effective.

Emil Hess developed a treatment whereby a weak solution of hydrogen peroxide is sprayed into the sheath under high pressure. Some investigators have reported good results from this treatment, but others have obtained poor results. Some bulls must be treated several times before the infection is eliminated, and sometimes injury to the bull results. Special equipment is required.

One shortcoming of any treatment has been that a bull could not be used for 3 or 4 months after treatment; otherwise, one could not be certain that the infection had been eliminated. Improved methods of diagnosis, especially the use of the culture method, have made it possible to shorten this period, but the minimum safe interval has not yet been determined.

Treatment of heifers and cows is usually not necessary, unless pyometra occurs. Methods for treatment of pyometra includes enucleation—the removal of an organ or a tumor in such a way that it comes out clean and whole, like a nut from its shell—of the corpus luteum (yellow body), which encourages emptying of the uterus, and administration of hormones to stimulate normal function of the reproductive organs. Also, the uterus may be washed out with disinfectants, such as iodine solutions.

MANAGING INFECTED HERDS requires eliminating the source of infection.

The use of infected bulls must be stopped immediately. The status of any other bulls in the herd should be determined by examinations. It is usually more practical to determine the approximate status of females in the herd by analysis of the breeding record than by clinical examinations.

All females bred to an infected bull should be considered as infected. Nonpregnant females should have sufficient sexual rest to allow the disappearance of any infection still present. They

therefore should not be rebred until at least 4 months have elapsed from the date of the first service by the infected bull. If interruption of the oestrus cycle have occurred, the female should not be rebred until at least 3 normal periods of oestrus have passed after the interruption.

Some females may be pregnant or apparently pregnant following breeding to an infected bull. They should be observed for possible interruption of pregnancy or development of pyometra. Any cows that may have completed a normal pregnancy since breeding by an infected bull may be considered to be free of infection, but should not be rebred until after an adequate interval from the date of calving.

Virgin heifers and other females that have not been bred to infected bulls may be considered free of infection. Ordinary breeding practices may be used then.

It is advisable to use artificial insemination in the infected herd in order to prevent further transmission of the infection. If that is not feasible, the next best plan is to use an uninfected bull of relatively little value until all infected or possibly infected females are settled. This method involves some risk of transmission of the infection, and the bull should be examined at regular intervals during his period of service.

After this plan of management has been in effect for about 18 months, trichomoniasis should have been eradicated, and normal breeding practices may be resumed.

Prevention of infection or reinfection of herds is favored by exercising caution in bringing new mature animals into the herd. The breeding record of individual animals and of the herd of origin should be examined carefully before purchase. If significant irregularities are found, advisability of purchase is questionable.

Breeding performance of new animals should be carefully observed after they are brought into the herd. Intercourse between animals within the herd and animals outside the herd should be avoided. The danger in this practice is shown by the high incidence of trichomoniasis in Europe, where use of community bulls is widespread. As an example, in 1954 Eduard Gollbeck of Stuttgart reported that 44 percent of more than 2,000 bulls in northern Württemberg were found by a single examination to be infected with trichomoniasis.

These methods of managing infected herds are applicable especially to dairy herds and to beef herds in which the breeding program can be controlled and carefully observed. This is not true of the grazing type of beef operation. In grazing operations, management is facilitated if bulls are allowed to run with the cows for only a part of the year, so that calving is confined to a definite period.

Trichomoniasis might be suspected if the calf crop is reduced or if the number of late calves or barren cows is larger than usual. In that case, all bulls should be examined for trichomoniasis during the most convenient time of year. Any infected bulls found should be treated or slaughtered. It is advisable to repeat this procedure for 1 or 2 years until positive bulls are no longer found.

Much progress has been made in understanding trichomoniasis and in learning how to diagnose and control it. The greatest need for further study is a more accurate method of diagnosis and a simple, infallible treatment for bulls. These developments would enable a significant reduction in losses caused by the disease.

DATUS M. HAMMOND *has been on the staff of the Utah State Agricultural College since 1936, except for 4 years when he worked in the Zoological Division of the Department of Agriculture and at the Regional Laboratory for Animal Disease Research at Auburn, Ala. Dr. Hammond became professor and head of zoology, entomology, and physiology in 1945. Since 1952 he has been a cooperative agent associated with the Animal Disease and Parasite Research Branch, Agricultural Research Serv-*

ice. That branch and the Utah Agricultural Experiment Station have been cooperating in investigation of trichomoniasis since 1950.

PAUL R. FITZGERALD *holds two degrees from Utah State Agricultural College. Since 1950 he has been doing research on trichomoniasis at Logan, Utah, first as cooperative agent and since 1953 as veterinary parasitologist in charge of the Logan Field Station of the Animal Disease and Parasite Research Branch, Agricultural Research Service.*

J. LEGRANDE SHUPE *has been a member of the Veterinary Science Department of Utah State Agricultural College since 1952. In addition to the work on trichomoniasis, he has been studying brisket disease and fluorosis. A native of Utah, he attended Weber College and Utah State Agricultural College, and holds the degree of doctor of veterinary medicine from Cornell University. He served in the Veterinary Corps of the Army from 1942 to 1945.*

For further reading:

David E. Bartlett: *Trichomonas foetus Infection and Bovine Reproduction,* American Journal of Veterinary Research, volume 8, number 29, pages 343–352, 1947; *Procedure for Diagnosing Bovine Venereal Trichomoniasis and Handling Affected Herds,* Journal of the American Veterinary Medical Association, volume 114, number 866, pages 293–305. 1949.

David E. Bartlett, Kenneth Moist, and Francis A. Spurrell: *The Trichomonas foetus-Infected Bull in Artificial Insemination,* Journal of the American Veterinary Medical Association, volume 122, number 914, pages 366–370. 1953.

Paul R. Fitzgerald, Datus M. Hammond, and J. LeGrande Shupe: *The Role of Cultures in Immediate and Delayed Examinations of Preputial Samples for Trichomonas foetus,* Veterinary Medicine, volume 49, pages 409–412, 454. 1954.

Paul R. Fitzgerald, Datus M. Hammond, and Merthyr L. Miner: *The Survival and Transmission of Trichomonas foetus in Diluted Bovine Semen,* American Journal of Veterinary Research, volume 15, number 54, pages 36–40. 1954.

Datus M. Hammond, Paul R. Fitzgerald, Wayne Binns, and Merthyr L. Miner: *The Efficacy of Bovoflavin Salve in the Experimental Treatment of Trichomoniasis in Bulls,* Cornell Veterinarian, volume 43, number 1, pages 121–127. 1953.

Emil Hess: *Treatment of Bovine Trichomoniasis,* Proceedings of the U. S. Livestock Sanitary Association, Fifty-Third Annual Meeting, pages 120–127. 1949.

Roundworm Parasites of the Digestive Tract of Cattle

DALE A. PORTER, HARRY HERLICH, AND HALSEY H. VEGORS

APPROXIMATELY 25 species of roundworms can live in the digestive tract of cattle. About 10 of them are of economic importance. Natural parasitism usually is a mixture of several or all of them in one animal, and each type of worm produces a specific effect on the infected animal.

Three species of roundworms are commonly to be found in the stomach (abomasum) of cattle.

THE COMMON STOMACH WORM, *Haemonchus contortus*, occurs throughout the United States in cattle and sheep. It is three-fourths inch to one and one-half inches long and about as thick as a common pin. The adult females are larger than the males. The red spiral effect often seen in the living worms gives rise to such common names as wireworm, barberpole worm, and the twisted stomach worm.

The free-living part of its life cycle is much the same as that of all the roundworm species in cattle (except two species of intestinal worms). Eggs are passed with the feces of the infected animal. In 5 to 8 days, depending on temperature and humidity, the eggs have produced infective larvae (immature worms), which are capable of further development if swallowed by susceptible grazing stock.

The larvae do not feed and are enclosed within the cuticle (skin) of the preceding stage of development. They also have an inner cuticle. The two cuticles make the larvae able to survive unfavorable conditions.

The infective larvae are eaten with the grass. They pass down to the stomach, where they cast off their sheaths and undergo further growth until they become mature males and females. Fer-tilization occurs, and 18 to 23 days after the larvae have been swallowed, eggs from the female are passed with the droppings of the host.

We used to think that a bovine and an ovine strain of the common stomach worm existed, but F. H. S. Roberts in Australia stated in 1954 that the common stomach worms from sheep and cattle were two distinct species. He proposed that the name *H. contortus* be continued for the sheep species. He proposed the name *H. placei* for the cattle species. Cattle are more susceptible to *H. placei* than are sheep, and sheep acquire greater numbers of *H. contortus* than cattle do.

THE COMMON STOMACH WORM appears to affect sheep and cattle in the same way and is one of the most harmful species to both.

The most common symptoms are anemia, which is shown in paleness of the mouth and eyes, and emaciation despite continued good appetite. Infected cattle may have a rough hair coat and "bottle-jaw," a fluid accumulation in the lower jaw. They may be stunted. Diarrhea is rare. The most acute stage of infection is usually during the first 2 to 3 weeks after larvae have been swallowed. Symptoms often disappear when the worms have reached maturity. Severe cases may result in death.

THE MEDIUM STOMACH WORM, *Ostertagia ostertagi*, is hard to detect with the naked eye. In clear water against a black background, however, it can be seen readily as a worm slightly less than one-half inch long and about half as thick as a pin. Living worms are often reddish.

Its infective larvae are susceptible to heat and resistant to cold, so that they often become a problem during the colder months. The larvae shed their sheaths 3 days after they have been swallowed and penetrate the lining of the stomach. There they undergo further development for about 7 days. The worms then return to the stomach lumen (cavity) and develop to maturity. Many worms remain in the stomach lining for months. Eggs are passed with the feces about 25 days after cattle swallow the larvae.

The worms damage the stomach lining severely as they bore into it. This action stimulates a host reaction, which produces small nodules—raised, hemorrhagic (bleeding) spots—in an attempt to overcome the invading larvae. Eventually the worms leave the nodules, or die within them. Thereupon the nodules degenerate and leave patchy, eroded areas.

Animals infected with the medium stomach worm show general symptoms of parasitism, including scouring, weakness, stunted growth, and anemia. Severe infections cause death.

Postmortem examination often reveals a highly edematous—or swollen—stomach wall, in which there are many hemorrhagic or eroded spots. In the West and Southwest, the losses that are directly attributed to roundworm parasites are due mostly to the medium stomach worm.

THE SMALL HAIRWORM, *Trichostrongylus axei,* is the smallest of the roundworms affecting cattle. It is less than one-fourth inch long and about as thick as a hair. Laboratory equipment is needed to detect it. The small hairworm can establish itself readily in sheep, goats, and horses. In horses it causes an extremely severe gastritis (a stomach inflammation). Rabbits, hamsters, and guinea pigs have been experimentally infected with it.

The life history of the small hairworm generally is like that of the common stomach worm and the medium stomach worm. The worms spend part of their developmental cycle within the stomach lining of cattle and produce ringwormlike lesions similar to those produced by this parasite in horses. About 4 weeks after cattle have swallowed infective larvae, eggs are passed in their feces.

THE SMALL HAIRWORM does not seem to affect the health of calves very much unless the level of exposure is high. Experimental findings, however, have borne out clinical evidence that the small hairworm has been the main cause of many cases of severe illness and death.

The detrimental effect of the small hairworms on calves is notably marked in cases of parasitism involving both the small hairworms and the medium stomach worms. Postmortem examination of stomachs of these cases shows a diffuse reddish-gray or slate-gray color, with evidence of edema. As many as 400,000 small hairworms have been recovered after death—the animal must have swallowed enormous numbers of larvae, because not all the larvae become adults.

A CLOSELY RELATED form, *T. colubriformis,* primarily a parasite of sheep and goats, occurs in the small intestines of cattle. It has been found in great numbers in New York in calves suffering from parasitism. It might become a serious menace to cattle as the practice of raising sheep and cattle together becomes more prevalent.

SEVERAL SPECIES OF ROUNDWORMS exist in the small intestines of cattle.

Three species of small worms are referred to as cooperids. One of them, *Cooperia punctata,* occurs in all parts of the United States. *C. oncophora* and *C. pectinata* are more often found in the Northern and Southern States, respectively. (A fourth species, *C. curticei,* primarily a parasite of sheep, is found occasionally in cattle.)

The cooperids are as thick as a hair and less than one-third inch long. The live worms are yellowish or pinkish brown. They occur most often on (and occasionally embedded in) the lining of the intestines, principally along the upper half of the small intestines.

All three species are similar in the essential details of their development, which resembles that of the common stomach worm. The main difference is the rapidity with which the cooperids complete their development within the animal. Eggs of *C. punctata* are in the feces of infected animals 11 days after infective larvae have been swallowed.

The cooperids have been implicated in field cases of severe parasitism in cattle, but other parasites usually were present and it was hard to determine the extent of the detrimental effects directly traceable to the cooperids.

C. punctata is potentially harmful to cattle. It can cause scouring, loss of appetite, weakness, and death. Anemia was not evident in any experimentally infected animals. The lesions consist chiefly of hemorrhages, which are usually no bigger than a pinhead. The intestinal wall is thickened. The surface of the intestinal lining has an unusual grayish-white appearance. The entire length of the small intestine may have an accumulation of white or yellowish, cheesy material, indicating irritation of the intestinal lining.

The hookworm, *Bunostomum phlebotomum*, occurs in cattle all over the world. It is most prevalent in regions of high rainfall and warm climate, as in the Southeastern States. Normally it is found in the upper half of the small intestine, chiefly in the first 8 or 10 feet. The male worms are about one-half inch long. The females are about three-fourths inch long. Both sexes are much stouter than the common stomach worm.

Cattle become infected when they swallow infective larvae. Larvae might also penetrate their skin when they are lying on contaminated bedding or ground. The larvae that enter through the skin migrate to the lungs, probably through the blood stream, and penetrate the lung. Then they are coughed up and swallowed and complete their development in the intestine. The time required for this migration and development is 52 to 79 days.

The head end of the hookworm has a large, cup-shaped mouth cavity armed with teeth, or cutting plates. With them it attaches itself to the intestinal wall. It sucks a part of the intestinal lining into its mouth and cuts the finer blood vessels with the teeth, and so gets its food from the blood of the animal. When many worms are present, the many small hemorrhages cause anemia.

Other symptoms are like those seen in infections of stomach worms. The calf may go off feed and eventually die. Diarrhea, weakness, and unthriftiness are apparent about a month after infection while the worms are still immature. Thus severe symptoms of a hookworm infection often are present during a period in which the infection cannot be detected by finding eggs in the droppings.

Adult hookworms may live in cattle as long as 10 months. Infected cattle acquire an immunity to further infection with this parasite.

THE INTESTINAL THREADWORM, the *Strongyloides papillosus*, is another skin-penetrating worm. It reaches maturity in the small intestine. It is very widely distributed and is common in young calves, especially in dairy calves and in the beef calves that are dropped in barnyards.

These roundworms are so tiny that they often are overlooked at postmortem examination. The adult females, about one-eighth of an inch long, usually are buried in the lining of the upper two-thirds of the small intestine. Parasitic males have not been found. The eggs contain fully developed larvae at the time they are passed in the feces. Intestinal threadworms have a cycle in which there are free-living males and females.

The worms may enter through the skin, or the infective larvae may be swallowed. Immature females are found in the small intestine as early as 7 days after infection. Eggs are usually in the feces 10 days after the animal is exposed.

Heavy infections cause severe inflammation of the intestinal lining.

Hemorrhages usually are evident in the first two-thirds of the small intestine. Diarrhea is frequent during the first 2 weeks of infection and continues intermittently for 2 to 3 months. A bloody, slimy discharge sometimes accompanies the diarrhea.

The calf may go off feed, lose condition and grow slowly, or lose weight rapidly, depending on the severity of the infection. Calves 4 or 5 months old can survive heavy infections for a longer period than calves a few weeks old, but the effects of parasitism may persist for some time after the infection is over.

THE NODULAR WORM, *Oesophagostomum radiatum*, gets its common name from the small, hard nodules that the larvae produce in the wall of the lower part of the small intestine and cecum, the large pouch at the beginning of the large intestine. Nodular worms are distributed widely, but are especially prevalent in the Southern and Eastern States. Because their eggs and larvae are susceptible to drought and cold, they occur less often in Northern and Western States.

Adult worms are found in the cecum and large intestine. They are one-half to three-fourths inch long. Like hookworms, they have a cup-shaped mouth, which, however, lacks teeth or cutting plates. The head end is hook-shaped. The females have a dark-colored spot near the tail.

Eggs pass out in the feces, hatch in 20 to 24 hours, and produce infective larvae in 5 to 6 days. Cattle become infected by swallowing the larvae.

When the larvae reach the calf's lower digestive tract, they burrow about halfway through the wall of the small intestine or cecum and remain there about 10 days. Then they return into the intestine and reach maturity in the cecum and large intestine. Eggs are passed with the feces 33 to 43 days after infection occurs.

The larvae in the tissue cause a thickening of the intestinal wall and a rupturing of small blood vessels. At the point of larval entry, small, raised nodules are formed as a reaction of the host, which is attempting to overcome the invading worms. The nodules get bigger as the worms grow.

A single exposure to nodular worm larvae does not cause nodule formation. Multiple doses of infective larvae at different intervals—the normal occurrence on contaminated pastures—result, however, in a severe nodular reaction. Large nodules are formed and the intestine is inflamed and hemorrhagic. Nodules are usually more pronounced in the older animals than in calves.

The larvae and the nodules, by interfering with the normal digestion and absorption, may produce a diarrhea of varying severity. The discharge becomes watery, sometimes bloody, and has a disagreeable odor. Diagnosis is difficult in the early stages because worm eggs do not appear until 3 to 5 weeks after onset of diarrhea. Calves may lose their appetite within 4 or 5 days after infection occurs, and then they may become weak and anemic.

Symptoms subside and damaged tissues heal after the larvae leave the intestinal wall and mature, but the animals may be weak and in poor condition for months. The adult nodular worm can live 11 to 14 months in an infected animal.

The larval stages of the nodular worm of cattle can maintain themselves for short periods in sheep. Although they do not develop to the adult form, the larvae penetrate the intestinal tissues and cause damage in sheep similar to that in cattle.

TWO SPECIES OF WORMS, the threadnecked strongyles, *Nematodirus helvetianus* and *N. spathiger*, occur in the small intestines of cattle, although

N. spathiger is found primarily in sheep. These worms are one-half to one inch long and about as thick as a pin.

Living worms are usually reddish in color.

The free-living stages of the two species develop differently from the other roundworms parasitic in the digestive tracts of cattle. Eggs are deposited on the ground. Development to the infective stage occurs entirely within the egg. Consequently these species are resistant to the effects of climate and can survive long periods of drought and cold.

Eggs containing infective larvae and infective larvae hatched from the eggs may be swallowed by cattle. They pass down the digestive tract to the upper 20 feet of the small intestine, where they shed the cuticles of the second-stage larvae. The worms lie in close contact in the intestinal tract with the intestinal lining, where they develop and become adult worms. Eggs are passed in the host's feces 21 to 26 days after infection occurs.

Large numbers of *N. helvetianus* are detrimental to the health of calves. Scouring, loss of appetite, weakness, and severe setbacks in weight result. Experimental infections in which as many as 1 million larvae were fed did not kill calves. In Wyoming, however, the deaths of 32 calves on a pasture were attributed to infections with enormous numbers of *N. helvetianus*. Postmortem examinations of the experimentally infected calves showed that the close contact of the worms with the linings of the intestines cause some destruction of tissue, with an accumulation of thick, milky colored material in the upper part of the small intestine.

The effects of *N. spathiger* on cattle have not been determined. In lambs it produces symptoms like those described for *N. helvetianus* in cattle. It is probable that *N. spathiger* in large numbers would be harmful to cattle.

CONTROL OF ROUNDWORM PARASITISM of cattle requires good husbandry and proper treatment.

Prevention is better than cure. Because the free-living stages of the roundworms develop on the ground and infection occurs primarily when cattle swallow infective larvae, preventive measures are most effective when they are aimed at the pasture phase.

Since moisture abets the development of the free-living stages and dryness kills them, practices that tend to reduce the moisture on a pasture lessens the parasitic contamination. Pastures should be well drained. Watering troughs should be raised above the ground. Grazing should be kept to a minimum along the edges of ponds and streams. Supplemental feeding should be away from wet ground, and the feeding site should be changed to a new location as often as possible. Cattle should never be fed hay and grain on the ground.

Free-living stages of roundworms gradually succumb to natural environmental factors in the absence of susceptible grazing stock. Maintaining the proper rate of stocking and rotating pastures as often as forage is available therefore greatly reduce pasture contamination. The fewer animals to the acre and the longer the pasture is left vacant, the greater is the reduction in the level of contamination.

Young animals, which generally are more susceptible to parasitism, should be isolated as much as possible from older stock. Rearing dairy calves in portable pens is a successful method of raising calves free of worm parasites (except *S. papillosus*).

The nutritional state of cattle is important, for it affects the numbers of worms acquired and the effects of parasitism. The use of temporary pastures, for which the seedbed is prepared each year, in conjunction with the rotation of permanent pastures will help prevent severe parasitism.

The most dangerous period for the development of parasitism in beef calves is during the few months just before and after weaning. Consequently creep-feeding before weaning and adequate pasturage, with or without supplemental grain after weaning, help to control parasitism. Calves protected from severe parasitism during this period may develop a resistance to later infections.

When animals that harbor parasites are added to a herd, they should be treated and kept isolated for 3 or 4 days. They should be treated again in 3 or 4 weeks.

Phenothiazine (offered free-choice to cattle in combination with a mineral base consisting of 1 part phenothiazine by weight to 3 parts each of bonemeal, limestone, and salt, or incorporated in feed pellets) has given excellent control of the common stomach worm, *H. contortus*, and the nodular worm, *O. radiatum*.

The amount of phenothiazine thus consumed daily averages only 3 grams or less per head. Although such small amounts of the drug may have little actual killing effect on the worms, the phenothiazine may lower the egg production of the female worms and have some killing effect on eggs passed in the feces. The drug used in this way seems to have little effect on other species of roundworms.

THE TREATMENT OF CATTLE with drugs has two main aims: To remove worms from the infected animal and to reduce the number of eggs in the pasture. Several drugs are available for removing worms from cattle. Phenothiazine, the drug of choice, has a number of advantages over other medications.

Phenothiazine may be given as a drench or in a capsule or bolus and the animals can remain on full feed. Other drugs require that the animals be fasted for several hours before treatment.

Phenothiazine is effective against a greater range of species of worms than any other known drug. Used at recommended levels, it is relatively nontoxic to cattle.

Cattle that are partly white occasionally may become sensitized temporarily and experience scaling or

sloughing of nonpigmented areas. Temporary blindness has been reported in a few animals following treatment with phenothiazine in bright sunlight. Whenever practical, therefore, cattle should be kept in barns or in shaded lots or woods for 24 to 48 hours after treatment.

PHENOTHIAZINE is partly absorbed into the blood stream of cattle. Milk from treated dairy cows is colored pink. The drug is eliminated quickly from the animal's body, and the milk can be used by people as soon as it loses its discoloration, usually 4 to 5 days after it has been administered to the cows.

Phenothiazine is given to cattle at a dosage rate of 0.67 ounce (20 grams) per 100 pounds of body weight. The maximum is 2 ounces (60 grams). Some parasitologists have used as much as 4.5 ounces of the drug without toxic effects, but without enough evidence that any greater efficiency of the higher dosage justifies the extra expense.

Phenothiazine at the recommended dosage removes 100 percent of the common stomach worms, the small hairworms, and the nodular worms. It also removes an average of 80 percent of all medium stomach worms, and 40 to 100 percent of the hookworms.

Its efficiency against the other species of roundworms is relatively low. It is effective only against adult worms; treatment consequently should be repeated in 3 to 4 weeks in order to kill the worms that reach maturity during that interval. Routine treatment of beef cattle in early spring and late summer and fall helps greatly to reduce parasitism.

DALE A. PORTER *is director of the Regional Animal Disease Research Laboratory at Auburn, Ala., of the Department of Agriculture. He has worked as a parasitologist in the Department of Agriculture since 1935 and is an author of several papers on parasites of swine and cattle. Dr. Porter is a graduate of Kalamazoo College, Kansas State College, and the Johns Hopkins University.*

HARRY HERLICH, *a parasitologist at the Regional Animal Disease Research Laboratory, Auburn, Ala., has conducted research on parasites of cattle since 1949. He is a graduate of Tufts College and Alabama Polytechnic Institute.*

HALSEY H. VEGORS, *a parasitologist, also is associated with the Regional Labora-tory and is stationed at Experiment, Ga., where he conducts investigations on control of cattle parasites by management in coop-eration with the Georgia Agricultural Ex-periment Station. He is a graduate of the University of California and has been asso-ciated with cattle parasite research in the Department of Agriculture since 1945.*

Verminous Pneumonia of Cattle

ROBERT RUBIN

MOST internal parasites of cattle live in the stomach or intestine, but the worms known as *Dictyocaulus viviparus*, which live in the lungs, in many respects are the most injurious.

They are 2 to 3 inches long, white, and threadlike. They live in the medium and small air passages of the lungs. The females lay eggs, each containing a very small worm (first-stage larva). The larva usually hatches in the lungs.

First-stage larvae are coughed up and swallowed and then pass out in the droppings. An infected animal can pass 5 million larvae in a day—an important fact, for 5,000 fully developed larvae can kill a young calf.

On the ground the first-stage larvae develop but do not grow. When a certain stage is reached, the small worms (third-stage infective larvae) are able to reach the lungs and develop into mature worms if they are taken into the body of a susceptible calf, yearling, or adult.

The time required for first-stage larvae passed in the feces to reach the infective stage depends on the weather. Only a week is needed in a warm, wet period. Larvae do not develop in extremely cold or dry weather. The larvae can survive for weeks or months in the infective stage. They reportedly can survive an entire winter in parts of Great Britain, but in the United States the infective larvae have not been known to survive more than a few months at any time of year.

There are many degrees of infection. Even a lightly infected animal may be quite dangerous—it may show only slight or possibly no effects, but it might produce larvae enough to infect an entire calf crop or a number of yearlings or adults. The only way such an animal can be detected is by finding larvae in the droppings. That requires skill, because the larvae cannot be seen without a microscope.

An animal that ingests a large number of infective larvae becomes sick in a short time, usually within 2 weeks. The first noticeable sign is a cough, which becomes more and more frequent. Breathing is faster and more forceful. Often a loud grunt follows each breath. The sick animal may stand away from the herd with head lowered and extended.

As breathing becomes more difficult, as it does in severe and fatal cases, the animal breathes with its mouth open and tongue protruding—much as a dog pants. At that stage, coughing apparently has become too difficult or too much of a discomfort, and is seldom heard. A foamy and sometimes bloody material may collect around the muzzle. The animal is reluctant to move, usually has a fever, is off feed and water, and becomes gaunt.

The worms usually are directly responsible for the symptoms. Large numbers of them in the air passages can cause a blockage sufficient to prevent enough air from reaching the lung tissue. Suffocation can result. The tissues also may react to the irritating presence of adults, eggs, and larvae by producing fluid (pulmonary edema), which collects in the small airspaces (alveoli) and keeps air from reaching the vital tissues. A fatal bacterial or viral pneumonia can develop because lungworms reduce resistance.

The stock owner can detect symptoms in a sick animal indicative of lungworm disease, but he must find larvae in the feces to be certain.

Only in animals that survive for about 4 weeks after their initial infection is it possible to detect larvae, because it takes that time for third-stage larvae to become adults; the latter produce first-stage larvae. Many infected animals become sick well in advance of this period, and in them a diagnosis cannot be made unless the animal dies or is destroyed and lungworms are found at autopsy.

A further complication is that an animal may die so soon after infection that the worms in the lungs are still microscopic and may be overlooked. Such cases are perplexing to the veterinarian, because the only way to differentiate lungworm (verminous) pneumonia from other lung diseases at autopsy is to find the worms.

Because there is no good treatment, control must be approached with the idea of preventing infections.

Pasture rotation, barn sanitation, and isolation of young stock are helpful but not completely effective. The climate in the Southeastern and Pacific Coast States, the major lungworm sites in the United States, favors the propagation of lungworm disease.

A different approach to control there and in the other regions may be to use phenothiazine, which in proper amounts reduces the number of larvae that become infective. As phenothiazine is effective against other internal parasites, the best recommendation that can be made is to administer phenothiazine, under veterinary supervision, to all in an infected herd.

The preceding facts refer to animals that are susceptible to lungworm infection. There are varying degrees of susceptibility, just as there are degrees of susceptibility or resistance to bacterial, viral, and other parasitic diseases. Such resistance is termed natural resistance.

A definite resistance develops in an animal that can survive a lungworm infection. Once an animal has recovered, adult worms usually do not develop in its lungs; it may pick up infective larvae and some of them may reach the lungs, but usually they do not become adults. These larvae in the lungs cause the animal some trouble, such as rapid breathing for a few days, an increase in temperature, and loss of appetite, but usually that is far less severe than the first time it became infected. That is active acquired resistance. Animals with this type of resistance have survived 15 times the number of infective larvae that have killed susceptible animals.

The blood of animals with an active acquired resistance apparently contains substances—antibodies—that, if put into the blood of a susceptible animal, can help protect it from the serious effects that would naturally accompany an initial infection. This type of resistance is passive acquired resistance. The potential value of active and passive acquired resistance could have great importance in control of this disease.

Robert Rubin *is a parasitologist in the Animal Disease and Parasite Research Branch, Agricultural Research Service. He was a staff member of the School of Veterinary Medicine, Oklahoma Agricultural and Mechanical College for 4 years. He holds degrees from Stanford University, Colorado Agricultural and Mechanical College, and Oklahoma Agricultural and Mechanical College.*

Cattle Scabies

IRWIN H. ROBERTS AND N. G. COBBETT

SCABIES is a contagious skin disease caused by minute parasitic organisms known as mites. It affects cattle of all ages and breeds. Sometimes it is referred to as scab, mange, or barn itch. Similar infections attack other classes of livestock, wild animals, and birds, as well as people.

Scabies, the medical term for which is acariasis, is common throughout the world. It generally causes a severe inflammation of the skin and itching.

Mites are related to ticks, spiders, and scorpions, and are not true insects. Unlike insects, adult mites have 4 pairs of legs instead of 3. They are wingless and usually are so small that they can barely be seen with the naked eye.

Of the thousands of known kinds of mites, four are commonly parasitic to cattle. Each of the four produces a different type of skin reaction. Two, known as psoroptic and chorioptic mites, live on the surface of the skin and cause a condition generally spoken of as scabies. Two others, the sarcoptic and the demodectic mites, burrow under the surface of the skin and produce mange.

PSOROPTIC SCABIES, also known as common scab, was prevalent in range cattle in the Western States until about 1938. It is caused by *Psoroptes equi* var. *bovis*, a whitish mite, which can be seen as a minute speck if it is placed against a dark background. It spends its entire life cycle on the animal. Female mites deposit about 20 eggs on the surface of the skin. The eggs hatch in about 4 days, and minute larvae, each with three pairs of legs, emerge. These molt, or shed their skins, become nymphs, molt again, become adults, reach maturity, and mate, and the females of the new generation begin laying eggs. The entire cycle takes no more than 12 days.

Psoroptic mites attack the hairy parts of the body. They generally begin an infestation over the withers, but sometimes also over the back or around the tailhead. The mites prick the skin to obtain food. Tissue fluids ooze from the wounds. After many mites have fed, the fluids dry, become mixed with tissue debris, and form scabs.

The lesions made by the mites spread as the parasites increase in number and involve large areas of the back and sides. The condition may advance over practically the entire body if it is not checked. As the disease worsens, hair falls out, and the body is covered with thick, rough crusts. The skin becomes hard and thickened and it takes on a corrugated look.

CHORIOPTIC SCABIES occurs chiefly in farm herds. It is widely distributed from the Atlantic coast to the States east of the Rocky Mountains. A persistent disease, it spreads slowly over the infected animal, but may travel from one animal to most of the animals in a small herd in a year.

The mite responsible for it is *Chorioptes bovis* var. *bovis*. Like the psoroptic mites, it lives on the surface of the skin. Its life history is similar to that of the psoroptic mites, and it obtains nourishment in the same way.

Chorioptic scabies mites do not usually produce such extensive and prominent lesions as psoroptic mites, and the injury they cause is less severe. This form of scabies usually begins on the inside surface of the hind legs in the fetlock region, high on the rear surface of the udder or scrotum, or on the inside of the flanks and thighs. The infection is known commonly as leg or foot mange.

Chorioptic mites produce an infection by piercing the skin. The serum, or tissue fluid, that exudes from this wound forms a minute blister. The mites multiply, the blisters unite and break, and their dried contents slowly build up into little scabs or crusts, beneath which the skin is raw and bleeds easily.

The mites live in colonies under the scabs. If a scab is removed with the fingers and placed on a dark surface in some warm place, the flesh-colored mites will be seen, just about visible to the naked eye, crawling rapidly away in every direction. A reading glass will help one find the parasites.

The mites from one small lesion spread after a few months to various places about the hindquarters, establishing new colonies. The disease eventually may involve large portions of the underparts, side, and back.

Sometimes the disease progresses so slowly that scabs the size of a half dollar, in various places about the hindquarters, may go unnoticed for a year or two.

In highly susceptible animals, the condition may eventually spread to the underparts of the body, forward along the midline, around the outer surface of the legs, and over the sides and back.

Sarcoptic mange used to be considered of no economic importance in cattle in the United States. By 1950, however, 30 percent of the scabies-infested cattle in one Northeastern State were infested with the sarcoptic variety of the disease, either alone or in combination with chorioptic scabies.

As in chorioptic scabies, sarcoptic mange often is found in purebred herds and may be spread about the country with the sale of breeding stock.

The mite that causes it is *Sarcoptes scabiei* var. *bovis*. It spends its entire life cycle on the body of the animal. The mature female makes long channels within the horny surface of the skin. In the burrows the female deposits her eggs, which are almost as large as she is. The mature female usually stays in the burrow her entire life. The mite begins laying eggs within a few hours after starting her burrow. She deposits the eggs every second or third day for as long as 2 months, stringing the eggs out behind her as she lengthens her burrow. She usually lays about 30 eggs in her lifetime.

The eggs hatch in about 5 days, after which the larvae leave the channels. They move about on the skin, where they molt, become nymphs, and molt again to become adult males or immature females.

Larvae and nymphs can be found in the skin follicles. The adult males and young females make short burrows, in which they remain briefly. Mating takes place on the skin. After mating, the fertilized female burrows into the skin to lay her eggs and start a new generation. The full cycle takes about 14 days.

A female theoretically could have more than a million descendants in six generations, or 90 days.

When huge numbers of mites are present on an animal, they are rather easily found under scabs, which can be removed from the skin with the fingers or a dull knife edge. Their burrowing habits in the early stages make it rather hard to find the mites. However, skin scrapings made with a knife edge, deep enough to draw the blood, will usually disclose the active parasites. They are barely visible, but a reading glass will show them as moving specks if they are placed against a dark background.

Sarcoptic mange mites may produce lesions anywhere on the body of cattle. They appear to adapt themselves best in locations where the skin is thin and tender and the haircoat is thin. They are commonly found high on the rear surface of the udder or scrotum, and on the rear and inner surfaces of the thighs, where the lesions they produce may exist side by side with those caused by chorioptic mites.

Sarcoptic mites may also start infestations at the root of the tail or the lower parts of the neck and brisket. Before many months a large portion of the body surfaces may be involved. Itching is more intense than in other forms of scabies or mange.

Shortly after the onset of the disease, hairless spots appear, dandruff is abundant, and the skin may become thickened, hard, and covered with crusts or scabs. The skin may crack and ooze blood and pus. It may bleed where the scabs become detached. The disease may spread rapidly—from one cow to practically every animal in a dairy barn in a winter.

DEMODECTIC, or follicular, mange of cattle is widespread in the United States, but few cattlemen are aware of its existence.

It is caused by the mite *Demodex folliculorum bovis*, a microscopic, cigar-shaped, sluggish organism that lives within the skin.

The lesions in the skin take the form of nodules, usually in the region of the neck, shoulders, and brisket, and sometimes on other parts of the body. The size of the nodules may vary from that of a match head to that of a hazelnut. The nodules appear to result from the formation of pus, which accompanies the mite. Frequently the nodules are pitted. Sometimes they break and discharge their cheesy-white contents over the surrounding hair.

The mite occasionally can be found in this material, but often one has to lance the nodule and extract the contents. It can be seen only with a microscope. Dairymen sometimes become aware of the swellings or nodules on the neck or brisket, which usually can be felt more easily than they can be seen. Little is known about the life history of this strange, wormlike mite.

THE SEASONAL OCCURRENCE of psoroptic and chorioptic scabies and sarcoptic mange follows a similar pattern.

The mites multiply the most rapidly, produce the most severe skin lesions, and cause the greatest annoy-

ance during the fall, winter, and spring. Owners have observed that the lesions appear to clear up and disappear spontaneously when an infested herd is turned out to pasture. Some mites, however, survive the summer, and infestations almost invariably become serious again when the weather gets cool.

Often there is much less change in the status of infestations on animals that remain housed or in close contact with each other during the summer. The presence of oils in the skin, the increased activity of skin glands, and the improved nutritional state of the animals when they are on pasture may be responsible for the diminished activity of the mites in summer.

Demodectic mange shows no response to the change of seasons. The nodules almost invariably discharge their contents or are reabsorbed on the body, regardless of time of year.

THE SPREAD OF SCABIES and mange mites from one animal to another nearly always takes place through direct contact. Infection in a herd usually starts when an animal with scabies lesions too small to be noticed is introduced into a clean herd. Mites spread most rapidly in a herd when the dairy barn, feed lot, or barnyard are crowded. A bull that has mites may infect many animals, even on the range.

Mites parasitic on cattle can live apart from their hosts for varying periods. The length of life varies according to species, humidity, and the temperature. When the weather is damp and cool, the scabies mites may survive up to 3 weeks, but direct sunlight and dryness may destroy them in 48 hours or less.

The eggs may persist on barn walls, stanchions, fence posts, railway cars, and cattle trucks, but it is not very likely that cattle will acquire infection in that way. It is possible, though, that infection may be spread by such objects as currycombs, brushes, and halters.

Sarcoptic mange is the most contagious of all forms of scabies and mange on cattle. The way in which demodectic mange is transmitted from animal to animal is not known.

THE DAMAGE done by parasitic mites to cattle depends on the extent of the disease. Scabies causes noticeable and sometimes intense itching in its early stage. Cattle may be so annoyed and spend so much time rubbing that they fail to eat properly or to gain weight.

When the affected areas of the body become extensive and the skin takes on a thickened, wrinkled appearance resembling elephant hide, there is loss of condition and weight. Emaciation and weakness may happen in severe, chronic cases.

Under range conditions or in any environment in which the injury is compounded by poor nutrition and exposure to cold, heavily infested animals may die from psoroptic scabies.

Rubbing and scratching by milking cows that have sarcoptic mange may cause mastitis or inflammation of the milk-producing glands. Severe itching may also cause the animals to rub so vigorously that abscesses develop on the shoulders and rump. A serious economic result of mange is the loss in milk production. Another evil is that the mites can transfer from dairy animals to people. In the Northeastern States that has been a matter of some concern, because children particularly suffer from mites they get from cows.

The injury caused by demodectic mange is of greatest concern to the leather industry. The nodules produced in the skin by demodectic mites appear in the tanning process as deep pits or holes in the hide. Because the disease may attack animals of all breeds and classes, the annual loss in terms of damaged leather is high.

The total annual loss to our cattle industry from the four species of mites was estimated in 1954 to total more than 4 million dollars. That figure does not include the sums spent to keep scabies under control.

THE HISTORY of efforts to control scabies in the United States by Federal and State agencies emphasizes the enormous effort required to keep scabies from becoming a catastrophe.

Scabies was widespread throughout the Western States by 1900. A bulletin describing the disease and methods for its control, issued by the United States Department of Agriculture in 1902, described psoroptic scabies as a serious disease, chorioptic scabies as a less important one, and sarcoptic mange as being almost unknown in cattle.

The Department of Agriculture, with the cooperation of stockmen and the State livestock sanitary officials, in 1904 inspected more than a million head of cattle in the West and supervised the dipping of nearly 160,000 diseased or exposed animals. A large force of veterinarians was placed in the field by the Department in 1905. Federal quarantines were imposed in areas in which the disease was prevalent, but cattle scabies increased rapidly in many States until about 1911.

Progress thereafter was slow but encouraging. The disease was reported in 1926 to be increasing in only three Western States. More than 3 million head were inspected that year, and half that many were dipped. The work continued until 1937, when it was finally reported that the psoroptic scabies was confined chiefly to Nebraska.

After 1938, with control in sight, the numbers of animals annually inspected and dipped gradually diminished. In 1942 with infection present only in Nebraska and Kansas, 1.5 million head were inspected in the entire West, 85 thousand were dipped, and known infected herds contained only 12,000 animals.

The inspection of 1.5 million head in 1948 revealed only 550 cases of scabies. Many were chorioptic infections that had been introduced into the Western States from the East.

More than 300,000 inspections in the West in 1950 disclosed fewer than 1,000 infected animals with not a single case of psoroptic scabies among them.

Only 320 infected animals were found in 1953. In that year, however, cattle with chorioptic scabies and sarcoptic mange were reported in 11 Midwestern and Eastern States and undoubtedly were present in many more.

An outbreak of psoroptic scabies of unknown origin involved 6 Western States in 1954. It was quickly arrested by prompt Federal and local action. The existence of scabies and mange infestations in midwestern and eastern herds of purebred beef animals and dairy cows indicates the need for constant vigilance against the return of the parasites into the range herds of the West.

THE CONTROL of scabies and mange of cattle requires the external application of chemicals capable of destroying the parasites without harming the animals. For many years lime-sulfur and nicotine sulfate were used.

Many infected animals have been treated since 1948 with benzene hexachloride (BHC) and lindane, which are better than the old chemicals. They are deadlier to mites than lime-sulfur and less likely to injure cattle than nicotine sulfate.

Another chemical, toxaphene, seems to be about as effective as BHC and lindane for chorioptic scabies. It is inexpensive and relatively harmless to cattle if properly used.

DIPPING is the preferred method in treating cattle for scabies. The animals are put into a tank or vat of medicated liquid. The animals are thoroughly wetted all over. Dipping plants are usually so arranged that the cattle enter a narrow vat, one at a time, swim through it, and emerge into a draining pen at the opposite end. Lime-sulfur and nicotine sulfate are effective only when applied in dip form.

Prepared concentrates of these chemicals may be purchased and should be used in amounts recommended on the containers. One difficulty associated with their use is the need to maintain a dipping solution temperature of approximately 100° F. In the case of nicotine sulfate, temperatures higher than 105° may injure cattle.

Two dippings 10 to 12 days apart will cure most cases of psoroptic and chorioptic scabies. Four dippings about 6 to 10 days apart may be needed for sarcoptic mange.

BHC and lindane applied in dip form have given good results. They may be used in cold water. The solutions are easily prepared. The animals need not spend so much time in the vats as when the older insecticides are used.

BHC or lindane should be used at a concentration of 0.075 percent of the active ingredient. A single dipping generally is enough, but for unusually severe, chronic cases, marked by heavy scab formation, two dippings applied 10 to 12 days apart are recommended.

BHC is usually obtainable in the form of wettable powders containing 6, 10, or 12 percent of the active ingredient, which is known as gamma isomer. Lindane wettable powders usually contain 25 percent of gamma isomer.

THIS TABLE SHOWS the amounts of wettable powder needed to prepare 100 gallons of dip:

Gamma isomer in product	Pounds per 100 gallons of water
6 percent	10
10 percent	6
12 percent	5
25 percent	2. 5

Cattle must spend at least 2 minutes in the dipping solution if lime-sulfur or nicotine sulfate is used. When BHC or lindane is used, 30 seconds to 1 minute are enough.

All the insecticides must be used with care in the dipping vat. Newborn calves and weak or emaciated animals of any age should not be dipped.

BHC and lindane are particularly dangerous to calves of the dairy breeds. Dairy calves less than 2 weeks old should not be dipped.

All cattle should be well rested before dipping.

SPRAYING CATTLE to control parasitic mites is done in many places because dipping vats are scarce. Spraying is less effective than dipping, because it is harder to wet thoroughly the haircoat and the skin on all parts of the body. Scabies and mange can be cured, however, if generous amounts of liquid are used and if the work is done carefully.

BHC and lindane at a concentration of 0.075 percent gamma isomer, as recommended for use in dipping vats, are the insecticides of choice for this purpose.

Two sprayings with either BHC or lindane, 10 to 12 days apart, are recommended. High-pressure, power-operated equipment is usually necessary. A pressure of 200 to 400 pounds per square inch should be maintained. Newborn and sick or weak calves and calves of the dairy breeds less than 2 weeks of age should not be treated.

The amount of spray used depends on the size of the animals, the length of the haircoats, the dimensions of the quarters in which the animals are confined for treatment, and the type of equipment. Large, heavily haired beef cattle require 4 to 5 gallons or more each. All parts of the haircoat and skin must be wet. Particular attention should be paid to the hindquarters, the undersides of the body, and the inner surfaces of the legs. Total saturation provides greatest assurance of successful treatment.

Several health hazards must be considered when BHC and lindane are used. Small amounts of both are absorbed through the skin and are deposited in the tissues of treated animals. They are partly eliminated from the body through the milk.

Sprays containing 0.075 percent of lindane may be applied to producing dairy cows, but their milk is regarded as unfit for use by people for 3 to 4 days after treatment. The milk may be fed safely to calves, swine, and nonlaying poultry. Moreover, if such milk, as part of the product of a milkshed, is mixed with large quantities of milk from untreated herds before it reaches the consumers, any health hazard is probably eliminated.

When treating producing milk cows, strict adherence to the manufacturer's recommendations for the use of an insecticide must be followed; the addition of too much of the insecticide concentrate to the spray mixture may allow the chemical to show up in harmful amounts in the milk.

Beef cattle that are intended for food for people should not be treated with BHC or lindane within 30 days of the date of slaughter.

Leftover dips of BHC and lindane should be disposed of carefully. Pools from which livestock may drink should not be allowed to collect. The insecticides should not be allowed to contaminate feed or the grass on which livestock may graze. BHC and lindane are poisonous to fish and should not be emptied into streams or ponds.

DEMODECTIC MANGE of cattle does not respond to any known treatment. If the nodules are small, they will cause no perceptible injury and may be ignored.

BHC or lindane washes containing 0.075 percent of the gamma isomer can be applied to open nodules to kill the mites that may live in the pus discharged onto the skin.

Open demodex nodules infrequently become abscessed as a result of bacterial infection. If the discharge persists, such abscesses, which occasionally are as large as a pigeon's egg, may be treated with local antiseptics. Accumulated pus can be expressed by means of light pressure and flushed away with warm, soapy water. The abscess should then be swabbed, as deeply as gentle probing will allow, with tincture of iodine applied by means of a small piece of sterile absorbent cotton tightly wrapped around the end of a toothpick.

IRWIN H. ROBERTS *is a parasitologist*

in the Department of Agriculture. He was graduated from Alfred University in *1933* and received the degree of doctor of veterinary medicine from Cornell University in *1937*.

N. G. COBBETT, *a veterinarian in the Department of Agriculture, is stationed at Albuquerque, N. Mex. Upon graduation from Colorado Agricultural and Mechanical College in 1921, he joined the Bureau of Animal Industry.*

For further reading:

D. W. Baker: *Cattle Mange and the Other Diseases Known Commonly as Barn Itch,* 36 pages, Ithaca, N. Y., Cornell University, 1946.

E. W. Baker and G. W. Wharton: *An Introduction to Acarology,* 465 pages, New York, Macmillan Company. 1952.

Joseph H. Camin and Wm. M. Rogoff: *Mites Affecting Domesticated Mammals.* South Dakota Agricultural Experiment Station Technical Bulletin 10, 11 pages. 1952.

Richard W. Hickman: *Description and Treatment of Scabies in Cattle,* U. S. Department of Agriculture, Bureau of Animal Industry Bulletin 40, 23 pages. 1902.

F. Hutyra, J. Marek, and R. Manninger: Special Pathology and Therapeutics of the Diseases of Domestic Animals, volume 3, pages 610–661, Chicago, Illinois, Alex Eger. 1946.

H. E. Kemper and H. O. Peterson: *Treatment of Cattle Scabies with Lindane,* Veterinary Medicine, volume 47, number 11, pages 453–455. 1952.

H. E. Kemper and H. O. Peterson: *Cattle Scab and Methods of Control and Eradication,* U. S. Department of Agriculture Farmers' Bulletin 1017, 26 pages. 1953.

Frank Kral and Benjamin J. Novak: *Veterinary Dermatology,* 325 pages, Philadelphia, Pa., J. B. Lippincott Company. 1953.

Rudolph Snyder: *Cattle Scab and Its Control.* U. S. D. A. Yearbook of Agriculture 1942, *Keeping Livestock Healthy,* pages 588–592.

B. I. Sparr, J. C. Clark, E. E. Vallier, and A. H. Baumhover: *Studies on the Stability of Toxaphene Emulsions in Dipping Vats,* U. S. Bureau of Entomology and Plant Quarantine publication E–849, 11 pages. 1952.

Verminous Dermatitis

JOHN T. LUCKER

THE ONLY truly parasitic worm known to cause a specific dermatitis, or skin disease, of cattle in the United States is a small filarial roundworm, *Stephanofilaria stilesi.*

The adult worms live and move about in the outermost, or epithelial, layer of the skin. Their progeny, known as larvae or microfilariae, are found mostly in the upper part of the underlying dermal skin layer.

The life cycle of the parasite has not been worked out, but an insect intermediate host probably is required for its completion. Transmission by one or more of the many kinds of sucking insects that attack cattle is strongly suggested by the life cycles determined for related filarial roundworms. Such dipteran insects as flies, "midges," and mosquitoes head the list of suspects.

The causative parasite has been found only in lesions in the skin of cattle. Presumably the intermediate host inoculates the skin with the infective larvae of the parasite. The irritation produced as they develop into adults apparently starts the lesions. An alternative possibility is that the transmitter is attracted to already existing sores or breaks in the skin and inoculates infective larvae into them. At any rate, the presence of the adults and their microfilariae causes tissue destruction.

Stephanofilariasis, also known as stephanofilarial dermatitis and stephanofilarial dermatosis, the skin disease caused by this parasite, was first recognized in western cattle in 1934.

It has been found in 11 of the Eastern, Southern, and Midwestern

States—New York, Maryland, Virginia, Tennessee, Alabama, Louisiana, Mississippi, Florida, Ohio, Michigan, and Wisconsin—and 16 Western States—Kansas, Nebraska, South Dakota, Colorado, Utah, Texas, New Mexico, Oklahoma, Arizona, Wyoming, Nevada, Idaho, Montana, Washington, Oregon, and California.

It seems to be more common in beef cattle than in dairy cattle. When it becomes established in a herd, up to 90 percent of the animals may be affected. Stephanofilariasis has been observed mainly in mature cattle but younger cattle sometimes are affected. Lesions suspected to be of stephanofilarial origin have been found on calves about 6 months old.

THE LESIONS vary in size and appearance. The smallest ones are about one-fourth to one-half inch in diameter. They appear marked with spots of dried blood and serum and are not hairless. The slightly larger lesions, about an inch or so in diameter, are hairless. Some are moist and exude fresh serum and blood. Scabs or crusts formed by these exudates cover others. Some apparently heal without spreading after scabs are formed. A patch of smooth, thickened, hairless skin denotes that healing has occurred. Actively spreading lesions, about 2 to 3 inches in diameter, have numerous small bloodspots on their margins and wrinkled, thickened, hairless centers. Some of the larger, and apparently older, lesions appear grayish and are covered by a heavy, dry crust, with cracks and crevices. A deep-red crust with bloody, moist cracks covers others.

ECONOMICALLY the most obvious loss from this disease is by lessening the value of hides for leather. The lesions are located mainly along the median line of the abdomen where the main cut is made in skinning the hide from slaughtered cattle. They are most often near the navel, but may be anywhere from the brisket to the pubic region. Often there is only one lesion a few inches in diameter, or a row of smaller ones. The diseased areas can be trimmed off with little labor and small loss per hide in these cases. Occasionally, however, there may be isolated lesions on the flanks, or a median strip a foot wide and up to 4 feet long may be diseased. When an untrimmed affected hide is manufactured into leather, the diseased areas produce noticeable disfiguration of the grain and the leather is inferior in strength and quality.

General health apparently is not noticeably affected by this disease. The sores probably cause discomfort. They attract flies, which annoy the animal. It has been stated that involvement of the teats may predispose to mastitis. Owners of show cattle become concerned over any blemish that may affect ability to win prizes, and show animals with disfiguring stephanofilarial lesions have been given useless and expensive courses of treatment on the mistaken assumption that mange or ringworm was the cause of the trouble. To avoid such useless expenditures, a positive diagnosis should be obtained wherever possible.

A PRESUMPTIVE DIAGNOSIS of stephanofilarial dermatitis often can be made from the location of the lesions because other skin diseases are not confined to or centered about the ventral midline. The gross appearance of the lesions is also somewhat diagnostic.

Positive diagnosis, however, requires recovery and identification of the larval or adult worms from the skin. Skin scrapings should be taken from active lesions that are moist or covered with recently formed scabs or crusts. Scabs and crusts must be lifted off before scraping. The scraping must be deep enough to draw blood. Classification of the lesion as stephanofilarial is fully justified only if microscopic examination of the scrapings reveals larvae or pieces of the adult worms. A special method must be used to recover the adults intact. Rather often neither worms nor larvae are found in seemingly typical small, bloody lesions and larger, older, dried ones. Only a tentative diagnosis is possible in such cases, unless other infested lesions are found on the same animal. Even if sections of worm-free lesions show microscopic tissue and cellular changes like the ones observed when this parasite is present, the diagnosis remains inconclusive because similar changes may be caused by other classes of parasitic organisms.

NO SPECIFIC DRUG treatment for this condition is known. Tartar emetic and antrypol (suramin) have been successfully used in India for the treatment of a related disease (hump sore, caused by *Stephanofilaria assamensis*).

NORMALLY FREE-LIVING, or saprophytic roundworms of the genus *Rhabditis*, occasionally infest bovine skin lesions, according to reports from California and other States. These worms are omnipresent in soil and moist, decaying, organic materials, including feces. They get on the skin of cattle by contact with such materials. They evidently become established only in already diseased skin areas. They apparently can cause extension of the sores and have been found associated with extensive dermatitis.

JOHN T. LUCKER *is a parasitologist in the Animal Disease and Parasite Research Branch and leads a unit which investigates the helminthic parasites and diseases of cattle. He is a graduate of the University of Washington and the George Washington University. He has worked in the Department of Agriculture since 1930, and has carried out investigations on roundworm parasites of swine, horses, sheep, cattle, and other hosts.*

Cattle Grubs

IRWIN H. ROBERTS AND ARTHUR W. LINDQUIST

NEARLY all cattlemen know the conspicuous swellings that appear in the backs of cattle in winter. The swellings contain grubs, which are the maggot stage of heelflies.

Of all the insect pests that prey on livestock, heelflies are among the hardest to control. They and the cattle grubs (which are known also as warbles and wolves) may be to blame for losses to producers, feeders, dairymen, packers, and tanners. The losses may nearly equal those caused by all other insect pests of cattle combined.

Two species of heelflies, or warble-flies, parasitize cattle in North America. The common heelfly, *Hypoderma lineatum*, and its larva, the common grub, exist in all parts of the United States and Canada. The northern species, *Hypoderma bovis*, is found in Canada and the northern half of the United States.

Heelflies are true flies of the order *Diptera*. They are closely related to other flies commonly encountered on farms, but look like small bumblebees—hairy, black, and striped with yellow. The common heelfly is nearly three times larger than the housefly.

The northern heelfly is much larger and stouter.

From the eggs that the flies lay on cattle emerge tiny, white larvae. The flies, their eggs, and the young maggots are seldom seen by casual observers. The young maggots penetrate the skin of the host animals, move through the body tissues, and eventually emerge—as the familiar cattle grub—in the backs. Mature grubs are black and may be an inch long. Heelflies develop from grubs that have dropped to the ground from the backs of cattle.

Common heelflies appear during the first warm days of spring. They have no mouth parts and do not bite or sting. They live only a few days, rarely as much as 2 weeks, but in that time they can deposit hundreds of eggs. The heelflies are active about 2 months. They lay their eggs in neat rows on hairs, usually low on the legs on and above the fetlock—hence the name "heelfly." If the animal is lying down, the eggs may be laid on the hairs closest to the ground.

The eggs hatch in 3 or 4 days. The minute, spiny maggots crawl down the hair and begin to burrow through the skin. Then they begin an amazing journey through the tissues of the body. They appear to limit their travels to the soft connective tissues between the muscles. Most of the larvae of the common heelfly congregate in the tissues of the gullet after about 5 months.

The larvae spend 3 months or so in the gullet. After that they begin their final migration, again through the connective tissues, to the region beneath the skin of the back. Almost immediately they make breathing holes in the skin.

In a very few days a pocket, or cyst, developed from the tissues of the host, surrounds each larva, and in this the grub remains for about 6 weeks. At all times during its stay in this swelling, the breathing hole is kept open. The tail end of the grub, with its two prominent breathing pores, lies just under this opening.

The grub molts twice in the cyst. When it is mature, it works out of the now enlarged hole in the skin. Once free of the animal, the grub seeks the protection of soil or trash. Its outer cuticle becomes hard and black. Within that protective or pupal case, in a month or so, the change from grub to fly takes place.

The fly emerges from its pupal case through a hinged cap at the upper forward end. It may crawl from the puparium in less than a minute, dry its wings, and be in the air within half an hour. Shortly thereafter, the flies mate, and if the weather is favorable, egglaying may begin on the same day the adults emerge.

NORTHERN HEELFLIES appear later in the season, after the egg-laying activities of the common species are well underway. The activities of the two flies overlap for a short time, and then, after the common fly has disappeared, the northern fly continues to plague cattle well into the summer months. The northern heelfly deposits its eggs at about the height of the hock, striking the animal a number of times in rapid succession and cementing an egg on a hair each time. Its eggs are deposited singly, but it can lay several hundred in its lifetime.

The young larvae penetrate the skin and travel through the soft tissues of the body (as do those of the common heelfly), but they congregate in the spinal canal instead of in the gullet on their way to the skin of the back. When fully developed, the grubs of the northern fly are larger than those of the common heelfly, but their appearance otherwise is much the same. By the time northern grubs reach the backs of cattle, the common grubs normally have been present for about 2 months, and most of them are ready to emerge from their cysts. The northern grubs are most abundant in the backs of cattle after the larvae of the common fly have practically disappeared. It is not unusual in Northern States to find a few of these grubs emerging from the backs of cattle as late as July.

IN ORDER TO CONTROL cattle grubs effectively, it is particularly important to know when they are likely to be found in the backs of cattle, so that they may be attacked when they are most vulnerable.

Common grubs are said to appear as early as the first week in September in southern Texas. They appear progressively later as one goes northward. Common grubs may not appear until February or March in Montana, and the northern grub generally appears a month later.

Along the Gulf of Mexico and in southern Arizona and California, all grubs are likely to have matured and dropped from their cysts by the first days of March, at a time when the arrival of the grubs in North Dakota, Minnesota, and northern New York has scarcely begun.

In each section of the country, the appearance of grubs can be anticipated annually with some accuracy, but an allowance must be made for seasonal variations of approximately a month. In an average locality, grubs may show up in January one year, December the next, and in February the third year. Greater year-to-year variations than those have been known to occur, but are uncommon.

HEELFLIES AND CATTLE GRUBS injure cattle in various ways.

One is the annoyance to cattle when the flies are laying eggs. The northern fly excites stock most. Heelflies cause no pain while depositing their eggs, but the reaction of cattle to them may be one of great fear. Animals attempting to escape them run with their tails held high in a characteristic manner. Occasionally they injure themselves in their wild flight from the flies. More often, however, they seek protection from the flies in shade or in water, and fail to graze for hours at a time. The fact that heelflies attack range cattle in early spring, when cows are poor and weak, with calves at their sides, intensifies the losses. Milk production of dairy cattle may drop 10 to 25 percent when heelflies are active.

The grubs migrating through the body tissues and the larvae boring into the backs of cattle cause injuries that one can appreciate but cannot assess easily. Losses after slaughter, however,

are obvious. When hides are removed from grub-infested cattle, a mass of yellowish, gelatinous meat may be seen around the grub holes. It must be trimmed out as inedible. Fourteen million pounds of choice meat were wasted because of such trimming in 1948. Carcasses so trimmed are lowered a full grade, or loins may be so badly damaged that they must be boned.

The damage grubs do to hides is the easiest of all cattle losses to evaluate. A third of all cattle hides produced in the United States in 1948 contained five or more grub holes and were sold at a discount of a cent a pound. Many grub holes impair the quality of the skin for leather. Occasionally 100 to 200 grub holes are found in a hide. Such hides are not worth tanning and are sold for use as byproducts.

Losses due to cattle grubs and heelflies in the United States have been set at 100 million to 300 million dollars a year.

AN ACCEPTABLE METHOD of controlling heelflies and cattle grubs has been the object of a diligent search by many investigators since 1890. Attempts to destroy or repel the adult flies have not been successful. Efforts to destroy the eggs after they have been deposited on the hair coats of cattle or to keep the larvae from penetrating also have resulted in failure.

Research was begun in 1947 to find a drug which, given internally, would destroy the grubs after they reached the backs of cattle and would kill all the young larvae as they wandered through the tissues of the body. By 1955, several insecticides showed promise against grubs when injected into cattle or when administered in the feed or mineral-salt supplements. Among the most successful were lindane, aldrin, dieldrin, as well as some of the organic phosphorus compounds. Work on the internal administration of those and related insecticides had not advanced beyond the experimental stage in 1956. Additional research is underway to determine their effectiveness and the hazards involved in their use.

A satisfactory method of attack is to destroy the grub after it has formed an opening in the skin of the backs of cattle. Killing the larvae at that stage interrupts the life cycle before a fly can be produced. Cattle thereby are spared the annoyance of attack by the heelfly and the hundreds of larvae that could hatch from the eggs produced by each female fly.

The larvae within the cysts of the skin can be killed in several ways. An early and simple method was the removal of the grub by pressing firmly with the fingers. That is a slow and laborious method, but many dairymen have used it.

Research workers the world over have experimented with hundreds of materials in the search for insecticides for the mass destruction of grubs, but few have proved effective.

The chlorinated hydrocarbon insecticides, among them DDT, lindane, chlordane, methoxychlor, and toxaphene, which are used against other insect pests, have little effect against cattle grubs when applied externally over the cyst openings.

A few of the organic phosphorus compounds, a group of insecticides developed during the Second World War, are highly lethal to grubs when applied in that way. They have been used experimentally but are not recommended for general use because they possibly may have toxic effects on the animals.

Benzol and carbon tetrachloride, injected into grub cyst openings with an oil can, will destroy grubs, but this method is not a great improvement over manual removal.

Rotenone remains the only effective toxicant that can be safely recommended for use by cattle owners. Rotenone occurs in tropical shrubs, especially *Derris eliptica* and *Lonchocarpus nicou*. The finely ground roots of the plants are known as derris and cube powders. The powders, adjusted to contain about 5 percent of rotenone, can be applied to the backs of cattle in ointments, dusts, washes, dips, and sprays.

A rotenone ointment can be prepared by mixing 1 part of cube or derris powder with 10 parts of petroleum. The preparation is applied with the fingers directly over each grub opening. It is highly effective, but, like manual removal or the use of an oil can, it is designed only for dairy cattle or individual animals. Stockmen in the United States rarely use ointments.

Rotenone dusts are more practical for treating larger numbers of cattle. Such dusts can be formulated by mixing 1 part of cube or derris powder with 2 parts of dry vehicle or carrier, preferably a powdered mineral known as pyrophyllite. The dust is placed in a large shaker can, applied liberally to the backs of the cattle, and rubbed into cyst openings with the fingers. Dusts are readily available for use. They are clean, quickly applied, and preferred by some stockmen who hesitate to chill their cattle with liquids in very cold weather.

Some farmers use washes to kill the grubs. Washes are made by mixing 12 ounces of cube or derris powder, one-half ounce of soapless detergent or 2 to 4 ounces of powdered soap, and 1 gallon of warm water. A pint or more of the thin, warm paste is poured on the back of each animal and brushed over the cyst openings with a stiff brush. A crew of 3 or 4 men can apply washes to several hundred head of cattle in a day. Groups of a thousand cattle or more have been treated periodically in South Dakota in this way by several stockmen working together. The washes, carefully applied, destroy a greater proportion of the larvae present at the time of treatment than any other large-scale method of grub control.

Dips may be used to treat large numbers of cattle quickly. Dipping vats are charged with from 7.5 to 10 pounds of cube or derris powder to each 100 gallons of water. Cattle are held in the vats for about 1 minute, with the backs submerged. Their backs also may be brushed with long scrub brushes at this time. This procedure has been used chiefly in the Southwest, but it is expensive and has never been accepted generally.

Spraying is an easy, fast, and economical way to apply rotenone to the backs of cattle. Cattle can be treated with power-driven, high-pressure orchard spraying equipment almost as fast as they can be driven through chutes or pens. Cube or derris powder should be used in the proportion of 7.5 pounds for each 100 gallons of water in the sprayer tank. The tank should be equipped with a mechanical agitator, or else frequent stirring will be needed to prevent settling of the powder to the bottom.

The spray should be applied to the cattle at a gauge pressure of about 400 pounds to the square inch. A coarse, driving spray is directed upon the back of the animal. The nozzle of the gun should be held not more than 24 inches from the back. Catwalks, on which the operator can stand, should be placed high along the side of the chute or directly above the pen in which the cattle are restrained. From this elevated position, the operator can apply sprays with great efficiency at right angles to the backs of the animals.

To obtain maximum results from any control program, it is best that no larvae escape contact with the insecticide. Grubs spend 35 days or so in their cysts within the skin of the back and continue to appear for several months. A succession of treatments, about 30 days apart, therefore is necessary. The first treatment in any locality should be applied about 30 days after the first grubs make their holes in the skin. Thereafter applications of rotenone should be made until no more grubs arrive in the back.

As many as four treatments may be required in localities where the two species of grubs exist.

Less involved schedules of treatment have been used in South Dakota and Montana. There it has been demonstrated that two accurately timed ap-

plications will destroy most of the grubs of both species and provide a satisfactory degree of control from year to year. The first treatment is applied just before the first of the common grubs commence to emerge from their cysts, when the great bulk of all common grubs are present in the backs of cattle at one time. That date usually follows the start of the grub season by about 60 days. The second treatment is administered when the northern grubs have reached their peak of abundance in the backs, at a time when the earliest of those common grubs which may have survived the first treatment begin to emerge. This second treatment should follow the first application by 40 to 60 days. Individual cattle owners must determine these dates by careful and frequent examination of their cattle.

Near Colorado Springs, Colo., where only the common grub was found to exist, a single application of washes, properly timed before the emergence of the first grubs, destroyed 90 to 100 percent of the grubs appearing in the treated cattle during the grub season.

THE HEELFLY does not travel far— probably 3 miles or less from the point where it emerged from its pupal case. Nevertheless, because it can cross fences and travel to nearby herds, attempts to control grubs in an individual herd are relatively futile. Community action is essential if grub control is to be practiced on a sound basis.

The effectiveness of community efforts to control grubs has been demonstrated repeatedly in the United States, Canada, and Europe.

Two noteworthy community programs were completed successfully in South Dakota in 1953 under the direction of the Department of Agriculture and the South Dakota Agricultural Experiment Station. In one of them, involving 20 thousand head of cattle in an area of 430 square miles in Hughes and Hyde Counties, systematic efforts at grub destruction reduced the grub population by 93 percent in 5

years. At the end of the program, only
2 grubs an animal were found in herds
at the center of the area, compared to
an average of more than 30 in untreated animals in herds outside of the
experimental area. The 175 cattlemen
who participated used dusts, washes,
and sprays. Each selected the method
that suited his needs.

In the other campaign, in Meade
and Pennington Counties, 10,000 head
in 85 herds were treated in an area of
about 375 square miles with equal
success. An average of fewer than 2
grubs remained in animals in centrally
located herds, compared to 30 in untreated animals in herds outside the
area where grub control was practiced.
High-pressure sprayers were used in
this program.

Successful community battles against
grubs also have been waged in Kittitas
County, Wash., and in Chaves County,
N. Mex.

Wherever grub populations are consistently high and so are an economic
problem, such a program will pay for
itself. Community control is most successful in regions where cattle are produced, rather than shipped in and fed,
and where both cattle and grub populations are more or less constant from
year to year.

A farm adviser or the county agent
can give information about the importance of grubs in a county. Should
a schedule of treatment be undertaken,
the Extension Service representatives
can offer technical assistance.

First one has to fix the boundaries of
the area in which control measures are
to be undertaken. The area should be
reasonably large and should be as
nearly square or circular as possible.

Community action in a small area
would be no more successful than grub
control in an individual herd. Even the
limited flight of the heelfly is enough
to permit flies from pastures on which
untreated cattle are grazed to reinfest
practically all cattle in an area of about
10 square miles. In a much larger area,
however, flies from surrounding pastures cannot make their way to cen-

trally located herds, and would normally reinfest only the cattle on farms
at the edge of the territory. Not less
than a township should be involved.
An area of that size, in northern Illinois, say, might involve 100 dairymen
and 4,000 head of cattle. From an administrative standpoint, it is a sizable
undertaking. Elsewhere in the country, as in the North Central States, a
program involving 8 or 10 townships,
100 farms and ranches, and perhaps
12,000 cattle, would not require much
more effort. In the Southwest, as in
New Mexico, grub populations in huge
areas might be reduced materially
through the cooperation of as few as
5 to 10 ranchers.

Wherever located, the area should
be blocked out into a roughly square
or circular shape, with as short a
boundary line as possible.

Wherever the district in which grub
control is to be undertaken is located,
it is necessary to consider the existence
of natural barriers against invasion by
heelflies. The perfect place for a control project is an island. Heelflies apparently do not cross large bodies of
water, and grub-free cattle on an island
a mile or more from the mainland are
not likely to be reinfested. In approxi-
mating such ideal conditions, it may
be advisable to extend the territory up
to the banks of a large lake or wide
river. Mountains and woodland are
similarly effective, and even croplands
on which there are no cattle provide a
barrier against heelflies. Every effort
should be made to separate the district
from nearby concentrations of untreated, grub-infested cattle and to
make it difficult for heelflies to reenter.

The administrative aspects of a program can be worked out with the assistance of Extension Service advisers
or instructors of vocational agriculture.
Thereafter the participants will find it
useful to select an executive or committee to be in charge. A county association of cattlemen or dairymen, or a
similar group, may have to assume
those duties if the undertaking is large.

All owners of cattle within the community should take part in the program, because any untreated cattle in the area will constitute a source of infestation for treated animals and will make control that much harder. Actually, if more than 80 percent of the cattle within the community can be treated systematically, the program will be worthwhile. Routemen should be appointed early to get in touch with all participants to outline the details of operation, and to discuss with the cattle owners the economic advantages to be gained and the methods of treatment.

Details that must be attended to are the purchase of enough cube or derris powder for treating all animals and arrangements for applying the insecticide. If hand treatment is to be employed, the distribution of the insecticide, properly mixed, weighed and sacked, will help expedite matters.

Spraying equipment will generally be required for large herds. Some associations of cattlemen have found it desirable to buy their own orchard sprayers. Other groups may obtain such equipment from the Extension Service office or may find it economical to contract with commercial pest control operators for the work. In still other instances, the cooperating members may own enough suitable equipment to provide facilities for all cattle owners in the community.

Usually systematic grub-control practices have to be continued for 3 years before appreciable results, in terms of reduced grub infestations and heelfly activity, will be obtained.

Often the establishment of a workable program requires able and persevering leadership during the first year, but once support and experience have been gained, a control schedule can be maintained for years with little effort. When grub populations have finally been reduced materially in a large area, only 1 or 2 applications of insecticide may be required each winter to keep the pests at a low level.

When all aspects of cattle grub control are considered, the problem may appear to be a formidable one, but is by no means insurmountable. Stockmen have demonstrated their ability to conduct successful control programs, despite the deep snows and the subzero temperatures encountered in Washington in midwinter, or the difficulties imposed by the repeated handling of cattle on the huge ranches of New Mexico. In any locality in which a majority of cattle owners are willing to expend the time and energy required, cattle grub infestations can be virtually eliminated, as in parts of South Dakota. It is a matter of record that community action against this pest is effective, practical, and rewarding.

IRWIN H. ROBERTS *is a veterinarian and parasitologist in the Animal Disease and Parasite Research Branch of the Department of Agriculture and has been stationed in Springfield, Ill., since 1953.*

ARTHUR W. LINDQUIST, *a graduate of Bethany College and Kansas State College, since 1931 has conducted and directed research on the biology and control of hornflies, tabanids, screwworms, blowflies, cattle grubs, mosquitoes, and other pests affecting man and livestock.*

For further reading on cattle lice:
Robert A. Hoffman: *The Effectiveness and Limitations of Homemade Self-treatment Rubbing Devices for Louse Control on Cattle.* Journal of Economic Entomology, volume 47, number 6, pages 1152–1153. 1954.
E. F. Knipling: *Ticks, Lice, Sheep Keds, Mites,* U. S. D. A. Yearbook of Agriculture 1952, *Insects,* pages 662–666. 1952.
J. L. Lancaster: *One Application for Lice Control,* Journal of Economic Entomology, volume 44, number 5, pages 718–724. 1951.
John G. Matthysse: *Cattle Lice, Their Biology and Control,* Cornell University Agricultural Experiment Station Bulletin 832, 67 pages. 1946.
H. O. Peterson, I. H. Roberts, W. W. Becklund, and H. E. Kemper: *Anemia in Cattle Caused by Heavy Infestations of the Blood-sucking Louse, Haematopinus eurysternus,* Journal of the American Veterinary Medical Association, volume 122, number 914, pages 373–376.
Charles L. Smith and Rowland Richards: *Evaluations of Some New Insecticides Against Lice on Livestock and Poultry,* Journal of Economic Entomology, volume 4, number 5, pages 566–568. 1955.

Cattle Lice

C. L. SMITH AND IRWIN H. ROBERTS

FOUR species of bloodsucking lice and one species of biting lice are pests of cattle in the United States.

The damage lice do to cattle varies in proportion to the degree of infestation. Infestations of lice on cattle generally appear in the fall and increase, slowly at first and later more rapidly, in winter and spring. Louse populations gradually decline as the weather becomes warmer, but seldom do they disappear from a herd until an effective insecticide is applied.

Lousy cattle rub and scratch themselves and lose patches of hair by the rubbing. The loss of hair generally is linked with the presence of the biting, or red, louse.

Animals heavily infested with the bloodsucking species, especially the short-nosed louse, *Haematopinus eurysternus,* often look as if they had been rubbed with used crankcase oil.

The bloodsucking lice that attack cattle are *Linognathus vituli, Solenopotes capillatus, Haematopinus eurysternus,* and *Haematopinus quadripertusus.* The biting louse is *Bovicola bovis.*

The bloodsucking louse *H. quadripertusus,* commonly called the tail louse, was discovered in Florida a few years ago. By 1956 it was found only in the Southern States in areas along the coast. All the other species of lice occur in all parts of the United States.

Infested animals usually are in poor physical condition. Calves, yearlings, and old, undernourished cattle suffer most. Large numbers of lice may retard the growth rate of calves, prevent proper weight gains in cattle on feed, and reduce milk production of dairy cattle. Deaths due to lice are rare, but old cattle of low vitality, particularly skinny range cows that are exposed to bad weather, may die from the effects of lice. Extensive infestations of the short-nosed louse can cause pronounced anemia, even in well-fed adults.

CATTLE LICE do not live long off the host. They are seldom seen except on animals. The habits and life history of the various species of cattle lice are similar. The adult females glue the eggs to the hairs of the host. The hatching time of the eggs varies with the species, their place on the animal, and temperature to which they are exposed. The nymphs of lice differ from the adults mostly in size and color.

G. H. Lamson, Jr., observed at Connecticut Agricultural Experiment Station, that the eggs of *B. bovis* hatched in about 7 days and that the nymphs reached sexual maturity in 15 to 18 days. The hatching time for the eggs of *Linognathus vituli,* a bloodsucking louse, was 8 to 14 days, and its nymphs matured in 11 to 18 days. Normally the eggs of *H. eurysternus* hatch in 12 to 18 days, and the nymphs reach maturity in 13 to 23 days. In Texas some of the eggs hatched in 33 days.

BECAUSE CATTLE LICE live nearly all of their lives on the host, they are more easily controlled than some other insect pests are. The residual insecticides used in summer against hornflies may reduce the louse potential so much that a heavy buildup in winter is impossible. Thorough treatment of animals when the last treatment is applied for hornflies in the fall delays the development of lice in the herd and often makes unnecessary a later treatment for lice.

Some older insecticides, such as rotenone, nicotine, pyrethrins, sodium fluoride, the arsenical dips, and coal-tar creosote preparations, have been used for controlling lice on cattle and for certain other pests. They have some disadvantages: They are effective for the initial kill of lice, but they have little residual value and two or more treatments usually are needed to control lice. Nicotine, sodium fluoride, coal tar, and the arsenicals are highly poisonous and have to be applied to cattle with utmost care.

We now have better materials—the chlorinated hydrocarbons, commonly called residual insecticides, such as DDT, toxaphene, chlordane, methoxychlor, and BHC. They have replaced most of the older insecticides for lice on cattle. The problem thus has become one of thorough treatment of each animal rather than a problem of choosing one of only a few not entirely satisfactory insecticides.

Nearly all the chlorinated hydrocarbon insecticides that are satisfactory against lice are commercially available as wettable powders and emulsion concentrates. Among them are: DDT, methoxychlor, chlordane, toxaphene, TDE, and BHC. A few of the insecticides also can be bought as dusts. Some are available in oil to be used in rubbing or the self-treatment devices.

The wettable powders and emulsion concentrates usually are prepared to be used as dips or sprays. Regardless of the formulation selected, the insecticide should be used according to recommendations issued by State agricultural experiment stations and the Department of Agriculture and at no greater concentration than is recommended for satisfactory control. There is little difference in the insecticidal performance of the wettable powders and emulsion concentrates.

The insecticides may be applied in the form of dips, sprays, dusts, and oil solutions. The method of application depends on what equipment is available and the location and number of animals to be treated. The amount of spray, dip, or dust required to treat an animal varies with the equipment, the breed of cattle, and the density and length of the animal's hair. The amount of spray required to wet an animal thoroughly may be as little as

2 quarts in the Southeast or as much as 2 to 6 gallons in the Southwest and Northern States. The important point is that the animal must be wetted thoroughly.

Dipping vats used to be considered the surest and best way to control lice on cattle, especially those in large herds. Improved power sprayers have come into use. They are of many types and makes. All are similar in operation. They differ mainly in capacity and output of spray.

The spray should be premixed in the spray tank before it is applied.

That can be done by running the sprayer as the insecticide is added to the water. Afterwards the spray stream should be directed back into the tank for a few minutes to insure a thoroughly mixed spray. The agitators with which the power sprayers are equipped will keep the spray well mixed as it is used. A pressure of 100 to 200 pounds to the square inch usually is adequate for spraying cattle with short hair. Pressures up to 350 pounds may be needed if the hair is dense and long. The animal's crotch, dewlap, forelegs, tail, and ears should be sprayed especially well. The spray stream should not be aimed directly into the ears, because damage to the inner ear may result at these pressures.

If there are only a few animals, hand-operated equipment can be used. A knapsack or cylindrical garden-type sprayer is satisfactory, although with them it may be harder to wet the animal thoroughly. Because some hand sprayers are not equipped with agitators, they have to be turned over or shaken every few minutes to insure a well-mixed spray.

Dusting may be preferable in winter in the colder climates because wetting the animals may endanger their health. Dusting is more laborious than dipping or spraying. Only gentle cattle can be dusted satisfactorily, because the dust must be sifted through the dense hair by rubbing the animal's back with the fingers. Because of the difficulty in obtaining good penetration and coverage, dusts are less effective than sprays or dips. Usually about 6 ounces of a 5- to 10-percent dust are required to treat an adult animal.

The application of insecticides with backrubbers or self-treatment devices has been recommended in many States. Robert A. Hoffman, of the Entomology Research Branch laboratory, Corvallis, Oreg., found that *B. bovis* and *L. vituli* could be controlled with DDT, chlordane, methoxychlor, and toxaphene by self-treatment devices. To be successful, they must be used consistently.

The backrubbers should be accessible to the cattle near watering places and places where the cattle rest. They may be placed in lanes where the cattle would be forced to use them. Unless the cattle are able to rub themselves thoroughly, however, satisfactory control might not be had. The backrubbers seem to be better adapted for use in small pastures or feed lots where there are few trees and other natural objects on which cattle can rub.

Generally the insecticides are used at 5-percent concentration in the backrubbers. The technical material may be dissolved in fuel oil or kerosene to the desired concentration. Used crankcase oil is not recommended for use in these devices. Homemade backrubbers are as efficient as manufactured ones and are less expensive.

ON DAIRY CATTLE, methoxychlor, lindane, rotenone, and pyrethrum have been recommended for use against lice. They are usually applied as sprays. Methoxychlor should be applied at 0.5-percent concentration in sprays, 5.0-percent concentration in self-treatment devices, and 5.0- to 10.0-percent in dust. Lindane should be applied at a concentration of 0.03 to 0.06 percent in sprays and 1.0 percent in dust.

A concentration of 0.006 percent of rotenone in sprays (1 pound derris or cube containing 5.0 percent rotenone to 100 gallons water) and 1.0 percent in dust is recommended. Sprays containing pyrethrum should contain 0.025 percent active ingredient.

One can buy pyrethrum concentrates that contain a synergist, which tends to increase the effectiveness of the pyrethrum. Piperonyl butoxide, sulfoxide, and *n*-propyl isomer are commonly used synergists. The ratio of synergist to pyrethrins should be about 10 to 1 in formulations for lice.

A second application of lindane, rotenone, or pyrethrum 14 to 18 days after the first may be necessary.

ON BEEF CATTLE, methoxychlor, lindane, rotenone, and pyrethrum at the concentrations used on dairy cattle will control lice. The following insecticides will also control lice on beef cattle:

DDT at 0.5 percent in sprays and dips; 5.0-percent in oil applied in a self-treatment device; and 5.0 to 10.0 percent in dust;

TDE at the same concentrations and in the same manner as DDT;

Toxaphene at 0.5-percent concentration in sprays and dips and 5.0 percent in oil in backrubbers;

Chlordane at 0.5-percent concentrations as a spray and 5.0 percent in oil for a self-treatment device.

BHC, the technical chemical from which lindane is made—the gamma isomer in the spray should be the same as for lindane (0.03 to 0.06 percent of lindane).

To control the tail louse, it may be necessary to spray beef cattle with a 1.0- to 1.5-percent concentration of DDT or the same concentration of methoxychlor as recommended on dairy cattle. A limited number of tests in Texas indicated that the tail louse can be controlled with the same concentrations of DDT, methoxychlor, BHC, toxaphene, and chlordane as recommended for the general control of lice.

C. L. SMITH *became assistant station leader in the Department's laboratory in Kerrville, Tex., in 1951.*

IRWIN H. ROBERTS, *a parasitologist and veterinarian in the Department of Agriculture, has been concerned with investigations of parasitic diseases of livestock since 1940.*

Cattle Tick Fever

T. W. COLE AND WM. M. MacKELLAR

TICK fever is marked by high fever, destruction of red corpuscles, enlarged spleen, engorged liver, thick and flaky bile, jaundice, emaciation, and death in 10 percent of the chronic cases and up to 90 percent of the acute cases.

Tick fever is caused by the development and activity of minute animal parasites known as piroplasms, which are conveyed to the animals by the cattle fever tick.

A peculiarity of the disease is that animals responsible for its spread are apparently healthy, while those that become diseased do not as a rule convey the infection, except as carriers and distributors of the cattle fever tick.

Tick fever probably was introduced into the United States by cattle imported from the West Indies during the early Spanish colonization of Mexico and the southern parts of the United States.

The disease caused large losses year after year during the early history of this country. In the summer of 1796 a severe outbreak in Lancaster County, Pa., was attributed to cattle brought from South Carolina. An investigation indicated that native cattle contracted tick fever when they mingled with the southern cattle. In one instance the Pennsylvania cattle got sick when they used a pasture previously occupied by the southern cattle. This strange malady always seemed to occur in summer and disappear after the first heavy frost. It was observed that the southern cattle apparently responsible for spreading the disease remained in good health.

Alarming reports of this trouble came from the West and Southwest in the mid-1800's, when many cattle were trailed out of Texas to Western and Midwestern States. The heavy death losses that followed in the wake of the trail movements from Texas led to the name "Texas fever," a misleading name which wrongly gives the impression that the disease originated in Texas or was confined to that State.

Several States made laws and regulations in undertaking to control the movements and prevent the spread of the disease. Nevertheless the disease advanced northward. It became evident that the problem was of national interest—if the cattle industry in the North were to receive effective protection, the Federal Government would have to establish control measures by dividing the infected areas from the free areas and by regulating the movement of all cattle from the regions where the disease existed.

A survey was undertaken in 1883 to locate the northern limits of the infection. By order of the Secretary of Agriculture, a Federal quarantine line was established on July 3, 1889, and regulations were issued that permitted only the shipment of southern cattle under special sanitary restrictions to northern markets for immediate slaughter. The quarantine and the regulations checked the spread of the disease, but they did little to improve conditions in the quarantined area, except to emphasize the need to combat the disease where it was established.

While field surveys were in progress to determine the limits of the territory involved, scientists were conducting investigations to solve the baffling problems posed by the disease. In 1889 investigators of the Department of Agriculture recognized and described as protozoa the minute parasites that are found in the red blood cells and are the direct causative agents of tick fever.

The theory that Texas fever was caused by ticks, which were carried to and scattered on northern pastures by southern cattle, had been advanced by some observing western cattlemen. Others considered the idea ridiculous.

The Department's chief of animal disease eradication activities decided to investigate the theory, and experiments conducted by two of its scientists, Theobald Smith and Fred L. Kilborne, in 1889–1890 established that transmission of the disease depended on infestations of cattle ticks. They demonstrated that an infectious disease could be transmitted by an intermediate host or carrier from one animal to another—a notable advance in medicine.

Cooper Curtice, another Department veterinarian, made noteworthy contributions by his studies and description of the life history and characteristics of the cattle tick. The combined work of these three scientists pointed the way for studies that later resolved similar problems with respect to parasitic vectors that spread such human diseases as malaria, yellow fever, typhus, and Rocky Mountain spotted fever.

THE DESIRABILITY of eradicating the ticks became apparent when investigators found that without the tick the disease would soon die out. So in 1906 a campaign was started to eliminate cattle ticks from the United States. The work, carried out by State officials, livestock owners, and Department representatives, has continued to this time.

At the outset, 985 counties in 15 Southern and Southwestern States—nearly one-fourth of the United States—were under Federal quarantine because of tick infestation.

The only known tick-infested area in 1956 was a narrow buffer area in parts of eight counties adjacent to the lower Rio Grande River in Texas, where reinfestations continue to occur through stray and smuggled animals from Mexico. The area has remained under quarantine as a protective measure.

In order to free the United States of cattle tick fever, workers had to eradicate the North American fever tick (*Boophilus annulatus*), which formerly infested most of the quarantined area, and the tropical variety of the same tick *B. annulatus* var. *microplus*, which occurred in Florida, Puerto Rico, and areas near the gulf coast. The ability of the tropical species to perpetuate itself on deer complicated the established procedures and delayed the completion of tick eradication in several of the larger swampy areas and game preserves in Florida.

Cattle fever ticks can be destroyed in the pastures and on the cattle. Pastures may be made tick free by vacating the premises of all the host animals—cattle, horses, and mules—until all the ticks on the ground have perished through starvation.

Another and more common method is to allow the cattle to remain on the infested pasture and treat them every 2 weeks by dipping in a permitted arsenical solution of standard strength.

A list of arsenical cattle dips permitted for use in the official dipping of cattle for fever ticks may be obtained from the Chief, Animal Disease Eradication Branch, Agricultural Research Service, United States Department of Agriculture, Washington 25, D. C.

Such treatments prevent the engorged female ticks from dropping to the ground alive and reinfesting the pastures. The seed, or larval, ticks that are on the ground and the ticks that hatch from eggs laid by females already there will get on the cattle from time to time and be destroyed by the dipping, but the ticks that cannot find a host die of starvation.

The time necessary for systematic dipping to insure eradication varies somewhat with the time of year the dipping starts and with the thoroughness of the work. Dipping at 14-day intervals for 8 to 12 months has given satisfactory results.

Cattle fever ticks feed only on the blood of their host. The ticks develop rapidly and suck large amounts of blood. The infested animals soon be-

The heavy black line indicates the northern boundary of the tick-infested territory at the beginning of tick eradication in 1906. The shaded patch in Texas indicates the quarantined area in 1956.

come impoverished. Heavily infested cattle need extra feed to meet the demands of the parasites. The growth of young animals is retarded. They are likely to remain emaciated, stunted, and unprofitable. Dairy cows drop off in milk production.

Tick-infested cattle cannot be shipped from one State to another. Tick-infested animals must be freed of ticks by dipping before shipment. Formerly cattle from a quarantined area were consigned to only a few market centers for immediate slaughter and therefore were sold at a reduced price. The cars used in shipping them had to be cleaned and disinfected, which added to the cost of transportation. Ticks lessened the value of the live animals and caused their hides to be downgraded by tanners in comparison with prices paid for hides from tick-free areas.

Southern cattlemen suffered losses when they bought northern purebred cattle with which to improve the native stock. About 10 percent of those cattle would die of tick fever even if they were immunized by the use of gradu-

ated amounts of blood from cattle that had recovered from the disease; 60 percent or more would die if they were not so treated.

Medical treatment of cattle sick with tick fever has been unsatisfactory. A measure of the losses once caused by tick fever is the estimate that at the beginning of this century the disease cost southern cattlemen 40 million dollars a year.

The death of cattle from tick fever has been stopped. The latest report of an outbreak of the disease was in August 1949. Southern cattle now move to market or elsewhere without sanitary restrictions for tick fever. Special quarantine pens for those cattle at northern market centers have been abolished. They now compete on an equal basis with other livestock. Purebred breeding animals for the improvement of native cattle are being shipped freely to all parts of the former quarantine area in the South, for no longer is there danger they will contract tick fever and die. This new blood has resulted in a substantial improvement in the quality of southern cattle and the economy of the entire area. The total cost to Federal, State, and county governments of their cooperative conquest in eliminating this parasite has amounted to little more than the toll taken from the South in a single year by the fever tick before eradication work was started.

T. W. COLE, *a veterinarian, as chief of the Public Stockyards Inspection Section, Animal Disease Eradication Branch, performs many activities in connection with the*

interstate movement of livestock. He spent 21 years combating the cattle fever tick in Texas and Florida and formerly was in charge of tick eradication activities.

WM. M. MACKELLAR *was formerly principal veterinarian in charge of cattle tick eradication and other disease control activities of the Department. When cooperative cattle tick eradication was inaugurated in 1906, he directed the work in California. Later he directed a similar activity in Georgia. He retired in 1948 after nearly 48 years of service in the Department of Agriculture.*

Infectious Keratitis, or Pinkeye, in Cattle

R. S. SUGG

INFECTIOUS KERATITIS—pinkeye—has been recognized as a contagious disease in cattle since 1889.

The eyelids swell. A discharge is watery at first and later contains mucus and pus. The lining of the lids becomes red and congested. Often a pink or red ring surrounds the white part of the eyeball. The eyes are closed. The animal shows evidence of pain, especially when it is in bright sunlight. The eyeball becomes cloudy and the animal may be unable to see for several days. Ulcers may form in severe cases on the front of the eye near the pupil. Sometimes the eyeball is destroyed and the animal becomes blind.

The disease occurs all over the world and may appear at all seasons. It is most commonly seen in summer. It affects animals of all ages, but animals under 2 years of age seem to be most susceptible.

THE CAUSE of pinkeye has not been determined definitely. The disease can be spread by transferring the secretions from the eye of an affected animal to a

normal susceptible animal. If the secretions are filtered through filters that remove all germs, the filtrate will not produce the disease—an indication that the disease is caused by a germ and not a virus.

The secretions usually contain several species of bacteria. The most common are the common pus-forming germs, the *staphylococcus* group; bacteria that usually are found in manure, the *colon* group; and *Corynebacterium*. An organism known as *Hemophilus bovis* or *Moraxella bovis* usually is associated with the disease.

Ralph D. Barner, of Kansas State College, isolated *H. bovis* (*M. bovis*) from 92 of 95 acute cases in cattle. He reproduced the disease in farm animals with pure cultures of *H. bovis*. C. H. Gallagher, of McMaster Laboratory, Sidney, Australia, also produced the disease with pure culture of *H. bovis*. Herman Farley, of Oklahoma Agricultural and Mechanical College, however, was unable to produce the disease with pure culture, and considered *H. bovis* as a secondary invader.

Infectious keratitis is usually introduced into herds by newly purchased animals that have been exposed to infection while in transit. Sometimes the disease appears, but no source of infection can be found. It is possible that cattle that have recovered from the disease may be able to spread the infection for several months after all symptoms have disappeared.

Beef cattle affected with pinkeye usually lose weight because they cannot find their way about the pasture to graze. The milk flow drops. Nursing calves lose weight. Young calves may become temporarily blind and unable to follow their dams. Cattle, unable to see where they are going, may hurt themselves by falling in ditches, ravines, and waterholes.

Production in dairy cattle may drop 25 percent or more.

CONTROL MEASURES consist of good herd management. There are no specific vaccines, bacterins, or serums that will prevent the disease. Affected herds must be given daily attention to see that they get feed and water and are kept out of ditches and other places where they may get hurt.

Because flies and gnats probably spread the disease, spraying the herd with fly repellents and insecticides at regular intervals will help reduce the number of animals affected. Newly purchased animals should be kept isolated for at least 60 days before being allowed to mingle with the rest of the herd.

Herd treatment of wild pasture cattle is not practicable. Handling the cattle through chutes daily would do more harm than the treatment would do good. Individual animals that are tractable or halter broken should be placed in dark stalls and treated by a veterinarian.

Mild antiseptic eyewashes and antibiotics have proved of value in individual cases. Argyrol, a 2-percent solution of zinc sulfate, mercurochrome (2 to 4 percent), and a 1-percent solution of silver nitrate have been used. The antibiotics usually used are Chloromycetin ointment (1 percent), Terramycin pellets, and penicillin solution or ointment.

R. S. SUGG *is the dean of the School of Veterinary Medicine, Alabama Polytechnic Institute, Auburn, Ala.*

Bovine Coccidiosis

LEONARD REID DAVIS AND GEORGE W. BOWMAN

COCCIDIOSIS is an extremely common but usually overlooked disease that weakens or kills many calves before they are 6 months old.

Coccidiosis is a parasitic protozoan disease. It is produced by small, one-celled organisms of the genus *Eimeria* (Protozoa). Eleven species have been reported in cattle in this country. Most of these species are found in varying numbers on routine examinations of young calves. As a result of a natural infection on the farm, sometimes as many as eight species may be found in one examination.

Coccidiosis has been considered the third most important parasitic disease in cattle, even though some investigators have overlooked it as one of the causes of scours in calves. It has been reported that coccidiosis in cattle may produce as great an economic loss as that caused by coccidiosis in poultry.

Coccidiosis usually affects calves between 3 weeks and 6 months of age when they are placed together in unsanitary lots contaminated by older cattle or other infected calves. Occasionally it attacks mature cattle when they are brought in from large pastures and are crowded into small feed lots or barns. It is extremely rare to find cattle manure entirely free of these parasites.

Calves that appear to be free of coccidia may pass low numbers of oöcysts (the cyst stage of coccidia passed in the droppings) without showing clinical symptoms and thus may build up greater numbers in susceptible calves, which, in turn, will pass dangerously high numbers.

The infection in a previously uninfected calf may be subclinical (without symptoms) or clinical, depending on the amount of infective oöcysts swallowed, the age of the calf, and the species of coccidia involved. Species such as *Eimeria zurnii*, *E. bovis*, and *E. auburnensis* may produce pathological symptoms when relatively small numbers of oöcysts are ingested, but ones such as *E. ellipsoidalis* and *E. alabamensis* may produce no observable symptoms unless large numbers are swallowed or unless the calf is weakened from other conditions.

The oöcysts that are passed from an animal are not infective for the host or other calves until a process called "sporulation" takes place. The rounded material inside the oöcyst shell has to undergo cell division, dividing into four round bodies, each of which lengthens and then splits lengthwise into two early stages of the parasite, called "sporozoites." The presence of these eight sporozoites in an oöcyst shell indicates that sporulation has been completed and that the oöcyst has become infective. The time required for sporulation may vary from 1 to 14 days or more, depending on the species, surrounding moisture, oxygen, temperature, and other environmental conditions.

When outbreaks of coccidiosis occur, microscopic examinations will show that infective oöcysts usually can be found in the litter, in the upper layers of soil, on contaminated troughs or buckets, and on the ears, body, and tail of calves in the pen. The ever-inquisitive, searching tongue of a young calf can pick up the infective oöcysts by licking or sucking its own body or other calves.

The coccidia in cattle do not attack other animals, and vice versa. There is no scientific foundation for the commonly encountered belief that cattle coccidiosis can result when rains wash oöcysts of poultry coccidia into calf lots from a poultry house and lot situated higher on a slope. However, chickens, other livestock, and man can step in manure of infected cattle and then carry the contamination on the feet into places used for raising calves.

THE SYMPTOMS of coccidiosis may include rough coat, weakness, listlessness, nervousness, poor appetite, diarrhea, and loss of weight or poor gains in weight. The general weakness may cause the calf to defecate without rising, thus soiling its tail, hindquarters, and lower part of the body.

When standing, the calf may attempt to defecate and not be able to pass feces; the intense straining results in an arched back, raised tail, and a "pumping" of the sides. The diarrhea may be watery or only slightly liquid, being quite unlike the "white scours" of calves less than 3 weeks old. Diarrhea caused by coccidiosis may contain many strands of gelatinous mucus and splotches or streaks of blood. In infections with *E. zurnii* and *E. bovis*, it may be extremely bloody and may even include shreds of intestinal tissue or occasionally short lengths of the tubular lining of the damaged intestine.

When a susceptible calf swallows infective oöcysts, the sporozoites are released from the oöcysts in the stomach or intestine. The sporozoites penetrate the cells lining the intestine and begin to divide into multitudes of intermediate stages. The stages continue to divide, and each division produces parasitic cells that cause damage to the host cell in which each lives. Many male and female parasitic cells are produced eventually in the intestinal lining. They unite to produce the oöcyst, which is covered by a resistant shell to protect it from the surroundings in the outside world. The oöcyst is then passed out of the animal's body in the feces. The life cycle is started again after sporulation occurs and the oöcyst is swallowed by a susceptible calf.

Calves may sometimes die from coccidiosis without passing blood. The only positive indication of the presence of the disease in cases like this would be the discovery of the parasites during a careful microscopic examination of scrapings or sections of the intestinal lining.

The temperature of the calf may be elevated during an attack of coccidiosis, but it may be below normal before death. The presence or absence of fever, therefore, would not be a good indication of coccidiosis.

TREATMENT is not effective in many cases when the digestive tract already is severely damaged. Some of the reports of so-called cures attributed to drugs may have been due to the removal of cattle from contaminated areas during the time of treatment. If a calf does not continue to swallow oöcysts, those already swallowed soon complete development and the disease terminates. Unless untreated control animals are used for comparison, it is impossible, therefore, to evaluate objectively the therapeutic value of a drug used to combat coccidiosis.

Sulfaguanidine, sulfaquinoxaline, and sulfamethazine have shown promise in the treatment of bovine coccidiosis. When equal amounts of sulfamethazine or sulfaquinoxaline were compared, sulfamethazine gave more protection than the other drug. Sulfamethazine was given in a course of four daily treatments—1 grain per pound of body weight on the first day and half that amount on each of the next 3 days. Two weeks should elapse before repeating the course of treatment.

As IN MOST DISEASES, it is easier to prevent clinical coccidiosis than it is to treat it. Because several days are required for sporulation, the oöcyst stage is the weakest link in the life cycle of the parasite.

Separating the calf from its accumulation of manure interrupts the cycle and controls the disease. It is nearly impossible to remove all traces of oöcyst-contaminated feces from stalls by scrubbing, and the remaining water furnishes perfect moisture conditions for sporulation. That explains some outbreaks of coccidiosis in concrete-floored stalls under conditions normally considered "clean."

Raised isolation pens with wire mesh or slat floors permit most contamination to pass down away from the calf and are useful for reducing clinical coccidiosis, but they must be used inside a building.

Segregation into three or four age groups will reduce gross contamination of young calves by infected older ones, but when calves are raised in groups, respiratory troubles may be encountered occasionally and may spread to others in the same age group.

A PRACTICAL system of raising calves without clinical coccidiosis has been developed. Detailed plans are available at the Regional Animal Disease Research Laboratory of the Agricultural Research Service, the United States Department of Agriculture, Auburn, Ala.

The method involves the outdoor use of individual portable pens that are moved to a clean site once each week. The calf is left with the dam for not more than 24 hours, so that it receives some colostrum. Calves left with the dam longer than 3 or 4 days develop more coccidia and worm parasites than those removed after only 1 day. The calf is placed in an individual pen, 5 by 10 by 3 feet, where it remains until it is 4 to 6 months old, depending on the size of the calf.

Moving the calf and its pen, preferably uphill, once each week, takes the calf away from its contamination before too many of the oöcysts sporulate. The calves are not completely freed of infection, but they swallow enough oöcysts to get slight, nonclinical coccidiosis and to develop sufficient immunity to be resistant when they are placed on pasture, unless the pasture is heavily contaminated by older cattle.

Calves raised in portable pens and then placed on pasture are no more susceptible to coccidiosis and other parasitic diseases than are calves raised in individual stalls in a conventional calf barn.

Besides preventing clinical coccidiosis, portable pens reduce the transmission of worm parasites and many other infectious diseases of calves. As compared with barn-raised calves, those raised in portable pens remain remarkably free from respiratory troubles and invariably make better weight gains and have fewer deaths. The portable pens are recommended primarily for use in Southern States, but they have been used successfully in milder weather in some Northern States.

LEONARD REID DAVIS, *a native of Georgia, is a graduate of Union University and Iowa State College. Dr. Davis was head of the Biology Department at Union University for 7 years before joining the staff of the United States Regional Animal Disease Research Laboratory at Auburn, Ala., in 1941.*

GEORGE W. BOWMAN *is a research technician in parasitology, also assigned to investigations of bovine coccidiosis at Auburn, Ala. He has been associated with the Department of Agriculture since 1927, and previously was stationed at Jeanerette, La., and Beltsville, Md.*

Diseases of Calves

M. G. FINCHER

CALF SCOURS is perhaps the most important of the diseases of calves. It is known also as diarrhea in calves, calf septicemia, and 3-day calf disease.

It takes many different forms and therefore is hard to define. Here, though, I describe the types that are seen a few hours after birth and those that appear later.

The most fatal form of calf scours appears at birth or within 6 to 72 hours after birth. The calf is found soon after birth in a cold, weak, and dying condition.

Sometimes there is little or no evidence of actual passage of watery feces, and several calves on a farm may be "found dead" unless they are closely watched following birth. In other herds a few calves may scour mildly or severely during the first 10 to 30 days of life and recover with little assistance. Oftener, however, calves with severe diarrhea become unthrifty and pot-bellied, show poor growth, and get pneumonia.

The middle ear, joints, and umbilicus in rare instances become seats of localized infection in beef or dairy calves when they are a few days to several weeks old.

WE DO NOT KNOW all the factors that favor development of the various forms of diarrhea in calves. Many causes are known, but others undoubtedly have escaped detection.

Various infections may be to blame. Usually a calf reared from an isolated family cow on a small farm remains free of scours and grows better than do calves in larger herds in expensive but crowded calf barns. Presumably, therefore, infectious agents may be regularly present in most large herds.

The organisms capable of causing scours include the coliform group. The salmonella group is involved infrequently in California and other parts of the world. Possibly viral agents are the cause. The salmonella or paratyphoid organisms seldom have been recognized in calves in the eastern part of the United States.

Calf pens, parturition stalls, barnyards, trucks, and railroad cars may be contaminated by these infectious agents and may be a source of infections that cause mild to fatal scours.

Adult or younger cattle very likely carry the agents on their feet and skins. It is believed that the uterus and digestive tract of adult cattle do not generally harbor the infectious organisms.

AN UNUSUALLY SEVERE type of acute calf septicemia or calf scours, with death of some calves, will occur quite regularly when a large group of very young calves is assembled from different farms, because the virulence and the variety of the causative agents associated with calf diseases are thereby increased.

The removal of pregnant cows from an area where fatal scours is rampant and allowing them to calve in isolated stables or grass paddocks or on pasture often stops an outbreak immediately.

Calves born in a particular set of buildings, stalls, or outside yards may die of severe septicemia with or without scours over a period of a few weeks or several months. If the pregnant cows are moved to one or preferably to several new, clean stables or yards, the losses may suddenly stop. This strongly suggests that some type of infection (virus, bacteria, or both) occurs promptly after the calf is dropped in an infected place on the farm or ranch. Leaving this infected area and moving the remaining pregnant females to one or several uninfected areas avoids the chance for exposure to infection of calves born after the move.

The cow's diet during the several weeks before she drops her calf influences the calf's resistance to scours. The dam's lack of vitamin A (and perhaps other vitamins) may weaken the calf even though she herself is not emaciated.

A low amount of vitamin A in the calf's liver and in the dam's colostrum may result from poor pasturage and too little roughage and concentrates during the last months of pregnancy. When cows have been on poor winter rations or on extremely dry pasture, one can expect severe outbreaks of scours and other diseases of calves.

Colostrum from the dam of the calf or from some other cow, fresh within 12 to 24 hours, contains gamma globulins rich in antibodies. If the calf gets no colostrum in the first several hours of life, scours are likely to ensue. Yet this colostral milk has a high content of fat (and perhaps other products), which produces scours if the calf gets too much. Calves of high-butterfat breeds especially may become extremely sick from too much colostrum even if infection is absent.

CALF DISEASES, including scours, seem to be more severe and widespread in some years than in others. We do not know why. It may be due to lack of agents that produce immunity—antibodies—in the cows and in their colostrum and, therefore, high susceptibility to viruses or other agents in the newborn calves. Then, as the diseases became widespread, the calves might have acquired some immunity, perhaps from their dams, and the incidence would be lower for several years.

A virus has been isolated from calves

and cows near Ithaca, N. Y., and other parts of the United States. It can cause virus diarrhea. It has not been classed as a true cause of white scours or scours in calves under 3 weeks old, but it deserves attention as a threatening or possible cause. Most 3-month-old calves in the Ithaca section are resistant to artificial inoculation with the virus. Therefore the virus may have entered the young calves and built up resistance in them. It is debatable whether it has caused clinical symptoms, except a mild fever and resistance to that particular virus.

SOME RESEARCH MEN have suggested that some cases of scours are due to the same cause that is connected with diarrhea in human infants. It is called metabolic acidosis and is accompanied by low blood sugar and a low potassium level in the blood. Great variation in the blood chemistry has been found, however. The presence of a severe to moderate acidosis and the variations in the sodium and calcium levels in the blood of affected calves deserves more study before they can be positively evaluated. No doubt metabolic acidosis is a cause or a result of scours.

Some calves, as the late D. H. Udall pointed out years ago, develop depraved appetites and eat contaminated bedding. Their true stomachs (abomasum) at a week of age may contain shavings, coarse straw or hay, and hair, mixed in an indigestible mass. They remain unthrifty and develop so-called dietetic scours.

Furthermore, many calves are deprived of cows' milk when they are 3 to 15 days old. Veterinarians generally believe that calves should get milk longer than that. Various milk substitutes are widely used. Most of them contain dried skim milk, antibiotics, chemicals, carbohydrate filler, and vitamins. We have seen many calves that died of dietetic or nutritional scours or did not thrive because they got no fresh whole milk. And we have seen calves that were fed such artificial diets and seemed highly susceptible to ordinary infections even though they grew well.

In sum, then, scours seems to be due largely to an overcrowded condition, poor hygiene, poor diet for the calves or for their dams, and to a variety of infectious agents, which may enter by ingestion, inhalation, or through the umbilical stump.

ACUTE CALF SEPTICEMIA is a striking and costly form of the syndrome—a complex set of symptoms—called calf scours.

Usually the calves with this condition die suddenly. A few calves have a fetid, white, watery diarrhea soon after birth. A series of losses may occur despite drastic steps to cure or prevent the diarrhea. Then for several years the disease may not appear in such a virulent form on the same premises. Or it may recur a few weeks each year on larger farms. Or, again, calves may have a fetid, watery diarrhea, may be clammy and cold, and may have sunken eyes when they are 6 to 24 hours old—a syndrome that is a continuous experience each year throughout the long calving season, especially in winter and spring in the Northeast. Severe outbreaks may occur in hot weather, too.

Calves that survive may respond well to good husbandry and become useful adults. A few will remain unthrifty and stunted, with conformation much poorer than their inherited potential, and develop considerable pneumonia. Chronic solidifed areas will be found in their lungs at autopsy.

The absence of a temperature in many of the so-called "3-day scours" or very acute cases often is confusing and surprising. It probably means that the loss of fluids through the bowels has been so rapid that the patient is approaching shock and more complete dehydration and death. Owners may not have noticed that the calves were sick and the veterinarian may have found nothing at autopsy. There is a total absence of gross changes in the tissues. If the examination is performed immediately after death, hemorrhages may be found on the sclera of the eye or in the stomach, kidneys, or intestines, and the contents of the stomach and intestines have a fetid smell. Feces on the buttocks and tail have an extremely offensive odor.

Calves in most herds may die before the onset of the acute type of the disease. They start showing white or greenish-gray, fetid feces at 24 hours (or as late as 10 days) after birth. Usually these calves are not especially depressed and cold and will get up to nurse or suck a nipple pail despite severe diarrhea. Like the more severe form, this common "white scours" may lead to an unthrifty calf. Fetid, purulent discharges may come from the ears or umbilicus. Joint changes and lameness (arthritis or tendovaginitis) may set in. Eventually pneumonia, repeated attacks of constipation, or scours and unthriftiness may occur.

Older calves that have escaped the baby-calf type of septicemia and scours occasionally may develop troublesome and apparently contagious diarrhea. This form of diarrhea affects one or several calves 1 to 6 months old in a herd. The liquid feces often are nearly black. That is due perhaps to a medicine that did not stop the diarrhea but changed the character and color of the feces, or it may be due to blood in the feces. That blood would have come from the true stomach or small intestines; any fresh blood might come from the large bowel or rectum.

These late cases of scours in older calves may be a symptom of an unrecognized chronic pneumonia or be part of other localized infections following sickness in early calfhood. Such chronic scours often represents evidence of a poor diet and poor housing or general environment. Standing or lying in the mud or water-soaked bedding seems to favor the development of this and other forms of scours.

PREVENTION of scours is not a simple matter. Years ago people concerned with rearing healthy calves learned the value of keeping straw or hay contaminated with feces and other coarse material out of the abomasums of calves less than 2 weeks old. To do that, muzzles were helpful for pail-fed calves.

Some farmers still use muzzles on calves that have unusual appetites. Many calves need such protection. Carefully prepared pellets or other dry-grain calf starters, placed in small amounts in clean containers, are something for the calf to eat after it has hastily consumed the milk. To feed pellets for that purpose, the owner may have to build small stanchions or stalls in which very young calves can be fastened when they drink milk. Their feed and water should be so placed that the calves may then turn to vitamin-enriched calf starter, small amounts of clear water, or fine timothy hay—all of which should be placed off the ground so that the calves will not befoul the food and water with manure.

Many dairymen prefer nipple pails, because from them the calf gets its milk with its head held as when it nurses a cow. This natural position keeps the calf from inhaling milk or gulping it too fast, as it does from an open pail. The nipple and pail must be cleaned thoroughly every day.

To combat scours, farmers have effectively used the open-pen, nurse-cow system for rearing dairy calves to 3 or 4 months of age.

Beef cattle of high quality are quite regularly reared on nurse cows of a dairy breed until the calves are a year old. This plan gives unusually good growth and perhaps vigor. If, however, dairy calves are allowed to remain on nurse cows after they are 2 months old, a degree of fullness in the neck region below the throat sometimes results. This throatiness is undesirable in a dairy calf intended to be used in competition in the show ring, but has no undesirable effect on the health of the calf.

The nurse cow must be free from chronic infectious diseases lest the calf get the infection. Parasitism can spread to the calves from infected cows, but if the cow and calf are kept in a covered shed (with sides open as needed for the particular climate) and if no soiled ground or water holes are nearby, the danger of spreading parasitism in this way in the northeastern United States is not serious. A tarpaulin is lowered over the one open side of the shed in cold weather. Four nurse cows are tied in the shed and eight or more calves allowed to run with them. A creep is provided where they can eat grain and hay. A suitable dry calf starter, consisting of pellets and a special calf ration, is desirable. Clean, fresh water should be available to calves after they are 5 days old.

These two practices do not solve all disease problems of calves—acute septicemia may kill calves before it is time to shift them from colostrum of the dam to the nurse cow or nipple pail.

Another recommended preventive practice is to use feeds or supplements rich in vitamin A for the cows during the final 3 months of their pregnancy in order to raise the resistance of newborn calves to infections.

The plan of having many places in the farm buildings or many areas on a ranch as calving places may help to keep down scours because chances of exposure to infectious agents are reduced thereby.

As I mentioned before, it often is necessary to move the pregnant cows away from a place where newborn calves are dying within a very few hours after birth or let the cows calve in a pasture. Breeding so that calves are dropped in May or June usually assures that a clean pasture will be available for calving.

The movable, isolated pen system for rearing calves is still popular in much of the United States where calves may always remain outdoors.

A wire mesh a few inches above the floor of the pens keeps them free of urine and manure. Another plan is to put 6 inches of new soil or cinders, covered with soil, in the floor of each pen before each newborn calf is placed in it. The calf is removed from this clean pen to a larger one with other calves at 3 weeks of age.

Calves must be kept from sucking each other's navels, ears, and teats. If several calves must be kept in one open pen, they might well be kept tied or stanchioned some distance from each other so they cannot suck each other. If a good dry-grain starter for calves is put near them, the calves will soon learn to eat and not start sucking each other.

Utensils used for milk or water must be washed and sterilized often. The fixed boxes for grain should be cleaned if they are so placed that the calves can soil them. Very little grain should be left in them after a calf has eaten for a short time. What is left becomes unpalatable and attracts rodents and birds, which might spread disease.

A good place to rear a few calves in a cold climate is in the same stable with the cows but separated from them so that their manure does not befoul the calves' feed or bedding. A theory—which has not been widely accepted—is that this close contact between adult cattle and calves improves the bacteria of the calves' rumen and other parts of the digestive tract. The bacteria produce vitamins, which help protect the calves from scours.

Another, and more drastic, preventive measure for acute scours in young calves is the use of a blood transfusion from the dam or from some other fresh cow.

Treatment of an outbreak of scours after all preventive measures have failed is a serious problem even to the most competent veterinarian. Much can be accomplished, however, with blood transfusions (or transfer) and with modern antibiotics, protectants, and other chemicals. Prevention so that disasters are infrequent should be the aim of the successful breeder, and a veterinarian should be called early in an outbreak. The rapid progress in the development of newer treatments offers the hope that a more satisfactory treatment or even a good preventive vaccine may be in the hands of your practicing veterinarian some time in the future.

CALVES often have slight coughs and nasal discharges, which may develop into a more severe respiratory condition. The farmer might think of the irritation as only a cold or coryza, but actually it might be a part of calf pneumonia.

In large herds especially it is common to find a few calves with symptoms like those shown by a person with a "cold." In outbreaks of so-called colds, some of the calves cough but have a low temperature and eat well, while their mates may be fatally ill.

These respiratory diseases in calves, which are not related to respiratory conditions in man, cause financial loss to the beef and the dairy industries through death and the production of calves of poor conformation and poor growth rates.

Scientists who have studied the diseases differ as to the cause. One theory, represented by the research of Dr. J. A. Baker and his colleagues at Cornell University, is based on the belief that one or more viruses initiate mild or severe pneumonia.

Two Irish scientists, H. G. Lamont and W. R. Kerr, in 1939 described severe losses from scours and pneumonia. An entire crop of 30 calves on one farm was lost one year from what appeared to be pneumonia. The scientists succeeded in causing pneumonia in healthy calves in 5 to 6 days by placing one calf that had pneumonia in a small pen with several normal calves. The intranasal injection of a filtered saline suspension of pneumonic lung tissue from other sick calves, which were destroyed while sick, caused the usual chain of symptoms that had been observed in regular outbreaks of the disease in calves in Ireland. The scientists could not isolate bacteria. They suggested therefore that an influenzalike virus was perhaps the cause of the pneumonia.

Another view is that many different kinds of bacteria are capable of living in a normal calf without producing symptoms until the calf meets some set of factors that lower its resistance. Many investigators would insist that a virus constitutes the resistance-lowering agent that is needed to touch off such bacteria as the shipping-fever organism (*Pasteurella multocida*) or *Corynebacterium pyogenes* or any one of a great variety of pyogenic organisms that a calf ordinarily harbors in his tissues. Rarely has *Brucella abortus* been involved.

Other environmental causes are numerous and important. Foremost among them is improper housing.

Calves are raised sometimes in temperate or in cold climates in stables where extreme changes in temperature occur. Calves left outdoors suffer from even greater exposure. The air in a calf barn that seems well ventilated may become foul and hot; a few hours later a change in weather and wind direction may cause a sharp drop in temperature in it. Or, a ventilator or window may be left open so that a calf is in a cold draft; a few hours later it might have pneumonia.

Chilling is dangerous for confined calves. Calves that are turned loose with their dams or nurse cows get heat from the cows even in a cold stable, but confined calves cannot escape from a cold pen. The thick concrete partitions formerly used around calf barns shut off the movement of air and were cold and damp, and the calves that rested against them suffered.

Ventilators and thermostatically controlled artificial heat have come into use in many calf barns. The ventilators allow air to enter from a conduit at the ceiling and to escape over the edges of a trough, which may be 4 inches high and 8 to 24 inches wide and is suspended just beneath the ceiling inlet. The air outlet should remove the foul air near the floor.

Dr. E. S. Harrison, formerly of the New York State College of Agriculture, developed a plan whereby individual pens were provided for eight calves in a small, well-ventilated calf barn. The unit was separated from similar units. Newborn calves thus could be placed in a barn that had been left vacant for a period after it had been disinfected with hot lye solution applied under pressure. This group of normal baby calves would remain in this clean setting in a stall 6 by 6 feet until all were at least 3 months old. Then that barn would be disinfected and left vacant for several days. This avoided the addition of normal calves less than a week old to a group of older calves that were more likely to be harboring some infection capable of causing pneumonia. Having many of these areas widely separated on a large farm further protects the susceptible calf from infection carried by a caretaker who moves from an infected group to a pen of normal calves.

More than one caretaker is needed when several eight-stall units at various locations are filled with calves.

Close confinement of many calves in one barn allows one sickly calf to infect normal calves. That has happened even when individual stalls 6 feet square are used—the air becomes fetid in them if they have tight walls higher than the head of the calf; lower walls let the calves nuzzle each other and so spread infection. Calves should not be placed in pens that allow less than 30 square feet of floor space per calf, lest bad air and overcrowding lead to conditions conducive to pneumonia.

Pneumonia occurs rather frequently in unthrifty calves that have survived a mild attack of scours. Sometimes we use the term "pneumoenteritis" to suggest that both diseases have the same cause. Many groups of normal calves, however, suddenly develop pneumonia without another ailment.

Pneumonia generally affects calves after they are 3 weeks old. It is common at 6 to 8 weeks, but becomes less frequent as the calves get older. One should not assume, though, that a 4-month-old calf is beyond getting this type of pneumonia. It is more frequent

in the cold months, but it may happen in any climate in any month. Spring is the peak period in regions where the calves are kept in stables.

Calves of any age are susceptible to respiratory trouble when they are transported, but in weaned beef calves 6 to 10 months old (so-called feeder calves) the ailment usually is due to shipping fever rather than to the virus of calf pneumonia.

In individual outbreaks, however, the pasteurella organism (which commonly is associated with shipping fever) may be absent in shipped calves that have pneumonia.

There is too great a tendency to assume that all pneumonia of calves is due to the shipping-fever organisms. Dr. John McAuliff, who has practiced intensively with cattle in Cortland, N. Y., has seen no pneumonia in calves due to this disease.

Nevertheless, it is very important to avoid exposure of young calves to cattle of any age that may have shipping fever or pneumonia from any cause.

Various infections and bad atmospheric conditions seem to be responsible for most of the serious outbreaks of calf pneumonia, but the addition of calves from outside herds to other groups of healthy calves may cause a more serious type of pneumonia than is usually encountered from exposure to cold alone.

SYMPTOMS of calf pneumonia include dullness, coughing, and rapid breathing in a calf that is 2 weeks to 3 months old. The temperature may reach 103° to 106° F., and a nasal discharge appears. A complete or partial loss of appetite may occur as the pneumonia develops.

Usually the calf loses condition rapidly even if it continues to drink milk. The hair coat becomes rough after a short period; diarrhea develops and may persist if the calf is not treated. Prostration and death in a few hours or days may follow in acute cases.

A few of a group of infected calves

may show no symptoms of pneumonia and yet have small, solid (pneumonic) spots in the lungs. Most calves that cough and have a nasal discharge but still are not considered seriously ill may be found by a clinician to have slight to severe bronchitis and pneumonia.

The solid spots of tissue in the lungs—which, of course, can be seen only on autopsy—may cause relapses later. The slight attacks of pneumonia may cause unthriftiness. Calves that have bilateral pneumonia may recover with or without treatment, but they often are stunted and have a depression behind the shoulders, which spoils their conformation.

Calves that suffer from neglect and severe pneumonia tend to have acute symptoms of pneumonia for 3 years or more. A few develop necrotic (dead) areas in the lungs, a chronic dilation of the bronchi, or abscesses in the lungs. Such diseased tissue may spread, and the abscesses may rupture months later and cause death.

The symptoms and course sometimes are changed promptly by early diagnosis and treatment. Prompt and complete recovery, though, may indicate that the ailment was not pneumonia but an uncomplicated cold.

Such a variable course makes calf pneumonia one of the most costly and unpredictable diseases of calves.

DIAGNOSIS is not always easy because examination of the living calf often fails to disclose rales or other symptoms of pneumonia.

The possibility of a toxemia (blood poisoning) or uremia (absorption of urea) from other causes—such as overdosing with sulfa drugs—or pneumonia from inhalation of milk or medicines given as a drench must be considered when one makes a diagnosis.

Calves that are suffering from coccidiosis, lungworm disease, calf diphtheria (foot-rot organism infecting mouth or throat), or leptospirosis may breathe rapidly at certain stages of those diseases and require an antemortem and possibly a postmortem and laboratory examination to determine the correct procedure. Lead poisoning in calves often gives rise to a high temperature and may occur in calves that are of the age group in which calf pneumonia is common. The presence of pneumonia should always be suspected in calves with a high temperature and rapid breathing, but one should bear in mind that an allergic reaction to a great variety of agents and many other conditions can cause similar symptoms.

PREVENTION is based largely on an elimination of the known causes and is the most satisfactory method of dealing with calf pneumonia.

In the early stages, that means removal of normal calves to small units and leaving the sick calves in the infected area where they were found.

The early use of antibiotics to control bacteria that act as secondary invaders may check many outbreaks—but no drug has an entirely satisfactory effect on all the bacteria and viruses that may be involved in calf pneumonia.

Calves and older cattle that have been trucked or shipped should not be placed immediately with healthy calves, but should be isolated for several weeks before they are added to the herd.

Good hygiene is essential. Quarters should be dry and free of drafts. Steel mesh or woven wire floors placed several inches above the base of a pen keep calves off concrete floors and, if the drainage is good, keep the pens dry and clean.

Visitors should be kept away from calf barns, because the virus of calf pneumonia and other infective organisms can be carried on shoes and clothing. Cats, dogs, rodents, and swine also might have a part in spreading infections. Care is needed always to keep calves from being exposed to all infections from outside sources.

Many dairymen have found that the open-pen, nurse-cow system of raising calves is an easy and successful way to prevent calf pneumonia.

The same system might well be used for high-class beef cattle, because beef calves, reared on their dams indoors or maintained in confinement between nursing periods on a nurse cow, also may get pneumonia. The nurse cows could be kept in the cooler months in a shed or pen, one side of which is open and has near it a small yard so the calves can go outdoors at will. A tarpaulin, fastened over the open end of the nurse-cow unit to allow ventilation, gives needed protection. Vitamin-enriched calf starter, early-cut timothy or some other fine green hay, and clean water should be made available to the calves in a creep.

The nurse-cow units should be small. Only six or eight calves of the same age should be put in one.

Autogenous bacterin has been used in attempts to prevent pneumonia in calves. It is a special killed culture in saline suspension of organisms derived from the spleen or lungs of calves that have died of pneumonia on the farm or ranch where the calves are to be vaccinated. Other shipping-fever bacterins, mixed or stock, have given disappointing results, and the autogenous bacterin seldom does all that is expected of it.

Until a vaccine, based on the viruses that may be involved in calf pneumonia, is produced, little can be expected or guaranteed from the use of immunizing agents.

Treatment has changed from the use of cow serums or whole blood from cows or from recovered calves to reliance on wide-spectrum antibiotics or chemotherapeutic drugs. As there is constant improvement from year to year in the methods of treating calves with such agents, it is safest to consult a veterinarian for specific directions.

TREATMENT, to be most effective, must be started early.

Overdosage with certain chemotherapeutic agents—such as several of the sulfa drugs—has caused losses at times.

Calves less than 2 weeks old may die suddenly from a hemorrhagic enteritis caused by *Clostridium perfringens* or *welchii*, type C. The toxins it produces, like the toxins of all the organisms of this group, are extremely dangerous. The beta toxin is thought to cause necrosis (death) of the mucous membrane of the intestine so that there is free hemorrhage into the bowel.

The true causes of hemorrhagic enteritis with fatal toxemia are unknown.

It has occurred oftenest in Hereford calves in Western and Southwestern States, but at times it affects calves of all beef or dairy breeds.

It is believed to be associated with overeating. It has killed calves that were large and growing well—possibly because they got more milk from their dams than they could digest or because they consumed more grain, grass, and feeds other than milk than their immature digestive tracts could handle. It has been suggested that climate might influence the activity of the clostridial organism.

A closely related organism, *Clostridium welchii* (not typed), which causes a slightly less hemorrhagic condition, has been found in Canada.

In calves in Canada and in the West, the disease caused by clostridial organisms resembles acute calf septicemia in that calves—usually 2 weeks old—often are found dead without warning.

Calves with hemorrhagic enterotoxemia may have colic, develop weakness and listlessness, quit nursing, and pass bloody feces. Afterwards the head is often pulled back by spasms of the neck muscles, general spasms occur, and death ensues in 2 to 24 hours. A tendency toward rigidity (instead of paralysis) is an important sign.

Strangely, in this acute condition, temperature seldom rises.

At autopsy the abomasum (stomach) often is filled with milk, and the small intestines contain blood in the lumen and wall. The inflammation is acute enough to be accompanied by a severe peritonitis.

A laboratory diagnosis is desirable

unless the disease has occurred regularly for several seasons in the area in which the affected calves are located.

Vaccination of the cows with a specific toxoid, an alum-precipitated killed culture of bacteria, before the birth of their calves is useful. A specific serum for the calves may be tried if the toxoid has not been used on the dams.

INFECTIONS with *Salmonella* organisms are so rare in cattle in the United States that little is known about the nature of the problem in calves. Actual cases have not been identified in the eastern part of the country. In 1954 an outbreak occurred in California. Perhaps the condition has existed in other areas but has been classified incorrectly as calf scours or has been overlooked entirely.

Many types of *Salmonella* organisms are believed to exist in places where calves are kept, but infection does not occur unless the calves are exhausted or starved or deprived of colostrum.

In the outbreak in California, 37 young calves had been deprived of colostrum and then shipped a long distance by truck—their exhaustion and starvation favored the development of the *Salmonella* infection. The specific germ was found in the spleen of eight of the calves. Veterinarians in California, on the basis of the animals' medical history and symptoms, have since diagnosed the sickness of many calves as salmonellosis.

Sick calves, 2 to 15 days old, usually have a brief period of fever. It may pass unnoticed and may be followed by sudden death. Other calves scour and sometimes pass bloody or watery feces. They may linger for weeks without any response to the usual treatments for diarrhea.

The intestines and sometimes the stomach are necrotic, but there may be no gross changes in the tissues of the dead calves at autopsy. Some hemorrhage may occur in the stomach and intestines, where many ulcers may be present. The condition may be mistaken for coccidiosis, acute scours, and (rarely) hemorrhagic enterotoxemia. A laboratory diagnosis would be desirable in most outbreaks.

The way to prevent the disease is to avoid improper handling of calves under 2 weeks old. Calves at this age should receive a small feeding of milk at least two or three times daily. Calves should get the proper amount of colostrum. They should be kept away from other scouring calves. They should not be moved long distances unless absolutely necessary.

All places where calves are kept should be completely disinfected. Feeding utensils should be sterilized after use.

No vaccine is available. No treatment is entirely satisfactory.

A CONDITION CALLED TETANY may occur in calves 3 months old or older. It supposedly is due to a lack of magnesium in the blood, perhaps because the calf's diet was low in magnesium. Calves that eat only milk are especially susceptible. The symptoms are stiffness and convulsions.

Efforts to prevent tetany should include adding magnesium to the diet.

The use of sedatives to relieve the tetanic spasms of muscle groups has been tried. While there is not ordinarily a simple calcium deficiency in these calves, it may be the only deficiency in some individuals. This is corrected by the use of calcium injections. As in "milk disease," vitamin E may be deficient. Some scientists have suggested the possibility of other vitamin deficiencies in tetany.

M. G. FINCHER *has been a large-animal clinician in the New York State Veterinary College at Cornell University since 1920 and professor of medicine, head of the Department of Medicine and Obstetrics, and director of the ambulatory clinic since 1942. He is director of the New York State mastitis control program. He is a member of the American Veterinary Medical Association, the United States Livestock Sanitary Association, and other professional organizations.*

Miscellaneous Diseases of Cattle

L. O. MOTT AND C. A. MANTHEI

MUCOSAL diseases are relatively new diseases of cattle in the United States. They affect the mucous membranes or tissues that line the digestive and respiratory systems.

Some of the diseases are caused by viruses (bacteria-free filtrates), but the causes of others have not yet been determined. Bacteria have been eliminated as the causative agent in nearly all instances.

When the disease affects the mucous membranes of the digestive tract, diarrhea is a common symptom; sometimes, therefore, it is called virus diarrhea.

These diseases are important because of the economic losses and because of their clinical resemblance to rinderpest, a serious virus disease that occurs in parts of Asia and Africa but has not appeared in the United States.

There are now recognized in the United States four or more different diseases of cattle that belong to the mucosal disease group: New York virus diarrhea, Indiana virus diarrhea, Iowa mucosal disease, and rhinotracheitis.

They are similar to (and probably should be grouped with) malignant catarrhal fever and bluetongue of cattle, both of which are exotic diseases but probably exist in this country. It is possible also that some of these diseases may have a part in the syndrome of shipping fever.

The first of the mucosal diseases was recognized and identified as New York virus diarrhea in 1946 by Peter Olafson, A. C. MacCallum, and F. H. Fox, of Cornell University. One or more of the diseases, however, may have been present in the United States before then, according to reports in the American Veterinary Medical Association Journal for March 1920.

New York virus diarrhea of cattle was the first mucosal disease in the United States identified (in 1946) as to virus origin and later differentiated from rinderpest by R. V. L. Walker, of the Dominion Department of Agriculture of Quebec, and Dr. Olafson. It is an infectious, febrile, transmissible disease, characterized by profuse diarrhea, ulcers, and erosions of the digestive tract.

An incubation period of 7 to 9 days usually is followed by a sudden rise in temperature, lack of appetite, depression, a drop in the number of white blood cells, diarrhea, coughing, ulcers, and erosions of mucous membranes. Pregnant cows may abort 10 to 90 days after the onset of the acute stage.

Young animals seem to react more severely and may be more susceptible than older ones. Animals that have recovered are immune to reinfection.

Incidence of the disease in early outbreaks was 33 to 88 percent. The variation might have been due to the strain of virus and individual resistance or partial immunity from previous exposure to the virus. The death rate in early outbreaks in New York averaged 4 to 8 percent of the affected animals. In later years the morbidity was less than 5 percent and the mortality was about 50 percent of the sick animals.

The geographic distribution and extent of the disease are probably greater than is generally supposed, because many animals from almost all sections of New York, exposed with challenge virus, were resistant to infection. Virus has been isolated from animals in New York, Connecticut, Maine, and California. Shortly after the disease appeared in New York, a similar disease was reported in Canada and in Sweden in 1951. Immunological comparisons of the virus strains in the United States indicate they are of the same immunological type. No comparisons have been made between the New York virus and the Canadian and Swedish viruses.

Serological identification tests, including complement-fixation and serum-neutralization tests, have been unsuccessful. A limited number of experimental inoculations were made into fertile chicken eggs, guinea pigs, swine, dogs, cats, goats, sheep, mice, and rabbits. They were successful only in rabbits.

When a virus can be inoculated into and live in an artificial host (the rabbit in this instance) and then is forced to live in this environment for many generations, it frequently loses its ability to produce sickness of the natural host (in this case, the cow). Such a changed virus, even though it no longer can produce disease, frequently has the ability to produce an immunity against the virulent disease in the natural host and may be of value for a live-virus vaccine. Because this virus that was transferred through 75 passages in rabbits became modified in virulence for cattle, it could be considered for vaccine immunization.

INDIANA VIRUS DIARRHEA, a mucosal disease of cattle similar in clinical appearance to New York virus diarrhea, appeared in Indiana in 1954.

The natural disease has been observed only in steers. The disease was transmitted experimentally to calves of both sexes with bacteria-free virus filtrates prepared from the blood of diseased animals. The incubation periods were 1 to 3 weeks. A sudden rise in temperature, loss of appetite, depression, increased heart action, and rapid respiration followed. Those symptoms were followed by nasal discharges, coughing, lameness, and diarrhea, accompanied with muzzle, mouth, and intestinal lesions characterized by circular areas of inflammation, and erosions of the mucous membranes. Similar lesions were observed in the openings in the nose and in the vulva and vagina of inoculated cattle.

The incidence of disease in affected herds was almost 100 percent. The mortality rate was 4 to 20 percent. The disease ran its course in 2 to 4 weeks in most instances.

This virus disease seems clinically, hematologically, and pathologically almost indistinguishable from New York mucosal disease virus diarrhea, but immunologically it appears to be a different disease. Animals that recovered from the Indiana virus disease were immune to challenge with the Indiana virus but were susceptible to exposure with the New York virus, whereas recovered animals from the New York virus were susceptible to challenge with the Indiana virus.

Iowa mucosal disease of cattle was first observed by F. K. Ramsey and W. H. Chivers in a 10-month-old Hereford steer admitted to the veterinary clinic at Iowa State College in 1951. By 1953 the disease had appeared on about 100 Iowa farms and on several farms of the adjoining States.

Reports from a national survey in 1955 indicated the disease had spread to all the States around Iowa and to other States. Eighteen States and one Territory reported presence of the disease.

The Iowa mucosal disease presents a clinical and pathological picture like the New York virus diarrhea and Indiana virus diarrhea, but it differs from them in that the number of sick animals in a herd is usually low, probably averaging 2 to 5 percent. The mortality rate in clinical cases is practically 100 percent.

Experimental transmissions of the disease were unsuccessful until 1955, when scientists at Purdue University reported transmission with bacteria-free disease tissue suspension filtrates. The cause of the disease appears to be a virus. No satisfactory treatment has been developed.

The body temperature rises for 24 to 48 hours during the early stages of the disease. Later it returns to normal. Other symptoms are complete loss of appetite, watery diarrhea (sometimes mixed with blood), drooling of saliva, depression, rapid loss of weight, and ulcers of the mucous membranes of the nostrils, muzzle, lips, gums, tongue, and mouth cavity. Some animals have a watery discharge from the eyes, opacity of the cornea, and lameness.

Nearly all the affected animals die within 3 to 10 days.

It is likely that many animals in affected herds have developed an inapparent or nonclinical form of the disease because there have been no records of recurrence of the disease on the same farm—an indication that a herd immunity developed. Some attempts at transmission from sick animals to normal calves resulted in incubation periods of 2 to 8 days after inoculation. Temperature reactions lasting 2 to 5 days followed, but no other evidence of a clinical disease developed.

All of the common beef and dairy breeds have been involved. Most of the animals have been 6 to 14 months old. No seasonal factor has been associated with the occurrence of the disease, but in Iowa most of the cases occurred in winter and early spring.

That affected herds may be 20 miles or more apart suggests that insects transmit the disease, although it is true that we usually associate insect vectors with seasonal diseases. There is no evidence that the Iowa mucosal disease is transmitted by contact.

RHINOTRACHEITIS (red nose, California influenzalike disease) is a contagious, acute virus disease of cattle. It involves mainly the mucous membrane of the upper respiratory tract. It occurred in the dairy cattle of Los Angeles County and surrounding counties of California from October 1953 to February 1954. An outbreak, which lasted 6 weeks, occurred in dairy herds in the Stockton area as the disease was subsiding in the Los Angeles area. The following year the disease appeared again in feeder cattle near Stockton. Almost simultaneously it appeared in feeder herds in the Imperial Valley and recurred in dairy cattle in the Los Angeles area. The outbreaks lasted 2 to 3 months.

About 10,000 animals were in those herds. About 22 percent of them became infected. The mortality rate was 2 to 3 percent.

An outbreak of a disease condition similar to the California influenzalike disease was reported in Colorado in January and February of 1955. It involved 250,000 feeder cattle in the northeast quarter of Colorado. An average of 50 percent of the animals in affected herds became sick. Mortality was about 1 percent. The disease was previously observed in Colorado as early as 1950 and continued occurring annually in a few scattered herds of feeder cattle until 1955, when the big outbreak developed.

The disease first caused an abrupt cessation of milk flow and high temperatures, with little evidence of other symptoms, among dairy cattle in California. Temperatures continued high for 3 or 4 days before returning to normal. During the second and third days of sickness there was some drooling of saliva, slight nasal discharges, slight depression, increased respiration, and occasional coughing. Some animals had impaired appetites. There was no change in white-blood-cell counts.

Most of the cows returned to the milking string after 7 to 10 days. Dairy calves had similar symptoms without any evidence of depression. They also had a conjunctivitis, with a marked discharge of tears.

The disease usually appeared in beef or feeder cattle 3 to 6 weeks after the animals had been placed on feed. High temperatures, which usually returned to normal after a few days, attended the initial stages. Temperature reactions are associated with depression, increased respirations, a marked inflammation of the upper respiratory tract (including the nose openings, pharynx, larynx, and trachea) with various degrees of mucous discharges, drooling of saliva, and eye trouble.

Some animals displayed lameness,

diarrhea, and weight loss after a few days, but little or no lung involvement, little or no change in white-blood-cell counts, no central nervous symptoms, and no visible mouth or tongue lesions.

Even though the disease is naturally highly contagious, most attempts to transmit it have failed to produce an agent that will reproduce clinical cases on successive animal passages. Frequently only slight rises in temperature are observed in inoculated animals.

Many experimental laboratory animals, including guinea pigs and mice, and fertile chicken eggs were inoculated without any evidence of disease transmission. The disease was successfully transmitted in 1955 from infected to normal cattle with bacteria-free virus filtrates by scientists at the University of California with the California disease and by scientists at Colorado Agricultural and Mechanical College with the Colorado disease. The virus from each State was proved to be similar or possibly identical by cross-immunity studies.

Infected herds seem to have a high degree of immunity after they have recovered. Recurrences of known infection have been rare. These observations suggest scientists may be successful in efforts to develop an immunizing vaccine.

The economic losses of the disease are largely due to weight loss, milk loss, and cost of treatment. Treatment has been attempted with many drugs, including the sulfa drugs and antibiotics. As with most virus diseases, however, drug treatment has proved to be of little or no value.

The malignant catarrhal fever (bovine malignant catarrh) of cattle is an acute, infectious, noncontagious, and generally a highly fatal disease.

It is characterized by a marked swelling and enlargement of lymphoid tissues, severe inflammation and necrosis of nasal mucous membranes and conjunctiva of the eye, and rapid loss of weight. There are discharges from the eyes and nose.

The causative agent is a virus in the blood and lymphoid tissues. The disease incidence in infected herds is usually only 1 to 2 percent, but the mortality of affected cases in this country is 80 to 90 percent.

The disease occurred in 1850 in Europe and in South Africa, where it still is a serious problem. Its first occurrence in this country was reported to be in Pennsylvania in 1918–1919. It has been reported in many parts of the country since then.

There is some question whether the disease recognized in the United States is the same as the disease of the same name as described by scientists in Africa and Europe. As far as we know, no tests have been made to prove that the diseases are caused by the same virus. It is not logical, without additional research on our part, to assume therefore that all the information published by foreign workers may apply to our disease.

The Europeans describe four forms of the disease: The peracute form, the alimentary form, the head and eye form, and the mild form.

Scientists in Africa reported that they recognized only the head and eye form and the mild form and that sheep might harbor the virus without showing symptoms and cause infection in cattle through contact or transmission by insect vectors.

The virus recovered from the blood and lymphoid tissues of clinically diseased cattle is difficult to store and preserve, because it will not survive freezing or storage at ordinary refrigeration temperatures for more than 30 days.

In their studies of the disease, scientists have found it hard to transfer the disease to test animals. Investigators in Africa reported it necessary to keep up a continuous passage of the virus in living cattle to maintain a source of virus for experimental work.

The incubation period—the period from inoculation to the first rise in temperature—in experimental animals varies from 14 to 60 days. Death usually occurs within 4 to 10 days after the initial fever.

It has been demonstrated experimentally that immunity in recovered animals lasts only 4 to 8 months. No reliable method of immunization or treatment of any value have been developed. Cattle of all breeds and ages and both sexes are equally susceptible to infection.

BLUETONGUE is an infectious, transmissible virus disease primarily of sheep. Scientists in Africa report it is characterized in cattle by catarrhal inflammation of the mucous membranes of the mouth, nose, and gastrointestinal tract. Frequently it involves the coronary band and sensitive laminae of the feet.

Bluetongue has occurred in many of our sheep-producing States. Some outbreaks of clinical bluetongue in cattle can be expected.

It is not unusual to observe clinical cases characterized by localized inflammation and necrosis of the mouth and tongue, swellings of the lower parts of the limbs, marked hyperaemia of the skin (especially in the regions of the accessory digits), and necrosis of the epidermis of the skin, udder, and teats, followed by scab formation. A dermatitis associated with scab formation may occur in other parts of the body.

The lesions of bluetongue, foot-and-mouth disease, and vesicular stomatitis occur on the same parts of the body of cattle and may not be differentiated during certain stages by even the most experienced workers.

Bluetongue may be differentiated from the vesicular diseases—foot-and-mouth disease and vesicular stomatitis—by the absence of true vesicles, but vesicles frequently are present with the vesicular diseases only for a short period of time. After the vesicles have disappeared, the lesions on the feet and in the mouth would resemble and could be confused with the lesions of bluetongue.

Bluetongue does not spread from animal to animal by direct-contact exposure within screened pens but is transmitted by insect vectors. The vesicular diseases are easily spread by direct or indirect body contact during their acute stages.

The history of herd infections as to incidence and rate of disease spread usually is different for each disease, so those factors may be of assistance in arriving at a differential diagnosis. The expected number of animals sick from bluetongue would be low—less than 5 percent—in contrast to an average of 30 percent with vesicular stomatitis and frequently as high as 100 percent with foot-and-mouth disease.

To obtain a positive diagnosis of bluetongue in sick cattle, it is necessary to transfer some of their blood to normal sheep, which should result in sickness of the inoculated sheep with symptoms of bluetongue after an incubation period of about 7 days.

Cattle infected with bluetongue virus are said to be carriers of the virus for 3 or 4 months. They may be reservoirs of infection during that time. Cattle that lose their carrier status regain their susceptibility to reinfection and may again become carriers of the virus for another 3 or 4 months.

No cattle-to-sheep subinoculation tests had been made in the United States up to 1956 to determine whether cattle are carriers of bluetongue virus, and no experimental transmission of the disease to cattle had been attempted.

NASAL GRANULOMA (snoring disease) attacks the nasal cavities of cattle. The nasal mucous lining thickens. The condition interferes with the passage of air in breathing and causes a peculiar snoring sound.

Nasal granuloma has existed among the cattle of India for a long time, but it had not been observed in any other country until a similar disease was reported in 1933 in the United States. The disease was first discovered in this country in a dairy herd at the Iberia Livestock Experiment Station at Jeanerette, La. Subsequently it has been observed in several other herds in Louisiana, but apparently has not been recognized in any other part of the United States.

Affected animals in the more advanced stages of the disease may lose weight, but few have died from it.

Nasal granuloma occurs in India in two forms. One is caused by a schistosome worm, or fluke. The other form is caused by a fungus of the genus *Rhinosporidium*. The specific cause of the disease in the United States has not been determined. Bacteriological studies and examination for the presence of parasites have given negative results. Experimental animal inoculations likewise have failed to yield specific information about the cause.

The first symptoms usually noticed are sneezing and a nasal discharge of a mixture of mucous and pus. In the more acute cases, this material frequently is mixed with blood and may also contain bits of necrotic mucous membrane. The bloody discharges may be seen on the stable floor or on the grass or the ground where the affected animals have been pastured.

As the disease progresses, difficult breathing is noticed and a peculiar droning sound, or snoring, can be heard for some distance. The affected cattle show a characteristic wrinkling of the skin around the wing of the nostril because the partial closing or obstruction of the nasal cavity makes breathing harder. The difficult breathing is more pronounced during the warm months. The disease tends to subside or becomes more or less dormant during the cool season.

Certain treatments have been tried without much success. None has given permanent relief.

The lesions or tissue changes are confined strictly to the nasal mucous membrane and rarely extend beyond the first 3 inches of the anterior nares, or nostrils. The lesions may extend entirely around the nasal cavity, including the mucosa of the nasal septum (the wall separating the nostrils).

The mucosa becomes markedly congested in the more acute cases. Hemorrhages and sloughing follow, leaving small denuded areas, from which blood or a mixture of blood and mucus escapes from time to time. The nasal mucosa also become thickly studded with many small, grayish, tuberclelike nodules. In cases of long duration, the nasal mucosa thicken noticeably because of the extensive chronic fibrous changes.

CALF DIPHTHERIA, an acute infectious disease, is characterized by the formation of a diphtheritic false membrane on the mucous lining of the mouth and throat.

The disease sometimes attacks calves as early as the third or fourth day after birth. Mature animals may become affected in severe outbreaks. The mortality is high.

Calf diphtheria is known also as necrotic stomatitis, gangrenous stomatitis, ulcerative stomatitis, necrotic laryngitis, malignant stomatitis, and sore mouth.

The disease is caused by a specific organism, *Spherophorus necrophorus*, which is widespread in nature. The organism is anaerobic—it grows only in the absence of oxygen. It gains entrance through wounds in the mucous membrane, or lining, of the mouth. Such injuries are usually caused by sharppointed particles of food or other objects. Infection may also occur during the eruption of the first teeth after birth. The parts of the mouth most often affected at the beginning are the base or sides of the tongue, the inside of the cheeks adjacent to the molar teeth, and the lips. If the infection persists, however, the lesions, or tissue injuries, may spread to the hard palate, the gums, the pharynx, the nasal passages, the trachea (windpipe), and the lungs.

Occasionally only 1 or 2 animals in a herd may be affected, but sometimes 70 percent may show evidence of the disease.

The first symptoms appear 3 to 5

days after the organism gains entrance to the tissues. The affected animal appears depressed, and even suckling calves will refuse feed. Drooling of saliva and swallowing movements may be noted. At times a swelling may be observed on the side of the cheek or in the region of the throat. The animal becomes weak and loses flesh rapidly. When the lesions have become extensive in the larynx and nasal passages, there are wheezing, coughing, and labored breathing. A sticky, yellowish or greenish-yellow discharge from the nostrils may be noticed. At that stage, the animal is greatly depressed, extremely weak, and emaciated, and lies down all the time. Slobbering is profuse. The tongue is swollen and sometimes protrudes from the mouth, which has an offensive odor.

Soon after they enter the tissues of the mouth, the organisms multiply rapidly, and a poisonous substance, or toxin, is elaborated. The toxin destroys the invaded tissues, so that an extensive ulceration of the mucous lining of the mouth cavity occurs. The mouth of an affected animal may have ulcers on the mucosa of the cheek, on the base of the tongue, or along the sides of the tongue. The destroyed tissue is grayish yellow. Around the borders of the ulcer the tissue will be slightly raised, reddened, and granulated. A discharge of albuminous material from the ulcerated areas combines with the dead cellular elements to form a fibrinous mass, or membrane, that gradually becomes dry, crumbly, and cheesy. This degenerated tissue sticks tightly and can be scraped or peeled off only with difficulty.

As the disease process spreads, the lesions may involve the deeper tissue structures to a depth of an inch or more. In those cases there usually is no tendency toward spontaneous healing, and the untreated lesions continue to spread and involve large areas of the mouth, tongue, upper part of the windpipe, pharynx, and nasal cavities.

The infection becomes more or less generalized in cases of long standing.

Lesions may be found in the lungs, stomach, intestines, and liver. Animals that have the very acute form may die within a week. The cause of death is toxemia, or blood poisoning, which results from the infection rather than the local effects of the disease. In less acute outbreaks, affected animals may live some weeks and have extensive lesions.

In mild cases, if the sick animals are given prompt attention in the early stages, treatment may bring about recovery. In the highly virulent outbreaks in which there is extensive involvement of the tissue, however, treatment is of little value.

Prevention consists in segregating the sick from the healthy animals, thoroughly cleaning and disinfecting the stables and sheds, and examining the healthy animals each day to detect new cases, which should be isolated as soon as they are found.

Treatment consists chiefly of alleviating the symptoms.

RED WATER DISEASE is caused by a micro-organism, *Clostridium hemolyticum*, and is confined mainly to the mountain valleys of the western United States. It has been reported also in Louisiana, Mexico, and Chile.

C. hemolyticum is a spore-forming bacillus. Because the spores are resistant to changes in temperature and moisture, the disease may persist in contaminated areas for a long time.

Cattle are the most susceptible. The disease, which is also known as bacillary hemoglobinuria, hemorrhagic disease, and infectious icterohemoglobinuria, has been seen in sheep and swine.

The symptoms and pathology are quite uniform. Appetite, rumination, and bowel movement suddenly cease. The temperature rises in the early stages but drops below normal before death. The urine is dark red, clear, and foamy. The feces are bile stained or bloody.

Affected animals stand apart from the rest of the herd, have a tucked-up abdomen, and move about very little. Lesions most often seen are infarcts in the liver, which are lighter in color than the liver tissue. Extensive hemorrhages occur on the serous membranes and subcutaneous connective tissue. A red exudate is found in the peritoneal and thoracic cavities. Besides subserous hemorrhages in the intestinal wall, extensive hemorrhage occurs in the intestinal mucosa.

A tentative diagnosis is usually made on the basis of symptoms, pathology, the kind of animal involved, and the section of the country where the disease occurs. A positive diagnosis can be made only by isolation and identification of the causative agent.

Several types of vaccines and bacterins have been studied. The aluminum hydroxide formalinized bacterin has given the best results. An immune serum also has been developed. It has given good results in treating affected animals in the early stages of the disease and in protecting animals against infection.

L. O. MOTT *is a veterinarian in charge of the Viral and Rickettsial Diseases Section of the Animal Disease and Parasite Research Branch. He received the degree of doctor of veterinary medicine from Kansas State College, where he served 2 years on the veterinary faculty. Dr. Mott joined the Department of Agriculture in 1934.*

C. A. MANTHEI *is a veterinarian and the head of the Bacterial and Mycotic Diseases Section of the Animal Disease and Parasite Research Branch at Beltsville. He has engaged in animal disease research since 1938.*

For further reading:

James A. Baker, Charles J. York, James H. Gillespie, and Grayson B. Mitchell: *Virus Diarrhea in Cattle,* American Journal of Veterinary Research, volume 15, number 57, pages 525–531. 1954.

T. Childs: *X Disease of Cattle—Saskatchewan,* Canadian Journal of Comparative Medicine and Veterinary Science, volume 10, number 11, pages 316–319. 1946.

Harry Hedstrom and Axel Isaksson: *Epizootic Enteritis in Cattle in Sweden,* Cornell Veterinarian, volume 41, number 3, pages 251–253. 1951.

C. J. Marshall, T. E. Munce, M. F. Barnes, and Fred Boerner: *Malignant Catarrhal Fever,* Journal of the American Veterinary Medical Association, volume 56, pages 570–580. 1920.

R. W. McIntyre: *Experimental Studies of Acute Upper Respiratory Infection in Calves,* Journal of the American Veterinary Medical Association, volume 125, number 933, pages 473–474. 1954.

D. G. McKercher, J. E. Moulton, and D. E. Jasper: *Virus and Virus-like Cattle Disease Entities New to California,* Proceedings of the United States Livestock Sanitary Association, Fifty-Eighth Annual Meeting, pages 260–269. 1954.

Peter Olafson, A. D. MacCallum, and F. H. Fox: *An Apparently New Transmissible Disease of Cattle,* Cornell Veterinarian, volume 36, number 3, pages 205–213, 1946.

F. K. Ramsey and W. H. Chivers: *Mucosal Disease of Cattle,* North American Veterinarian, volume 34, number 9, pages 629–633. 1953.

Robert J. Schroeder and M. D. Moys: *An Acute Upper Respiratory Infection of Dairy Cattle,* Journal of the American Veterinary Medical Association, volume 125, number 933, pages 471–472. 1954.

R. V. L. Walker and Peter Olafson: *Failure of Virus Diarrhea of Cattle to Immunize Against Rinderpest,* Cornell Veterinarian, volume 37, number 2, pages 107–111. 1947.

DISEASES

AND PARASITES

AFFECTING

swine

Lung Parasites of Swine

JOHN S. ANDREWS

SEVEN species of roundworms and one species of flatworm may exist in the lungs of pigs.

Three of the roundworms, *Metastrongylus elongatus*, *M. salmi*, and *Choerostrongylus pudendotectus*, are the common lungworms of swine and grow to maturity in the lungs, as does the much less common flatworm or lung fluke, *Paragonimus westermanii*.

The four remaining roundworm species, the large roundworm, the intestinal threadworm, the hookworm, and the kidney worm, live in the lungs only during their early development. They complete their growth in other organs.

The effect of pulmonary parasitism on the growth and health of pigs is hard to evaluate on the farm because it is often complicated by other disease-producing agents, like bacteria,

viruses, and other species of parasites. In fact, lungworms have been reported to act as reservoir and intermediate hosts for swine influenza virus. The affected pigs may suffer also from malnutrition and other conditions brought about by poor management and lack of sanitation.

The common lungworms of swine are whitish, threadlike, and up to 2 inches long. They occur in the smaller air passages of the lungs (bronchioles) and—in heavy infections—in the larger air passages (trachea and bronchi).

Except for *M. salmi*, which are chiefly in swine in the South, lungworms are among the most widespread of swine parasites and occur in all parts of the United States. Investigators in the Southeast found that 70 percent of the swine they examined had lungworms.

335

The lungworms of swine require a second or intermediate host in order to complete their development. Female lungworms produce large numbers of thick-shelled eggs, which the infected hog coughs up, swallows, and ejects with the feces.

Earthworms, particularly the red-striped worms of the genus *Helodrilus* that exist chiefly in manure piles and rich soil, swallow the eggs, which hatch in the earthworms' intestines. A single earthworm may harbor 2,000 lungworm larvae. The tiny worms bore into the glandular part of the intestine (the part that contains the calciferous glands) and also get into one or all of the five to seven pairs of hearts of the earthworm. The larvae become infective to pigs 3 or 4 weeks later. They are freed from the earthworms by the process of digestion.

Pigs become infected with lungworms by swallowing the earthworms that harbor the larvae. The larvae penetrate the pig's intestinal wall and are carried by the lymphatic and circulatory systems to the lungs. There they burrow through the walls of the capillaries into the alveoli, become localized in the bronchioles, complete their development, and mate. The females produce eggs about 33 days after the pig ingests the larvae.

The outstanding symptom of lungworm infection in pigs is a cough. Even lightly infected animals may be subject to fits of coughing, which can weaken them and lower their vitality. The coughing seems to be caused by the presence of the lungworms in the bronchioles and by their moving about in the air passages. This movement irritates the mucous linings of these tubes. The worms block the air passages, interfere with breathing, and cause greater secretion of mucus. The pig therefore has to breathe faster, and that in turn makes the cough worse.

Hemorrhages appear on the surface of the lungs during the early stages of lungworm invasion. The constant irritation of the lungs by the worms and the plugging of the bronchioles subse-

quently can bring about the consolidation of the lung tissue around the sites occupied by the worms. The tips of the lungs become grayish or whitish and very hard in some cases of long-standing infection.

Pigs infected with lungworms tend to go off feed, become unthrifty, and fail to grow normally.

No EFFECTIVE MEDICINAL treatment is available for removing lungworms from swine. A change in diet may be helpful by temporarily stimulating the appetite of the affected pigs.

Infected swine should be removed from the lots on which they acquired the parasites and put in dry, clean pens that have concrete floors. They may be placed on temporary pastures that have not been used for pigs for several years so as to insure against further infestation from swallowing infected earthworms. Sick pigs, while they are kept in isolation, should be supplied with nutritious feed, safe drinking water, and good bedding, which should be changed fairly often.

A pasture or lot that has many infected earthworms may remain dangerous for several years. In soil at Beltsville, Md., on which lungworm eggs were deposited 4 years earlier, investigators found earthworms in which were infective larvae. The parasites and their intermediate hosts undoubtedly survived because a dense plant growth had kept the soil moist. Eggs remained viable for several months in soil in which the roots of vegetation growing on the surface penetrated to the level at which the eggs were located. But in soil bare of vegetation the period of survival was much shorter; in dry soil lungworms failed to survive more than a month in the summer.

Lungworm eggs can withstand low temperatures when adequate moisture is present. They have survived continuous freezing at 14° to 20° F. for more than a year.

Lungworm infection in swine can be prevented by keeping pigs in lots where they cannot come in contact with infected earthworms. Because the worms thrive in old hog lots in which manure and litter have accumulated, in old strawstacks, on permanent pastures, and in low fields that receive drainage from higher ground, a farmer who avoids grazing swine on such areas will do much to control lungworm infection. If he has to use such places for raising pigs, he can discourage rooting by putting rings in the noses of the animals and so reduce the number of earthworms ingested by the pigs.

THE LUNG FLUKE, *Paragonimus westermanii*, is a thick, oval worm, about one-fifth to three-fifths inch long and about one-fifth inch wide. It occurs in sacs, or cysts, in the lung tissue of many mammals, including man. It has been found in swine in Kentucky, southern Ohio, and southern Georgia. It has a limited distribution because the completion of its life cycle in the United States depends on the presence of various species of crayfish and a small amphibious snail, *Pomatiopsis lapidaria*, which live along the edges of small, sluggish streams less than 30 feet across.

The lung fluke has been of limited economic importance in swine, but it could spread rapidly in areas favorable to its propagation.

The eggs produced by the adult fluke, which is hermaphroditic, are coughed up, swallowed, and discharged with the feces of the infected pig. The larval flukes (miracidia) develop in a warm, moist environment to the stage infective to the snail host in about 3 weeks. The eggs hatch, and the miracidia penetrate the soft body of the snail.

After about 12 weeks and two stages of reproduction within the snail, in which the number of individual parasites has been vastly increased, the second infective stage, or cercaria, is produced. These actively motile organisms emerge from the snails in the greatest numbers in the late afternoon or night—when the crayfish also is most active. The cercariae penetrate the underside of the tail of the crayfish.

The fully developed stages (metacercariae), which are infective to pigs (the final host), develop in the crayfish 46 days after exposure to cercariae. Pigs can also become infected with the lung fluke by eating another final host in which immature forms of the parasite have not yet reached the lungs.

Pigs acquire lung flukes by eating infected crayfish, which they bring to the surface of the ground by rooting in wet and boggy pastures. The encysted flukes (metacercariae) are freed by digestion in the pig's stomach and small intestine. They then bore through the intestinal wall and migrate through the body cavity, penetrate the diaphragm, and enter the lung tissue. There they may form cysts, or pockets, which usually contain two worms, and develop to maturity in about 6 weeks.

No special symptoms have been noted in affected hogs. In other hosts, heavily infected with lung flukes, the pulmonary mucus is tinged yellowish-brown by the thousands of fluke eggs in it. Finding these eggs in the bronchial secretions or in the feces is the only sure way of diagnosing this infection in the living animal.

The presence of the flukes in the lungs produces an inflammatory reaction. When the worms are located near the surface of the lung, the cysts appear as bluish-gray protuberances. If the cysts are deep in the lung, the surface of the lung may show only a swelling. Sometimes there is a brownish cast because of the large number of eggs that lodge there.

There is no known treatment that will remove lung flukes from swine or any other animal.

Infection can be prevented by keeping hogs off wet and boggy areas along small creeks or rivers, where infected crayfish may live.

JOHN S. ANDREWS, *a parasitologist in the Animal Disease and Parasite Research Branch of the Agricultural Research Service, has studied the internal parasites of the larger domestic animals since 1930.*

Kidney Worms of Swine

JOHN S. ANDREWS AND FRANCIS G. TROMBA

THE KIDNEY worm of swine, *Stephanurus dentatus*, used to be considered of economic importance only in swine raised in the Southeastern States.

Surveys in 1947, however, disclosed that 20 to 40 percent of the livers of the general run of hogs sent from the Corn Belt to the meatpacking plants showed damage that was attributed to kidney worms. Kidney worms also have been found in pigs originating in Massachusetts, Kansas, Nebraska, and central Washington. They have caused estimated annual losses of more than 72 million dollars.

Kidney worms attack swine almost exclusively, but they occasionally occur in cattle.

The mature worms are 1 to 2 inches long and have a rather thick, black and white body. They usually live in cysts, or pockets, along the walls of the ureters (the tubes connecting the kidneys with the urinary bladder) and in the kidney. A female that happens to be in a cyst near a ureter pierces its wall and deposits its eggs in the opening. If she is in the kidney, she deposits the eggs in the ducts there.

In either instance, the eggs are swept into the bladder and are voided with the urine. If they fall on warm, moist soil, where they are protected from direct sunlight and from drying, they hatch in 18 to 24 hours into very small, free-living larvae, which are not infective. In another 3 to 5 days, under favorable conditions, the larvae undergo two molts and then can infect pigs.

As one infected pig may pass a million kidney worm eggs in a day, a pasture or hog lot can soon become heavily infested.

PIGS BECOME INFECTED with kidney worms in two ways—by swallowing the larvae while feeding on or rooting in infested soil and by lying on infested soil—the larvae, stimulated by the warmth of the pig's body, are able to penetrate its unbroken skin. After gaining entrance into the pig, whether by way of the mouth or by the skin, the larvae begin their migration through the body.

The larvae that are ingested penetrate the intestinal wall and presumably are carried to the liver by way of the blood stream; most of them leave the blood vessels and invade the liver. They damage the liver tissue and produce hemorrhages, which are visible on its surface just beneath the transparent capsule that encloses it. When these injuries heal, the liver becomes badly scarred, and the lesions appear as hard, grayish areas of varying sizes and shapes.

The unhealed or incompletely healed liver injuries are far more unsightly than the healed lesions. The latter usually no longer contain worms, but the unhealed lesions are soft and contain pus and live, dead, or degenerated worms. The entire liver may be covered also with a fibrinous deposit and may adhere rather firmly to the stomach and diaphragm.

Some of the larvae may leave the liver and invade other parts of the body. Immature kidney worms have been found in the body cavity, lungs, kidney fat, various blood vessels, the loin and other edible muscle tissue, and the spinal cord.

Larvae that enter through the skin invade adjacent tissues and blood vessels and become as widely distributed throughout the pig's body as those that entered the digestive tract.

Most of the larvae die in the pig's organs and tissues before they attain maturity. Usually they form abscesses wherever they happen to be. Some of the parasites can migrate to the region of the kidney and ureters, where they mature and mate and the females deposit their eggs. The period necessary for the worms to attain egg-laying maturity is about 6 months to a year from the date of infection.

THE ECONOMIC LOSSES due to kidney worms (estimated at more than 72 million dollars a year) are of two main kinds—those occurring on the farm and those sustained when the pigs are marketed.

The first group includes losses resulting from unthriftiness, from the additional cost of labor and feed necessary to bring a parasitized pig to market weight, and from the death of pigs because of gross parasitism.

The second group of losses results from lower market prices because of damage done to otherwise edible parts of the carcass.

An example of the losses due to unthriftiness and increased consumption of feed is a report that uninfected pigs gained 30 percent more weight than their infected litter mates and that infected pigs gained about one-half pound less a day than their uninfected litter mates during the growth period.

In meatpacking plants, all parts of the carcass in which kidney worms are found or which show evidence of damage due to the migration of the parasites are condemned entirely or are trimmed so as to remove the damaged parts. The condemnations may run as high as 66 percent of the kidneys and 94 percent of the livers of pigs from farms where infestation is heavy. Condemnations of the loins and hams are somewhat less, but the overall damage to the hog carcass caused by kidney worms has been estimated to be as much as 50 cents a hundredweight of live weight.

NO SATISFACTORY TREATMENT has been devised for removing kidney worms after they have established themselves in the pig's body. They cannot be reached by drugs or chemicals administered by mouth, and no chemical has been found that can kill the parasites without harming the pig.

Kidney worms can be controlled, however, in a number of ways.

Eggs of the worms and the larvae are quickly destroyed by exposure to direct sunlight, drying, low temperatures, and moderate degrees of heat.

If pastures grazed by pigs that pass eggs of kidney worms in their urine are planted so that the amount of soil surface exposed to sunlight is increased, the number of larvae surviving to the infective stage can be reduced greatly. That can be done by planting the forage crop in rows instead of sowing broadcast. Another way is to plow a bare strip about 3 feet wide inside the fence around the lots used by grazing pigs and place the shelter and feeding and watering equipment in places bare of vegetation.

The infective larvae can crawl from the soil to blades of grass or other herbage when the vegetation is wet with dew or rain. Their chances of being picked up by grazing pigs thus are increased. The use of forage plants with leaves that can be grazed several inches above the soil surface has the effect of reducing the number of larvae ingested by the pigs.

Several months may elapse before infected pigs pass eggs of kidney worms in their urine. Gilts farrowing their first litters may pass few eggs at farrowing time, but older sows from the same herd often pass large numbers of the eggs. By restricting his breeding herd to young sows farrowing their first litter, therefore, a farmer should be able greatly to reduce reinfestation of the pastures.

The infective larvae that are not exposed to sunlight, drying, and extremes of temperature may survive 6 months or more on pastures. They also can survive and remain infective for a month or more when ingested by common earthworms.

Attempts have been made to use chemicals to kill the eggs and larvae in the soil. All of the methods tried have been expensive, and the chemicals have been difficult to apply effectively or have harmed the vegetation.

Methyl bromide, a gas used to destroy nematodes in soil, destroys larvae of kidney worms to a depth of 12 inches in loose, sandy, loam soil. It is applied in the airspace between the soil surface and a layer of vaporproof paper placed immediately above it and is allowed to remain for 24 hours.

Commercial benzene hexachloride and the delta isomer destroy preinfective larvae in laboratory cultures, but its effectiveness on larvae in soil is unknown.

Polyborate, a mixture of sodium pentaborate tetrahydrate and sodium tetraborate pentahydrate, applied dry or in solution to soil at the rate of 5 pounds of the chemical per 100 square feet, has been used experimentally to destroy larvae on small plots, but it was found to be injurious to vegetation and could not be used on pastures.

It appears, then, that any plan of control must be based on the susceptibility of the eggs and larvae to sunlight and drying and on the relatively small numbers of eggs in the urine of gilts farrowing their first litters.

Good feeding and management also help to minimize the direct effects of kidney worms on infected pigs, as they build up the general health of the herd.

JOHN S. ANDREWS *is a parasitologist in the Helminth Parasite Section of the Agricultural Research Service.*

FRANCIS G. TROMBA *is a parasitologist in the Helminth Parasite Section. Dr. Tromba is a graduate of the University of Maryland. He has done extensive research on the swine kidney worm.*

The Large Intestinal Roundworm

LLOYD A. SPINDLER

LARGE intestinal roundworms are pinkish worms about as thick as an ordinary lead pencil. The mature females may be about a foot long. The males are smaller and have curved tails. The adults normally live in the small intestine but may wander into the liver and elsewhere.

About 7 of every 10 pigs and 1 of every 3 hogs of breeding age on farms may have these parasites in the gut.

Commonly known as ascarids, large intestinal roundworms cost hog raisers of the United States an estimated 50 million dollars a year. Those losses result chiefly from unthriftiness and death of young pigs. They can be avoided to a large extent by good livestock management and treatment with approved remedies at the proper time.

Farmers combat ascarids and other parasites when they follow good husbandry practices—sanitation, proper feeding, pasture rotation—which tend to protect pigs against infection and help them to withstand the injurious effects of the parasites they do acquire.

Pigs become infected with ascarids by swallowing the eggs. Each female ascarid may lay 250,000 eggs a day. These microscopic eggs pass from the pig's intestine with the droppings. When they reach the outside, they are in an early stage of development and are not infective. Within a few weeks, especially when the weather is warm and the eggs remain moist, a tiny worm develops inside the egg shell.

The eggs are then infectious to pigs. The eggs have thick, tough shells.

They can withstand severe cold, dryness, and most chemical disinfectants, and can live up to 7 years in soil.

When a pig swallows infective ascarid eggs, they hatch in its small intestine. A tour through the pig's body, from the intestine through the liver and lungs and back again, is then taken by the larval—young—ascarids. First they leave the intestine by burrowing into its wall and getting into the blood stream, which carries them to the liver. Next they travel to the lungs, passing through the heart on the way. From the lungs they pass up the windpipe to the throat and are swallowed, passing down the esophagus or gullet into the stomach and at last into the small intestine.

This journey usually takes about 10 days. By the time they have returned to the intestine, they are about 10 times as large as when they began the journey, but they are too small to be seen without a microscope. They grow rapidly and become mature in about 2 months. The fully grown females begin laying eggs, which pass out of the intestine and become infectious to swine.

Because of the enormous numbers of eggs produced by ascarids and because many hogs are likely to harbor the parasites, pastures and lots much used by swine are apt to be heavily seeded with the eggs. Such premises can be a source of trouble when pigs are kept thereon. Pigs are subject to damage by ascarids from the time they are born, and in general it is the younger ones that are victims of the heaviest infections.

ASCARIDS DAMAGE the health of pigs in many ways. Young ascarids passing through the lungs injure them severely, causing hemorrhages, or bleeding. If numerous, they may give rise to pneumonia, which may kill the pig.

Pigs that live in surroundings contaminated with many ascarid eggs frequently have so many of the young worms in the lungs at one time that they develop thumps, a sort of spasmodic, labored type of breathing that wears them out and may kill some of them. There are other causes of thumps, but many thumpy pigs are suffering from ascarids. Nothing can be done for thumpy pigs in the way of treatment, since the young roundworms are in the lungs, where it is impossible to get at them with medicines. Thumps are a warning to the farmer that more trouble may be expected, especially when the pigs are weaned and put on feed. Pigs that survive the stage of lung infection often fail to grow normally, develop poorly, and remain small, stunted, and unprofitable.

Pigs kept where they pick up enough ascarid eggs to cause thumps will continue to pick them up every day. By weaning time they may have collected enough of the parasites to injure seriously their health and retard growth.

Even a few ascarids in the intestine may cause the pig to utilize its feed poorly and make poor weight gains. For example, in experiments to show how much ascarids can retard the growth of weanling pigs, the experimentally infected animals weighed at slaughter 45 to 54 pounds less than their worm-free litter mates. Those that had the most ascarids gained the least. One that acquired about 100 of the worms lost weight rapidly and died. All the wormy pigs suffered severely from thumps, did not eat well, and failed to grow as fast as the clean pigs.

Ascarids cause losses in other ways. While the young worms are passing through the liver, they often injure it so that small, whitish scars may form. Livers that have been severely damaged by young ascarids may contain many scars and are unfit for food.

Occasionally the adult and partly grown worms move into the liver and dam up the flow of bile from the liver to the intestine. The bile is then carried to the flesh and skin by the blood and gives them a yellowish color, which is spoken of as icterus, or jaundice. Flesh of jaundiced pigs is unfit to eat. At times about 8 percent of all hogs condemned by Federal meat inspectors are condemned for this reason. Market prices for hogs generally are adjusted downward to account for expected losses caused by ascarids and other parasites.

COMPLETE ERADICATION of ascarids from a herd is difficult, because so many eggs are produced by the worms and because the eggs are so long lived. It is possible, however, to manage in such a way as to reduce or eliminate the losses caused by the worms. The best method is to keep pigs from becoming infected until they are about 4 months old. Thereafter they are less likely to be affected so seriously even though they may acquire some worms. Good livestock management and treatment at the proper time are the ways to do that.

TREATMENT IS DESIRABLE when pigs are kept on premises that are much used by older hogs and are therefore likely to be contaminated heavily with roundworm eggs. Pigs in such conditions may benefit from two treatments before they reach marketable age and weight, one shortly after weaning time and the other about 2 months later.

The most generally satisfactory treatment consists in feeding pigs for a day on a mixture containing from 0.75 to 1 percent of sodium fluoride (technical grade) in dry ground feed (never in slop or in wet feed).

Instructions for the use of sodium fluoride are contained in the Department of Agriculture Farmers' Bulletin 1787, *Internal Parasites of Swine.*

But treatments are only aids to sound control measures. Prevention of infection is of the utmost importance because young ascarids do so much damage while they are in the lungs, before they can be reached by medicine. Control measures, to do the most good, should start before the pigs are born.

An effective program for the control of large intestinal roundworms is the McLean County system of swine sanitation, which is discussed in the De-

partment of Agriculture Leaflet 5, *Prevention of Roundworms in Pigs.*

The main features of the program are:

Remove all litter and trash from farrowing pens and houses and thoroughly clean them with hot water, soap, and lye to destroy and remove eggs of ascarids and other parasites.

A few days before her farrowing time, scrub the sow thoroughly with a brush, using soap and warm water to remove dirt and worm eggs from all parts of her body. Then put the clean sow into the clean farrowing pen.

Ten days or so after farrowing, haul (do not drive) the sow and little pigs to clean pasture, which has a suitable forage crop and on which there have been no hogs since the crop was sown.

Keep older pigs away from the pasture and keep the young pigs away from dirty hog lots.

Leave the pigs on clean pasture until they weigh about 100 pounds each. Better still, leave them on clean pastures until they are ready to be fattened for market.

MUCH CAN BE GAINED by feeding adequate amounts of a well-balanced diet. Feeding skim milk or whey may help control ascarids and other roundworm parasites. Milk or whey may be fed once daily instead of a grain feeding, or it may be fed instead of all other feed and water for periods of 3 days at intervals of 2 weeks. One should always feed all the milk or whey the pigs will drink. Pigs so fed remain free of worms, or nearly so. They also gain weight faster than pigs fed only grain.

LLOYD A. SPINDLER *was trained in parasitology at the Kansas State College of Agriculture, and the Johns Hopkins University School of Hygiene and Public Health. He joined the Department of Agriculture in 1929. Until 1955, when he was put in charge of the Protozoan Parasite Section, Animal Disease and Parasite Research Branch, he conducted investigations of parasites and parasitic diseases of swine and parasites of importance in meat inspection.*

The Intestinal Threadworm

LLOYD A. SPINDLER

INTESTINAL threadworms (*Strongyloides*) cause pigs to suffer from diarrhea, have a poor appetite, be unthrifty, lose weight, and die. Suckling pigs kept under crowded conditions in unclean pens are the ones most apt to be affected.

The cost of intestinal threadworms to hog raisers in the United States has been estimated at about 25 million dollars a year. Good husbandry practices help to avoid losses from threadworms as well as from other parasites.

Intestinal threadworms are slender, whitish, and about one-sixth inch long when fully grown. The adults, all of which are females, live in the small intestine. They lay microscopic eggs, which already are partially developed. The eggs pass from the intestine of the pig with its droppings and may hatch within a few hours.

The young worms (larvae) that emerge from the eggs follow one of two courses of development. Some develop directly to a stage that is infective to swine. Others develop into tiny males and females. These mate, and the females produce eggs, which hatch within a day or two. The larvae that issue from these eggs quickly become infective.

Intestinal threadworms are the only roundworm parasites of swine that multiply thus on soil.

Pigs acquire threadworms by swallowing the infective larvae or when the larvae burrow through the skin. In general, the larvae then travel by way of the blood stream to the liver, the lungs, up the windpipe, down the esophagus, or gullet, to the stomach, and through it to the small intestine, where they quickly mature and begin producing eggs.

Some of the larvae wander more extensively in the pig's body. They even enter the brain and spinal cord, the muscles of the body and heart, the tongue, the voice box, the kidneys, and other places. Eventually, however, most of them make their way to the lungs and then to the small intestine.

Only about a week is required for threadworms to make this journey through the pig's body, grow to maturity in the intestine, and begin laying eggs.

The pigs are injured severely by both adult and young threadworms. The adults burrow into the wall of the intestine, where they may be overlooked, except by trained observers. The damage they do may cause severe scouring. As a result, the pig becomes weak and unthrifty and may lose weight. When large numbers of the worms are present, the damage they do to the wall of the intestine often causes it to bleed. When the bleeding is severe, the pig soon dies.

Threadworm larvae that enter the body muscles cause the pig to be stiff and sore. When they invade the heart muscle or the brain and spinal cord, the pig may die suddenly. Sows in a weakened condition from suckling their litters may die as a result of damage inflicted on the heart, brain, and spinal cord by wandering threadworm larvae.

A few threadworms may have little noticeable effect on pigs fed adequate amounts of a well-balanced diet. The adult worms have been found, generally in small numbers, in a fair proportion of the apparently healthy swine that have been especially examined. Even a few threadworms in the intestine of a sow may be a source of possible danger to her pigs, however.

The pigs sometimes become infected with threadworms before they are born. Threadworm larvae wandering through the body of a pregnant sow invade the unborn pigs, but it is not known whether any die from this cause.

No treatments based on thorough tests have been devised for removing intestinal threadworms from swine. Consequently sanitation must be used to combat the parasite.

The best way to fight threadworms is by cleanliness: Keeping the farrowing pens and other premises occupied by little pigs clean and dry, and providing the pigs with plenty of fresh, dry bedding. Eggs and larvae of threadworms are killed by dryness, but they live well in manure and damp bedding.

It is important to clean and wash the pens frequently and destroy the old bedding. Young pigs should be kept away from the droppings of older animals and from bedding that has been used by older animals.

Pigs that are farrowed and raised on temporary pastures generally are troubled less with intestinal threadworms than are those raised indoors.

LLOYD A. SPINDLER *joined the Department of Agriculture in 1929.*

Thorn-Headed Worm of Swine

KENNETH C. KATES

THE THORN-HEADED worm, *Macracanthorhynchus hirudinaceus*, has a big hooked snout by which it attaches itself firmly to the wall of the small intestine of pigs. It belongs to an unusual group of parasites, the Acanthocephala, which look somewhat like roundworms but are unlike them in body structure.

This parasite is found in swine throughout the United States.

It is a giant of its kind. The adult female is more than a foot long and has a maximum diameter of one-third inch. The male, smaller than the female, attains a length of 4 inches and width of about one-fourth inch. It is milk white and somewhat flat when alive, but it becomes more or less cylindrical when it is kept in water or preserving fluid.

The muscular snout, which protrudes from the front end, is about one twenty-fifth inch long and has hooks arranged in six spiral rows of six hooks each.

The thorn-headed worm has no digestive system or mouth. It absorbs predigested food materials through the body wall in the intestine of the host.

Female worms are essentially elongated, tubular sacs, which contain large numbers of eggs, or embryos in shells, in various stages of development. A complicated organ at the hind end rejects eggs that have not completed their development and ejects the fully developed eggs.

The male reproductive system consists of two small organs, or testes, arranged in tandem and connected with the exterior by a tube or duct.

A female worm can produce more than 10 million eggs during a normal lifetime of several months in the host. Fully developed eggs contain small larvae (acanthors), which are encased in a thick shell. After the eggs are eliminated from the host, the larvae remain in the shell and undergo no further development until they are swallowed by the white grubs of many species of beetles—particularly June-beetles—as they burrow through the soil and manure.

Larvae hatch in the midgut of the

grubs, penetrate to the body cavity, and develop into another larval stage (acanthella). Eventually juvenile worms (cystacanths), about one-eighth inch long, and with the snout inverted into the body, develop from the acanthellas. Larval development in white grubs takes 2 to 3 months at average summer temperature. The worms reach maturity in swine in about 2 months.

Pigs become infected by eating infected grubs while rooting in the soil. Young worms, which are freed from the grubs in the host animal's digestive tract, attach themselves to the small intestine with their thorny snouts.

That is how the parasite does most of its damage. A pea-sized nodule forms at each place of attachment. Worms move about in the small intestine and form a new nodule each time the snout bores into the wall. At first the nodules may be surrounded by a red, inflamed border. Later they become filled with cheeselike material. The snouts may perforate the intestinal wall. Then the escape of bacteria into the body cavity may cause an inflammation of its lining (peritonitis).

No specific symptoms are associated with these infections in pigs, but the worms contribute to general unthriftiness. The nodules formed by the worms lower the value of the casings that are prepared from pig intestines in abattoirs for use as skins for sausages and other meat products.

It is difficult to control thorn-headed worms. No effective drug is available to remove them from swine; it is uneconomical to employ control measures for white grubs in the soil of hoglots and pastures. Furthermore, eggs in soil will remain infective to white grubs for several years.

Some control measures have value. The noses of pigs may be ringed to keep them from rooting and eating infected grubs. The use of old hog lots and permanent pastures should be avoided. The elimination of old straw piles and other debris from places where hogs are kept will help to reduce the number of white grubs and thereby the chances of infection.

KENNETH C. KATES *is parasitologist in charge of investigations on helminth parasites of sheep and goats in the Helminth Parasite Section, Animal Disease and Parasite Research Branch, Beltsville, Md.*

The Hog Louse

N. G. COBBETT AND R. C. BUSHLAND

THE HOG LOUSE, *Haematopinus suis,* is a bloodsucking parasite. It is the largest of the lice that prey on domestic animals. The full-grown female often attains a length of one-fourth inch. The males are slightly smaller.

The lice are easily seen on swine. They are brownish gray and have a peculiar habit of traveling sidewise over the skin and through the bristles.

They are parasitic on swine only and pass their entire life cycle on the host.

Hog lice may attack swine of any age or condition. They infest both domesticated and wild hogs in practically all parts of the world. Hog growers generally recognize them as a pest responsible for considerable losses to the swine industry.

The lice feed frequently. They puncture the skin and suck blood in a different place at each feeding. Each puncture produces irritation and itching, which cause the infested hogs to rub themselves vigorously against any available object.

The frequent scratching and rubbing destroy the hair in patches and often wound the skin. The lice congregate around the abrasions and cause further irritation. As the lice increase in numbers, the infested animals suffer constant irritation. They are restless and do not eat properly. They become unthrifty and do not grow or gain weight normally. Young animals especially suffer a lowering of vitality so that they may be more susceptible to attack by other parasites and to contagious diseases.

The female louse attaches her yellowish-white eggs to the bristles of the hog, usually in or around the ears and on the neck, shoulders, and flanks. She lays 3 to 6 eggs daily and an average total of 90 eggs during her life span, which is about 35 days. The eggs hatch in 12 to 20 days. The eggs farthest out on the bristles away from the body warmth usually hatch last.

After emerging from the egg, the nearly colorless, young louse becomes active. It seeks the tender skin nearest the point of its emergence and begins feeding. Clusters of young lice are often found inside the ears, in the region of the armpit and flank, and on the belly of infested swine. The young lice become sexually mature in about 10 days. The females may begin laying eggs when they are 12 days old.

The lice transfer readily from one hog to another when the animals are in close contact. Since it is the habit of swine to rest and sleep closely together, the lice spread rapidly in a herd and suckling pigs soon acquire them from their infested mothers.

Because hog lice live only a few days when separated from swine, enclosures, trucks, and cars in which infested swine have been are seldom a source of infestation if left unoccupied for several days.

Oils and medicated liquids are usu-

ally used against hog lice. They are best applied as dips or sprays or in well-constructed and maintained hog wallows. Used in hog oilers or applied by hand, the remedies will usually reduce and hold the lice infestation in check but seldom eliminate them entirely because it is hard to get a thorough coverage of all infested animals with them.

Crude petroleum and oils derived from crude petroleum are economical and commonly used in hog wallows and are preferable for use in hog wallows.

Coal tar-creosote preparations, properly used in soft water, are also effective, but they have been largely replaced by BHC, lindane, DDT, chlordane, and toxaphene, all of which are available as wettable powders or oil emulsions.

Dips and sprays made up with BHC or lindane should contain 0.06 percent of the gamma isomer—the insecticidal ingredient—when they are used for hog lice. The DDT dips or sprays should contain 0.75 percent of DDT. Those made up with chlordane or toxaphene should contain 0.5 percent of either chemical.

These chlorinated hydrocarbon insecticides will kill all the lice present on the swine. They also remain active on the bodies of treated animals long enough to kill most of the young lice that hatch after treatment, and they destroy some of the lice eggs. Nevertheless, a few eggs and late-hatching lice may survive a single dipping or spraying, and a second treatment in 10 to 14 days should be applied.

In treating swine for lice, it is important that all the body surfaces, including the inside of the ears, be thoroughly covered with the remedy and that all animals in the herd are treated.

N. G. COBBETT *joined the Department of Agriculture soon after he was graduated from Colorado Agricultural and Mechanical College in 1921.*

R. C. BUSHLAND *is in charge of the Kerrville, Tex., laboratory of the section of Insects Affecting Man and Animals, Entomology Research Branch.*

Hog Mange

N. G. COBBETT

MANGE in hogs is a contagious skin disease caused by mites—tiny, insect-like parasites that live in the skin.

Two kinds of mange affect swine. Each is caused by a different mite. The more common kind is known as sarcoptic mange. Demodectic, or follicular mange, is less common.

The mites spend their entire lives on infested swine. They produce wounds or lesions in the skin as they take food from the tissues and blood of the host.

Each kind of mite has distinctive habits in its feeding and other activities and causes peculiar skin lesions.

THE SARCOPTIC MANGE is caused by *Sarcoptes scabiei* var. *suis*. They are tiny, round, whitish mites, just visible to the naked eye. The mature female is about one-fiftieth and the male about one-sixtieth inch long. The bluntly rounded head is as broad as it is long and is equipped with strong mouth parts designed for piercing the skin tissues. Mature mites have four pairs of short, thick legs.

They penetrate the outer layers of the skin and excavate shallow burrows, or galleries, in which the females lay their eggs. Each female may deposit 10 to 25 eggs during the egg-laying period, which probably lasts 12 to 15 days. After that she dies in her burrow.

The eggs hatch in 3 to 10 days. The young mites escape from the burrow and excavate new burrows of their own, in which they begin laying eggs when they are about 10 or 12 days old.

As the average period of incubation is 4 days and the average period after hatching until egg laying begins is 11 days, a new generation of mites may be produced every 15 days or so.

Lesions of sarcoptic mange may start on any part of the body, but usually they appear first on the head, around the eyes, nose, or ears. They are often present inside the ears and may be overlooked when the hogs are examined or treated for mange. Since infested swine scratch the first lesions with their hind feet, the disease usually appears next on the hind legs.

The lesions grow gradually and may spread over the whole body.

The feeding and burrowing of the mites then cause irritation, itching, inflammation, and swelling of the affected tissues. Nodules and vesicles appear over and around the burrow.

The vesicles break and discharge serum, which dries into hard granules, or scales. The hair over the lesions stands erect, and much of it drops out.

As these mites multiply and the disease advances, increasingly large areas become involved. The intense itching causes the animals to scratch and rub the affected parts vigorously.

This mechanical injury to the skin causes it to become thicker, wrinkled, hairless, and crusted over with hard, granular-appearing scabs, which remain firmly adhered to the underlying skin and are difficult to remove.

The frequent rubbing of the hard scabs has a sort of polishing effect on them and gives them a slightly glistening, silver-gray appearance.

Occasionally the heavily scabbed-over areas are broken by movements of the animal, and blood and serum ooze out of the cracks. Then the lesions are moist and may be reddish or yellow.

SARCOPTIC MANGE SPREADS by direct contact with infested swine.

The disease can be transmitted to people and to some other animals, but the mites usually live only a limited time on such new hosts. It is advisable, however, to bathe and change clothes as soon as possible after handling mangy swine.

Because the sarcoptic mites live in their burrows, they do not spread to other animals so rapidly as the varieties that live solely on the surface of the skin.

Because of the hog's habit of resting and sleeping in close contact with one another, however, the disease frequently makes great headway in herds of swine. The infestation spreads most rapidly among swine kept in crowded or unclean quarters, especially when the animals are undernourished and exposed to cold or under other circumstances that tend to lessen their vitality.

The spread of the disease is not limited to any one season, although healthy hogs become infested less often during the summer and the mange lesions are usually less severe in summer, especially if the swine have access to good pasture.

Hogs of all classes, ages, and conditions are susceptible to sarcoptic mange but usually the disease is less severe and spreads less rapidly in well-fed, well-kept, vigorous animals than in weak, unthrifty swine.

Visible lesions of mange may develop in 14 to 45 days after exposure to the disease, or a much longer time may elapse before the exposed hogs show typical lesions. Cases of mange may become generalized in 6 weeks, but sometimes the lesions take much longer to spread to any great extent.

One or more attacks of the disease do not confer immunity. After the disease has been cured, the animals may become reinfested by contact with mangy hogs or possibly by confinement in quarters where infested swine have recently been kept.

While practically all cases of hog mange seem to originate from contact with infested animals, the possibility that swine may contract the disease from infested premises should not be overlooked.

Although the mites do not reproduce except when on the bodies of animals,

they can live for 2 or 3 weeks when removed from hogs. They may live much longer if conditions are favorable. Therefore swine of questionable origin or swine that have been held in commercial yards or transported in commercial carriers should be regarded as potential carriers of sarcoptic mange. They should be held apart and treated before they are added to clean herds.

TREATMENT OF SWINE infested with sarcoptic mange mites consists of killing the parasites, without injuring the animal, by applying recommended parasiticides.

The commonly used methods of applying treatment are dipping, spraying, medicated wallows, medicated bedding, hog oilers, and hand application.

Dipping is the most thorough and effective method. Spraying, if thoroughly done, also is effective. Medicated wallows, if properly constructed and maintained, often give satisfactory results. The use of hog oilers, medicated bedding, and hand applications usually checks the spread of hog mange but seldom produces a cure.

Oils and lime-sulfur solution used to be the most commonly and successfully used remedies for sarcoptic mange of hogs. Some of the newer insecticides have largely replaced the older remedies. Among them are benzene hexachloride (BHC), lindane, and chlordane, all of which are marketed in the form of wettable powder and oil emulsions.

BHC was the first to be tested widely and recommended for sarcoptic mange. Its greatest drawback is its disagreeable, pungent, musty odor, which persists for weeks on treated swine and all objects with which it comes in contact. Lindane is practically odorless and has largely replaced BHC as a remedy for mange and many other external parasites of livestock.

DIPS, SPRAYS, OR MEDICATED WALLOWS made up with BHC or lindane preparations should contain at least 0.1 percent of the gamma isomer—the principal insecticidal ingredient. A concentration of 0.13 percent is most satisfactory. Like remedies made up with chlordane should contain 0.5 percent of that chemical.

Sarcoptic mange can be kept from spreading in a flock if the swine and their bedding are thoroughly dusted with lindane or BHC dusts that contain 1.0 percent gamma isomer. In very cold or inclement weather, dusting may be resorted to until dipping or spraying is feasible.

In treating swine for mange, it is important to see that all body surfaces, including the inside of the ears, are thoroughly covered with the remedy being used, and that all animals in the herd are so treated.

When spraying a swine herd for mange, only a few animals should be treated at one time. In that way the thorough wetting of each individual can be assured. It is usually advantageous to dip the smaller pigs in a barrel or tub containing the spray material.

After dipping or spraying, swine should be kept out of the sun and wind for a few hours if possible. That practice allows the dip or spray material to soak into the mange lesions, so that the mites in deep wrinkles and beneath the crusts can be destroyed before it dries on the surface.

One thorough dipping or spraying with BHC, lindane, or chlordane will usually eradicate sarcoptic hog mange from swine. Extensive cases, especially those of long standing with thickly crusted lesions, sometimes require a second treatment. It is good practice to treat such cases a second time about 10 days after the first application.

DEMODECTIC, OR FOLLICULAR, MANGE of swine is caused by minute, wormlike mites known as *Demodex folliculorum suis* or *Demodex phylloides*.

Similar follicle mites infest dogs, cattle, other animals, and people.

The parasites are truly microscopic in size. The full-grown female is only about one one-hundredth inch long. They penetrate the hair follicles and oil glands of the skin, where they complete their life cycle. Small numbers of them apparently cause the animal no serious inconvenience, but occasionally they increase rapidly and cause well-marked lesions in the skin of the animal.

THE DISEASE IS CONTAGIOUS to hogs of all classes but is encountered much less often than the more common sarcoptic form of mange.

The lesions usually appear first on the snout or around the eyelids. They spread slowly over the underside of the neck, breast, abdomen, inner sides of the legs, and other parts of the body, where the skin is thin and tender. The back and upper parts of the sides, where the skin is thick and tough, are seldom affected.

In the early stages, the affected skin may be red and scurfy. Small, hard, nodular lumps, ranging in size from that of a pinhead to that of a hazelnut, appear in the skin. The nodules may be dark red or light red, with a whitish or cream-colored center.

As the disease advances, the nodules break and discharge a creamlike pus or lumps of matter of a cheeselike consistency. Two or more of the nodules may break and run together, forming cavities in which pus may form.

No SPECIFIC CURE for demodectic mange is known. Frequent dippings or sprayings with crude petroleum check its progress and heal many old lesions.

Repeated treatments with some of the newer insecticides, especially BHC or lindane, likewise may control the disease.

Herds in which demodectic mange appears should be treated. Any animals that have advanced cases and do not respond to treatment should be killed. The rest of the herd should be fattened for market and disposed of.

The premises should then be cleaned and disinfected before they are restocked with healthy swine.

N. G. COBBETT, *a veterinarian in the Animal Disease and Parasite Research Branch, Agricultural Research Service, is* *stationed at Albuquerque, N. Mex. Upon graduation from the Colorado Agricultural and Mechanical College in 1921, he joined the former Bureau of Animal Industry. Since 1928 he has engaged in research investigations pertaining to external parasites affecting livestock and poultry.*

Atrophic Rhinitis in Swine

RICHARD D. SHUMAN, JOHN S. ANDREWS, AND F. L. EARL

ATROPHIC rhinitis affects mainly the upper respiratory tract of the pig. It causes atrophy or shrinkage of the turbinates and distortion of the nasal septum. The disease process also can involve the bones of the face.

Atrophic rhinitis was first reported in the United States in 1944 by L. P. Doyle, C. R. Donham, and L. M. Hutchings, of Purdue University. Records indicate that it may have been present before then.

It has been encountered throughout the swine-raising areas of the United States and Canada. Rhinitis has been observed in the Scandinavian countries, England, Germany, and France.

It may be identical to a condition known as "sneezing sickness," which has been recognized in Europe for more than 100 years.

This disease caused alarm among swine producers and veterinarians in the United States in the late 1940's and early 1950's and has come to be considered a major disease of swine.

Atrophic rhinitis alone does not seem to kill pigs. But litters farrowed by affected dams tend to have greater losses than litters farrowed by dams that do not have the disease.

F. K. Kristjansson and R. Gwatkins, in Canada, reported that pigs affected with rhinitis were significantly lighter at 56, 84, 112, 140, and 168 days of age than their normal litter mates. Work at the Agricultural Research Center at Beltsville has shown that under Record-of-Performance conditions, the average weight of normal pigs at 56 and 140 days of age exceeded that of affected pigs by 3.9 and 6.4 percent, respectively. The normal pigs also exceeded affected ones in daily gain by 5.2 percent.

R. S. Smiley, of the Division of Animal Industry in Columbus, Ohio, summed up the effect of this disease on farm herds as follows: In some farm herds there is a 30-percent mortality rate after weaning. Some of the affected pigs stop growing after they attain a weight of 40 to 50 pounds. Some of the hogs take 3 to 5 months longer to reach market weight than others. Other animals belonging to the same herd show no apparent ill effects from the disease.

It is possible, however, that the damage attributed to the disease may be caused mainly by secondary conditions, such as pneumonia: Severe upper respiratory disturbance that causes a complete or partial loss of the turbinates when accompanied by a suppurative process could easily result in a type of pneumonia caused by mechanical inhalation of bacteria and debris.

On the other hand, while pneumonia and atrophic rhinitis can be seen in the same pig, the two conditions can also exist separately. In addition, malformation of the jaw, irritation of the nose when eating dry feed, and the lack of aggressiveness on the part of weakened pigs would have a cumulative effect and lead to an inadequate consumption of food. That in turn would be reflected by a deficiency in the normal rate of development.

How ATROPHIC RHINITIS is transmitted from aninal to animal is not known exactly. The disease has been traced from one specific source of infection to 50 farms.

The disease may possibly be spread through contact with droplets of infective material blown from the noses of affected animals. W. P. Switzer, of Iowa State College, has observed that some of the baby pigs in a pen next to an infected litter became infected although separated from it by a solid tile partition more than 3 feet high.

Baby pigs can be infected experimentally through the intranasal instillation of fresh material from the noses of affected pigs. Experiments at Beltsville, Md., have shown that this type of material will produce the disease in baby pigs after being stored at the temperature of dry ice (—94° F.) for about 7 months. Some evidence also was found that the atrophy-producing factor may survive in the nose of the albino rat for about 3 weeks—an indication that wild rodents may be able to transmit the disease to pigs.

F. W. Schofield, of the Ontario Veterinary College in Canada, reported in 1955 that the domestic cat can be a carrier of the disease.

Not all pigs in constant contact with affected pigs develop the characteristic lesions of the disease. This occurred in experiments at the Agricultural Research Center at Beltsville, when littermate pigs were inoculated with material from the noses of pigs affected with atrophic rhinitis. It also occurred naturally in litter-mate weanlings, on Record-of-Performance tests, which were in direct contact with pen litter mates and pigs in adjacent pens that did not have atrophic rhinitis. The findings indicate that pigs differ in their susceptibility to the disease or that affected pigs lose their infectiveness. In the same herd, contact with the soil seemed to have been important in the high incidence of atrophic rhinitis in the pigs on pasture (67 percent), compared with the incidence in the pigs kept on concrete floors (27 percent). The following year, however, the disease was distributed almost equally in both pasture-raised pigs and the pigs raised in concrete pens.

Atrophic rhinitis is not transmitted to the offspring at birth or through the milk of the dam. Hand-raised baby pigs have not become affected with the disease after having been fed or injected with pooled bacteriologically sterile swine sera obtained from two affected herds.

THE CAUSATIVE AGENT or agents of atrophic rhinitis also must be considered as unknown. Investigators have presented experimental evidence pointing to the identification of the etiological agents of the disease, but as of 1956 their findings await conformation.

"Sneezing sickness" has been attributed in Europe to a bacterium, *Pseudomonas aeruginosa*, as well as a particular localization of the cause of lung inflammation or pneumonia in influenza.

Dr. Switzer first found that species of *Trichomonas*, a microscopic parasitic organism, were present in a greater number of affected animals than in those not affected.

Observations at the Agricultural Research Center indicated that trichomonads may not be essential to turbinate atrophy. Attempts by other research workers to produce the condition experimentally, using pure cultures of trichomonads, were unsuccessful.

R. Gwatkins, L. Dzenis, and J. L. Byrne, of the Animal Disease Research Institute, Canada, and J. L. Flatla and M. Braend, of the Norwegian Veterinary College, Norway, reported that the disease could be transmitted experimentally by a bacterium, *Pasteurella multocida.*

K. A. McKay and G. R. Carter, of the Ontario Veterinary College, reported that they repeatedly produced rhinitis in young pigs by the nasal instillation of *Pasteurella multocida* and *Spherophorus necrophorus.*

Dr. Switzer found that filter-passing agent or agents could produce atrophy of the turbinates.

THE FIRST SYMPTOMS of atrophic rhinitis may be limited to persistent sneezing, which usually appears about 3 weeks after the farrowing. A clear mucous discharge may come from the nose. As the disease progresses, the discharge sometimes may become mucopurulent. The mucus from the nose is tinged at times with blood. Some mucopurulent debris may be passed from the nose following violent sneezing. Persistent bleeding also may occur following sneezing, vigorous exercise, or injury to the nose.

The irritation in the nose may become so severe that the pig will rub its snout on the ground or against some solid structure. The atrophy of the structures within the snout in some animals leads to visible distortion of the facial bones, and the snout may be turned to either side or upward and have an accordionlike appearance. Affected pigs with crooked noses have been found to be more the exception than the rule, however.

In light-colored hogs, a blackish streak that extends from the inner corner of the eye and bulging of the facial bones also may be circumstantial evidence of atrophic rhinitis. Associated conditions, such as pneumonia, diarrhea, and unthriftiness, may occur in affected herds.

A postmortem examination of the normal animal reveals the turbinate bones as delicate, scroll-like structures of bone and tissue, which fill up the right and left nasal passages. They are separated by a relatively thick cartilaginous structure, called the nasal septum. The function of the turbinates

is to warm the air before it passes into the lungs and assist in filtering out such foreign material as dust and bacteria. The mucous membrane that covers the structures inside the nose normally is pink and not excessively moist.

Considerable gross variation in the appearance of the structures within the nose occurs in animals affected with atrophic rhinitis. The variation can range from a decrease in size or loss of whorls of one or both turbinates, leaving fleshy residual stumps, to the absence of all the turbinates. One side may appear completely normal; the other side may show considerable variation in the extent of shrinkage. The nasal septum may be perpendicular and normal in appearance or somewhat thin. It may also show varying degrees of bowing. Marked bowing of the septum in many instances apparently causes flattening of the turbinates on one side and leads to distortion or compensatory enlargement of the turbinates on the other side. The resulting decrease in size and loss of turbinates with or without a change in the nasal septum brings about a varying increase in size of the nasal passages.

The surface of the membrane lining the structures within the nose may show an excessive amount of mucus. There may be a collection of mucopurulent exudate on the floor of the nasal passages. Occasionally one passage will be completely plugged with a mass of dirty, cheeselike material.

The postmortem findings usually are quite characteristic. Some individuals, however, will present changes that may be normal defects or are not differentiated enough to permit reaching a definite conclusion as to whether or not the animal is affected.

THE DIAGNOSIS of atrophic rhinitis may not appear to be difficult. When it is not suspected, however, the disease can be present in a herd for a year or two before it is recognized, because the various symptoms can easily be attributed to other causes. The sneezing may be thought to be due to inhalation of dust or particles of dry feed. The coughing could be considered as caused by the migration of larvae of intestinal worms. The bleeding could be considered insignificant in the mistaken belief that it may have been due to a ruptured blood vessel following injury or extreme exercise. A crooked nose could be thought of as having been due to injury, "bull nose" (or necrotic rhinitis), or the influence of a breed characteristic.

A postmortem examination, however, conducted on a few individuals that showed symptoms will confirm a herd diagnosis.

In most instances, to see within the nose, it is sufficient to make a cross section with a saw midway between the eyes and the end of the snout. For more detailed observations, the snout and face can be divided lengthwise down the midline and the nasal septum removed. This will reveal the nasal cavities in their entirety.

Although a herd diagnosis of atrophic rhinitis can be reached, the number of individual animals affected can only be approximated on the basis of clinical findings. In order to arrive at an individual diagnosis, a rhinoscopic examination may be conducted. That is done with the aid of an otoscope, a lighted instrument for examining the external ear. The instrument can be used with speculums of various sizes, depending on the size of the pig to be examined. When the attached speculum is inserted in the nostril, the light will reveal the anterior portion of the turbinates and nasal septum. Unfortunately the nasal structures cannot be seen completely or in the most desirable perspective; therefore there may be inaccuracies of diagnosis, particularly when the changes are not far advanced. This method is about 75 percent accurate.

A rhinoscopic examination cannot be conducted unless the animal is restrained properly. Several methods can be used: An anesthetic agent, a castrating trough with a crosspiece at one end, or a chute equipped with an adjustable stanchion or yoke to accommodate pigs of any size. The stanchion or yoke must be designed so that it is somewhat wider at the bottom than at the top to conform to the shape of the neck.

The X-ray can be employed in making a diagnosis on the individual live animal.

No satisfactory treatment has been devised for atrophic rhinitis. Adequate treatment cannot be evaluated until the causes are established. Because it appears doubtful that regeneration of atrophied parts occurs, any treatment must necessarily be directed towards its prevention or arrest in the early stages.

R. Gwatkins, P. J. G. Plummer, J. L. Byrne, and R. V. L. Walker, of the Animal Disease Research Institute, Canada, found experimentally that penicillin and streptomycin inhibited the infective agent or agents when added to the inoculum before being instilled into noses of susceptible pigs.

Gwatkins and Dzenis also found that the early use of streptomycin intranasally will reduce the number of pigs that develop atrophic rhinitis. T. L. Jones, also of the Ontario Veterinary College, reported that intramuscular injections of streptomycin administered three times during the first month after birth reduce the incidence of rhinitis but will not eliminate the disease.

Control measures must proceed along generally recognized principles of disease control.

The most satisfactory method of control is to try to keep the disease out of a herd. Much can be accomplished by learning everything possible about conditions in the herd from which replacements are to be obtained.

A more drastic method is to dispose of the affected herd. Thorough cleaning and disinfection of the buildings and equipment should follow. It would be well to renovate the lots by filling in wallows and by providing drainage in the low, boggy areas. Replacements from disease-free herds can be made after several months. The disadvantages of such a program are obvious, however, especially when valuable breeding animals are implicated or when it is doubtful that healthy replacements can be obtained.

A third method involves the selection within the herd of normal-appearing pigs for breeding purposes and the elimination of those that are obviously affected. Such a program could be improved by using the rhinoscope to aid in the selection and rejection of the pigs.

At the Agricultural Research Center we found that we could minimize the incidence of atrophic rhinitis by raising rhinoscopically negative weanlings to maturity in an isolation area under conditions of litter segregation and raising a second generation of pigs under the same conditions.

A fourth method offers a means of obtaining swine free of atrophic rhinitis but has practical limitations. This method consists of removing the baby pigs from the dam by hysterectomy or Caesarean section, or catching them in

sterile bags or on sterile cloth as they are born and removing them 24 hours after birth. In all instances the baby pigs must be hand raised under isolated conditions. Such procedures can be used when it is necessary to obtain valuable breed strains free of the disease and when adequate facilities and sufficient help for the sanitary care and management of the baby pigs are available.

RICHARD D. SHUMAN *is a veterinarian in the Bacterial and Mycotic Diseases Section of the Animal Disease and Parasite Research Branch.*

JOHN S. ANDREWS *is a parasitologist in the Helminth Parasite Section of the Animal Disease and Parasite Research Branch at Beltsville. He majored in parasitology at Purdue University.*

F. L. EARL *is a veterinarian in the Viral and Rickettsial Diseases Section of Agricultural Research Service. Following graduation from Michigan State University in 1947, Dr. Earl was employed by the State veterinarian's office in Missouri to investigate pullorum and Newcastle disease. In 1948 he joined the Department of Agriculture as station veterinarian in Beltsville.*

Hog Cholera

J. P. TORREY

HOG CHOLERA is a 40-million-dollar annual expense to the 4-billion-dollar swine industry in the United States.

It occurs in every State and in parts of every country where hogs are raised, except those—Northern Ireland, Denmark, and Australia, among them—that have undertaken vigorous and continuing eradication measures. Reports are that hog cholera broke out in countries where meat from the

United States was shipped for use by American Armed Forces.

We have the means to stamp out hog cholera, would we but use them.

THE FIRST AUTHENTIC REPORT of hog cholera in the United States came from Ohio in 1833. The disease spread rapidly. By 1887 it existed in 35 States. It became unusually prevalent at intervals of about 10 years between 1887 and 1926—1887, 1896, 1913, 1926.

The annual loss of hogs that died was placed at 65 million dollars. The average for a 10-year period was not less than 20 million dollars. The indirect costs doubled that figure.

THE CAUSE of hog cholera is a virus, which has a mean diameter of 27 millimicrons. (25 million millimicrons equal 1 inch.) This virus readily passes through Berkefeld and Chamberland filters. It is killed in 30 minutes by heat at 55° C.; in 10 minutes at 60° C.; and in 60 minutes in dried blood at 72° C.

The virus is destroyed by a 2-percent cresol solution in 60 minutes. A 3-percent solution of sodium hydroxide in combination with 2-percent milk of lime kills the virus in 15 minutes.

The virus lives best in an acid solution. The optimum pH for preservation of virulence is 5.0 to 5.5. The virus is quite resistant to phenol, and will survive long periods in a 0.5-percent solution. Phenol is used as a preservative when the virus is produced for immunization purposes. It has been kept in a perfect state of preservation for 7 years at −40° C. It will survive in meat products for months and will live at least 6 months in pickled, salted, and smoked meats. Putrefactive processes destroy the virus in about 5 days, except when it is in the bone marrow, where it survives for at least 15 days.

When it enters the pig's body, the virus passes to the blood stream and develops there. It is therefore a viremia, or blood infection. The blood of a pig becomes infectious within 24 hours after the virus is injected into its body. The urine and feces usually contain the virus within 48 hours. The secretions of the eyes and nose become infectious by the third day.

Rarely do pigs show visible symptoms earlier than the fourth day. Infected pigs therefore can transmit the disease before any symptoms can be seen. The maximum growth of virus is reached in 6 to 8 days.

The virus moves to all parts of the body, primarily in the red blood cells.

The liver and spleen contain more of the virus than other organs do.

Some viruses will cause infection in pigs when 1/5,000,000th of 1 cubic centimeter is injected. Others will not cause disease when less than 1/10,000th of 1 cubic centimeter is injected.

The incubation period—the time that elapses between the invasion of the first cells of the body and the first symptoms of the disease—is quite variable and depends on the virulence of the virus and the individual resistance of the pig. Symptoms may be observed 3 days after the injection of virus, but sometimes it may be 7 days before the pig is visibly sick.

When susceptible swine are exposed by contact or in other ways, one cannot know the exact time when infection occurs, but visible symptoms are rarely observed within less than 5 or 6 days after such exposure.

HOG CHOLERA may be introduced into a herd in many ways. When the disease is introduced in a small amount of infected material, such as a scrap of raw pork or small amount of dirt on an attendant's shoes, one or two pigs that eat it become sick first. Several days may pass before more animals become sick.

At least 2 days pass before the urine of the first exposed pig contains virus and other pigs eating feed contaminated with the urine will become exposed. The period of incubation must elapse before these pigs show symptoms. Thus when cholera is introduced in a herd, about 7 days will elapse between the time the first sick pig was exposed and other susceptible pigs begin to show symptoms. This characteristic of the disease shows the importance of being concerned when only one pig in a herd becomes sick. Immediate isolation of the first sick pig and early diagnosis, followed by proper immunization, will prevent heavy losses in the herd if the trouble is due to hog cholera.

When hog-cholera virus is introduced into a herd in large amounts, as in a bone brought from the neighboring farm by the farmer's dog or litter thrown from a stock truck, the outbreak will be more explosive, and a number of animals will become sick about the same time. These cases are more difficult to handle and the loss usually is greater.

Birds, such as pigeons and sparrows, and insects have been suspected of spreading hog cholera, but experimental evidence has failed to incriminate them.

Man is most to blame for the spread of the virus. Improper handling and use of the virus used for vaccinating pigs may start an outbreak of cholera. Men who visit sales barns, stockyards, slaughterhouses, and rendering plants and do not disinfect their shoes or truck and change clothing when they return to the farm may spread the disease.

The virus is spread within a herd by contact with sick animals or material infected with excrements from a sick animal. Animals recently vaccinated with virulent virus may spread the disease, especially if they show some reaction to the vaccination. Such animals should never be mixed with susceptible swine.

THE VIRUS of hog cholera differs from most other infectious agents in its relation to the white cells of the blood. Most infections, especially bacterial infections, cause an increase of white blood cells. The function of white corpuscles is to pick up infecting or invading particles and to try to carry them from the body. Hog-cholera virus has the opposite effect on white corpuscles. It destroys the corpuscles and apparently stops the production of them. The number of white cells in the normal pig may vary between 7,000 and 30,000 per cubic centimeter. Any number below 7,000 is subnormal, and the condition is called a leucopenia.

This characteristic of hog cholera can be used as a diagnostic agent, but it cannot be relied upon if the count is

higher. An animal may be infected with cholera and another disease at the same time. The cell count might then be high and a wrong diagnosis would be made.

The American strains of the virus are more virulent than the European strains. They differ also from the Canadian viruses.

The American strains seem to vary in virulence among themselves from time to time. Because there is no known serological method of differentiating the viruses, they have been considered the same virus. Heavy death losses in 1949 and 1950 in swine after vaccination with certain serials of viruses and serums indicated, however, that the viruses were different.

After extensive investigation, C. N. Dale and other scientists of the Department of Agriculture learned that the viruses differed from regular viruses in their antigenic properties—ability to produce immunizing properties—in a serum. The immunizing properties produced by a regular virus would not protect against the irregular viruses unless the amount of serum was greatly increased. These viruses are called variant viruses.

Since this discovery, variant viruses have been isolated from sick pigs that were not vaccinated with serum and virus. Variant viruses may have been involved in post-vaccination losses for a long time, but the cause of the losses may not have been determined.

The differences between variant viruses and regular viruses are: Variant viruses have low antigenic properties and therefore will not make good hyperimmune serum or vaccine. Hyperimmune serum made from regular viruses will not protect pigs against variant viruses in the same dosage as is used for regular viruses. The minimum lethal dose of variant viruses is greater than the dose of regular viruses. The variant characteristics are not stable, and after several passages in pigs the characteristics are the same as regular viruses. The variant characteristics are retained when the virus is injected into susceptible pigs simultaneously with subprotective doses of immune serum.

Hog-cholera virus has been propagated in swine tissues implanted on the chorio-allantoic membrane of chick embryos.

It has been cultivated more successfully in tissue cultures that employ various swine tissues, such as lymph node, spleen, kidney, testicle, and choroid plexus. More recent methods used only spleen as a culture medium.

THE SYMPTOMS of hog cholera differ in different hogs and in different herds, depending on the strength of the virus and the ability of the animal to resist the disease attack. Because of the variations, the disease is said to exist in two forms. In the acute, or severe type, the hogs sicken and die quickly. In the chronic, or less severe type, the hogs may be sick for weeks or months before they succumb or (in a few cases) recover.

At first the pig's temperature quickly rises to 105° to 107° F. The temperature continues high for a few days. Then it gradually drops. The temperature may go to subnormal if the pig lingers for a time.

A few pigs (or possibly only one) sicken at first. They refuse to come for feed with the herd but remain in the nest. They may appear to be cold and shivery, and their backs may be arched when they are driven from the bed. The sick hogs become gaunt or tucked up in the flank as the disease progresses. They have a weak, stilted, staggering gait; the weakness is most noticeable in the hind legs. Constipation is commonly present in the early days, but it may be followed by a diarrhea.

A red or purplish discoloration of the skin on the belly, ears, and inner surface of the legs may happen in some cases, but not all. Because the same discoloration may be found in other diseases, it cannot be a diagnostic symptom.

The eyes in the early stages may have a watery discharge. Later this becomes thicker and gums the eyelids shut. The eyes may be congested.

POSTMORTEM EXAMINATION of sick pigs is important in making a diagnosis, but one cannot rely on it entirely. All the lesions described for hog cholera rarely are found in one animal. Only a few organs may be involved, or there may be no visible changes at all. The absence of lesions is more often encountered in the early stages of the disease; therefore, it is important to make more than one postmortem examination in a herd.

Lesions are often in the spleen, kidney, lymph glands or nodes, and urinary bladder, but they are by no means constant findings.

The spleen may be enlarged and congested, or it may have irregular raised areas of a dark color, called hemorrhagic infarcts, along the edges.

The kidney may be congested, or it may have small, red spots, called petechiae, in the surface just under the outside covering or capsule. The spots may be as small as a pinpoint or as large as a pinhead. They may be few or numerous, like the specks on a turkey egg.

Lymph glands or nodes are normally gray, but they become enlarged and bright red or dark when they are infected with cholera. The redness may be on the outside surface, while the inside has a normal color. Sometimes the entire gland may be dark red.

The glands of the neck (cervical glands), of the lower jaw (submaxillary glands), beneath the kidney (renal glands), along the small intestines (mesenteric glands), and between the hind legs (inguinal glands) may have hemorrhages. One or more of the glands may be involved at a time.

The urinary bladder may be congested or may have hemorrhages on either the inner or outer surface, or both. The hemorrhages may be very small or quite large. Hemorrhages may occur in the stomach, small intestines, and large intestine.

DETECTION of hog cholera in the early stages often is difficult because postmortem findings may be negative or may be indistinguishable from a number of septicemic diseases.

A positive diagnosis can be made only by inoculating filtered blood from one or more sick pigs into healthy, cholera-susceptible pigs, to some of which hyperimmune serum is given at the same time. The pigs receiving the serum should remain well, and the others should get sick if cholera virus is present. That obviously takes time and is not practical in the field.

One has to rely on a careful study of the history, clinical symptoms, autopsy findings, and experience in making a diagnosis. A complete accounting of the farmer's movements, the happenings around the farm, and the management of the herd during the previous 2 weeks often gives some idea as to how the infection might have been introduced into the herd.

No DEPENDABLE TREATMENT is available for hogs visibly sick with cholera. Prevention, therefore, is of prime importance.

Proper sanitation and other preventive measures often will check the spread of virus.

The swine raiser should know how the virus is carried. Hog cholera does not occur in a herd unless the specific virus is introduced. The most certain way to do that is to bring an infected hog into a herd. Any hog added to the herd must be considered a potential source of danger until it has been isolated long enough to allow cholera to develop if the hog had been exposed to virus.

Because hogs affected with cholera discharge the virus from their bodies in the urine, feces, and secretions of the nose and eyes, the manure, bedding, and dirt in their pens are contaminated. The virus may enter the hog's system in food and drink and possibly through wounds or abrasions of the skin.

Infected hogs sometimes are shipped to market in order to get rid of them. Public stockyards, unloading chutes, railroad cars, and susceptible hogs may become contaminated or exposed in that way.

Cholera may be carried to a farm in infected litter, manure, or other material from public stockyards or cars. Infected material may adhere to other animals, wagon wheels, tires, and to the shoes of men who have entered such places. That also applies to farms where cholera exists—it may be carried from an infected farm to healthy herds when, for example, farmers exchange labor and implements or deliver grain and stock to market.

Cholera may be spread by stock buyers and sellers of stock remedies who go from farm to farm, and by animals bought at public sales.

Feeding garbage containing scraps of uncooked pork and bones also is dangerous. They may spread cholera and other swine diseases, particularly vesicular exanthema and trichinosis. The only safe garbage is cooked garbage.

A good ounce of prevention is to disinfect all things that might carry the virus. A 2-percent solution of ordinary lye is recommended. In places where lye cannot be used, a cresol compound disinfectant will do.

IMMUNIZATION is another means of prevention. Because the virus is highly contagious and can spread fast, some method had to be devised for protecting the hog. For that, hyperimmune serum was developed, but the men who discovered it realized that cholera could never be stamped out as long as a virulent virus was being spread. So the investigators continued to search for a better immunizing agent. They produced a killed-virus vaccine, but it, too, had limitations.

Other research workers tried to perfect an immunizing agent and developed five types of products for immunizing hogs against cholera:

Anti-hog-cholera serum of swine origin;

A fully virulent virus of pig origin used in conjunction with anti-hog-cholera serum;

A killed or inactivated virus vaccine made from swine tissues, inactivated with crystal violet or eucalyptol;

Modified virus vaccine passed through a nonspecific host, like the rabbit;

A modified tissue-cultured virus vaccine, grown upon tissue cells from the pig.

AFTER IT WAS DETERMINED definitely that a filterable virus was the cause of cholera, the investigations were directed toward finding a way to protect hogs from infection by the virus.

The first attempts at preventive measures were to develop a vaccine by attenuating or destroying the disease-producing properties of the blood in liquid or dried form and by using a mixture of virulent blood and the blood from immune hogs. All those experiments were fruitless.

Efforts then were turned to making a protective serum. These experiments were started in 1903, when the first hog was hyperimmunized. This hog had been used in experiments on hog cholera by Marion Dorset, at the Federal Experiment Station, Bethesda, Md., and was identified as number 844. It had recovered from an attack of hog cholera. It was given an injection of one cubic centimeter of blood from a sick pig, which had been injected with infected blood by W. B. Niles, at the Hog Cholera Research Station in Iowa, and shipped to Bethesda. The dosage was gradually increased to 400 cc. of virus blood. The hog remained normal. Eleven days after the last injection of virus blood, the end of its tail was cut off with a chisel and hammer, and 100 cc. of blood were collected in a pan.

The blood was defibrinated (prevented from clotting) by constant stirring and then tested for potency by injecting 20 cc. of it into each of two susceptible pigs with and without virus blood. The two pigs were tested 5 weeks later by injecting infected blood. The pig that received only serum died. The one that got serum and virus lived. Thus the first hyperimmune serum was produced. It is referred to as anti-hog-cholera serum.

MANY EXPERIMENTS were carried out at the Hog Cholera Research Station, Ames, Iowa, from 1905 to 1907 to make sure that adequate protection was afforded in almost 100 percent of the pigs. In 1907 the serum was put to a practical test by vaccinating farm herds. The results were good. The method of preparing the serum was then patented by Dr. Dorset, who had discovered the methods, and all rights were dedicated to the public.

Notice of the successful results was sent by A. D. Melvin, chief of the Federal Bureau of Animal Industry, to livestock officials of every State, with an invitation to send representatives to the Hog Cholera Research Station to observe the work and consider plans for the practical applications of this method of combating hog cholera. Representatives from 25 States attended a conference in Ames in 1908.

A number of States began to produce and distribute the new serum to their farmers. The preparation and sale of serum was undertaken by commercial concerns. As the commercial establishments began to increase in size and number, the States discontinued making the serum. Only commercial firms now make anti-hog-cholera serum.

The basic principles of producing serum are the same as when the first hyperimmune serum was made from hog number 844. The mechanics of producing serum have been improved greatly by research workers in the United States Department of Agriculture, in various States, and in commercial companies. These improvements give a more refined standard serum free from the disease-producing organisms.

The serum is prepared by the intravenous injection of 5 cc. of virus blood for each pound of body weight into the hogs that have been immunized against hog cholera for at least 90 days. After 11 days, blood is drawn from the tail three times at intervals of 7 days. The next week—that is, after the three intervals— all the blood is taken by bleeding from the throat. The blood is mechanically defibrinated as it is collected. The fibrin is removed by a centrifuge.

The red blood cells are removed by passing the blood through a milk separator after a small amount of bean extract (Wisconsin pea bean) and salt solution are added to the blood to facilitate the removal of the cells. The clear serum is then pasteurized at 58.5° C. for 30 minutes. Phenol is added so as to make a 0.5-percent concentration.

The serum is tested for potency by injecting 15 cc. of serum and 2 cc. of virus into 40- to 90-pound pigs. The pigs must pass a satisfactory test before the serum is released for sale. Purity tests for swine erysipelas and other contaminating organisms as well are made. No serum more than 3 years old can be sold.

HOG-CHOLERA VIRUS is prepared from the blood of the pigs that have cholera, show the characteristic symptoms, and on postmortem examination disclose lesions typical of hog cholera but no lesions of other infections. Five or seven days after the injection of the virus, the blood is drawn aseptically and defibrinated. Phenol is added as a preservative. This virus is the active agent that produces disease. If it is improperly handled it can cause an outbreak of cholera.

Two methods of serum treatment are used.

The serum-alone treatment consists in injecting hyperimmune serum into the pig at one of three places—the axillary space between the shoulder and body, the loose skin in the flank, or the abdominal cavity.

The length of time immunity will last varies with the individual pig. Some will be protected for 2 weeks and others 2 months.

Serum alone is used when only a temporary immunity is required. It may be recommended for pregnant sows and in an emergency when it is necessary to immunize pigs affected by a condition or disease, other than cholera, that has lowered their vitality so that they are not in proper condition to receive virus. The dosage of serum must be judged according to the size of the pig and the conditions under which it is given.

In simultaneous inoculation, hog-cholera virus and anti-hog-cholera serum are administered at the same time but in different places. The combined use of the two products results in permanent immunity in most herds. The serum protects the pig until the body has had time to develop immunity to the virus. For some unknown reason, some pigs do not develop immunity and are a source of danger and a loss to the owner. This failure to develop immunity after treatment with serum and virus is one of the reasons hog cholera cannot be eradicated by the simultaneous immunization method.

The dosage of virus remains the same for pigs of all sizes—that is, 2 cc. each. Some veterinarians prefer, however, to give larger doses of virus, 3 to 5 cc., and increase the serum accordingly. We have no experimental evidence to support this practice. Virus may be injected into the axillary space on the opposite side from where the serum is administered or it may be injected into muscles in the hind leg.

The dosage of serum is adjusted to the size of the pigs. The dosage recommended on the label of the serum bottle varies from 20 cc. for suckling pigs to 75 cc. or more for grown hogs. Many veterinarians increase the recommended dosage 50 to 100 percent in the belief that it is better to give a large dose of serum than to give too little. Good judgment and experience must determine how much serum to use. The serum may be injected into the axillary space between the front leg and body, into the loose tissue in the flank, or into the abdominal cavity. A large dose should not be injected in one place nor should it be injected too fast, lest the surrounding tissue be destroyed and an abscess form.

HOG CHOLERA VACCINES may be called modified hog-cholera-virus vaccines. They may be either live virus or killed virus.

The killed-virus type may be made of blood or of tissue from pigs that have cholera. The vaccine made from tissue is prepared by treating lymphoid tissue, principally spleen, from cholera-infected pigs with 1-percent oil of eucalyptol. After about 8 weeks at 45° F., the virus is killed, but the antigenic properties are retained. This vaccine commonly is spoken of as BTV—Boynton's Tissue Vaccine.

The other killed vaccine of blood origin is known as crystal violet-glycerol vaccine. It was first prepared in 1934 under the direction of Dr. Dorset. Since then other men in the Department of Agriculture have gathered and have made many improvements in the production and use of the vaccine.

Crystal violet-glycerol vaccine is prepared by adding 20 parts of a solution of crystal violet in glycerol (also called glycerine) to 80 parts of defibrinated blood from a cholera-infected pig. The crystal violet-glycerol solution is prepared by adding 1 part of crystal violet to 400 parts of glycerol. The method of use and the results of the two killed vaccines are almost the same.

A dose of 5 cc. of the killed vaccine is injected subcutaneously into each pig. Immunity is produced in about 14 days. Although some protection is given in 7 days, the vaccine should not be used in herds where cholera already exists and pigs should not be exposed to cholera within 14 days after treatment. Immunity will last 8 to 12 months in most pigs. In some it will last longer.

The chief advantage of this type of vaccine is that it produces immunity but does not introduce active virus into the hog. Therefore it can be used in herds infected with diseases other than cholera, because the use of virulent virus would be dangerous with them.

MODIFIED-LIVE-VIRUS VACCINES of rabbit origin are of two types. One type is made from a virus that has been passed from one rabbit to another until only a very slight reaction is observed when the virus is injected into a pig. The virus is injected into pigs, and certain tissues of the pig are harvested, treated, bottled, and dried in vacuum. The vaccine is tested for safety, potency, and purity before it is sold. It is necessary to inject 10 cc. of anti-hog-cholera serum at the same time this vaccine is used.

The other type of rabbit-origin vaccine is made from a virus that has been passed from one rabbit to another more than 200 times so that it lost its disease-producing properties; when it is put back into the pig no lesions or symptoms are observed. This type of vaccine is prepared from rabbit tissues which are collected, treated, and dried in vacuum the same as the other vaccine. No anti-hog-cholera serum is recommended for use with this vaccine. However, serum can be used if desired.

VACCINES were not used very widely to protect pigs against cholera until the modified-live-virus vaccines were produced. Since their introduction in 1951, their use has steadily increased; 11,072,295 doses were sold in the 12 months ending June 1952 and 15,800,-577 doses were sold in the year ending June 1953. The production of serum and virus produced declined proportionately.

An important question came up: Are the modified vaccines as good as serum and virulent virus in the prevention of hog cholera? The answer will come after further use of the modified vaccines. In 1955 we might have been in the low phase of the 10-year cycle that characterizes the field outbreaks of the disease. The cycles seem to occur without respect to the amount of vaccination and therefore should be taken into account when one attempts to evaluate the efficiency of the new vaccines. The incidence of cholera declined from 1952 to 1954, but we cannot attribute the drop to the increased use of modified vaccines until the end of the 10-year cycle.

When the new vaccines were introduced, claims were made that these new forms of virus would be totally incapable of producing cholera. Field usage and experimental evidence have disproved the claims under certain circumstances. Some pigs are highly susceptible to cholera and acquire the disease easily when vaccine is injected into them, although the same vaccine may make other pigs immune.

I know of no way in which to determine which pigs are hypersusceptible. Sows injected with modified-live-virus vaccines during the first 30 days of pregnancy may abort, or many of the fetuses will have abnormalities, such as ascites, edema, asymmetry of the head, lengthening and twisting of the snout, and malformations of the limbs.

Eradication of hog cholera in the United States has been talked about since the first experimental work on it was begun. When the simultaneous method of immunization was discovered, many thought the method would eliminate hog cholera, but the men who developed the procedure were aware that it would never eradicate the disease. The swine industry could never have grown to a major farm industry without this method of immunization, but the availability of other methods of immunization have made the goal of eradication seem more attainable.

The United States Livestock Sanitary Association in 1951 appointed a committee to study further the possibility of stamping out cholera in the United States. The committee presented its first report in 1951. Its recommendations influenced some States—Alabama, Georgia, and Tennessee—to prohibit the sale of virulent virus. Idaho, Utah, and Wyoming require a special permit for each shipment of virus coming into the State.

The recommendations also led to the establishment of a pilot test area, in which more than 2,500 hog raisers participated, in Florida. The first reports of the project were encouraging.

Alabama undertook an area plan of eradicating cholera in 1952. After 2 years, the death losses from cholera were negligible.

J. P. TORREY *is veterinarian in charge of the Hog Cholera Research Station, United States Department of Agriculture, at Ames, Iowa. He holds degrees from Mississippi State College and Michigan State University.*

The Enteritis Complex

L. P. DOYLE AND L. M. HUTCHINGS

A GROUP of diseases having similar manifestations is called a complex. Several ailments that cause inflammation of the digestive tract of swine make up the enteritis complex—as enteritis means an inflammation of the intestine.

Inflammation of the gut is often accompanied by necrosis, or death, of tissues in the gut wall. The word "necrosis" has been shortened to "necro" and is used widely in referring to disease of the intestine. The term has little definite value because it does not distinguish between the various intestinal diseases.

Some diseases, such as swine dysentery, affect the intestine without causing much change in other organs. Other diseases, such as hog cholera, seriously affect other organs as well as the intestine. Other specific diseases in the enteritis complex are swine dysentery and transmissible gastroenteritis (TGE). Other diseased conditions of the gut are less well defined.

SWINE DYSENTERY is one of the important diseases of the intestinal tract.

Several common names have been given to it, such as bloody diarrhea, bloody or black scours, and bloody flux.

Dysentery affects swine of all ages. The death rate may vary from less than 10 percent to 90 percent of the herd. Death losses average about 25 percent unless treatment is effective.

The disease is caused by a germ, which is given off in the bowel discharge from infected animals. A small amount of bowel discharge may infect a large number of healthy animals. Brood sows and boars may be carriers of infection even if they appear to be healthy.

The lesions of dysentery are in the large intestine. The small intestine is usually normal. The lining of the stomach frequently is inflamed, but a similar inflammation occurs in several other diseases. Early in dysentery the lining of the large intestine shows small, red spots and diffuse reddening. The intestine content consists of bloody mucus mixed with feces. Later there is sloughing of exudate and of the bowel lining. This sloughed material mixes with the intestinal content, giving a "rice-water" appearance. Usually mucus exists in the intestine in all stages of the disease.

After several days the large gut lining shows necro. The necrosis is superficial instead of being deep, as in hog cholera.

Dysentery is usually brought to a farm by hogs that have recently been in an infected herd or in an infested sale barn or stockyard. Animals that went through an outbreak several weeks or months previously may bring the disease into a healthy herd.

The first symptoms usually appear 5 to 14 days after contact with infection, although a longer period may pass before symptoms are seen. The symptoms are usually easily recognized. Diarrhea, or scours, probably always occurs. The bowel discharge may not differ at first from what occurs in relatively harmless scours. Soon (usually not later than 2 or 3 days) blood or mucus, or both, appear in the bowel discharge. Blood in the bowel discharge is one of the most reliable signs of dysentery. Occasionally hogs that have other diseases, such as cholera, also bleed from the bowels.

Affected animals may quickly become gaunt and lose considerable weight. Individuals that have the disease can often be detected by sunken sides. In many cases there are surprisingly few symptoms, except scours.

The animals may remain on feed while scouring profusely. Sometimes the disease runs such a rapid course that death occurs before diarrhea is noticed. Return of scours is likely in hogs that recover temporarily.

When dysentery starts in a herd, promptly moving the healthy hogs away from the infection helps reduce losses. If the healthy animals are ready for market, it is usually advisable to market them for immediate slaughter. If the healthy animals are kept for a time, they should be moved to a clean place and divided so as to reduce the spread of infection.

It is doubtful whether any animal that has passed through the disease should be kept for breeding because of the danger from carriers. Affected hogs should be fed lightly on easily digested feed. Milk seems to help recovery.

Yards and houses where dysentery has been should not be used for hogs for a while after all the hogs have been removed. The houses and yards and all the equipment should be carefully cleaned. The interior of the houses and equipment should be sprayed with a disinfectant.

Direct sunlight soon kills the germs in a clean yard, but the germs may live for a longer time when protected by manure or in some other way.

Some antibiotics, given in large doses, reduce the severity of symptoms temporarily and lower the death losses. The antibiotics do not definitely cure the disease and prevent it from recurring. Arsenic, properly used, reduces losses but fails to effect a final cure. These drugs should be used by a veterinarian or under his supervision. Arsenic is always potentially dangerous.

The experience with treatments and so-called cures has emphasized the importance of depending upon fundamental control measures—quarantine to prevent introducing the disease into a herd, sanitation for preventing its spread, and disposing of the infected herd and restocking with hogs from a healthy herd in order to eradicate it.

THE TRANSMISSIBLE GASTROENTERITIS (TGE) is a destructive disease among young pigs. It is highly contagious and affects swine of all ages, but the death losses are limited mostly to pigs less than 3 or 4 weeks old. Shoats and breeding animals usually recover from an attack in about 7 or 10 days. Younger pigs that survive may be stunted for some time.

The cause is a virus.

Symptoms may be seen within 18 hours after pigs are exposed to infection. Practically all the animals may become sick within 2 or 3 days. Scours always occurs, and some of the sick animals vomit. The scouring is watery and profuse in older swine. Scouring and some loss of weight may be the only symptoms in older hogs. Vomiting may occur. Some of the older animals may die.

Young pigs scour, and some vomit. The scours is usually light-colored or white. The pigs lose weight rapidly,

and death usually occurs within 4 or 5 days after symptoms appear. The pigs usually continue to nurse; some stand at the water fountain or trough as if they were thirsty. The mortality may be as high as 90 to 100 percent in pigs less than a week old.

The significant lesions of TGE are an inflammation of the stomach and intestine and an abnormal fullness of the intestine with liquid. The stomach and intestine are fiery red in some cases. The abnormal filling of the intestine often is the only symptom, except dehydration and emaciation.

No sure way to prevent outbreaks of TGE is known. Precautions to be taken to lessen the danger of an outbreak are to keep away from infected farms and to keep visitors away from the farrowing houses and pens, particularly while the pigs are young.

When an outbreak starts, moving and scattering the sows that have not farrowed helps reduce the spread of the disease. It is difficult or impossible to prevent the spread of infection in a central farrowing house or under conditions where litters of young pigs are close together.

Sows that have passed through an outbreak and have lost some or all of their pigs can be kept for breeding. Such sows are often able to transmit resistance to the next litter of pigs. This resistance, or immunity, probably does not last for more than a year. Early breeding of the sow after the loss of pigs is advisable. Continuous farrowing should be avoided, because it tends to perpetuate the disease.

ENTERITIS ATTRIBUTED TO paratyphoid or *Salmonella* bacteria has been given a good deal of attention. Cultures of *Salmonella cholera suis* can cause enteritis.

Still a question remains as to how important these bacteria alone are in causing disease in swine. The question arises from the fact that *Salmonella cholera suis* plays only a secondary part in some diseases that affect the intestine, such as hog cholera and dysentery. When disease is produced experimentally by cultures of *S. cholera suis*, there is little tendency for the trouble to spread to contact animals. Moreover, the feeding of tissues or organs containing *Salmonella* bacteria usually fails to cause disease in healthy hogs that are immune to cholera.

THE DISEASES that we have discussed do not account for all of the enteritis that occurs. Other kinds of enteritis are not all clearly understood as to causes. Coccidiosis causes serious disease of the intestine, particularly in young poultry, calves, and lambs. Comparatively few important outbreaks of enteritis in swine can be attributed to coccidia, however. Other protozoa, such as balantidia, spirochetes, trichomonads, and ameba are found in diseased intestine, but their primary importance is questionable. Some bacteria, such as *Actinomyces necrophorus*, multiply in damaged or dead tissue in the intestinal wall and elsewhere.

It is doubtful if such bacteria alone cause serious disease in healthy animals. The "cork lined" intestine is a familiar form of necrotic enteritis, in which necrophilous bacteria are found. An effort should be made to locate and remove the primary cause of obscure forms of enteritis.

An enteritis commonly occurs in pigs about weaning age or older. It is characterized by scouring, loss of weight, and unthriftiness. It is sometimes called "pig typhoid." Some veterinarians believe it is caused by paratyphoid or *Salmonella* bacteria. A good many cases occur in which these bacteria cannot be found. A filterable agent or virus is found sometimes in this type of disease.

Good care and careful feeding usually bring affected pigs through without many deaths. Swine affected by this disease, as well as by other forms of enteritis, should be fed easily digested, nutritious feed. Milk and molasses are good for cases of inflamed intestine.

Scours in baby pigs is common. Overloading of the digestive tract with milk or other food may cause scours. Scours sometimes indicates a destructive infectious disease, such as TGE. At other times it may not be important.

Debilitating conditions or an unfavorable environment may cause scours. Baby pigs that are allowed to become anemic are likely to scour.

The effects of nutritional deficiencies in enteritis have not been fully determined. A lack of certain nutritional factors may cause enteritis. A deficiency of nicotinic acid and perhaps other members of the vitamin B group are regarded as the most likely nutritional factors concerned. Many errors have been made in attributing enteritis to nutritional deficiency when the cause was infection.

Chemical poisons and irritants, such as arsenic and mercury, may result in enteritis when eaten or even when applied to the body surface. The general and careless use of poisons may be of increasing importance in causing enteritis.

A prompt and accurate diagnosis is of the greatest importance in successfully handling enteritis in swine. It is no longer sufficient to recognize a condition as necrotic enteritis. The diagnosis should be specific and indicate definitely the nature of the disease affecting the intestine. Successful treatment and control depend upon a correct diagnosis.

Determining the cause of enteritis frequently requires considerable time and skill.

L. P. DOYLE *is professor of veterinary science and* L. M. HUTCHINGS *is chief veterinarian in Purdue University, Lafayette, Ind.*

Dr. Doyle holds degrees from Purdue, the University of Michigan, Michigan State University, and the University of Chicago.

Dr. Hutchings became head of the Purdue Department of Veterinary Medicine in 1950. He has degrees from Maine, Michigan State, and Purdue Universities.

Swine Influenza

RICHARD E. SHOPE

SWINE influenza is an acute, highly contagious, infectious disease caused by the concerted activity of a tiny bacterium, *Hemophilus influenzae suis*, and a filterable virus.

The disease made its first appearance, as far as anyone knows, in the autumn of 1918, when a great outbreak of severe and highly fatal influenza was prevalent in the human population. Many veterinarians and farmers at the time believed that swine had acquired their influenza infections in the first instance from man. Subsequent laboratory work has tended to support the belief.

At any rate, when the cause of human influenza was discovered in 1933 to be a filterable virus, it was soon found that this virus from man bore a striking similarity to the one earlier discovered in swine influenza. Furthermore, the blood serums of most human beings born before 1918, and hence living at the time of the great 1918 epidemic, contain immune substances (antibodies) specific for the swine influenza virus, whereas serums from people born after 1918 are largely without these specific antibodies.

While the evidence is strong that swine may have acquired their influenza from man, there is nothing to suggest that the swine virus now presents a health hazard for people, because its long sojourn in swine has apparently "fixed" it for that species.

Swine influenza is essentially a disease of the late autumn and early winter months. It seldom appears, as a farm infection, at other times of the year. Its occurrence is largely limited to swine droves in the Middle Western States. It is primarily a herd disease, and single cases within a herd are unknown.

Ordinarily swine influenza begins explosively in October or November, depending on whether the onset of wet, inclement weather has been early or late that year. It frequently appears to start up in many different swine droves in an area almost simultaneously, a characteristic that early gave the disease a reputation for spreading like wildfire. After the initial flareup, new droves sicken in sequence for a period of 6 weeks or 2 months. Then the disease subsides and largely disappears as a farm ailment until the following year.

PERHAPS THE BEST WAY to outline the symptoms ordinarily seen in swine influenza would be to describe a typical outbreak of the disease as it might be encountered on any one of hundreds of Midwestern farms almost any autumn.

We will suppose it is the third day of illness for the hypothetical drove under observation. About 100 shoats are bedded in the runway of the barn. All are lying down, most of them on their sides. A few rest on their bellies, assuming a partly sitting position with the body propped on the forelegs; apparently they are in extreme respiratory distress. All show a rapid, jerky type of breathing. They are obviously very ill; one can walk among them without rousing them from the ground.

Their temperatures may range from 104.5° to 107° F. The animals have shown little interest in food for 3 days, and most are exhibiting early evidence of gauntness. One has died. To a person unfamiliar with the extreme prostration so characteristic of swine influenza, it would seem that many others are doomed. The animals are finally aroused by pulling some of them to their feet.

Most of them begin coughing soon after getting up. The cough is paroxysmal in character, the back being often arched, and is of sufficient violence as sometimes to cause vomiting. When the coughing attacks have passed, the animals stand for a short while in a listless attitude with their heads down and their tails limp. They soon return to their nests.

The owner says that only 4 days ago the drove was apparently in perfect health, was eating ravenously, and was making a nice gain; 3 days ago they appeared listless in the morning and showed little enthusiasm for their food. Practically the entire drove appeared ill. By afternoon most of them were markedly depressed and had taken to their nests in the runway of the barn. The few animals that had eaten in the morning were off feed by afternoon. By the following day the illness was full blown.

Visits to the drove on the fourth and fifth days of illness reveal little change in its condition, except that on the fifth day a second animal is dead. On the sixth day, when a person unfamiliar with the course of swine influenza might have expected to discover most of the herd dead or dying, the animals have left their nests, are up and around, and are hungry once again. Still coughing severely, they show definite improvement in their condition. Their temperatures are found now to have dropped to normal, ranging from 101° to 103°. Aside from a noticeable gaunt appearance, the pigs seem little the worse for their influenzal attacks. From this point on, recovery is rapid and usually is uneventful, although regain of the weight and condition lost during the illness is slow. The troublesome postinfluenzal cough may last for 3 weeks or longer after recovery.

The salient features of the outbreak, which may be summarized as characteristic of swine influenza, are the sudden onset, with most of the animals sickening almost simultaneously; the extreme prostration exhibited by the affected swine; the persistence of the illness without abatement for a period of about 5 days; and the remarkably sudden and unexpected cessation of the illness, almost by crisis, on about the sixth day. As one observer has said, "the patient begins to recover about the time death is expected." The 2-percent mortality assigned to the hypothetical drove I described is about the overall figure generally given for swine influenza.

THE POSTMORTEM findings in a pig with influenza are quite characteristic. In an animal sacrificed on the third or fourth day of illness, the trachea and bronchi will be found to contain a thick, sometimes frothy, mucus exudate, usually in copious amount. The lungs will show a patchy pneumonia, purple in color in contrast to the white nonpneumonic lung, involving the smaller anterior lobes.

The line of demarcation between the pneumonic and nonpneumonic areas is sharp. Ordinarily the large posterior lobes are not involved. The lymph nodes lying along the lower part of the trachea are greatly enlarged and very juicy. The lining of the stomach is reddened. Ordinarily the remaining organs and tissues are normal in appearance. In fatal cases the findings at autopsy are similar to those just described, except that the pneumonia seen in the anterior lobes of the lungs is apt to be extensive and the large posterior lobes are distended, bloody, and filled with fluid.

Animals fully recovered from swine influenza are ordinarily immune for life and their blood serums contain antibodies capable of destroying the influenza virus. These antibodies can be tested for in the laboratory, and their presence is sometimes used for diagnostic purposes.

SWINE INFLUENZA, though highly contagious, would die out and disappear forever at the end of an epidemic if its causative virus did not have some mechanism for lasting through the 9-month period during which the disease disappears as a farm infection.

To take care of this, nature has provided the organism with an ingenious mechanism for survival which involves lungworms (thin, white worms present in the bronchi at the bases of the lung) and earthworms. The eggs laid by the female lungworms in the lung of a pig sick of influenza contain virus. The eggs are coughed up, swallowed, and eventually passed in the feces.

Earthworms eating this manure ingest the lungworm eggs, and the eggs hatch inside the earthworm. The baby lungworms develop through several stages and finally imbed themselves in the hearts and gizzards of the earthworm. There they remain until the earthworm harboring them is rooted out and devoured by a pig.

The baby lungworms burrow through the lining of the pig's intestine and, after a period of wandering, finally reach the lung, where they locate in the basal bronchi and develop to adults. These lungworms have carried the influenza virus throughout the whole of their cycle but in a latent, noninfectious form. Because of this, the pigs acquiring the lungworms do not immediately come down with influenza. They remain normal to all appearances until such a time as they are exposed to an unusual set of weather conditions, in which they become wet and chilled.

In some manner, not at present understood, this chilling renders the latent virus present in the lungworms in the pig's respiratory tract active, and it infects the animal. After a short period of usually 2 or 3 days, the pig shows beginning signs of illness and comes down with influenza.

Ordinarily the incidence of infective lungworms in a drove is high. That accounts for the onset of the disease in a large proportion of the herd simultaneously. The few pigs not infected at this time acquire their influenzas by contact with the sick animals. The weather condition responsible for provoking a swine influenza infection in one drove is apt to be operative over a large area, thus accounting for the appearance of the disease in many droves in an area at the same time.

There is little in the line of specific treatment that proves beneficial in swine influenza. Bedding the animals down in a dry, nondrafty, warm place and leaving them completely undisturbed is probably the best procedure. They should, of course, have free access to all the clean water they might care to drink. Being febrile, they are frequently thirsty.

Although a vaccine prepared from the swine influenza virus would probably be effective, none was commercially available in 1956.

The matter of lungworm control by rearing pigs on cement or pasturing them in areas where the earthworms are free of lungworm larvae could be of value in preventing swine influenza, but is not practical on most farms.

RICHARD E. SHOPE *is a member of the Rockefeller Institute for Medical Research, New York. He was trained as a physician, but his scientific work has dealt entirely with diseases of animals. He has worked with swine influenza, hog cholera, pseudorabies, the filterable rabbit tumors, and cattle plague.*

For further reading:

C. N. Dale: *Swine Influenza.* U. S. D. A. Yearbook of Agriculture, *Keeping Livestock Healthy,* pages 703–713. 1942.

Richard E. Shope: *Old, Intermediate, and Contemporary Contributions to Our Knowledge of Pandemic Influenza,* Medicine, volume 23, pages 415–455. 1944.

Bureau of Entomology and Plant Quarantine and Bureau of Animal Industry: *Control of Hog Lice,* U. S. Department of Agriculture Leaflet 316, 4 pages. 1951.

H. E. Kemper and I. H. Roberts, and H. O. Peterson: *Hog Lice and Hog Mange, Methods of Control and Eradication,* U. S. Department of Agriculture Farmers' Bulletin 1085, 21 pages, (revised). 1952.

H. E. Kemper and I. H. Roberts: *Preliminary Tests with DDT for Single-Treatment Eradication of the Swine Louse, Haematopinus suis,* Journal of American Veterinary Medical Association, volume 108, number 829, pages 252–254. 1946.

N. G. Cobbett, J. E. Peterman, and A. G. Beagle: *Eradication of Sarcoptic Mange of Hogs by a Single Treatment of Benzene Hexachloride Sprays,* Veterinary Medicine, volume 43, number 10, pages 407–409. 1948.

Vesicular Exanthema

F. J. MULHERN AND W. C. PATTERSON

VESICULAR EXANTHEMA of the swine became a national problem in the summer of 1952. The disease suddenly escaped from California, where it had been confined for more than 20 years, and within 6 weeks it spread to 18 States. By September of 1953 it had appeared in 42 States.

Vesicular exanthema causes weight losses in mature hogs, slower gains in the feeder pigs and runts, and sometimes death in the suckling pigs. Because it resembles foot-and-mouth disease, vesicular exanthema creates fear, which depresses hog prices whenever it appears in auction and sales markets and stockyards.

A VESICULAR DISEASE that affected only swine and looked like foot-and-mouth disease was discovered in swine fed on raw garbage in Orange County, Calif., in April 1932. It spread to Los Angeles and San Bernardino Counties and was diagnosed as foot-and-mouth disease. All animals involved in the outbreak were killed and buried.

The lesions of vesicular exanthema—commonly called V. E.—consist of vesicles (blisters), that develop on the feet and snouts of infected hogs and rupture quite rapidly. The name given to the disease tends to describe the lesions presented. Vesicular refers to the vesicles, or blisters, while exanthema refers to the eruption of them. These lesions are identical with the lesions produced by foot-and-mouth disease and vesicular stomatitis in swine.

When a suspected case is reported, animal inoculation tests or laboratory tests are needed to determine whether the infection is vesicular exanthema, vesicular stomatitis, or foot-and-mouth disease.

A similar disease in hogs that were

366304°—56——25

fed raw garbage occurred in San Diego County in March 1933. It also was confined to swine. When test animals were inoculated, swine and horses developed lesions, but cattle and guinea pigs did not. Opposite results are produced when test animals are inoculated with tissue infected with foot-and-mouth disease virus. All cloven-footed animals, including cattle and swine, and guinea pigs are susceptible to foot-and-mouth disease. Horses are not susceptible. Therefore, because of the findings of those tests, no official diagnosis was made, but all animals involved were slaughtered, and indemnities were paid.

A new disease of swine was described in 1934 by Jacob Traum, of the University of California, as the cause of the 1933 outbreak. Dr. Traum reported that the agent that caused the disease was different both from that of foot-and-mouth disease and vesicular stomatitis. Animals that recovered from it were not immune to those two diseases. Dr. Traum also considered the 1932 outbreak to have been caused by this new agent, for which he suggested the name vesicular exanthema.

The vesicular exanthema that occurred in 1934 was found only on premises where raw garbage was fed. A strict quarantine was imposed until no other animals in that vicinity were reported as having the disease. Mild outbreaks occurred, however, in 1935 and 1936. Then 42 months passed before it was reported again. When it did reappear, it was for a more serious disease than it was previously considered to be.

A serious outbreak started in 1939 in San Mateo County. One-fourth of the hogs in California were involved within 6 months. The disease subsequently appeared each year there.

Vesicular exanthema appeared at a plant manufacturing biologicals in Grand Island, Nebr., in June 1952. That was the first time the disease had been detected outside California. The source of the infection was traced to swine near Cheyenne, Wyo., which had been fed garbage from transcontinental trains whose point of origin was California.

Before the disease was detected, hogs from Grand Island had been shipped to the stockyards in Omaha, Nebr., and moved out to various parts of the country. In slightly more than a month, 18 States were under Federal quarantine because of vesicular exanthema. The Secretary of Agriculture declared a state of emergency on August 1, 1952—an action that provided funds for an eradication program.

VESICULAR EXANTHEMA is caused by a virus, which is concentrated in the fluid in the blisters as well as in the tissue that makes up the cover of the blister. The blisters, vesicles, are formed during the fever stage. The virus also is present in the blood during the fever stage and for a short period thereafter. The virus is said to be 0.000002 inch in diameter.

The virus can remain infective for 2.5 years at 45° F. in unground vesicle coverings stored in a 50-percent glycerine phosphate buffer.

Meat scraps from infected pigs can remain infectious after storage at 45° for at least 4 weeks and for a much longer time when they are frozen. Hams infected with vesicular exanthema virus are inactivated (made noninfectious) when the internal temperature of the meat is held at 150° for 30 minutes. A fresh 2-percent lye solution (caustic soda) kills the virus.

We know of five virus types, which have been identified as A–48, B–51, C–52, D–53, and E–54. The letter indicates the order of isolation and the numbers indicate the year when they were found. Of these five types, none

immunized against the other. Only B–51 has been identified as the causative agent of outbreaks outside California.

There is reason to believe there are still other types. R. A. Bankowski started this classification of types when all previously isolated types were no longer available.

Vesicular exanthema is confined almost entirely to swine. A. B. Crawford, of the Department of Agriculture, in 1937 isolated four strains of the virus, identified as A, B, C, and D. All four affected swine, but only B and D were infectious to the horse.

Of the many outbreaks reported since June 1952, only in one outbreak has a horse been reported as being susceptible, and he was used in a differentiation test. Material collected from him would not produce lesions when inoculated into a second horse. Other horses and cattle used in tests have not been susceptible.

Experimental attempts to infect sheep, goats, guinea pigs, rats, suckling and adult mice, ferrets, chickens, and chicken embryos have failed.

S. H. Madin and Dr. Traum reported that hamsters could be infected with the 1940 A and B strains when the inoculations were made on the skin on the abdomen—these strains are no longer available. Inoculations of hamsters with A–48 and B–51 virus types were negative. Dogs have been infected but not with regularity, according to R. A. Bankowski and M. Wood, of the University of California.

THE FIRST SYMPTOMS of vesicular exanthema usually noted are the formation of vesicles on the snout and lips and lameness, caused by the formation of vesicles on the feet. The lesions usually develop 24 to 72 hours after exposure to the virus. During the vesiculation period, the temperatures usually range from 104° to 106° F. and persist for 24 to 36 hours. Then they recede rapidly, but a second rise in temperature may occur 24 to 72 hours later.

Those rises in temperature coincide with two stages of the disease. The first may occur when a primary lesion forms on the snout. The virus then enters the blood stream, and secondary lesions appear on other parts of the body. The spread of virus to all parts of the body is termed generalization. It is at this time that the second rise in temperature occurs, and it is the point at which most livestock owners first observe the disease. The pain and swelling of the foot lesions cause the animal to limp or refuse to move.

Vesicles may also form on the lips and tongue and other parts of the lining of the mouth cavity and on the area around the top of the hoof in the space between the toes and the soles of the feet. Lesions have been reported on the teats of nursing sows.

As the vesicles begin to form, there is a whitening of the affected area, which then forms a blister filled with fluid and containing great amounts of virus. The blisters will pit on pressure. Slight friction or pressure will tear away the epithelium covering and leave a red, raw, eroded surface. Shreds of tissue will cling to the margins of the wounds.

The primary lesions may spread over the whole surface of the snout and lips. Foot lesions, which commonly are found after generalization has taken place, may be so severe that the entire hoof will slough off. Formation of another hoof may take 3 to 6 months. The junction of the new and old hoofs is often marked by a black line.

It is of great importance that a differential diagnosis be made of any known vesicular disease. The lameness and blisters are easily recognizable evidence of a vesicular condition. But the determination of which vesicular disease is present is made by a specially trained diagnostician through a differential diagnosis by inoculations of horses, cattle, and swine. This method is like the one used to determine the presence of foot-and-mouth disease.

THE SPREAD of vesicular exanthema comes about principally in three ways:

The feeding of raw garbage containing infected raw pork scraps; direct contact with infected swine; and contact with mechanical carriers, including people and vehicles.

Infected swine in the early stages of the disease, when they show no signs of the disease, can be marketed without being detected as being ill. Scraps of pork from such animals or from other infected and exposed or recovered swine may be thrown into the garbage of restaurants, institutions, hotels, and households. Such garbage, fed uncooked to swine, may spread the disease. In California, before most farmers cooked the garbage they fed hogs, the chances of vesicular exanthema in garbage-fed swine were a thousand times greater than in grain-fed swine.

Swine in the early stage of the disease and recovered swine might be marketed undetected as carriers of the disease. Discharges from them may infect others with which they come in contact before slaughter in markets, sales barns, and stockyards.

Hogs with fresh lesions spread the disease quite readily. Large amounts of virus are liberated when the blisters rupture, both in the fluid and tissues that make up the cover.

Human beings do not contract vesicular exanthema, but they can carry the disease to swine on their clothing, especially their shoes, if they have been walking on infected premises or have been in contact with infected swine.

CONTROL AND ERADICATION of vesicular exanthema are carried out cooperatively by the State and Federal regulatory officials. Each State develops its program to control the disease within its own borders.

The Federal Government develops a program that controls the interstate spread of the disease.

The programs are based on seven major points: Quarantine, prompt disposal of infected and exposed swine, cleaning and disinfection, inspection, prohibition of feeding raw garbage, control of the marketing of garbage-fed swine, and the dissemination of helpful information.

QUARANTINE should be placed into effect as soon as swine suspected of having vesicular exanthema are located. The quarantines usually are invoked under the authority of the State department of agriculture. The quarantine may prevent the spread to neighbors' swine and others. While the quarantine is in effect, the movement of livestock from the premises is prohibited.

All persons leaving the premises should wear freshly laundered clothing. Their footwear and vehicles should be cleaned and disinfected.

The herd is under quarantine until a diagnosis reveals that it is not vesicular exanthema or, if it is, that the animals have been disposed of and the premises cleaned and disinfected.

PROMPT DISPOSAL of all infected and exposed swine by immediate slaughter and burial on the premises is the ideal way to dispose of swine infected with vesicular exanthema.

The meat can be salvaged without spreading the disease, however, and permission is granted to ship swine that have been infected and exposed to the disease to approved slaughtering establishments for slaughter and special processing. The swine should be moved under State or Federal supervision in leakproof trucks to an establishment that can handle them properly. Sick animals are condemned and rendered for fertilizer or other nonfood purposes. Other animals, such as those exposed to vesicular exanthema, are carefully inspected before and after slaughter. When passed, the carcasses are handled under special safeguards to insure wholesome food products and to prevent any possible spread of the infection.

The swine are appraised before slaughter. Usually the money received by the owner from the slaughtering establishment and indemnity by the State and Federal Governments equal the market value of the swine destroyed.

CLEANING AND DISINFECTING infected premises and all facilities and equipment used to handle infected and exposed swine are important. The entire operation must be done under State or Federal supervision. Recommended disinfectants are 2-percent lye solution or 4-percent soda ash (sodium carbonate).

INSPECTION is essential. All swine on premises where garbage is fed should be inspected twice a month or oftener to determine whether infection is present or has developed between inspections. Frequent inspections protect other swine and make it possible to localize the disease.

Swine arriving at stockyards and other concentration points should be inspected before being mixed with other hogs in the yards. If they arrive during hours when inspectors are not working, the animals should be held separately until they can be inspected. The hogs also should be inspected while in the yards and when they leave the yards.

FEEDING RAW GARBAGE to swine should be prohibited. Garbage-cooking laws have been passed by State Governments. Garbage should be heat-treated at 212° F. for 30 minutes. That treatment destroys the virus and makes the garbage safe for swine. Cooking breaks up one important cycle by which the disease is spread.

The consistency of the garbage will prevent uniform temperature readings throughout the mass, but fluctuations of more than 25° should not be permitted. Farmers that do not comply with the law or do not use adequate temperatures should be subject to quarantine and forbidden to ship swine.

Controlling the marketing of garbage-fed swine will hinder the spread of the disease by them if they are infected. Shipment of such hogs should be restricted as long as the disease exists in this country. The marketing of swine fed raw garbage should not be permitted at any time, unless the pork from them is specially heat treated. Any vehicles used to haul swine that are fed raw garbage should be cleaned and disinfected after they are used.

Swine fed cooked garbage could be sent to market if inspected by a State or Federal inspector and if all swine on the premises are free of the disease. The swine that move should be accompanied by a certificate issued by a Federal or State inspector.

All vehicles, facilities, feed, watering and rest stations, and loading and unloading points used for swine within or from the State or States involved in an outbreak should be cleaned and disinfected each time they are used.

The informational phase of an eradication program is important. The cooperation of all parts of the livestock industry is necessary to control and eradicate the disease. Therefore, a first step is to give all of them the facts about the disease and the need to control it. Problems should be discussed with representatives of the industry as the program progresses. They should be kept informed of gains made and setbacks encountered.

F. J. MULHERN *became head of the Vesicular Exanthema Eradication Section of the Agricultural Research Service in 1952. Previously he was employed in the foot-and-mouth disease eradication program in Mexico and was the Department's representative during an outbreak of foot-and-mouth disease in Canada. He holds the degree of doctor of veterinary medicine from Alabama Polytechnic Institute. He joined the Department of Agriculture in 1945.*

W. C. PATTERSON *is a veterinarian in the Animal Disease and Parasite Research Branch of the Agricultural Research Service. He is a graduate of Pennsylvania State University and has the degree of veterinary medicine from the University of Pennsylvania. Dr. Patterson joined the Department of Agriculture in 1951.*

Swine Erysipelas (Diamond Skin Disease)

RICHARD D. SHUMAN AND O. L. OSTEEN

SWINE erysipelas is present in the United States wherever hogs are raised. It is worst in regions, like the Midwest, where the hog population is dense. It is serious in Europe, parts of Asia, and North America.

R. Koch, F. A. J. Löffler, L. Pasteur, and M. L. Thuillier—all of whom are famous in scientific history—are associated with the discovery of the causative organism of erysipelas in the 1880's. Previously swine erysipelas was confused with anthrax. The work of Theobold Smith, in the former Bureau of Animal Industry, showed that the disease was present in this country before 1900. G. T. Creech, also of the Bureau of Animal Industry, in 1921 demonstrated the relationship of diamond skin disease (a clinical form of swine erysipelas) and the causative agent of erysipelas. The disease caused little trouble until the 1930's, when A. A. Fosterman, a veterinarian in South Dakota, directed attention to its acute aspect. Swine erysipelas has since become one of the most serious hazards of the swine industry.

The causative agent is a bacterium, *Erysipelothrix rhusiopathiae*. It is a hardy organism and can live in dead animal tissue and decaying matter. It can resist the effects of pickling, smoking, freezing, and drying of meats for long periods. It is rather sensitive to heat, however, and is killed at temperatures necessary to cook the chop or roast well.

The organism is considered to live in the soil as a saprophyte and can multiply under favorable conditions of moisture and in soil rich in humus.

Disinfectants commonly available and used according to directions will destroy it.

The organisms have been found in all parts of the world—and in a wide variety of animals, birds, fish, and insects. Of major economic importance is the effect of the disease in swine, turkeys, and sheep.

Infection of people is not uncommon (erysipeloid). It is an occupational hazard of veterinarians, persons who handle fresh meat and meat products, and commercial handlers of marine fish. Home butchering and processing of pork also has been the source of infection of people.

Probably the chief source of swine erysipelas infection is the organism present in the soil. A saprophyte, the organism can live on dead and decaying organic material—it does not require a living animal to maintain itself. Perhaps it has always been present as a soil organism.

Another source is the animal carrier. The organism can exist in the tonsils and the lymphoid tissue of the intestinal tract of apparently normal swine.

Hogs that become affected with swine erysipelas may or may not show actual clinical symptoms of the disease, but in each instance it is possible for the organism to be eliminated from the animal's body through the feces and urine. Hogs that die from the disease and remain undetected in the field can contaminate the soil and can be the source of an outbreak when eaten by other hogs.

Very likely birds and other wildlife that carry the organism contaminate the soil in the hog lots with their droppings.

Animals become infected through contact with the soil that contains the organism—by ingestion of contaminated feed and water and by infection of wounds. Fighting may lead to wounds of the lips, face, and shoulders. Sharp rocks, glass, and other objects cause wounds in and around the claws or lips while rooting. Protruding nails or broken boards and pieces of wire fence also can cause tears and breaks of the skin.

One sick hog can cause an outbreak of the disease through its elimination of the organism in its dung and urine.

Because the organism can be found also in the circulating blood of an infected animal, there is a possibility that bloodsucking insects may transmit the disease to other hogs. G. Wellmann of Germany has shown this to be possible by experimentally transmitting the disease with biting flies.

SWINE ERYSIPELAS has a peculiar behavior: Why did the disease apparently lie dormant for many years and then become a menace in the early 1930's? Why does it show itself on a farm for several seasons and then seemingly disappear? Why do some areas remain known as erysipelas areas? Some outbreaks years ago could have been confused with hog cholera (they can occur at the same time), but the real reason is not known.

The other peculiarities can be explained on the basis of what is known to be possible. We have known for a long time that the causative agent can be one of relatively low virulence or one of great virulency: Because it is not always the same, its ability to produce disease can vary a lot. It is possible that we may even be dealing with different strains or variants of the same organism. At any rate, since the infectiveness of an organism can be increased or lowered by artificial means in the laboratory, it is very likely that such external factors as climate and soil conditions also can alter its disease-producing ability. This could then be demonstrated on the farm by either a high incidence of disease, with many dead animals, or a low incidence, with just a few sick ones in the herd.

Swine erysipelas also can be present in a herd in such a mild form that it remains unnoticed. Many animals therefore become immune through natural infection. On a farm where this condition occurs, one could easily conclude that erysipelas died out or disappeared, although actually it was still there. All that would be needed to change this situation into an outbreak would be an increased virulency of the organism and the presence of susceptible hogs.

THE CLINICAL SYMPTOMS of swine erysipelas are classed as acute, subacute, and chronic.

Acute swine erysipelas is characterized by its sudden onset. Many animals in the herd may be affected at once. Only a few may be visibly sick, but a number of others may run temperatures of over 104°. Sick pigs tend to stay where they are bedded, yet at the same time their eyes give an impression of alertness. If stirred up and forced to move, they will protest with squeals as though it were painful to put weight on their feet. Sometimes the animals may show a peculiar stilty and stiff gait, or they may stand with their feet under them, and head hanging down, so that the back line has an arched appearance. The attitude becomes one of dejection or depression. Left alone, they quickly make themselves as comfortable as possible in the bedding again. Most animals show little desire for food or go off feed altogether. A not uncommon symptom is nausea and vomiting. Some animals breathe with difficulty and have a husky cough. If there is any change in the feces, it is more likely to be dry and reduced in quantity. Several of the pigs may die suddenly; others will be obviously sick, as we described, and a few may die in 7 or 10 days.

During the acute phase, many hogs may develop what is called diamond skin disease, or the urticarial form of swine erysipelas. This phase is marked by light-pink to dark-purple areas on the skin that usually become raised and firm to the touch and in most instances have clearly defined borders. The shape is quite characteristic when seen or felt, because the outline of the skin lesion assumes a square, a rectangular, or a rhomboidal geometric pattern. The lesions might join and cover quite a large area of the skin. Although the lesions are best seen on a light-skinned animal, they can be felt (but are easily overlooked in either case, particularly if they are not too numerous) on animals with darker skins. The number of "diamond skin" lesions can vary from one to so many that it would be hard to count them.

The skin lesions may disappear in several days, or they may become areas of dry, firm, darkened, scabby, dead skin and under tissue. These areas of dead skin will eventually fall off, leaving an ugly scarred area. It is here that one will also see loss of tips of the ears and tail. Secondary infection usually takes place during this stage and prolongs the healing process. Although the mortality rate of hogs showing diamond skin disease may not be particularly high, animals that have it will probably be affected with arthritis and the owner will be left with a number of pigs, which are unprofitable to feed out.

It is easier to think of the subacute form as being less severe than the acute form. The animals seem to be less sick. The temperature may not be so high. The hogs may show more interest in food. A few diamond-skin lesions may appear. The animals do not stay sick for so long a time.

Many hogs that live through the acute and subacute forms do not always recover completely, because an infection of the joints commonly occurs during the attack and can progress to a chronic or arthritic form. Infection of the joints also can occur without the animal's being noticeably sick. Infection of the knee, hock, and the toes is most frequent. Besides the noticeable lameness, shifting of weight, and other signs of pain in the legs, there is a gradual enlargement of the affected joint, which will also feel hot to the touch. Sometimes the symptoms disappear altogether, but may show up again. Many, however, get progressively worse, and the arthritis leads to bony enlargements and thickening of the soft parts, resulting in permanent deformity of the affected joint. This condition in hogs is similar to rheumatoid arthritis in man. Involvement of the heart is not uncommon. It is referred to as endocarditis and brings about a cauliflower-like growth at the site of the inflammation.

Injuries and the absence of a proper nutritional balance or adequate assimilation of the mineral elements can cause lameness. Thus it might be confused with swine erysipelas. Other recognized causes of arthritis include infection with streptococcus, staphylococcus, brucella, and salmonella organisms. S. H. McNutt, T. S. Leith, and C. K. Underbjerg, as well as W. P. Switzer, isolated a filterable agent that may be of significance in this regard. Despite all these possibilities, we know of no survey into the causes of arthritis in swine that would alter the picture presented by C. G. Grey, O. L. Osteen, and H. W. Schoening in 1941. They examined 472 joints of hogs that came from 91 counties in 14 States; they found the swine erysipelas organism in 375, or 76.5 percent, of the joints.

DEATH LOSSES can run from none to 75 percent, but swine erysipelas is more noted for its crippling effect than for the deaths it causes. The hogs cannot get around so well; for a while they show little interest in food, and therefore they become unthrifty. This systemic effect of the disease—plus the permanent damage to the joints and even the heart—leaves an animal in such a condition that it never does very well. It remains rough, undersized, or backward in growth.

Those that do reach the market may be docked at the packinghouse. Many thousands of dollars are lost annually in this manner, as diseased tissue requires trimming out as well as the removal of visibly affected joints.

THE DIAGNOSIS of swine erysipelas at times can be quite difficult, and it is well to remember that diseases—hog cholera and salmonellosis, for example —other than erysipelas can be present in herds at the same time.

Whenever an owner experiences sudden deaths in hogs for no apparent reason, he should consult his veterinarian immediately.

Diagnostic serological tests have been developed, but there are still definite limitations on their general use. Service laboratories are invaluable in assisting the veterinarian in his diagnosis.

Early diagnosis and treatment can put hogs on the road to recovery sooner and with less overall damage to the herd. Antibiotics alone and antibiotics with a specific immune serum are useful in treating swine erysipelas.

Biologics are available to the veterinarian. Hyperimmune serum was the only tool available before 1938, and it was not always adequate. Vaccination, for which a living virulent culture of the causative organism of swine erysipelas was used along with hyperimmune serum, had been practiced in Europe for many years.

The Department of Agriculture, in cooperation with the Nebraska Bureau of Animal Industry and the University of Nebraska, set up a program for introducing that method of control on an experimental basis. In the beginning only a few States were permitted to use live-culture vaccine, but as the results from the field were quite encouraging, the program was extended under the terms of a cooperative agreement. Up to 1956, 26 States were permitted to use the vaccine. The number of pigs vaccinated has increased; in 1954 they numbered more than 5 million head. An average of more than 2 million swine has been vaccinated annually since 1943.

Other methods of vaccination have used the principle of a living but mild vaccine, or what has been called an "avirulent" vaccine. This type of vaccine does not require the use of the protective serum.

There also have been introduced bacterins that do not contain living organisms. One is called the adsorbate and the other is the lyso bacterin. The advantage of such products is that they eliminate any possibility of spreading the disease and accidentally infecting the veterinarian while vaccinating the swine. These bacterins show considerable promise as additional tools for the control of swine erysipelas.

No vaccination procedure offers complete protection in all circumstances, however, and it is a common mistake to think that they do.

AN OWNER can do much to prevent disease by following established principles: Inspect his animals regularly; learn as much as possible about the health of animals and the conditions on the premises where replacement animals are bought; isolate newly purchased animals for at least 30 days before introducing them into the herd; keep pens and pastures clean and sanitary; use disinfectants often and according to directions; and feed a balanced ration.

RICHARD D. SHUMAN *is a veterinarian in the Bacterial and Mycotic Disease Section of the Animal Disease and Parasite Research Branch. Following graduation from the College of Veterinary Medicine, the State College of Washington, he was in charge of the Federal Bang's Disease Laboratory at Oregon State College in Corvallis. Since 1947 Dr. Shuman has studied diseases of swine, principally swine erysipelas and atrophic rhinitis.*

O. L. OSTEEN *received the degree of doctor of veterinary medicine from the University of Georgia in 1928. He has been in the service of the Department of Agriculture since 1932. He served in meat inspection for 3 years and has engaged in research work on equine infectious anemia, swine erysipelas, equine encephalomyelitis, Newcastle disease, and vesicular diseases.*

Diseases of Baby Pigs

N. R. ELLIS AND RICHARD D. SHUMAN

NEARLY one-third of all pigs born each year die from various disorders and hazards.

Not all of the loss can be said to be due to diseases in the strict sense. The causes, which often are ill-defined and overlapping, include various management factors that involve housing, facilities, and care; various prenatal factors, which involve several variables such as genetics, physiology, disease organisms, and nutrition; and postnatal factors reflected in physiological well-being of dam and pig, nutrition,

infections, parasites, numbers of pigs per litter, and others.

The multiple nature of the causes is evident in the cataloging of deaths outwardly apparent as due to mashing or injury. Many of the deaths are entirely physical. They are caused by the sow and often indirectly by inadequate housing and lack of protective guardrails, brooder lamps, and other pen facilities, of which the undersized, weak, and sick pigs are more prone to become victims.

The reasons why they are undersized, weak, and sick in turn are multiple. Hereditary, physiological, nutritional, and infectious-disease factors and parasitic infestations are involved. Bacterial and viral infections create a variable that may range from an extremely mild or latent contributing cause of weakness and unthriftiness to extremely virulent diseases of epidemic proportions. Some pigs that do not die from these causes often are permanently stunted or unthrifty in growth and use of feed. Examples of such diseases are the various enteric (intestinal) disorders, ranging from those forms that respond to antibiotics and other medication and to improved care and nutrition to the highly fatal transmissible gastroenteritis (T. G. E.).

Other diseases, such as pneumonia, cholera, erysipelas, atrophic rhinitis, and edema, add to the complexity of the possible causes of death.

Nutrition and management studies—directed at the gestation and lactation periods—at the Agricultural Research Center at Beltsville showed that the losses of young pigs are of various forms. Seasonal losses among farrowings of 350 to 500 baby pigs from 1949 to 1955 ranged from 30 percent to 10 percent of all pigs born. The average was about 20 percent.

Stillbirths averaged 3 percent between 1952 and 1954—a relatively low figure, compared to 5, 10, and 18 percent in some of the earlier studies, in which more severe dietary treatments were included in the tests.

Mashing or injury as the immediate cause of death averaged nearly 5 percent in 6 years, even though pen facilities and care were better than average.

Scours, especially in the first few days of life, claimed nearly 4 percent of the pigs.

Classifications of deaths due to other causes included chilling, 2 percent; starvation, more than 1 percent; uremia, 1 percent; and runtiness and weakness, about 1 percent. These totaled about 17 percent, leaving 3 percent as not further classified.

The studies at Beltsville emphasized the importance of good nutrition and good management. Inadequate care, overcrowding, unfavorable weather, and related factors can nullify benefits of good nutrition, and vice versa. Good nutrition and good management can keep losses to 10 percent or less if there are no epidemics of a virulent nature.

So far we have considered the multiple nature of the causes of losses of baby pigs and the general nature of the more specific nutritional and infectious diseases that are involved. Let us consider now a number of the diseases with the object of bringing them to the attention of the swine raiser. Many are discussed in detail in other sections of this book.

ENTERIC DISORDERS are the predominant group of diseases of baby pigs. More than a dozen forms, both infectious and nutritional, have been listed, among them T. G. E., baby pig scours, bloody dysentery, salmonellosis (necro), hog cholera, influenza, pneumonia, swinepox, erysipelas, internal parasites, chemical fungi, molds, plant poisons, and the nutritional deficiencies.

Nutritional deficiencies or imbalances are important among these forms of diarrhea. Enteric disturbance often results from too little niacin, pantothenic acid, riboflavin, and other vitamins in the feed. Necrotic enteritis (necro) for many years was considered an important and baffling disease, which sometimes was helped by adding niacin and tryptophan (a crystalline amino acid) to the feed.

Young pigs are highly susceptible to enteritis. They can get sudden and severe diarrheas if the sanitation is neglected, the quality of the feed is low, and the manner of feeding the dam and the nursing pigs are below standard.

Practical treatments that involve improvements in nutrition, feeding, and care do much to clear up the trouble. Outbreaks of diarrheas often can be brought under control or prevented by such remedies as vitamin and mineral concentrates, sulfonamides, antibiotics, and arsanilates.

ANEMIA was a great hazard until the discovery that lack of iron and copper was responsible for nutritional anemia. Development of methods of providing iron, especially to young pigs, and widespread recognition and adoption of these methods has brought improvement. The recommended dosage is 10 to 15 milligrams of iron daily, preferably in the form of an iron salt. Commercial compounds are available and suggested directions for their use are printed on the containers. Neglect of these precautions can result in the development of weak, unthrifty pigs, and frequently is either the direct cause or at least a contributing cause of deaths.

ANOTHER DISORDER, goiter or hairlessness, is due to a deficiency of iodine. The general use of iodized salt in the mineral mixture or in the mixed diet of the sow in regions—especially in those States bordering on the Great Lakes and westward to Montana— that are deficient in iodine has brought about great improvement.

When the disease does occur, it is manifested by enlargement of the thyroid gland, hairlessness, and weakness. A high proportion of pigs may be dead at birth.

UREMIC POISONING often causes runtiness and the death of young pigs. It is also called toxemia-uremia syndrome. A study at the Agricultural Research Center revealed that the disorder is especially fatal among pigs less than a week old.

The onset is relatively sudden. Growth is interrupted. The pigs become sluggish and weak. Vomiting and diarrhea frequently occur. The hair becomes rough, and the pigs die or are accidentally crushed by the sow. A postmortem examination discloses emaciation and evidence of uremic poisoning, including precipitates of uric acid salts in the kidneys, an increase in urea and uric acid in the blood, and uric acid in the kidney.

The disease seems to have some connection with the amount and quality of the milk that the pigs get by nursing. Studies by W. W. Green and others in Minnesota in 1949 showed that a condition, characterized as a toxemia-uremia syndrome, similar to that seen in suckling pigs, could be induced by feeding young pigs on reconstituted skim milk simply fortified with a mineral mixture along with vitamins A and D. Addition of yeast generally prevented the symptoms.

Its sporadic and unpredictable nature has made study and control of the disorder difficult.

HYPOGLYCEMIA affects young pigs 1 to 3 days after birth. The blood sugar in affected pigs is much lower than in healthy pigs. It indicates some derangement of carbohydrate metabolism. The symptoms are sluggishness, weakness, convulsions, and failure to nurse. The amount of sugar in the blood is a measure of the severity of the trouble. The young pig in this condition may be crushed by the sow or it may burrow into the bedding, where it passes into a coma and dies. This condition may affect some or all pigs in a litter.

Pigs may be treated successfully in the early stages by injections of sugar, such as glucose, or by feeding them milk by bottle or by medicine dropper.

EDEMA may cause the death of many embryos, even up to time of birth. Some live pigs are abnormal at birth, and many of them die. The edema— an excessive amount of watery fluid in the tissue and in the body cavities—is evident by the potbellied appearance, swollen legs, and other body parts.

The trouble has been traced to the vaccination of the sows for hog cholera within 30 days after breeding. Vaccination should be avoided during that critical stage in pregnancy. It is possible that damaged fetuses, stillbirths, and weak and undersized pigs that show a high death rate after birth are the product of various infections in early gestation.

This form of edema should not be confused with idiopathic toxemic paralysis, or "gut edema," which occurs chiefly in pigs 8 to 14 weeks old.

BRUCELLOSIS is important in regard to baby pigs not because of its immediate effect—although arthritis, spondylitis, and paralysis can develop in affected pigs—but because continued herd infection (by retention of affected animals) may cause temporary or permanent sterility of breeding animals, loss of baby pigs by abortion, and the birth of stillborn or weak pigs. (See page 202.)

LEPTOSPIROSIS was first reported in swine in the United States in 1952. As with brucellosis, the immediate effect on baby pigs may not be of marked significance, although stunting and unthriftiness of young pigs has been observed. Its apparent economic seriousness lies in the loss of sow productivity through abortions and farrowing of weak pigs, which die shortly after birth. (See page 226.)

SWINE ERYSIPELAS may be a serious threat to growing hogs and to newborn pigs. The infection in baby pigs can result in a high mortality rate; the survivors may remain unthrifty and stunted the rest of their lives. Because the disease can appear a few days after birth, the organisms causing it apparently gain entrance through the umbilicus. Pigs farrowed by immune dams, however, have a relatively high degree of immunity, which persists at least up to 8–10 weeks of age. (See page 373.)

SALMONELLOSIS (suipestifer or necro) is caused by an organism that generally is considered to be a secondary infective agent, which becomes active in the animal's body after some physiological disturbance has taken place.

The organism, once it becomes active, may spread readily to other ani-

mals and produce a definite primary disease condition.

The disease affects pigs of any age, but young pigs appear to be more susceptible than older hogs. Its acute form may kill the animals in a few days.

A chronic form is also recognized; it is marked by diarrhea and failure to gain weight.

LISTERIOSIS is of greater significance in sheep and cattle. It should be suspected when pigs manifest disturbed locomotion, nervousness, and excitability. A positive diagnosis can only be reached by a laboratory examination.

OMPHALITIS, or inflammation of the navel cord, is the result of exposure to infection by organisms shortly after birth. It is associated with poor management and lack of sanitation.

Bacteria, such as staphylococci, streptococci, coliforms, and the organisms causing swine erysipelas and tetanus, can be related to this condition. Affected pigs that remain untreated may die or become uneconomical to raise.

Swollen, deformed joints, or arthritis, are a common result of infection of the navel cord, but they do not necessarily indicate infection with swine erysipelas organisms.

PNEUMONIA can be associated with poor management and unsanitary practices, which reduce the ability of young pigs to withstand a variety of infective agents.

Pneumonia can also accompany such primary conditions as hog cholera, salmonellosis, erysipelas, pasteurellosis, atrophic rhinitis, and parasitism.

NECROTIC RHINITIS and necrotic stomatitis are known also as "bullnose" and "infectious sore mouth."

Mismanagement, lack of sanitation, wounds, and either crude removal of the needle teeth or not removing them at all contribute to these two conditions. Lesions of the face, snout, lips, and mouth can interfere with eating. The result is that pigs are uneconomical to raise unless treatment is successful. (See page 382.)

TRANSMISSIBLE GASTROENTERITIS (TGE) is of particular importance because it is the cause of high mortality in baby pigs. Litter loss may be greater than 90 percent if the infection cycle cannot be broken. Symptoms may appear several hours after birth; death may occur in 2 to 5 days. The mortality rate declines as the pigs get older.

Sows that have been affected with this disease confer a protective level of immunity to their offspring through the milk. (See page 362.)

HOG CHOLERA is capable of destroying an entire herd unless preventive measures are applied. Baby pigs farrowed by immune dams rarely contract cholera because of the passive immunity they receive through the milk. They become susceptible toward the end of the suckling period, however. (See page 354.)

VESICULAR STOMATITIS has grown in importance since 1952, because its lesions are like those of foot-and-mouth disease and vesicular exanthema and because a differential diagnosis must be made.

While vesicular stomatitis has been recognized in cattle and horses a long time, its significance in swine, other than in the laboratory, was considered to be of little importance. Its dangers are now recognized but not fully understood.

VESICULAR EXANTHEMA can spread rapidly through a herd and cause a temporary setback to growing market hogs. Sows affected with it early in the gestation period may farrow undersized or runty pigs. Sows affected late in the gestation period may abort.

An eradication program was started in 1952 to control this serious disease. (See page 369.)

SWINEPOX is not considered to be of serious economic importance but is of significance because of the appearance of characteristic lesions on the skin of pigs. (See page 385.)

PSEUDORABIES (Aujesky's disease or "mad itch") is highly contagious. Its symptoms may be mild and therefore unrecognized. In baby pigs the mortality rate can be high.

Restlessness, some incoordination of movement, and convulsions, followed by death, may be experienced. In those that survive, restlessness and irritability of the skin, as evidenced by scratching, may be seen. One of its more important aspects is that it is readily transmitted from swine to cattle.

In cattle the disease is more disastrous and more dramatic; the symptoms may resemble the furious stage of rabies, from which pseudorabies gets its name.

SWINE INFLUENZA may suddenly attack a large proportion of hogs of all ages in the herd. The clinical symptoms are alarming, but all the animals may recover quickly.

If the management and sanitary conditions are poor, however, secondary complications can cause substantial economic loss through death or unthriftiness. (See page 366.)

ATROPHIC RHINITIS may afflict baby pigs a few weeks after birth. It may retard growth in varying degrees. Losses in litters farrowed by affected dams tend to be heavier than in litters farrowed by those not affected.

PARASITISM may be overlooked by a farmer who is confronted with diseases that may strike with considerable suddenness and alarm. The economic inroads of parasitism, although less startling, can be very severe, however.

N. R. ELLIS *is chief of the Animal and Poultry Husbandry Research Branch.*

RICHARD D. SHUMAN *is a veterinarian in the Bacterial and Mycotic Disease Section of the Animal Disease and Parasite Research Branch.*

Miscellaneous Diseases of Swine

PAUL C. BENNETT, J. P. TORREY, AND C. N. DALE

NECROTIC RHINITIS is referred to as bullnose in many localities. Because swine producers have tended to regard any diseased condition of the nose or snout of pigs as necrotic rhinitis or bullnose, misunderstanding arose when atrophic rhinitis became widely recognized.

Both necrotic rhinitis and atrophic rhinitis are observed oftenest in growing pigs. Both may be present at one time in one animal.

The names by which they are identified merely describe the condition produced by the disease. In atrophic rhinitis it is a gradual atrophy or disappearance of some of the bony and cartilaginous tissues that make up the air passageway in the central part of the snout. In necrotic rhinitis it is an abscess or ulcer of the soft, fleshy tissue that surrounds the harder tissue forming the air passageway; the abscess or ulcer is much the same as those found in many other locations and is caused by bacterial infections.

The abscesses of necrotic rhinitis often develop to considerable size, and their presence can be seen easily. Atrophic rhinitis, though, is limited to changes that occur within the bony air passageway; in most cases no evidence of these changes can be detected from the external appearance of the snout.

Still another difference exists between the two conditions—their cause or causes. We do not know the cause of atrophic rhinitis.

The specific cause of necrotic rhinitis for many years was thought to be the bacterial organism *Spherophorus necrophorus*. Studies of this bacterium have brought some doubts as to its primary significance as the causative agent of the necrotic processes in which the organism usually can be found. The organism is quite common in nature, especially in localities of high animal populations, and is readily available to contaminate any wounds, abrasions, or other such injuries of the mouth and snout areas of the pig. Poor and inadequate sanitary conditions favor such contamination of wounds.

Other bacterial organisms always are found in the abscesses and ulcers. The most common belong in the *Micrococcus, Streptococcus, Corynebacterium,* and *Pseudomonas* groups. They are usually the most abundant organisms in the rhinitis lesions. The original site of the necrotic abscesses and ulcers is in some of the soft tissues, but the development of the lesion sometimes involves the bones of the nose and face, and considerable destruction of bony tissue may occur.

The development of the lesions in either soft or bony tissues can result in interference with the ability of the animal to eat. That and the toxic effect of the necrotic tissues results in a lowering of the general health and resistance to other diseases. The pigs develop into rough, unthrifty individuals.

Some pigs may overcome the infections through natural processes. Surgery or drugs, penicillin and other antibiotics, and several of the sulfa compounds in the early stages may give good results. In many cases the infection is well established before it is noticed, and treatment is unsatisfactory. Prevention is more effective than treatment. Good sanitation and farm safety practices, such as the elimination of as many hazards as possible, will reduce the incidence of these infections.

PASTEURELLOSIS has been known also as hemorrhagic septicemia and swine plague. It is caused by a bacterial organism, *Pasteurella multocida*.

It occurs in many species besides swine, but apparently it does not always produce a diseased condition. The reason is that there is more than one strain or variety of the organism. Some strains have more ability to cause disease than others. The fact that more than one type is recognized means that any resistance developed in the animal body as the result of infection with one strain will not give protection against infection with strains of the other types.

In regions where many hogs are raised in the United States, *Pasteurella multocida* occurs most commonly in association with abnormalities of the respiratory system. Occasionally it becomes a form of infection that spreads rapidly through the blood stream to all parts of the body, but in most cases other diseases are present, and the pasteurellosis seems to be a secondary complication. There is considerable doubt even in the pneumonic form of pasteurellosis that the organism is of primary significance.

Research in swine disease has shown the presence of formerly unknown causative agents of pneumonic conditions. Both viral and bacterial agents have been added to the list of causes of pneumonia, and the importance of pasteurellosis as a primary cause of pneumonia has decreased.

Two types of products for the prevention and treatment of pasteurellosis have been popular for a long time. Bacterins for vaccination purposes and antiserum for quick treatment and preventive benefits have been used extensively. These products sometimes gave good results and sometimes indifferent results, probably because of the variety of strains of the *Pasteurella* organisms. With the introduction of effective drug treatments, the use of bacterins and antiserum has decreased considerably.

When drugs and antibiotics, such as sulfathiazole, sulfamethazine, penicillin, streptomycin, Aureomycin, and Terramycin, became available, all of them were used either singly or in various combinations. Because pasteurellosis is so often associated with other diseases, it is quite likely that the best results will be secured with combinations of drugs and antibiotics, which are effective against both pasteurellosis and its associated diseases.

MILK FEVER in sows includes several conditions that occur shortly after farrowing. Veterinarians generally agree that it is not the same condition that is observed often in cows after calving.

One form of milk fever that occurs in sows is believed to be caused by a parathyroid dysfunction. It is called parturient hypocalcemia. It is a result of a reduction of the blood calcium below normal at farrowing time.

Sows may be attacked within a few hours of farrowing. The appetite and milk secretion fall off, and the sow appears to be restless. Later she lies down. She may get up and make some convulsive movements around the pen before she goes down again and passes into coma.

Treatment consists in injecting under the skin a solution of calcium and magnesium chloride with glucose.

HYPOPITUITARISM is sometimes called milk fever, but it does not have the symptoms of milk fever. It is caused by improper functioning of the pituitary gland. It may occur within 3 days after farrowing.

The characteristic symptoms are lack of appetite, constipation, and a high temperature. Affected animals lie down and are reluctant to move. If they are forced to their feet, they soon lie down again and seem to be stiff in the joints. The mammary glands may be swollen; little or no milk can be pressed from the teats.

Treatment consists in the injection of pituitary extract. The mammary gland should be massaged well to assist a return of the milk flow. The milk flow will return in a short time if there are no complications.

A lack of enough minerals, especially calcium, in the rations of brood sows often leads to a condition like milk fever. Most sows are not fed enough minerals during gestation and lactation. When the demand for calcium increases with the milk flow, the body becomes depleted in 1 to 2 weeks after farrowing. The milk flow may gradually become less or may stop in a few days. The sow loses her appetite, refuses to nurse the pigs, and cannot stand. She may linger a while and then die unless calcium is supplied.

MASTITIS, also known as garget, is an inflammation of the mammary glands or udder. The most common cause is the invasion of the glandular tissue by bacteria. The organisms enter through the opening in the teats or through cuts and abrasions. The organisms most often found in this condition are Actinomyces (which also infect cattle), Streptococci (also found in cattle), and Actinobacillus.

The symptoms may be a local reaction or a general disturbance of the system resulting in loss of appetite, rise of temperature, and possibly constipation. The inflamed udder becomes swollen, hot, and painful. The sow, because of intense pain, often refuses to let the pigs suckle. The milk may be stringy and clumpy or may be absent.

Prevention is important. Proper care and feeding of sows just before and after farrowing lessens the possibility of infection.

Sows should not be kept in muddy barnyards or in places where stones, rubbish, and straw might harbor the infective organisms and cause injury to the mammary glands.

The udder should be washed thoroughly before moving the sow to clean, dry, farrowing quarters that have been disinfected and bedded.

Reduction in the quantity of feed, especially proteins, and the use of molasses and antibiotics will prevent the development of predisposing factors. Treatment with penicillin has been successful. Hypodermic injections of penicillin and hot applications have given the best results.

PARALYSIS IN SWINE is commonly called posterior paralysis. It covers all conditions from leg weakness to complete loss of function in the hind quarters. The causes are varied and often obscure but may be included mostly under infectious diseases, nutritional deficiencies, mineral poisons, and mechanical injury.

Such infectious diseases as hog cholera, erysipelas, rabies, and tetanus, or lockjaw, in their late stages may cause paralysis. In most instances, however, a diagnosis can be made before the paralytic stage develops.

LISTERIOSIS, an infectious disease that commonly results in paralysis, is hard to diagnose. The infectious organism, *Listeria monocytogenes*, may cause sporadic outbreaks anywhere in the United States. Swine of all ages are susceptible. The method of transmission has not been discovered.

A central nervous infection causes incoordination, stilted gait, and dragging of the hind legs. A queer, stilted gait of the front legs is evident before the hind quarters become paralyzed. Ten to 20 percent of the herd may be infected. The highest mortality is in suckling pigs.

The disease can hardly be distinguished clinically from a deficiency of calcium and vitamin A. Therefore a laboratory test of affected animals has to be made for an accurate diagnosis. The infective organism localizes in the medullary part of the central nervous system.

We know of no specific treatment for listeriosis.

Paralysis commonly follows a long period of nutritional deficiencies, particularly a shortage of calcium. The relationship among calcium, phosphorus, and vitamin D, however, is complex and the three items must be considered together. Paralysis is observed oftener in sows than in younger stock.

Sufficient mineral may be fed the sows before the breeding period, but the extra demand for calcium during pregnancy and after farrowing may mean that the calcium has to be taken out of the bones to supply the demand for milk. The result then is a softening of the bones, or osteomalacia, and paralysis. That condition may occur any time during the lactation period, depending on the amount of calcium supplied in the feed. When the supply of calcium is quite short, paralysis may occur about 2 weeks after farrowing.

The sow goes off feed, the milk flow stops, and she lies down most of the time. In a day or so the sow cannot stand at all and dies in a short time. Secondary infection often is the immediate cause of death.

A postmortem examination will show that the liver is light in color and brittle, the spleen may be enlarged and congested, and the kidney may have a parboiled appearance. Congestion may be observed in other organs. The ribs will be soft—they can be cut with a knife and will bend almost double before breaking, instead of snapping, as a normal rib does.

No treatment is effective after the sow goes down. Sows that show uneasiness or difficulty in standing should be given an injection of calcium gluconate. The entire herd should be fed molasses and calcium, which can be readily utilized by the body. Vitamin D should be increased in the ration, especially in winter.

Avitaminosis A, which is due to too little vitamin A, may lead to paralysis. An important function of vitamin A is to keep the surface tissues of the body's mucous membranes healthy so that they will resist bacterial infection. A shortage of the vitamin changes and weakens the tissues so that bacteria can invade the body and the animal is subject especially to respiratory ailments. It is evident therefore that many other symptoms may be observed before paralysis occurs and the true cause of the paralysis will not be determined. The head may be carried tilted to one side because of infection in the middle ear. Night blindness, a weaving gait of the posterior parts, and a stunted growth precede paralysis.

Paralysis is caused by nerve degeneration in parts of the spinal cord, and in the sciatic and femoral nerves.

Vitamin A is supplied in green feeds, yellow corn, and well-cured alfalfa hay. Dehydrated alfalfa leaf meal is a good source of vitamin A.

Large amounts of mineral poisons may cause paralysis. Generally speaking, hogs get those substances—arsenic, lead, and coal tar pitch—only accidentally.

Mechanical injury, which may cause paralysis of the hind legs in shipping hogs, is not uncommon, because large hogs are inclined to be weak in the loins, and a blow there may cause them to go down. The hind legs may spread apart when a hog slips on a slick floor or concrete. Paralysis of pigs in feed lots is often caused by butting or pawing by cattle.

SWINEPOX, an acute infectious disease, affects swine of all ages. The pox lesions, like those of pox diseases of other animals, form on the skin.

The first signs of the disease usually are reddened, round areas, about one-fourth to one-third inch in diameter. The spots progress through the common stages of pox lesions, first as pustules and vesicles and then in a few days as scabs, which may drop off in several days.

Sometimes one finds symptoms of fever, poor appetite, diarrhea, and depression, but in such cases many pox lesions may be scattered over many areas of skin and the symptoms may be due to coexisting or secondary infections.

Swinepox is caused by a pox virus that is thought to affect only swine. The disease is not generally considered as being transmitted from animal to animal by contact, but it is easily carried from affected pigs to unaffected pigs by lice.

Swine that recover from the disease are immune to further attacks.

Swine are not susceptible to the viruses causing pox in other species of animals except vaccinia virus, the virus used for vaccination against smallpox. Vaccinia virus produces a disease with skin lesions in pigs much like those produced by swinepox virus. The outstanding differences are the more superficial location of the pox lesions and their earlier disappearance. Swine that recover from vaccinia infection are permanently immune to that disease but remain susceptible to swinepox. Swine that are immune to swinepox are still susceptible to vaccinia.

No medicinal treatment is known for swinepox.

Good care and general sanitary measures are recommended for controlling the disease and preventing complications.

PAUL C. BENNETT *is a professor of veterinary pathology and supervisor of the Iowa Veterinary Medical Diagnostic Laboratory at Iowa State College. He is a graduate of the University of West Virginia and Ohio State University.*

J. P. TORREY *is a veterinarian in charge of the Hog Cholera Research Station, United States Department of Agriculture, at Ames, Iowa.*

C. N. DALE *is a veterinarian in the Viral and Rickettsial Diseases Section of the Animal Disease and Parasite Research Branch. He received the degree of doctor of veterinary medicine from Ohio State University and the master of arts degree from the George Washington University. He has worked in the Department of Agriculture since 1927. He has engaged in research work on hog cholera.*

Various references on disorders of swine:

R. A. Bankowski and Margaret Wood: *Experimental Vesicular Exanthema in the Dog,* Journal of the American Veterinary Medical Association, volume 123, number 917, pages 115–118. 1953.

A. B. Crawford: *Experimental Vesicular Exanthema of Swine,* Journal of the American Veterinary Medical Association, volume 90, number 3, pages 380–395. 1937.

S. H. Madin and J. Traum: *Experimental Studies with Vesicular Exanthema of Swine,* Veterinary Medicine, volume 48, number 11, pages 443–450. 1953.

S. H. Madin and J. Traum: *Vesicular Exanthema of Swine,* Bacteriological Reviews, volume 19, pages 6–29. 1955.

L. O. Mott, W. C. Patterson, J. R. Songer, and S. R. Hopkins: *Experimental Infections with Vesicular Exanthema. Parts I and II. Direct and Indirect Contact Procedure,* Proceedings of the United States Livestock Sanitary Association, Fifty-Seventh Annual Meeting, pages 334–360. 1953.

W. C. Patterson and J. R. Songer: *Experimental Infections with Vesicular Exanthema. Part III. Viremia Studies in Swine and Their Relationship to Vesiculation,* Proceedings of the United States Livestock Sanitary Association, Fifty-Eighth Annual Meeting, pages 396–405. 1954.

J. Traum: *Vesicular Exanthema of Swine,* Journal of the American Veterinary Medical Association, volume 88, number 3, pages 316–327. 1936.

K. C. Kates: *Development of the Swine Thorn-Headed Worm, Macracanthorhynchus hirudinaceus, in its Intermediate Host,* Journal of Veterinary Research, volume 4, pages 173–181. 1943.

K. C. Kates: *Some Observations on Experimental Infections of Pigs With the Thorn-Headed Worm, Macracanthorhynchus hirudinaceus,* Journal of Veterinary Research, volume 5, pages 166–172. 1944.

Benjamin Schwartz: *Internal Parasites of Swine,* U. S. Department of Agriculture Farmers' Bulletin 1787, 41 pages. 1952.

Harley J. Van Cleave: *Acanthocephala of North American Mammals,* 179 pages, Urbana, Ill., University of Illinois Press. 1953.

sheep and goats

Coccidiosis of Sheep and Goats

JOHN C. LOTZE

COCCIDIOSIS is caused by microscopic, one-celled parasites (Protozoa), known as coccidia. It is a common but generally overlooked disease of lambs and kids throughout the United States.

The developing stages of the parasites live in the lining of the intestine and destroy parts of it. This causes diarrhea, or scours, which may or may not be bloody. Severely affected animals become unthrifty, fail to grow, and may die.

Sheep and goats acquire coccidiosis by swallowing feed and water contaminated with the droppings of infected animals.

THE LIFE CYCLE of coccidia has two main phases—a free-living phase outside the body of the animal and a parasitic phase in its intestine.

The free-living phase, known as oöcysts, is the one by which the parasites spread to new hosts. The oöcysts are discharged in the manure of infected animals. In moist places with temperatures above freezing, eight tiny, wormlike bodies—sporozoites—form inside each one in about a week. They are then known as sporulated oöcysts and are infective.

Oöcysts have thick shells and are resistant to drying and most chemical disinfectants. The parasites in this phase may live for several months on soil. Generally they occur in large numbers on pastures and in pens and other places where infected animals are kept. The parasites are readily killed by ammonia produced by fermenting manure.

The parasitic phase begins when

387

the sporulated oöcysts are swallowed.

When the oöcysts reach the upper part of the small intestine, the sporozoites inside them become active and escape. Each sporozoite then enters one of the cells that line the small intestine and divides a number of times. It is then known as a schizont.

As the schizont grows, the host's cell grows also, sometimes to a tremendous size. It finally dies. Enormous numbers of tiny, cigar-shaped bodies, known as merozoites, develop within each schizont. The merozoites escape from the schizont, and each invades a separate, different cell. Millions of cells may be affected at one time.

Some of the merozoites develop into eggs. Others divide into numerous wormlike forms, which migrate to the eggs and fertilize them. A thick shell develops around each egg and it is now called an oöcyst. The oöcysts are released into the cavity of the intestine and pass to the outside with the droppings. The first oöcysts are produced about 16 to 21 days after inoculation. An infected animal may void enormous numbers of oöcysts in 10 or 15 days.

Destruction of large areas of the lining of the intestine may begin 5 to 7 days after infection, but severely affected animals usually do not appear to be sick until about the 11th day of the infection—when the young stages or merozoites in the schizonts are reaching maturity.

TEN SPECIES of coccidia, all of the genus *Eimeria*, have been reported in sheep and goats. It is generally assumed—but not proved—that the same species affect both sheep and goats. It has been assumed also that the different species are equally harmful.

The three species that occur oftenest in sheep may differ in their ability to damage the animal. Lambs, raised free of parasites until they were 3 to 5 months old and maintained on a good diet, were studied in a research project at the Parasite Station of the Beltsville Research Center.

Some of the lambs were given one-half million sporulated oöcysts of one of the most common species, *Eimeria ninae-kohl-yakimova*. About half of these lambs died from severe coccidiosis. Some lambs were fed one-half million oöcysts of either *E. arloingi* or *E. faurei*, but did not seem to be affected seriously. Others got 5 million oöcysts of *E. arloingi;* none died. Still others were fed 50 million oöcysts of *E. faurei*—a tremendous dose—but none died.

SYMPTOMS OF COCCIDIOSIS depend on the amount of damage the parasites do to the intestine. That in turn depends on the number of oöcysts swallowed at one time and the species involved. At birth or shortly thereafter, most or all sheep and goats acquire light infections of one or more species of coccidia, apparently without bad effects.

The development of large numbers of the parasites in the intestine at one time may injure extensive areas of the intestine and thereby interfere with digestion and cause diarrhea, loss of weight, and death. Breaks in the wool may occur about a month after the sheep acquires a heavy infection.

TO DIAGNOSE COCCIDIOSIS of sheep and goats one needs a microscope to detect the parasites, either the oöcysts in the droppings or the parasites in their various stages of development in the intestines. One needs experience to recognize the parasites and to judge whether the infections were severe enough to produce the symptoms and deaths encountered, because other disorders may be present and produce like symptoms.

When animals become heavily infested, symptoms may occur and the animal may die before oöcysts are formed. Furthermore, the number of oöcysts in the droppings may not always reflect the severity of the infection because of resistance or some factor that tends to check the formation of oöcysts.

In general, however, coccidiosis should be suspected when lambs have diarrhea.

No specific chemical treatment of proved reliability is available for coccidiosis of sheep and goats.

Sulfonamides, especially sulfaguanidine, sulfamethazine, and sulfasuxadine, have been used advantageously in several instances. At the proper time and in proper amounts, they may destroy some of the intestinal stages, reduce the production of oöcysts, and help the animal withstand the injurious effects of the parasites. Since the developing stages of coccidia injure the lining of the intestine and make it easier for bacteria to invade the intestinal wall, these drugs may be of help in stopping invasions by certain bacteria.

Fly strike is favored by the watery feces of coccidial scours, which keeps the wool on the hind parts moist. The odor of the feces attracts blowflies, and they lay tremendous numbers of eggs on the soiled wool. The larva, or maggots, that hatch from the eggs live close to the skin and attack the tissues of the living animal. Severe infestations of the larva may cause death unless they are detected early and proper treatment is given.

Treatment consists in removing the soiled wool and applying a medicated smear or ointment to destroy the maggots and to promote the healing of lesions. Commercial screwworm remedies are recommended for this purpose.

Control of coccidiosis of sheep and goats rests largely on the use of management practices that help to keep the animals from contaminating their feed and water with droppings, which may contain oöcysts. That, in turn, helps keep the animals from swallowing large numbers of oöcysts at one time and thus prevent severe cases.

Some suggestions:

Clean pens often and keep them dry.

Ordinary disinfectants have little or no effect on oöcysts. Washing pens with disinfectants may be of little value against coccidiosis, but may help to control bacterial diseases.

Crowding animals together in close quarters favors coccidiosis. With increased use of improved pastures and more intensive farming, there is an increasing tendency to keep larger numbers of sheep and goats in small areas. Pastures should not be overstocked. A plan of pasture rotation should be followed.

Feed good diets and use prescribed medicines in recommended ways to help prevent severe infections, especially when animals are crowded. Sulfur mixed in the feed of lambs kept in feed lots is reported to have given good results against coccidiosis.

JOHN C. LOTZE, *a parasitologist in the Animal Disease and Parasite Research Branch, has done research on protozoan diseases of livestock at the Agricultural Research Center since 1938.*

Roundworms of the Digestive Tract

KENNETH C. KATES, REX W. ALLEN, AND JAMES H. TURNER

ROUNDWORMS, or nematodes, in the digestive tract may seriously affect the health of sheep and goats. It is not uncommon for sheep and goats to die of the effects of roundworms, but even greater losses come about through reduced weight gains, less meat and fiber production, lower vitality of breeding animals, and a considerable rise in cost of production.

More than twenty-four species of roundworms occur in the digestive tract of sheep and goats in the United States. The worms are tiny, cylindrical, threadlike parasites. Some are hard to see with the unaided eye.

THE COMMON and scientific names of roundworms that occur more or less frequently in sheep and goats in this country are given in the list that follows. (When more than one species is listed under one common name, the first species named is usually the most important one. Practically all species listed occur in sheep and goats, but some are commoner in sheep than in goats, and vice versa. Some species normally are parasites of cattle but have been reported also in sheep and goats. In fact, about half of these species have been found in cattle and several kinds of wild ruminants.)

IN ESOPHAGUS AND RUMEN—gullet worms: *Gongylonema* species.

IN FOURTH STOMACH (abomasum)— large stomach worm: *Haemonchus contortus;* medium stomach worms: *Ostertagia circumcincta, O. trifurcata, O. occidentalis, Marshallagia marshalli, Pseudostertagia bullosa;* stomach hairworm: *Trichostrongylus axei.*

IN SMALL INTESTINE—intestinal hairworms: *Trichostrongylus colubriformis, T. vitrinus, T. capricola;* hookworm: *Bunostomum trigonocephalum;* thread-necked worms: *Nematodirus spathiger, N. filicollis, N. abnormalis;* threadworm: *Strongyloides papillosus;* cooperias: *Cooperia curticei, C. punctata, C. oncophora, C. pectinata;* capillarids: *Capillaria brevipes, C. bovis.*

IN LARGE INTESTINE and blind gut, or cecum—nodular worms: *Oesophagostomum columbianum O. venulosum;* whipworms: *Trichuris ovis, T. globulosa, T. discolor;* large-mouthed bowel worm: *Chabertia ovina;* pinworm: *Skrjabinema ovis.*

Parasitic gastroenteritis, a term that means irritation or inflammation of the stomach and intestines caused by parasites, usually roundworms, often is applied to a disease caused by several kinds of roundworms. It is not always possible to separate the effects of one kind of parasite from the effects caused by others.

The term "parasitic gastritis" is used when only the stomach is involved. "Parasitic enteritis" is used when only the intestines are involved. Sometimes more specific terms derived from the common or the scientific names of the parasites are applied when only one kind of roundworm is concerned in disease. For example, "haemonchosis" refers to infections with the large stomach worm, "ostertagiasis" to medium stomach worms, "trichostrongylosis" to hairworms, "hookworm disease" or "bunostomiasis" to the hookworm, "strongyloidiasis" to the threadworm, and so on.

The injurious effects of roundworms on sheep and goats are many and varied according to the species, numbers of parasites present, the age and nutritional status of the animals, and other factors.

Some kinds of roundworms are well tolerated by their hosts or seldom occur in numbers large enough to produce perceptible effects.

Some of the clinical symptoms of roundworm infections are diarrhea (scours), anemia (reduced number of red blood cells and quantity of their contained red pigment), edema (swelling caused by excess fluid in the tissues), emaciation (unthriftiness from failure to gain or from loss of weight), loss of appetite, and physical weakness. The acute effects of roundworms, or less severe chronic effects of long duration, may cause death of the host.

Both immature and adult roundworms may injure the tissues of the digestive tract. For example, larvae of the nodular worm stimulate the formation of pea-sized nodules in the wall of the small and large intestines. Medium stomach worms and cooperias cause the formation of very small nodules in the wall of the stomach and small intestine, respectively. The large stomach worms, the hookworms, and large-mouthed bowel worms cut or pierce the inner lining of the part of the digestive tract in which they live with special mouth structures, at the same time ingesting blood, lymph, and cells from the gut wall.

Additional blood is lost from such small cuts or abrasions by seepage into the cavity of the digestive tract, from which it is eliminated in the droppings. When the worms make many small perforations of the gut lining, the total daily loss of blood may be greater than the animal can replace, and anemia ensues.

Hairworms, thread-necked worms, and threadworms do not usually inflict discrete, visible injuries to the tissues of the gut or cause anemia but cause diffuse damage to the gut lining, often to the extent that it may be partly destroyed.

Affected animals refuse food. Fluid may be lost from the body from a diarrhea and excessive urination. Normal digestion and absorption of nutrients are interrupted.

THE LIFE HISTORIES of these roundworms are called direct, as transmission from host to host occurs without intervention of an intermediate host, such as an insect, mite, or snail. The gullet worms are exceptions; their larvae develop in dung beetles.

Adult worms of both sexes live in the digestive tract. (The threadworm is an exception; only its females are known.)

Females deposit eggs in the cavity of the gut after fertilization by the males. The eggs are very small, usually contain one to many cells or a small larva, and are eliminated from the host in the droppings. On pasture under favorable conditions, the free-living development takes place. Small, active larvae, infective to sheep and goats, develop in a few days from the eggs. When a film of moisture is present on vegetation, they move onto the plants.

Infective larvae, after being swallowed by the host, develop to maturity in the digestive tract in 1 to 5 weeks, depending on the species. The young worms penetrate into the lining of the gut of the host, or are lodged between the small, fingerlike projections (villi), and usually cause damage to the tissues. As the worms mature, they usually, but not always, move to the cavity of the gut and spend their adult lives there.

Some variations of this typical life history occur in some species of roundworms. Knowing what they are helps one to understand the damage done and the symptoms.

Infective larvae of the hookworm and threadworm, which likewise can produce infection after being swallowed, also can enter the animal's body through the skin.

Many larvae penetrate the small blood vessels of the skin and are carried by the blood to the lungs. In the lungs they migrate from the small blood vessels through the lung tissue to the small air sacs. Infective larvae of these roundworms when swallowed may also penetrate the gut tissues, much as they penetrate the skin, and may be carried to the lungs by the blood. When the larvae reach the air passages in the lungs, they migrate up the windpipe or are coughed up and swallowed. Development to maturity takes place when they again reach the small intestine.

An interesting variation from the typical life history occurs in the threadworm, besides the fact that only females are known in the parasitic phase. Some of the small larvae, which are in the eggs when deposited in manure on pasture, may develop directly into infective larvae. Others, however, may develop into adult, free-living males and females that differ in structure from the parasitic females. These in turn give rise to a much larger number of infective larvae than would develop directly from eggs deposited on the pasture.

In the following more detailed account of these parasites, emphasis is placed on the roundworms that cause the greatest losses to farmers. No further mention will be made of the gullet worms, which seldom occur in large numbers in sheep and goats. Therefore, the following discussion concerns the roundworms of the abomasum (hereafter referred to as "stomach"), the small intestine, and large intestine, including the blind gut, or cecum.

IN THE TRUE STOMACH of sheep and goats are three important kinds of roundworms, the large stomach worm, several species of medium stomach worms, and one species of hairworm. These are the common roundworms found in the stomach of these hosts, but occasionally some of the species that normally live in the small intestine are found in the stomach, and vice versa.

When small numbers of stomach worms are recovered from the intestines after death, it is usually thought these worms are being eliminated from the host. The stomach not only performs important digestive functions; it also insures the regular passage of food materials into the small intestine in the proper form and quantity for further digestion. Therefore, when the stomach cannot function normally because of the injurious effects of roundworms in it, the digestive processes, appetites, and general health of the parasitized animals are seriously impaired.

The large stomach worm is the main roundworm of sheep and goats in most of the United States. Its life history is direct. Heavy infections and clinical disease, called haemonchosis, are more common in localities with long summers and moderate to heavy rainfall or where pastures are irrigated than in cold, arid localities. The reasons are that infective larvae develop best during warm, wet weather, and the free-living stages are killed by relatively short exposure to drying and subfreezing temperatures. When arid land in warm localities is irrigated and made into productive pasture, it becomes ideal for the development of the larvae of large stomach worms and other roundworms. Heavy infections are rapidly acquired by stock under such conditions, and losses are serious. This roundworm is also common in cattle and wild ruminants throughout the country, and its injurious effects on these animals are much the same as for sheep and goats. This parasite is such a common cause of losses that sheepmen and goat raisers routinely take measures to prevent haemonchosis from developing in their flocks and herds.

Haemonchosis is a serious disease. Its most important symptom is anemia. Infective larvae of the large stomach worm develop into adult worms in the stomach in 2 to 3 weeks. The males are one-half to three-fourths inch long. The females may be more than 1 inch long and look like pieces of coarse thread. The worms are very vigorous. Each has a small, sharp tooth on the upper surface of a small mouth cavity, by which small cuts are made in the wall of the stomach. Blood seeps into the cavity of the stomach from the cuts. More blood is sucked from the stomach wall by the worms. The intestines of living worms are usually filled with blood and are deeper red than the light-pink body of the worms. The whitish reproductive organs of the female are wrapped around its intestine; the names "twisted stomach worm" and "barber-pole worm" therefore are often applied to the parasite. The stomach of an animal that dies of haemonchosis usually contains much chocolate-colored material, which is blood altered by chemical action in the stomach.

Animals seriously ill of haemonchosis may seem to be in good health and flesh, except when the infection is of long duration or other parasites are involved, which often is the case. When the anemia is severe, the whites of the eyes and skin are pale, there may be a swelling under the jaw (bottle jaw), and the animals are incapable of much exertion because of the lack of red blood cells to carry oxygen to the tissues of the body.

Normally there are 10 million or more red blood cells in 1 cubic millimeter of blood in healthy sheep and goats. When the number is reduced to 3 million or below, animals may die suddenly. The number of red blood cells may be reduced in acute haemonchosis to a fatal low level in just a few weeks.

Medium stomach worms are about one-half inch long. The males are smaller than the females. They occur in sheep and goats throughout the country, but they cause clinical disease in the Western States oftener than in other parts of the country.

Five species of medium stomach worms occur more or less commonly in sheep and goats in this country, but only *O. circumcincta* and *O. trifurcata* are of much importance. Three other species occur in restricted localities in small numbers.

The life histories are direct. Their early parasitic development takes place in the lining of the stomach, where they form small, red, elevated spots or, at times, larger, flattened nodules. The mature worms usually move out of the tissues and live close to the inner surface of the stomach wall. When large numbers of young and adult worms are present, they irritate the stomach and generally interfere with digestion. Heavily infected animals may lose weight, scour, and become anemic.

The stomach hairworm is only about one-fourth inch long. It is like a short piece of fine thread. It is the smallest roundworm of sheep and goats and cannot be seen without a microscope when the stomach of an infected animal is opened for inspection. The stomach contents and scrapings of the lining must be washed thoroughly so that the worms are obtained relatively free of debris before they can be seen. This worm is unusual in that it infects cattle, horses, and various wild animals, besides sheep and goats. It has been reported only once in a wild rabbit, but domesticated rabbits, guinea pigs, and hamsters have been infected with it experimentally.

Its life history is direct. Infective larvae after ingestion develop into mature worms in the stomach in about 2 or 3 weeks. Young worms penetrate deep into the glands of the stomach, but most of the adults live near the inner surface or in the crevices of its lining.

The stomach hairworm severely injures all its hosts, particularly sheep and goats. Because the worms live in the rear part of the stomach near the valve between the stomach and small intestine, they can exert great effect on digestion and the movement of food and fluids to the small intestine.

In heavily infected animals the lining of the rear of the stomach, the pyloric valve, and the first few inches of the small intestine are acutely irritated, inflamed, and swollen. Affected animals refuse feed and water, lose weight, and become diarrheic, with copious watery feces. Many die, after experiencing acute symptoms for a week or more.

In chronic infections of long duration, especially when the animals are poorly nourished, the failure to gain weight is a common symptom and a nutritional anemia may develop. Small ringwormlike ulcers may also form in the stomach in chronic infections. In acute infections, however, the opposite of anemia may occur—an increase in concentration of red blood cells, brought about by excessive fluid loss from the body.

IN THE SMALL INTESTINE of sheep and goats several different kinds of roundworms may be found—intestinal hairworms, the hookworm, thread-necked worms, the threadworm, cooperias, and capillarids. All (except possibly the capillarids) can injure their hosts. (In addition to these worms, the larvae of the common nodular worm produces nodules in the small intestine, as well as in the large intestine and the cecum.)

All these roundworms have direct life histories. Infections are acquired by sheep and goats by swallowing infective larvae. The larvae of the hookworm and threadworm may also penetrate the skin.

Intestinal hairworms are only slightly larger than the stomach hairworm and usually must be recovered from the small intestine after death by special techniques and identified by a microscopic examination. They are found in the first one-third of the small intestine. Their injurious effects on the small intestine are like those produced by the stomach hairworm. Their general effect on sheep and goats also is much the same.

The disease caused by stomach and intestinal hairworms is called trichostrongylosis. In Australia it is commonly known as "black scours," because in affected sheep the wool around the anus usually is soiled by fluid feces. Actually, fluid feces in acute cases of pure hairworm infections is usually light brown or medium brown, but when considerable blood is lost into the cavity of the gut because of concurrent infections of large stomach worms or hookworms, decomposed blood blackens the fluid feces.

Trichostrongylosis is a serious disease, whether caused by hairworm species in the stomach, in the small intestine, or both. When sheep and goats are scouring, thin, and emaciated and poor feed is not entirely to blame, hairworms are often found to be the cause of their poor condition, although certain other kinds of roundworms may produce similar symptoms.

The characteristic symptoms of hairworm infections are loss of appetite, scouring, and loss of weight or failure to make normal gains. Scouring is often absent, however, unless the infection is overwhelming. When trichostrongylosis is made worse by haemonchosis or hookworm disease, the affected animals may scour and be anemic at the same time.

The hookworm is one of the large roundworms. The females are about an inch long. The males are slightly smaller. They are stout, muscular worms of a light-pink color. They live in the middle part of the small intestine. Their front ends are slightly bent, somewhat like a hook. Usually they are not encountered in as large numbers in sheep and goats as are large stomach worms, but several investigators have found several hundred worms in an animal.

The hookworm is potentially a dangerous parasite, particularly in localities with long periods of warm weather and high rainfall or on irrigated pastures in warm climates. Its life history is direct, but infective larvae may enter the hosts either by mouth with feed or through the skin.

Hookworms feed upon blood and cells while attached to the lining of the small intestine. They may move from one spot to another, making small punctures in the lining from which blood oozes into the cavity of the gut. Surrounding the mouth of the hookworm is a hard structure, called a buccal capsule, which contains cutting plates and a large tooth. Its esophagus is very muscular, and it can suck blood from the host's intestinal tissues.

The effects of heavy hookworm infections on sheep and goats are nearly the same as those produced by large stomach worms. The same kind of anemia occurs in hookworm disease as in haemonchosis, even though the loss of blood occurs in one case in the small intestine and in the other in the stomach. Other side effects of the two roundworm diseases also are similar. Hookworm disease is less common than haemonchosis in goats and sheep.

Thread-necked worms inhabit the first third of the small intestine. They cause nematodirosis. They are common in sheep and goats, particularly in localities of low average temperatures, as their pasture stages survive exposure to cold weather very well.

The females are about an inch long. The males are three-fourths inch long. All are threadlike. The hind half of the female is fairly broad and contains unusually large eggs. The front end of the body tapers toward the mouth and is quite narrow. Living, adult worms are light pink and sluggish in their movements. Immature worms are vigorous. When the small intestine of an infected animal is cut open, the adult worms can be seen tightly coiled in masses in the cavity of the intestine. Immature worms are hard to see, as they are smaller than adults and often are in the spaces between the intestinal villi.

Like the hairworms, thread-necked worms injure the lining of the small intestine and cause loss of appetite, a diarrhea, poor gains, and a loss of weight.

The threadworm causes strongyloidiasis in sheep and goats. Closely related species cause a similar disease in cattle, swine, dogs, monkeys, certain other animals, and man.

This roundworm is common in lambs and kids, but heavy infections may also occur in adult animals. Only females are known in the parasitic phase of the life history. They inhabit the first part of the small intestine, where they are found with their front ends deep in the spaces between the villi. Threadworms are about as long as hairworms, a quarter of an inch or less. They are slender and transparent and are hard to see with the unaided eye.

Strongyloidiasis is usually a disease of young animals. Injury to lambs and kids may be done in three ways. A skin irritation, or dermatitis, may occur when the larvae are penetrating the skin. The lungs may be affected. Bleeding may occur from the lung capillaries when larvae are passing through these organs on their way to the small intestine. Adult female parasites may injure the lining of the small intestine, causing an enteritis and symptoms similar to those associated with infections of hairworms and thread-necked worms.

Cooperias are small roundworms, one-fourth to one-half inch long. They inhabit the middle part of the small intestine. They can be distinguished from other kinds of small roundworms only with the aid of a microscope. Cooperias are common in all parts of the United States. Their life histories are direct.

Cooperia curticei is the most common one in sheep and goats. Its injurious effects are less severe than those we described for intestinal hairworms and thread-necked worms. They cause some irritation to the lining of the intestine. In chronic cases, small nodules form around immature worms in the tissues of the gut. Some of the other species of cooperias listed are known to cause more severe effects in cattle, but usually do not occur in large numbers in sheep and goats. Like most of the injurious roundworms, the cooperias, when present in large numbers, adversely affect the utilization of feed and rate of gain of lambs or kids.

Capillarids are slender roundworms, about one-half to three-fourths inch long, and are more closely related to whipworms than other kinds of roundworms of sheep and goats. They inhabit the small intestine. They seldom occur in large numbers and are not known to be injurious.

THE LARGE INTESTINE AND CECUM of sheep and goats commonly harbor several kinds of roundworms, nodular worms, whipworms, the large-mouthed bowel worm, and the pinworm. Nodular worms, which are discussed in another chapter (page 399), are by far the most injurious roundworms found in the large intestine of these hosts in this country. The others may cause some trouble.

The whipworms look like the whipworms of other animals and man. Females may be 3 inches long. The males are slightly shorter. The front part of the body is slender and usually is embedded in the lining of the cecum, or upper part of the large intestine. The rest of the body is broader, contains the reproductive organs, and lies free against the lining. The life history is direct. Infection takes place when the host swallows eggs that contain small larvae.

As far as we know, no serious injurious effects have been ascribed to whipworms of sheep and goats, but in heavy infections (which are rare) the lining of the large intestine and cecum probably suffers some irritation from their presence.

The large-mouthed bowel worm is about the same size as the two species of nodular worms, about an inch in maximum length, and resembles them superficially. At the head end is a large, cup-shaped buccal capsule, which has no teeth. This roundworm is much less common than some others. It has a direct life cycle. It is attached to the lining of the coiled parts of the large intestine by its buccal capsule, which is like a small suction cup. Damage is caused to the lining in a manner similar to that of the hookworm. This roundworm may cause diarrhea, bloody feces, loss of weight, and moderate anemia in heavy infections.

A species of pinworm, related to the pinworms that infect horses and man, is harbored by sheep and goats in some localities. It is found in the large intestine and usually is more common in goats than in sheep. Females are about one-fourth inch long. Males are about half as large. The life history is probably direct, but it has not been investigated thoroughly. Whether this roundworm is injurious to its hosts has not been determined.

DIAGNOSIS of roundworm infections of the digestive tract of sheep and goats is done by one or more of three methods: Microscopic fecal examinations for roundworm eggs; postmortem examinations to recover adult and immature worms; and observations of clinical symptoms displayed by affected animals.

The eggs of roundworms passed in the droppings are too small to be seen with the unaided eye. They are thoroughly mixed with the manure when they are voided by the animal. The eggs therefore must be concentrated, partially cleared from the fecal debris, and studied with a microscope. That is done by a simple technique. Fecal preparations for microscopic examination are made by mixing a small amount of feces, usually a half or quarter of a pellet or the equivalent in mushy or fluid manure, with a solution of higher specific gravity than the eggs, which will float the eggs to the surface. The usual flotation solutions used are saturated solution of common salt in water, a concentrated solution of sugar (about 1 pound of sugar to 12 ounces of water), or a 33-percent solution of zinc sulphate in water.

The fecal sample and the solution can be mixed in a small vial. Flotation of the eggs can be accomplished in a few minutes by gravity, or the mixture can be placed in a small centrifuge tube and centrifuged for about a minute or two at moderate speed. The eggs that float to the surface of the solution are removed to a glass slide and examined microscopically. This technique is very useful, as the number and kinds of eggs in the feces are often roughly proportional to the number and kinds of roundworms in the animal. (Infrequently, however, when an animal has a heavy infection of immature roundworms, a fecal examination will not reveal any eggs.) This technique has a further advantage in that it can be used with living animals.

Research workers in Australia have devised a special slide for flotation and counting of helminth eggs in feces, known as the McMaster egg-counting slide. This slide, when used with a special technique, has been found to be efficient for processing large numbers of fecal specimens in the minimum of time. Also, some diagnosticians prefer the fecal-culture method of diagnosis. Small quantities of feces are cultured in small bottles, and larvae of the roundworms are subsequently obtained therefrom for examination and identification.

Postmortem examinations for parasites are performed in order to establish a diagnosis based upon the presence of adult or immature roundworms in the digestive tract. The abdominal cavity is opened, and the digestive tract is removed and opened for examination. Large roundworms are easily seen and can be removed for study, but the small and immature worms of all kinds must be separated by special techniques from the food material and studied microscopically. Direct total counts of the large roundworms usually can be made, but when large numbers are present or the worms are small, those in a small sample or samples are counted and the total number is calculated.

The clinical symptoms we described as associated with roundworm infections often are helpful in making a diagnosis, but one cannot rely entirely on them because other diseases and conditions often cause similar effects. In sheep and goats, however, when such symptoms as diarrhea, anemia, emaciation, edema, loss of appetite, poor weight gains on good feed and forage, weight loss, and physical weakness are seen, roundworm parasites of the digestive tract are often involved.

The effects of poor or inadequate nutrition are often associated with the effects of parasitism, and the two factors are difficult to separate.

CONTROL OF ROUNDWORMS of the digestive tract of sheep and goats is of utmost importance if one is to raise the animals profitably. Parasite-free, or relatively parasite-free, animals make better weight gains and are more productive than animals with moderate to heavy parasitism.

It is not practicable now to raise parasite-free sheep and goats on the farm, although under experimental conditions that goal has been approached. It is possible, however, to control roundworms in sheep and goats so their effects are small or insignificant. This objective can be accomplished by the use of proper management procedures that check the transmission of roundworms from animal to animal and by judicious use of medication.

Sheep and goats acquire infections by grazing on pastures contaminated with larval stages of the parasites. All practices designed to reduce the numbers of the infective larvae aid in control. The numbers of infective larvae on pastures may be reduced to low levels if strict attention is given to three practices:

First, resting pastures, to take full advantage of the killing effect of adverse climatic conditions on larvae,

Second, maintaining animals on a high level of nutrition, to develop maximum resistance to roundworm infections and to their injurious effects, and

Third, reducing the numbers of adult egg-producing worms in grazing animals by medication. The drug most effective in removing roundworms of sheep and goats, phenothiazine, also has important secondary effects of inhibiting egg production of female worms not removed from the hosts and preventing the development of infective larvae from eggs deposited in manure on pastures.

Most of the larval stages of many kinds of roundworms are killed by exposures of a few weeks to 2 months of drought in the summer or by subfreezing weather in winter. Most larvae will survive best during periods of high rainfall and moderate temperatures. Irrigation probably lengthens the survival time of larvae. The killing effect of subfreezing weather on roundworm larvae is minimal in the Southern States. Larvae of a few kinds of roundworms are resistant to adverse effects of certain weather conditions. Significant numbers of larvae of medium stomach worms and thread-necked worms survive over winter even in the coldest parts of the country. Most other kinds of roundworms are primarily carried over winter in the breeding stock. Knowledge of the lethal effects of climatic conditions on free-living stages of roundworms is helpful in planning a pasture rotation program for parasite control.

Roundworms are easier to control if sheep and goats are fed well. A well-fed, healthy animal generally withstands the injurious effects of roundworms better and tends to have fewer worms than a poorly nourished one.

Animals subjected to massive invasions of large stomach worms, hookworms, and other roundworms that can produce anemia, need a high intake of iron, protein, and other nutrient elements (including carbohydrates and minerals) to replenish the blood lost as the result of infection. In some localities forage may not contain all the nutrients needed to maintain a high level of nutrition, and dietary supplements, including minerals, are helpful in maintaining nutrient levels and lessening the effects of parasitism.

A number of chemicals or combinations of chemicals are in use against roundworms in sheep and goats. In order of their usefulness they are:

Phenothiazine, copper sulphate and nicotine sulphate, copper sulphate, carbon tetrachloride, tetrachlorethylene, hexachloroethane, copper sulphate and sodium arsenite, and copper sulphate and arsenic pentoxide. These chemicals are of little or no value in treating some kinds of roundworm infections.

Phenothiazine is the most useful drug for removing and controlling roundworms of the digestive tract of sheep and goats and is used more widely in the United States than any other. It is particularly effective against large stomach worms, the medium stomach worms, hairworms, hookworms, large-mouthed bowel worms, and nodular worms. Phenothiazine is less effective, but still useful, against cooperias, thread-necked worms, and the whipworms. Phenothiazine has been found so useful in control of so many kinds of roundworms of sheep, goats, and cattle that several million pounds are used annually in this country.

Phenothiazine is remarkable in its action against many kinds of adult roundworms of sheep and goats, but it cannot be relied upon to remove immature roundworms from the digestive tract.

Phenothiazine may be administered in capsule, bolus, and tablet form and as a drench. It may be mixed in feed. The dose of the drug is usually 1 ounce (25 grams) for adult sheep and goats and about three-fifths ounce (15 grams) for lambs and kids under 60 pounds. Doses for adult animals may be safely varied from 20 to 40 grams, and about one-half those amounts for lambs and kids. The lower dose range is adequate for removing large stomach worms and nodular worms, but the higher dose range is needed when hairworms and thread-necked worms are the main roundworms present.

It is helpful to give treatments to breeding stock in the late fall or early winter, or a month before lambing and kidding time, and to treat again before they are put out to pasture in the spring. Because many kinds of roundworms are carried over the winter primarily in breeding animals, the spring treatment is helpful in preventing early contamination of pastures and early exposure of lambs and kids to infective larvae.

Phenothiazine also may be used preventively by a free-choice method of administration. Phenothiazine may be mixed with loose salt or suitable mineral mix in the proportion of 1 part by weight of the drug to 9 to 14 parts by weight of salt or minerals. This mixture is made available to the animals in a suitable container that protects the mixture from rain.

Sheep and goats should get about one-half gram of phenothiazine a day. That amount has the effect of preventing to a considerable extent the development of roundworm larvae in the droppings. The free-choice method may be used continuously and combined with therapeutic treatments when needed. If animals eat less of the medicated salt or supplement than is desirable, a small amount of grain may be added to make it more palatable.

Salt blocks medicated with phenothiazine have also been used in some localities, but it is not certain that they are economical or efficient.

KENNETH C. KATES *is parasitologist in charge of investigations on helminth parasites of sheep and goats in the Helminth Parasite Section, Animal Disease and Parasite Research Branch, Beltsville, Md.*

REX W. ALLEN *is parasitologist in charge of the State College, New Mexico, field station of the Animal Disease and Parasite Research Branch. He joined the Department in the Meat Inspection Service in 1934 and has conducted research on parasites of domestic animals since 1939.*

JAMES H. TURNER *is a parasitologist investigating helminth parasites of sheep and goats in the Helminth Parasite Section, Animal Disease and Parasite Research Branch, Beltsville. He holds degrees from the University of Maryland and has been engaged in research since 1948.*

Nodular Worms of Sheep and Goats

REX W. ALLEN

SHEEP and goats harbor two species of nodular worms, the common nodular worm (*Oesophagostomum columbianum*) and the lesser nodular worm (*O. venulosum*).

The adult stages of both species live in the lower part of the digestive tract. They are whitish and about one-half inch long and one-fiftieth inch wide.

The common nodular worm causes the condition known as pimply gut, or knotty gut, in which growths—nodules—occur in the walls of the intestines.

Intestines of sheep are used in the meatpacking industry chiefly as casings for sausage and as material for surgical sutures. Intestines containing nodules are unsuitable for those uses.

The developmental cycle of the common nodular worm begins with the eggs that are produced by the adult female worms. The eggs pass out of infected animals in the manure. After a period of development, a small, immature worm—a first-stage larva—hatches from each egg. The larva grows into a second-stage and finally a third-stage larva.

The third stage is the infective stage. It is about one thirty-second inch long.

It can develop further only in a susceptible animal, such as a sheep or goat. Development from the egg stage to the infective stage takes 6 or 7 days if the weather is favorable. Lower temperatures prolong the time or prevent development entirely.

In experiments conducted at Beltsville, Md., in 1945, A. G. Dinaburg found that mean air temperatures of 65° F. or above are necessary for their development. That means that in most parts of the United States little development takes place during winter.

The infective larvae are swallowed with feed or water. They penetrate the intestinal wall, usually in the lower part of the small intestine. After about 5 days, the larvae have attained a length of about one-twelfth inch. Now they migrate out of the wall into the lumen, the hollow part of the intestine, where growth to the adult stage takes place. Infective larvae usually reach the adult stage in 4 to 8 weeks.

The lesser nodular worm develops in much the same way.

Nodules, which often are as big as a pea, form as a direct result of penetration of the intestinal wall by the larval worms. Nodules are sites where larvae become encapsulated, or walled off, as the tissues of the affected animal try to ward off the encroachment of the parasites.

The common nodular worm is responsible for retarded growth, reduced weights of pelts and organs, a lower dressing-out percentage, and poor quantity and quality of wool. These effects are due mainly to the nodules and the penetration of the intestinal wall by the immature worms rather than to the adult stages of the parasite. The adults may cause diarrhea, increased secretion of mucus, and slight anemia.

Nodules are sometimes so numerous as to form a firm, tumorlike mass. There is a scarring, hardening, and thickening of the intestinal wall. Such extensive involvement undoubtedly interferes with the digestion and absorption of food.

The effects of the lesser nodular worm are less serious. It causes diarrhea and has some effect on gains in weight.

Symptoms of nodular worm disease include loss of appetite and loss of weight. The wool becomes dry, brittle, and yellow; it is often soiled because of a chronic diarrhea. Affected animals are weak and assume a hunched-up posture. Rectal temperature may rise slightly. Often a slight anemia follows.

Diagnosis on the basis of symptoms is complicated by the fact that some other worm parasites cause symptoms similar to those of nodular worm disease. It is hard to identify the eggs of the nodular worm because they look like some of the other worm eggs. But a slight anemia and the presence in the manure of a large number of eggs of typical size and shape is indicative, particularly if diarrhea is present.

Nodules can be detected in some cases in the wall of the rectum by feeling with the finger. A presumptive diagnosis may be made in this way. Postmortem examination reveals the typical nodules as well as the adult worms.

MEDICINAL TREATMENT is an effective weapon against nodular worm disease.

A single dose of phenothiazine, the drug of choice, will remove a high percentage of the adult worms from affected animals and so cut down the source of new infection.

Medicinals have no effect on nodules, however, and animals suffering from nodules cannot be expected to recover promptly.

Good sanitation practices aid materially in the control of nodular worms. The more heavily contaminated a pasture becomes, the more dangerous it is as a source of nodular worms. Much is to be gained therefore by shifting flocks occasionally from one pasture to another. This practice reduces the amount of contamination and the risks of infection as well.

Overstocking and overgrazing invite nodular worm disease.

CONTROL MEASURES that combine good sanitation and medicinal treatment and are carried out in the light of present knowledge concerning the seasonal development of nodular worms and their free-living stages will go far in abating this widespread parasitic disease.

REX W. ALLEN *is parasitologist in charge of the State College, N. Mex., field station of the Animal Disease and Parasite Research Branch, Agricultural Research Service.*

For further reading:
Aaron Goldberg: *Effects of the Nematode, Oesophagostomum venulosum, on Sheep and Goats,* Journal of Parasitology, volume 38, pages 35–47. 1952.
Merritt P. Sarles: *Effects of Experimental Nodular Worm (Oesophagostomum columbianum) Infection in Sheep,* U. S. Department of Agriculture Technical Bulletin 875, 19 pages. 1944.
M. P. Sarles and A. O. Foster: *Nodular Worm Disease of Sheep,* U. S. Department of Agriculture Leaflet 228, 6 pages. 1942.
United States Department of Agriculture: *Losses in Agriculture, A Preliminary Appraisal for Review,* U. S. D. A., A. R. S. 20–1 publication, 190 pages. June 1954.

Lungworms in Sheep and Goats

AARON GOLDBERG

THE thread lungworm (*Dictyocaulus filaria*), the hair lungworm (*Muellerius capillaris*), and the red lungworm (*Protostrongylus rufescens*) are serious parasites of sheep and goats in the United States. The first two species are widespread. The red lungworm occurs sporadically.

The thread lungworm causes more sickness and death than the other two species. Lambs and kids seem to be more susceptible to it than older animals are. Some mature sheep and goats acquire resistance to it after recovery from an attack, and others apparently have a natural resistance to it. In sections where the thread lungworm is a disease factor, the use of naturally resistant animals for breeding may be desirable.

Lambs less than 6 months old usually do not have serious infections of hair lungworm.

THREAD LUNGWORMS are white, up to 4 inches long, and as thick as coarse thread. When the air passages of the lungs of infected animals are opened at autopsy soon after death, the worms can be seen wriggling about.

The female worms deposit their eggs in the lungs, where they hatch. The larvae are coughed up or carried up in mucus, swallowed, and passed onto the pasture with the droppings.

After about a week's development on the ground, if temperature and moisture are favorable, the larvae reach the stage that is infective to the host.

Low temperatures delay development. Drying destroys the preinfective larvae. The infective larvae are more resistant to unfavorable influences and many remain viable on pastures for at least several weeks.

In favorable conditions the larvae migrate onto herbage and are swallowed by grazing sheep and goats. The larvae also may be swallowed with water. Once they get to the intestine, they penetrate its delicate membrane, enter the lymph system, and reach the abdominal lymph glands, where further development occurs.

About a week after infection, the young worms are carried by the blood stream to the lungs. Prenatal infection of lambs may occur when the larvae migrate from the placental blood vessels of the ewe into the blood vessels of the fetus. The larvae migrate in the lungs from the blood vessels to the air passages. They are still small at this time; they develop to maturity while they are in the lungs. The worms reach fertile maturity, and the new generation of larvae they produce is usually first found on the droppings about 5 weeks after infection.

The irritation of the mucous membrane of the air passages by the worms produces an inflammation, which may cause excessive amounts of a watery, straw-colored fluid and of mucus to form. The mucus and fluid sometimes contain traces of blood. Pus also forms. In massive infections, the air passages may be packed with worms. This blockage at times causes death by suffocation. The accumulation of worms and fluid in the lungs and drainage into the air spaces also may result in the partial blocking of the air passages. Breathing becomes difficult and noisy.

Coughing may begin 17 days after infection. The cough is usually strong and harsh in light infections, but in heavy infections it may be soft or absent. If the animal does not succeed in expelling the worms and fluid, affected areas of lung tissue collapse, become consolidated and of fleshy consistency, and sometimes atrophy. Considerable portions of the lungs may thus be rendered functionless. To get enough air, the animal breathes rapidly and sometimes keeps its mouth open and its neck extended.

Marked coughing may result in emphysema, the enlargement, and at times rupture, of some of the remaining functional alveoli, or air cells. The animal becomes weak, is not inclined to feed, and loses weight. The condition may lead to extensive pneumonia, sometimes complicated by the invasion of the tissues by bacteria, and death. Because the blood has too little oxygen, the skin often becomes blue just before death.

THE HAIR LUNGWORM is one-half inch to 1 inch long and as thick as a fine hair. It occurs embedded in the tissues of the lungs and is easily overlooked in casual postmortem examination. The presence of the worms is frequently indicated by slightly raised, yellowish-gray or greenish-gray areas, about one-fourth inch to 1 inch in diameter, on the surface of the lung. The deeper lesions are detected less readily. The lesions contain adults, eggs, larvae, and usually dead tissue and pus.

The eggs are deposited in the lungs and the larvae reach the pasture in the same way as thread lungworm larvae.

Unlike the thread lungworm, the hair lungworm does not have a direct life history—an intermediate host is required. The larva must enter the tissues of any of several different species of small land snails and slugs, where it develops in about 2 weeks to the stage that is infective to the final host. It may remain viable in the intermediate host for many months, and infection of the final host occurs when the snail or slug is swallowed by the grazing animal. The larvae are released in the process of digestion and reach the lungs in the same manner as the thread lungworm. The worms develop to maturity and their larvae are usually first recoverable from the droppings about 6 weeks after infection.

Although symptoms are not marked, the worms cause the destruction of lung tissue. The lungs are permeated in severe infections with nodular lesions, which result from the body's attempts to wall off affected tissue and parasites by surrounding them with fibrous connective tissue. The infection results in a catarrhal lobular pneumonic condition, contributes to the debilitation of the animal, and opens the way for invasion by bacteria.

THE RED LUNGWORM is reddish, about 1 inch to 2.5 inches long, and as thick as a hair. Usually it occurs in the medium and smaller air passages.

Its life history is like that of the hair lungworm. It seems to require a longer period and warmer conditions during the development of its larval stages than the other species of lungworms. Unlike the hair lungworm, it can use only a few species of snails as intermediate hosts. Such factors may account for its sporadic distribution.

Symptoms are usually not marked in animals infected with the red lungworm. When the worms are present in considerable numbers, they may cause pathological conditions similar to those produced by the thread lungworm.

Diagnosis of lungworm infections often can be made readily by floating a few fresh droppings in a small amount of water and examining the water for larvae, after about 15 minutes, with a dissecting microscope. The larvae occur in the mucous layer surrounding the pellets and migrate into the water. Lungworm larvae are the only kinds that may occur in fresh droppings of sheep and goats.

THE LARVA of the thread lungworm, the largest of the lungworm larvae, has a cuticular knob at the anterior end of the body and a blunt tail.

The larva of the hair lungworm, the smallest of the three species, has a sinuous, sharply pointed tail with a short, dorsal, subterminal cuticular spine.

The larva of the red lungworm is intermediate in size. It has a sharply pointed, straight tail.

No satisfactory medicinal treatment for the destruction of thread lungworms is known. Inhalants and intratracheal injections of various drugs have been tried, but frequently they are more injurious than beneficial to the host and they are hard to give.

The hair lungworm can be killed by an intramuscular injection of emetine hydrochloride, but such a treatment should be administered by a veterinarian. Emetine hydrochloride is a potent drug, and an overdose may result in serious damage or death. Care must be used to keep it from contact with the eyes, as it is highly irritant. It should not be used near shearing time because it may cause sheep to shed.

Preventing infection is the best means of combating lungworms. The general measures recommended for keeping livestock healthy apply.

The following measures are especially important in minimizing lungworm infection. The use of wet areas for pastures should be avoided as they are favorable habitats for the development of the thread lungworm larva and the intermediate hosts of the hair lungworm and the red lungworm.

It is desirable to rotate animals to clean pastures whenever practicable.

The use of dry feed, in racks designed to prevent contamination with droppings, and uncontaminated water will minimize the acquisition of parasites.

Sick animals and heavily infected ones should be kept from contaminating pastures with their droppings. They should be removed to dry lots to prevent additional infection with lungworms.

An adequate diet, and removal of gastrointestinal parasites by anthelmintics, remedies for worm infections, are deemed to be of considerable value in building up the vigor of the animal and consequently counteracting the effects of lungworm infection.

AARON GOLDBERG *is a parasitologist in the Helminth Parasite Section, Animal Disease and Parasite Research Branch, Agricultural Research Center at Beltsville.*

Scabies in Sheep and Goats

H. E. KEMPER AND H. O. PETERSON

FIVE KINDS of parasitic mites cause scabies, or scab, in sheep and goats.

Common scabies, or psoroptic scabies, is highly contagious to all classes of sheep. It is transmitted readily and quickly from one animal to another by direct contact.

It is caused by tiny, ovoid, pearl-white mites, *Psoroptes equi* var. *ovis.* The female mite is about one-fortieth of an inch long. A hand lens should be used when one examines infested animals for the mites. The adults have four pairs of brownish legs and sharp, pointed, brownish mouth parts.

The mites live on blood serum that oozes from skin punctures, which the mites make with their sharp mouth parts. Into the tiny wounds they probably secrete a poisonous substance. Bluish-red, inflamed, swollen areas surround the punctures. The serum on the skin becomes mixed with debris, which soon dries, hardens, and forms a crust, or scab. As the lesion develops, the skin becomes thickened, hard, and wrinkled. It might crack and bleed when it is manipulated with the fingers. The uniformly thickened condition of the diseased skin is readily detected by comparing it with the pliable, healthy skin.

Chronically diseased areas become hardened and covered with a tightly adhering, scaly, grayish crust. The grayish color results from the accumulation of dried flakes of skin. The wool falls out and leaves bare areas, which enlarge as the disease advances and make the sheep look naked. The mites seek the healthier skin at the outer edges of a lesion, produce more punctures, and thereby cause the lesions to spread. The mites can be found most easily at the outer edges of the lesions.

The mites cause intense irritation and itching. Infested sheep become restless and furiously scratch, rub, kick, and nibble at their wool. The fleece soon has a broken, disturbed appearance. From the fleece hang tags or tufts of wool, which the sheep have pulled out with their mouths or scratched out with their hind feet. Their discomfort is especially noticeable after they have been active. The wool on affected areas within reach of the animals' mouths may be dirty and wet with saliva. Licking the lips and champing the jaws while scratching are characteristic movements of sheep affected with scabies.

The first lesions usually are on the back or sides, but may start on any part of the body.

The only way to be sure that a sheep has scabies is to find the mites. Any condition that causes the sheep to bite and scratch themselves should be investigated at once.

As the wool is parted over a lesion, the mites move away from the light and may be picked up on the edge of a knife blade. The best way to find mites is to scrape the outer edge of the lesion with a blunt blade of a pocketknife, transfer the scrapings to a sheet of black paper, and examine the material under bright light. If the material is slightly warmed by sunlight or a lamp, the mites become active. They are plainly visible with a hand lens.

Clean sheep do not commonly contract scabies from infested premises, but they may become infested from premises or bed grounds very recently occupied by infested sheep. Premises that have been vacant for about a month are safe for use by clean sheep.

Freshly dipped sheep do not become infested from contaminated premises and therefore may be safely held there between the first and second dippings. It is a good sanitary practice, however, to avoid old bed grounds and unclean corrals.

The disease may be contagious at all seasons, but new infestations are uncommon in summer. Scabies often remains dormant during hot, dry weather and may seem to be cured, but usually it becomes evident again with the arrival of cold, rainy weather.

An attack does not give immunity. A flock may become infested any number of times.

Goats and cattle herded with sheep may be temporary carriers and may even develop lesions of short duration. Therefore they should be included when the flock is treated.

We used to think that psoroptic mites of sheep were not transferable to cattle or to any other class of livestock.

Tests at the Animal Disease and Parasite Research Laboratory at Albuquerque, N. Mex., showed, however, that common sheep scabies could be transmitted from sheep to cattle and then back to clean sheep. Lesions containing psoroptic mites were found on December 27, 1950, on a cow that had been kept with 10 scabies-infested sheep for 15 months. Six months later the disease appeared on a bull that also had been with the sheep. The original infestation on the cow and bull was maintained continuously on them for more than 4 years. Skin scrapings containing live psoroptic mites were removed from the cow every day for 2 weeks and placed in the wool of scabies-free sheep. Live mites became established in the wool 4 days after the first transplant. Small lesions and some loss of wool were observed during the first month. The sheep developed extensive and typical scabies within 3 months.

FOOT SCABIES, also called chorioptic or symbiotic scabies, is caused by mites known as *Chorioptes bovis* (of the variety *ovis*, if they are on sheep, or the variety *caprae*, if they infest goats).

The mites resemble the common scab mites and live in groups on the surface of the skin, usually on the lower parts of the legs and around the feet. They spread to the inner surfaces of the thighs and to the udder and abdomen in severe cases.

Chorioptic scabies is much more common in goats than in sheep. The visible lesions usually occur initially around the feet and are most pronounced during cold weather when the flock is housed.

SARCOPTIC SCABIES, often known as head scab or black muzzle, has been found on sheep in Europe but not in the United States. It is caused by the mite *Sarcoptes scabiei* var. *ovis*.

The mite burrows into the skin on the head and face, where there is little or no wool. Like common scabies, it causes intense itching and irritation. The infested animals rub and scratch the affected parts and hard, firmly attached scabs are formed.

Sarcoptic scabies may be told from common scab by the nature and location of the lesions and its tendency to remain localized on parts that are not covered with wool.

DEMODECTIC SCABIES usually is referred to as demodectic or follicular mange.

It is quite common in goats. It is found only rarely in sheep—usually in the small glands of the eyelids. The infestations in sheep do not cause much trouble.

In goats the mites infest the sebaceous, or oil, glands of the skin, which become filled with a thick, cheesy substance that contains thousands of mites. The swollen glands look like nodules in the skin. They may be as small as a wheat seed or as large as a walnut. The nodules are found oftenest at the base of the neck in front of the shoulders. They also occur over the back, hips, flanks, ears, and jaws. To find them, one must run his hands over the animal's body.

The contents of some nodules can be squeezed out between the fingers, but sometimes they must be incised. In order to see the mites, the material from the nodules must be examined under a microscope. They look quite different from other mites that infest livestock. The elongated body is divided into the anterior part, which bears the head; thorax, with legs attached; and the abdomen. About 100 or 125 of them measure an inch. The legs are short and stout. The mites have sucking mouth parts.

PSORERGATIC SCABIES was first found in the United States on sheep in Ohio in 1951. It had been reported on Merino sheep in Australia in 1941.

The mite causes a mild irritation and itchiness like that caused by lice. The sheep bite and scratch the parts most easily reached, such as the sides, flank, and rump. Tags of wool are pulled out, and the fleece has a ragged, tangled appearance. The tips of the wool fibers are twisted or curled into locks or matted and hang loosely from the sides.

The psorergatic mites are about one-third as big as the common scab mite. The head is short and broad. The general form of the body is rounded. Eight short legs extend from the sides of the body at equal distances from one another. Each leg has a double hook. The mite burrows into the skin, causing a slight thickening, roughening, and scaling of the affected area. The scabs are usually loose, dry, and crumbly. Moist spots sometimes exist in the lesion.

The small size and burrowing of the mites make them hard to find. One has to make deep skin scrapings with a scalpel or pocketknife and examine the material in light mineral oil under a microscope. The infestation spreads slowly and may take 3 or 4 years to become generalized on a sheep. The intensity of infestations may vary year to year. Some animals appear to recover, but usually there is a recurrence.

TREATMENT of sheep and goats infested with psoroptic and chorioptic scabies is with dips approved by the Department of Agriculture. The approved dips contain lime-sulfur, nicotine sulfate, wettable BHC, or wettable lindane.

Lime-sulfur dips are made in the proportion of 8 pounds of unslaked lime and 24 pounds of flowers of sulfur, or sulfur flour, to 100 gallons of water. If commercial hydrated lime, not air slaked, is used, 11 pounds per 100 gallons of water is required. If nicotine sulfate is used, the dip should contain not less than 0.05 percent nicotine. These two dips must be heated and maintained at 95° to 105° F. The sheep and goats must be dipped at least twice at intervals of 10 to 14 days.

Dips prepared from BHC (benzene hexachloride) or lindane should be prepared from wettable powders and the content of gamma isomer, the active insecticidal ingredient, should be maintained at 0.06 percent. BHC and lindane were approved by the Department of Agriculture in 1954 for the treatment of sheep infested with scabies or exposed to it. They have several advantages over lime-sulfur and nicotine sulfate.

Dips prepared from BHC and lindane must not be heated above 80° F. One treatment with BHC or lindane, properly applied, is enough to cure the common form of sheep scabies and foot scabies of goats.

The dipping vat should be filled with enough clean, unheated water to cover the animals—ordinarily 40 to 48 inches deep. After the water is measured and put into the vat, the required amount of BHC powder is added and thoroughly stirred. The dip should be stirred again after any interruption in dipping.

Each animal must be held in the dip not less than 1 minute to assure saturation of the skin and fleece. The head of each animal should be submerged at least twice for an instant so that the wool and hair about the head and face are thoroughly wet.

Small lambs should be dipped in a barrel. After they are a month old, it is safe to let them swim through the vat, but they should not be put into the vat with adult sheep.

The dip should be changed as soon as it becomes filthy, regardless of the number of sheep that have been dipped in it.

Because BHC, lindane, lime-sulfur, and nicotine sulfate do not kill or check bacteria, open cuts or wounds may become infected with dirty dip. Sheep that are weak and in poor physical condition should not be dipped because of the danger (especially when BHC or lindane are used) of killing them.

NO SPECIFIC RECOMMENDATIONS are made for treating sarcoptic, demodectic, or psorergatic scabies.

Many treatments have been suggested for controlling the demodectic mange of goats, but none of them has been completely effective. The lesions in goats are prominent enough to be treated locally. Some of the investigators report good results by opening the nodules, removing the contents, and irrigating the pockets with a 2-percent solution of coal tar-creosote dip. Good results also have been had from a few drops of a saturated solution of carbolic acid used in a similar manner.

In the absence of a satisfactory treatment, the infested animals should be isolated from the rest of the flock.

Attempts to control psorergatic scabies with BHC have shown some promise, but precise recommendations depend on further experiments.

One dipping in suspensions containing 0.06 percent of gamma isomer of wettable BHC or lindane makes it possible to eradicate psoroptic and chorioptic scabies from sheep and goats.

The use of this simple and reliable dip and the effective cooperation of livestock owners and State and Federal officials can eradicate this scourge of the sheep and goat livestock industry.

H. E. KEMPER *was graduated from the Kansas City Veterinary College in 1914. He retired from the Department of Agriculture after more than 40 years of work in the field of animal diseases and parasites in the former Bureau of Animal Industry.*

From 1943 to his retirement in 1955, he directed research on external parasites of livestock at the Department's field station at Albuquerque, N. Mex.

H. O. PETERSON, *parasitologist in the Agricultural Research Service, joined the Department's field station at Albuquerque in 1946. He has been engaged in research on the development of treatment of livestock affected with ectoparasites.*

Head Grubs of Sheep

N. G. COBBETT

HEAD grubs inhabit the nasal passages and adjoining cavities in sheep. They cause heavy losses everywhere.

The grubs are the larval, or maggot, stage of the sheep botfly, *Oestrus ovis*, which also is called the sheep gadfly or nasal fly. The fly is slightly larger than the common housefly. It is brownish gray and hairy. It can dart quickly in and out among sheep and occasionally hovers in front of a sheep's nose. Sometimes it remains motionless for some time on the ground.

The fly has no functional mouth parts; so it does not bite or feed. It has no stinger. Its sole purpose in life apparently is to reproduce its kind and deposit its young in sheep's nostrils.

The female fly deposits tiny larvae—not eggs—through a small, flexible tube, which she extends from the rear of her abdomen. She makes repeated, persistent attacks on different sheep, depositing a few larvae at a time. A fly can deposit 500 young grubs during her lifetime. When conditions are favorable she completes her deposition of larvae within a few days and then dies. During periods of cold or stormy weather, when conditions are not favorable for flight, she conserves her energy for later attacks on sheep by

remaining motionless in some sheltered spot and so may live for 2 weeks.

The sheep botfly is hard to see—it flies fast, and at rest its coloring usually blends with the surroundings. But sheep recognize its presence at once and become nervous and agitated. They stop feeding and gather in groups with their noses held close to the ground. They become alert, stare at the ground, stomp their feet, and snort or sneeze.

Just how the fly accomplishes the deposition of its young in the sheep's nostrils we do not know. It is thought that since practically all sheep become infested with head grubs, the fly must somehow come in contact with the nostrils. Perhaps she does so by quick, darting attacks while hovering in front of the sheep's nose or from the position she assumes on the ground near the places where sheep are feeding or resting.

After the sheep botfly makes a deposit of her young in or on the moist edges of the nostrils, the tiny grubs crawl quickly back into the nasal passages. There they move about over the mucous membranes, feeding on the mucus secreted by the tissues. Many conceal themselves within the many folds and crevices of the interior nasal structures, from which sheep cannot expel them by sneezing. They are then too small to be seen readily. They are only about one-sixteenth inch long, slender, and nearly colorless, like the mucous secretion in which they are found. Some of the tiny larvae soon molt and become second-stage grubs in about 2 weeks. Others remain unchanged for varying periods.

In the second stage of growth, the grubs are about three-sixteenths inch long, whiter, and somewhat thicker than when first deposited by the botfly. The second-stage grubs crawl further back into the nasal cavity and on through small passages into the more remote head cavities—the frontal sinuses. There they soon molt again, passing into their third and final stage of development.

The third-stage grubs are white or yellowish at first and slightly larger than second-stage grubs. They grow fast, getting darker as they develop. Some become fully grown in 2 weeks. The mature grubs are about 1 inch long and one-fourth inch thick and have several dark stripes on the back.

The grubs have two dark mouth hooks and many rows of sharp spines across their under surface. This armament increases in size and becomes darker as the grubs grow. They use it for moving about and for attaching themselves to the mucous membranes that line the head cavities. In so doing, the grubs irritate the membranes and cause them to secrete large amounts of mucus.

The fully grown grub works its way back out to the nostrils, drops to the ground, and burrows into the soil. There its skin hardens, and it becomes a pupa, or crysalis, from which a sheep botfly emerges in 4 to 6 weeks. Thus some grubs may complete their life cycle from tiny, newly deposited maggot to botfly in about 2 months.

The space within the frontal sinuses of sheep is limited in size. Ordinarily, therefore, only 2 to 8 grubs occupy those cavities at a time. Each nasal passage, however, may harbor as many as 25 of the smaller, first- and second-stage grubs.

As the mature grubs vacate the frontal sinuses, the second-stage grubs enter from the nasal passages and complete their growth to maturity. This process is continuous during warm weather and goes on the whole year in regions of mild winters.

In regions where the winters are cold, however, the botflies and the grubs that drop from the nostrils of sheep cannot survive freezing temperatures. Nature has provided for the perpetuation of the species under such conditions. The tiny first-stage grubs that are still in the nasal passages when the first cold days of fall arrive become dormant. They remain in this inactive state until the following spring. They then resume their development, become second-stage grubs, and migrate to the frontal sinuses, where they grow to maturity, leave the sheep, and subsequently become botflies.

LOSSES due to sheep head grubs are twofold—those produced by the grubs while living in the head cavities of sheep and those caused by the botflies.

The pests are found in practically every region where sheep are raised.

Goats are sometimes infested. Occasionally the grubs are found in deer, especially if goats or deer occupy the same range with sheep.

The damage caused by the grubs themselves is usually most apparent in old or weak animals and occurs oftenest when large grubs are present in the head cavities. The grubs cause the production of excessive amounts of mucus, which flows from the head cavities to the nostrils. In the nostrils it often accumulates in thick, stringy masses, which sheepmen call snotty nose.

Strong, healthy sheep usually have no difficulty in expelling the excess flow of mucus from the nasal passages and ordinarily show little distress or evidence of illness from infestations of head grubs.

Old or weak sheep usually lack the strength to rid themselves of the excess mucus. It accumulates in their nasal passages, becomes thicker, and often stops up the passages, so that breathing becomes difficult. Bacterial invasion sometimes occurs and causes inflammation and thickening of the mucous membranes that line the head cavities. That produces further difficulty in breathing and may kill the animal. The thickening of the membranes often obstructs the escape route of mature grubs, and they die in the deeper head cavities. Abcesses, which may cause severe illness or death, may then form in the cavities.

The greatest loss produced by this pest is that caused by the botflies. When the flies are active among sheep, the animals become nervous and are constantly on the alert as they attempt to protect their nostrils from the attacks. Thus throughout the summer grazing season sheep frequently are prevented from feeding or resting normally during the daytime. The result is a great loss of growth.

CONTROL MEASURES for head grubs in sheep have been attempted by many workers over the years, but none has proved universally practicable.

The measures have included the application of repellants to the noses of sheep in attempts to prevent the botfly from depositing her young in the nostrils and the introduction of larvicides into the head cavities to destroy the grubs therein. The sheep botfly is not easily deterred from depositing her young. Field tests involving the thorough and frequent application of some of the best known fly repellents, such as pine tar and fish oils, to the noses of sheep have proved unsuccessful. When slaughtered, lambs so treated were found to have as many grubs as untreated lambs in the same flock.

The presence of large, dead grubs in the deeper head cavities of sheep often produces severe inflammation and abcesses. Methods of treatment designed to destroy the grubs in those places therefore are not advised. Furthermore, the difficult procedures involved in such treatments make their use on a large scale impracticable. Killing head grubs of any size in the head cavities of sheep when the botflies are active is a waste of time and effort. At those times the flies reinfest the sheep with young grubs soon after the animals have been treated.

One method of controlling head grubs in sheep has been quite successful, but it is practicable only in regions where the winters are cold. It is applied in the late fall and winter and is designed to kill all the tiny dormant grubs that overwinter in the nasal passages, thereby destroying the maggots that would otherwise resume development the following spring.

The treatment consists of irrigating the nasal passages with a 3-percent Lysol solution. The solution mixes readily with the nasal mucus and makes it lethal to the small grubs.

A small stream of the solution is forced first into one nostril and then into the other, backed by 35 to 45 pounds of air pressure. During treatment the sheep is held on its back, with the head resting on its top surface. The nose is raised slightly. In that position the stream of solution irrigates most of the crevices and folds inside the nasal passages before it gravitates to the pharnyx. If the solution is injected while the head is in an upright position, it takes a direct course to the pharnyx, where it might be swallowed and produce toxic effects to the animal. Only about 1 ounce of the solution is injected quickly into each nostril, and the animal is immediately returned to its feet. Occasionally a treated sheep, after being released, will hold its breath, stagger, and fall to the ground. Such animals make a quick recovery, however, when promptly assisted to their feet.

Many tests have shown that this treatment, applied once after the botfly season is over, can eliminate more than 90 percent of the small dormant grubs in the sheeps' nasal passages.

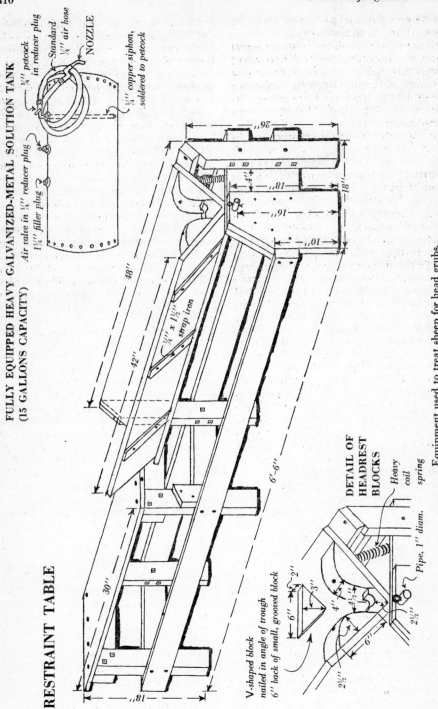

FULLY EQUIPPED HEAVY GALVANIZED-METAL SOLUTION TANK
(15 GALLONS CAPACITY)

Air valve in 1/4'' reducer plug
1 1/4'' filler plug
3/8'' petcock in reducer plug
Standard 1/4'' air hose
NOZZLE
1/4'' copper siphon, soldered to petcock

RESTRAINT TABLE

1/4'' x 1 1/2'' strap iron

V-shaped block nailed in angle of trough 6'' back of small, grooved block

DETAIL OF HEADREST BLOCKS

Heavy coil spring

Pipe, 1'' diam.

Equipment used to treat sheep for head grubs.

SPECIAL EQUIPMENT that includes a restraint table, a solution tank capable of holding the required air pressure, hose, and nozzle, as shown in the accompanying sketch, are essential for properly administering the treatment to large numbers of animals. With this equipment 350 to 400 sheep can be treated in an hour.

The nozzle is made of brass. It has a curved spout about 3 inches long and about five-sixteenths inch in diameter. The end of the spout is smooth and blunt and has an opening three thirty-seconds inch in diameter. The flow of solution is controlled by pressing or releasing a button that opens and closes a valve in the base of the nozzle. Such nozzles are obtainable at most stores where automobile parts are sold.

The restraint table is equipped with a trough made of two 1-inch by 12-inch boards. The trough is mounted on a pipe axis, which allows it to be tipped to one side. Sheep are placed in the trough on their backs for treatment. When the treatment is completed, the trough is tipped, discharging the animal onto its feet. The trough is returned to its upright position by a heavy coil spring attached to the left side of the trough and anchored to the frame of the table.

In use, the restraint table usually is placed so as to form one wall of a small catch pen. The sheep enter the catch pen through a chute or gate from a larger holding corral. An operator and four helpers usually work at each restraint table. Two men hold a sheep in the trough for treatment, and two helpers catch and hold another animal in readiness.

The operator forces the nose of each sheep downward into the notch in the headrest of the table with the palm of the left hand while holding the nostrils open by grasping each side of the upper lip firmly with the thumb and forefinger. To complete the injections quickly, it is important to maintain a firm grasp until both nasal passages have been treated. The operator handles the nozzle with the right hand.

The point of the nozzle is placed a short distance (1 to 2 inches, depending on the size of the sheep) into first one nostril and then the other. Only enough solution is injected into each nostril to cause a return flow through the opposite nostril.

N. G. COBBETT, *a veterinarian in the Animal Disease and Parasite Research Branch, Agricultural Research Service, is stationed at Albuquerque, N. Mex. Upon graduation from Colorado Agricultural and Mechanical College in 1921, he joined the Bureau of Animal Industry. Since 1928 he has engaged in investigations pertaining to external parasites that affect livestock and poultry.*

Lice of Sheep and Goats

H. O. PETERSON AND R. C. BUSHLAND

SHEEP and goats are commonly infested with lice, which usually go unnoticed until the infestation becomes extensive and harmful.

The heaviest infestations occur in winter when the animals are closely herded or confined to shelters. Goats usually suffer more than sheep.

Two kinds of lice attack sheep and goats—sucking lice and biting lice. Both may be present in a flock at the same time.

Sucking lice are more harmful because they live on blood and pierce the skin to obtain it. They are blue or dark gray and have pointed heads and sucking mouth parts. The heads are usually longer than broad.

Biting lice live on the surface of the skin and feed on scales, bits of hair, and other debris on the skin surface. They are yellow or reddish brown and have short, broad, rounded heads, which are usually broader than long.

Some of the sheep lice can be distinguished from others by noting the region of the body they inhabit. Foot lice, for instance, are found on the legs of sheep. To find them one should look in the coarse, dense hair above the hoofs near the dew claws. When foot lice are numerous on sheep, they may be on the upper region of the legs and even on the ventral surface of the thorax or abdomen. The African blue louse usually afflicts the sides of the body. The common body louse of sheep, *Linognathus ovillus*, is found on several parts of the body.

Three species of sucking lice live on sheep: *Linognathus ovillus*, the common body louse; *L. africanus*, the African blue louse; and the foot louse, *L. pedalis*.

On goats, the most common sucking louse is *L. stenopsis*. At times the African blue louse is found on goats, especially those on the western ranges. It closely resembles *L. stenopsis*.

Only one biting louse, *Bovicola ovis*, is commonly found on sheep.

At least four species of biting lice are found on goats. The most common is *B. caprae*.

Both biting and sucking lice are completely parasitic. They spend their entire life cycle on the infested animal. They can live for only a short time off the host.

Their eggs are firmly attached to the wool fibers or hair about 1 inch from the surface of the skin on animals in full fleece. The eggs are oval or barrel-shaped, attached at one end to a single wool fiber or hair, and firmly closed at the other end by a cap, called the operculum. They vary from straw color to a pale or dark brown. The eggs hatch in 1 to 3 weeks, depending on the weather.

Newly hatched lice, the nymphs, are similar to the adults except that they are slightly smaller. Several molts occur during the nymphal stage. Nymphs become adults in 2 to 3 weeks after hatching. As they become adults, mating takes place and eggs are laid, thereby completing the life cycle.

As the numbers of lice increase, they spread through the flock by direct contact between individual animals. Close herding, crowded corrals, and confinement to stables aid in spreading the lice.

SUCKING LICE pierce the skin to obtain blood for food. In doing so, they cause intense irritation.

Biting lice do not pierce the skin. They move about on the skin surface much more than the sucking lice and irritate the infested animals by their constant movements. They live on particles of hair, dried skin, dried serum, and other bits of skin debris.

Because sucking lice consume blood, they are considered more harmful than biting lice. The damage done by both biting and sucking lice is confined largely to that done the wool or mohair. The attempts made by the infested animals to relieve the irritation caused by lice results in injury to the fleece. The wool or mohair becomes soiled, matted, and broken by the rubbing, scratching, and biting done by the infested animals. The value and utility of both are reduced, and the loss sustained by the producer is considerable.

TREATING sheep and goats for lice is usually by dipping. If a dipping vat is available, it should be used, because it is the most certain method for eradicating lice, especially if the animals are in full fleece.

Louse-infested animals need not be held in the dip longer than necessary to wet the fleece and skin thoroughly.

About 1 minute is usually long enough. The animals usually get thoroughly wet if they are allowed to swim slowly through the length of the vat. Their heads should be submerged at least twice for an instant while swimming through the vat. It is not necessary to heat the dip, but the temperature should not be allowed to fall below 65° F.

All the animals in the flock should be dipped whether they show infestation or not. The dipping fluid in the vat should be 40 to 48 inches deep. The amount necessary to complete the work should be ascertained before it is prepared. Freshly shorn sheep and goats and short-wool lambs and kids carry out 1 to 2 quarts of dip. In the late fall, when they are in full fleece, each will carry out and retain in the fleece 1 gallon. The amount carried out and retained by the animals and the amount required to change the vat will be a fair estimate of the total amount of dip needed.

Lindane and BHC are recommended for treating sheep and Angora goats for sucking lice. Control has been obtained sometimes—but not always— with dips containing 0.025 to 0.03 percent of gamma isomer, the active insecticidal ingredient. Dips and sprays having a concentration of 0.05 to 0.06 percent are considered better. A single treatment with either BHC or lindane is enough.

Milk goats should be treated with methoxychlor in a 0.25-percent dip.

Flocks of sheep and goats may be treated satisfactorily in dips prepared from cube or derris powder containing approximately 5 percent rotenone. Rotenone is the active insecticidal ingredient in the powder, and the recommended concentration of rotenone in the dip is 0.006 percent. To make a dip containing this concentration, 1 pound of cube or derris powder is added to 100 gallons of water.

Sheep infested with foot lice need not be necessarily dipped. They can be waded through a water suspension prepared as though for a dip. Infestations of foot lice have been effectively treated in wading troughs with 0.5-percent suspensions of DDT.

SHEEP AND GOAT LICE can be eradicated by dipping once in DDT, TDE, methoxychlor, toxaphene, or chlordane in concentrations of 0.25 percent.

Because it is hard to wet the animals completely with sprays, it is recommended that sprays be used in twice the concentration of dips—namely, 0.5 percent.

Dips prepared from emulsifiable concentrates should be used with great care. They are more hazardous than wettable powders and should be used only as directed by the manufacturer.

Only fresh formulations should be used, and all quantities of insecticide and water should be measured.

To CONTROL sheep and goat lice with sprays prepared from lindane or BHC, the gamma isomer should be the same as for dips; namely 0.06 percent. These lice pests can be eradicated only by destroying the motile lice, their eggs, and the nymphs that hatch after the treatment. Complete and thorough wetting is therefore required but is rarely achieved by spraying; consequently consistent eradication cannot be expected from spraying. If other insecticides, such as DDT, methoxychlor, toxaphene, or chlordane, are used for spraying sheep or goats, they should be used in concentrations of 0.5 percent.

The insecticidal chemicals referred to here will not dissolve in water, but are soluble in oils. Liquid concentrates for mixing with water are prepared by dissolving the chemical in a suitable petroleum solvent along with a wetting agent so that the oil will mix with water. This three-way mixture of insecticide, oil, and wetting agent is called an emulsifiable concentrate. Emulsifiable concentrates suitable for livestock use should mix readily with water to form milky-white emulsions that do not separate on standing.

An owner who prefers to use spray

should spray as soon as possible after shearing. All the animals should be treated, and attempts should be made to wet all parts of the body. Particular attention should be paid to the underline. If the animals are in full fleece, more spray is required than on newly shorn sheep.

The amount of spray required varies with the size of the animals, the length and density of the fleece, and the circumstances under which they are sprayed. The amount usually will run near a gallon for one animal.

When infested sheep or goats cannot be sprayed or dipped because of unfavorable weather, as is often the case in areas where the winters are severe, the animals can be dusted, either by hand, if the flocks are small, or treated with a dusting machine. These devices are usually set up in a runway leading from a corral. The insecticide most often used for dusting is cube powder containing approximately 5 percent of rotenone. The cube powder is formulated for treatment so that it contains 0.5 percent of rotenone.

Goats producing milk for consumption by people should not be treated with DDT, toxaphene, TDE, chlordane, benzene hexachloride, or lindane, because of possible contamination of the milk.

Methoxychlor or rotenone can be used to treat milk-producing animals.

H. O. PETERSON, *a veterinarian, has been employed at the Ectoparasite Research Station at Albuquerque, N. Mex., since 1946.*

R. C. BUSHLAND *since 1951 has been in charge of the Kerrville, Tex., laboratory of the Department of Agriculture.*

Sore Mouth in Sheep and Goats

C. L. DAVIS

SORE MOUTH, or contagious ecthyma, is a highly contagious disease of sheep and goats.

It is common in lambs and kids but rare in animals more than a year old, although lesions have been seen on the udders of nursing ewes and goats. It is most prevalent among lambs being fattened for market but it may appear in range bands and farm flocks. Feeder lambs frequently develop the disease, usually within 7 to 10 days after arrival in the feed lots.

Sore mouth occurs in spring and summer wherever sheep are raised.

The lesions appear mostly on the lips and sometimes on the face and ears and near the eyes. Vesicles, pustules, ulcers, and scabs form. The lesions in severe cases may reach the mouth, where extensive ulceration of the cheeks, hard palate, and tongue may develop.

The disease in the ordinary outbreak runs a rather benign course, with few or no fatalities, unless complications set in. The greatest loss results from debilitation due to inability of the animals to eat for long periods and from stunting of growth at the age when normal gains should be greatest.

Uncomplicated cases heal spontaneously in about a month, usually without treatment. The scabs fall off within 3 or 4 weeks. Healing takes place without formation of scars. The dried scabs retain the virus, which is resistant to heat and cold and can survive in the soil from year to year. The disease may therefore recur annually on premises where it previously existed, unless the new crops of lambs are protected by vaccination.

When the lesions on the face become infested with maggots or secondary infection has resulted in deep ulceration, many fatalities may occur—particularly in the Southwestern States, where the screwworm larvae invade the tissues through the lesions of sore mouth.

Complications from secondary infections, chiefly by *Psorophora necrophorus*, occur in the more northerly States where the screwworm does not exist. The bacterial infections may result in necrotic lesions in the lung, liver, stomach, and intestines. Fatalities may range from 10 to 50 percent of the animals so affected.

PREVENTION of screwworm infestations and secondary infections are of chief concern to avoid complications.

Lesions should be cleansed of maggots and a fly repellant should be applied to prevent further infestation. Secondary infections can be avoided for the most part by local antiseptic treatment. Deep-seated ulcerations and secondary lesions in the lung and gastrointestinal tract are harder to treat.

The value of antibiotics and the sulfa drugs in the treatment of such cases has not been established.

A LIVE VACCINE for the prevention of sore mouth was developed in 1935. It is applied to the skin in a manner similar to the technique used in vaccinating against smallpox in man— that is, by rubbing the vaccine in scratches made in the skin. The common sites for vaccination are in places where the wool is absent, such as inside the flanks or under the tail. A successful inoculation, or "take," is indicated in susceptible animals by the formation of a local pustular lesion at the site of application. The scab that forms afterwards dries and falls off in several weeks. The immunity thus conferred lasts up to 2 years or longer. Animals that recover from natural in-

fection and those vaccinated are considered, from a practical viewpoint, to be immune for life.

In places where contagious ecthyma occurs regularly, it is advisable to vaccinate all lambs or kids before the pasture season begins.

Some ranchers may find it more convenient to vaccinate at the time when castration, docking, and earmarkings are done.

Because exposure to infection may occur during shipping, range lambs consigned to feed lots should be vaccinated at least 10 days before shipment to allow time for immunity to develop.

Ordinarily it is advisable to vaccinate animals before the disease appears, but some beneficial results may be expected even when vaccination is done as an outbreak impends— the normal course of the disease in animals already showing symptoms is usually shortened.

MAN IS SUSCEPTIBLE to the virus of contagious ecthyma. Ranchers, sheepherders, and others who may handle infected sheep are subject to infection, usually through abrasions on the hands. Those who treat or vaccinate lambs therefore should wear rubber gloves.

The lesions in man consist of one to several rather large vesicles, or blisters, with painful reddening and swelling of the skin. There may be a slight rise in temperature and some swelling of the lymph glands in the armpits.

C. L. DAVIS *attended Colorado Agricultural and Mechanical College and received the degree of doctor of veterinary medicine in 1921. He has been with the Department of Agriculture since 1922, devoting most of his time to the study of the pathology of animal diseases. He is a charter member of the American College of Veterinary Pathologists and was elected president of the organization in 1954. He was the director of the Animal Disease Research Laboratory in Denver from 1947 until 1955, when he was transferred to the Animal Disease Eradication Branch in Washington, D. C.*

Scrapie in Sheep

C. R. OMER

THE DISEASE of sheep known as scrapie is caused by a filterable virus. It represents a chronic neurosis characterized by symptoms of intensive and progressive pruritis, or itch, progressive debility, and locomotor incoordination. The course of the disease may extend over several months. Almost invariably it ends in death.

Scrapie was found in New Zealand and Australia in 1952 in animals imported from Great Britain.

The first case of scrapie in the United States was reported in Michigan in 1947. The disease appeared in California and Ohio in 1952. Since that time scrapie has been diagnosed in Illinois, Indiana, New York, Connecticut, Oregon, Texas, and Tennessee.

All breeds of sheep are susceptible. It has recently occurred only in the Suffolk or Cheviot breeds or their crosses. Most of the affected sheep found in the United States have been imported from Canada or are the progeny of such importations—an indication that infection possibly has been carried by sheep imported into Canada from English flocks that may have been either infected or exposed.

At one time it was thought that the disease followed only certain blood lines of sheep. An experiment was carried out in Scotland, starting in November 1932, by Dr. J. Russell Greig. Healthy sheep were placed in a pasture that had contained scrapie-infected sheep, without coming into direct or indirect contact with the infected animals. This exchange was made twice weekly between healthy and diseased sheep.

In 1936—3 years and 3 months later—the first symptoms appeared in the healthy group. Seven cases showed typical symptoms of scrapie between February 1936 and May 1938, when the experiment was concluded. This exposure afforded experimental evidence that scrapie is an infective disease, the period of incubation is prolonged, and the causal agent can be transmitted through the medium of pasture.

The exact method of elimination of the virus from the infected animal is not known.

THE SYMPTOMS of the disease are slow to develop. Only an experienced sheepman may be able to recognize the earliest symptoms. The sheep are nervous, apprehensive, and more excitable than usual. Slight tremors in the head and neck are observed. The animal becomes tense with excitement when it is moved. Rapid muscular tremors, affecting particularly the thighs and flanks, are manifest. The head and neck are carried high and somewhat stiffly. The facial expression is staring and fixed. The ears frequently assume unnatural positions. Grinding of the teeth is commonly noticed. The wool loses its luster and becomes dry.

The outstanding symptom is that the animal rubs against fixed objects. At first the owner may suspect that the animal is infected with scabies, but a close examination of the skin discloses no evidence of scabies. The scratching usually begins in the region of the rump, particularly around the tail head, and gradually extends over the sides, shoulders, and neck. When the sheep is rubbed by the hand over the loin or rump, it will usually show a definite "scratch reflex"—nibbling movements of the lips and sometimes vigorous wagging of the tail.

The itch becomes more intense, as the disease progresses and the animal spends a great deal of time rubbing. One can see evidence of this rubbing on fences and sides of buildings where pieces of wool hang. The skin of the animal will show no evidence of any diseased condition, except possibly abrasions from the scratching. Some sheep do not rub their wool but bite the skin on their legs and pull wool with their mouths.

The temperature of the infected animal remains normal throughout the course of the disease. Thirst is a frequent symptom. There is no diarrhea. The bleating is weak and tremulous.

The animal's appetite remains good. The sheep gradually loses weight, becomes weak, and walks with an unsteady or staggering gait. It may fall after running a short distance, particularly if it tries to jump over objects on the ground. Eventually it will be unable to stand. It will then lie on its side and make running movements of the feet. It will continue to eat in this position if feed is within its reach.

The course of the disease varies in duration, from 6 weeks to 6 months before the animal dies. Instances are known in which the animal dies within 14 days after the first symptoms are noticed.

THE NUMBER OF ANIMALS actually infected in a flock may vary from 4 to 20 percent, although it is possible that 50 percent of the flock may be affected, or there may be only an occasional case over a period of several years. Interviews with farmers in whose flocks the infection was diagnosed brought out that some of them had lost a few sheep without knowing that such a disease existed. Scrapie is a new disease in this part of the world.

As the disease has an extremely long incubation period, only seldom does one find an animal under 18 months that shows the symptoms. Animals as old as 11 years have been infected. Most of the cases in the United States have been in animals about 3 years old. It is possible that some animals may harbor the infective agent and never show symptoms of the disease themselves.

Scrapie is different from parasitic skin diseases commonly found in sheep.

In scabies, the mites can be located and the scabs they form can be seen with the naked eye, and there is no incoordination of gait. Ticks and lice also can be seen on the skin and in the wool. Dipping the animals in special preparations for the elimination of these parasites will stop their rubbing.

Scrapie must also be differentiated from listeriosis, a bacterial disease of short duration. Animals that have listeriosis draw their heads to one side, circle in one direction, and push against fixed objects.

No specific postmortem lesions are present in the animals infected with scrapie, except those that microscopic examination of sections of the brain stem and adjoining spinal cord will reveal. Evidence of vacuolar degeneration of nerve cells characteristic of this disease is seen then.

WE KNOW OF NO TREATMENT for sheep infected with scrapie.

The most effective method of eradication has been the slaughter of all infected and exposed animals. This method has been recommended in England and has been actually carried out in infected flocks in New Zealand, Australia, Canada, and the United States.

Thorough cleaning and disinfecting of premises after slaughter is important. Federal indemnity is available for partial payment of sheep destroyed under this program in the United States. Several States also have made funds available for indemnity payments.

A program has been developed in all States whereby flocks containing sheep that have been imported or purchased from flocks that may have been exposed to scrapie are inspected at 6-month intervals by State or Federal veterinarians. In this way the flock owner learns about the symptoms of this disease and which officials to notify if he suspects scrapie in his flock.

C. R. OMER *is veterinarian in charge, Animal Disease Eradication Branch, Agricultural Research Service, the United States Department of Agriculture, Albany, N. Y.*

Bluetongue of Sheep

D. G. McKERCHER, B. R. McCRORY, AND J. L. HOURRIGAN

BLUETONGUE, or catarrhal fever, is a virus disease of sheep. Typical symptoms are fever, depression, and lack of appetite. Inflammation and ulceration of the mucous membranes of the nasal cavity, mouth, and the tongue may occur. The tongue may sometimes be swollen and cyanotic (bluish).

The acute phase is relatively short, but recovery may take a long time and may be marked by lameness, debility, and extreme emaciation. A "break" in the staple lowers the value of the wool. The fleece is sometimes shed. The mortality occasionally is high but usually does not exceed 15 percent of the affected animals in an outbreak. Because of loss of condition, long convalescence, interruption of breeding schedules, and lower value of the wool, however, the indirect economic losses from bluetongue are considerably greater than those suffered directly in terms of actual deaths.

Bluetongue has been serious in some countries for many years but is relatively new to the United States. For a long time it apparently was confined to the Union of South Africa and other parts of Africa. It has been studied extensively in the Government Veterinary Research Laboratories at Onderstepoort, Union of South Africa. The disease was reported on Cyprus in 1943 and later in Israel. It has been reported, without confirmation, in Palestine, Turkey, and Syria.

The presence of bluetongue in the United States was suspected in 1948 and confirmed in 1952 on the basis of studies by American and South African investigators, who could not find out, however, how it was introduced or when. Its presence in Arizona, California, Colorado, Kansas, Missouri, and Texas has been verified, and it was diagnosed clinically in Montana, Nebraska, New Mexico, Oklahoma, and Utah. Suspected outbreaks were reported in Idaho, Indiana, Oregon, and Wyoming in 1954 and 1955.

ALL BREEDS of sheep are susceptible to bluetongue, but severity of infection depends on several factors.

Certain breeds are less susceptible than others. In South Africa the native Afrikander and Persian breeds are considered quite resistant; the Merino is less so; and the Dorset Horn and other British breeds display but little natural resistance. The susceptibility of individuals in each breed also seems to vary.

Another factor is the strain of the virus. Some strains produce relatively mild infections, irrespective of breed; others regularly give rise to a severe form of the disease.

Age is a factor. Sheep about 1 year old are most susceptible. Lambs of susceptible ewes suffer a much milder form of the disease, possibly because of the natural resistance of youth. Lambs of dams that have recovered from the disease have a passive immunity, which gives a measure of protection for 2 months or more after birth.

Environmental circumstances also have a part: Sheep born and bred in an area where bluetongue exists are more resistant than those introduced from a place where the disease is less prevalent or absent.

Bluetongue is seasonal. (Very likely insects transmit it.) It is more prevalent during wet years and occurs mainly in low-lying localities, although conditions suitable for the vector, rather than the absolute elevation, may be the critical factor. The disease usually begins in early June and ends abruptly with the first severe frosts. Its onset and duration, therefore, vary for different areas of the country. The peak of the disease coincides generally with the period of greatest insect activity in any particular area.

THE FILTERABLE VIRUS that causes bluetongue is present in the blood, blood serum, organs of circulation, and tissue fluids of the infected sheep. Sheep are regarded as the natural hosts. The virus is also found in cattle, but in cattle the clinical manifestations of disease are negligible or absent.

Infant mice, hamsters, and chicken embryos can be infected by experimental inoculation.

The bluetongue virus can remain viable in decomposed blood and tissues for long periods. In suitable storage it retains its viability for years.

A number of strains of bluetongue virus exist. Most of them differ in virulence. Thus, in fully susceptible sheep, some strains — the virulent strains—regularly produce a severe form of bluetongue, whereas others—of low virulence—give rise to a relatively mild infection.

When a strain of low virulence is passed from sheep to sheep by injection, the virus tends to become weaker and eventually loses its capacity to produce a recognizable clinical infection. The virulent strains retain full power to cause disease when they are passed in this way. When passed through a succession of chicken embryos, however, strains of high and low virulence alike lose their ability to cause bluetongue in susceptible sheep. The weakened virus is then said to be "modified" or "attenuated." Such viruses are used to protect or immunize against their fully virulent counterparts.

Of utmost importance in vaccinating and immunizing against bluetongue is that all known strains of the virus are divisible into four distinct groups, or types. Recovery from an attack of bluetongue caused by a strain of one particular type fails to protect the individual against subsequent exposure to a strain of virus belonging to any of the other three types. Type and virulence are unrelated, however, because a mild strain of virus protects against infection with a fully virulent strain of the same type, and vice versa. The significance of this point is referred to later.

BLUETONGUE is not a contagious disease. It can be transmitted only by the injection of infectious blood and other virus-containing tissues. The evidence we have strongly suggests that under natural conditions transmission is by a nocturnal bloodsucking insect, or insects, which transfer the blood from diseased to susceptible sheep.

Circumstantial evidence originally implicated the mosquito as the vector, but investigations have not proved that to be true.

Limited experiments later demonstrated that a night-feeding gnat of the genus *Culicoides* could possibly transmit the infection. It has not been possible to raise these gnats in captivity, however, and research men have been unable to determine whether this gnat might be a biological vector (that is, one in which the virus undergoes multiplication) or merely a mechanical vector of the virus. In any event, we think it is highly significant that these gnats are found wherever bluetongue occurs in the United States, although bluetongue does not necessarily occur where these gnats abound.

Of equal importance is the manner in which the virus is maintained from one bluetongue season to the next. The disease does not occur in late fall, winter, and early spring, a period of about 6 months; yet, as far as we know, the virus does not persist for longer than 4 months in recovered sheep. These two points can be reconciled only on the premise that the virus is maintained from year to year in a host other than sheep.

Although species of the *Culicoides* gnat can harbor the virus, that the gnats normally maintain the virus is considered highly improbable. Much more likely is that some vertebrate species is involved from which the insect obtains the virus before the beginning of each bluetongue season. The fact that cattle harbor the virus for variable periods while showing little or no evidence of clinical infection might therefore be significant.

IN SHEEP into which the virus is injected experimentally the disease appears usually 6 to 9 days after the injection. The time required for the disease to develop naturally has not been determined but is believed also to be about 6 to 9 days.

Rarely will all the signs of the disease be observed in any one sheep or even in any one outbreak. A definite pattern of symptoms may predominate in one flock, but another set of symptoms may be found in an outbreak nearby. Likewise the morbidity and mortality vary greatly. Sheep may occasionally contract the disease and experience only a febrile reaction. Others may display the typical clinical symptoms and have no fever.

The early stage of the disease is characterized in most cases only by a temperature, which ranges from 104° to 106° F. or even higher. The fever begins to subside after 3 or 4 days, and clinical symptoms appear.

The first symptoms consist of a flushing of the skin over the sternum, inside the thighs and forelimbs, and sometimes over the shoulders, ribs, and flanks; swelling of the lips and tongue; and reddening of the mucous membranes of the mouth and nasal cavity. A watery discharge and an excessive amount of salivary secretion, often stringy, also are observed. The nasal discharge soon becomes quite thick, dries on the nostrils, and forms encrustations, which leave a raw, bleeding, underlying surface when removed.

In many cases the swelling of the lips extends to the ears, muzzle, and intermandibular space and less frequently to the neck and sternum. The ears become hot and pendulous. The lower part of the head looks swollen. Affected animals show variable degrees of depression. The appetite is diminished or absent. Breathing and the pulse rate speed up. The animals lie down much of the time.

Parts of the mucous membranes of the mouth and tongue may slough, leaving bleeding areas on the margin, inner surfaces of the lips, at the corners of the mouth, on the upper surface and tip of the tongue, and on the dental pad and gums.

The tongue may be greatly swollen and bluish and protrude from the mouth, so that breathing is difficult. Necrotic ulcers often are observed in severe cases on the sides of the fixed part of the tongue. Sometimes raw sores develop on the muzzle and in the nasal passages. Animals that develop pneumonia as a sequel to the febrile reaction breathe with great difficulty, and the saliva becomes frothy and sometimes tinged with blood. These cases usually die.

The flushing of the skin results ultimately in the formation of localized areas of dermatitis and is associated with the development of a bluish-red or purplish band at the coronet (skin margin of the hoof), which moves down with the growth of horn. This inflammatory process is believed to account for the lameness that often occurs. This band is not observed in all naturally occurring cases of the disease, however, and is seldom observed in animals that are infected experimentally.

Most deaths occur during or shortly after the acute stage. A few deaths occur just afterwards; they usually are due to secondary pneumonia. Most of the other animals recover in a relatively short time, but some develop emaciation, weakness, stiffness, and lameness. Sometimes the fleece is shed. In some cases the head is held to one side—a condition that is known as torticollis or wryneck. It is caused by a muscular weakness resulting from the degeneration (wasting) of the neck muscles. Such animals, which survive a long period of convalescence, rarely if ever regain their former condition and are of little economic value.

MOST OF THE TISSUE DAMAGE in bluetongue is apparent in the living sheep and includes swelling of the ears and lower head; inflammation and ulceration of the mucous membranes of the nasal cavity, mouth, and tongue; localized inflammation of the skin; the presence of a purplish band around the coronets; and a wasting of the muscles.

Less striking internal changes are observed at autopsy. These include hemorrhage in the form of dark-red, gelatinous areas, which look like bruises. They usually are found in the tissues under the skin and often extend into the muscles of the back, shoulders, and neck. In many instances when gross hemorrhage is absent, small pinpoint hemorrhages, seen only by careful examination, are present in the skeletal muscles. In all or most cases of bluetongue a clear or reddish gelatinous fluid is present in the muscle tissues and in the skin of the lower neck.

Degeneration appears as whitish areas of various sizes throughout the skeletal muscles. Pneumonia is present to a variable degree in many cases but is not regarded as being characteristic of bluetongue. Changes visible only by microscopic examination of affected tissues include capillary hemorrhage and the degenerative process in the individual muscle fibers.

ONCE THE PRESENCE of bluetongue has been established in an area, a diagnosis can be made with reasonable confidence on a strictly clinical basis. However, clinically diagnosed or suspected cases of the disease in an area presumably free of bluetongue should always be confirmed by laboratory studies.

Conditions occurring in the United States that are most likely to be confused with bluetongue are contagious ecthyma (soremouth) and photosensi-tization (big head). The following details will help one tell them apart.

Contagious ecthyma occurs mainly in lambs and is characterized by the formation of vesicles—blisters—on the lips and tongue, which ulcerate, leaving granulating sores. Vesicles on the lips become encrusted with thick, grayish-brown scabs. After some time the scabs drop off and the lesions heal, leaving no scars. Rarely is the disease accompanied by fever or depression, which is so common in bluetongue.

Photosensitization occurs only in white-faced sheep. There may be considerable depression, but muscular stiffness and oral lesions are absent. (The term refers to the process whereby something becomes sensitive to light.)

BECAUSE INSECTS probably transmit bluetongue, efforts to eradicate or restrict the spread of the disease by regulatory measures would appear to be futile. Attempts to control it by means of insecticidal dips and sprays likewise are impracticable under most conditions of sheep raising in this country and appear to be of little value.

Treatment is useless, although the disease can be made less severe by protecting affected animals from direct sunlight.

Bluetongue can be prevented by vaccination procedures, which were developed by scientists in South Africa.

The original vaccine used in that country consisted of a mild strain of virus, which was further weakened by successive passage in sheep. That vaccine was dangerous, however, because occasionally it produced clinical bluetongue in highly susceptible animals. Another disadvantage was that the vaccine afforded protection against only the same type of virus. The subsequent attenuation of the bluetongue virus by serial passage in chicken embryos made it possible to develop a modified live-virus vaccine containing the four known virus types. It has given excellent results.

In the United States a similar vaccine is available. It contains the only type of bluetongue virus known to exist in this country in 1956. It is recommended that vaccination be carried out well before the onset of the bluetongue season. It may be resorted to in the face of an outbreak, however, because the development of new cases can be arrested in nonvaccinated flocks within several days.

Ewes should be vaccinated before breeding, but if that is impracticable it may be safely done during late pregnancy. While a high incidence of weak and abnormal lambs results when vaccination is done during the first 6 or 8 weeks of gestation, limited field observations seem to indicate that the adverse effects do not occur when vaccination is done before breeding or during the fourth or fifth month of pregnancy.

The earliest age at which lambs can be vaccinated and develop a satisfactory immunity has not been definitely established, but available information indicates 3 to 4 months of age.

Occasionally reactions occur after vaccination. These are manifested by fever, mild depression, and a reluctance to feed about a week after vaccination. The affected animals will return to normal, however, in 24 to 36 hours. The severity of the reactions conceivably may be minimized by affording protection against direct sunlight during that time.

D. C. McKercher *is associate professor of veterinary medicine and associate veterinarian in the experiment station of the School of Veterinary Medicine, University of California, in Davis. He holds degrees from the Ontario Veterinary College, in Guelph, Canada; Queens University, Kingston, Canada; and Cornell University.*

B. R. McCrory *is a veterinarian of the Animal Disease Research Laboratory at Denver, Colo.*

J. L. Hourrigan *is head of Special Diseases Eradication Section, Animal Disease Eradication Branch. He received the degree of doctor of veterinary medicine from Kansas State College in 1940 and joined the Department of Agriculture that year.*

Enterotoxemia of Sheep

B. R. McCRORY AND C. L. DAVIS

ENTEROTOXEMIA is a highly toxic and usually fatal disease of suckling and feeder lambs. Mature animals are less susceptible to it. Investigators in different countries have described it under the various names of enterotoxemia, overeating, pulpy kidney, apoplexy, milk-colic, and braxy-like disease. It has been very costly to the sheep industry of the world, but effective control has resulted from good management and the use of biological products for immunization.

Most investigators agree that enterotoxemia is of nutritional and bacterial origin, the predisposing cause being the overeating or gorging by the animal of highly nutritive feed ingredients, which causes a digestive disturbance and creates an ideal environment for the multiplication of the organism, *Clostridium perfringens* Type D. This organism is commonly present in the stomach and intestinal tract of normal warm-blooded animals and in the soil. The immediate cause of the disease is the absorption into the blood circulatory system of the toxin liberated by the organism. The mechanism by which the toxin is absorbed from the intestines has not been determined.

Invariably the lambs affected by the disease are the largest, thriftiest, and greediest feeders. Nursing single lambs that consume too much milk are similarly affected, as are older animals that are given access to a good, lush grass pasture or winter-wheat pasture. The practice of "lambing down" corn and other grain fields has been discontinued in many districts because the death loss from enterotoxemia makes it unprofitable. Severe losses occur every year in feeder lambs that are being finished for market on a grain ration.

Symptoms of illness are manifested by most of the affected lambs a few hours before death. It is common to find dead animals in the pens in the morning even though all appeared healthy the night before.

Many lambs may suddenly jump, fall to the ground in a convulsive seizure, and die. Others show symptoms of a brain disturbance by holding the head to one side and walking in a circle, holding the head high and extended or thrown back and staggering about the pen, or standing with the head down and pushing against the fence, feed bunker, or other objects.

Extreme excitement may be shown by a lamb. It may run blindly about the pen for a few minutes, then collapse, and go into a coma or die. The temperature may be raised 2° to 3° F. Loss of appetite, depression, vomiting, paralysis, constipation, diarrhea (which may persist for several days), and a rapid loss of weight are some of the symptoms frequently observed.

I. E. Newsom, in experiments at the Colorado Agricultural Experiment Station, determined that sugar in the urine may run from 2 to 6 percent and should be regarded as characteristic of acute cases of enterotoxemia.

Characteristic lesions revealed at postmortem examination are many large, blotchy hemorrhages along the wall of the intestines, in the diaphragm, and in abdominal muscles. Small hemorrhages frequently are observed under the covering of the heart. An accumulation of straw-colored fluid containing small clots may be found in the sac surrounding the heart. When the animal lives for a few days after symptoms are noticed, it is usual to find an inflammatory reaction in the tissue lining the fourth stomach and especially in the first few feet of the small intestine attached to it. Often no lesions are visible when lambs die suddenly. Pulpy kidney is considered a postmortem change that occurs 3 or 4 hours after the lamb dies.

Enterotoxemia must be differentiated from such infectious diseases as listeriosis, anthrax, paratyphoid, coccidiosis, and hemorrhagic septicemia and from plant poisoning.

A diagnosis of enterotoxemia is justified when some of the most vigorous and fattest lambs on full feed show signs of brain disturbance; dead lambs are found in the pens a few hours after they were seen to be normal; symptoms and losses stop abruptly when grain is removed from the ration; nursing lambs stop dying when the ewes are placed on sparse pasture or a less nutritive feed; during postmortem examination, large blotchy hemorrhages are found along the intestinal wall, in the diaphragm, and in abdominal muscles; there is no evidence of pneumonia; *Clostridium perfringens* Type D toxin occurs in the contents of the intestines.

GOOD MANAGEMENT is an essential part of the program for preventing the disease in fattening lambs because they vary considerably in their individual abilities to assimilate grains or concentrated feeds. Lambs that are received from the range may be placed on pasture or sorted according to size and penned. If they are penned, it is advisable to feed only hay or other good roughage for a few days. Water should always be available to the lambs. There should never be any extra feeding space left at the grain trough. The grain should be spread evenly the length of the trough to assure a more uniform consumption of feed.

The ration for lambs that are being started on feed should consist mostly of hay or other good roughage and a small amount of grain. The grain allowance is raised gradually as they become accustomed to it. Sudden or radical changes of ingredients in the ration or in feeding time should be avoided.

When enterotoxemia develops in lambs nursing ewes that are on lush pasture or rich feed, the flock should be placed on sparse pasture or penned in a dry lot for a part of the day to restrict grazing.

It requires close observation, especially for the inexperienced feeder, to detect the lambs that are about to go off feed and those that show early signs of scouring. When lambs show either tendency, an immediate reduction of one-half to three-fourths of the daily grain allowance for 4 or 5 days will prevent other lambs from gorging and dying, but it will also reduce the rate of gain.

Following the reduced-feed period, the daily allowance of grain or concentrate should be increased gradually until the lambs are on full feed. It is important that close observation of the lambs be maintained.

A. W. Deem and his colleagues at the Colorado Agricultural Experiment Station have shown by several feeding experiments that the addition of sulfur to the daily grain ration greatly reduced (but did not completely prevent) the death loss from enterotoxemia. The addition of one-third ounce of the sulfur (325-mesh commercial ground), added to the daily grain ration of each sheep, was an effective control that did not affect appreciably the rate of gain.

Losses can be prevented near the end of the feeding period by sorting out and shipping to market the fat lambs that are ready for slaughter and by reducing the amount of ration and trough space to the requirements of the remaining sheep.

The administration of antitoxin and bacterin has given excellent results in preventing enterotoxemia.

ANTITOXIN gives an immediate immunity that lasts 2 or 3 weeks. It is used to stop death losses in lambs of all ages in the face of an outbreak of enterotoxemia and may also be used to immunize feed-lot lambs on short-term (21 days) feeding.

Bacterin is intended to stimulate the development in healthy animals of an immunity that will last at least 5 or 6 months. About 10 days are required to develop a protective immunity. Bacterin therefore should be administered at least 10 days before sheep are placed on full feed.

There may be a reaction in the tissues at the site of injection. Because it may persist for at least 30 days, it is inadvisable to use bacterin if the animals are intended for slaughter within that time. Bacterin should not be injected into lambs under 2 months.

Antitoxin and bacterin should not be injected at the same time, because the immediate immunity established by the antitoxin will prevent the body tissues from reacting to the bacterin.

The antitoxin or bacterin is injected by aseptic means, usually under the skin in the wool-free area back of the place where the foreleg joins the body. Injection there helps to prevent unnecessary lameness.

B. R. McCRORY *is a veterinarian of the Animal Disease Research Laboratory in Denver, Colo. He was graduated from Colorado Agricultural and Mechanical College and received an advanced degree from Ohio State University. He served as associate professor of pathology at the Colorado Agricultural and Mechanical College and Colorado Agricultural Experiment Station, and later became professor and head of the Department of Veterinary Medicine and Anatomy. Dr. McCrory joined the Department of Agriculture in 1953.*

C. L. DAVIS *in 1955 joined the Laboratory Section, Animal Disease Eradication Branch, of the Department of Agriculture.*

Vibriosis of Sheep

HADLEIGH MARSH

IN SHEEP in the United States, the only known important cause of infectious abortion is infection with *Vibrio fetus*. The situation differs from that of cattle in that brucellosis has not been found in sheep in this country. Vibriosis occurs in sheep in many States.

The occurrence of the disease is sporadic. The total incidence in any one area or flock over a period of years is not great, but in some years and in individual flocks the losses may be serious. In some seasons the lamb loss in several of the western range States has run into many thousands. The percentage of the flock which aborts varies from 5 percent to 70 percent. A loss of 10 to 20 percent is common. There is also considerable mortality in the infected ewes in some outbreaks, but the death loss in the ewes generally is slight.

The characteristic symptom of vibriosis in sheep is abortion, usually starting about 30 to 40 days before the band is due to begin lambing. At first, in a band of 1,000 ewes, there may be 1 or 2 abortions a day, and the number gradually increases until as many as 10 may be aborting in a day.

Some of the infected ewes will carry their lambs to full term, but the lambs may be born weak and may not survive. In the aborted fetus there is often some subcutaneous edema, and the body cavities contain a bloodstained fluid. The liver in some of the fetuses shows a number of gray spots, but this lesion usually is absent.

Usually no symptoms are noticed before abortion, but close observation may reveal vaginal discharge several days before abortion, and the ewe may appear sick. After abortion there is usually a brown vaginal discharge for several days. *Vibrio fetus* can be recovered from the vagina for about a week after abortion. Usually the ewes recover rapidly. In a few instances the disease is fatal to the ewe.

After abortion the ewes lose the infection within a few weeks. Reports from the field and records of ewes in large experimental flocks show that lamb production is usually normal in the season following an outbreak of abortion and that the previously infected ewes do not act as carriers. The lapse of 7 months between lambing and the next breeding helps prevent a carryover of infection.

THE SOURCE of the infection and the principal means of transmission have not been finally determined for the disease as it occurs in sheep. In vibriosis in cattle, cows become infected by being bred to infected bulls, and the bulls may be carriers of the infection indefinitely. In the sheep disease, the evidence available indicates that probably the ram is not the chief source of the infection in ewes. It has not been possible to identify specific infected rams as responsible for infecting ewes by serving them.

In two large experimental flocks where extensive outbreaks of vibrionic abortion occurred, the numbers of abortions were distributed quite equally through almost all of the breeding lots. In one of the flocks, in which 644 abortions occurred in 2,513 ewes bred in 116 breeding lots, the abortions were distributed throughout 112 of the lots. If the rams were responsible for the infection, one must conclude that all of the rams were carriers of the infection, but that seems quite unlikely.

A few experimental infections of rams have not resulted in infection of the ewes bred to them. Further negative evidence as to the role of the ram is the experimental finding that it is difficult to infect a ewe at breeding time by any method of inoculation. The susceptibility of the ewe appears to be relatively low until she has been pregnant more than a month.

Nevertheless, research workers at three experiment stations have started studies of the possible role of the ram as a carrier and transmitter of the infection.

Although experimental infection of the ewe by any means except inoculation directly into the blood stream of the pregnant ewe is rather difficult, research workers have established that the disease can be produced by feed or water carrying *Vibrio fetus*. Perhaps that is an important source of the infection—in the range States, outbreaks of vibrionic abortion seldom if ever occur in flocks that are grazed on the range throughout the year, as compared with flocks that are fed during the winter.

THE DIAGNOSIS of vibriosis in sheep is made most satisfactorily by isolating *Vibrio fetus* from an aborted fetus. If the fetus is submitted to a laboratory in good condition, the organism can be quite readily obtained in cultures from the stomach, liver, or heart blood.

The blood from ewes in the acute stages of the infection will show reaction to the agglutination test, but this test is of little practical value because the agglutinins in the blood decrease rather rapidly after abortion occurs and because there is seldom occasion to make a diagnosis except when abortions are occurring. It is possible therefore to base the diagnosis on laboratory examination of the aborted lamb. As the ewes are not carriers of the infection, blood tests on individual ewes are of little value except as an aid to diagnosis in an outbreak of the disease. Although artificially infected rams react to the blood test, it is not known whether the test would be of value in identifying a carrier ram, because the existence of carrier rams has not yet been demonstrated.

Treatment of infected ewes seems to offer little hope, because the affected ewe is not recognized until it is too late to save the lamb and because a high proportion of the ewes recover quickly after abortion without treatment.

Of the small number of ewes that do not recover, it might be possible to save some by treatment with antibiotics.

Definite recommendations for prevention and control cannot be made with the information now available. We know that there is no advantage in disposing of ewes that have been through an outbreak of abortion, as they will lamb normally in the next breeding season and will not infect other ewes or rams.

If further investigation shows that infected rams transmit the disease, such rams should be identified and eliminated as breeders. Because pregnant ewes can become infected by feed or water contaminated with the discharges of aborting ewes, aborting ewes should be isolated immediately and the fetuses and discharges destroyed.

We have some evidence that standing surface water or contaminated shallow wells may be reservoirs of infection. Pregnant ewes therefore should have access only to clean running water.

No vaccine or other immunizing agent has been developed.

HADLEIGH MARSH *is State veterinarian of Montana. He obtained his degree in veterinary medicine from the George Washington University. He was formerly head of the Montana Veterinary Research Laboratory, Montana State College.*

For further reading:
Anonymous: *Sheep Husbandry in Ontario*, Ontario Department of Agriculture Bulletin 499, 51 pages. 1954.
C. G. Potts: *Sheep Raising on the Farm*, U. S. Department of Agriculture Farmers' Bulletin 2058, 18 pages. 1953.
C. G. Potts and V. L. Simmons: *Milk Goats*, U. S. Department of Agriculture Farmers' Bulletin 920, 38 pages, (revised). 1955.
J. F. Ryff and Ralph F. Honess: *Internal Parasites of Sheep*, Wyoming Agricultural Experiment Station Circular 42, 16 pages. 1951.
G. P. Williams: *The Angora Goat*, U. S. Department of Agriculture Farmers' Bulletin 1203, 21 pages, (revised). 1946.

Pregnancy Disease

W. A. ANDERSON AND C. L. DAVIS

PREGNANCY disease is a highly fatal metabolic disorder of ewes. It occurs during the fourth or fifth (last) month of pregnancy and is associated with an inadequate supply of carbohydrates.

It affects older ewes, particularly those carrying twins or triplets, but occasionally an animal bearing a single large fetus will succumb. The disease occurs wherever sheep are raised. It has been reported from all parts of the United States and in Australia, South Africa, Canada, Great Britain, and Europe. In this country it is primarily a disease of small farm flocks; large bands of range sheep are seriously affected less often.

Synonyms include lambing paralysis, hypoglycemia, preparturient paresis of ewes, staggers, and old ewe disease. Ketosis is probably the most satisfactory term that has been suggested, because the condition in ewes bears a physiological similarity to that disease in cattle.

Death losses are severe. It is estimated that 90 percent of the animals showing visible symptoms die. O. H. Muth and J. N. Shaw, of the Oregon Agricultural Experiment Station, have reported that losses reached 10 percent and sometimes 20 percent in bands of ewes in that State. To the loss from the death of a ewe must be added the potential value of the unborn lambs and the disruption of management practices that follows a lamb crop smaller than expected. Thus the overall economic loss involved makes this disease one of the outstanding hazards of the sheep industry.

It was formerly believed that pregnancy disease chiefly involved fat ewes, but further experience has shown that animals in poor condition also are frequently affected. The disease is definitely associated with an insufficient or unbalanced diet. This may be complicated by lack of exercise, the effects of parasitism, or exposure.

The essential cause of pregnancy disease is an insufficient intake of carbohydrates. The conditions under which that may occur are fairly well understood. A particular blood-sugar level necessary to meet the normal metabolic requirements is supplied primarily by the carbohydrates and to a lesser extent by fats and proteins.

In late pregnancy, the nutritional demands of the fetus upon the pregnant animal are extremely high and are increased by the added requirements of twins or triplets. When for any reason carbohydrates in the diet become inadequate, the blood-sugar level is lowered, and pregnancy disease develops.

Regardless of whether the disease occurs in fat animals or in thin and poorly nourished animals, the pathology is the same. Only the predisposing conditions differ. In well-nourished animals an attack may be precipitated by cessation of feeding because of storms, a radical change in diet that lowers appetite, irregular feeding, or the upsets of a long drive or railroad journey. Outbreaks have developed when owners, thinking their animals were too fat, reduced the rations. Lack of exercise is also a contributing factor in fat ewes.

Most cases, however, develop in sheep that are in poor condition and on inadequate diets, such as straw, cornfodder, wild hay, or poor pasture, and too little grain. The increasing demands of the growing fetuses finally become too great for the limited supply of carbohydrates, and pregnancy disease results.

R. F. Bourne, formerly of Colorado Agricultural and Mechanical College, in his discussion of the physiology of pregnancy disease, pointed out that the body's supply of carbohydrate is represented by the relatively small amounts of sugar in the blood and lymph. In addition, there is a considerable reserve of glycogen stored in the various tissues, 80 percent of which is in the liver and skeletal muscle. When the intake of carbohydrate is insufficient to meet the increasing demands, the liver gives up glycogen to make up the deficit. The glycogen in the liver cells is then replaced by fat, which may increase from a normal 3 percent to as much as 30 percent by weight in that organ. The reserve glycogen stored in the muscle is not immediately available for use but is released in the form of lactic acid under the influence of exercise and is utilized to replenish the depleted supply of glycogen in the liver. That helps explain the well-established value of moderate exercise in the prevention of pregnancy disease, particularly in fat ewes.

As the reserves of glycogen are depleted, the body turns increasingly to the fats as a source of body energy. Fats, however, burn well only in the presence of an adequate amount of blood sugar, and since this is low, the resultant imperfect metabolism evolves quantities of unburned intermediate products, known as ketone bodies. The ketone bodies accumulate first in the blood and later in the urine, and are always present in pregnancy disease. The resultant ketosis further depresses the appetite, and the already damaged liver cannot efficiently utilize the fatty acids for energy in place of glycogen. The condition thus becomes progressively worse, the animal becomes comatose, and a fatal toxemia develops.

THE FIRST SYMPTOMS are loss of appetite, dullness, and an inclination to lag behind and remain outside the flock. The ewe becomes unsteady and urinates frequently. There is grinding of the teeth and labored breathing.

Vision is impaired, and blindness may result. There is a tendency to walk in circles or push against some solid object. Finally, the ability to stand is lost; in a few hours or at most in 1 or 2 days, the animal becomes prostrate.

The ewe remains recumbent in a comatose condition, sometimes on her side but more frequently lying on the breast, with the head turned to one side. Occasionally the fetuses are delivered, in which case recovery is prompt. Otherwise the disease is fatal in 1 to 7 days. The temperature remains normal throughout the course of the disease. The urine is usually acid and becomes strongly positive for ketone bodies.

Almost invariably more than one fetus is found at autopsy. The most striking pathologic change is in the liver, which is light yellow, friable, and perhaps mottled. The cut surface is found to be greasy as a result of the fatty infiltration. In extreme cases, because of the high fat content, it will be found that pieces of liver will float in water. The kidneys and sometimes the heart show microscopic evidence of fatty infiltration, but usually no gross changes are evident.

THE MANAGEMENT of pregnancy disease resolves itself into two phases—prevention and treatment.

Pregnant ewes should be fed an abundance of a balanced ration, which must be increased during the last 2 months of gestation. It may consist of good pasture or a liberal amount of legume hay, such as alfalfa or clover. The amount of grain fed should not be less than one-half pound, and may be gradually increased to 1 pound during the last month of pregnancy. It is desirable that the ewe herself should be gaining some weight in addition to the weight of the fetus.

In the face of an outbreak it is advisable to supplement the grain mixture by adding directly to it small amounts (up to one-fourth pound) of blackstrap molasses or corn sugar (dextrose).

Radical changes in diet should be

avoided. Intake should not be cut sharply. Care should be taken that the sheep do not go unfed during periods of storm or while being shipped. A moderate amount of exercise is important. An adequate water supply should be provided. A constant supply of salt is desirable.

The theory of treatment is simple: It is necessary to raise and maintain the sugar level of the blood. In practice, however, treatment on an economically feasible basis is difficult.

Loss of appetite is a constant symptom, and force feeding is necessary until the animal again begins to eat. That may be done by injections of dextrose (in a 10 percent solution) intravenously, intraperitoneally, or subcutaneously. Dextrose or molasses in water may be given by mouth, but, since a comatose sheep may be unable to swallow, it should be administered by a stomach tube. Injections must be given daily or, if treatment is by stomach tube, 2 or 3 times a day.

It is evident that the treatment of affected sheep involves considerable time, labor, and expense, and the results generally have not been encouraging. Most of the ewes that are down and comatose eventually die, but a reasonable proportion of those showing symptoms but still on their feet may be expected to recover. Probably the chief benefit of adding sugar to the ration derives from tiding over ewes that are starting to show symptoms.

Other treatments that have been used on an experimental basis include injections of adrenocorticotropic hormone (ACTH) and cortisone. The value of concentrated vitamins, injectable amino acids, and rumen inoculation is also being investigated. Those treatments, alone or in combination, show promise, but they are costly.

W. A. ANDERSON *is a veterinarian at the Animal Disease Research Laboratory, Denver, Colo. He received his degrees from Colorado Agricultural and Mechanical College and Purdue University and has been associated with the Department of Agriculture since 1936.*

C. L. DAVIS *received his degree in veterinary medicine from Colorado Agricultural and Mechanical College in 1921. In 1922 he joined the Bureau of Animal Industry of the Department of Agriculture.*

White Muscle Disease in Lambs and Calves

O. H. MUTH

WHITE MUSCLE disease was recognized in this country as a serious disease of lambs in the early 1920's. Some called it "stiff lamb disease." In later years it has been recognized also as a killer of calves. It is marked by a degeneration of muscle tissue.

It is known to occur in lambs and calves across the northern half of the United States. Probably it is most serious in some of the fertile irrigated districts of the western intermountain area. It varies considerably in extent from year to year, but no correlation has been noted between climatic differences and the extent of the trouble.

It may occur at any time of year. Although it does occur in calves whose dams have spent the previous 6 months on good irrigated pasture, most cases occur in the spring, when calves and lambs are most numerous.

Losses range from a few to a high percentage of the young in the flocks, bands, and herds. Many farmers have stopped keeping breeding animals because of the losses, which in small herds in irrigated districts may reach 100 percent.

Animals from birth (or earlier) to several months of age and otherwise in good physical condition are affected. The finding of the young affected at birth suggests that the disease at times may be the cause of stillbirths.

Injuries are seen oftenest in lambs 3 or 4 weeks old and calves 4 to 6 weeks old. We have no evidence that any breed is more susceptible than others.

The injuries and losses result from the deterioration of muscles. An animal whose muscles are severely affected moves with difficulty and is generally weak. Some animals cannot rise and nurse, although their appetites remain good. The leg muscles may contract in time.

When the heart muscle is affected, breathing is labored, and death may occur a few hours after the symptoms appear. Calves that die in this way often discharge blood-tinged foam from the nostrils just before death.

A degeneration of the muscles of movement is most frequent in lambs. Heart injury is most common in calves. The heart and other muscles may be affected in either. This is not an inflammatory disease, such as might result from an infection, and rises in body temperature are not constant.

Many affected animals recover without change in feeding or management. A considerable number (especially among lambs) may show some injury, yet there may be no losses. The evaluation of a treatment therefore is apt to be difficult. Animals showing signs of injury of the skeletal muscles may die suddenly from heart failure due to heart injury. Those with heart injury usually live several hours after symptoms develop, but some die without outstanding symptoms.

The heart and other muscles, when they are examined after death, are seen to be affected in varying degree. Most of the damage in some animals will be in the heart. The damaged tissues appear as discolored areas from which the normal pigment is gone. They may be slightly lighter than normal or markedly bleached, with white streaks. The lining of the lamb's heart may contain white patches suggestive of white enamel. In cases where damage impaired the function of the heart and the breathing is labored for some time before death, the lungs are congested with blood and fluid—a condition that a person not trained in pathology might mistake for a sudden and severe pneumonia.

Under a microscope, the damaged heart and muscle tissues are revealed to have lost their normal substance, which in some instances has been partly replaced with calcium salts.

Because other diseases occur in lambs and calves that have white muscle disease, diagnosis may be uncertain if the animals are not carefully examined by a qualified person. Symptoms of pneumonia and various types of arthritis might be confused with those of white muscle disease.

The cause of white muscle disease is not understood fully. As I said, it often occurs in lambs and calves in western irrigated districts, where dry climate, productive soil, and controlled irrigation favor the production of feed, especially excellent hay. The dams of the affected young are usually well managed.

The disease has been associated with the feeding of legume hays during the winter feeding period. Some cases occur after the dams of the young have been maintained on irrigated legume pastures for as long as 6 months. A similar, if not identical, disease occurs in New Zealand in lambs from ewes maintained on irrigated clover pastures.

The disease has occurred where alsike, ladino, sweetclover, native clovers, alfalfa, and vetch have formed a large part of the feed—with and without supplements of grain and molasses. It has occurred also where clover silage has been fed.

The disease is not generally a problem in localities where animals have access to range in winter.

White muscle disease seems to have become more common following improved forage production. Many producers have related the disease to fertilization of their meadows, although the kinds of fertilizer have varied greatly. A similar or identical disease occurs in Sweden in years of heavy rainfall—which also stimulates plant growth.

When animals are maintained experimentally on rations deficient in vitamin E, which was first linked with reproductive functions in rats, muscle injury similar to that of naturally occurring white muscle disease occurs. In some parts of Scotland where beef cattle are normally maintained on a ration consisting largely of rutabagas, mangolds, fodder beets, and oat straw—feeds that are deficient in vitamin E—muscular degeneration occurs in the calves. The condition responds to supplements of vitamin E or disappears when the animals are turned on grass. The situation thus is different from the one found in the irrigated areas of this country where the dams are wintered on liberal rations of excellent feed and calves may get the ailment after the dams have been on pasture for a long time.

Experimental supplementation of ewes' rations with vitamin E has failed to prevent white muscle disease in their lambs. Vitamin E has also been used in lambs and calves as a preventive and treatment, but the results have not been wholly satisfactory.

Although investigations point to the cause of white muscle disease as being nutritional or metabolic in origin, the disease does not appear in the light of present information to be an uncomplicated vitamin E deficiency. Biochemical investigations of the problem were under way at several agricultural experiment stations in 1956.

O. H. MUTH *is a veterinary pathologist at the Oregon Agricultural Experiment Station, Oregon State College, Corvallis, where he has been engaged in research with diseases of sheep and cattle since 1929. Dr. Muth is a graduate of Michigan State College, where he received the doctor of veterinary medicine degree in 1929 and master of science degree in 1935.*

Other Diseases of Sheep

HADLEIGH MARSH AND E. A. TUNNICLIFF

FOOT ROT sometimes is thought of as including several conditions of the feet of sheep, but we use the term firmly for only one specific infectious disease.

Its main symptom is severe lameness in one or more feet. A sheep whose fore feet are affected often feeds on its knees. Only the hoof is involved. No swelling or other change occurs in the foot or leg above the hoof.

The condition starts with a small sore on the inside of the claws or in the soft tissue of the bulb of the heel. From there it spreads under the horn of the sole and inside the horny wall of the hoof. The dirty-gray, cheesy material formed between the horny wall of the hoof and the softer tissue beneath causes the horn to separate from the tissue beneath. The loosened horn becomes overgrown and the foot deformed. The diseased tissue stinks.

Foot rot develops and spreads among

sheep when they are on wet ground, like swampy pastures and wet corrals. But pasturing on wet or muddy ground will not of itself produce foot rot. The infection must be brought in on the feet of a sheep that has foot rot. Then, if the ground is wet and the feet are softened, the infection may spread quickly through a flock. The disease does not spread when the sheep are on dry, hard range.

The infection lives only a short time in the soil. One need not be afraid of pastures or corrals where foot-rot sheep have been if the premises have had no sheep on them for a month—although the infection actually dies out in less than a month.

Foot rot may be confused with festering conditions of the foot that are caused by infection with ordinary pus-producing organisms. The hoof itself in such cases is not primarily involved, but abscesses form in the tissues above the hoof. Sore feet may also occur in connection with contagious ecthyma (sore mouth) and lip-and-leg ulceration, but those lesions also are above the hoof itself.

The treatment of foot rot should start immediately after the diagnosis. The way to avoid a long and expensive experience with a diseased band of sheep is to tackle the condition vigorously with the aim of stamping out the infection as quickly as possible.

It is no good to spot the visibly lame sheep and treat them with something to make them feel better. Every sheep—lame or not—should be set up and every foot examined.

All feet that show anything wrong must be thoroughly trimmed to expose all diseased tissue. Enough of the horn must be cut away to expose every spot of infection, even if it is necessary to remove nearly all the horn. The sheep are then walked through a foot bath containing a saturated (30 percent) solution of copper sulfate. The unaffected sheep must also be walked through the foot bath. After treatment, the sheep should be moved to fresh dry pasture or range.

The feet will be cured if the trimming has been thorough. It seldom happens in actual practice that every foot is cleaned up on the first round. The sheep must be carefully examined at short intervals, and the process should be repeated until no infected feet can be found.

PROGRESSIVE PNEUMONIA is a slowly developing, chronic, progressive disease of the lungs. It is marked by a gradually increasing difficulty in breathing and emaciation.

Sheep affected with this disease are commonly known as "lungers" or "heavers" in the Northwestern States. Progressive pneumonia in the United States is a disease of range sheep. It has not been reported as occurring in the farm flocks of the Central and Eastern States.

The percentage of cases in infected flocks is difficult to estimate, but probably 2 to 3 percent a year is a reasonable figure. None of the affected sheep recovers.

It is less apparent in the young sheep than in older animals. Some of the ewes culled for age are actually lungers and are sold out of the range bands before progressive pneumonia kills them. Most of the sheep in which symptoms are observed are relatively old ewes—4, 5, and 6 years old. Clinical cases occur in younger sheep, but symptoms rarely appear in yearlings.

The main symptom is the gradually increasing difficulty in breathing. The rate of breathing, particularly after exertion, increases slightly at first.

As the condition advances, the affected ewes may be easily picked out after a drive, because their heads rise and fall with each breath. There is a double expiratory effort, which can be observed even in the early stages when the sheep are standing quietly after being moved. Over a period of several months the respiratory distress increases, and the sheep become emaciated and die. Lunger sheep live 2 or 3 months or even a year or more after symptoms are first noticed.

The pathological lesions are confined to the lungs. When the chest of a sheep dead of lunger disease is opened, the lungs do not collapse. They retain the shape of the chest cavity; when they are removed, they are three times as heavy as a normal lung. Instead of the normal bright-pink color, they have a combination of a dull-gray and dull, pale-red appearance. The tissues are so thickened that there is little air-space.

The cause of progressive pneumonia has not been determined. It is transmissible. The infective agent may be a virus.

No method of treatment has been developed. The slow development, the difficulty in recognizing the first stages, and the uncertainty as to the cause make treatment difficult.

The only method of control we can recommend is the elimination of affected sheep from a flock as soon as they are detected. Those that are detected early enough may have some slaughter value. A lunger will never raise a lamb. Any feed she consumes is wasted. The general practice of culling range ewes for age helps to eliminate lungers, because the disease is recognized oftener in old sheep than in the younger ones.

BLACKLEG is thought of generally as a disease that affects only cattle, but the fact is that it also causes serious losses among sheep.

Almost always it is possible to trace the source of the infection in sheep to a wound, which may be the result of shearing, dogbites, fighting among rams, difficult lambing in ewes, or docking of lambs. Where blackleg has developed in freshly sheared sheep or after docking, it usually is found that cattle have died of blackleg in the area and that the carcasses have not been burned.

The symptoms and lesions of blackleg in sheep are like those in cattle.

The treatment and prevention are the same as for cattle. The vaccine that is used for cattle can be used for sheep. When the dosage of vaccine for cattle is 5 milliliters, a dose of 3 ml. is enough to immunize a sheep. Because blackleg in sheep is somewhat sporadic, it has not become routine procedure to vaccinate. When blackleg losses occur following shearing, for instance—indicating that the shearing plant and corrals are infective—the flock should be vaccinated. Each year thereafter the young sheep should be vaccinated before exposure to the infected premises.

MASTITIS, also called mammitis, garget, or blue-bag, is an inflammation of the udder. Losses from mastitis in the western range States generally are considered to be of economic importance, for often it occurs in 4 percent of the ewes.

Without treatment, about 20 percent of the affected ewes die. One side of the udder of ewes that survive is permanently spoiled. The loss of lambs from stunting and bumming also is heavy.

Some of the cases that occur soon after lambing are caused by infection with filth bacteria, such as those found in unsanitary lambing quarters.

The more common type of mastitis in sheep may appear at any time from lambing to the time when the lambs are 3 to 4 months old. Investigations at the Montana Veterinary Research Laboratory showed that this type is caused by infection with a specific organism, *Pasteurella mastitidis*. This mastitis occurs quite generally in the Western States. It has been identified in Montana, Wyoming, Utah, Texas, and Oklahoma.

A band of 1,900 ewes, shed-lambed in Montana in April 1948, developed four cases by June 1. They then were moved to hard, dry, clean range, where they remained until fall. The sanitary conditions were excellent during the three summer months— but 23 cases were detected in the first 45 days and 27 cases in the second 45 days.

Infection may develop in an udder

that looks normal, but it is more apt to attack the abnormal or injured tissue. Heavy lambs are rough with the ewes when they nurse; sometimes they raise the mothers off the ground. The gland may easily be bruised so that the pasteurella organism gets a chance to grow and set up an infection. Nodules or cysts of any size, consistency, or location in the udder are potentially dangerous, for some of them harbor the organism and eventually break down to produce mastitis. Even the udder that looks and feels normal may harbor the organism for an entire season without producing the disease, but this same udder may be a source of infection for other ewes.

Transmission of the infection would seem to take place by contact of the end of the teat with infection on the bedground.

The first noticeable symptoms are loss of appetite and dejection. The ewe stands off by herself, drops behind while being moved or trailed, and does not allow her lamb to nurse. Forced to move, she shows lameness in one hind leg because of the painful udder. That is an important early symptom. She swings the hind leg of the affected side outward to avoid contact with the painful side of the udder. The first day the udder is painful and hot, without too much enlargement or discoloration, and the milk is normal.

Within 24 hours after the first symptoms are noticed, the glands enlarge and begin to harden. The secretion changes through the successive stages of whey separation, casein coagulation, and finally a caking of the udder in which there is no secretion. This process usually takes place in 4 to 6 days.

The udder may or may not become discolored. The bluish discoloration is responsible for the term "blue-bag"— a misleading term, because the condition occurs in few cases. The infection is practically always on one side. The unaffected side and milk are normal unless the animal remains extremely ill for some time; then milk secretion ceases. The process terminates in a hard, enlarged udder, or abscessed udder. Either way, the ewe's economic reproductive life is ended. She should be marked for culling.

Treatment has value when it is given at the first sign of the disease. Two good treatments are available. Streptomycin has been effective.

Sulfamethazine is also effective. It is economical and efficient. It is administered in a 15-gram bolus by the mouth. A second dose is given in 18 hours. If the treatment is started early, at least 50 percent of affected udders can be restored to normal milk production. Without treatment, no udders are saved, and 20 to 25 percent of affected ewes die. Regardless of recovery, the ewe should be culled in the fall.

None of the vaccines available in 1956 had any value in preventing blue-bag.

Control of the disease is furthered by isolating the affected ewes to avoid spreading the infection from the discharging teats and udders. One should not milk the affected udders on ground or bedding where other ewes may become infected. After handling these mastitic cases, one should wash his hands.

Vigorous culling of all sheep with visibly abnormal udders, including the nodular or cystic types, should be followed. Repeated annual culling will reduce the number of cases but will never entirely eliminate the disease. Until a satisfactory immunizing agent is produced, the procedure we recommend is the best for the present.

ULCERATIVE DERMATOSIS OF SHEEP embraces a group of skin diseases known as lip and leg ulceration and venereal disease (posthitis, balanoposthitis, ulcerative vulvitis), affecting the sheath, penis, and vulva of sheep.

The condition is marked by destruction of the outer layer of skin and the tissue immediately beneath. A raw, easily bleeding, ulcerous (craterlike) lesion follows. The ulcers are between the borders of the upper lip and nasal opening, the lower lip, the legs above the hoof, the front of the foot between the toes, the end of the sheath, the penis, and the external lips of the vulva.

The process is primarily one of tissue destruction—an ulcer containing a mass of diseased tissue covered by a brownish, raised scab. The round lesions have sharply defined borders, one-eighth to three-eighths inch deep and three-fourths inch to one and three-fourths inches in diameter. The base and walls of the ulcer are composed of raw, easily bleeding tissue, spotted with gray and red areas. Beneath the scabs there is a thick, creamy, odorless material. All lesions have the same characteristic ulcerated appearance, regardless of their location on the body.

A filterable virus causes the lesions of the genital-organ type. The cause of the lip and leg ulceration form has never been proved but there is evidence that the same virus produces the venereal type.

Differential diagnosis is important. With the ordinary cases, a diagnosis of ulcerative dermatosis is not hard to make. But it may be confused with the lip and foot lesions of contagious ecthyma (sore mouth), the interdigital (between the toes) lesions of footrot, and a noninfectious type of sore sheath. The basic difference is that they are entirely different pathological processes. Ulcerative dermatosis causes tissue destruction. Sore mouth results in the proliferation (building-up) of tissue similar to a cold sore in human beings. Foot rot produces dead tissue.

The foot lesions of ulcerative dermatosis are always on the skin above the hoof itself either on the outside or between the toes. On the other hand, if the lesions involve the bulb of the heel, undermining the sole of the foot and extending into the vascular part of the horny wall, one need have no fear in making the diagnosis of foot rot.

Another difference is the foul odor of the young, coagulated, scalded-looking lesion of foot rot. The odor is not present in ulcerative dermatosis. Furthermore, foot rot is always limited to the feet.

The virus of ulcerative dermatosis attacks only the skin and is limited to the lightly wooled areas of the body. Seldom does it extend to the mucous membrane. The virus of sore mouth tends to attack the lips where the mucous membrane and the skin join.

No vaccine or other immunizing product is available for ulcerative dermatosis. Since there is a good vaccine for sore mouth, it is important to tell the difference between the two diseases.

Treatment is not advisable unless the disease is so severe as to interfere with eating or breeding. It is best to let nature take its course. The recommended treatments are not entirely effective.

Caustics and astringents kill the infective agents but destroy so much tissue that the benefit is doubtful. Caustics, such as a styptic pencil (silver nitrate), astringent solutions (such as a saturated solution of copper sulfate), and commercial formaldehyde, have been used with indifferent results. The treatment should be applied after removal of the scab and careful cleaning of the ulcer. It is usually necessary to repeat the treatment every 10 days for a month.

Should lesions exist before the breeding season, attempts should be made to eliminate the infected sheep. The animals therefore should be carefully observed 45 to 60 days before the breeding date, because elimination of all sheep showing the lip and leg form of the disease may prevent the development of the venereal form in the rams.

When the disease has occurred in a band of ewes before breeding, the rams should be inspected each time they are to be used before being turned in with the ewes. Any rams with lesions should not be used for breeding.

BLACK DISEASE—infectious necrotic hepatitis—is an acute infectious disease. The cause is a sporebearing bacterium, *Clostridium novyi*. It is characterized by sudden deaths and a dark, bloodshot appearance of the flesh surface of the pelt—hence the name "black disease."

Losses occur year after year between July and February on some ranches. Ewes in the best condition are usually the ones that die. Death comes suddenly, without evidence of a struggle or any previous sickness. The entire bunch will appear to be well at night, and one or more may be found dead on the bedground the following morning. Such deaths have been attributed to an infestation of immature liver flukes—but that is not the cause of black disease, which is an infectious disease.

From the intestinal tract, the bacteria get into the liver via the blood stream, where some survive, until the liver tissue becomes damaged or irritated. Small, immature liver flukes cause this damage. Following the irritation or tissue destruction in the liver by the fluke, the bacteria that are stirred up grow rapidly and produce a potent toxin that kills the sheep—thus accounting for the sudden deaths.

Black disease can be prevented by using an inexpensive, commercially available, one-dose vaccine (toxoid). Properly administered, it produces a lifetime immunity against black disease. The toxoid should be given to the lambs after weaning in the fall.

NAVEL INFECTION following birth results in the formation of abscesses in the liver and other parts of the body. For several hours after the lamb is born, the navel cord can pick up germs from the wet ground or dirty bedding.

The result of navel infection does not usually show until the lamb is 1 to 3 weeks old, at which time it may die without showing any definite symptoms. Postmortem examination may disclose many large, gray spots in the liver or abscesses in the leg joints or backbone.

Most sheepmen who lamb in sheds or around dirty corrals consider proper disinfection of the navel a necessary procedure. Tincture of iodine is the best antiseptic to use for the purpose. It penetrates, thereby drying the cord.

The iodine must be properly applied. Swabbing is not effective. The recommended method is as follows: The iodine is carried in a wide-mouth container, like an ointment jar. The navel cord is cut with scissors so that about one and one-half inches remains. The stump of the cord is placed in the bottle of iodine. The neck of the bottle is held tightly against the lamb's belly. The lamb is turned up, so that the iodine completely covers the cord and skin around it. The treatment should be applied within an hour after birth.

ARTHRITIS may occur without noticeable swelling of the joints and without pus in the joints. It may appear in lambs 2 or 3 weeks old as an acute lameness in one or more legs, or it may not be noticed until the lambs are several months old. It may become particularly noticeable when they are being moved down from summer range. Little lambs that have acute cases usually recover temporarily, but later the lameness reappears, and the lambs are undersized.

It is a disease of shed lambing. It does not occur in sheep that are lambed on the range. The disease can be prevented by thorough disinfection of the navel and by proper docking and castration methods. If docking is done with a hot iron there is less chance that the tail stump will become infected than if other methods are used.

HADLEIGH MARSH *has been in the veterinary service of Montana since 1919.*

E. A. TUNNICLIFF, *bacteriologist and veterinarian, joined the Montana State College Agricultural Experiment Station in 1930. He has been professor and head of the Montana Veterinary Research Laboratory and Department of Veterinary Science since 1950.*

DISEASES

AND PARASITES

AFFECTING

poultry

Coccidiosis of Chickens and Turkeys

EVERETT E. WEHR AND MARION M. FARR

COCCIDIOSIS costs poultry raisers millions of dollars each year because of the unthriftiness, poor utilization of feed, loss of weight, and death of infected birds.

Coccidiosis is caused by coccidia, which are microscopic protozoan parasites. Coccidia of poultry are nearly always host specific—each species is so adjusted to a life within the body of one kind of bird that it may not survive very long in another.

The coccidia that affect chickens and turkeys follow a similar course of development. They develop within the cells that line the wall of the intestine and cecal pouches. In their resistant stage—as oöcysts—they are discharged into the cavity of the intestine and pass out with the droppings.

Before they can infect birds, the oöcysts must develop, or sporulate. When the weather is warm and the oöcysts remain moist, development is completed in about 1 to 3 days. Oöcysts have tough shells. They can withstand cold and dryness and have been known to survive on soil and elsewhere for many months.

Poultry get coccidiosis by swallowing the sporulated oöcysts with feed and water that have become contaminated with the oöcysts of infected birds. The droppings are spread from place to place by the birds themselves and by mice, cats, dogs, flies, and other insects. Persons that care for poultry may carry the oöcysts on their hands, feet, and clothing. Dirty sacks and crates and contaminated litter may also be responsible for the spread of coccidiosis.

437

Not every bird that swallows infective oöcysts develops symptoms of coccidiosis. Some birds may pick up just enough oöcysts to produce a light infection, which may cause them little or no discomfort.

Repeated light infections may cause the bird to build up a resistance to the particular species involved. Resistant birds may then pick up large numbers of the same species of oöcysts without serious effects. Once a bird becomes immune or resistant to one or more species of coccidia, it may remain resistant to them for several months.

Two types of coccidiosis occur in chickens. In one, the infection is limited primarily to the blind pouches, or ceca. It is known as cecal coccidiosis. In the other, the parasites attack the part of the intestine between the gizzard and the opening of the ceca—the ceca may or may not be involved. This type is known as intestinal coccidiosis.

In cecal coccidiosis, the parasites enter the cells lining the walls of the ceca, multiply rapidly, and destroy them. Severe bleeding and death may be the result. Bloody droppings are an important sign of cecal coccidiosis. This disorder is caused by only one species of coccidia, *Eimeria tenella*. It occurs mostly in chickens less than 2 months old. Chickens of any age may get it, however. It strikes suddenly. Sometimes the poultryman is taken completely by surprise.

The following is a typical picture of an outbreak of cecal coccidiosis: Yesterday the birds appeared healthy—eating, drinking, and chasing each other around the pen. Today some or many are dead. Others are visibly sick, while still others are eating and drinking and are apparently healthy. Bloody droppings are seen on the ground or litter.

THE SEVEN SPECIES of coccidia that cause intestinal coccidiosis occur mainly in the small intestine—occasionally in the large intestine or bowel and ceca. They give rise to a serious but usually

less acute condition than occurs in cecal coccidiosis. This type may affect chickens of any age, but serious losses occur oftenest in young pullets.

Economic losses to the poultryman from intestinal coccidiosis are due primarily to the slowness with which many of the birds recover. The laying flocks may be unprofitable for several weeks.

Intestinal coccidiosis frequently appears soon after pullets are confined to the laying houses. Generally only a few birds are affected at first, but more develop symptoms from day to day until many are affected. Deaths occur mostly after several days to 2 or 3 weeks, but some die in the early stages. Many of the affected birds gradually regain their appetite, become stronger, and recover.

Loss of appetite, loss of weight, weakness, and an abnormal drop in egg production in pullets are some of the first indications of intestinal coccidiosis. The droppings may be watery or slimy, and greenish or brownish, or may consist almost entirely of bloody mucus.

The small intestine of a bird that has a severe case of intestinal coccidiosis may be greatly distended and have tiny white and red spots on the lining, which are visible on the outer wall (*Eimeria necatrix*); thickened intestinal walls, with numerous transverse white bars or streaks, which are visible from the outside as well as the inside and are particularly abundant in the intestinal loop or duodenum (*E. acervulina*); distended intestine, with walls thickened and filled with thick, greenish or brownish mucus (*E. maxima*); short, red streaks arranged in a ladderlike fashion in the lower part of the intestine and a cheeselike material in the narrow, tubular portion of the cecum (*E. brunetti*).

Three other species (*E. praecox, E. mitis,* and *E. hagani*) occur in the intestinal tract of chickens but are not known to be associated with any pronounced visible changes in the wall of the intestine.

TURKEYS harbor seven species of coccidia. One of them, *Eimeria meleagridis*, develops in the ceca. Three others, *E. innocua*, *E. meleagrimitis*, and *E. subrotunda*, develop in the intestine. The remaining ones, *E. adenoeides*, *E. dispersa*, and *E. gallopavonis*, occur in the ceca and intestine.

The species that are most important apparently are *E. adenoeides* and *E. meleagrimitis*.

The symptoms of coccidiosis in turkeys are not distinctive or specific.

None of the species causes severe hemorrhage, such as occurs in severe cecal coccidiosis of chickens.

Affected poults eat very little, lose weight, and stand huddled together with drooping wings and ruffled feathers. They may discharge cylindrical fecal pellets or fluid droppings containing small amounts of blood, blood flecks, or plugs of mucus.

The injuries produced in the intestine and ceca of turkeys tell little about the species of coccidia present. All, except *E. innocua* and *E. subrotunda*, produce inflammation of the intestinal tract, with a whitish discharge. The intestine may be swollen, the walls thickened, and the lining congested with blood or whitened. The intestine may contain large amounts of fluid, white or green mucus, or a cheesy material. Small strands of clotted blood may occur in the droppings. The ceca may be distended with granular, creamy material or with a cheesy plug. The walls may be slightly thickened. Rows of bloody spots or petechial hemorrhages may occur on the lining.

SEVERAL IMPORTANT FACTS have been discovered in studies on coccidiosis of poultry: Coccidia are present wherever poultry is raised. Repeated light infections help the bird build up a resistance to the species it harbors, but not against the others. The severity of the disease depends largely on the number of oöcysts swallowed. Young birds are usually affected more severely than older ones. The infection generally lasts only a short time, provided reinfection is prevented. Sick birds recover slowly, if at all, when treated. Resistant birds, although healthy, shed oöcysts and thus serve as sources of infection, which may overwhelm others.

THE BEST WAY to control coccidiosis of poultry is to prevent severe infections, and the best way to do that is to develop resistance to the disease.

Birds that recover from a light infection become resistant to coccidiosis. Experimentally repeated light infections confer a stronger resistance than a single infection, whether it be light or heavy.

Farm-raised flocks generally suffer less from coccidiosis than flocks raised under crowded conditions. Because of the space over which farm birds can range, their chances of picking up heavy or fatal doses of coccidia are less great—the droppings are scattered over a wide area and the sun and wind dry them quickly, so that the oöcysts are destroyed.

Outbreaks of coccidiosis have occurred in farm flocks, it is true, but they occur less often and are less severe than outbreaks in large commercial flocks that are crowded together. Instead of being exposed to large numbers of oöcysts in a short time, the farm-raised bird may pick up a few oöcysts each day and eventually develop a resistance. This may explain the relatively few deaths from coccidiosis in farm-raised poultry.

Poultry production has increased tremendously in a few years. Flocks numbering thousands of turkeys are common. The increase in numbers of birds and higher costs of production have brought about a tendency to grow two birds where one grew before. This tendency to crowd birds sometimes has been carried to the point where control measures for parasites and other disorders, particularly respiratory disease, are inadequate.

Sanitation and other measures are necessary to keep up the birds' resistance and keep down disease.

Crowding should be avoided because it favors disease by contributing to a buildup of the number of disease organisms. It also deprives the birds of the exercise they need.

A comfortable, sunny, well-ventilated poultry house, free from drafts or dampness, favors good health. Damp litter is an ideal place for the multiplication of parasites and germs.

Birds of different ages should be reared separately. Older birds may be immune or resistant to a particular organism but young birds may be highly susceptible to it.

Poultry houses should be thoroughly cleaned and disinfected before clean birds are placed in them. Oöcysts of coccidia, eggs of worm parasites, and other disease-producing agents may remain infective in litter and soil for many months. You should first remove all dirt and manure from the walls, floors, and windows and bury it or take it to a remote place where birds cannot get at it. Then you should scrub the entire house thoroughly with hot water, to which lye and soap have been added. A thorough spraying with household ammonia (10 parts to 100 parts of water) is advised in houses where coccidiosis has occurred.

In the case of birds in houses, the litter should be kept dry and loose. Frequent turning of the litter and removal of any wet litter and replacing it with dry material helps to do that. Stirring the litter helps to keep it dry and buries disease germs and parasite eggs so that the birds cannot get at them easily.

Leaky founts and broken feeders should be repaired or replaced. They should be placed on wire platforms wide enough so that wasted water and feed and droppings will fall through the openings and collect underneath out of reach of the birds. Spilled feed is attractive to birds and often it becomes mixed with droppings that may contain infective eggs and oöcysts.

It is highly important to isolate any new stock for several days. There is always the possibility that the new birds may harbor disease-producing organisms, which should be eradicated before they spread to clean birds. Any birds that die should be buried or burned promptly. Otherwise their entrails may become scattered about the premises.

The owner or attendant of another poultry flock should be discouraged from entering the poultry yards or houses lest disease germs or parasitic material be carried in on his shoes or clothing.

Even when all the essential precautions have been taken, outbreaks of disease occasionally occur. The earlier the signs of disease are detected, a correct diagnosis made, and something is done to check its progress, the more effectively can the outbreak be brought under control.

Not always are reliable sources for diagnoses close at hand. If your veterinarian or county agent is unable to help you, it will be necessary to take or send two or three sick birds to the nearest State Livestock and Poultry Diagnostic Laboratory, State Veterinary College, or the State Agricultural College for diagnosis.

As soon as a diagnosis has been made, and if coccidiosis is the cause of the trouble, the treatment should be started. If several days must elapse before obtaining the diagnosis, it may be wise to start treatment anyway. It will do the birds no harm, and it may mean saving the lives of a number that might otherwise die.

Every poultryman should have on his supply shelf one or more of the drugs that have proved useful against coccidiosis for emergency use. These drugs are available either as solutions for mixing with the drinking water or as a premix (a small amount of mash containing the drug) for mixing with the feed.

One of the first steps is to remove the sick birds from the flock and place them in separate pens, where they will have a better chance to get plenty of feed and water and will not infect other birds. There is not much you can do for sick birds except to see that they get plenty of feed and water and hope that some of them will recover.

The other birds should be placed on a medicated mash or given water in which the right amount of the drug has been added. Some poultrymen are equipped with a water system that is well suited for the administration of medicated water; for others, the use of medicated water would require a large amount of extra time and labor. They will find that medicated feed is more economical.

A number of drugs for preventing and treating coccidiosis can be bought from feed companies, commercial drug houses, or drug salesmen.

Nitrofurazone and sulfaquinoxaline, nicarbazin, and nitrophenide have been thoroughly tested and found to be satisfactory for the prevention of the disease. Any one of them can be administered in a low concentration for a period of several weeks without causing any ill effects.

In the event of an outbreak, however, the drug of choice is sulfaquinoxaline or sulfamethazine. The medicated water or mash must be prepared exactly as directed on the package or bottle containing the drug.

EVERETT E. WEHR, *a parasitologist, is engaged in research in parasitology in the Animal Disease and Parasite Research Branch, at Beltsville, Md. He has been associated with the Branch since 1928 and has been in charge of its investigations on the parasitic diseases of poultry since 1936.*

MARION M. FARR *is a veterinary parasitologist in the Animal Disease and Parasite Research Branch at Beltsville. She joined the Department in 1934. Her investigations have dealt primarily with the protozoan parasites of poultry.*

Blackhead of Turkeys and Chickens

EVERETT E. LUND

BLACKHEAD is caused by a microscopic, single-celled animal, *Histomonas meleagridis.*

It was a devastating disease in turkeys in the East and Midwest a generation or two ago. It still causes heavy losses in some flocks of turkeys and is recognized as a serious disease in chickens whose resistance is lowered by other diseases, by vaccination, or by undue exposure to adverse conditions.

The death rate in individual flocks of turkeys may run as high as 50 percent. Most of the survivors are seriously affected. Turkeys of any age may contract blackhead, but losses are usually greatest among birds 8 to 18 weeks old.

Outbreaks are most common in the spring and fall and usually are more serious in wet seasons than in dry ones. A study in Minnesota in 1951 revealed that of every 1,000 poults started, 87 died with blackhead after being placed on the range; only 6 were lost while poults were still in the brooder house. The average age of birds succumbing to blackhead on range was 17 weeks.

The symptoms of blackhead—which is known also as histomoniasis and infectious enterohepatitis—are quite distinct, but the name is misleading in that the head does not always turn dark. Other diseases also may cause the head to get black.

The first symptoms are not specific for blackhead but are suggestive. The birds stand with their heads tilted downward or drawn to the body. Their feathers are ruffled. The wings droop.

Their eyes are partly closed. At first the birds are alert when they are disturbed, but they quickly become indifferent if they are seriously ill. Young poults may die within 2 or 3 days after the first signs of illness, but older birds may suffer for several days before dying or starting a slow recovery.

The passage of thin, sulfur-colored droppings is characteristic of blackhead, but the disease is well advanced in turkeys before this is conspicuous and it often does not appear as a symptom in chickens.

When birds that have just died from blackhead are opened, fairly characteristic symptoms may be expected. The ceca—the blind pouches—are inflamed and ulcerated; they may be filled with a greenish-white material as thick as curdled milk or consolidated into cores. If the birds have been ill a long time, the cores will have become a foul-smelling, brown residue of a creamy consistency. The two ceca need not be affected equally.

By the time the sulfur-colored droppings have been passed, the liver also is visibly involved and has round, grayish-white lesions one-half inch or more in diameter. Nearby lesions may merge. Large lesions often are marked by concentric rings. Small lesions are elevated, but as they increase in size the centers flatten, and then shrink below the level of the margins, until finally the entire lesion may appear as a depressed and pox-marked area. Secondary infections sometimes set in and alter the appearance of the lesions.

The membranes covering the visceral organs and the lining of the visceral cavity sometimes become involved, and they may have a slippery feel. Peritonitis develops in extreme cases and causes death if the blackhead does not.

BLACKHEAD OCCURS when the parasites gain access to the ceca of the bird and are able to multiply in the cecal wall and in the cavity.

Occasionally the bird ingests the naked organism in contaminated feed or water or while picking gravel or preening itself. But in most instances a second parasite, the cecal worm (*Heterakis gallinae*), is involved. This little worm lives in the ceca of chickens, turkeys, and some other birds. Either the worm itself (which is one-third to one-half inch long and as thick as basting thread) or its egg (which is microscopic) can harbor the blackhead germ and carry it from one bird to another.

Passage by means of the worm eggs seems to be the usual method. Thus the blackhead organism, which is fragile and can live by itself outside the bird for only a few hours and which only rarely reaches its destination in a vigorous state if swallowed alone, has in the cecal worm's egg a nearly perfect means of survival outside the bird's body.

The cecal worm itself usually does little harm. But most chickens reared on the ground eventually harbor cecal worms. A great many also have histomonas, the blackhead organism. Many turkeys also become infected with cecal worms. When that happens, the danger of blackhead becomes great, for it may then be spread rapidly if the histomonad gets into the flock. In such a situation, contamination of feed, water, soil, or feathers with cecal worm eggs, now likely to be carrying histomonads, becomes a serious problem. The cecal worm egg is sturdy and may survive in the soil for a year or longer. Temperature, soil humidity, the action of micro-organisms, and probably other factors influence its survival and may account for the relative ease or difficulty experienced in controlling blackhead.

PREVENTION depends first of all on proper management. Turkeys must be kept entirely away from other fowl. Poults should never be brooded in houses that have been used by chickens, unless the buildings are of materials that can be made scrupulously clean and disinfected thoroughly. Even then they must be allowed to become entirely dry throughout before they are used. Buildings with earth floors or floors that are rough and broken or of porous material are hard to make entirely safe. The litter in brooder houses must be kept clean and dry. Good ventilation will help.

Traffic between places where chickens and turkeys are kept must be held to a minimum. If one person or one vehicle or other piece of equipment must service both chicken yards and turkey yards, absolute sanitation must be practiced. Shoes, boots, the bottoms of pails, the tires of carts, and other objects that come in direct contact with the soil or litter of both chicken yards and turkey yards and houses should be rinsed freely with water before bringing them into the turkey yard or house. If they can be left to become thoroughly dry after such a rinse, that, too, will help.

Sun porches with wire floors are recommended. Otherwise, runways should be rotated every 7 to 10 days in cool, moist climates. The runways should not be used until they have been cleaned and the surfaces are completely dry or have been turned under.

Turkeys should not be ranged on land recently occupied by other fowl, particularly chickens. Light soils in warm, arid climates, if barren, may become safe for use in a few weeks or months, but it may take years before heavier soils in moist climates become safe. Land on which poultry manure has been spread is to be regarded as having been occupied.

Turkeys should not be ranged in places to which drainage from chicken yards may carry eggs of the cecal worm. Turkey grounds should be fenced off from streams and low ground subject to such drainage.

The poultryman should provide ample range and be prepared to move the flock as often as conditions dictate. If blackhead is prevalent in the locality and the climate is cool and damp, he may need to move the flock as often as every 10 days until they are 18 to 20 weeks old. In dry climates the interval may be extended considerably. In very dry regions changing may be unnecessary if the soil about the feeders, waterers, roosts, and shelters is kept clean and dry.

Feeders and waterers should be on wire platforms so that the manure falls through and is out of reach of the birds and off their feet and feathers. If that is impractical, the location of feeders and waterers should be changed often enough to prevent accumulations of manure, which might contain cecal worm eggs in an infectious stage. It usually takes 7 to 10 days in a favorable environment for the eggs to reach that stage.

Poults should not be ranged with older birds or on land recently occupied by them. The owner might well institute a program of land utilization or reconditioning that will be effective in providing fresh, clean range as often as it is necessary or practical to return to the same plots. The farm adviser, county agent, or the State Experiment Station will be able to advise the farmer about the practical alternatives—which differ widely according to geographic, climatic, and economic considerations—in a locality.

If hazards are exceptional or management practices cannot be maintained at levels needed for effective control, drugs may have to be used.

If a heavy infection of cecal worms is the great hazard, a medicated ration containing 1 pound of phenothiazine per 100 pounds of feed may be given for 5 to 7 days and repeated after an interval of 15 to 20 days, from the time the birds are placed on the range until about 3 weeks before going to market. Phenothiazine has no direct effect on the blackhead organism, but it will greatly reduce the cecal worms and so reduce the hazard of transmission of blackhead. It reduces the number of cecal worm eggs reaching the soil and makes the range better for reuse later.

Drugs specifically for the control of the blackhead organism have been marketed under various trade names. If principles of good management are ignored, none will be satisfactory, and all can be harmful if mishandled. The grower contemplating the use of such drugs should explore the situation well and use the drug as directed by the manufacturer. Three drugs offered as aids to the control of blackhead in 1956 are identified chemically as 2-acetylamino-5-nitrothiazole, furazolidone, and 4-nitro-phenyl arsonic acid.

IF AN OUTBREAK OCCURS, the first thing to do is to get a diagnosis. Take 2 or 3 typical sick birds to your nearest poultry diagnostic laboratory, your State Experiment Station, or to a veterinarian who includes poultry in his practice. Other diseases cause symptoms resembling some of those of blackhead.

Isolate sick birds. Quarantine all pens or plots in which such birds have appeared. Always care for the unaffected flocks first, then those from which sick birds have been removed, and last of all those in the isolation quarters. Allow no traffic in the reverse order.

Intensify all measures recommended for preventing blackhead. You are now faced with preventing its spread. Claims have been made regarding the value of a few drugs in treating af-fected birds, but prevention must still be the major means of attack.

Be prepared to move the birds at least once a week. Cecal worms are almost certainly present, and any droppings are potentially infective within a few days of their passage.

Record carefully the houses, pens, or plots in which outbreaks have occurred or which are used later by birds from such sources. They must not be reused until they are made free of cecal worm eggs.

The successful interruption of an outbreak of blackhead may not be apparent until 2 to 3 weeks after the strict control measures have been invoked. Do not be discouraged or relax your efforts. It sometimes takes 3 weeks from the time a turkey takes in the cecal worm eggs containing the blackhead parasites until the bird is obviously ill: What you have done probably has not influenced the course of the disease in this bird, but you have saved others and your continued efforts will save still others.

EVERETT E. LUND *joined the Department of Agriculture as a parasitologist in 1946. He received his training at Iowa State College and the University of California at Berkeley.*

Hexamitiasis of Turkeys

EVERETT E. LUND

HEXAMITIASIS is an intestinal disease caused by a microscopic, single-celled animal (*Hexamita meleagridis*).

The parasite remained unnoticed until about 1938. The disease it caused was confused with other diseases for several years thereafter. Hexamitiasis was seldom reported in some large areas in which the turkey industry was extensive, but reports of it became more frequent after 1954—probably because it was recognized more generally.

Hexamitiasis is usually most serious in poults still in the brooder house, where losses as high as 75 percent have been reported. Poults on the range are also affected, and losses may continue until the birds are 14 to 16 weeks old, or occasionally even later. Mature birds often harbor the parasite but seldom show symptoms. They are a source of infection for younger birds.

Light cases usually show no symptoms, and outbreaks commonly start this way because only a few parasites were introduced. These infected birds soon shed many parasites, however; contamination increases, and other poults pick up enough organisms to be affected seriously. They soon have a ragged appearance, are nervous, keep on the move, and chirp incessantly, but do not gain. Small poults especially tend to crowd close to the hover.

As the infections become more severe, the droppings become fluid and foamy and often are yellow. Water is voided faster than it is replaced, and the poults lose weight rapidly.

In the later stages of the disease, the birds stand with heads drawn in, feathers ruffled, and wings drooping, as they do with several other disorders, particularly those of the lower digestive tract. Chirping is less frequent and more muffled than before.

In the final stages, the birds go into a coma, struggle convulsively, and die.

The greatest changes internally are in the upper intestine, just below the gizzard. The intestinal wall is inflamed, and the cavity contains mucus, which may be thin and watery or heavy and like phlegm. The flesh of birds dying with hexamitiasis is usually dark and dry.

The diagnosis of hexamitiasis depends on finding the organism, which is very small, even as parasites go, and hard to identify. If hexamitiasis is suspected, several sick birds should be taken to the nearest diagnostic laboratory, State agricultural experiment station, or a veterinarian who includes poultry in his practice.

Turkeys get hexamitiasis by consuming food, water, or soil contaminated with the droppings of infected birds. Several kinds of wild, game, and domestic birds harbor hexamita, but the parasites often are of different species than that of the turkey. Consequently, while it is still necessary to regard some of those other fowl as possible carriers, none is nearly so dangerous as the mature turkey or the poult of a previous brood that may be carrying the parasite and showing no symptoms.

If most infections started only after the poults were placed on the range, one might believe that wild fowl or visitors were responsible for the first introductions of hexamita into flocks of turkeys. But so many outbreaks occur or appear to have originated in the brooder house that it seems likely the grower himself introduces the parasite by tracking it in from a nearby yard occupied by older birds. Or it may be carried in with utensils used in both places. Mud or fresh droppings clinging to boots, tires, or on the bottom of buckets or other utensils could keep the parasites alive for several hours.

Growers who raise two or more broods of turkeys a year, using the same brooder houses and equipment, frequently suffer the most difficulty with hexamitiasis in the second brood. The parasites may have been introduced with the first brood, but the buildup in numbers of parasites was not rapid enough to do much damage until the second brood of poults was exposed to contamination.

Thorough cleaning, disinfecting, and drying of houses and equipment between broods eliminates the hazard of passage by means of the house and its equipment, but parasites may still be introduced from the birds of the first brood, now possibly carriers, and on the range.

The prevention or control of hexamitiasis need not be difficult. Hexamita are fragile and apparently have no resistant forms or protective devices, other than the body of the bird they inhabit. Consequently, once they have been shed in the droppings, they live but a few hours in air that is warm and dry, and only a few days, at most, in moist soil or litter.

To minimize the danger of the introduction and spread of hexamite into your flock, do these things:

Dispose of all breeding stock and other mature turkeys at least 2 weeks before starting your first brood of poults, or else keep the mature stock on a distant part of the farm that has its own equipment and caretaker, so traffic between the two operations is unnecessary.

Have your feed house so arranged that men delivering supplies need not enter buildings or yards occupied by your turkeys or handle equipment that your birds use.

Have feeders and watering devices so constructed that they stay free of droppings.

Start each brood with houses and equipment scrupulously clean.

Keep litter clean and dry always.

Isolate all sick birds, quarantine all affected pens, and bury or burn all birds that die. Always take care of clean stock first, pens having shown sick birds next, and isolation quarters last of all.

Move birds on the range frequently to avoid excessive contamination of the ground. As far as hexamitiasis is concerned, plots may be reused safely 2 to 3 weeks later, but if blackhead or coccidiosis also are present that should not be done.

Some growers have had satisfactory results with the use of Aureomycin (chlortetracycline) administered at levels of 180 to 200 grams per ton of ration.

Other growers have preferred to administer the medicant in the water, because birds will sometimes drink after they no longer feed. They use 10 grams of soluble Aureomycin for 50 gallons of water. In either instance, the drug may constitute only a small part of the preparation available on the market, so the mixture must be made to contain the stated amount of the active ingredient. If the drug is effective, improvement usually is noted in 2 or 3 days.

Frequently other disorders accompany or follow hexamitiasis. If control measures or treatment fail after 3 or 4 days, a second diagnosis may be necessary for the situation may have changed.

EVERETT E. LUND *is a parasitologist in the Department of Agriculture.*

Pullorum Disease of Chickens and Turkeys

J. E. WILLIAMS, PAUL B. ZUMBRO, AND A. D. MacDONALD

PULLORUM DISEASE, which occurs in all parts of the world, is caused by a microscopic organism, *Salmonella pullorum*. The chicken seems to be the natural host of the organism, but the disease has become increasingly serious among turkeys as the commercial hatching of turkey eggs has increased.

Pullorum disease may also strike ducks, guinea fowl, pheasants, sparrows, quail, bittern, geese, pigeons, doves, parakeets, and canaries. The organism, which was discovered in 1899, is rarely found in mammals.

Pullorum disease causes heavy death losses in chicks and poults and reduces the productivity of adult birds. The deaths occur mainly during the first 3 weeks after hatching. Losses may be as high as 80 to 90 percent of the brood. Pullorum disease is not commonly encountered in the acute form in birds more than 1 month old. The infected adults usually show no outward evidence of infection.

Once commonly known as bacillary white diarrhea (B. W. D.) of chicks, pullorum disease for more than a half-century has been recognized as one of the worst of all poultry diseases.

Great strides have been made toward eradicating it through a national program of blood testing adult breeding flocks, supplemented with the widespread practice of sound sanitation.

The main reservoirs of pullorum infection are the egg-producing organs of the infected hen. The disease is transmitted from her to the chick or poult directly through the egg.

The infection may be spread among the brood through breathing or consuming contaminated dust, down, or other material in the incubator, shipping box, brooder, or pen. The disease is transmitted also through consumption of litter, feed, or water contaminated with infected droppings. One infected chick or poult at hatching time may be responsible for transmitting the disease to the entire brood. The infection is usually spread during the first few days. Unsanitary conditions, improper heating or ventilation, and the occurrence of other diseases hasten the spread.

Infected chicks or poults that do not die of the disease may grow to maturity and remain lifetime carriers. Infected hens may lay infected eggs that may hatch diseased chicks; thus the cycle is repeated. Transmission sometimes happens among adult fowl through consumption of infected droppings or broken eggs.

THE SYMPTOMS exhibited by infected chicks and poults are by no means specific but may lead one to suspect the disease. Losses may start in the incubator or shortly after hatching, when infected eggs are the source of the disease. As a general rule, however, several days elapse before heavy losses start. Losses tend to decline during the third and fourth weeks.

Pullorum-infected chicks and poults show symptoms of extreme depression, huddling together with closed eyes and with drooping heads and wings, ruffled feathers, frequent passages of liquid feces, which results in pasty vents, shrill chirping, and loss of appetite.

When the infection reaches the lungs, the birds may breathe with difficulty and extend their heads in an effort to breathe. Surviving birds may be runts.

Listlessness, a lack of appetite, diarrhea, increased water consumption, and a paleness of the comb may be observed when the infection is acute among adults.

Postmortem findings in chicks and poults are usually observed in the liver, spleen, heart, and lungs as a generalized infection. Those organs are enlarged and often covered with streaks of hemorrhage or minute white spots, in which the organisms are centered. Larger areas of infection in the form of abscesses—lumps—may occur in the heart wall and through the lungs. The lumps may be observed also along the intestines and in the muscle of the gizzard. The sac covering the heart may be thickened and cloudy. The contents of the yolk sac often are dry and cheesy. The blind sacs (ceca), located toward the end of the intestinal tract, frequently contain a dry core.

The findings in maturing and adult birds that die of acute pullorum infection are like those in young birds. The more frequently observed lesions of adults are in the chronic carrier. On postmortem examination, one generally finds the most clear-cut lesions in the ovary of the chronic carrier. The ova are thickened, misshapen and discolored, and filled with a cheesy or watery material. Diseased ova may be clustered among normal ova or suspended on stemlike extensions from the main body of the ovary. Ovarian lesions are suggestive of pullorum disease. Other lesions in chronically infected adults include abscesses on the heart wall, thickening of the heart sac, and generalized infection of the abdominal cavity, with an accumulation of fluid and pus.

For accurate diagnosis, bacteriological tests must be made in a laboratory, because the symptoms and postmortem findings merely suggest the infection.

Adult or maturing birds that react suspiciously to the pullorum blood test and chicks and poults that show symptoms of acute pullorum disease should be submitted to a State diagnostic laboratory for examination.

This service is available at most State agricultural colleges. The laboratory culture tests are essential in distinguishing pullorum disease from fowl typhoid and paratyphoid infections, which are also eggborne diseases closely related to pullorum. Birds infected with fowl typhoid react to the pullorum test. Occasionally birds infected with certain paratyphoid types, as well as other micro-organisms, may react to the test. After the organisms have been isolated in the laboratory, their biochemical activity can be determined and a detailed report can be issued on the exact type of infection involved. This information is often useful in guiding the pathologist in making recommendations regarding treatment and control.

When an acute disease outbreak occurs, it is usually best for the owner to take several live birds and several dead ones to the laboratory for examination. The laboratory procedures for pullorum diagnosis generally take 48 to 96 hours to complete.

CONTROL AND ERADICATION of pullorum disease must be based on breaking the cycle of transmission. That is done by detecting and eliminating adult carriers, because the disease is largely eggborne. Such a procedure makes the owner reasonably sure that only noninfected eggs are set and noninfected chicks and poults are hatched.

Blood testing of adult chickens and turkeys in breeding flocks is done throughout the United States. The agglutination test, used in detecting pullorum carriers, is conducted by one or more of the three officially recognized methods; namely, the tube agglutination test, the rapid whole-blood plate test, and rapid serum plate test.

Each test is based on the fact that infected birds carry in their blood stream immune substances (antibodies), which will clump (cause to stick together in a compact mass) a liquid suspension of killed-pullorum organisms (antigens) when the test suspension is mixed with the serum or the whole blood of the infected bird. The clumps are visible to the unaided eye and indicate that the living organisms and the antibodies that they stimulate are present in the bird. The blood of noninfected birds does not contain any antibodies, and therefore no clumps form when the whole blood or serum of such birds is mixed with the antigen.

The rapid whole-blood test has been most widely used for testing chickens. The test is easily conducted in the field by anyone trained in its use.

State agricultural colleges for years have held schools to train poultrymen in conducting blood tests and practicing other procedures for controlling pullorum disease.

The three agglutination tests mentioned as being used for diagnosing pullorum disease are described in *The National Poultry Improvement Plan and National Turkey Improvement Plan and Auxiliary Provisions.* This publication is available from the Agricultural Research Service, Washington 25, D. C.

A VARIANT TYPE of pullorum disease was recognized in Canada in 1941. Outbreaks occurred in chicks in flocks that tested negative to the standard agglutination test and were maintained on uninfected premises. The outbreaks had the same history and symptoms as typical pullorum disease. Cultures were isolated and studied. All were identical to *Salmonella pullorum*, except that they varied in their antigenic makeup from the official pullorum strains that were used

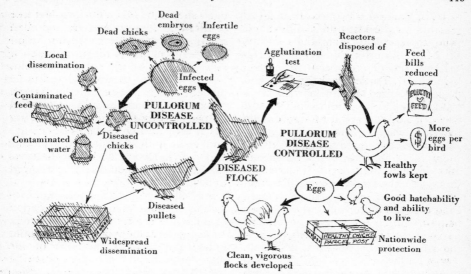

A comparison of the serious effects of uncontrolled pullorum disease and the results of the use of the agglutination test and the disposal of reactors.

to produce antigens (liquid testing fluids containing killed-pullorum organisms). These usual or so-called "standard" antigens often did not react in the presence of serum from the outbreaks noted. This new form of pullorum disease was designated "variant type." It has been found in many sections of the United States.

In order to detect both the standard (usual) and the variant forms of pullorum infection, a polyvalent-type whole-blood antigen has been widely used in testing. The polyvalent antigen consists of a mixture of both standard and variant-type cultures of *Salmonella pullorum* organisms; the standard antigen contains only standard-type cultures. Both standard and polyvalent whole-blood type antigens are available commercially.

A polyvalent-type tube agglutination antigen has been used occasionally to test chickens and turkeys in flocks where the variant type of pullorum disease has been encountered or is suspected. Most diagnostic laboratories can determine if the variant form of pullorum disease is present in a flock by analysis of cultures isolated on postmortem tests.

THE KEY to the control of pullorum disease is to get healthy chicks and poults. Because most chicks and poults raised in the United States are bought from hatcheries, the first step in the control of pullorum disease for most poultrymen is to buy from a hatchery that produces clean stock.

The identification of such sources is an important function of the National Poultry Improvement Plan (NPIP) and the National Turkey Improvement Plan (NTIP), both of which are administered by the Department of Agriculture and an official agency in each State.

Hatcheries participating in the plans follow a systematic program of pullorum-typhoid control. They use eggs from participating flocks only. They are inspected by a representative of the official State agency and must be kept in sanitary condition.

Flockowners participating in the National Poultry Improvement Plan and National Turkey Improvement Plan must test their flocks annually for pullorum disease. To qualify, the flock must have no reactors. The testing is done by trained men. The flocks are subject to inspection and qualify either as U. S. Pullorum-Typhoid Passed (no reactors on the last official blood test prior to producing hatching eggs) or U. S. Pullorum-Typhoid Clean (no reactors on two consecutive official blood tests). Turkey flocks and chicken flocks acquired from participating sources qualify as Pullorum-Typhoid Clean if no reactors are found on the first or any subsequent official test.

Lists are published annually giving the names and addresses of hatcheries and dealers participating in the National Poultry Improvement Plan and the National Turkey Improvement Plan and the pullorum-typhoid classification of their products. The chicken hatcheries are listed in ARS 53–6 and the turkey hatcheries in ARS 53–8. These publications are available upon request to the Agricultural Research Service, Department of Agriculture, Washington 25, D. C.

TREATMENT of pullorum disease is advisable only as a salvage or preventative measure and for chicks and poults that are not to be kept as a source of hatching eggs.

Sulfamethazine, sulfamerazine, and sulfaquinoxaline have been used successfully to reduce the death losses in chicks and poults.

Furazolidone, a chemical derivative of furfural, checks losses in acute outbreaks. It may be incorporated in the feed at a low level for continuous feeding to prevent outbreaks and spread of the infection.

We have little evidence that the antibiotics are effective or practical for the control of pullorum disease. Bacterins are of no value in the prevention or treatment of the disease.

Sanitation and disinfection are important, especially with regard to the hatching and the brooding operations. S. pullorum is rather easily destroyed by the common disinfectants, heat, and direct sunlight, but the organisms may survive for months in soil, manure, and sheltered places.

After each hatch, incubator egg trays and the other readily removable parts should be taken out, washed free of dirt and foreign matter, and then scrubbed with a 2-percent lye solution or other acceptable disinfectant, such as a 3-percent solution of cresylic acid. Lye is caustic and the operator must take precautions against exposure in using it.

Incubator rooms should be cleaned by periodically brushing and washing down dust and cobwebs from ceilings and walls and from around windows and doors. Debris and miscellaneous stored material should not be allowed to accumulate.

Formaldehyde gas is good for disinfecting incubators during incubation or following the removal of the hatch. In using formaldehyde gas, one should follow the recommendations of the manufacturer of the incubator being used. Chick brooders, brooder rooms, feeders, waterers, and similar equipment should be cleaned frequently by washing and disinfecting with an approved disinfectant.

Following removal of reactors to the blood test, poultry houses and equipment should be cleaned and disinfected. An empty pen in each house will facilitate these operations. Since yards in which infected birds have been kept should be considered unsafe for new stock, clean ground should be provided for replacements.

Feedbags, shipping cartons, and the egg crates preferably should be new. Otherwise they should be cleaned and disinfected properly. Trucks, in which the chicks or poults are transported, should be kept clean and sanitary. They always should be disinfected immediately after being used to haul any material that may be contaminated.

The persons who handle shipments should take precautions to insure freedom from contact with any source of contamination to newly hatched chicks or poults. Hatching operations in general should be off limits to visitors and unsupervised persons. Workers assigned to field jobs or other hatchery business where they come into contact with adult birds and other animals, which may or may not be known to be infected with disease, should never enter the hatching area. If it is necessary for employees to work in other places in some of their work, they should remove their coveralls before leaving the area and put on overshoes. On reentering the hatching area they should wash their hands, disinfect the overshoes, and put coveralls on again.

Further information about disinfection methods is available in the following Department publications: *An Outline of Disinfection Procedures for Poultry Service Personnel* and Farmers' Bulletin No. 1991, *Use of Disinfectants on the Farm.*

J. E. WILLIAMS *became a project leader in the Bacterial and Mycotic Diseases Section of the Agricultural Research Service in 1951. He has the degree of doctor of*

veterinary medicine from the Alabama Polytechnic Institute and the degrees of master of science and doctor of philosophy in veterinary medicine from the University of Minnesota.

PAUL B. ZUMBRO *is a poultry husbandman in charge of poultry improvement in the Animal and Poultry Husbandry Research Branch of the Agricultural Research Service. He is a graduate of Ohio State University and served as extension poultryman in Ohio before he joined the Department in 1935.*

A. D. MacDONALD *is a veterinarian in the Animal Disease and Parasite Research Branch of the Agricultural Research Service. He is a graduate of the former U. S. College of Veterinary Surgeons, Washington, D. C., and has been associated with the Department of Agriculture in research work on poultry diseases since 1924.*

Fowl Typhoid

WALTER J. HALL

FOWL TYPHOID, a septicemic disease, may be acute or chronic, depending largely on the pathogenicity of the causative organism, *Salmonella gallinarum.* It is primarily a disease of pullets and mature chickens, but it may attack young chickens and turkeys, ducks, guinea fowl, pheasants, and some other birds.

It occurs throughout the United States and throughout the year but is most common in summer.

Symptoms are not distinct enough to be diagnostic. There is fever, loss of appetite, increased thirst, and usually a yellowish-orange diarrhea. Paleness of the head and shriveling of the comb are usual.

The changes seen inside birds dead of fowl typhoid are variable. Few abnormalities may be noted in the more acute cases that die at the beginning

of an outbreak. Later, especially in young chickens, a marked swelling and redness of the liver, spleen, and kidneys are commonly observed. The more chronic cases may develop grayish spots on the heart muscle, with swelling and a bronze or dark-green coloring of the liver. The ovary may show flaccid, angular, or hemorrhagic ova, as in pullorum disease.

Rupture of the diseased ova frequently cause peritonitis (infection of the abdominal cavity), and salpingitis (infection of the oviduct). This infection disturbs the functioning of the oviduct, so that there is a loss of motility, resulting in the dropping of some yolks into the abdominal cavity, and the stagnation and hardening of those that enter the oviduct, with consequent cessation of laying.

Fowl typhoid should be differentiated from pullorum disease, fowl cholera, and blue comb. A positive diagnosis can be had only by isolating the causative organism.

Fowl typhoid may be spread from pen to pen, from house to house, and from farm to farm by people, animals, and equipment that are contaminated by manure, dirt, feed, or water, in which the germs can survive.

An acutely infected bird is the most dangerous spreader of the disease, because it gives off millions of germs constantly from its mouth and nostrils and through its droppings, thus quickly contaminating feed, water, and litter. Prompt segregation of the sick birds from the healthy birds is recommended.

In almost any outbreak of disease, some individuals survive, and many of the survivors become carriers.

The germ localizes in the ova. Some of the eggs will be infected and upon hatching may start an outbreak of fowl typhoid. Carrier pullets may lay infected eggs on the range or in the henhouse. An outbreak may start when those eggs get broken and are eaten by other pullets.

Since the bird dead of fowl typhoid is such a dangerous source of disease, it should be buried or burned promptly so that animals and insects cannot come in contact with it.

Animals may spread the disease by carrying contaminated material on or in their bodies. Among them are rats, other predatory or scavenger wild animals, buzzards, and possibly other free-flying birds. Flies and some other insects may also be involved.

Control procedures depend somewhat on the age of the birds and the purpose for which they are kept. The best control procedure is prevention, including the practice of sanitation, and the removal of carriers by agglutination testing.

Vaccination does not give effective immunity against fowl typhoid.

When an outbreak occurs in large breeding flocks, the pens or the part of the flock that is affected should be shut off from the remainder of the flock, and every practical sanitary precaution should be taken to prevent spread of the disease to healthy birds.

The following procedures will be helpful: Attend the sick birds last; disinfect footwear, hands, and utensils after caring for the sick birds; prevent contamination of feed and water by providing grilled covers; change the water often; give feed in small amounts to prevent waste and ground feeding.

Within 2 weeks after the outbreak has subsided, all birds should be tested by the agglutination test (using pullorum antigen), and all reactors should be removed.

The test should be repeated at 30-day intervals until no more reactors are found.

The easiest way to eradicate the disease in small flocks is to dispose of the entire flock, disinfect the premises, and restock with healthy birds.

No drugs are entirely satisfactory as curative agents. The sulfonamide drugs are used both as feed mixes and in drinking water to control mortality. These drugs reduce mortality while they are being administered, but mortality increases again upon withdrawal of the drug. The sulfonamides are toxic when fed continuously or in too large doses. This effect may be avoided by intermittent feeding.

Antibiotics, including Aureomycin, streptomycin, and penicillin, also have been used to some extent but results have been disappointing.

More recently furazolidone has been used to control the *Salmonella* diseases, including fowl typhoid, pullorum disease, and paratyphoid. This drug is nontoxic. Experimental and field reports on its effectiveness in controlling losses from the *Salmonella* diseases have been encouraging.

WALTER J. HALL, *a graduate of the New York State College of Veterinary Medicine, taught in the veterinary science department of Montana State College before he joined the Department of Agriculture in 1924.*

Poultry and the Paratyphoids

J. E. WILLIAMS

ALL TYPES of poultry are important reservoirs of paratyphoid infections.

As applied to poultry diseases, the term "paratyphoid" denotes diseases caused by micro-organisms of the Salmonella group other than *Salmonella pullorum* (pullorum disease) and *Salmonella gallinarum* (fowl typhoid).

More than 60 of the 200-odd types of Salmonella that are known to exist cause diseases in poultry.

With the rapid expansion and increased traffic in the poultry industry in recent years, paratyphoid infections have become a problem of utmost concern. The wide natural distribution of the Salmonella organisms has made the establishment of efficient control methods most difficult.

The distribution of paratyphoid infections is worldwide. Unlike pullorum disease and fowl typhoid, which are essentially restricted to poultry, the paratyphoids can infect practically all animal species, including man.

Among avian types, these infections cause severe losses among the young of most domesticated and wild fowl, including turkeys, chickens, pigeons, geese, ducks, quail, canaries, parrots, finches, sparrows, and guinea fowl.

Mammalian types that may be infected with Salmonella and transmit the disease to poultry include swine, cattle, horses, sheep, dogs, cats, and foxes. Mice, rats, snakes, flies, and roaches may also carry the organisms.

The discussion that follows is restricted to the disease as it occurs in turkeys; however, paratyphoid infections as they occur in other fowl are quite similar in symptons, postmortem lesions, treatment, and control.

Micro-organisms belonging to the genus *Paracolobactrum* (so-called paracolons), which are closely related to the Salmonella, have been reported as the cause of a septicemic disease of young fowl. Laboratory procedures are required for accurate identification of this group of diseases. Members of the Arizona group of paracolons are especially pathogenic for young turkeys and may be eggborne. Like the Salmonella, the paracolons are distributed in a wide variety of animal species under natural conditions and are usually eliminated in the droppings of infected animals. The symptoms and postmortem lesions as well as the control and treatment of paracolon infections are identical to those described for the paratyphoids.

The microscopic organism that causes paratyphoid infection was first reported in turkeys in 1933. The bacteria can be readily cultivated in the laboratory and through a special procedure, called serological typing, the various types can be identified. Information derived from typing the organism aids in tracing the origin of disease outbreaks and permits men who work to control disease to concentrate their efforts toward the eradication of the more widespread and deadly types.

Salmonella typhimurium is the most frequently encountered paratyphoid in poultry and most other animal species. Other types frequently encountered in turkeys include *S. anatum* (common also in ducks), *S. bredeney*, *S. derby*, *S. newport*, and *S. senftenberg*.

HEAVIEST LOSSES from paratyphoid infections occur among young birds during the first month after hatching. The age at which losses start depends on whether the infection takes place in the incubator or after the young birds are placed in the brooder. The disease spreads rapidly. Deaths may continue for several weeks. Losses vary widely and may exceed 90 percent of the hatch.

Birds that survive the infection may remain lifetime carriers of the organisms and are capable of laying infected eggs, which may spread the disease to the young.

Paratyphoid is not frequently encountered as an acute disease in adult turkeys. Infected adults generally show no outward symptoms.

Paratyphoid organisms are spread from bird to bird by consumption of litter, feed, or water contaminated with infected droppings. Adult birds may pass large numbers of the organisms in their droppings and readily infect younger birds. Droppings of rodents often contain huge numbers of the organisms. People may carry the organisms when feces and litter adhere to their shoes or clothing.

The infection may be spread also by way of the egg. One way is by direct transfer from the ovary of the infected hen. The other is by penetration of the egg shell by the Salmonella organisms that may be present in dirt on the surface of the egg. Only clean eggs should be used for hatching.

THE SYMPTOMS of paratyphoid infection in young poults cannot be told from pullorum disease and fowl typhoid. Diarrhea, weakness, sagging wings, and pasting of feathers around the vent are common. Infected birds often appear to be sleepy. They congregate in groups as if chilled. Surviving birds may be emaciated.

Acute outbreaks of paratyphoid infection in older birds are evidenced by diarrhea, loss of appetite, and emaciation. Death may occur in a few days.

Postmortem findings in young poults include inflammation of the intestinal tract and enlargement of most of the internal organs, including the liver, spleen, and kidneys. Minute white spots may also be seen on various internal organs. The sac around the heart may be filled with a straw-colored fluid. Plugs of dry, cheesy material in the blind sacs (ceca) toward the end of the intestinal tract are common. Lesions in the lungs and heart are infrequent.

Enlargement of the liver and spleen and inflammation or ulceration of the intestinal tract may be observed in infected adult birds. In grown pigeons the infection may be manifested by the formation of abscesses, which particularly affect the joints of the wings.

Diagnosis of paratyphoid infections depends on isolation and identification of the causative bacteria. Most States have diagnostic laboratories to which infected birds may be sent for examination.

PREVENTION AND CONTROL of paratyphoid infections depend to a large extent on the use of paratyphoid-free stock as a source of hatching eggs and prevention of exposure to the numerous other animal species that serve as reservoirs of the infection.

Adult birds and other animals should be kept confined and separated from poultry-rearing operations. Rats and mice should be eradicated.

Every effort should be made to insure that the infection is not introduced from a source outside the farm.

Diseased birds should be isolated from healthy stock and disposed of as soon as possible, because infected groups should never be maintained as a source of breeders.

Blood testing has never been widely applied against paratyphoid infections of poultry because of the numerous antigenic types of the organism and the wide distribution of Salmonella bacteria under natural conditions. The agglutination test for paratyphoids is more complicated and has been subject to more variation than is the one used for pullorum disease and fowl typhoid. Some birds may be intestinal carriers of the organisms and will not react to it.

A few paratyphoid carriers may be detected through the use of pullorum antigen. Anyone who uses the agglutination test for paratyphoid, however, should use antigens prepared from the particular type or types identified in the flocks to be tested. Thus the services of a laboratory with trained personnel and adequate facilities for paratyphoid testing are essential. Only a few States in 1956 conducted blood testing programs for paratyphoid infections of turkeys. The programs were aimed mostly at the detection of *S. typhimurium* infection.

Treatment of paratyphoid infections is advisable only as a salvage or preventative measure and only for birds that are not to be maintained as breeders, as some of the treated birds may remain permanent carriers of the paratyphoid organisms.

Furazolidone, a chemical derivative of furfural, is effective in treating and preventing acute outbreaks of the disease. It is mixed with the feed.

Several of the sulfonamide drugs (sulfamethazine, sulfamerazine, sulfaquinoxaline) and antibiotics (Terramycin, Aureomycin) have been used successfully to reduce death losses.

Bacterins have been found to have little or no value for preventing and controlling the disease.

Salmonella organisms are destroyed readily by the usual disinfectants and direct sunlight, but they may survive for months in soil, manure, and sheltered places.

All equipment used in hatching operations should be frequently washed free of all foreign matter and scrubbed with a 2-percent commercial lye solution or a 3-percent solution of cresol or other acceptable disinfectants.

Formaldehyde gas is effective for fumigating incubators and eggs. Anyone who uses formaldehyde gas should follow closely the recommendations of the manufacturer of the incubator he has. Direct spraying with a 5-percent formalin solution has also been recommended for fumigating incubators.

Poult brooders, brooder rooms, feeders, waterers, and similar equipment should be cleaned frequently by washing and disinfecting with an approved disinfectant.

J. E. WILLIAMS *is project leader in the Bacterial and Mycotic Diseases Section of the Animal Disease and Parasite Research Branch.*

Newcastle Disease

O. L. OSTEEN

NEWCASTLE DISEASE is a specific, highly contagious disease primarily of chickens and turkeys. Other domestic poultry, various species of wild birds, and people are susceptible to it, but in man it is usually mild and is characterized by inflammation of one eye, seldom both.

Among young chickens the loss may be as high as 100 percent. The average is usually 30 to 40 percent. The death losses may vary greatly from one outbreak to another. Chicks that survive

an outbreak are retarded in growth and efficiency of feed utilization. It requires at least 2 extra weeks to finish birds in affected broiler flocks.

Turkey poults are somewhat less severely affected, but the loss among them may be 15 to 20 percent of the brood.

The death loss among laying birds usually is quite low but occasionally may be as high as 80 percent of the flock. Production and quality of eggs usually drop sharply. The disease in breeding flocks also results in lower fertility and hatchability of the eggs.

Additional losses to the poultry industry arise from the restriction on exportation of live and dressed fowl from the United States to other countries.

Dr. T. M. Doyle of England first recognized Newcastle disease as a distinct and separate disease of chickens in 1926. He discovered that the disease in a flock near Newcastle upon Tyne, England, was a virus disease, which differed from fowl pest. He named it after the town.

The disease apparently reached California about 1940, but because of its unusual nature it went unrecognized until 1944. Then the virus of the new respiratory-nervous disorder, which research workers in California called pneumo-encephalitis, was shown to be identical with the virus of Newcastle disease.

Newcastle disease was found in 1945 on the eastern seaboard—first in New Jersey and New York. By 1947 the infection had been reported in 30 States. Within a year or two it had spread to every State reached by traffic in poultry and poultry products.

After Newcastle disease was first recognized as a disease of chickens, other species of poultry and birds and certain mammals were found to be susceptible to it by natural exposure.

Turkeys usually are less severely affected than are chickens. Pheasants, guinea fowls, geese, ducks, pigeons, swans, quail, sparrows, parrots, doves, owls, gannets, starlings, and martins are reported to have become infected under natural conditions. Thus these birds, as well as people, dogs, and cats, may be unrecognized or mechanical carriers and spreaders of the virus of Newcastle disease because they often show little or no evidence of the disease.

THE VIRUS that causes Newcastle disease is present in actively infected individuals and in apparently healthy carriers. It is too small to be seen except through an electron micro-scope. It appears to be shaped like a tadpole. About 250 thousand of them measure an inch.

Nasal secretions, saliva, and droppings of infected birds contain the virus 1 or 2 days after they are exposed to the infection. Birds that survive attacks of the disease seldom give off the virus for more than 3 or 4 weeks, but the virus has been recovered from the lungs of a few chickens 2 or 3 months after recovery.

The portion of healthy, recovered carriers of the virus is ordinarily quite low, but the persistence for a month or more of only a small percentage of carrier cases often is enough to set up new centers of infection and thus to favor spread of the disease.

The possibility of transmission of the virus from an infected hen through her egg to the hatched chick is not important in the spread of the disease—few, if any, infected eggs hatch.

Conditions outside the living bird are usually unfavorable for the survival of the virus for any great length of time. When the virus is protected against heat, light, moisture, and other factors that destroy it, however, its livability may be prolonged for months.

The virus is extremely hardy at low temperatures. It can live in frozen poultry carcasses for more than 2 years. Quite resistant to heat, it can withstand a temperature of 132° F. for at least 30 minutes. On ordinary farm materials—feedbags, egg flats, feathers, eggshells and such—it may survive at the usual temperatures for 2 to 8 weeks.

Boiling water destroys it instantly.

The usual coal tar disinfectants quickly destroy the virus.

One-percent saponified cresol, 1-percent Lysol, and 10-percent quaternary ammonium compounds are effective in 5 to 10 minutes, but are ineffective when the virus is protected by dirt, droppings, body secretions, or tissues.

Fumigation of cleaned incubators with formaldehyde as it is used against pullorum disease destroys the virus.

THE SYMPTOMS vary with the age of the bird. In chicks a few days to a few weeks old, the first symptom usually is difficulty in breathing. The birds are depressed and weak. Sometimes a marked stupor develops. Twitching of the head and neck, marked weakness, and paralysis may occur within a few days. Generally the symptoms subside rapidly, or the chicks die in a few days.

The symptoms in broilers resemble those in chicks. Apparently broilers have a greater tendency to a more lasting illness and paralysis.

The disease usually begins in older or adult birds with a drop in feed consumption and with respiratory symptoms. A characteristic symptom in laying flocks is an abrupt and almost complete interruption of egg production. Soft-shelled or rough-shelled eggs are found on the henhouse floor. Eggshells are often off color. The loss in egg production may last 4 to 8 weeks. The birds may go into a molt, which is usually much heavier than that normally observed. Paralysis is less frequent generally and the mortality is much lower in laying birds than in other groups.

The symptoms in turkeys are quite similar to those seen in chickens but generally are less severe.

Postmortem findings are variable and inconsistent. Hemorrhages are found in acute infections in the body membranes, heart, stomach, and intestine, but infrequently in less severe outbreaks. Often there is a thickening and clouding of the abdominal and thoracic air sacs, which are covered with slimy exudate. The trachea contains an inflammatory mucous exudate, but the lungs are not seriously affected. Clouding of the eyes occurs in a few birds. The spleen may be mottled, pale, and small.

Symptoms alone are not a reliable basis for determining whether a given lot of sick birds has Newcastle disease. The disease resembles other maladies, such as infectious bronchitis, air-sac infection (chronic respiratory disease), laryngotracheitis, and avian encephalomyelitis, or epidemic tremor. It may appear to be leucosis. It simulates nutritional deficiencies, such as encephalomalacia and ariboflavinosis.

The only exact means of diagnosis is by laboratory procedures. The most conclusive evidence of Newcastle disease is obtained by isolation of the specific causative virus.

PREVENTION or control of Newcastle disease by vaccination is considered to be a valuable supplement to a sound, basic, long-range program of sanitary management.

Two types of vaccine are available for immunizing poultry against Newcastle disease. Before being released for use, the vaccines are tested for ability to immunize, safety, and freedom from contaminating bacteria or other disease-producing agents. The expiration date of usefulness of the product is shown on the label.

Killed-virus vaccine has the important advantage of not producing active disease. The immunity resulting from the killed-virus vaccines depends on the reaction of the bird to the virus present in a single dose. Slight immunity may develop 1 week or so after vaccination, although 2 to 3 weeks are required for its maximum protection to develop. The immunity begins to disappear within 6 to 8 weeks after vaccination and gradually is lost entirely. Revaccination after a period of 2 weeks or longer will strengthen and prolong the immunity. Because of the irritating effect of the large dose needed, it is not recommended that this vaccine be used in chicks less than 10 days old.

Live-virus vaccines are available for several methods of administration; namely, the wing-web, intranasal, and intramuscular routes and in water. Other routes include dropping the vaccine into one eye or atomizing (spraying) the vaccine for inhalation.

The virus employed in the wing-web method vaccine usually produces a mild form of Newcastle disease in most healthy birds more than 4 or 6 weeks old. Given by other routes—intranasally or intramuscularly—it may cause rather severe shock or fatal infection, especially in young chicks or devitalized birds of any age.

The virus employed in the intranasal-method vaccine is adapted to growth in the respiratory tract and to stimulate a moderate degree of immunity in most healthy birds. While its use has been advised in baby chicks and laying flocks, the systemic reaction in some cases has been so severe as to impair production appreciably and to contribute heavily to chick mortality.

Because of the relatively small amount of virus introduced with the living vaccines, the blocking effect is seldom so substantial as it is with the killed vaccines. The specific immunity given by the living-vaccine infection should appear within a week after vaccination and should be of substantial degree after the second week. The immunity from living vaccine begins to wane within 10 weeks, and proper revaccination is usually recommended within 2 months to a year.

Neither the killed nor living vaccines have given fully satisfactory results, and efforts are continuing to improve them. The killed vaccines can be used in birds of any age or status of production or health, but the immunity produced by them has not been so strong or durable as desired.

Nevertheless, vaccination of baby chicks, or those less than 6 weeks old, may not be expected to give a maximum immunity to a satisfactory proportion of the brood or lot. Likewise, use of killed vaccine in birds of low vitality may fail to produce a satisfactory degree of immunity although the health is not further impaired, as may be the case with live-virus vaccination.

While a stronger and more lasting immunity usually may be expected with the living than with the killed vaccine, these advantages of the living vaccine are often offset by a relatively severe vaccination-disease reaction even in broods and flocks of suitable age and production status that appear to be in normal health.

The use of living vaccines may also present the problem of introducing Newcastle disease infection into previously clean flocks and areas. The possibilities that the vaccine virus may become fully active and destructive are small but cannot be ignored.

Another factor that may alter the response to vaccination is the immunity the hen that has had Newcastle disease or has been vaccinated against it transmits to her chicks. Where the hen's immunity is of high grade, the chick will carry a yolk-borne immunity up to 30 days of age. If the hen has a partial immunity, the passive immunity of the chicks may be lost at 2 weeks or earlier. The immunity gives the chicks a degree of protection against natural infection and also prevents a "take," or immunity from vaccination. Failure to recognize the influence of the previous Newcastle disease status of the breeding flock and the degree of immunity which the chick or flock may carry at any time may lead to apparent failure of vaccination.

Obviously the indiscriminate, careless, and improper use of vaccines will result in difficulty, confusion, and loss. Only when vaccination is practiced as a supplement to a long-range sanitation program of a community, State, and national scope can it be fully effective.

Sanitation practices recommended for your climate and locality by the livestock sanitary officers, State universities, and the poultry pathologists should be followed.

O. L. OSTEEN *received the degree of doctor of veterinary medicine from the University of Georgia in 1928. Dr. Osteen has been in the service of the Department of Agriculture since 1932. He served in meat inspection for 3 years and has engaged in research work on equine infectious anemia, swine erysipelas, equine encephalomyelitis, Newcastle disease, and vesicular diseases.*

Ornithosis and Psittacosis

JOHN P. DELAPLANE

PEOPLE can get ornithosis—or psittacosis—through contact with sick birds, notably parrots and other birds of the psittacine, or parrot, family. Epidemics have occurred since 1879 in Switzerland, Germany, France, England, and the United States.

The disease used to be known as "parrot fever" because people thought parrots and parakeets were the only sources of infection. Now we know that some 70 species of birds can get the infection.

Since 1938, epidemics in people traceable to contacts with fulmars, petrels, chickens, ducks, pigeons, shore birds, pheasants, and turkeys have been recorded.

K. F. Meyer, of the Hooper Foundation, University of California, has suggested that "psittacosis" be used to designate infections that have parrot or psittacine origin and "ornithosis" to designate the infections that arise from nonpsittacine birds.

Diagnoses of the epidemics in 1948, 1951, and 1952 among workers in poultry-dressing plants in Texas were based on positive complement-fixation serological tests. Turkeys were suspected as the source of infection in man because the incubation period of the disease indicated repeatedly that the infection followed the processing of turkeys. The isolation of the virus from turkeys and the fact that the virus infected laboratory technicians who worked with it proved that turkeys were the source of those epidemics. Thereafter persons concerned with problems of public health and poultry diseases became deeply interested. About 200 workers in poultry-dressing plants got the disease in 1954.

The first description of a disease marked by an atypical pneumonia was reported in 1879 among persons having contact with sick parrots. A severe and sometimes fatal atypical pneumonia was observed in various European countries and the United States in later years. An unusually severe epidemic occurred in Paris in 1892. Then the disease was thought to originate as a result of gram-negative bacterial organisms, which could be isolated readily from the tissues of the sick and dead parrots. The subsequent failure of investigators to find the gram-negative bacterial organism consistently in sick or dead parrots created doubt that the organism actually caused the disease. We now recognize that the organism originally reported was merely a common complicating agent, rather than one of primary significance.

The name "psittacosis" was suggested for the disease in 1895. From 1895 to 1929 the disease was recognized as single or group infections in Europe and the United States.

An epidemic involving more than 100 cases of atypical pneumonia, diagnosed as psittacosis, occurred in Argentina in 1929. A year later epidemics in Europe and the United States were traced to parrots newly imported from South America, and the virus character of the psittacosis disease agent was found by scientists in England and the United States.

They discovered that white mice could be infected with the virus and would therefore be used in laboratory studies. The finding contributed greatly to our knowledge of the disease.

We refer to the ornithosis and psittacosis agents as large, particle-size viruses—they can be seen with an ordinary microscope and are susceptible to antibiotics, while true viruses cannot be seen or are not affected by antibiotics.

An epidemic of pneumonitis among

persons who were processing fulmars and petrels in the Faroe Islands in 1938 was found to be a "psittacosis-like" disease. The finding emphasized the importance of birds other than parrots as sources of human infections.

A highly virulent virus isolated from snowy egrets in Louisiana and indistinguishable from the one causing a severe human pneumonitis in that State in 1944 suggests that this bird was the possible source of the infection in man.

Since the 1930's, ornithosis and psittacosis viruses have been found to be closely related to a group of agents affecting mammals, such as bovine sporadic encephalomyelitis, lymphogranuloma venereum, mouse pneumonitis, feline pneumonitis, and agents isolated from calves, ewes, and opossums.

THE CLINICAL SYMPTOMS and pathology of the disease are better known in psittacine birds than in turkeys.

Latent infections occur in most species of birds. Virus may be shed from time to time and can infect man and other birds.

The infection may or may not be apparent in psittacines. The sick birds seem to be sleepy and have ruffled feathers, fits of shivering, labored breathing, and a rapid loss of body weight. Diarrhea, with greenish stools, may soil the feathers. Nestlings become infected through feeding. Virus has been recovered from eggs, but the importance of a direct transmission through the egg has not been well established among these birds.

The mortality among parakeets is 5 to 10 percent when they are raised under satisfactory conditions; otherwise, the mortality rate may be higher. Stress factors, such as changes in environment, shipping, exposure to cold, and unfavorable temperatures, are thought to excite latent infections into activity.

The incubation period upon contact exposure usually is 5 to 20 days, but it might take as long as 100 days for infection to occur in individuals exposed to contamination.

The disease may persist for weeks in an individual and may be marked by frequent relapses.

The gross pathological changes observed in typical specimens include enlarged, saffron-colored livers, with many partly healed, whitish foci. The spleen is usually enlarged during the various stages of the disease. The air sacs show catarrhal inflammation and accumulations of whitish exudates. Degenerative changes may be seen in the kidneys. Occasionally there is evidence of pericarditis.

Microscopic studies of the various tissues show changes in the normal structure of the spleen, with increased numbers of white blood cells, which are recognized as body defense mechanisms in combatting infections such as psittacosis. The large spleens commonly seen in diseased psittacines occur from the increases of blood and the large numbers of white blood cells.

The liver has many small, distinct areas of whitish, dead cells irregularly distributed throughout the organ. In lesions of longer duration, collections of leucocytic types of white blood cells are observed. The serous membranes covering the liver become affected, and depositions of a thin film of fibrin (false membranes) may cover the surface of this organ. More frequently this type of film on the surface of the liver is referred to as "plastic exudate."

The lesions found in other birds, such as the pigeon, are similar fundamentally to those in psittacine birds.

IN MAN the disease is characterized by an atypical pneumonia with the incubation period of 7 to 15 days after contact with the infective birds. The symptoms parallel those of influenza. Fever may persist 3 or 4 weeks. Cough may be slight or absent.

Relapses following recovery are not uncommon. Death may result from toxemia or pulmonary insufficiency.

The use of broad-spectrum antibiotic therapy, such as Aureomycin,

Terramycin, and Chloromycetin, will bring the disease readily under control. Relapses have occurred when the antibiotic therapy has been stopped.

IN MAMMALS, such as the calf, ewe, opossum, mouse, and cat, that are infected with their respective virus strains, the pathology varies.

In sheep, the infection causes necrosis of the fetal membranes and abortion or premature lambing.

The virus may cause no symptoms in calves.

It causes highly infectious pneumonitis in cats.

The virus induces paralytic-convulsive symptoms in opossums.

The serological test studies of the viruses isolated from mammals are so closely related to those of birds that more research will be necessary to determine the role of mammals in the psittacosis problem.

THE DISEASE IN TURKEYS has not been studied enough to warrant an extensive description of the symptoms or pathology.

The only indications of the disease in some flocks are occasional sick birds, some of which die. The turkey grower may not become unduly alarmed, because the small number of deaths may lead him to think the cause is one of the miscellaneous noninfectious diseases, which he recognizes as a part of turkey production. Egg production in laying flocks and hatchability of eggs have varied from poor to good. That is not a reason to suspect the disease, because various factors of management frequently account for such difficulties.

Symptoms are droopiness, difficult and rattled breathing, yellowish to greenish droppings, and diarrhea. Some birds die suddenly without previous symptoms. These symptoms are like those of other poultry diseases, such as infectious sinusitis and Newcastle disease.

The pathology of turkeys seems to parallel that of parrots and psittacine birds. In typical specimens, the liver is enlarged and covered with a fibrinous exudate. Pericarditis, cloudiness, and accumulations of cheesy exudates in the air sacs occur. The pathology resembles the lower form of infectious sinusitis (or air-sac disease) so closely that the two diseases can be told apart only by isolating the causative agents.

The cause of infectious sinusitis was unknown before 1948. That probably delayed the recognition of ornithosis in turkeys because of the confusing pathology of the two diseases.

It is not known whether latent or inapparent infections, as found in parrots and parakeets, occur in turkeys.

The spleen in turkeys may or may not be enlarged. The enlargement, though, may be due to factors other than ornithosis and in itself is therefore an unreliable index of infection in turkeys.

The mode of infection in turkeys had not been determined in 1956—whether through the egg or through food and water contaminated by free-flying birds or other animals.

Many of the young poults and chicks that were experimentally infected with turkey virus died—a possible indication that natural reservoirs of infection (rather than transmission through the egg) are major sources of the disease in turkeys.

Problems that needed further study in 1956 were whether carriers of the virus exist among recovered turkeys; whether the birds that react to the indirect complement-fixation test following infection continue to remain positive or become negative over a period of weeks or months; whether infection affects only individuals or eventually involves all of the birds in the flock; and how fast the disease spreads from infected to susceptible turkeys.

Diagnosis is reliably established only by isolating and identifying the causative virus. Chick embryos and mice are useful for isolating viruses of turkey origin. Mice inoculated intracerebrally may become ill within 48 hours and die. Nine- or ten-day embryos also may be inoculated with tissue suspensions treated with streptomycin to overcome bacterial contaminants and without affecting the virus. Of some 12 isolations made from spontaneously infected turkeys, virus has been isolated through the use of chick embryos. The infection is characterized by deaths among the embryos on the fourth and fifth days following inoculation. It has not been necessary thus far in working with the turkey viruses encountered to make blind passages in mice. The mice have shown typical symptoms during the initial passage from diseased turkey tissues.

Failure of the turkey ornithosis virus to grow in a cell-free pleuropneumonia medium distinguishes it from the pleuropneumonialike organisms (PPLO) of infectious sinusitis, which can be propagated in such a medium.

The mouse also serves to distinguish between the two agents, since the PPLO organisms of turkey sinusitis is without effect in mice.

Virus tissues of Newcastle disease from turkeys has caused illness in mice, but virus could not be recovered. Serial transfer from mouse to mouse is without effect. The hemagglutination of chicken red blood cells serves to identify and differentiate Newcastle virus.

By preparing antigens of an unknown virus and using a known ornithosis antiserum, it is possible to prove or disprove whether the agent in question belongs to the psittacosis-ornithosis group of agents.

The toxigenic tests are used to determine whether the agents are further closely related or unrelated by the ability of known positive and negative antiserums to neutralize the toxins produced by the viruses.

Rising titers of serums from individuals collected at intervals of one or more weeks and using a known antigen give supportive information in the identification of ornithosis.

Laboratory infections have been acquired from cultivating ornithosis virus in chick embryos. Precautions should be taken therefore to prevent infection when propagating unknown disease agents.

The prophylaxis and treatment in control of ornithosis in turkeys is too recent to be properly evaluated. The use of Aureomycin, as in human therapy, at the rate of 3 ounces per ton of feed has value in preventing fatal infection in young poults in which the untreated infected controls experienced heavy losses. Experiences in the limited number of flocks under field conditions indicate Aureomycin is effective in preventing deaths and new infections.

The indirect complement-fixation test is the only serological test available for detecting the disease in turkeys. It is of value in research studies of ornithosis, but probably too involved and expensive for use in detecting individual birds in a flock. Much research will be required to evaluate the efficiency of the test as a reliable index of the actual ornithosis status of a flock.

Recommendations for procedures for preventing or eradicating the disease in turkeys must await further information concerning the sources of infection, rate of spread, the persistency of carriers, and the lack of a reliable economical serological test. Until then, recognized poultry management and sanitary practices, as used in the prevention and control of various infectious diseases, are to be encouraged.

JOHN P. DELAPLANE *in 1951 became head of the Department of Veterinary Bacteriology and Hygiene, School of Veterinary Medicine, Texas Agricultural and Mechanical College, College Station, Tex. He was graduated from Ohio State University, College of Veterinary Medicine. He joined the staff of the University of Rhode Island in 1931. From 1942 to 1946, he was associated with the Texas Agricultural Experiment Station as poultry pathologist. From 1946 to 1951, he was professor and head of animal pathology of the University of Rhode Island and the Agricultural Experiment Station.*

Blue Comb

WALTER J. HALL AND G. B. VAN NESS

BLUE COMB, a disease of young laying fowls, is known also as pullet disease, avian monocytosis, new wheat disease, X-disease, summer disease, mud fever of turkeys, and contagious indigestion. It has occurred in the Northeastern, Middle Atlantic, North Central, and Southern States and California.

It occurs more commonly in the warm months, June to November, in chickens 4 weeks to 2 years old, and in poults of all ages. Mortality from blue comb may range from zero to 50 percent and the morbidity to 20 percent in chickens.

Research workers have tried for a long time to discover the cause of blue comb. The disease resembles an infection in its spread through the flock, but in most cases it is a metabolic disturbance without an infectious cause. A virus has been suspected.

D. E. Stover, of the California Department of Agriculture, Sacramento, Calif., found the virus of Newcastle disease in outbreaks of blue comb; the association of this virus with explosive outbreaks of blue comb is common. Birds in a subclinical stage of leukosis often develop blue comb before the lesions of leukosis are well developed.

Other infections, among them staphylococcal and streptococcal infections and trichomoniasis of the intestinal tract, can be involved in outbreaks of blue comb, but those diseases are secondary to the injury and dysfunction of tissues incidental to blue comb.

Poultrymen's suspicion that wheat was involved was confirmed by G. D. Quigley, of the University of Maryland, who in further studies considered the possibility that blue comb is due to a mineral imbalance.

The disease cannot be entirely prevented in susceptible flocks, because as R. K. Cole, at Cornell University, discovered, genetic makeup is a factor.

Poultrymen in localities where blue comb is prevalent have found that birds brought into production rapidly are more susceptible, that losses in the spring are more likely in high-producing flocks, and that blue comb is most common 3 or 4 days after a hot spell or when temperatures are above 85° F.

Symptons of blue comb vary according to the stage of the disease and may include depression; loss of appetite; cyanosis of the head (bluish-red comb) and skin because of poor circulation; fever; sunken eyes; and dehydration, with a shriveling of the skin of shanks, comb, and wattles. The crop may be distended and sour. A sudden drop in egg laying and a slow return to normal are usual. Poults have a fetid diarrhea and tend to pile in the brooder house. Blue comb lasts 1 to 2 weeks.

A high proportion of chickens recover, but mortality may be 25 to 100 percent in young poults.

Sometimes birds are found dead before symptoms are noted. Sudden deaths may produce few or no lesions (tissue changes). The more prolonged cases on autopsy may show a focal necrosis of the liver, hemorrhages on the serous membranes, chalkiness of the pancreas, and tenacious mucus in the intestines. Renal (kidney) damage is a prominent lesion in the subacute and a constant lesion in the chronic form of the disease.

Chronic blue comb is indistinguishable from visceral gout, a disease characterized by marked paleness and swelling of the kidneys and ureters due to accumulations of uric acid salts.

Blue comb must be differentiated from fowl cholera and fowl typhoid. The latter diseases may be identified by culture of the dead bird and isolation of the respective causative organisms, but in blue comb disease no specific causative micro-organism has been isolated.

Good management will do much to alleviate the impact of stress factors on young pullets just coming into production and may prevent the onset of the disease. These stress factors include an unbalanced laying diet, forcing for higher production, sudden changes in diet, unfavorable weather (especially excessive heat and humidity), inadequate supplies of fresh water, rough handling or excitement of the birds, and changes in environment.

After the onset of an outbreak, such management procedures as the provision of an ample supply of fresh water, restriction of grain consump-

tion, and cool quarters are advised. Also recommended is the administration of molasses and some form of potassium, such as muriate of potash, fertilizer grade.

Antibiotics, such as Aureomycin, Terramycin, streptomycin, and penicillin, are used by some in place of molasses or potash.

WALTER J. HALL *joined the Department of Agriculture in 1924.*

G. B. VAN NESS, *a graduate of Kansas State College, is a veterinarian in the Animal Disease and Parasite Research Branch of the Agricultural Research Service. He was a member of the research staff of agricultural experiment stations in Washington, Arkansas, and Florida before joining the Department of Agriculture in 1953.*

Fowlpox

WALTER J. HALL

FOWLPOX, also called avianpox, birdpox, avian diphtheria (no relation to human diphtheria), sorehead, and canker, is a widespread disease.

The filterable virus that causes it occurs as inclusion bodies in the cells of the skin or mucous membranes. These bodies may be viewed by sectioning (slicing) the skin cells, staining them, and observing them under a powerful microscope.

One inclusion body may contain as many as 20 thousand elementary bodies, each of which can cause fowlpox. These bodies are thought to be the real virus carriers, and, when liberated from the inclusion body and stained, can be seen under the microscope.

The late J. R. Beach, after research at the University of California, in 1939 classified avianpox as fowlpox, turkeypox, pigeonpox, and canarypox.

Fowlpox and turkeypox cross-immunize; that is, fowlpox will immunize both chickens and turkeys, although some strains differ.

The lesions—tissue changes—produced by an attack of fowlpox occur on the unfeathered parts of the body, comb, wattles, face, and eyelids and sometimes on the feet and around the cloaca. Lesions in turkeys may occur on the breast.

Pock lesions begin as a small, round blister, which contains a serous—watery—fluid. As the pock, or pimple, enlarges, the center becomes yellowish from an accumulation of virus and pus. Later the pock ulcerates, ruptures, and discharges a sticky fluid. The ulcer dries in a few days, and a dark-red or black scab forms over the raw lesion. The scab sticks for some time before it drops off. The pocks develop at different times. Usually it takes 3 to 4 weeks before all the scabs have been shed and the lesions are completely healed. Several pocks may coalesce to form a large lesion.

An internal form of pox usually is seen in the pharynx and sometimes in the nasal passages as a thick, caseous membrane, which sticks firmly to the mucous membranes. The diphtheritic membrane may restrict the air intake and cause suffocation if it extends down around the glottis. The false membrane may build up around the tongue and interfere with swallowing so as to cause emaciation or death.

Fowlpox may be diagnosed by the nature of the skin lesions; by microscopic examination of the lesions for inclusion bodies and elementary bodies; and by inoculation of immune and susceptible birds.

The incubation period of fowlpox is 1 to 2 weeks. The disease may appear at any time but is more common in fall and winter. The cutaneous form is more common in summer. The diphtheritic, or internal, form occurs oftener in winter, and mortality usually is higher.

If there are no complications, the disease usually lasts 30 days from exposure until the scabs drop off. The percentage of recovery is high if no complications ensue.

Fowlpox is transmitted by contact of infected or recently vaccinated birds with susceptible birds and by mosquitoes, which may carry the virus on the proboscis from infected to susceptible flocks. Mosquitoes are said to be able to infect susceptible fowls for 2 months after a single feeding on an infected bird.

A good preventive (there being no cure) is a prophylactic vaccine that gives lifelong immunity to chickens. The vaccines against pox most commonly used are fowlpox and pigeonpox and are propagated on chicken embryos. They are live-virus vaccines and must be handled with care to prevent spread of disease to unvaccinated birds.

To prepare the avianpox vaccine, the infected membranes of the embryo are collected, dried, ground to a fine powder, sealed under vacuum in ampules, and stored under refrigeration. A vial of diluent for reconstituting the vaccine is packaged with the dried virus. Only enough vaccine for a day's use should be taken out of the refrigerator at one time and reconstituted. Care should be taken to avoid spilling the vaccine on the poultry premises during this operation. Empty vials should be burned or disinfected.

Fowlpox vaccine is used to vaccinate chickens, turkeys, and pheasants.

It should not be used to vaccinate pigeons or hens that are laying.

Pigeonpox vaccine may be used to vaccinate chickens, pigeons, and pheasants, but not turkeys. It may be used on chickens in lay and on chickens that are in a debilitated condition from malnutrition or an intercurrent disease. In such circumstances, pigeonpox gives the protection of a temporary immunity for 2 or 3 months without a systemic reaction and without interfering with egg production.

Only canarypox vaccine should be used on canaries.

Chickens may be vaccinated against pox in two ways.

In the stick method, two needles (about one-fourth inch apart in a cork or other holder) are dipped into the vaccine container and then applied by puncturing the wing web. This gives four cutaneous inoculations simultaneously, two on each side of the wing web, since the needles pierce both layers of the skin. This method is fast, accurate, and economical of vaccine.

In the older follicle method, four or five feathers are plucked (usually from the upper lateral surface of the thigh) and the vaccine is applied to the feather follicles with a stiff bristle brush. The vaccinated birds should be checked for takes a week to 10 days after vaccination. A take is indicated by swelling and redness of the vaccinated follicles or the stick wounds.

The flock should be revaccinated if most birds do not show takes.

The recommended age for vaccinating chickens is 6 to 12 weeks.

Vaccination of baby chicks has been tried but is not generally satisfactory because systemic reactions may slow growth rates. Mortality may be high.

Chickens should not be vaccinated within 4 weeks of the beginning of lay. Turkeys may be vaccinated at any age, except that they should not be vaccinated within 8 weeks of marketing in order to give time for the scabs and vaccination lesions to disappear.

Turkeys should be vaccinated only by the follicle method and on the upper thigh. When the stick method is used, turkeys put their heads under the wing and spread the disease to the head and other parts. Generalized cases of fowlpox are the result. Fowl-pox vaccine gives turkeys an immunity that lasts about 6 months. Turkeys that are kept for breeders should be revaccinated before winter.

Chickens do not need to be vaccinated against fowlpox unless pox is prevalent in the neighborhood, the flock is likely to be exposed to the disease, or the flock had the disease the previous year.

After pox vaccine (a live virus) is used on a place, vaccination every year thereafter is necessary.

All susceptible fowls on the premises, including chickens, turkeys, guineas, and pheasants, should be vaccinated at the same time or else segregated.

WALTER J. HALL *is a graduate of the New York State College of Veterinary Medicine. He joined the Department in 1924.*

Avian Lymphomatosis

B. R. BURMESTER AND NELSON F. WATERS

LYMPHOMATOSIS, an infectious disease, leads to tumorous accumulations of lymphoid cells in various parts of the body. Three forms of the disease complex reflect the location of the pathologic alterations—visceral (internal organs), neural (nerve), and ocular (eye) lymphomatosis.

The disease is widespread in flocks of chickens throughout the United States and the world.

An estimate of its importance was had in results of the New York Random Sample Test, in which many poultry breeders from different sections of the country entered their stock from 1950 to 1954. The yearly average total mortality of the hens, which were hatched and reared from eggs received at the test, was 34 percent. Lympho-matosis was responsible for 13.4 percent; the visceral form caused three-fourths of this mortality. If that death rate were applied to the total number of chickens on farms, it can be estimated that in 1954 more than 59 million mature chickens died of it.

Heavy losses from neural lymphomatosis occurred on many farms in the 1920's. The visceral form became more prevalent after 1930 and has been responsible for two-thirds to three-fourths of all mortality caused by this disease complex.

At no time has the ocular form caused so high a death rate as the other two forms.

Soon after this disease complex became a definite economic hazard in poultry production, many State experiment stations and other laboratories began investigations for the purpose of developing measures for its prevention and control. Because of the many difficulties encountered in this research, certain agricultural experiment stations sponsored the establishment of a central laboratory. The United States Regional Poultry Research Laboratory, at East Lansing, Mich., was approved on December 23, 1937, by the Secretary of Agriculture. Its purpose was designated as the improvement of viability in poultry. Since its inception, most of the work has been devoted to investigations on lymphomatosis and associated diseases. The work at the laboratory and that done at the State agricultural experiment stations has resulted in much information about many phases of this disease, but a great deal more research will be needed before adequate prevention or controls can be developed.

The three forms of lymphomatosis are related to several other neoplastic (cancerous) conditions, all of which are grouped in "the avian leukosis complex." These associated diseases—of minor or no economic importance—include osteopetrosis (bone disease), the true leukemias, erythroblastosis, granuloblastosis, and myelocytomatosis (blood diseases). The names are based on the pathologic alterations observed without regard to their causes.

Lymphomatosis is limited primarily to chickens. We have indications that its occurrence in turkeys has been increasing. It has been reported in pheasants. Symptoms and lesions typical of neural lymphomatosis have been noted in ducks.

Pathologic manifestations of the disease are varied. The common indication is the uncontrolled accumulation of blood-forming cells and closely related cells.

THE VISCERAL LYMPHOMATOSIS—also known as big liver disease, lymphocytoma, or lymphomatic leukosis—may occur at any age after 4 weeks. Most deaths usually occur soon after the pullets are in heavy production. Mortality then drops gradually but continues as long as the chickens are kept.

Outward signs of the disease are variable. It may be acute or chronic. Fast-growing pullets may become listless, droopy, and succumb within a few days. Laying hens may cease laying abruptly and soon die. Other birds may show similar symptoms over a long period, becoming emaciated and dying after a long illness.

As the disease advances, the comb becomes shrivelled and pale or bluish. A white, pasty deposit of uric acid alone or in combination with greenish bile pigments often is found on the abdominal feathers.

Certain internal organs of birds that are not excessively fat may be felt; enlargement of the liver may be recognized in that way by its projection beyond the keel and the margin of the ribs.

The lesions characteristic of visceral lymphomatosis are found oftenest in the liver, spleen, and kidneys, but all organs, including the skin, at times are affected. The gross alterations may be a general enlargement, with a variation in color from dark red to light gray in organs such as the liver, spleen, and kidneys. These represent the diffuse type of involvement and often require microscopic examination for diagnosis. More frequently discrete tumor nodules, one-sixteenth to one-half inch or more in diameter, are located in the organs. These nodules are spherical. When they are on a surface, they are flattened or merge with other nodules. They are grayish, and the cut surface is uniform in color; similar nodules seen in tuberculosis are white and usually contain yellowish centers.

The microscopic picture is comparatively uniform and is characterized by massive accumulations of lymphoid cells, which are of two types. The small round cells, resembling lymphocytes, usually make up the tumors of chronic cases. The large cells, like lymphoblasts, occur in the acute type.

Intermediates and mixtures of the two types are often found.

In the absence of large accumulations, difficulties often arise in the interpretation of microscopic changes. Birds, with few exceptions, are without organized lymph nodes, but microscopic lymphoid foci are present in the glandular organs and the digestive tract. Because these foci respond to the presence of several disease agents, it often is difficult to state whether a given lymphoid focus represents normal, reactive, or neoplastic tissue. All such foci should be considered abnormal; they may represent a predisposition toward lymphomatosis.

The NEURAL LYMPHOMATOSIS—also known as neurolymphomatosis, fowl paralysis, or range paralysis—occurs oftenest in birds 2 to 6 months old, although the rate of its appearance reduces only slowly after 6 months and it has been seen in birds as early as 3 weeks of age.

The sign of this disease most familiar to the poultryman is a spraddling position, in which the chicken may lie on its side with one leg extended forward and the other backward. Less advanced cases may show a weakness or lack of coordination of the legs, wings, or neck, so that the bird has trouble in standing or walking, and a drooping of wings and head.

Nerves supplying the digestive tract may be affected, so that there are loss of weight and appetite, dilation of the crop, and diarrhea.

Respiratory distress, such as gasping, may result when one or both vagus nerves are involved. Only one of several nerves of the same bird may be affected. Survival depends largely on the extent, location, and function of the nerve or nerves affected.

Partly paralyzed birds may live many months and sometimes show partial recovery when placed in individual cages with access to feed and water.

Similar symptoms may occur in chickens with other diseases, such as those due to riboflavin deficiency or avian encephalomyelitis. A microscopic study of the affected nerves is the basis of a differential diagnosis.

The gross pathologic alterations of the affected nerves are characterized by localized or extensive soft swellings of the peripheral nerve trunks, which are yellowish or slightly grayish. In less obvious cases, the affected nerves may show only a loss of cross-striations, which are seen in normal nerves. Microscopic examination is often necessary for an accurate diagnosis. The nerves most commonly affected are the sciatic (large nerve in thigh) and its roots, the vagus (easily seen in the neck), and the brachial (shoulder and arm), celiac, and lumbar (viscera) plexuses.

Microscopic examination of affected nerves shows an infiltration with the small, round lymphocyte with a few large cells not unlike the lymphoblast. Occasional infiltrations are made up predominately of cells of the latter type.

OCULAR LYMPHOMATOSIS, formerly known as gray eye, pearly eye, or iritis, causes impairment of vision or complete blindness in one or both eyes. That is because lymphoid cells enter the iris and other vascular parts of the eye. This infiltration occurs over a period of several weeks and finally stops the normal dilating and constricting movements of the iris. The iris becomes fixed, usually in a restricted state, and the pupil becomes small. The pupillary border may become irregular, show indentations, and lose its regular circular shape.

These changes in form and loss of movement are perhaps more diagnostic than the change in iris color, which is a more commonly observed symptom.

The infiltrating cells also mask the pigments of the iris and cause a change from an orange or reddish brown to a pearly gray. The amount of pigment in the iris is influenced by the diet, the rate of egg production, and the age of the chicken; furthermore, some breeds and crosses naturally have a gray iris. It is important to consider these normal variations in the color of the iris in arriving at a diagnosis of ocular lymphomatosis.

Osteopetrosis, commonly known as marble bone or thick leg disease, afflicts an occasional bird in some flocks or a sizable number in other flocks, but it is not so widespread as to be of major economic importance. An enlargement of the shanks, giving a convex appearance, is usually the first symptom in chickens.

As the disease progresses, other bones, especially the long bones of the wing and of the leg, become enlarged. Articulation becomes restricted, and the chicken walks in a stiff, stilted manner. The histopathologic picture varies with the stage of the disease in the bone examined. The excessive deposition of hard bone appears to be due to a greatly increased proliferation and activity of the bone-forming cells of the inner and outer surfaces of the shaft and a reduced activity of the bone-dissolving cells.

The true leukemias in chickens are of two types.

In erythroblastosis, the immature forms of the erythrocyte (the red blood cell) are dominant in the blood. When the leukemia is due to an overabundance of the immature forms of the granulated white cells, it is known as myeloblastosis or granuloblastosis. Often both cell lineages are involved. This condition is referred to as erythromyeloblastosis.

The occurrence of erythro- and myeloblastosis is similar to osteopetrosis and is in contrast to the various forms of lymphomatosis in that the occurrence is comparatively rare and sporadic. Symptoms are similar for the two types of leukemia. The comb and other unfeathered parts of the body become pale and often yellowish. The bird becomes emaciated, listless, droopy, and shows evidence of diarrhea.

The blood appears watery and grayish red, instead of the bright red or dark red of normal blood. Microscopic examination reveals a high proportion of immature blood cells. The liver and spleen are usually enlarged and are gray or bright red, depending on the cell type involved. The red bone marrow increases and takes over portions that are normally a fatty yellow.

Myelocytomatosis, an aleukemic neoplasia of the granular white blood cells, occurs only occasionally and is of no economic consequence. The cells are massed into distinct white nodules, which are located in the muscle and visceral organs. The cell type is the myelocyte, which contains red staining granules.

The causative agent or agents of the various forms of lymphomatosis and associated diseases are submicroscopic and are believed to be viruses. Conclusive evidence that such is the case has been obtained only for visceral lymphomatosis, osteopetrosis, and erythromyeloblastosis. The rapid spread of neurolymphomatosis from one farm to another and from one section of the country to another suggested that the disease is contagious and is caused by an infectious agent. Attempts to reproduce neural or ocular lymphomatosis experimentally, however, have not been sufficiently successful to warrant any conclusions regarding their cause.

Early investigators considered the different forms of lymphomatosis as separate entities, caused by different agents. Later many research workers obtained the different forms, including the leukemias, in chickens of the same experimental lots and even the same chicken. In fact, under natural conditions two or three forms of lymphomatosis are usually present in any flock, with one form predominating. It is not unusual to find individual chickens with visceral-neural, visceral-ocular, or ocular-neural involvement. A combination of the three forms also occurs. These observations led to the theory that one agent causes all forms of lymphomatosis, osteopetrosis, and erythromyeloblastosis.

Recent investigations have led some research workers to return to the earlier view that most, if not all, of the neoplastic conditions described here are caused by similar viral agents that are different but have some similarities. Thus the virus causing visceral lymphomatosis does not result in the neural or ocular form or in erythro- or myeloblastosis. The virus causing the latter does not produce lymphomatosis in any of its forms.

The appearance of several forms in one flock or in one chicken may be explained by a tendency of the causative agent to remain latent and create inapparent infections in many chickens. Thus, a bird that has died of one type of neoplasm also may have been infected with viruses that cause other types. An inoculum obtained from such a bird is likely to contain a mixture of viruses and result in different types of tumors in the chickens.

Experimental studies at the Regional Poultry Research Laboratory disclosed that only a part of the naturally occurring cases of visceral lymphomatosis could be transmitted readily to susceptible chicks. Why this is so has not been determined.

The readily transmitted tumors may be reproduced in two different ways. Living tumor cells in suspension, when injected into almost any part of chickens of any age, will grow into a tumor in 5 to 20 days. Some of the tumor cells escape into the blood vessels during that time and are carried to the liver and other organs, where they multiply rapidly and cause the death of the bird.

Some birds survive such transplants of tumor cells and are then immune to further transplants of the same type of tumor, but they are not immune to the action of the viral agent, which requires a much longer time for its action.

The second method of propagating such tumors is by the use of cell-free viral preparations. The virus may be obtained from such sources as feces,

saliva, or embryos of eggs from infected chickens. A more concentrated source is blood plasma of lymphomatous birds and extracts of the tumors. Such materials may be centrifuged and passed through fine filters capable of removing all bacteria and particles of tissue. In order to produce a high incidence of disease with this type of preparation, baby chicks of a susceptible line must be exposed. The exposure may be by one of several routes, such as intravenous or intraperitoneal injection or application to the eye, nose, or trachea.

The development of the disease is similar to that which takes place after natural means of exposure. Tumors develop in the viscera irrespective of the route of infection, and the birds die of lymphomatous involvement of the visceral organs over a wide range in age. When large doses are used and when the chickens are very susceptible, most of the deaths occur in from 4 to 16 weeks, but when small doses or more resistant chickens are employed, the birds die at ages more nearly approaching those occurring after natural exposure.

The dose and susceptibility, which together determine largely the range of the age at death, also determine the type of microscopic pathology, which is easily recognized in sections of the liver. Thus, in several inoculation experiments, about 90 percent of the chickens that died within 4 months had the intravascular type of tumor involvement (the lymphoid cells were located within the walls of the blood vessels), whereas about 90 percent of those that died after that age had the extravascular type—the lymphoid cells were outside the walls of the blood vessels. The latter is the type found in more than 90 percent of the cases that occur after a natural exposure.

Potent inoculums which have passed through bacteria-retaining filters have been obtained from lymphomatous liver. In one test, 73.5 percent of the chickens died with visceral lymphomatosis before they were 9 months old, after being inoculated at the age of 1 day by the intraperitoneal route. The dose was at the rate of filtrate equivalent to that obtained from one hundred millionth of a gram of tumor. The virus causing visceral lymphomatosis contained in blood plasma or tumor filtrate has been kept viable for several hundred days when stored at the temperature of dry ice and has been inactivated at a temperature of 131° F. by treatment with low concentrations of formaldehyde or by ultraviolet irradiation.

VISCERAL LYMPHOMATOSIS is transmitted by contact and through the hatching egg. The virus is spread widely by various means, by chickens of various ages, and in various stages of the disease.

Research workers at the Regional Poultry Research Laboratory have made extensive infectivity tests of oral washings, of extracts of feces, and of extracts of embryonating eggs by injecting such materials into susceptible chicks and noting the incidence of visceral lymphomatosis. The studies have revealed that the virus is shed in the feces and in the saliva of chickens having gross lymphoid tumors, but—more important—it is also shed in this manner by chickens apparently normal in every way except for a latent or an inapparent infection.

Chicks inoculated at 1 day of age have, in turn, shed the virus in their saliva at 10 days of age. Noninoculated chicks of the same hatch in direct contact with the inoculated ones became infected and started to shed significant amounts of virus at 90 days of age. The average amount shed gradually increased for the first 6 months.

It was also found that day-old chicks, hatched from hens which have a latent infection, shed virus in their saliva and feces. Thus it is quite evident that many apparently normal chickens may shed the virus of visceral lymphomatosis in their saliva at any age from the baby chick to the mature hen. It is evident that virus from either the saliva or the feces may serve to infect the environment including the drinking water, the feed, and the air.

Studies on possible natural modes of entry of the virus showed that it is possible to induce a high incidence of visceral tumors by applying the inoculum to such natural body openings as nasal passages, conjunctiva, mouth, trachea, and cloaca. Transmission was also obtained when the virus was sprayed into the air above the baby chicks. Thus any mucous membrane normally exposed to the external environment may serve as the avenue of entry.

The infected egg is another major means by which the disease is spread. Workers at the Regional Poultry Research Laboratory have provided direct proof of transmission by eggs. They selected hens of an infected flock at random. They marked the eggs as to source, incubated them, and prepared inoculums from embryos of eggs of individual hens. The presence of the virus in such inoculums was then tested by intraperitoneal inoculation of susceptible baby chicks.

Results from many tests show that the embryos of most of the hens tested harbored significant amounts of the virus of visceral lymphomatosis—even though all the hens appeared healthy at the time the eggs were laid and none of the embryos showed any evidence of gross or microscopic pathology.

Thus it would appear that large numbers of chickens, apparently normal in all respects, can transmit the virus of visceral lymphomatosis to their eggs. The virus in turn is taken up by the embryo. No test which could be used to identify such carrier hens in a breeding flock is available. Hatcherymen, therefore, should not be held responsible for the dissemination of the disease by egg transmission.

The progeny of carrier hens may not develop a high incidence of lymphomatosis. Experiments conducted at the Regional Poultry Research Laboratory show that the visceral lymphomatosis among progeny of infected hens was not significantly greater on the average than that found in progeny of hens classified as noninfected. The chicks of carrier hens are an important source of infection for chicks of noninfected stock, however.

It has been demonstrated that an extract of dust, down, and other debris collected from the hatching unit of an incubator containing chicks of an infected flock, when injected into other susceptible chicks, caused a high incidence of visceral lymphomatosis. Furthermore, when chicks of an infected flock were hatched and brooded with chicks of a noninfected flock, the latter developed a high incidence of tumors, but the former did not. In this experiment the brooding period appeared to be more important than the hatching period in the transmission of the disease.

Thus it is quite possible that the importance of egg transmission lies not in the disease, which may or may not occur among chicks hatched from infected eggs, but in the disease that is transmitted by direct or indirect contact from chicks hatched from infected eggs to chicks hatched from eggs of hens that have had no contact with the virus.

NEURAL LYMPHOMATOSIS appears to be transmitted primarily by contact with an infected environment during the early brooding period.

In experiments at the New York Agricultural Experiment Station, the distance between chicks and adult chickens has influenced greatly the incidence of this form of the disease.

When chickens were reared in an isolated area, only a few cases of neurolymphomatosis developed. There is no direct evidence and little circumstantial evidence for the transmission of the causative agent of neural lymphomatosis from the hen to the chick through the hatching egg. It therefore would appear that the most important source of infection must be the growing or the adult chicken.

Nothing definite is known concerning the transmission of ocular lymphomatosis.

MANY FACTORS affect the resistance of chickens to lymphomatosis. Among them are genetic resistance, virus-stimulated antibodies, and the age of the chicken at the time of exposure.

A partial control of naturally occurring visceral or neural lymphomatosis can be accomplished through selective breeding. Workers at the Regional Poultry Research Laboratory and the New York Agricultural Experiment Station demonstrated that breeding for resistance is practical and will reduce losses materially.

Only breeders whose practices permit the identification of all chickens hatched are in a position to select toward resistance to either form of lymphomatosis. Pedigree breeding will permit the identification of the most viable families, together with their sires and dams, which show the greatest resistance to the disease. Continued selective breeding from the most viable families will show, within three or four generations, a marked improvement of resistance to either the neural or the visceral form of the disease.

A program of breeding for increased resistance to either of the two forms of lymphomatosis often is difficult because of a lack of adequate infection among the breeding chickens.

The history of many flocks indicates that continued elimination of families of chickens that show high mortality from lymphomatosis will reduce losses to a low figure. This reduction encourages the breeder to believe his chickens have become more resistant. Actually the chickens may have stopped dying because the disease complex and the causative agents disappeared, or nearly so, from the flock. Thus, when this breeder's chickens are placed on many different farms, certain of these farm flocks encounter substantial losses. So it would appear that the chickens going to some farms are subjected to a greater exposure of lymphomatosis than those on other farms—an indication that the stock was not so resistant as indicated by the performance on the farm.

In any attempt, then, to use selective breeding as a means of increasing family or strain resistance, one must first subject the chickens to a reasonably constant level of infectious agent. Since a proved method of artificially infecting chickens is not available, any exposure must come from naturally infected stock. If resistance to both neural and visceral lymphomatosis is desired, then the infectious agent of both of these forms must be present.

Experiments indicate that an immunity to visceral lymphomatosis may be induced. When certain adult hens were given a series of intraperitoneal injections with preparations of the virus, the chicks from such hens showed a high degree of resistance. In contrast, chicks from the same dams were highly susceptible when hatched from eggs laid before the hens received the injections. Neutralization tests demonstrated that the injections stimulated the formation of antibodies in the dams. Presumably sufficient antibodies were transferred to the hatching egg to give the chick a passive immunity, which protected them from the inoculated virus. This type of immunity may be the basis for the low incidence of disease encountered in the progeny of known carrier hens. It would appear that such hens shed the virus into their eggs and also shed antibodies, which give some protection to the progeny from the egg-transmitted infection.

The younger the chicks are at the time of exposure to the infectious agent—under natural conditions, by inoculation, or by contact with inoculated chickens—the greater will be the incidence of the disease. Thus many experiments have shown that age increases the resistance of chickens to the disease. This resistance is acquired rather rapidly, but it is still not known at what age the maximum resistance is first attained.

In one experiment fewer than half as many chicks exposed to natural infection at 30 days of age developed lymphomatosis as those exposed at 1 day of age. In another experiment, chicks 1, 30, and 60 days old were exposed to others of the same hatch that were inoculated at 1 day of age with the virus of visceral lymphomatosis. The incidence of tumors resulting from this contact exposure was 70, 56, and 21 percent, respectively. Similar results were obtained in chickens inoculated at those ages.

Other factors, some of which are unidentified, influence significantly the expression of the disease.

Females and capons generally are more susceptible than males. We have some indication that the female hormone increases and the male hormone decreases the susceptibility of chickens to lymphomatosis.

Some poultrymen believe that coccidiosis or other intestinal parasites may act as predisposing or precipitating factors. Nutritional factors have not been ruled out. Various stress factors may also determine the incidence of the tumors.

NONE OF THE VARIOUS forms of lymphomatosis can be prevented by vaccines available in 1956 or by the use of other prophylactic measures. No chemotherapeutics, antibiotics, or other therapeutic treatments are known to be effective in the cure of chickens with this disease.

Chickens affected with lymphomatosis sometimes spontaneously show a partial recovery. Even though such cases are rare and never complete, they may be the basis of an erroneous assessment of a therapeutic treatment unless adequate controls are maintained during the same treatment period.

Isolation and quarantine procedures during the hatching and brooding period are helpful in restricting the spread of lymphomatosis.

Neural lymphomatosis is transmitted primarily by direct or indirect contact with older growing or adult poultry with no indication of significant egg transmission. The primary consideration therefore is to rear the chicks at as great a distance as possible from such stock and to restrict the interchange of personnel and equipment between chicks and older stock.

The primary source of infection for visceral lymphomatosis appears to be the maternally infected baby chick—there is no indication that the adult stock is an important source. Therefore the procedures that were recommended for checking the spread of neurolymphomatosis are not effective for the visceral form. A practical test for the identification of birds having a latent or inapparent infection is not available. Elimination of such carrier birds from the breeding flock thus is not possible at present. The only recourse available is to hatch and brood chicks from different flocks in separate compartments, pens, or houses insofar as possible. This recommendation is based on the premise that the extent of this disease in a breeding flock, and hence the proportion of chicks with a latent infection and protective antibodies, will vary from flock to flock. This procedure would prevent the mixing of chicks, most of which have a latent infection and shed virus, yet are protected by maternal antibodies, with chicks from other flocks, most of which are from disease-free parents and are highly susceptible to the virus shed by chicks of infected parents. Because most flocks are infected with both neural and visceral lymphomatosis, it is desirable to follow the isolation procedures suggested for both forms of the disease.

B. R. BURMESTER *is a biologist at the laboratory at East Lansing. He is in charge of the pathological phases of investigations of avian lymphomatosis. He has undergraduate and graduate degrees from the University of California. Later he obtained the degree of doctor of veterinary medicine from Michigan State University.*

NELSON F. WATERS *is the geneticist at the United States Regional Poultry Research Laboratory at East Lansing, Mich. He has been investigating the inheritance of resistance and susceptibility to avian lymphomatosis since 1939.*

Turkey Erysipelas

RICHARD D. SHUMAN AND O. L. OSTEEN

TURKEY ERYSIPELAS is caused by the same bacterium that causes swine erysipelas, *Erysipelothrix rhusiopathiae.* The organism also attacks ducks, chickens, pheasants, pigeons, parrots, peacocks, quails, and a variety of small wild birds.

Since 1934, when the disease was first recognized in the United States in New Jersey, by F. R. Beaudette and C. B. Hudson, turkey erysipelas has been reported in turkey-raising areas throughout the country. Officials in 17 rather widely separated States indicated in 1953 that turkey erysipelas ranked first to fifth in economic importance among the bacterial diseases. But of 16 States that produced more than 1 million birds each in 1952, 10 indicated that turkey erysipelas was not a problem. The others ranked the disease from first to fifth in importance.

Estimated annual losses in 1942–1951 approached 2 million dollars. Death losses and the setback turkeys have from the infection usually come about the time they are ready for market and the death of even one bird of that age is a sizable financial loss to the owner. Besides, affected birds that might otherwise have commanded top price may be downgraded or rejected.

THE OCCURRENCE of turkey erysipelas is not necessarily associated with erysipelas in swine, although it can originate from contact with infected pigs. Four States in the Corn Belt, where erysipelas in swine commonly exists, reported that turkey erysipelas was not a statewide economic problem. One other State in this region reported it to be second in economic importance, and two ranked it fifth. It has been also suggested that this disease may be associated with areas where sheep have been ranged, but this may be only coincidental.

Because *E. rhusiopathiae* is so widespread, the soil must have an important part in keeping it alive. Because turkeys are resistant to infection with ordinary laboratory strains of the organism, which in turn can cause sickness in susceptible hogs, some unusual situation must occur to start an outbreak of this disease.

A. S. Rosenwald and E. M. Dickinson observed that in Oregon the disease occurs at the time of increased rainfall and when the turkeys are reaching maturity. Possibly the increased moisture along with the additional nitrogen from droppings in the soil favors the multiplication of the organism.

The toms, which are maturing at that time, fight and cause head injuries, in which infections could start. It has been shown in the laboratory that repeated transfer of the organism from a bird dying of the disease to a living susceptible bird increases the virulence, or killing ability, of the organism. Occurrence of the same situation in the field might account for the sudden severe losses and seasonal occurrence of the disease.

Feed that contains inadequately cooked fish offal has also been suspected as a possible source of the infection.

The death rate following infection may vary from 2 to more than 40 percent.

Outbreaks usually occur in the fourth quarter of the year. The disease rate is much higher in the males than the females, not because of a sex difference in susceptibility but apparently because of infected wounds incurred in fighting among the males.

An outbreak of turkey erysipelas can occur with no warning, and all that will be seen are some dead birds. Dr. Rosenwald and Dr. Dickinson noted that in several outbreaks in Oregon the owners suspected poisoning, stampeding, or some mysterious predators.

In other instances the birds may first appear weak or listless and with wings and tail feathers drooped. The snood, wattles, and bare parts of the head and neck may be swollen and purplish. In birds that live long enough, erysipeloid lesions may appear on the head and resemble somewhat the lesions of diamond skin disease of swine.

An examination of a dead bird reveals evidence of a septicemia. Hemorrhages in the muscles particularly in the breast and thigh, may be seen. The liver and spleen are usually swollen and dark colored, and there may be some degree of enteritis. The blood vessels of the viscera will usually be full. Despite the possible presence of noticeable symptoms and lesions in the bird, a definite diagnosis can only be made in the laboratory. Finding the organism eliminates any doubt as to the diagnosis of the disease.

THE ONLY AVAILABLE TREATMENT for many years was specific immune serum, as used in swine. For the most part, however, the results did not appear satisfactory, probably because of the manner in which the serum was used. At any rate, if serum is used it should be administered early in the course of the disease. Sulfonamides have not proved to be worthwhile.

Antibiotics, particularly penicillin, are useful. Used early enough and at adequate levels, they usually give satisfactory results. One should not expect all sick birds to recover, however, and relapses may occur.

Erysipelas adsorbate bacterin has shown promise as a biologic for vaccination, but a final estimate of its value must await further reports from users. For a long time we have needed an immunizing agent that will protect the growing turkey right on through to market time.

Removal of the snood, or dewbill, of day-old turkey poults in areas where the disease is prevalent has been suggested by W. A. Billings, of the University of Minnesota. The basis for such a procedure is that the snood is especially apt to be injured because of its location; removing it would reduce the hazard of wound infection with the erysipelas organism. Debeaking at about 14 weeks also has been suggested in an effort to minimize the effect of fighting among the toms.

Segregation of sick birds, moving the remainder to a new range, and the use of antibiotics will help to control an outbreak. An infected range should not be used for turkeys for a year. Any low points should be landscaped to eliminate areas of standing water, and a cover crop should be put in. As a precaution, particularly in the places where erysipelas is known to exist in hogs or sheep, turkeys should be kept away from any contact with them.

One should remember that the causative organism of turkey erysipelas can infect people (erysipeloid). A person should therefore handle sick or dead birds only with proper care.

RICHARD D. SHUMAN *is a veterinarian in the Bacterial and Mycotic Disease Section of the Animal Disease and Parasite Research Branch. He was graduated from the College of Veterinary Medicine of the State College of Washington in 1938.*

O. L. OSTEEN *joined the Department of Agriculture in 1932 and has engaged in research in diseases of animals, and poultry.*

Chronic Respiratory Disease in Chickens

J. F. SULLIVAN, CLARENCE H. THOMPSON, JR., AND O. L. OSTEEN

CHRONIC respiratory disease (air-sac infection), a respiratory disease of chickens, has a slow rate of spread and a persistent nature.

The average annual mortality from chronic respiratory disease (CRD) in chickens from 1942 through 1951 was more than 14 million birds. Each year additional losses are due to the decreased gains and lowered feed utilization that accompany the disease, extra time needed to bring broilers to market, a larger number of unmarketable birds, and lower egg production and hatchability.

A pleuropneumonialike organism causes CRD. The organism is extremely small and, like viruses, can pass through certain filters designed to retain bacteria. Like bacteria, it can be seen, following appropriate staining, with an ordinary microscope. It grows readily in the yolk sac of 7-day-old embryonating chicken eggs and can be propagated in suitable cell-free cultural media. The organism has varying degrees of sensitivity to antibiotics, ranging generally from complete inhibition by streptomycin to total resistance to penicillin.

Observations made in the field and investigators' inability to produce in the laboratory the entire picture of CRD as it occurs in nature suggest that various factors have a part in starting severe outbreaks—extremes of climate, lack of sanitation, mismanagement, or other diseases.

Sometimes it seems that Newcastle disease, infectious bronchitis, and vaccination against them provoke CRD.

Investigations by Canadian scientists attribute the occurrence of CRD to a specific virus acting simultaneously with the pleuropneumonialike organism. This agent has not been recovered by American investigators.

CRD might be spread to healthy flocks by introducing apparently healthy carriers as flock replacements or by putting clean and infected flocks close together on the same premises. The unusually long duration of the disease once it has gained access to a flock makes its spread more certain.

The disease may be transmitted from infected hens to the chicks through the eggs. The agent causing CRD has been recovered from young cull chicks. CRD has been observed in chicks hatched from eggs laid by infected hens and maintained in isolation about 15 weeks. Although this suggests that transmission by eggs is related to outbreaks in growing birds, the true importance of this means of spread has not been determined. The presence of the CRD organism in incubator eggs that are pipped but do not hatch at the usual time indicates that incubator transmission likewise may have an undetermined part in the general dissemination of the disease.

The course and severity of CRD reflect environmental factors and the individual status of the exposed bird. Aside from the slow rate of spread and tendency toward chronicity, CRD in many respects seems similar to Newcastle disease and infectious bronchitis.

A drop in the consumption of feed by broiler flocks usually is the first indication of infection. Soon generalized symptoms of respiratory distress appear. They may include nasal discharge, audible breathing, sneezing, and coughing. Coughing is more noticeable at night, when the cooler air makes it worse. In some cases the face may swell up in the area of the infraorbital sinus—below the eye.

Mortality in broilers may run as high as 10 or 20 percent of the flock. The heaviest losses occur in the first few weeks. The mortality among adult or laying birds is negligible, but the drop in their productivity means serious economic losses.

The most commonly observed postmortem findings are inflammatory involvements of the air sacs and other serous membranes in the body cavity. These tissues, appearing as thin, transparent membranes in health, are somewhat thickened and may show varying degrees of opacity. Small curds of caseous material are often found in or on the air sacs or within the trachea. The serous membranes covering the lungs, heart, liver, and intestines often are involved. The organs themselves are also affected in some cases. The mucous membranes lining the upper respiratory passages are often inflamed and secrete abnormal amounts of mucous material.

Any diagnosis based entirely on clinical observations is subject to question because of the similarity of symptoms observed in CRD, Newcastle disease, and other common respiratory diseases of poultry. A definite diagnosis can be made only through certain laboratory techniques.

A tentative field diagnosis may be confirmed in the laboratory by isolating and identifying the causal agent of CRD in embryonating chicken eggs, where it is known to grow well, or in certain enriched bacteriological media.

The microscopic examination of appropriately stained tissues, obtained from affected birds, also is an effective means of confirming a field diagnosis.

In other commonly employed laboratory procedures, the chickens and poults are given hypodermic injections of suitably treated tissues obtained from birds suspected of having CRD. The development of characteristic symptoms and lesions in birds immune to Newcastle disease and infectious bronchitis is highly suggestive of CRD.

Diagnostic blood serum tests (similar to those used in the pullorum testing program), although still in an experimental stage have been used in some laboratories.

ANTIBIOTICS have been used to treat CRD, although opinions have differed as to their true worth. In view of the many known and unknown factors that may initiate an outbreak and the possibility of infection at the same time with other poultry diseases, the recorded variation is to be expected. Low levels of antibiotics incorporated in the feed promote growth; high or therapeutic levels, administered to individual birds or to flocks, are costly and in many instances fail to offer a worthwhile return.

The best way to control CRD is to keep it out of clean areas and flocks. Replacements should never be obtained from an unknown source or from a flock with a recent history of respiratory disease because of the danger of obtaining an apparently healthy carrier. Baby chicks should be obtained from a reliable hatchery where healthy breeder flocks are maintained under constant supervision. They should be raised in isolation. Eggs from flocks showing any active respiratory infection should never be set.

The numerous stress factors—climatic extremes, improper sanitation and management, and concurrent bacterial, viral, and parasitic diseases that may initiate a severe outbreak of CRD as well as the chronic nature of the disease—emphasize the need of adequate sanitation and management throughout the growing and laying period.

Birds should be raised in properly ventilated houses that provide adequate protection against extreme variations of temperature. Overcrowding should be avoided. Litter, whether fresh or built up, should be dry and crumbly. Waterers and other equipment should be cleaned and disinfected (with a 2-percent lye solution) periodically. Houses should be thoroughly cleaned and disinfected after one flock has used them and before another flock is put in them.

CRD can be eradicated by marketing the entire flock immediately. If conditions favor a less drastic method, the flock should be kept well isolated, and all birds known to be infected should be removed. Identification of infected birds is usually accomplished by physical examination of all birds in the flock and (in a limited number of instances) by the use of experimental blood tests. Unless extremely valuable birds are involved, the rest of the flock should be marketed as soon as that is possible.

In either instance, the entire premises should be cleaned thoroughly and disinfected before new birds are bought.

J. F. SULLIVAN *joined the Department of Agriculture in 1953. As a veterinarian in the Agricultural Research Service, he has done major research in respiratory diseases of poultry.*

CLARENCE H. THOMPSON, JR., *was formerly a veterinarian in the Animal Disease and Parasite Research Branch, where he worked on diseases of poultry. He joined the State Experiment Station Division of the Department in 1954.*

O. L. OSTEEN *received the degree of doctor of veterinary medicine from the University of Georgia in 1928. He joined the Department of Agriculture in 1932.*

For further reading:

J. P. Delaplane and H. O. Stuart: *The Propagation of a Virus in Embryonated Chicken Eggs Causing a Chronic Respiratory Disease of Chickens*, American Journal of Veterinary Research, volume 4, number 13, pages 325–332. 1943.

E. L. Jungherr and R. E. Luginbuhl: *Air Sac Infection in Poultry*, Proceedings of the United States Livestock Sanitary Association, Fifty-Sixth Annual Meeting, pages 275–283. 1952.

H. Van Roekel, Olga M. Olesiuk, and H. A. Peck: *Chronic Respiratory Disease of Chickens*, American Journal of Veterinary Research, volume 13, number 7, pages 252–259. 1953.

Infectious Sinusitis in Turkeys

J. F. SULLIVAN AND CLARENCE H. THOMPSON, JR.

TURKEYS, like chickens, are subject to a respiratory disease that has a chronic course.

The name "infectious sinusitis" (IS) has been suggested to differentiate it from a similar appearing ailment caused by a deficiency of vitamin A.

The term "swellhead" is used commonly to describe the characteristic appearance of infected birds once the sinuses have become distended with exudate.

The name "air-sac infection" is applied to this disease when the symptoms and lesions are confined to the lower part of the respiratory tract.

In a study conducted by the National Poultry Improvement Plan in 1953, "sinusitis" was cited as one of the four most important diseases of turkeys in 11 of the 19 leading turkey-raising States. It is serious because affected turkeys lose appetite and weight and treatment takes time and money.

The agent that causes IS in turkeys is a pleuropneumonialike organism, which cannot be distinguished from the agent that causes chronic respiratory disease (CRD) in chickens. Agents recovered from either chickens or turkeys, when injected into susceptible birds in the laboratory, produce characteristic symptoms and changes in tissues.

IS is contagious—a point that distinguishes it from deficiency of vitamin A. IS may be spread by direct contact or indirectly in contaminated air and dust. The causative agent has been isolated from eggs laid during certain stages of the disease. That fact strongly suggests that transmission through eggs and incubation has some part in the general spread of the disease.

The first symptoms may be overlooked or discounted as being unimportant. Birds at first shake their heads in an effort to dislodge the discharge that accumulates in the nasal passages. The discharge often can be seen on the feathers of the wings. Foamy secretions appear later in the eyes. A noticeable swelling of the sinuses follows.

These symptoms, unchecked, may culminate in impaired vision, inability to find food, and rapid loss of weight.

In some cases the main lesions are confined to the lower part of the respiratory tract, where they cause the development of generalized symptoms of respiratory distress (air sac infection).

The primary lesions usually are confined to the sinuses and their lining membranes. The excessive amount of exudate resulting from the inflammation of these membranes causes the sinuses to dilate until they produce a visible swelling of the face. The consistency of the discharge is variable. It is watery in the early stages and becomes progressively thicker as the infection continues. In a few advanced cases the material is cheesy.

In outbreaks where the lesions are confined to the air sacs and lower parts of the respiratory tract, the findings at autopsy are like those noted in CRD infections in chickens.

The symptoms and lesions observed in infected poults are characteristic and furnish ample evidence to justify a presumptive diagnosis of infectious sinusitis. Confirmation of a diagnosis of this type may be established in the laboratory by bird or egg inoculation techniques, or by isolation and identification of the causal agent of the disease in enriched bacteriological media.

Antibiotics, including streptomycin, Aureomycin, and Chloromycetin, have been used to treat infectious sinusitis of turkeys with varying degrees of success. These drugs may be mixed in the feed, injected directly into the affected sinus, or, in the lower respiratory form of the disease, administered intramuscularly. The intramuscular methods, which assure each bird an adequate therapeutic dose, seem to be best.

PROGRAMS designed to prevent the spread of infectious sinusitis to clean areas and flocks serve as one of the chief means of combating the disease. Poults should be obtained from a reliable hatchery where healthy breeder flocks are maintained under adequate supervision. Eggs from flocks showing any active respiratory infection should not be set. Breeder flock replacements should never be obtained from an unknown source or from a flock with a recent history of respiratory disease, because of the danger of obtaining apparently healthy carriers.

Infectious sinusitis can be eradicated by marketing the entire flock. If flock conditions are such that a less severe method is desired, the flock should be isolated, and all birds known to be infected should be removed. Infected birds may be identified by physical examination.

It is generally advisable to market the rest of the flock as early as possible.

J. F. SULLIVAN *is a veterinarian employed by the Animal Disease and Parasite Research Branch of the Agricultural Research Service.*

CLARENCE H. THOMPSON, JR., *is a veterinarian employed by the State Experiment Stations Division of the Agricultural Research Service. He has degrees from Kansas State College. Dr. Thompson was formerly with the Animal Disease and Parasite Research Branch.*

Infectious Bronchitis

E. L. JUNGHERR AND J. F. SULLIVAN

INFECTIOUS BRONCHITIS, a widespread respiratory disease of chickens in North America, attacks poultry of all ages.

A. F. Schalk and M. C. Hawn, at the North Dakota Agricultural Experiment Station in 1931, separated infectious bronchitis from the group of ailments known as the "common cold." Because they observed the disease primarily as a hatchery-transmitted condition, it became known as "chick bronchitis."

The disease since has become less common in brooder chicks but more common in growing and laying stock. That change in susceptible age is due probably to the widespread natural occurrence of the disease or artificial immunization for it. A transfer of temporarily protective substances—antibodies—to the offspring follows occurrence and immunization.

The cause of infectious bronchitis is a tiny virus, which passes through bacteria-retaining filters and is visible only under the electron microscope.

The virus can be grown in embryonated chicken eggs, in which it kills or stunts the embryo. The inoculation of embryonated eggs is the only well-developed method of propagating the virus other than in live chickens. Propagation by tissue culture has been studied.

The virus is killed by ordinary disinfectants and dies in drinking water after 12 to 24 hours. Large amounts of water are effective for cleaning the premises. The virus is not affected by sulfa drugs or by antibiotics. Different strains of the virus of infectious bronchitis vary in disease-making power.

The disease is spread by direct or indirect contact with infected birds. The virus is present in the discharge from the respiratory tract and spreads from bird to bird or from contaminated feed, drink, and litter. It may live for a short time, probably not more than 2 or 3 days (except in cold, dry weather) on contaminated clothing, feedbags, crates, and utensils.

The air in an infected poultry house becomes contaminated heavily with virus, perhaps attached to dust particles or droplets, and thus can spread the disease far. The virus can enter all except specially constructed poultry houses.

The virus has been recovered from eggs laid by infected birds as long as 4 weeks after a naturally occurring outbreak or one initiated by a live-virus vaccine. Such eggs should never be set, as they may cause contamination of a hatchery.

Recovered birds carry the virus for a limited time, perhaps 5 weeks.

Recurrence of the disease in certain areas year after year is not fully understood. Only chickens are known to be susceptible to the disease.

The period between exposure and the onset of symptoms is 18 to 36 hours.

The shortness of that incubation period and the ability of the disease to spread through the air make infectious bronchitis the most contagious respiratory disease of poultry.

The symptoms of infectious bronchitis resemble those of other respiratory diseases and are not diagnostic. They consist of nasal discharge, rattling, sneezing, and coughing. Mild symptoms are best observed by pressing on the nostrils and holding the bird close to one's ear to detect gurgling in the windpipe.

The mortality in brooder chicks may be high because of suffocation. Growing birds rarely die from uncomplicated bronchitis but eat much less and have a setback in growth. Egg produc-

tion drops. The eggs become bleached, thin-shelled, misshapen, rough on the outside, and watery on the inside. Hatchability drops. Some of those effects may persist weeks or months after recovery from the respiratory phase and even after return to full production. An early molt may ensue.

Research by D. I. Broadfoot, B. S. Pomeroy, and Wade M. Smith, at the University of Minnesota, disclosed that natural bronchitis infection in brooder chicks less than 3 weeks old may cause permanent injury to the oviduct so that such birds—so-called false layers—cannot produce fully formed eggs.

In brooder chicks dead of the disease, one can see yellowish casts in the windpipe and grayish-yellow turbidity in the air sacs. Older birds have increased mucus in the windpipe and in the large bronchi. The lesions are not diagnostic; furthermore, birds dead for some time often show accumulation of mucus without indications of a respiratory disease.

Accurate diagnosis can be made only in a well-equipped laboratory. The diagnosis during an acute outbreak is made by virus isolation on live birds submitted to the laboratory in person (to avoid shipment by common carrier) or on a whole windpipe shipped in a stoppered glass tube and packed with dry ice. Virus isolation is a long, costly technique, however, and does not always succeed.

Three to four weeks after recovery, a diagnosis can be made by demonstrating immunity. Two laboratory methods are available for that. Live recovered birds are exposed to infectious bronchitis virus and a "take" is not obtained. Blood serum from recovered birds is mixed with an embryo-killing bronchitis virus and the mixture is used to inoculate embryonated chicken eggs. These embryos are not killed or stunted. The latter is the serum neutralization test. Both tests indicate past exposure to infectious bronchitis virus and present immunity to the disease, even if previous symptoms have not been noted.

Treatment of infectious bronchitis is nonspecific and often is unsatisfactory. Extra moist heat, increased ventilation, and appetite stimulants are recommended.

It is unwise to resort to vaccination in places where infectious bronchitis does not exist, as proved by laboratory examination. Vaccination may introduce the disease, which, aside from its own damaging effect, may also act as a stress factor for other respiratory diseases, such as air-sac infection. Some poultry premises have a mild bronchitis infection, which immunizes the chicks early without causing severe symptoms. These strains protect the layers and even transfer parental immunity to the chicks. On such premises vaccination is not necessary, but the situation should be clarified by laboratory tests.

Timely vaccination is the only means of prevention in densely populated areas. Only live-virus vaccines are effective. Certain States offer the poultryman a fully virulent virus, which is inoculated into a few birds during the growing period to start an outbreak. This method generally gives good results, but it cannot be standardized. At times it induces severe reactions and endangers neighboring flocks. It is not applicable to broilers.

Commercial bronchitis vaccines utilize naturally mild or artificially weakened strains. The products are subjected to extensive tests under Government supervision for potency, purity, and safety. Progress has been made toward standardization. The resulting immunity is of shorter duration than that following contact with fully virulent virus.

Repeat vaccinations or booster shots should be applied according to the direction of the manufacturers. Even natural outbreaks occasionally fail to induce permanent immunity, especially for the second laying season. Vaccines may be applied individually into the nostril or eye, or by mass techniques as spray and dust or through the drinking water.

General rules should be followed, such as vaccination of only healthy birds, keeping the vaccine package under refrigeration, and using the vaccine immediately after dilution.

The need for bronchitis vaccination and the choice of vaccine must be decided by the poultryman. Diagnostic laboratories can advise as to the occurrence of the disease in the area and the status of immunity of the mature stock on the particular premises.

Any vaccination program should be planned for an entire year in advance—consideration being given to the incidence of bronchitis in the area, to the immune status of birds on the farm, and to existing physical facilities.

Vaccination of susceptible birds causes a "take," or mild respiratory ailment similar to the natural disease. This "take" is noticeable within 2 to 3 days, but may be delayed in immune brooder chicks for 7 to 14 days.

The reaction to the vaccination lasts about 7 to 10 days. Everything possible should be done during that time to keep the birds comfortable and to maintain feed consumption. Replacement stock must be vaccinated at least 4 weeks before the expected beginning of egg production.

Unfavorable results from vaccination are usually due to unnoticed diseases in the vaccinated birds, such as coccidiosis, quail disease, or air-sac infection. Bronchitis vaccination acts as an extra burden on the birds and thus may precipitate other diseases. Vaccination itself does not improve the birds but constitutes an insurance policy for areas of increased risk.

E. L. JUNGHERR *is professor and head of the Department of Animal Diseases at the Storrs Agricultural Experiment Station, University of Connecticut. He received the degree of doctor of veterinary medicine from the Vienna, Austria, Veterinary School in 1923.*

J. F. SULLIVAN *is a veterinarian employed by the Animal Disease and Parasite Research Branch of the Agricultural Research Service.*

Infectious Laryngotracheitis

O. L. OSTEEN

INFECTIOUS laryngotracheitis is an acute, highly contagious respiratory disease of chickens.

The cause is a filterable virus, which can remain alive and infective in the trachea—windpipe—of dead birds for 60 days at 4° to 6° C. It dies within 48 hours at 37° C. It is readily destroyed by a 3-percent cresol solution or a 1-percent lye solution in 1 to 3 minutes.

Pheasants are the only other fowl that are susceptible to laryngotracheitis under natural or experimental conditions. Embryonating turkey and chicken eggs are experimentally susceptible to the virus.

Susceptible birds get the disease 6 to 12 days after being in contact with sick birds. Transmission of the disease by contaminated crates and other equipment is possible but is of minor importance in its spread.

The virus is not carried through the egg to the hatched chick. Recovered birds can be carriers of the virus for long periods—up to 16 months—and are the usual means by which the disease is spread. A person can act as a mechanical carrier and should not go from sick to healthy flocks without washing and changing to clean clothes and shoes.

Laryngotracheitis is seldom observed in chickens younger than the brooding age, although they are fully susceptible. The disease spreads rapidly to all the birds in an infected flock.

A symptom is difficult breathing, which causes the birds to extend the head and open the mouth for each respiration. A usual rattling sound is caused by obstruction of the windpipe with mucus, which often is tinged with blood. The bird may throw its head from side to side as it tries to dislodge the mucus. Coughing and a watery discharge from the eyes also occur.

A sudden drop in laying flocks of 10 to 30 percent in egg production occurs.

As the disease progresses, the accumulation of excessive amounts of the thick, bloody mucus in the back of the mouth and windpipe causes death by asphyxiation. Death losses in most outbreaks is about 10 percent but may be up to 85 percent. The disease usually lasts 2 to 4 weeks. Egg production in layers stays down for about a month.

Postmortem examination of dead birds shows an inflammation of the respiratory tract. The highly inflamed windpipe with bits of blood in the mucus is significant of infectious laryngotracheitis.

Because the symptoms are so similar to Newcastle disease and infectious bronchitis, it is most advantageous to rely on a positive diagnosis made in a poultry diagnostic laboratory.

No known medicine is effective against the disease.

Preventive measures include the rigid application of sound management and sanitary practices. Hatching eggs or day-old chicks should be obtained from flocks known to be free of the disease. Clean equipment should be used and the flock kept in isolation.

An effective live-virus vaccine is available. It should be used only in areas where the disease is known to be prevalent year after year and not as a substitute for isolation and good management where outbreaks occur in widely separated areas. As the vaccine is a living virus, it is best used only after a diagnosis by qualified laboratory technicians and under their supervision.

O. L. OSTEEN *received the degree of doctor of veterinary medicine from the University of Georgia in 1928. He has been employed in the Department of Agriculture since 1932.*

Tapeworms of Chickens and Turkeys

J. L. GARDINER

AT LEAST ten different species of tapeworms may exist in chickens in the United States. About a dozen species are found in turkeys and a half dozen in ducks. Geese, guinea fowl, peafowl, and pigeons also harbor a few species.

The total number of kinds of tapeworms infesting American poultry is smaller than the figures might indicate, however, because in most instances a given species lives in more than one kind of host. Tapeworms of poultry are less important than roundworms or protozoans. Nevertheless, should any of them be present in sufficient numbers, particularly in young birds, they will make their presence felt—to the detriment of both the bird and its owner.

Tapeworms are parasites in the true sense. Most of the creatures that we call parasites are, strictly speaking, micropredators—they attack and eat their victim, just as a weasel attacks and eats its prey. The weasel, like most so-called parasites, prefers to confine its feeding to certain favored portions of its kill.

Tapeworms, however, do not eat their host. They live within it and partake of its food, thus robbing it of nourishment. If many of them are present, they cause the host to lose weight and appetite and to become droopy and unthrifty. Intestinal catarrh and diarrhea frequently are linked with the presence of tapeworms.

Young birds are affected more seriously by tapeworms than are older birds.

The most serious tapeworm parasite of poultry throughout the United States probably is the small chicken tapeworm, *Davainea proglottina*. It occurs in the small intestine, and particularly favors the duodenum (the horseshoe-shaped part of the small intestine immediately behind the gizzard) as the site of its activities. It is one of the smallest species infesting poultry and can be seen only by careful examination. Mature worms are about one-sixth inch long and consist usually of two to five segments, although there may be as many as nine.

Poultry kept in damp areas are most likely to harbor the small chicken tapeworm, which is understandable enough, as its intermediate hosts are several kinds of snails and slugs.

The small chicken tapeworm occasionally occurs in turkeys, which also play host to another species of the same genus, *Davainea meleagridis*. Neither has been reported as doing any harm to turkeys.

The nodular tapeworm, *Raillietina echinobothrida*, is one of the largest of poultry tapeworms. It may become several inches long. It is distributed widely through the country, but it is less common than some other species. Ants are its intermediate host. The adult tapeworms infest chickens, turkeys, and occasionally pigeons, and produce bumps, or nodules, in the lower third of the small intestine wherever they attach themselves to the intestinal wall. The nodules are like the nodules caused by tuberculosis and may fool the poultryman into thinking his flock has that disease.

Ants also are the intermediate hosts of the related *Raillietina tetragona*, a parasite of chickens, turkeys, guinea fowl, and peafowl.

The broad-headed tapeworm, *Raillietina cesticillus*, is common in chickens, turkeys, and guinea fowl. Its name describes it. It generally locates itself in the front and middle parts of the small intestine of its host. Two dozen or more species of beetles may be its intermediate hosts. Among them are

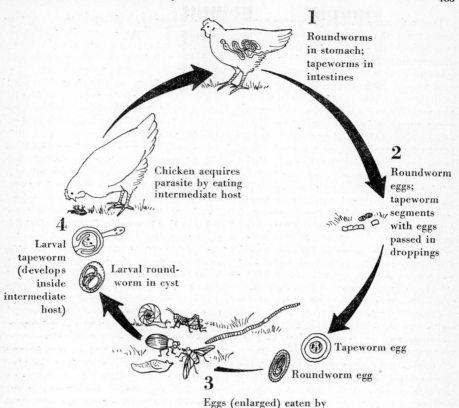

1 Roundworms in stomach; tapeworms in intestines

2 Roundworm eggs; tapeworm segments with eggs passed in droppings

Chicken acquires parasite by eating intermediate host

4 Larval tapeworm (develops inside intermediate host)

Larval round-worm in cyst

Tapeworm egg

Roundworm egg

3 Eggs (enlarged) eaten by beetles, flies, slugs, earthworms, grasshoppers, etc. (intermediate hosts)

The various stages in an indirect life history of a tapeworm and a roundworm of poultry.

the common meal-beetles that infest poultry feeds.

Domesticated fowls harbor a number of other species of tapeworms, but none seems to be important.

Seven species of *Hymenolepis* occur in ducks and geese. Two other species of that genus are parasites of chickens and turkeys. The hymenolepids have no common name, but you might call them the fragile tapeworms because of the way in which they break into pieces when they are handled.

Metroliasthes lucida, a common tapeworm of turkeys, also is found in chickens and guinea fowl. *Amoebotaenia sphenoides* is a species primarily parasitic in chickens.

Choanotaenia infundibulum lives in both chickens and turkeys.

The pigeon tapeworm, *Aporina delafondi*, which is confined to the pigeon among domesticated fowl, has been reported occasionally.

No drug has yet been found that will remove all tapeworms in poultry. For the species that do not fasten themselves too deeply in the intestinal wall of the host (such as the broad-headed tapeworm and *Hymenolepis carioca*), butynorate, hexachlorophene, and certain tin compounds have proved effective. The catch to using these drugs is that you have to be sure you are dealing with one of the tapeworms against which they are of value.

The best way to control tapeworms is to attack them at their most vulnerable point—the developing stage in the intermediate host.

If the droppings of the fowls are removed and attended to in such a way that they are not usable as a breeding place or shelter for beetles, ants, flies, earthworms, slugs, or snails, the tapeworm eggs in the droppings cannot reach the intermediate host, which is necessary for their further development, and the tapeworms die.

The droppings may be treated with some substance, such as benzene hexachloride dust, that kills the insects and other invertebrates that are attracted to them.

The fly problem may be greatly reduced by the use of poison baits and residual sprays. Malathion is a recommended fly poison for use in baits. Several substances, such as DDT, lindane, chlordane, and methoxychlor, make good residual sprays.

Keeping the poultry yards and houses as free as possible of boards, boxes, and trash, which shelter the potential intermediate hosts, is another step in control.

Other helpful measures are the liming of damp places, especially near feed and water containers, and the plowing up of poultry yards and seeding them to low-growing vegetation.

JOHN L. GARDINER, *a parasitologist in the Agricultural Research Service, has worked in the field of poultry parasites since 1948.*

Roundworms

J. L. GARDINER

MANY kinds of roundworms attack poultry. Two or three of them occur in all parts of the country and are troublemakers everywhere. Several others occasionally cause severe losses. A roundworm that gets out of hand has a great potential for harm.

The digestive tract of the host is the habitat favored by most poultry roundworms, but some roundworms attack the eyes, air sacs, thoracic and abdominal cavities, and the windpipe. Among those that favor the digestive tract are specialists that prefer such an unlikely organ as the gizzard for their base of operations.

Roundworms do damage in two ways: By a direct attack on the tissues of the host, which serve them as food, and by the elimination of toxic substances into the host's system.

Satisfactory treatments have been worked out for some kinds of roundworms, such as the gapeworm, cecal worm, and large intestinal roundworm, but no drugs have been found that will deal adequately with most of the roundworm parasites of poultry. Prevention is better than cure.

Taking first things first: The location of the poultry runs should be chosen with sanitation in mind. The ideal spot is a gently sloping piece of land with sandy or gravelly soil and the best possible drainage.

It is wise to rotate the runs. The four-yard system is perhaps the most satisfactory. The ground assigned to one kind of fowl (chicken, turkey, or whatever it may be) is divided into four equal lots by cross-fencing. The poultryhouse is placed in the center, with a door opening into each lot. The birds are rotated from one lot to another and are left not more than 3 months at a time in any one lot. After the birds have been removed from a lot, it may be plowed and planted to some green crop, plowed and left fallow, or simply left undisturbed. Of these alternatives, the first is probably the best.

Proper disposal of droppings and removal of trash that might afford shelter and breeding places for insects and other invertebrates that are intermediate hosts are important in good poultry management.

Another important precept to follow is never to raise young and old birds, or different kinds of birds, on the same piece of ground. Grown chickens, turkeys, and guinea fowl can carry gapeworms without any visible ill effects, but young chicks or poults that are allowed to run with them may become infected, with serious consequences.

Another example of the inadvisability of raising different kinds of poultry together: Blackhead occurs in chickens of all ages, along with its carrier, the cecal worm. It happens frequently that the chickens do not suffer enough ill effects for the poultryman or farmer to be aware that the disease is present among them, but turkeys that are put in the same lot with the chickens will contract blackhead from their associates—and the owner will not be left long in doubt that blackhead is present in the turkeys.

THE LARGE INTESTINAL ROUNDWORM, *Ascaridia galli*, is the roundworm best known to poultry raisers. It is common and large enough to be seen easily. Primarily a parasite of chickens, it is found in the intestines, sometimes in numbers great enough to block the passage.

As are most parasites, this worm is a much more serious problem with young birds than with older ones. Large numbers in young chicks sometimes kill them. In lesser numbers, it stunts the growth and prevents proper bone development. In grown chickens its presence may cause a drop in laying.

This roundworm occasionally wanders up the oviduct and becomes entrapped in the egg as it forms.

The large intestinal roundworm has no intermediate host. Its eggs pass out in the droppings of its host and continue to incubate while lying about on the ground. The eggs reach the infective stage in 15 to 20 days when weather conditions are favorable. They are then ready to hatch if a chicken (or possibly a turkey, duck, or goose) swallows them.

The egg having been swallowed by an acceptable host, the young worm that emerges from it spends the first 10 to 20 days of its active life burrowing in the inner surface of the host's intestinal wall, where it damages the glands. It then emerges from the intestinal wall and from that time on lives within the intestinal passage.

Preventive measures against the large intestinal roundworm include general sanitation, rotation of runs, and keeping young birds off the ground where older birds were kept.

This is one species of roundworm for which treatment has been developed. Nicotine sulfate (in combination with Fuller's earth), tetrachlorethylene, piperazine compounds, and carbon tetrachloride are effective.

SEVERAL RELATED SPECIES of ascarids, as this group of roundworms is called, occur in other kinds of domestic poultry, but none is considered to be of great importance. The guinea fowl, pigeon, and turkey each has its own particular ascarid, which lives in the small intestine of its respective host.

The small intestine is the base of operations for a few other roundworm parasites of poultry. The threadworm, or pigeon capillarid, *Capillaria obsignata*, a slender, colorless worm about one-half inch long when mature, occurs in pigeons, chickens, and occasionally in turkeys. Large numbers of threadworms can cause a considerable loss in weight; the birds may die from the damage done to the intestines, if the infestation is especially severe.

Like the large intestinal roundworm, the threadworm has a direct life history. Its eggs are passed out by one bird and swallowed by another without going through a stage of development inside some invertebrate intermediary.

No satisfactory treatment for threadworms is known. The only method of combatting them is by sanitation.

A related species, the hairworm, *Capillaria caudinflata*, looks like the threadworm. It infests chickens and turkeys and may seriously affect their health.

Pigeons are parasitized by an intestinal roundworm, *Ornithostrongylus quadriradiatus*, which has no common name. It apparently does its damage by sucking the blood of its host. It has no intermediate host, but its eggs, after being passed from the pigeon, hatch on the ground. The young larvae, rather than the eggs, are picked up by the next host.

The ceca, or blind guts (the two little pouches that grow out of the sides of the intestines of many birds), are the seat of infestation of several kinds of roundworms.

The most important is the cecal worm, *Heterakis gallinarum*, which parasitizes chickens, turkeys, and guinea fowl. In large numbers, it may cause a serious inflammation of the ceca, but the main reason for concern about it is not for the direct damage it may do. More serious is that it is a carrier of the organism that causes blackhead in turkeys. Because chickens, which are little affected by blackhead, are favorite hosts for cecal worms, they and turkeys should not be turned loose in the same runs.

The cecal worm, which is small and hard to see, has a life history like that of the large intestinal roundworm. Its eggs pass to the ground in the droppings of one host and are swallowed by another host, in which they hatch and in which the larvae grow to maturity. Earthworms often swallow the eggs. The eggs are not digested by the earthworm and do not hatch within it; they just stay in its alimentary canal. Should an earthworm that has swallowed cecal worm eggs be eaten by a chicken or other suitable host, the eggs hatch and the young worms continue to develop.

Sanitation measures and rotation of runs are important in keeping down the numbers of cecal worms.

Phenothiazine is effective in ridding birds of cecal worms.

The ceca of chickens and turkeys harbor the strongyloid, *Strongyloides avium*, a very small species of roundworm. It may seriously endanger its host's health, especially if the host happens to be a young chicken. The activities of the strongyloid thicken the walls of the ceca. Bloody diarrhea is sometimes a symptom of its presence. A host that survives the acute stage of this illness may continue to harbor the parasite with no more apparent bad effects. The strongyloid can mature and reproduce in the soil, without a host.

The only way to cope with the strongyloid is to keep premises clean and to manage the flock well.

One gizzard worm, *Cheilospirura hamulosa*, attacks chickens and turkeys. It tunnels through the horny lining of the gizzard, riddling it with holes and passages and causing the loss of a good deal of blood. It requires an intermediate host, such as flour beetles, grasshoppers, and sandhoppers. It does not seem to be serious. No satisfactory treatment is known for it.

Farther up the digestive tract is the proventriculus, or glandular stomach, where the globular roundworm, *Tetrameres americana*, is sometimes found. The young female enters one of the glands of the proventriculus. The eggs that form within her when she becomes mature cause her body to swell into a globular shape, and she turns a bright red. The intermediate hosts are grasshoppers and cockroaches. The chicken is a favored host, but turkeys occasionally are victimized. Grown birds seem not to be greatly inconvenienced by the presence of the worm, but young chicks sometimes are affected seriously. No treatment for it is known.

Also inhabiting the glandular stomach is the spiral stomach worm, *Dispharynx nasuta.* This short, white roundworm holds its body in a curved position or twisted into a spiral. It is found in chickens, turkeys, guinea fowl, and pigeons. Large numbers of the worm can seriously affect the health of its host. Its life history is indirect. The intermediate host is the sowbug or pillbug.

No treatment is known for the stomach worm. Control depends on sanitation.

Two CAPILLARIDS, some of whose relatives we have discussed as parasites of the intestine, occur in the crop. The cropworm in chickens and guinea fowl is *Capillaria annulata*, which can damage the walls of the crop and the part of the esophagus next to the crop. The inner wall of the crop becomes greatly thickened and rough, and much tissue, containing masses of worms, is sloughed off. This cropworm often is fatal to pheasants and quail and sometimes is fatal to chickens. Its intermediate hosts are some species of earthworms.

A related cropworm, *C. contorta*, occurs in turkeys and ducks but not in chickens and guinea fowl. On occasion it uses the earthworm, but ordinarily it has a direct life history, no intermediate host being involved—perhaps the earthworm is merely a carrier. *C. contorta* takes a heavy toll once it gets established on a piece of ground where turkeys are being raised.

No remedy (other than sanitation and good management) is known for cropworms. Their location inside the host makes it hard to get at them with drugs.

One rather rare kind of cropworm, *Gongylonema ingluvicola*, causes little damage. It occurs in chickens and turkeys. It has an indirect life history, but the intermediate host is not known for sure. The dung beetles and cockroaches are suspected.

The trachea, or windpipe, of chickens, turkeys, and guinea fowl might harbor the interesting roundworm known as the gapeworm, *Syngamus trachea*. Gapeworms attach themselves to the inner wall of the windpipe in pairs. The male and female worms become permanently joined and form a Y. The bodies of the worms clog the windpipe and prevent the host from getting a proper supply of air; the birds open their beaks and "gape" in an effort to get air. Because of loss of blood and difficulties in breathing, which prevent them from feeding properly, birds heavily infested with gapeworms waste away and die. Young chicks and turkey poults are especially susceptible. Older chickens are rarely bothered with gapeworms, but turkeys and guinea fowl may carry them at any period of their life.

The eggs of the gapeworm are coughed up from the windpipe and swallowed by the host. They then pass out with the manure. They may be picked up by another bird when they reach the ground; failing that, some of them will hatch and may be picked up by a bird. Either way, the result is the same—a fresh infestation. The eggs or young worms also may be swallowed by earthworms, in which they can live for a long time. The earthworm is not an intermediate host, merely a carrier; but an earthworm carrying gapeworms, when swallowed by a chicken or other suitable gapeworm host, causes the bird that found it to become infected.

The best thing to do to prevent gapeworms is to raise young turkeys and chickens entirely apart from older turkeys or guinea fowl and on ground not recently used by either.

Should birds become infected despite all precautions, gapeworms can be removed safely with the aid of barium antimonyl tartrate dust.

ONE OTHER ROUNDWORM is occasionally serious in the States bordering the Gulf of Mexico, particularly Florida, Alabama, Mississippi, and Louisiana. It is the eyeworm, *Oxyspirura mansoni*, a slender, colorless worm, about three-quarters inch long. It flourishes under the transparent membrane covering the eyeball of the host, which may be the chicken, turkey, or peafowl. Birds that have these unwanted guests wink their eyes continuously and frequently rub their heads on their wing feathers or scratch at their eyes with their feet. The eyes puff up and become inflamed, and blindness may result. The eye-worm has for its intermediate host a cockroach found in warm climates.

The best way to prevent eyeworm infection is to keep the poultry runs clear of any sort of trash that might serve as shelter for the roaches. Roaches coming into a clean yard are apt to be spotted by the birds and eaten before they can pick up eyeworm eggs. Thus they have less chance to spread infection than would be the case if the roaches were able to live in the poultry yard long enough to pick up worm eggs in the droppings.

J. L. GARDINER *is a parasitologist in the Protozoan Parasite Section of the Animal Disease and Parasite Research Branch of the Agricultural Research Service.*

Poultry Lice

IRWIN H. ROBERTS AND C. L. SMITH

LICE infest chickens, turkeys, ducks, geese, pigeons, and other birds.

Each class of poultry is parasitized by its own kind of lice. Ten species of lice are common on chickens. Six of them may be found anywhere in the United States. At least three occasionally cause serious losses. Because they are common and easy to see, lice probably get more attention from poultrymen than all other parasites.

Most commercial poultry operators manage to keep their establishments relatively uninfested, but the losses lice cause in small farm and barnyard flocks are great. The average annual loss to the whole poultry industry in 1942–1951 from all external parasites was estimated to be 80 million dollars. We can stop such losses; at small cost and with little effort, any flock can be kept practically free of lice.

Poultry lice seldom are more than three-sixteenths of an inch long. Most of them are brownish to grayish yellow and flat, as though compressed from above.

Lousiness can be detected by parting the feathers and looking for the insects on various parts of the body. They may be found on the skin, the shafts of the feathers, or the fluff of the feathers. All but a few species can dart among the feathers so quickly that some experience may be necessary to find them unless great numbers are present. Their eggs sometimes may be seen in large masses at the base of the feathers. Some species lay their eggs singly on the feathers, and then the eggs may escape detection. All bird lice have biting or chewing mouth parts and ordinarily eat castoff bits of skin and feathers.

All have similar life histories. They are permanent parasites, spending their entire lives on the birds. They die in about 5 or 6 days if they are removed from the living fowl. Louse eggs require a week or less to hatch. The adult stage is reached in 3 weeks or less. The young lice molt two or three times in that time.

Mating takes place on the birds.

Egg laying may begin 2 or 3 days later. Each female may lay as many as 300 eggs. Because one pair of lice may produce 120,000 descendants in a few months, infestations can increase fast. In cold weather, when the heaviest infestations occur, 6 thousand to 7 thousand lice may be present on a single chicken. Infestations are acquired through contact; the lice crawl from one bird to another.

Chicken lice are identified commonly by their usual location on the body. We therefore call them head lice, wing lice, body lice (or vent lice), and shaft lice. Such distinctions are not always satisfactory, for in heavy infestations the vent louse can be found anywhere on the skin, the head louse on the neck and sometimes over the body, and the wing louse on the tail and back feathers. Three or more species may be on a bird at one time.

The body, or vent, louse (*Menacanthus stramineus*) is one of the commonest parasites of poultry everywhere in the United States. It is large, vigorous, and active. It is the most destructive species found on adult birds, where it congregates on the skin just below the vent. Extremely heavy infestations may be on the back, under the wings, and, in fact, from head to the thighs. In young chickens it is found commonly on the back. Its eggs often are in large clusters at the base of the feathers around the vent.

The chicken head louse (*Cuclotogaster heterographus*) also is of primary importance. A grayish louse, it is found on the head and neck. It may cause considerable injury to young chicks. Its eggs, laid singly, are attached to the down or fine feathers of the head.

The shaft louse (*Menopon gallinae*) is widespread. It is a parasite of adult birds. It is pale yellow. You can usually see it when parting the feathers of the thighs and breast; then, in heavily infested fowl, you can see a row of the lice running quickly down the shafts and dispersing when they reach the skin. The eggs are deposited singly at the base of the shaft.

The wing louse (*Lipeuris caponis*) is grayish. It infests the underside of the primary wing feathers or in heavy infestations, the tail and back feathers. It does not move about a great deal. It is easily detected, especially on white birds. Its eggs are laid on the large wing feathers and are not readily seen.

Two other species likely to be found on chickens throughout the United States are of minor importance. The fluff louse (*Goniocotes gallinae*) is pale yellow and so broad that it appears almost circular. Small numbers of this little louse may be found on the fluffy feathers anywhere on the body. Like the wing louse, it is rather sluggish.

The large chicken louse (*Goniodes gigas*) is widely distributed geographically, but only a few are apt to be on a bird at one time. It is the largest, darkest, and most formidable looking of the lice on chickens, and can be seen anywhere on the body as it darts among the feathers.

TURKEYS MAY BE INFESTED with five species of lice. Three of these—the vent louse, the shaft louse, and the head louse of chickens—may be abundant.

Two others, the large turkey louse (*Chelopistes meleagridis*) and the slender turkey louse (*Oxylipeurus polytrapezius*), appear to be restricted to turkeys.

Lice do not appear to be abundant on ducks and geese or to cause appreciable injury.

Several species attack pigeons. The large pigeon louse, the small pigeon louse, and the slender pigeon louse are most important. All three species may attain large enough numbers to cause injury.

THE DAMAGE caused by lice on fowl is not easily determined. Some species, particularly those that live on the feathers and do not become very numerous, are probably of little economic importance. But the vent, head, and shaft lice of chickens multiply so fast that even a light infestation should be regarded as potentially dangerous.

When very large numbers are present, birds may appear unthrifty and show damaged plumage. Vent lice may cause pronounced skin irritation and produce small blood clots on the skin below the vent. Heavily infested chickens may fail to gain weight as a result of restlessness.

Tests conducted at the Alabama Agricultural Experiment Station showed that infestations of body lice depressed egg laying by 11 percent in 11 months and that mortality was greater and body weights less among infested birds than among clean ones.

LICE ON POULTRY can be controlled in many ways. Many insecticides are available.

To get rid of lice, you have to destroy the lice on the birds. Because the lice live only a short time off the fowls, it is not necessary to treat houses, litter, and runs.

Dusts, dips, and sprays can be applied directly to the birds. Insecticides with fumigant action against lice may be applied to the roosting surfaces of poultry buildings. The vapors from insecticides thus applied rise among the feathers and destroy the lice.

One way to apply dusts is to hold the bird in one hand and with the other apply pinches of the powdered insecticide to the skin at various places on its body. One pinch, taken between thumb and index finger, should be placed on the head, neck, tail, breast, vent, and each of the wings and thighs. Two pinches should be placed on the back. Powdered sodium fluoride used in this way is effective.

Dusts also may be applied to the skin with a shaker can—one operator holds the bird and a second administers the powder while ruffling the feathers. When used in this way, sodium fluoride should be diluted with 3 parts of flour, talc, pyrophyllite, or some other inert carrier.

Dusts containing 5 percent or 10 percent of DDT or 1 percent or rotenone are equally satisfactory. Powdered sulfur may be applied from a shaker can, but it is effective only if large amounts are used.

A 10-percent DDT powder also has given good results when applied as a mass treatment to many birds at one time. The powder should be applied at the rate of one-half ounce per bird with ordinary plunger or rotary hand dusters. This is a quick method of administering dusts, but the results sometimes are erratic, and breathing the dust often is annoying.

Dips are effective and faster than dusting individual birds. The bird is held in one hand by the wings and plunged up to the head into a tub containing the dip. The feathers are raised with the other hand to allow the dip to reach the skin. Then the head is submerged once or twice. A sodium fluoride dip can be prepared by adding 1 ounce of powder to each gallon of water. An ounce of soap or detergent can be added.

For head lice, dusts applied by the pinch or shaker method are advised, or the fowl should be dipped.

Lice on turkeys may be controlled with dusts applied by the pinch method. Grown turkeys may require about 15 pinches.

It usually is necessary to dip pigeons because their feathers are so close; enough detergent should be added to the dip to insure complete wetting.

Sodium fluoride is poisonous and must be handled and stored with care. DDT may be purchased in the form of a 50-percent wettable powder. To prepare a 5-percent dust, use 1 part of the 50-percent wettable powder and 9 parts of a diluent, such as pyrophyllite or tripoli earth. A 10-percent dust should contain 1 part of the 50-percent DDT powder and 5 parts of diluent. Powders containing rotenone, ready for use, can be bought.

A much faster method of controlling chicken lice is to apply an insecticide to the roosts. The lice on the roosting birds are killed by the vapors of the insecticide. Several materials are satisfactory, including nicotine sulfate, lindane, BHC, and malathion.

Lindane probably is the most effective. Lindane may be applied to the roosts with a small paintbrush or sprayed over the roosting surfaces, nesting boxes, and floor. To prepare a paint containing about 1 percent of lindane, you mix 5 ounces of lindane wettable powder containing 25-percent gamma isomer (or 6 ounces of 20-percent lindane emulsifiable concentrate) with a gallon of water. You apply the paint to the roosts with a small paintbrush to the point of runoff.

Spraying poultry houses is a little more effective than painting in that coverage of roosting surfaces is usually better. If many birds are involved, spraying is easier and takes less time. To prepare a spray containing about 0.5 percent of lindane, you add three-fourths pound of 25-percent lindane wettable powder (or 1 pint of 20-percent lindane emulsifiable concentrate) to each 5 gallons of water.

Malathion also is effective against lice when used at a 1-percent concentration as a roost treatment. Sprays should be applied liberally, to the point of runoff, on roosts and perches and, if desired, lightly to nesting boxes and floor. A small knapsack sprayer is suitable for all but large establishments. Five gallons of spray are enough to treat buildings housing 750 to 1,000 chickens.

IRWIN H. ROBERTS *is a parasitologist in the Animal Disease and Parasite Research Branch. He was graduated from Alfred University and has the degree of doctor of veterinary medicine from Cornell University. He entered the former zoological Division of the Department of Agriculture in 1937, and since 1940 has been engaged in investigations of parasitic diseases.*

C. L. SMITH *is an entomologist in the Entomology Research Branch. He is a graduate of Mississippi State College and Louisiana State University. Since 1946 he has been project leader for research on the control of lice, mites, and fleas affecting livestock. In 1951 he became assistant station leader of the Department's laboratory at Kerrville, Tex.*

Mites on Poultry

IRWIN H. ROBERTS AND C. L. SMITH

MITES on fowl are sometimes mistaken for lice. Actually they are quite different.

Parasitic mites are so small that they are barely visible to the naked eye. All mites have four pairs of legs in their adult stage. Lice have three pairs of legs. Some of the mites are bloodsuckers. They may live for a long time without food. They and lice are controlled by different methods.

Two groups of mites attack poultry. One spends the greater part of its life cycle in crevices about the poultry houses, from which it makes nightly forages upon the roosting birds to suck their blood. The second group spends the entire life cycle on the birds; they burrow into the skin, into the shafts of the feathers, beneath the scales of the legs, and into the internal organs.

Of the several kinds of mites that may infest poultry anywhere in the United States, the commonest and perhaps the most injurious is the chicken mite (*Dermanyssus gallinae*). It is also known as the red chicken mite or the roost mite. The adult is not more than one thirty-second inch long when fully engorged with blood—about the size of the head of a pin. Chicken mites are gray when unfed and reddish after having had a blood meal. When many of them infest a poultry house, they can be found by lifting a clod of manure off the roosts. Joints in the roosts are often surrounded by tiny, salt-and-pepper specks, which are the excrement of the hidden mites.

After taking a blood meal from the bird, the female chicken mite finds a crevice, usually on the roost, and deposits a few eggs. She then returns to the bird for additional meals. She may deposit 35 eggs in her lifetime. Larvae, which hatch from the eggs in 1 or 2 days, do not feed but shed their skins and then become nymphs. The nymphs attack the birds, suck blood, molt, suck blood a second time, molt again, and become adults. In warm weather or in heated buildings, the entire cycle may take only 1 week. Enormous infestations may build up in poultry houses in 3 or 4 weeks.

The northern fowl mite (*Bdellonyssus sylviarum*), also called the feather mite, is distributed widely over the United States, but is encountered less frequently than the chicken mite. It looks like the chicken mite but has a different life history.

Northern fowl mites normally spend their entire lives on chickens or other birds, but they are sometimes found in birds' nests and can breed on or off the birds. Their entire life cycle lasts 8 to 12 days. They can be found on the birds during the day. They move rapidly. If infested birds are picked up, the mites crawl over the handler's arms and sometimes on his clothing. They usually congregate about the bird's vent and give the feathers a soiled appearance. Their voracious blood-sucking habits may irritate the skin severely. Heavy infestations may develop in a short time.

Another mite that lives continuously on chickens and other birds is the scaly-leg mite (*Knemidokoptes mutans*). It attacks the unfeathered parts of the legs, burrows into the skin, and causes a condition like mange of livestock. It is generally found on older birds in the flock. It is less prevalent than the chicken mite and the northern fowl mite.

Scaly-leg mites usually are first noticed between the toes. As they multiply they work their way up the leg. They cause the scales to separate from the skin and the feet and legs to swell and become deformed. Occasionally they may spread to the comb and wattles. Scaly-leg mites are too small to be seen with the naked eye, but the symptoms they produce are detected easily.

The practice of culling old birds has eliminated the scaly-leg mite to a large degree, and it is now rarely seen except in small farm flocks.

Closely related to the scaly-leg mite is the depluming (or body-mange) mite of chickens and other birds (*Knemidokoptes laevis* var. *gallinae*). It also passes its entire life on the bird. It burrows into the skin at the base of the feathers. It is found only on the feathered areas of the body, usually over the back and sides. The mites cause intense irritation, so that the fowl may pluck out or break off their feathers. You can see this tiny mite only with a lens or microscope.

Most of the mites parasitic on chickens also can live on turkeys and other fowl, but they do not trouble turkeys quite so much as they do chickens. Apparently the management practices used for turkeys are not conducive to the propagation of mites. The most common mite affecting turkeys is the chicken mite. The northern fowl mite occasionally is troublesome. Both may be controlled with the same measures used against mites on chickens.

Severe infestations of mites do more damage than lice do. Mites that burrow into the skin produce intense skin irritation and heavy formation of scabs. Such injury retards the birds and spoils their appearance when dressed. Some species cause the loss of feathers, thereby interfering with the regulation of body heat. The nests of laying hens sometimes have so many chicken mites that the birds cannot remain in them.

Anemia, caused by the loss of blood, is common. Heavily parasitized fowl become thin, weak, and restless. Egg production falls. Young and laying birds may die. The injury due to mites that live in the internal organs has not been calculated, but may be sizable.

An indirect loss due to bloodsucking mites results from their ability to transmit disease, such as fowl cholera and Newcastle disease, among flocks.

For each of the four kinds of mites commonly found on chickens, a different method of attack is required. It is therefore essential to determine what species is present. If two or more species are present simultaneously, separate treatments will be necessary.

To CONTROL infestations of the chicken mite, an insecticide should be applied to the poultry house. It is not necessary to treat the birds.

The first step is to clean the building, nesting boxes, floor, and dropping pits thoroughly; burn the litter; and dispose of manure. Dried manure should be scraped from roosts and perches.

This cleaning should be followed by a liberal application of 0.5-percent lindane or 2.5-percent DDT spray to the entire interior. Lindane or malathion applied to the roosts as a 1-percent paint is also satisfactory against the chicken mite. Lindane and malathion have a further advantage in that if the birds are returned to the buildings at the close of the day, all their lice will be destroyed.

With any of these insecticides, a second application may be required in 10 to 14 days, particularly in heavy infestations. It is not easy to eradicate chicken mites entirely.

Because the northern fowl mite remains on the birds most of the time, insecticidal dusts and dips applied directly to the birds are effective control measures.

Sulfur has been used for many years. The treatment of individual birds with powdered sulfur is satisfactory if liberal amounts of dust are used and if application is thorough. Dipping the birds in sulfur baths is laborious, but the results are gratifying. Dips may be prepared by mixing 2 ounces of finely ground sulfur (325 mesh) and 1 ounce of powdered soap or detergent to a gallon of lukewarm water. The feathers should be wet to the skin, and the head ducked. It is always advisable to dip fowl on warm, sunny days or in heated buildings. Treatment with either sulfur dusts or dips should be repeated as required.

An effective and quick treatment to eliminate northern fowl mites consists of applying to the roosts or litter a chemical, the vapors of which will destroy the mites on the birds. Undiluted nicotine sulfate (40 percent) may be applied with a brush to the roosts, perches, and other roosting surfaces, at the rate of 1 to 1.5 ounces for each 30 feet of roost. As nicotine sulfate volatilizes rapidly, it should be used shortly before roosting time. About three applications a week apart are required to end infestations. The buildings should be ventilated after nicotine sulfate is used.

Another easy and less hazardous way is to treat the litter with malathion. A 4-percent malathion dust applied to the litter only, 1 pound to 50 square feet of floor space, will control the northern fowl mite. The dust should be applied uniformly with a plunger or rotary hand duster or a shaker can or jar.

An old, simple, and effective treatment for the scaly-leg mite consists in dipping the feet and legs of infested birds in crude petroleum. Usually one treatment is enough, but a second treatment about a month later may be required in heavy infestations.

A mixture of 1 part of kerosene to 2 parts of raw linseed oil also may be used as a dip for the feet and legs. Repeated treatments every 2 to 4 weeks, until healing takes place, may be required with this mixture.

For controlling the depluming mite, old, established remedies continue to be effective. The birds may be dipped in a bath containing 2 ounces of wettable sulfur per gallon of water. If spot treatment on a few birds is all that seems necessary, a sulfur ointment can be rubbed into the affected areas of the skin. The ointment can be prepared by mixing 1 tablespoonful of flowers of sulfur in one-half cup of lard or vaseline.

IRWIN H. ROBERTS, *a parasitologist in the Department of Agriculture, has studied parasitic diseases of livestock in Southwestern, Western, and North Central States. He is stationed in Springfield, Ill.*

C. L. SMITH *in 1955 became project leader at the Department's laboratory in Orlando, Fla., in charge of methods and procedures for eradicating the screwworm.*

Diseases of Ducks

E. DOUGHERTY III

DUCKS are waterfowl and scavengers by nature and are relatively resistant to many common diseases of birds.

The large, modern, commercial duck ranch is a long step from nature, however. Confinement creates such problems as a damp, ammonia-laden atmosphere; rapid spread of some diseases that are almost unknown in wild ducks (paratyphoid, serositis, and fowl cholera); heavy insect populations; and leg weakness.

On the other side of the ledger, confinement rearing (with a controlled water supply) has all but eliminated western duck sickness (botulism), parasitism, and attack from predatory animals, which are scourges of wild ducks.

The duck rancher has to provide an escape for moisture to prevent ammonia burn. To accomplish that he replaces the litter daily or provides wire floors over washable pits on at least part of the building. Other problems, such as botulism, have been solved by the use of pelleted feed and a constant water level.

Flies can be controlled by modern chemicals. They must be checked before use, however, because some of the thiophosphates, which are safe to use in chicken houses, are highly toxic to ducks.

PARATYPHOID, or keel, is an infectious disease of young ducklings (also of turkeys and other birds). It is caused chiefly by a bacterium, *Salmonella typhimurium*, and to a less extent by other species of salmonellas. Mortality is usually low (less than 10 percent) on Long Island, but poor incubator and brooder management increase the death rate.

The name "keel," which stems from early observations that the ducks suddenly keel over when dying, is misleading. Often the ducklings become dehydrated and emaciated and die slowly. They may gasp for air or tremble, as though chilled.

The common lesions are small, white spots on the liver, cheesy plugs in the blind gut, and a thickening of the wall of the large gut.

The best preventive measure we know of is to fumigate the eggs during early incubation and the hatching unit between hatches. Potassium permanganate and formalin are recommended.

Potassium permanganate crystals should be used at the rate of one-half ounce (weighed) and 1 ounce of formalin (measured) to every 80 cubic feet of incubator or hatcher space. The potassium permanganate crystals are placed in an earthenware vessel with a capacity of 1 pint for each ounce of formalin required. The vessel is placed on the floor of the machine and the formalin poured over the crystals. The doors and vents should be closed for 15 minutes. This procedure should be followed in the incubator 3 to 5 days after each new lot of eggs is set, and in the hatcher between hatches after the hatcher has been cleaned. Fumigation should not be done while the ducklings are hatching. The farmer should not inhale the fumes and should handle the poisonous formalin carefully.

Treatment consists of rigid culling and sulfonamide medication in the feed or drinking water. NF-180 can be used in the feed at the rate of 2 pounds to the ton for a week to 10 days. Sulfamethazine can be used in the drinking water at the rate of 1 ounce (2 tablespoons) to the gallon of drinking water for 2 days; the treatment can be repeated after 4 days, if necessary.

The ducks should be kept on clean bedding, because *S. typhimurium* may be found in the feces of affected ducks and can be transmitted by ingestion of infected material. The bacteria can live 28 weeks in feces. Thorough cleaning and disinfecting of the brooder house after removal of an infected flock therefore is important.

VIRUS HEPATITIS—baby duck disease—is a highly fatal virus disease of young ducklings. It runs rapidly through a flock and kills many. The dead and dying birds are found with their heads thrown back.

The disease was first discovered in white pekin ducks on Long Island in January 1950. The virus since has been isolated from wild ducks (mallards) on Long Island and from domesticated ducks in Massachusetts, western New York, Illinois, and England.

Losses up to 90 percent are common and occur within 2 days of the first death. The biggest ducklings in a flock die first and without warning. Individuals are dead 30 minutes after showing the first signs. They lie on

their sides with their heads thrown back. The feet may paddle as though they were swimming, and the beak often is purple. Lesions consist of small hemorrhages on the liver and mottling of the spleen and kidneys.

Treatment with serum from ducks that have recovered from the disease has been used successfully. A serum bank sufficient to treat many thousands of ducklings is maintained on Long Island. The bank consists of about 2 million milliliters of blood serum collected at slaughter from ducks that had the disease and recovered. The serum is separated from the clots and treated with a preservative. The serum is then stored under refrigeration and issued, as needed, to the duck farm.

Geese, muscovies, chickens, turkeys, and game birds reared in contact with infected ducks have failed to show any evidence of the disease.

ASPERGILLOSIS, a respiratory disease of young ducklings, is caused by the fungus *Aspergillus fumigatus*. It is also known as brooder pneumonia and gaps. Ducklings less than 2 weeks old are most susceptible, but the fungus has been found growing in the air sacs of ducks of all ages, including breeders.

Affected birds gasp for air and the head and neck are extended. Many become weak and actually may die of thirst.

Cheesy nodules, from pinpoint size to one-eighth inch across, occur in the lungs and air sacs. The filamentous type of growth, similar to that seen on moldy bread, may be present in the air sacs of older ducks.

Moldy litter, the most common cause of an outbreak, should never be used for young ducklings. Moldy feed should be avoided. Every effort should be made to keep the area around the water fountains dry through the use of wire platforms and drains.

Treatment of individual birds is unsatisfactory. The litter in affected pens should be removed or covered with fresh litter.

INFECTIOUS SEROSITIS—anatipestifer infection or "new duck disease"—is so widespread as to be the most important disease problem of the duck industry. It is a bacterial disease caused by *Moraxella anatipestifer.*

The symptoms are coughing, staggering, and loss of equilibrium. Frequently the ducks lie on their sides or backs and paddle their feet. Death often is due to water starvation, rather than to the primary infection. Loose green and white droppings are common in a pen of affected ducks. Losses up to 75 percent have been recorded.

The characteristic lesion consists of a cream-colored, gelatinous membrane, one-sixteenth inch or more thick, over the heart and liver. The air sacs may contain a yellow, cheesy exudate. The liver and spleen are enlarged. Hemorrhages may be present beneath the capsule of the liver.

Terramycin suspension in oil gives good control for about 5 days. The treatment consists of injecting the drug under the skin of the neck at the rate of 12.5 milligrams per pound of body weight. Treatment may have to be repeated.

Sulfa drugs have been widely used, with varying results. One and one-half pounds of sulfaquinoxaline per ton of feed is the recommended level. The ducks should be starved for 4 to 6 hours and the medicated feed given for the remainder of a 24-hour period. This treatment may be repeated if necessary.

FOWL CHOLERA—pasteurellosis—is an infectious bacterial disease of ducks and other birds. The cause is a bacterial organism, *Pasteurella multocida.*

Chickens, turkeys, geese, and other species are susceptible.

Losses from fowl cholera are seldom seen in ducks under 4 weeks old. Affected ducks are hot to the touch, the skin is usually red, and the healthy birds in the flock frequently pick the feathers from the sick and dying birds. Swollen hock joints may be seen in flocks following an outbreak of fowl cholera.

Hemorrhages usually are found on the heart. Cheesy masses may be seen in the air sacs and on the heart. The liver and spleen are enlarged and mottled. Small, white spots may be found in the liver. The blood vessels of the intestines and other organs are engorged with blood.

Diagnosis must be made by isolation and identification of the causative organism, since the lesions of fowl cholera and infectious serositis are easily confused.

Fresh drinking water and clean quarters appear to be of some importance in the control of cholera in ducks. Bacterins consisting of either chemically killed or heat-killed liquid cultures of *Pasteurella multocida* have been used successfully. Two doses of 1 to 2 milliliters (determined by the size of the duck) of duck-origin bacterin a week apart are inoculated intramuscularly at least a week before an anticipated outbreak. The egg-embryo vaccine is more effective than broth bacterins for the control of the fowl cholera in ducks.

Treatment with sulfonamides is of some value, but not all outbreaks respond to it. Terramycin oil, as given for infectious serositis, is effective for short periods.

Ducks dead of cholera should be burned or buried deep, because the cholera organism can survive for long periods in carcasses.

LEUCOCYTOZOON infection has not been reported in the duck-growing area of Long Island, but it is a major problem in some areas of the United States where the blackfly (*Simulium*) is present in large numbers.

The disease is caused by a protozoa, *Leucotozoon simondi*, which attacks the blood cells.

Affected birds may exhibit thirst, become weak, and be highly excitable. Death usually occurs a few hours after symptoms are noted.

The blood is thin and does not clot readily. The spleen may be swollen and dark or mottled.

Control consists of rearing ducks in a screened area or discontinuing production during the blackfly season.

No adequate treatment is available.

BOTULISM—limberneck—is poisoning caused by the toxin formed in putrefying animal and vegetable matter by the growth of bacteria known as *Clostridium botulinum*. When the toxin is consumed, the ducks develop a paralysis of the neck muscles (limber neck), and the feathers become loose.

Diagnosis is made by finding the toxin in the blood of sick ducks; to do that, the suspected serum is inoculated into immune and nonimmune mice.

Pellet feeding, maintaining a constant water level in streams and ponds, and prompt removal of all dead animals and birds aid in the control.

The treatment of the birds with antitoxin is recommended only when the individual value of the bird is high.

COCCIDIOSIS is a minor problem in ducks, although some outbreaks, with losses up to 24 percent, have been reported.

External parasites of ducks include the duck louse (*Anatoecus dentatus*), which is frequently found on the heads of breeding birds on Long Island. Control consists of dusting 5-percent DDT under the feathers on the head of the affected ducks at the time of selecting breeders.

INFLAMMATION of the eye, eyelids, and the mucous membranes of the nose and throat resulting from ammonia fumes generated in feces is common in ducks. Frequent removal of the litter and good ventilation are the best control measures.

SALT POISONING—the toxic level for salt is 2-percent sodium chloride in the feed, 4,000 parts per million in the drinking water, or any combination.

High salt levels depress growth in ducklings and lower the fertility and hatchability of eggs of breeder ducks.

FOREIGN BODY PENETRATION—ducks are known for their habit of eating shiny objects. Nails, wire, screws, and other objects that are ingested penetrate the gizzard or intestine. Special care must be exercised to remove such objects from pens or yards, especially after making repairs on buildings that house ducks.

SUCH CONDITIONS as prolapse of the oviduct and paralysis of the penis occur in breeding flocks. The true cause of these conditions is unknown. Forcing the birds into production is thought to play a part.

All birds thus affected should be removed from the breeding flock immediately, so as to prevent the development of cannibalism. Ducks that have a tendency to prolapse of the oviduct or paralysis of the penis should not be used in a breeding flock, even if they recover.

Impaction of the oviduct may occur as the result of infection or other unknown causes, which prevent the movement of partly or fully formed eggs down the oviduct.

Internal layers are found occasionally in laying ducks. Reversed peristalsis in the oviduct deposits the fully formed eggs in the abdominal cavity.

Ascites, or water belly, is a common condition in ducks. The accumulation of fluids in the abdominal cavity is usually the result of interference with the circulation of blood through the liver.

The incidence of tumors in domestic ducks is extremely low. Tumors of the liver, lungs, kidneys, and oviduct have been reported in ducks.

E. DOUGHERTY III *has been the director of the Duck Disease Research Laboratory of the New York State Veterinary College, Cornell University, since 1950. Previously he was an assistant professor of poultry diseases there and an assistant research specialist in poultry pathology at the Vineland Laboratory of the New Jersey College of Agriculture.*

Parasites Affecting Ducks and Geese

EVERETT E. WEHR AND MARION M. FARR

NOT MANY internal parasites attack our domestic ducks and geese, but some of them cause large losses in individual flocks.

Roundworms are more numerous and generally more injurious than the others.

The gizzard worm, *Amidostomum anseris*, is a slender, reddish worm, up to three-fourths inch long. The young worms penetrate the softer parts of the gizzard lining and migrate to a position between the lining and the muscular part below. There they feed, grow, and injure the lining. Many tunnel-like impressions in the lining and in the muscular part of the gizzard, visible on separation of the two, is evidence of their presence.

Young birds lose their appetite and become dull and emaciated. Severely infected birds may die. The gizzard lining of a heavily infested bird appears loosened, necrotic, and riddled with worms. The softer parts are dark brown or black and often separated in places.

The eggs of the gizzard worm are microscopic. They are discharged from the female and pass out in the droppings. They are partly developed when they reach the outside. If moisture and temperature are favorable, the eggs complete development and hatch. The larvae become infective in about a week. Susceptible birds become infected by swallowing the free-living infective larvae with food and water. Adult worms have been found in the gizzard about 25 days after infective larvae were fed in experiments.

The cecal strongyle, *Trichostrongylus tenuis*, is related to the gizzard worm and has a similar developmental cycle. It is much smaller than the gizzard worm and is often overlooked in a casual examination of the cecal con-

tents. It is straw colored and does not ingest blood as does the gizzard worm.

Large numbers of the worm produce definite clinical symptoms. The changes in the ceca consist of a thickening and reddening of the walls. Small hemorrhages are sometimes present. Loss of weight, anemia, and chronic toxemia are signs of heavy infections. The cecal strongyle has been transmitted experimentally to domestic turkeys, guinea fowl, and chickens.

A species of gapeworm, *Cyathostoma bronchialis*, has been encountered only occasionally as a parasite of domestic geese in the United States but is said to be a rather common parasite of geese in Europe. This roundworm was responsible for extensive losses among goslings in Minnesota in 1951. The morbidity in that outbreak reached about 80 percent, and the mortality was about 20 percent. As this gapeworm is common in the wild geese of the North Central States, it is possible that domestic geese acquire their infections from them.

Gapeworms are associated with respiratory distress—the bird throws its head back and gasps for breath. Some birds die within a few days after symptoms appear. Others may linger for several weeks.

One can tell the gapeworms that occur in geese from *Syngamus trachea*, which attacks chickens and turkeys, by the disjoined condition of the male and female worms. Gapeworms of chickens and turkeys are joined permanently in the adult stages.

A species of hairworm or threadworm, *Capillaria contorta*, occurs in both wild and domestic ducks in the United States. Domestic and wild turkeys and other wild gallinaceous birds often harbor these worms also.

Tapeworms occur occasionally in

domestic ducks and geese in the United States but are of less economic importance than the roundworms.

One kind of tapeworm, *Hymenolepis tenuirostris*, caused the death of a large flock of geese in Oregon in 1921. The affected birds showed weakness, emaciation, incoordination, and diarrhea. It is the only time this tapeworm has been associated with death of geese in this country, but it has been reported on several occasions in Europe.

Ducks and geese become infected by swallowing certain small aquatic animals, which are said to serve as the parasite's intermediate hosts.

No satisfactory treatments for the removal of roundworms and tapeworms of ducks and geese are known. Sanitary measures which prevent the contamination of feed and water with the droppings of infected birds are of value in keeping parasitism at a low level.

BLOOD PARASITES, which resemble the parasites that cause malaria, are responsible for considerable losses in ducks in the United States. The parasites are known as leucocytozoa, and the disorder they cause is called leucocytozoon disease.

One, *Leucocytozoon simondi*, is the cause of sickness and death among domestic and wild ducks, especially the young ones. It is most common in flocks in the region of the Great Lakes. Some ducklings that recover may be permanently stunted. Occasionally adult birds become affected severely and may die. They usually recover, however, but continue to harbor the parasite in their blood stream and thus serve as sources of infection for young birds.

This disease strikes suddenly. A flock may appear normal and healthy one day. Many of them may be dead the next day. Some affected birds refuse to eat. Others may continue to drink until they are too weak to move. Some of them crawl about in a sitting position as though it were an effort to exert themselves. Shortly before death their breathing may be fast and la-

bored, and they may pass through a period of nervous excitement.

The spleen of a severely affected bird is enlarged and blackened. The liver also is enlarged. The blood is thin, pale, and watery, does not clot readily, and contains large numbers of leucocytozoa.

These parasites are transmitted from one bird to another by blackflies (*Simulium* species), which ingest the parasites when they suck the blood of an infected bird. The parasites grow and multiply within the fly's body. When they reach the infective stage they are discharged, along with the saliva, into the next bird, on which the insect feeds.

In the duck, the parasites penetrate the cells of the lungs, liver, and spleen and multiply several times. Enormous numbers of parasites are produced. Eventually the parasites are liberated into the blood stream and supposedly invade the blood cells, where they appear as large rounded and spindle-shaped bodies.

The entire life cycle requires 3 days in the blackfly and 6 to 12 days in the duck.

The disease can be controlled in ducks and geese by protecting them from blackflies. That may be done by raising susceptible birds in regions where there are no blackflies or by raising them in houses screened to keep out the insects.

A secondary method of control is to detect and destroy carrier birds.

Chemical treatment of blackfly-infested streams will also aid in the control of the disease by reducing the number of blackflies.

COCCIDIOSIS is responsible for serious losses among geese. It is caused by coccidia, microscopic protozoan parasites that invade the tissue cells and eventually destroy them.

One species of coccidium, *Eimeria truncata*, causes a highly fatal renal, or kidney, disorder in geese. This type of coccidiosis is widespread in the United States and Canada. Goslings 3 weeks to 3 months old are particularly susceptible.

Affected birds lose weight rapidly, become emaciated and weak, and often die 2 or 3 days after symptoms appear. A mortality of 80 to 100 percent has been reported in severe outbreaks.

Enormous numbers of coccidia develop within the kidneys. They plug up and destroy the uriniferous tubules (minute passages). The kidneys of a severely affected bird are swollen, pale, and flecked with small yellow-white nodules and fine white streaks.

Other species of coccidia, *Eimeria anseris*, *E. nocens*, *E. parvula*, and the *Tyzzeria anseris*, have been found in the intestine of geese, but the extent of their injuries is not known. One species, *Tyzzeria anseris*, has been found in geese in the United States.

We have had relatively few reports of serious losses among ducks from coccidiosis, and in them the species of coccidia were not identified positively.

One species, *T. perniciosa*, is known to cause sickness and death under experimental conditions. E. Allen, of the Department of Agriculture, experimentally infected 10 ducklings, 8 of which died. The walls of the intestines were thickened and their muscular exterior was dotted with round white spots. The contents of the intestine consisted of blood, cheesy material, and pieces of intestinal lining.

E. Dougherty III, of the New York State Veterinary College, in 1952 reported two outbreaks of intestinal coccidiosis in ducklings in New York. He observed that many of the birds were not eating and appeared moribund; 20 percent of them died. He tentatively identified *T. perniciosa* as the cause.

An intestinal flagellate, *Cochlosoma anatis*, is common in the intestinal tract of ducks. It has a rounded, cuplike depression in the front half of the body. It moves by means of six long, hairlike structures (flagellae), which are attached near the front end. The parasite has been found in birds suffering from intestinal disturbances, but there has been no evidence that it was responsible for the trouble.

Sarcocystis rileyi, a parasite of the muscles, often is found in wild ducks and has been found in domestic ducks. It forms tubular sacs up to one-fourth of an inch long. The saclike parasites often occur in huge numbers, particularly in the breast muscles.

EVERETT E. WEHR, *a parasitologist in the Animal Disease and Parasite Research Branch, has been with the Department of Agriculture since 1928.*

MARION M. FARR, *a veterinary parasitologist in the Animal Disease and Parasite Research Branch, joined the Department in 1934.*

For further reading:

Animal Disease Eradication Branch: *Cresylic Disinfectants Permitted for Use in Official Disinfection*. Animal Disease Eradication Branch, Agricultural Research Service, U. S. D. A., Washington, D. C., 1956.

Animal Disease and Parasite Research Branch: *An Outline of Disinfection Procedures for Poultry Service Personnel*, Animal Disease and Parasite Research Branch, Agricultural Research Service, U. S. D. A., Washington, D. C.

Frank W. Tilley: *The Use of Disinfectants on the Farm*. U. S. D. A. Farmers' Bulletin 1991, 17 pages. 1947.

———

E. H. Peterson: *Field Tests of Some Insecticides in the Control of the Red Mite of Poultry and of the Northern Fowl Mite*, Poultry Science, volume 28, number 3, pages 411–414. 1949.

L. E. Vincent, D. L. Lindgren, and H. E. Krohne: *Toxicity of Malathion to the Northern Fowl Mite*, Journal of Economic Entomology, volume 47, number 5, pages 943–944. 1955.

———

J. R. Beach and M. A. Stewart: *Diseases of Chickens*, California Agricultural Experiment Station Bulletin 674, 151 pages. 1942.

H. E. Biester and L. H. Schwarte editors: *Diseases of Poultry*, Edition 3, 1245 pages, Ames, Iowa; Iowa State College Press. 1952.

S. A. Edgar and D. F. King: *Effect of the Body Louse, Eomenacanthus stramineus, on Mature Chickens*, Poultry Science, volume 29, number 2, pages 214–219. 1950.

Morley A. Jull: *Raising Turkeys*, 467 pages, New York, N. Y.; McGraw-Hill Book Co., Inc. 1947.

DISEASES

AND PARASITES

AFFECTING

dogs and cats

Internal Parasites of Dogs and Cats

F. D. ENZIE AND EMMETT W. PRICE

EVERY seventh American in 1956 owned a dog. At least 20 million cats lived in American homes that year, but anybody who knows cats that it is not entirely correct to say they were "owned."

Along with the ownership of dogs and association with cats goes the responsibility for their proper feeding, housing, grooming, and protection from preventable disease. We are here concerned with the last responsibility—the duty and responsibility of the owner to become familiar with the common parasites that affect dogs and cats, particularly with respect to the sources of infection, modes of transmission, and methods of control.

The internal parasites of dogs and cats include a few one-celled organisms, the protozoa, and a much larger

and more important group known as helminths or worms. All of these parasites live within the body of the host as compared with the arthropods, or external parasites, which usually infest the surface of the body.

Many of the internal parasites of dogs and cats occur infrequently and are of little concern to most owners. A few are widespread and produce serious losses, particularly among puppies and kittens.

This discussion includes a description of only the more important species. We give particular consideration to the sources of infection, manner of transmission, and methods of control.

The external parasites, including fleas, lice, ticks, and mange mites, are discussed in the chapter that follows.

The nematodes—the roundworms—

503

comprise the largest group of internal parasites affecting dogs and cats, and they are by far the most injurious.

Some species, notably hookworms and ascarids, have a simple, direct life history and are distributed widely wherever dogs and cats are raised. They usually are acquired at an early age and may be responsible for the loss of entire litters before the animals are weaned.

Other roundworms, such as heartworms, the kidney worms, and certain lungworms, require intermediate hosts to complete their life cycles. These species generally occur in older animals and are restricted mostly to certain geographical areas. Although spectacular death losses are seldom associated with these nematodes, the usefulness of infested animals, particularly hunting dogs and animals serving with the Armed Forces, is largely destroyed.

THREE KINDS OF HOOKWORMS may be found in dogs and cats in the United States. *Ancylostoma cannium* is widely distributed throughout the country. *A. braziliense* is limited primarily to the Southern States. *Uncinaria stenocephala* occurs in the more northerly areas.

Hookworms are white or grayish roundworms about one-half to three-fourths inch long and about as thick as an ordinary straight pin. The front end is bent slightly upward to give a hooklike appearance, and the mouth is provided with teeth or cutting plates. Hookworms generally are firmly attached to the lining of the small intestine, but in heavy infestations they may occur also in the cecum, colon, and rectum.

The life histories of the hookworms are comparatively simple and are similar for all species. The adult females produce many eggs, which are eliminated with the fecal material of the host. When temperature and moisture are favorable, wormlike larvae hatch from the eggs within a few days.

In a week or so the young larvae molt twice and are transformed into the infective stage. Susceptible animals become parasitized when the infective larvae are swallowed in contaminated feed or water or when they are brought into contact with the mouth on balls, rubber bones, or other objects. Infective hookworm larvae may also penetrate the skin of susceptible hosts. In pregnant females they may pass by way of the circulatory system to the developing young.

Larvae that penetrate the skin are carried with the blood to the lungs, where they escape to the air passages. They are eventually coughed up and swallowed and pass to the intestine, where they develop to maturity.

Infective larvae that are swallowed with contaminated feed and water pass directly to the intestine without going through the lungs.

Hookworm eggs first appear in the feces 3 to 6 weeks after the larvae reach the intestine, the worms generally maturing more rapidly in young animals. In prenatal infections, however, eggs may be found in the feces as early as 13 days after birth. In the absence of reinfection, hookworms may persist in the intestine of the host for as long as 2 years, although most of them are eliminated within 6 months.

Because these parasites are voracious bloodsuckers, the principal symptoms of hookworm disease are the ones associated with chronic hemorrhage. There is a pronounced anemia, manifested by extremely pale mucous membranes, marked depression, and a reluctance to move about.

The animal may have a persistent diarrhea in the early stages of the disease. The feces may be streaked with blood. As the condition advances, the feces contain progressively larger amounts of blood and mucus. Shortly before death the bowel movements may consist almost entirely of pure blood. Since the bitch generally keeps the puppies and bedding free of fecal material during the first few weeks, prenatal infections may end fatally before hookworm disease is suspected.

Forty hookworms may withdraw as much as an ounce of blood every 24 hours. Infections of several hundred worms are not uncommon, even in nursing puppies. But that is only part of the blood loss: The worms have a tendency to migrate to new areas, and the abandoned sites continue to bleed for some time. That is what makes hookworm infections so serious, particularly in puppies and young dogs.

The common hookworm, *A. caninum*, is the species most frequently encountered in cats, but cats seldom harbor sufficient numbers to produce clinical hookworm disease. This parasite is the same species that occurs in dogs, but it is a strain especially adapted to cats, and the two strains are not readily transmitted from one host to the other.

The infective larvae of *A. braziliense* occasionally penetrate the skin of man and produce a condition known as creeping eruption. Tortuous burrows are formed in the superficial layers of the skin. The itching is intense. The larvae move at the rate of an inch or so a day and may persist for several days or weeks. The larvae may be destroyed in the skin by spraying the lesions with ethyl chloride or carbon dioxide snow, although the larvae die before they reach the intestine, even without treatment.

The larvae of the common hookworm may produce a transient inflammation of the skin of people, but they do not produce the typical lesions associated with *A. braziliense* larvae.

Large intestinal roundworms, or ascarids, are second only to hookworms in their injuriousness to puppies and kittens.

The dog is parasitized by two species, *Toxocara canis*, which occurs principally in puppies and young dogs, and *Toxascaris leonina*, a species generally found in older animals. The latter occasionally is found also in cats, although cats, particularly kittens, usually are infested with *T. cati*, a species closely related to the common ascarid of young puppies.

Large roundworms are white or yellowish and 2 to 8 inches long. They occasionally are passed in large numbers in the feces or vomitus of young animals, and while still alive they have a tendency to coil in a spiral.

The life histories of dog and cat ascarids are similar to that of the large roundworm of man. Numerous eggs are passed in the feces of the host and become infective within a few days under favorable conditions. The infective eggs are swallowed in contaminated feed or water and hatch in the small intestine. After penetrating the wall of the digestive tract, the young worms pass to the lungs with the blood and escape from the blood vessels to the air passages. They are subsequently coughed up, swallowed, and develop to maturity in the small intestine within a few weeks.

The larvae of *T. leonina* do not pass through the lungs but penetrate the intestinal lining, where they grow and develop. They return to the lumen of the intestine after about 10 days and mature in a few weeks. Ascarid larvae, like those of the hookworms, may pass from the circulatory system of the pregnant female to the developing embryos. This is particularly common in mature animals that are resistant to (and seldom harbor) the adult worms. The need for preventing exposure of the pregnant animal to sources of infection therefore is apparent.

The most common symptoms of ascarid infection in puppies and kittens are marked enlargement of the abdomen, unthriftiness, and digestive disturbances. The animals appear listless. Large numbers of worms may be eliminated in the feces or in vomitus when the infections are heavy. Coughing may be noted when larvae are passing through the lungs. Pneumonia commonly follows massive invasion of the lungs.

The larvae of dog and cat ascarids, like those of the hookworm, may invade the body tissues of people and produce a condition known as visceral larva migrans. The disease generally occurs in children less than 3 years old and may be mild or severe, depending on the numbers of larvae involved. After the eggs hatch in the small intestine, the larvae penetrate the gut wall, enter the circulation, and invade the liver, lungs, heart, kidney, brain, spinal cord, and other internal organs.

Because no treatment is known for this condition, every effort should be made to prevent exposure of children to the infective eggs of these parasites.

THE WHIPWORM of dogs, *Trichuris vulpis*, is a white or gray-colored worm that is usually found in the cecum, or blind gut. It is 2 or 3 inches long when mature. It resembles a small whip. Closely related species have been reported in cats in other parts of the world, but they are not known to occur in this country.

The life cycle of the whipworm is direct—that is, infection occurs when susceptible animals swallow embryonated eggs in contaminated feed or water. The eggs hatch in the small intestine, and the young worms reach maturity in the cecum about 3 months later.

The damage produced by the whipworm is not well understood, although a variety of symptoms have been associated with heavy infestations. Symptoms commonly attributed to whipworm infections are abdominal pain, unthriftiness, and chronic diarrhea, or alternate periods of diarrhea and constipation. In many cases, however, the worms appear to do little or no harm.

THE HEARTWORM, *Dirofilaria immitis*, is primarily a parasite of the dog. It is found occasionally in cats and other hosts. It is encountered in all parts of the United States, but it occurs oftenest in the South and along the eastern seaboard. The worms are long, slender, and whitish. The males and females are, respectively, about 6 and 12 inches long. Heartworms are generally located in the right ventricle and pulmonary artery but may occur under the skin, between muscles, and in other places.

The life history of the heartworm differs materially from that of the intestinal roundworms. The adult female does not lay eggs but deposits living larvae, called microfilariae, directly into the blood stream. The microfilariae are removed from the blood by fleas, mosquitoes, and perhaps other bloodsucking arthropods. Experimental findings suggest that fleas may be the most important vectors in the transmission of heartworms.

After a period of growth and development in the body of the intermediate hosts, the larvae become infective and capable of becoming established in susceptible dogs or cats. The transmission of infective larvae occurs while the vectors are feeding on the primary host. The young worms undergo development in various extravascular tissues before migrating to the heart and adjacent vessels. The time required for the worms to reach maturity has not been definitely established, although it is presumed to be several months.

The symptoms associated with heartworm infections are generally observed during or after vigorous exercise, although some heavily infested animals may show no symptoms whatever.

Probably the most characteristic symptom is rapid fatigue. The animal may lie down and gasp for breath or collapse completely, but after a short rest it recovers and is apparently normal for a while. Sometimes the animals develop a rather distinctive cough, which fails to respond to medication. Abdominal dropsy and swellings in the legs and other parts of the body may be seen in cases of long standing because of poor circulation.

Positive diagnosis of heartworm infection can only be made by finding the active microfilariae in the blood. It should be recognized, however, that microfilariae may persist in the blood for as long as 2 years after the adult worms are dead and that adult worms may occur in locations other than the heart and adjacent vessels. It is possible, therefore, that adult worms may not always be found in the heart of animals that show microfilariae in the circulating blood.

THE INTESTINAL THREADWORM of dogs, *Strongyloides* species (possibly *S. stercoralis*), is a small, slender worm about one-tenth inch long. Only the female worms are present, and they are generally buried in the intestinal lining. The eggs of this parasite usually hatch shortly after they are deposited, and the liberated larvae are eliminated in the feces.

Some of the larvae evolve directly to the infective stage in the usual manner, but others first develop into a generation of free-living males and females. Ultimately infective larvae are produced by both developmental cycles, and infection of susceptible animals occurs when the larvae penetrate the skin or are swallowed with contaminated feed or water.

After penetrating the tissues of the host, the larvae migrate to the lungs by way of the blood stream, ascend the trachea, pass to the small intestine, and develop to maturity within a few days.

Parasitized animals generally show a persistent or intermittent diarrhea accompanied by general weakness, depression, dehydration, and emaciation. Pneumonia may develop following massive invasion of the lungs by migrating larvae or in consequence of continued exposure to infective larvae.

The parasite is encountered with increasing frequency throughout the United States and should be considered as a possible causative agent in cases of persistent diarrhea.

One should avoid handling infested animals, although it has not been proved that intestinal threadworms can be transmitted to people.

THE ESOPHAGEAL WORM of dogs, *Spirocerca lupi*, is usually found in nodules, or tumors, in the walls of the esophagus, stomach, trachea, or aorta. The worms are 1 to 3 inches long and are bright red. They are generally coiled in a spiral.

The esophageal worm has an unusual life history. The eggs are embryonated when deposited by the female worms and are passed in the feces or vomitus of the host. They do not hatch until dung beetles swallow them.

The liberated larvae develop to the infective stage and encyst in the body cavity of the beetles. Susceptible dogs, or closely related animals, become infested when they swallow the beetles. Occasionally the infected beetles are swallowed by certain abnormal hosts, such as snakes, frogs, birds, or small mammals. The infective larvae cannot develop to maturity in those animals but may reencyst and remain infective. The dog may become infected therefore by eating either infected dung beetles or the so-called transport hosts. In the definitive or natural host, the larvae are liberated in the stomach, penetrate the stomach wall, and either stimulate nodule formation there or migrate to the aorta, esophagus, or trachea before doing so.

The symptoms associated with infestations of the esophageal worm are governed by the location and size of the nodules or tumors. In mild infestations the animal may have difficulty in swallowing but show no other signs of discomfort. Large, tumorous masses in the esophagus, however, may cause persistent vomiting and a considerable loss of weight. Death may result from rupture of the aorta when tumors weaken its wall. When the tumors occur in or near the trachea, they may cause difficult breathing, coughing, or suffocation.

The migrating larvae sometimes injure the fibrous membrane covering certain thoracic vertebrae; the result is bony enlargement and deformation of the spinal column. It has been suggested that the parasites may incite the formation of malignant tumors in the esophagus.

THE EYEWORM, *Thelazia californiensis*, is a small, whitish worm about one-half inch long. It occurs under the eyelids and in the tear ducts. It is chiefly a parasite of dogs, but it has been found rarely in cats, other animals, and people. It is not known to occur outside California.

The life cycle of the eyeworm is unknown, but the parasite is closely related to an eyeworm of poultry that requires an insect intermediate host.

The worms move about over the surface of the eyeball and cause considerable irritation and inflammation. This results in profuse watering of the eye, swelling of the lids, and marked sensitivity to light. In heavy infestations the activities of the worms may result in ulceration of the eye and blindness.

THE GIANT KIDNEY WORM, *Dioctophyma renale*, is the largest nematode known. The mature worms may be as large around as the little finger. The male and female may attain a length of 18 and 40 inches, respectively. The worms are bright red and may be found in the kidney or free in the abdominal cavity.

The kidney worm is not encountered often in dogs in this country, but it may be more common than reports indicate, as it is generally found only when animals are examined after death. In wild animals it is especially common in mink and has been reported also in other fish-eating mammals. It has not been found in cats.

Its life history is not fully known but is said to include two intermediate hosts. The dog, or other host animal, becomes infested by eating fish that contain the infective stages of the parasite. The life cycle of the kidney worm may take 2 years to complete.

When the worm occurs in the kidney, the functional tissue of the organ may be destroyed, leaving only the fibrous capsule surrounding one or more worms. The other kidney is not involved but may be much larger than normal in order to compensate for the loss of the parasitized organ.

The worms may be found free in the abdominal cavity; then the eggs dispelled by the female worms produce a chronic peritonitis. Symptoms of infection are not distinctive but may include lack of appetite, loss of weight, abdominal pain, depression, and evidence of abdominal dropsy. The urine may contain blood and pus when the worms occur in the kidney itself; in that event, diagnosis may be established by finding the characteristic eggs in the urine.

THE BLADDERWORM, *Capillaria plica*, is occasionally encountered in the urinary bladder of dogs in the United States. It occurs mostly in foxes.

They are whitish, hairlike worms, 1 or 2 inches long. They generally are attached to the bladder lining. Ordinarily only a few worms are present and cause no apparent discomfort. In heavy infestations they may produce an inflammation of the bladder lining, so that the animal urinates frequently and with some pain.

This parasite (*C. plica*) may occur also in cats, but a closely related species, *C. felis-cati*, is more commonly found in this host.

Bladderworms are related to the dog whipworm and produce eggs that may be confused with those of the latter.

LUNGWORMS are not encountered often in dogs and cats, although three kinds are known to occur in the United States. One species, *Capillaria aerophila*, is very closely related to the bladderworms and occurs in both dogs and cats.

Lungworms are found in the large and small air passages and large numbers of them may produce symptoms of bronchitis and pneumonia. The eggs, which closely resemble those of the whipworm and bladder worms, are coughed up, swallowed, and eliminated in the feces. They become infective in about 2 months, and the dog or cat gets an infection when it swallows them in contaminated feed or water.

The cat lungworm, *Aleurostrongylus abstrusus*, is a fine, hairlike worm about one-fourth to three-eighths inch long. The adult worms occur in the lung tissue and appear as small black spots throughout the lung and underneath the membrane covering its outer surface. Small white or grayish spots in the vicinity of the adult worms consist of accumulations of eggs and first-stage larvae. The latter ascend the air passages, pass out in the feces, and reach the infective stage in snails or slugs. Infection becomes established in the cat when it ingests the gastropod host or a transport host, such as mice and certain other small animals. The adult worms are comparatively harmless, but the eggs and larvae, which are a source of irritation to the lung tissue, give rise to symptoms and lesions of pneumonia.

The dog lungworm, *Filaroides osleri*, is a small, transparent, hairlike worm about one-fourth to one-half inch long. It occurs in nodules or tumorlike masses on the inner lining of the large air passages. These lesions are found oftenest near the junction of the trachea and bronchi, and in heavy infestations they may be sufficiently large and numerous to cause labored breathing and suffocation. Infested dogs generally have a persistent and rasping cough. The eggs generally hatch shortly after they are deposited by the female worms. The larvae are passed in the feces. The life cycle and method of transmission are not known.

TAPEWORMS of at least 14 kinds are known to infest dogs and cats in the United States.

Some species occur only rarely and may be limited to certain geographical areas where suitable intermediate hosts exist.

The injury tapeworms produce is not well understood, although digestive disturbances, abdominal pain, nervousness, and unthriftiness have been associated with heavy infestations. By and large, however, the chief importance of dog and cat tapeworms concerns the transmissibility of certain stages to man and livestock and the nuisance associated with infestations in house pets. Segments of tapeworms may be passed involuntarily by infested animals and may soil rugs, furniture, and bedding. Also, the irritation produced by motile segments in the rectum and around the anus causes the animal to assume a sitting position and drag itself forward over the rugs or ground.

Because the symptoms and damage associated with the various species are similar, only the more important differences in their life cycles and potential hazard to man and livestock need be considered here.

THE DOUBLE-PORED TAPEWORM, *Dipylidium caninum*, occurs commonly in both dogs and cats.

The adult worm is 12 to 16 inches long. The gravid segments are shaped like melon seeds. Infection is established when the definitive host swallows fleas or biting lice, in which the larval stages are found.

This tapeworm may be transmitted to people, particularly children, as a result of the accidental swallowing of the intermediate hosts.

THE INFECTIVE LARVAE of a number of tapeworms affecting dogs and cats develop in various mammals. The immature stages, usually called bladderworms, consist of one or more tapeworm heads in a thin, membranous sac filled with fluid. These tapeworms are more common in rural areas where dogs and cats (particularly dogs) are more likely to encounter the carcasses of infected animals.

Among the commoner tapeworms of this group are *Taenia pisiformis*, which is obtained by dogs from the entrails of rabbits, and *T. taeniaformis*, the immature stage of which occurs in the liver of rats and mice.

The larval stage of the hydatid tapeworm, *Echinococcus granulosus*, occurs in the liver and lungs of sheep, cattle, swine, and other animals. It also occurs occasionally in people and is a serious public health problem in some parts of the world.

The adult worm is primarily a parasite of dogs. The smallest species that occurs in dogs, the mature worm consists of only 3 or 4 segments and measures about one-fourth inch in length.

Immature stages of other species occur in cattle, sheep, swine, and various small wild animals.

THE BROAD FISH TAPEWORM, *Diphyllobothrium latum*, and the related species *D. mansoni* and *D. mansonoides*, differ substantially from all species we have described so far. The head of these worms has long, narrow, sucking grooves, rather than cup-shaped suckers. They require two intermediate hosts instead of one.

The first intermediate host of all species is a small crustacean, or crayfishlike animal, called Cyclops. The second intermediate host of *D. latum* is a fish. The infective larvae of the other species occur in frogs, snakes, mice, and other small animals.

The broad fish tapeworm occurs in dogs and related carnivores in Florida and in the Great Lakes region, where it is also found in people. The other species are encountered only rarely in the United States.

THE FLUKES, or trematodes, that parasitize carnivores are generally small, unsegmented, flat worms that require two intermediate hosts in order to complete their life cycles. Certain snails invariably serve as the first intermediate host. The second is usually a fish or some other aquatic animal. Only one trematode, *Troglotrema salmincola*, the so-called salmon-poisoning fluke, is of major importance in the United States. This parasite occurs only in northern California, Oregon, Washington, and southwestern Canada, where it is associated with a fatal disease of dogs, foxes, and coyotes. The parasites are hardly visible to the unaided eye and are generally deeply embedded in the lining of the small intestine.

Cats may become infested with the flukes, but they do not develop the disease commonly seen in dogs.

The eggs of the fluke are passed in the feces and hatch after several weeks of development in water. The liberated larvae, called miracidia, eventually penetrate a fresh-water snail in which certain developmental changes occur.

They emerge later as tadpolelike larvae (known as cercariae), penetrate the body of fish of the salmon family, and encyst in the muscles and other organs as the infective stages, which are called metacercariae. The definitive host becomes infested after eating raw or improperly cooked fish. The flukes reach maturity in a week or 10 days.

So-called salmon poisoning is caused by a rickettsialike organism, *Neorickettsia helminthoeca*, which is transmitted by the fluke. The rickettsia occur in the blood and lymph tissue of infected animals, and the infection can be transmitted by injecting those substances into susceptible dogs. Animals that recover spontaneously or because of treatment with established remedial agents are immune to the disease, although the flukes may become established in their intestinal tract.

The symptoms of salmon poisoning develop 7 to 10 days after the infected fish are ingested by susceptible hosts. At first there is an elevated temperature, marked depression, loss of appetite, and increased thirst. Vomiting and diarrhea begin after a few days. The feces are mucoid and watery, but in time they become blood-tinged and are nearly all blood in the final stages of the disease. Death usually occurs within a week or 10 days if the patient is not treated.

THE PROTOZOA—minute, one-celled organisms—are responsible for four diseases of dogs and cats that are of some importance in the United States. Two, coccidiosis and giardiasis, involve the intestinal tract. The others, canine piroplasmosis and leishmaniasis, are parasites of the blood and associated organs.

COCCIDIOSIS is widespread throughout the country but is particularly prevalent in the warmer areas of the

South. The disease is less frequently encountered in cats than dogs, possibly because of their cleaner habits.

Three species of coccidia, *Isospora bigemina*, *I. rivolta*, and *I. felis*, are commonly found. A fourth, *Eimeria canis*, is encountered occasionally.

These parasites invade the cells of the small intestine, where they multiply rapidly and destroy considerable tissue. The organisms eventually give rise to the resistant egglike forms—oöcysts—which are eliminated in the feces. Under favorable conditions of temperature and moisture the oöcysts become infective in a few days and are transmitted to susceptible hosts in contaminated feed or water.

The disease is marked by a severe diarrhea, in which the feces are mucoid and frequently consist largely of blood.

Usually marked depression, loss of appetite, general weakness, anemia, and dehydration also are noted. Heavy infections in young animals commonly end in death.

GIARDIASIS, an intestinal infection of dogs, is caused by the protozoan, *Giardia canis*. The disease occurs mainly in young animals and is characterized by dysentery and diarrhea. In heavy infections the feces are bloody and mucoid and generally have an offensive odor. The disease is becoming more frequent all over the country.

The parasites live in the small intestine and pass through two stages in their life cycle.

The parasitic stage, called a trophozoite, is pear shaped and active. It may be seen in fluid or semifluid feces when the feces are examined under a microscope.

The oval-shaped, inactive cystic stage is found only in formed stools. It is this stage that is transmitted from one host to another.

It has been reported that a closely related human species is transmissible to dogs and produces fatal infections in them, but it has not been established whether the dog form can be transmitted to people.

CANINE PIROPLASMOSIS is caused by an organism known as *Babesia canis*. In this country it occurs principally in Florida and the adjacent States. The disease is not known to occur in cats.

The pear-shaped parasites are found in the red blood cells. Ticks transmit them from one animal to another. In the United States the brown dog tick, *Rhipicephalus sanguineus*, is considered to be the chief vector.

The disease may occur in either an acute or chronic form. Animals affected with the acute form are off feed but generally show an increased thirst. The pulse and respiration rates are increased, and the animals commonly have an elevated temperature. The mucous membranes of the mouth and eyelids often are reddened in the early stages but may become yellowish as the condition progresses, an indication of jaundice. The acute cases frequently terminate in death. The symptoms in the chronic form are less pronounced. There may be an intermittent fever, diminished appetite, and loss of weight. The animals are generally anemic and become weak and indifferent to their surroundings. Death may be delayed for several days or weeks; sometimes the animals recover.

LEISHMANIASIS, or kala azar, of dogs has been recognized recently in the United States. In each instance the disease was found in dogs that were brought into the country by servicemen returning from duty overseas.

The disease is caused by *Leishmania donovani*, an oval or round nonmotile cell that occurs in the liver, spleen, bone marrow, and lymph nodes of affected vertebrates. A chronic inflammation of the skin may be spotted or diffuse. Loss of hair and marked enlargement of the superficial lymph glands occur. The disease is transmitted by the sandflies and is transmissible to man and other animals.

THE CONTROL OF PARASITISM in dogs and cats is important for several reasons. In North America dogs and cats are subject to infestation with more than 70 kinds of internal parasites.

Some of the pests, particularly hookworms and large roundworms, are extremely destructive and are often formidable obstacles to the successful rearing of dogs and cats. Indeed, it has been estimated that at least 10 percent of all puppies and kittens born each year in the United States die from the effects of parasitism.

Of equal or greater significance are the unspectacular losses that are manifested by lowered resistance to infectious diseases, retarded growth, reduced efficiency, and general ill health. Furthermore, a number of dog and cat parasites, notably hookworms, large roundworms, and certain tapeworms, can be transmitted in some form to people and to the food-producing animals on the farm.

It is evident therefore that the importance of controlling parasites in dogs and cats is threefold: Their welfare and survival, safeguarding human health, and the protection of livestock.

Parasite control in dogs and cats is of two general types—preventive and medicinal.

Prevention, largely the duty and responsibility of the animal owner, includes establishing and maintaining proper sanitary conditions, carefully supervising the animal's food habits, and maintaining an adequate control over its whereabouts.

Medicinal control involves the administration of chemical agents to the parasitized animals. It should not be attempted by an owner who is unfamiliar with the need for the chemicals and their potential toxicity.

The formulation of control measures to prevent parasite infections hinges on a thorough knowledge of the life cycle of the parasite, including the sources of infection, the modes of transmission, and the resistance of its preparasitic stages to physical and chemical agents.

One of the main sources of infection with many of the roundworms affecting dogs and cats is premises contaminated with feces or other excrement that contain parasite eggs or larvae. Freshly deposited eggs and larvae are not an immediate hazard; they must undergo a period of development before they can become established in susceptible hosts.

The dog or cat becomes parasitized when it swallows the infective stages with food or water or when the larval worms burrow through the skin. It is therefore apparent that strict sanitation—the frequent and thorough removal of excrement—is important. Applying chemicals to the soil that destroy parasite eggs and larvae is an effective supporting measure.

Dogs and cats acquire other parasites, particularly tapeworms, by eating raw or insufficiently cooked meat or fish, discarded viscera, or carcasses of cattle, sheep, swine, rabbits, squirrels, and other animals that contain the larval stages of the worms. Obviously the control of parasites so obtained requires the close supervision of the animal's food supply and a restriction of its freedom to run at large.

A few of the parasites affecting dogs and cats, notably the heartworm, double-pored tapeworm, and blood protozoa, are transmitted by fleas, flies, lice, ticks, and mosquitoes. The control of these infections therefore depends on the eradication of the intermediate hosts or protection of the animals from their bites. That may be accomplished by the judicious use of suitable chemical agents and by limiting the freedom of the animals to roam at will.

The prevention of losses from parasitism also may be aided materially by regular grooming, by providing dry, comfortable sleeping quarters free from drafts, and by maintaining the animals on a balanced diet.

The importance of diet in the control of parasitism has been demonstrated in dogs by a greater susceptibility to hookworm infections in animals maintained on an inadequate diet; a loss of acquired resistance to infection when animals are changed from an adequate to an inadequate diet; and an increase in resistance to infection and a loss of worms when an inadequate diet is improved. Dogs are more susceptible to infection with large roundworms when kept on a diet deficient in vitamin A.

The symptoms exhibited by parasitized animals are seldom distinctive and are easily confused with the signs in other diseases. Therefore many pet animals die each year from improper treatment by their owners or because proper treatment was not given or was unduly delayed. The owner must recognize the need for medical attention, but it is equally important for him to realize that improper treatment will delay or preclude recovery. Consequently a prompt, accurate diagnosis is imperative in formulating control measures and in selecting appropriate medicinal agents. The drugs used for removing parasites are poisonous to a certain degree, and the dosages employed must be determined individually on the basis of age, weight, and general condition of the patient.

Ordinarily little difficulty is encountered in giving pills and capsules to dogs, but cats are less tolerant of manual restraint and resist medication. Cats also are generally more sensitive to the toxic effects of most drugs than are dogs; particular care therefore must be exercised in selecting appropriate drugs and calculating proper dosages for use in cats.

To avoid possible injury to the animal and to the owner, it would be prudent in all cases to entrust the medication of dogs and cats, particularly cats, to a veterinarian.

The practicability of the general control measures we discuss hinges in large measure on the conditions under which the animals are maintained. On farms or in suburban areas where the animals generally run at large, the chief control measures consist in the judicious use of appropriate medicinal agents and in the proper disposal of viscera and animal carcasses that may contain infective stages of para-

sites transmissible to dogs and cats. In kennels or catteries, on the other hand, the animals are usually closely confined and the dispersal of excrement containing preinfective stages of the parasites is limited. Under those conditions, most of the suggested control measures are feasible and should be employed to the fullest extent.

The diagnosis of parasitism, the selection of suitable drugs, the computation of proper dosages, the administration of the medicament, and the use of appropriate supportive measures including tonics, changes in diet, and blood transfusions are all responsibilities that should be entrusted to a veterinarian. He is best qualified by virtue of specialized training and experience to manage all aspects of parasitism, and other disease conditions, with skill and dispatch. For the information of the owner, however, we give brief consideration to the more important parasites of dogs and cats with respect to the availability of specific remedial agents and with regard to appropriate preventive measures that tend to minimize the need for medication.

The commonest and most injurious internal parasites of dogs and cats are the hookworms and large roundworms or ascarids. The former are particularly destructive to dogs, especially nurslings and weanlings, and only occasionally produce serious losses among cats. Ascarids, on the other hand, are commonly found in both hosts. A number of chemicals are available for removing these worms from the intestine of the host. The most useful of these, toluene, n-butyl chloride, and tetrachloroethylene, are employed against either type of worm in both hosts. Another drug, hexylresorcinol, is commonly used against ascarids and, to a lesser extent, hookworms, in dogs, but it is not generally recommended for use in cats.

Because cats seldom require medication for the removal of hookworms, diethylcarbamazine and other piperazines, drugs highly effective against ascarids but without significant action against the common hookworm in the United States, are probably preferred treatments for cats because of their greater safety. Piperazines are also useful in dogs infested primarily with large roundworms or ascarids.

Migrating ascarid and hookworm larvae in the body of the host are not affected by chemotherapeutic agents.

In the prevention of large roundworm infections, it is imperative to bear in mind the two main modes of infection, namely, the swallowing of embryonated eggs and the passage of migrating infective larvae to developing offspring through the placenta. To this end, large roundworms in the intestine of the dam should be removed by an appropriate medication before breeding or, at least, by the middle of the gestation period. Thereafter, the animal should be kept under conditions that preclude exposure to embryonated eggs of this parasite until after the young are weaned. This may best be accomplished by housing the animal in an area not previously occupied by dogs or cats because it is not feasible, at present, to destroy the eggs of this parasite by chemical means.

Before the animal is moved to clean quarters, all accumulations of dirt and feces in the hair and on the skin, particularly around the mammary glands, should be thoroughly removed. In the prevention of prenatal infections, it is imperative to prevent exposure of the dam to embryonated eggs. It is of little use to keep the dam free of these worms by medication if she is constantly exposed to new sources of infection. The larvae that hatch from embryonated eggs in the body of the dam and migrate through her blood stream may be incapable of developing to maturity in her intestine because of an acquired immunity, but they are fully capable of passing through the placenta to the unborn young and, indeed, may have a greater tendency to do so in a mature, resistant animal.

Insofar as hookworms are concerned, the preventive measures described for large roundworms are equally applicable since infections may be acquired in a similar manner.

An additional mode of infection obtains with hookworms, however, since their infective stage is an active, aggressive larva, rather than an immobile egg. Infective hookworm larvae may penetrate the skin of the host and become established in the intestine after migrating through the blood stream and lungs. Unlike the thick-shelled, embryonated eggs of the large roundworm, however, infective hookworm larvae are subject to destruction by chemical agents and thus afford a vulnerable point for their control.

Hookworm larvae on hard surfaces or on bare dirt runs in kennels and catteries may be destroyed with saturated salt solution, sodium borate, and other chemicals. The brine is prepared by stirring common salt into boiling water at the rate of 1.5 pounds of salt to a gallon of water. The salt solution is sprinkled over the desired surfaces with an ordinary sprinkler can in amounts sufficient to provide thorough coverage of hard surfaces and to assure saturation of the soil to a depth of 1.5 inches or so. The amount required for the latter will depend upon the type of soil, but about 1 pint of brine per square foot of soil surface will probably be enough. The interval between treatments with the brine is governed by the amount and the frequency of the rainfall.

An effective alternative method consists in applying sodium borate to runs at the rate of 10 pounds per 100 square feet. The applications should be repeated at 4-week to 8-week intervals during the spring and summer in the northern part of the country and on a year-round basis in the warmer sections. The frequency of soil treatments depends on the degree of infestation of the animals and the type of soil; heavy clay requires fewer applications than sandy loam. This chemical is preferable to brine in areas of heavy rainfall because of its lower solubility. Both chemicals harm vegetation, and therefore should not be applied to lawns, flowerbeds, or other cultivated plots.

The heartworm is an especially serious menace among dogs that are used for hunting, racing, sentry or guard duty in the Armed Forces, and herding livestock on the farm. This parasite is of no clinical importance in cats, although occasional infections are encountered in them. Three chemicals—stibophen, thiacetarsamide, and diethylcarbamazine—may be used separately or in various combinations in the treatment of heartworm infections.

Stibophen is given in graduated doses by intravenous or intramuscular injection. Treatment may take several weeks. This drug sterilizes the female worms and destroys the circulating microfilariae.

Thiacetarsamide is given daily for 15 days by intravenous injection. Because the drug is extremely irritating to the perivascular tissues, care must be taken to avoid leakage during or following the injection. This chemical destroys the adult worms but has little or no effect on the microfilariae.

The other common heartworm remedy, diethylcarbamazine, is given three times daily by mouth for about 3 weeks. It is effective against microfilariae and has some action against the adult worms.

Because of the selective or limited action of these drugs, they may be given in combinations that will destroy both the adults and circulating microfilariae. It is evident therefore that the treatment of heartworm infections is frequently prolonged.

The prevention of heartworm infection is difficult because the parasite is transmitted through the bite of fleas and mosquitoes. Control, aside from periodic treatment, consists largely in protecting animals from the bites of the intermediate hosts, a rather impractical procedure in working dogs insofar as mosquitoes are concerned.

Of particular interest, however, is a preliminary study in the latter part of 1954 which indicated that heartworm infections were prevented with three daily doses of diethylcarbamazine given at intervals of 6 months. This regimen is a practical and economical procedure that warrants prompt and thorough study in endemic areas.

The whipworm is hard to remove successfully with medicinal agents because of its sheltered location. The drugs most commonly used against the whipworm are toluene and *n*-butyl chloride, but neither is completely satisfactory. Promising results have been reported with a drug called phthalofyne. It is possible that further experimental trials and field use may show this preparation to be the treatment of choice.

The prevention of infection with whipworms depends primarily on prompt, thorough disposal of feces and the use of clean utensils for feed and water. The thick, impervious egg shell of this parasite, like that of the large roundworm, does not permit its destruction by chemical agents.

No established, dependable treatments can be recommended for the removal or destruction of other roundworm parasites affecting dogs and cats in this country. Only strict sanitation and good husbandry practices can be suggested for their control. These species occur infrequently, however, and do not present serious hazards to the rearing of dogs and cats.

The control of tapeworms affecting dogs and cats, aside from the welfare of the host animals, is desirable because of the transmissibility of certain stages of these parasites to people and livestock. Satisfactory medication against these worms is frequently difficult because some remedial agents frequently fail to remove the scolex (head) of the parasite but produce only a "shearing" action on the strobila, or chain of segments. In that event, another complete strobila develops from the undisturbed scolex; and in time (depending on the particular species of tapeworm involved) ripe segments again are eliminated with the bowel movements.

A variety of medicinal products are

available for removing the different kinds of tapeworms that parasitize dogs and cats. None is effective against all species, and selection of the appropriate drug depends on an accurate determination of the particular tapeworm involved.

Arecoline hydrobromide, Nemural, Anthelin, and Di-phenthane-70, the last three being proprietaries, are the remedies most widely used against the common tapeworms affecting these animals, namely, *Taenia* species and *Dipylidium* species; but only arecoline is a satisfactory treatment for the removal of Echinococcus, the hydatid tapeworm.

The treatment of choice against the broad fish tapeworm and related species is Nemural, although male fern is an acceptable alternative choice if proper consideration is given to its greater toxic potential.

The prevention of tapeworm infections in dogs and cats is especially difficult because their intermediate or infective stages occur in natural feedstuffs and in such common external parasites as fleas and lice. Nevertheless, every effort should be made to prevent the animals from ingesting infective material, a recommendation that necessitates the control of fleas and lice, proper disposal of offal on the farm and in slaughter houses, and restriction of the animal's freedom to roam at large under conditions that permit it to kill and eat rabbits, squirrels, and other intermediate hosts.

House pets and animals that are raised in kennels or catteries have little chance to acquire tapeworms other than the common double-pored species that is transmitted by fleas and lice. For cats and dogs, therefore, prevention of tapeworm infections may be achieved largely by the application of such insecticides as methoxychlor, lindane, or chlordane to the host animals, bedding, and premises. The prevention of infection in dogs and cats on the farm and in other animals that are permitted to roam at large is virtually impossible. Control under these conditions, therefore, consists largely in the removal of worms from the infested animal with appropriate medicinal agents.

Only two protozoan diseases, coccidiosis and piroplasmosis, are of major clinical importance in dogs in this country although two others, giardiasis and leishmaniasis, are being encountered with increasing frequency.

The medicinal treatment of coccidial infections is not well established, although Di-phenthane-70 and certain antibiotics and sulfonamides have shown promise in limited experimental trials. The control of coccidiosis, therefore, is largely preventive and consists in providing and maintaining strict sanitary conditions, proper nutrition, and good nursing.

The drugs most widely used in the treatment of piroplasmosis, phenamidine and acaprin, are given by subcutaneous or intravenous injection, and a course of treatment generally requires several days. The dosages of these chemicals, like other drugs similarly administered, must be calculated carefully on the basis of age, weight, and general physical condition.

Favorable results have also been reported with chlortetracycline given by mouth, but more information must be obtained with this material before it is recommended for general use.

Prevention of infection depends largely on tick control. That may be accomplished by dipping or washing the animal in suitable insecticidal preparations and by applying residual insecticidal sprays to dwellings and runs occupied by the animals.

Tick control is covered more fully in the article on external parasites of dogs and cats. (Page 519.)

The treatment of giardiasis is largely experimental, although favorable results have been reported with quinacrine hydrochloride. Control measures for this infection are similar to those described for coccidiosis, because the infective stages are transmitted directly rather than by intermediate hosts.

Leishmaniasis in the United States

has been observed only in imported dogs and as a consequence no preventive measures are possible. In areas where the disease is commonly encountered, however, control measures are directed against sandflies, which transmit the parasites. Although phenamidine has been used in the treatment of leishmaniasis, relapses are common and specific medication is generally unsatisfactory.

The only trematode that concerns dog owners in this country is limited in its distribution to the Pacific Northwest. This parasite is responsible for the transmission of rickettsialike organisms that cause "salmon poisoning" of dogs and related carnivores, but it does not produce symptoms of disease by itself. Treatment of salmon poisoning, therefore, is directed against the rickettsia rather than the flukes, for which there is no effective treatment.

The drugs that have been most effective in the treatment of salmon poison-

ing in dogs are sulfamerazine, sulfamethazine, chlortetracycline, penicillin, and chloramphenicol. The prevention of infection with this particular fluke consists in preventing dogs from eating salmon or trout that contain the infective stages of the parasite.

F. D. Enzie *is a parasitologist in the Parasite Treatment Section of the Animal Disease and Parasite Research Branch, Agricultural Research Service. He received his veterinary degree in 1940 from the Ohio State University and has been engaged in parasite treatment investigations since 1942.*

Emmett W. Price *is head of the Helminth Parasite Section, Animal Disease and Parasite Research Branch, Agricultural Research Center, Beltsville, Md. From 1919 to 1926 he taught pathology and parasitology at the Agricultural and Mechanical College of Texas. He joined the Department of Agriculture in 1926, and from 1936 to 1953 was assistant chief of the former Zoological Division of the Bureau of Animal Industry.*

External Parasites of Dogs and Cats

CARROLL N. SMITH AND F. D. ENZIE

ALMOST everyone who keeps dogs or cats is concerned at some time with their external parasites. Among them are several kinds of mange mites, ticks, fleas, and lice. Fleas are the most annoying. Mange mites and ticks also are common and can quickly reduce an animal to a condition of misery or death. Lice are less common on dogs and cats in the United States.

Mange is an unsightly and painful skin condition caused by the burrowing or feeding of mites, several species of which attack dogs and cats. The mites are related to ticks and spiders. Many are microscopic in size, and the others are barely visible. The condition

is contagious and is spread by contact with infested animals.

Sarcoptic mange of dogs is related to the human infection called scabies and is caused by the mite *Sarcoptes scabiei canis*. The female mite burrows into the upper layers of the skin, where she lays 20 to 40 eggs. The eggs hatch after 3 to 7 days and produce larvae, which are tiny mites with three pairs of legs. The larvae grow to nymphs by molting—shedding the skin—and the nymphs grow to adults in the same way. The nymphs and adults have four pairs of legs, but the nymphs are sexually immature. The entire life cycle requires 2 to 3 weeks. The larvae, nymphs, and males do not burrow into the skin, but live under crusts or scales on the surface.

Sarcoptic mange may occur on any part of the body, but usually it appears first on the head. It spreads rapidly. Red spots appear and develop into small blisters. The scratching of the animal causes the reddish area to spread.

The burrowing of the female causes the skin to exude serum, which dries in crusts or scabs. The infected part of the skin becomes dry and covered with crusts, the hair may come out, and the skin may thicken and become wrinkled.

Itching is intense. The scratching may give rise to secondary bacterial infections and sores. Bacterial action in the scabs and sores causes an unpleasant odor. If the infection is not checked, digestion and other body functions become impaired, and death may result.

This species of mite can live for a time on people. Unnecessary handling of infected dogs should be avoided.

A related mite, *Notoedres cati*, causes a severe type of mange in cats, which usually starts about the head, forming crusts, until the skin becomes hard, thickened, and creased.

Demodectic, or red, mange of dogs is caused by a long, wormlike mite, *Demodex canis*, which lives principally in the hair follicles of the skin. It has been found also in certain lymph glands and in the liver, spleen, lungs, and other internal organs. The mites are found in typical cases in great numbers in association with bacteria, which cause the most unpleasant symptoms of the infection.

The first evidence of demodectic mange is usually the appearance of bald areas, from which the hair has been lost. Itching becomes pronounced as the spots spread, and the area becomes reddened. After invasion by the bacteria, the infection becomes pustular, the skin becomes thicker, poisons formed by the bacteria affect the general health of the animal, and a dis-

agreeable odor is produced. The infection may last for several years. It usually causes death if it is unchecked.

Ear mange of dogs and cats is caused by the mite *Otodectes cynotis*. The mites do not burrow in the skin but live deep in the ear canal, near the eardrum, and feed through the delicate skin. Irritation results. The ear canal becomes congested. The dog scratches and rubs its ears and shakes its head in an attempt to relieve the itching, or it may run in circles or show other evidence of nervous disturbance.

Mange may be confused with other skin conditions. It can be diagnosed positively only by a microscopic examination of scrapings from the diseased parts.

PREVENTION OF MANGE in dogs and cats is largely a matter of good care and management. A well-balanced, nutritious diet; clean, dry, comfortable quarters; protection from the debilitating effects of internal parasites; and regular, thorough grooming all promote good health and tend to increase resistance to skin diseases of all kinds.

Above all, however, the dog or cat should not be permitted to mingle with mangy animals or to frequent premises occupied by them, since they are the main sources of infection.

Rational treatment is contingent upon a prompt, accurate diagnosis, because the various types of mange differ in their response to remedial measures. Improper treatment is costly and may cause injury to the patient or permit the condition to reach an incurable state.

Ear mange will generally respond promptly to one or two weekly applications of olive oil containing 1 percent of rotenone or 0.25 percent of lindane. The materials may be applied with cotton swabs or put into the ear canal with a medicine dropper. Accumulations of foreign matter should be carefully removed from the ear canal before treatment. That can be done more easily if the accumulations are soaked first with the medicated oil.

Demodectic mange is difficult to treat. The results often are disappointing. The response to specific medication varies among individual animals and seems to be influenced by the patient's general condition. In addition to the use of chemical agents for the destruction of the mites, therefore, every effort should be made to build up the general health of the animal by improving the diet and combating secondary bacterial infections.

Several chemical agents are available for use against the mites, but none appears to be uniformly effective. Alternative treatments therefore should be tried when little or no improvement is noted after a reasonable period of medication. Among the preparations that have proved most satisfactory are 1 percent of rotenone in vegetable oil; a 25- to 33-percent benzyl benzoate emulsion; 0.15-percent aqueous lindane suspension; 2- to 5-percent tetraethylthiuram monosulfide; and a 0.25-percent chlordane emulsion.

Most of these agents are applied once or twice weekly, as necessary.

The finding of demodectic mites in lymph glands, liver tissue, and other internal organs has suggested the possible need for internal medication to supplement the application of remedial agents to the skin.

Sarcoptic mange may be treated effectively with any of the remedies suggested for demodectic mange. The treatment of sarcoptic mange, however, is less tedious; the disease often responds to a single application of the chlorinated insecticides, such as lindane and chlordane.

Similar response may be had with some of these materials in head mange of cats, although extreme caution must be exercised in the treatment of cats because of their marked sensitivity to most drugs. It is, in fact, advisable in all cases of mange to entrust treatment to a veterinarian.

TICKS of several species may infest dogs, but cats are rarely infested.

Many of the dog ticks are also known as wood ticks and infest dogs when they run through woods or fields. The brown dog tick is a truly domestic species that feeds almost exclusively on dogs.

The brown dog tick, *Rhipicephalus sanguineus*, is particularly troublesome because it is adapted to life in the relatively dry environments of kennels, heated houses, and apartments. Dogs pick up ticks in infested premises and in turn infest their own living quarters. Yards as well as houses in the southern States may be infested. The ticks may survive the winter outdoors in the extreme South. The brown dog tick is the principle vector in this country of canine piroplasmosis, a protozoan infection encountered most frequently in Florida and adjacent States.

The adult ticks are about one-eighth inch long when unfed, flat, and reddish brown. Both sexes feed on dogs. Mating takes place on dogs. The males remain about the same size.

The females become engorged with blood, reach a length of about one-half inch, and turn dark gray. After engorging, which takes about 6 days, the females drop from the dog and seek a hiding place. They usually hide in cracks in the woodwork, under rugs, or behind pictures, mirrors, or draperies. They lay 1,000 to 3,000 eggs, which hatch after 3 to 8 weeks into tiny, six-legged larvae, or seed ticks.

The larvae are light brown and about one-fiftieth inch long when unfed. They feed on dogs and become about one-twentieth inch long and slate gray. Feeding requires 3 to 6 days, after which they drop and hide like the females. They molt after 1 to 3 weeks and become eight-legged nymphs, about one-twentieth inch long and flat and brown. The nymphs feed on dogs becoming about one-eighth inch long and slate gray. They drop, hide, and molt to the eight-legged, sexually mature males and females. Engorgement requires 4 to 9 days and molting about 12 to 29 days.

Ticks crawl about the walls, floors, and furniture in heavily infested houses in search of a host. They very rarely bite people. Their mere presence is annoying. Heavy, continuous infestations on dogs cause irritation and loss of condition. Pulling the ticks off leaves open wounds, which may become infected.

The other ticks that infest dogs also infest other animals. They live outdoors and will not live long in dry, unheated buildings. They pass through the same stages—egg, larva, nymph, and adult—but all stages do not always have the same host.

The American dog tick, *Dermacentor variabilis*, is the most widely distributed species. It is most abundant along the Atlantic and gulf coasts, in the Mississippi Valley, and along the Pacific coast as far north as Oregon. Scattered infestations occur in most other parts of the country, except in the Rocky Mountain region and in the Pacific Northwest.

A closely related species, the Rocky Mountain spotted fever tick, *D. andersoni*, occurs in the Rocky Mountain region. Another, the Pacific coast tick, *D. occidentalis*, occurs in California and southern Oregon.

The gulf coast tick, *Amblyomma maculatum*, occurs along the gulf and Atlantic coasts as far north as South Carolina. The lone star tick, *A. americanum*, occurs from New Jersey west to Iowa and south to Florida and Texas.

Adults of all the foregoing species are reddish or dark brown and marked conspicuously with one or more patches of white.

The black-legged tick, *Ixodes scapularis*, occurs along the Atlantic and gulf coasts from Massachusetts to Texas and in the lower Mississippi Valley. A closely related species, *I. pacificus*, occurs along the entire Pacific coast of the United States. These species possess a smoky-black shield. The body of the females behind the shield is yellow or light brown.

All stages of the lone star tick and adults of the other species feed on dogs and other carnivorous or hoofed ani-

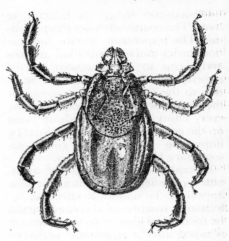

The adult female of the brown dog tick, a parasite of dogs and cats. (Magnified about 13 times.)

mals. Larvae and nymphs of the two *Dermacentors* feed on rodents, those of the two *Amblyommas* on rodents or birds, and those of the *Ixodes* on rodents, birds, or lizards.

The American dog tick, Rocky Mountain spotted fever tick, and lone star tick may carry Rocky Mountain spotted fever, tularemia, or other less common diseases from animals to people.

Dogs do not show the clinical symptoms of those diseases, but persons may become infected by picking infected ticks from dogs, particularly if the ticks are crushed.

The distribution of Rocky Mountain spotted fever is sporadic; some suburban or rural communities have a number of cases each year, others only an occasional one or none. Children playing in the woods or overgrown fields, or adults working there, may be bitten by infected ticks which, if not removed within a few hours, may transmit the disease. People living in neighborhoods where wood ticks occur should inspect themselves and their children once or twice each day for attached ticks. The scalp should be examined especially carefully. Any ticks found should be removed immediately. They should be grasped as near the skin as possible with forceps, or the fingers, and removed with a firm, even pull. The bite should be disinfected in the same manner as a small cut. In localities where Rocky Mountain spotted fever is prevalent, a protective inoculation may be desirable, and any fever of uncertain origin should be treated immediately by a physician.

The American dog tick and the Rocky Mountain spotted fever tick may also cause paralysis of dogs or children if the females attach and engorge at the base of the skull or along the spinal column. The paralysis usually begins in the hindquarters and moves toward the front of the body. It is caused by a toxic secretion produced by the ticks while feeding. Recovery is rapid as soon as the ticks are removed, but if they are not removed, death may follow.

CONTROL OF TICKS may require the treatment of the dogs and the infested area as well.

Dogs may be freed of ticks by washing or dusting them with insecticidal preparations containing rotenone (the active principle of ground derris root), DDT, or lindane. Washes or dips are usually more effective than dusts, as they are better able to penetrate the hair and reach all the ticks.

Derris root should contain at least 3 percent of rotenone and should be applied at full strength as a dust or at the rate of 2 ounces per gallon of soapy water as a wash. Commercial formulations of extracted rotenone also are available.

DDT should be used at a concentration of 10 percent in a dust or 1 percent in a wash. The wash is best made by adding 2 ounces of a 50-percent DDT wettable powder to 3 quarts of water. Lindane is used as a 1-percent dust or 0.05-percent wash, using, in this instance, one-fourth ounce of a 25-percent wettable powder to 3 quarts of water.

The treatments should be repeated every 3 or 4 days if dogs are constantly exposed to reinfestation.

Infestations of brown dog ticks in houses may be eradicated by thorough use of one of the common household sprays that contain 5 percent of DDT, 2 percent of chlordane, or 0.5 percent of dieldrin in deodorized kerosene. The spray should be applied as a wet spray to the woodwork, edges of carpets, behind pictures and draperies, and other possible hiding places of the ticks in all the rooms to which the infested dogs have had access. This will kill the ticks that are active at the time it is applied and will leave a residual deposit that will kill ticks that come out of hiding later. As the residual deposit kills slowly, active ticks that have emerged and are not yet dead may be found in steadily declining numbers for several weeks after treatment. If active ticks persist for more than 3 weeks, a second treatment should be applied.

The outdoor areas infested by wood ticks are often too extensive for practical control measures to be applied. However, it is sometimes desirable to eliminate lone star ticks, American dog ticks, or black-legged ticks from limited areas. That can be done by applying dusts containing 10 percent of DDT or 5 to 10 percent of toxaphene, chlordane, or dieldrin at the rate of 20 to 40 pounds to the acre. These insecticides may also be applied as sprays at the rate of 1 to 2 pounds of actual insecticide per acre. Lindane may be applied as a dust or spray at 0.1 to 0.2 pound of actual insecticide per acre.

FLEAS of four species commonly infest dogs and cats—the dog flea, *Ctenocephalides canis;* the cat flea, *C. felis;* the human flea, *Pulex irritans;* and the sticktight flea, *Echidnophaga gallinacea.*

The first three are quite active and run through the hair when disturbed. The sticktight flea attaches permanently on the less hairy parts, such as the regions around the eyes and ears.

Otherwise the habits of all four species are similar. Cat and dog fleas frequently infest houses in the Eastern States, as does the human flea in the West.

All fleas pass through four stages— the egg, the larva, the pupa, and the adult. The eggs are laid while the female is on the host, and they drop to the ground, where they hatch in a few days into wormlike larvae.

The larvae are not parasites, but live on organic matter in the dust or soil. The dust in habitual sleeping or resting places of heavily infested animals contains dried blood that was passed in the feces of the adult fleas, which makes an especially favorable food for the larvae.

In about 2 weeks the larva becomes full grown and spins a tiny cocoon, in which it transforms to the pupa. The pupa changes to an adult flea after a week or more, but the adult may not emerge for some time unless it is disturbed, as by the presence of a host.

Fleas often breed in tremendous numbers in rooms or buildings where dogs or cats are kept. The larvae proceed with their development even when the hosts are taken away, and the resulting adults may continue to appear for several weeks. If no cats or dogs are present, the fleas become particularly noticeable and annoying to people.

Dogs and cats can be freed of fleas by dusting with derris or cube powder, or commercial products containing 0.5 to 1 percent of rotenone. Since most fleas move about over the animal, it is usually satisfactory to treat only the back, neck, and head.

To kill sticktight fleas, it is necessary to apply the powder directly on the fleas. Rotenone is slow in action, and the fleas will not die for several hours. Furthermore, the residual effectiveness of the powder is not great, and animals that are constantly exposed to reinfestation require treatment every 3 days to 2 weeks.

Pyrethrum powders may also be used to free dogs and cats of fleas. If

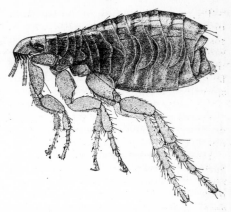

The female of the cat flea, a parasite of dogs and cats. (Magnified about 20 times.)

pyrethrum is the only agent present, the powders should contain at least 0.9 percent of pyrethrins, the active insecticidal principle of pyrethrum. Commercial preparations may contain an activator, such as piperonyl butoxide or sulfoxide, with which the content of pyrethrins can be greatly reduced. Pyrethrins cause a quick knockdown, but sometimes, especially with unactivated pyrethrins, the fleas may recover later unless they are collected on a paper and burned.

Neither pyrethrins nor rotenone is considered hazardous to dogs or cats, although cats may be temporarily upset by licking it from their fur.

Powders containing 10 percent of DDT or methoxychlor, or 1 percent of lindane, or 4 percent of malathion will also rid animals of fleas, and are safe for use on dogs. They have also been used satisfactorily on cats, but are not recommended for this use, because the cats may lick off enough of these insecticides to be harmful.

To control infestations of fleas in houses, spray the floors and lower portions of the walls with a commercial household spray containing 5 percent of DDT, 2 percent of chlordane, or 0.5 percent of dieldrin or synergized pyrethrum household spray. Be sure the beds of dogs or cats are cleaned frequently.

To control infestations in yards or under houses, dust or spray with a suspension of wettable powders of the same insecticides or lindane. Where these materials do not provide satisfactory control, malathion dust or spray is recommended.

THREE SPECIES OF LICE may be found on dogs and one on cats, but they are not common in the United States.

The sucking louse of dogs, *Linognathus piliferus*, is a bloodsucking species. It also infests some wild carnivorous animals. The biting louse of dogs, *Trichodectes canis*, has chewing mouth parts and feeds on dead epidermal tissue or secretions from the skin.

A second chewing species, *Heterodoxus longitarsus*, is normally parasitic on kangaroos, but has become established on dogs in several localities in North America.

The cat louse is also a chewing species, *Felicola subrostrata*.

The sucking lice and biting lice are quite different in structure and feeding habits, but their life histories are similar. All pass through the egg stage, several nymphal stages, and the adult. The eggs are fastened to the hair of the host. The nymphs are similar to the adults in appearance except for size and lack of sexual organs. The entire life cycle may be completed in a few weeks, and is passed entirely on the host, other animals becoming infested by direct contact.

Lice on dogs may be controlled by the thorough application of dusting powders containing 10 percent of DDT or methoxychlor or 1 percent of lindane, and by washes containing 1 percent of DDT or methoxychlor as a wettable powder. DDT is not always fully effective in the control of sucking lice on dogs, however.

Commercial preparations containing pyrethrins or allethrin plus an activator may also be used on dogs, and should be used in preference to the other insecticides on cats, as they may lick off enough DDT or lindane to be harmful.

CARROLL N. SMITH *is entomologist in charge of the Orlando, Fla., laboratory of the Insects Affecting Man and Animals Section, Entomology Research Branch, Agricultural Research Service. He received the degree of doctor of philosophy in entomology at the George Washington University and has been with the Department of Agriculture since 1931.*

F. D. ENZIE *is a parasitologist in the Agricultural Research Service.*

Infectious Diseases of Dogs and Cats

J. E. GREENE

DISTEMPER in dogs, like influenza of the human family, is an acute, infective disease caused by a filterable virus usually complicated by many bacterial secondary invaders.

Distemper occurs throughout the world—even in Iceland and Greenland.

Few unimmunized dogs reach 1 year without having contracted distemper. It is most common at about 7 months of age, less common after 2 years, and practically unknown in suckling pups. Unconfirmed diagnoses have been reported in dogs as old as 9 years.

A young dog usually begins to show the first symptoms about 5 days after it is exposed to the disease. The eyes become sensitive to light, as shown by squinting and the presence of a clear discharge. The rectal temperature usually rises to about 103° or 105° F. Swelling usually can be detected at that time in the lymph nodes of the throat. Death can occur during convulsions within a few days.

The fever reaches a peak in about 5 to 7 days and begins to drop to nearly normal until the 7th to 10th day. Then it begins to rise again. The temperature chart is irregular throughout the rest of the disease.

The animals become languid. The coat roughens. Loss of appetite develops. Usually rhinitis—inflammation of the lining of the nasal cavities—begins 1 to 2 days after the first fever, as shown by sneezing, rubbing the nose with the forepaws, and a nasal discharge, which at first is watery but later becomes thicker and whitish and sometimes streaked with blood.

Catarrh of the respiratory tract, as manifested by a short, soft, spasmodic cough and rapid breathing, inflammation of the eyes, a discharge of tears mixed with pus, and a tendency to avoid light, develops almost simultaneously with the rhinitis.

Digestive symptoms begin early. Loss of appetite, vomiting, constipation, diarrhea, extreme thirst, dehydration, and coating of the tongue are signs of that.

Nervous symptoms may begin with the other initial symptoms, or they may occur as late as the fifth or sixth week. They occur as rhythmic, brief spasms of the muscles that control the lips, cheeks, ears, and the fore or hind limbs, or in any group of skeletal muscles.

Early nervous symptoms often are manifested by epileptiform fits. Paresis (partial paralysis) usually begins in the hind limbs and progresses forward. Death occurs when any group of vital muscles is affected by the paralysis.

Some cases are affected by eruption of the skin, which begins as small pimples, which may contain pus and later become encrusted and emit a repulsive odor. The urine may contain bile pigment, indican, acetone, and albumen. Significant changes usually occur in the white blood cells. The disease usually lasts 10 days to 6 weeks.

Exposure to cold, parasites, inbreeding, malnutrition, and unhygienic conditions are believed to make dogs more susceptible to distemper.

From 30 to 80 percent of the dogs that develop distemper die.

As is true of most virus diseases, present-day antibiotics, biologicals, and drugs seem limited in their ability to alter the course of the disease once it has become well established. Careful nursing is necessary. Particular attention should be paid to forced oral or intravenous feeding of the essential food elements.

A number of different methods have been developed through the years for protecting dogs from this disease by vaccination. They include formolized tissue vaccine, followed by attenuated or unattenuated virus, serum and live or unattenuated virus, and modified live virus.

The vaccine and virus method is based on increasing the animal's resistance to the virus by one or more injections of the formolized (formalin-treated) vaccine before one introduces the live virus.

The simultaneous use of immune serum and unmodified virus, a method that was popular in the early 1930's, is not widely used today because of the apparent instability of the virus.

The modified-virus methods are based on cultivating the virus in an unusual host, such as ferrets or egg yolk, in order to render it incapable of producing the disease in dogs while maintaining its ability to stimulate resistance to disease.

It seems advisable to use occasional booster injections to maintain immunity regardless of the method of vaccination used.

INFECTIOUS CANINE HEPATITIS is one of the specific viral diseases of dogs. It affects primarily the endothelial and liver cells. It often includes symptoms of acute shock, followed by coma and death.

Infectious canine hepatitis has been miscalled fox encephalitis and infectious canine encephalitis.

Since most of the investigators credit Sven Rhubarth, of Sweden, with the original observations and differentiations, the virus usually is known as the virus of Rhubarth.

Transmission is usually by means of virus-carrying urine, which is passed by healthy carriers or by nonclinical cases. The disease usually is transmitted from dog to dog, although it may be carried indirectly by the hands, clothing, and implements of the handlers. James A. Baker, of Ithaca, N. Y., has shown that the disease is not carried across enclosures as narrow as 2 feet.

The virus withstands heat of 133° F., is stable at 4° F., and will withstand repeated thawing and refreezing. H. B. Parry and N. M. Larin, of the Canine Research Station, Newmarket, England, detected the virus in lice collected from sick dogs and were able to transmit a mild infection with inoculations of suspensions of such lice. This is not conclusive proof that the dog louse is a vector, but it may be accepted as circumstantial evidence that such a possibility exists.

Some investigators believe that the best way to destroy the virus is to use plenty of hot water, soap, and detergents and to follow that with a harsh disinfectant, such as the phenols (carbolic acid) and phenol-containing products, and a very caustic one, such as sodium hydroxide (caustic soda).

According to the studies of Parry and Larin, when the disease is introduced into a susceptible kennel or community, the percentage of sick dogs usually approaches 70, but the mortality rate usually is 12 percent or even less.

The more susceptible animals are apt to die within the first 24 hours.

Others may run a very mild course for 2 weeks or longer and show only hemorrhage of the urinary mucous membranes and the membranes of the eye and mouth, severe tonsillitis, and some loss of weight. They usually maintain their appetite throughout the course of the disease. Most of the affected animals will recover with supportive treatment.

A hyperimmune serum is available that seems to be effective in preventing the disease and slightly effective in treating the disease. A vaccine for immunizing dogs has been available since 1952. Statistics on the effectiveness of this vaccine are limited, but evidence does indicate its effectiveness in controlling the hepatitis.

Some investigators believe that the incubation period is 5 to 10 days, at the end of which time a rise in temperature can be expected, the white blood count may decline, and the development of tonsillitis and hemorrhagin visible mucous membranes occur. However, the appetite is rarely affected as is the case in canine distemper.

The more susceptible animals develop severe and rapid enteritis (inflammation of the intestines) which may be accompanied by massive bleeding from the rectum and end in sudden death.

The least susceptible animals develop tonsillitis and lesions of the mucous membrane, usually become jaundiced, have a loss of energy and sometimes soreness over the area of the gallbladder, and may develop opacity of the cornea (white eye).

Infectious canine hepatitis is difficult to differentiate from leptospirosis and canine distemper. Differentiation often is possible only by examination of tissues microscopically for inclusion bodies (tiny bodies that are in cells).

This disease is diagnosed by finding inclusion bodies in the cells of the blood vessels lining the liver, in contrast to inclusion bodies of distemper (which are found in cells lining the urinary bladder and the respiratory tract), and to leptospirosis (which produces no inclusion bodies).

The primary physical difference in the symptoms of hepatitis and distemper seem to be in the maintenance of appetite in hepatitis and the loss of appetite in distemper. A fairly common late symptom of hepatitis is inflammation of the cornea of the eye, giving it a bluish appearance.

Because the virus may be shed in urine for 6 months or longer, recovered animals should be considered as carriers. It is advisable to use immune serum liberally in kennel outbreaks and to keep careful daily records of the temperatures.

LEPTOSPIROSIS is produced by a spirochete, a bacterial organism, *Leptospira icterohemorrhagiae* or *Leptospira canicola*. It has been known as Weil's disease or Stuttgart's disease and sometimes has been called blacktongue, sore mouth, or canine typhus.

These spirochetes are shed in the urine of infected animals and healthy carriers.

The brown rat is a carrier of *L. icterohemorrhagiae*, but it is not a carrier of *L. canicola*, which is the commoner species in dogs.

Despite the known ability of leptospirosis to invade and attack the skin, the dermis of the dog probably offers an impenetrable barrier, except in the very tender places joining the footpads.

Most investigators believe the disease is transmitted directly from the contaminated genitals of one animal to another animal. Like hepatitis, this disease is not airborne. It must be transmitted by direct contact and it can be controlled by practical hygiene.

Because the spirochete is susceptible to heat and drying, the disease seems to be most prevalent during the wet, cool months. Because of the less resistant nature of these spirochetes in comparison with the virus of hepatitis, however, the disease does not seem to assume the epidemic proportions of hepatitis.

It is hard to differentiate between this disease and distemper and hepatitis; the general course usually is milder and more chronic than in the others. The sudden and dramatic death that occurs from hepatitis does not occur in outbreaks of leptospirosis.

The onset of the disease usually follows constipation and lameness in the hind legs and tenderness around the groin. In the early stages, the kidney region is extremely tender and the rear legs are lame. In that stage the animal loses its appetite and may begin vomiting and develop a fever of 103° to 106°, which may last 1 day to 3 weeks.

The visible mucous membranes of the eyes and mouth usually look congested. The temperature may drop to normal or subnormal within a short time, and signs of severe dehydration may develop. During this stage the affected dogs may die within 5 to 10 days, or convalescence may begin in the second week and extend to the sixth week. The tonsils remain unchanged. Jaundice may occur.

The tenderness in the abdomen is less pronounced and is centered usually in the region of the kidney, rather than in the liver region. The white blood count is high. Mouth lesions may be severe, with ulcerations and sometimes actual sloughing of the tongue. Nosebleed occurs occasionally.

No inclusion bodies are found in this disease, but spirochetes can be demonstrated in the liver tissue by staining with silver nitrate and on examination may be found in the concentrated urine and blood serum by dark-field examination.

A serological test has been used in detecting animals that at one time have been exposed to this spirochete. This test is difficult to use as a clinical aid, however, because as many as one-third of the animals may react positively to it, although they show no clinical symptoms of the disease.

Inoculation of hamsters helps in reaching a diagnosis.

M. K. Heath, who conducted research at Alabama Polytechnic Institute, found that the antibiotics, particularly streptomycin, offer an excellent means of treatment if started early.

In contrast to virus diseases, animal serum does not seem to be of any particular value in preventing or treating leptospirosis, except that it may be of value in adding normal blood constituents when needed.

The tissues attacked are primarily the kidney and liver, but the clinical symptoms are difficult to tell from those of canine distemper and those of hepatitis.

Because surveys show that 11 to 30 percent of the dogs are temporary or permanent carriers of leptospirosis, the disease apparently is mild and is unrecognized in most cases.

BABESIOSIS is caused by *Babesia canis*, a parasite in the blood cells. It occurs almost everywhere.

Many species of ticks transmit it. The incubation period is 7 to 10 days. It is accompanied by fever, lassitude, anemia (later cyanosis), jaundice, loss of appetite, extreme thirst, and bile-stained urine.

It may be diagnosed by finding the parasites in the blood cells.

Trypan blue given intravenously in a 1-percent solution is a useful treatment.

TULAREMIA is caused by *Bacterium tularense*. It has been reported occasionally in at least 46 States and the District of Columbia.

Rabbits and other rodents are reservoirs of the disease. Ticks or insects that have fed on infected animals may transmit tularemia to dogs. It may be contracted by eating uncooked infected meat, by drinking infected water, or by having infected materials come in contact with the skin.

The clinical signs are nausea, fever for 10 to 15 days at 104° to 106°, loss of appetite, anemia, and an increased white blood cell count. In the cutaneous (skin) type, the lymphatics may abscess. The ophthalmic (eye) type is characterized by itching, discharge of tears, severe inflammation of the eyes, punched-out ulcers, and sensitiveness to light.

Because this disease is transmissible to people, dogs with tularemia should be handled only by those who are familiar with the precautions that should be taken.

NOCARDIOSIS is a rather rare disease of dogs. Symptoms include generalized weakness, lameness of hind legs, edema of the extremities, rapid breathing, generalized soreness, and fever. A pathologic examination discloses small nodules in the heart, liver, lymph nodes, lungs, and kidneys.

Nocardiosis is either acute or chronic. The general symptoms are like those of influenza, with rapid loss in weight and general emaciation. Abscesses are present in most of the lymph nodes in the chronic cases. Enlarged spleen, accumulation of pus around the lungs, and catarrhal enteritis are rather common.

HISTOPLASMOSIS, caused by the fungus *Histoplasma capsulatum*, is an infection characterized by diarrhea, chronic cough, weakness, anemia, and general emaciation.

Cases of canine histoplasmosis have been reported all over the world. Most cases reported in the United States have been in the East Central States. The mortality rate in the acute cases is high.

No definite proof has been found to indicate that histoplasmosis is transmitted from one animal to another. Because the fungus has been isolated from soil, it is probable that the infection is airborne.

No successful treatment for canine histoplasmosis was commonly available in 1956.

J. E. GREENE *is director of clinics at the School of Veterinary Medicine, Alabama Polytechnic Institute at Auburn, Ala. He is chairman of the Council on Education of the American Veterinary Medical Association.*

Miscellaneous Ailments of Cats and Dogs

M. K. HEATH AND W. M. DILLARD

FELINE distemper is known also as feline infectious enteritis and feline infectious panleukopenia. It is a highly infectious and contagious disease of cats. It is characterized by a sudden onset, pronounced leukopenia, a rapid course, and high mortality. A virus causes it.

Symptoms usually do not appear until 6 to 9 days after the cat is exposed to the infectious agent or to an animal that is sick with the disease. Some infected cats may seem well or have only slight impairment of appetite, and recover in a few days. But the more severe cases have fever and then become listless, remain prone, and refuse all food. Vomiting, diarrhea, and nasal and eye discharges may occur. The disease runs its course in 6 to 9 days.

Death may occur anytime after the cat refuses food. Death often comes before weakness develops—sometimes in a few hours.

Recovery—if there is recovery—usually begins 2 to 4 days after the onset of symptoms. The first sign of recovery is improvement of appetite. Once the animal begins to eat, it very likely will recover. The period of recovery usually lasts 5 to 6 days.

Diagnosis can be confirmed by making a count of white blood cells.

The antibiotics are useful in treatment of feline distemper. Among them are Chloromycetin, Aureomycin, and Terramycin.

Feline distemper serum has some value if it is given in the early stages of the disease. A 5-percent dextrose solution and the vitamin B complex should be given in the treatment of the more severe cases.

Active immunity is produced by a tissue vaccine prepared from the spleen and liver of artificially infected cats.

Approximately 3 weeks, calculated from the time of the first injection of the vaccine, are required for the complete development of active immunity. The duration of the immunity is not known. Passive immunity is produced by giving serum from hyperimmune cats.

All cats that recover from the disease are immune the rest of their lives. A naturally immune cat may transfer immunity to her offspring.

INTESTINAL OBSTRUCTION is the complete blockage of movement of the contents of the intestines. Incomplete blockage of the intestinal canal can be termed intestinal stasis. A differentiation of the two conditions therefore is merely one of degree—intestinal stasis may lead to obstruction.

Obstruction is usually mechanical in origin and occurs oftenest in very young and old animals. There are several causes. Dogs and cats often eat sticks, straw, garbage, and hair; all might cause obstruction. Hair balls are peculiar to cats and are due chiefly to their cleaning and grooming habits. Intestinal parasites (roundworms) are another common cause of obstruction in young puppies. Hernia and twisting or telescoping of the bowel are common causes or contributing causes of intestinal obstruction.

The first step in treatment is to remove the cause, if it is known. Normal evacuation of bowels is accomplished through surgery or the use of laxatives. In most instances, the laxatives should be lubricants (mineral oil) and such drugs, as milk of magnesia, and epsom salts.

If necessary, enemas should be used with caution to avoid rupture of the intestine and peritonitis.

Early treatment is necessary in order

to prevent toxemia, which may be caused by the reabsorption of intestinal toxins.

HEAT EXHAUSTION is the direct result of long exposure to abnormally high temperatures. It may occur without sunshine.

Symptoms develop quickly. The animal becomes depressed and then may stagger and become unconscious. The body temperature may rise to 110° F. Respiration becomes difficult, the nostrils are dilated, and mucous surfaces are greatly congested. The animal may die without regaining consciousness.

Recovery usually takes several days. Early treatment is necessary. The body temperature should be lowered gradually and steadily by sprinkling cool water over the body, applying ice packs to the head, and establishing adequate ventilation. Electric fans are a valuable aid in providing ventilation. Cool water enemas may be given carefully. Constant observation of body temperature is necessary in treatment to avoid chilling and shock. Removal of the cause in heat exhaustion should be given primary consideration.

Heat exhaustion, of course, is of seasonal occurrence. It happens oftener in dogs than in cats.

ECLAMPSIA, a disease of females in lactation or the final stage of pregnancy, is marked by excitability, stiffness, staggering, and convulsions.

Affected animals are unable to stand. The muscles become rigid. Respiration is rapid. The temperature rises. The patient emits cries of pain. This condition may resemble tetanus, or lockjaw, and poisoning by chlorinated hydrocarbons, particularly in the cats. Death may come quickly if there is no proper care.

The administration of calcium salts provides prompt relief from symptoms. Nursing offspring should be permanently removed, or at least temporarily, if possible. Complete rest should be provided. Sedatives may be necessary.

Recurrence of symptoms, necessitating repeated treatment, is not uncommon. Eclampsia seldom occurs in the latter half of the lactation period.

MOTION SICKNESS—or carsickness—is a systemic condition of dogs and cats that results from continued motion. Salivation, nausea, and vomiting are symptoms. Younger animals, less used to motion, are most susceptible.

Fear often is a contributing factor. Depression and yawning may recur.

Prevention should be directed to adapting the animal first by taking it on short, frequent rides; withholding feed and water 4 hours before a ride (or very light feeding if food is necessary); and sedatives, in recommended dosages.

Prompt recovery, with relief from symptoms, usually follows removal of the cause, regardless of severity.

WOUNDS in small animals are frequent and result from various causes.

The more common causes are automobile accidents, bites of other animals, cuts or punctures from glass, wire, and similar objects; and placement of rubber bands, wire, and similar materials accidentally or intentionally around the neck, tail, and limbs.

Wounds in animals may be obscure, and careful observation often is necessary to detect them. Puncture wounds of cats are an example. Hunting dogs should be examined carefully following hunting exercises for wounds and the possible presence of such things as wire, sticks, thorns, and glass.

Treatment and care of wounds in animals should include control of bleeding by direct pressure over the bleeding part or applying a tourniquet to bleeding limbs, ears, or tail. It is important to prevent infection of wounds; that can be done by applying a bandage and confining the animal in clean quarters.

Proper healing should be promoted with daily application of healing oils or salves. Healing powders are of equal value and convenient for use. Kero-

sene, turpentine, and similar solvents
should not be used because they often
cause further tissue destruction and
discomfort.

Injuries suffered in automobile accidents should be checked by qualified
individuals for possible fractures and
rupture of the internal organs. Many
wounds of small animals, including
extensive lacerations, may be sutured,
or closed, by the veterinarian if he is
called in time.

M. K. Heath *is professor of small animal surgery and medicine in the School of
Veterinary Medicine, Alabama Polytechnic
Institute at Auburn. He is secretary and
treasurer of the Alabama Veterinary Medical Association and a past vice president of
the American Veterinary Medical Association.*

W. M. Dillard *is assistant professor of
small animal surgery and medicine in the
School of Veterinary Medicine, Alabama
Polytechnic Institute.*

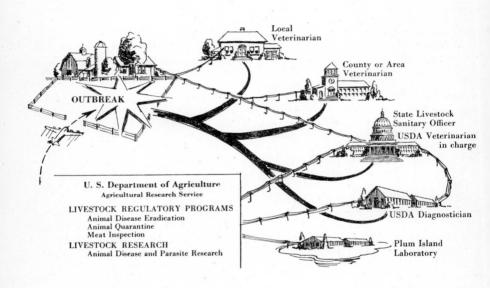

horses and mules

Equine Periodic Ophthalmia

T. O. ROBY AND L. O. MOTT

PERIODIC ophthalmia, or moon blindness, is the most common cause of blindness in horses and mules.

It is primarily a recurring inflammation of the inner portions of the equine eye and its associated structures. Nonacute stages follow acute attacks. One eye alone or both eyes together or alternately may be affected. Acute attacks begin suddenly. The time the acute symptoms lasts varies among animals and in the same animal. The extent of damage to the eye caused by one acute attack also may vary.

This disease has occurred in most of the countries of the world except Australia. It occurs often in the eastern half of the United States and much less frequently in the West.

Horses of all ages are susceptible. Most cases are in animals that are mature or are approaching maturity. The disease frequently occurs sporadically in a given group of horses.

Mules seem less susceptible than horses.

The diagnosis of periodic ophthalmia is based on the recognition and evaluation of several factors, the most important of which are the history of the animal with regard to previous eye disease; the nature of the abnormal changes; and the permeability of the blood vessels within the eye. If the animal's history is known, a positive diagnosis is reached much more easily because of the characteristic attacks and the frequent appearance of the disease in other animals in the locality.

The acute stage is essentially a marked inflammation of the iris and ciliary body. The ciliary body is deep

531

within the eye—behind the iris—and so cannot be seen. Outward signs are detectable, however. Some occur in other diseases of the eye and must not be taken in themselves as being diagnostic. A complete examination of the eye is indicated when any abnormality is observed. Knowledge of the structure of the eye is essential in making a diagnosis. In acute iridocyclitis—inflammation of the iris and ciliary body—the eyelids are usually inflamed, sometimes swollen, and very tender. An excessive quantity of tears runs down the face from the corner of the eye. The cornea—the outer surface—may look cloudy or milky if the inflammation is severe.

Practically all cases show some degree of corneal vascularization (penetration of blood vessels toward the center of the cornea). In the normal eye, no blood vessels occur in the cornea. If the horse is placed in a dark stall and examined with a strong light that has a narrow beam, it will be observed that during acute iridocyclitis the pupil is contracted and fails to dilate normally.

During acute symptoms an exudate (abnormal discharge) forms within the eyeball. The exudate contains clotted blood, white blood cells, and sometimes red blood cells. The exudate develops behind the lens and may not be seen unless some enters the front of the eye. The acute stage may last several days to several weeks.

Many of the acute inflammatory symptoms usually subside after the first attack. The eye outwardly may look normal again. An examination with an ophthalmoscope, however, usually discloses a sprinkling of small, opaque spots or a diffuse cloudiness in the fluid behind the lens. Small pieces of the iris may adhere to the lens capsule.

The eye looks more abnormal after successive acute attacks. Eventually the damage to the tissues of the eye persists permanently and is of greater extent. Then serious loss of vision results, and the animal's sight remains impaired.

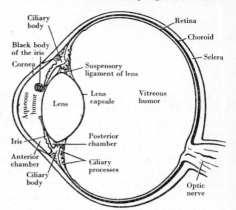

Diagram of normal equine eye.

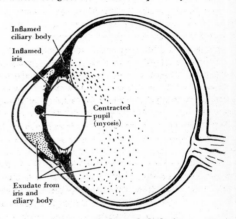

Acute periodic ophthalmia.

The final stage is almost complete blindness. No single case of periodic ophthalmia can be described as being average in terms of degree of severity and frequency of acute attacks, but it is usually true that once the eye has become affected, further attacks and blindness may occur later. Total blindness can result from the initial attack if the acute reaction is severe and long.

Regardless of the variability in the acute symptoms and in the number of previous acute attacks, an eye that has once been affected differs from a normal eye that has never been affected. That difference is the increased permeability of the vascular system of the iris, and particularly the ciliary body of the affected eye. This subtle but definite pathological feature can be denoted by the intravenous injection of fluorescein, a chemical dye, and by observing the emergence of the dye into the eye, as seen with the aid of an ultraviolet light. Only eyes which have been affected with iridocyclitis will allow the dye to become visible. Normal eyes prevent the penetration of the dye into their fluids. This technique has certain hazards and should not be undertaken without experience. It is indicated only when no other manifestations of the disease are detectable and a question of previous periodic ophthalmia is important.

The cause of periodic ophthalmia is not clearly understood as the disease is not yet reproducible under controlled experimental conditions.

Many theories as to its possible infectious, hereditary, parasitic, hormonal, nutritional, and allergic nature have been proposed. Most of these have been extensively studied without finding conclusive positive evidence of the exact cause. The sum of knowledge regarding the causes indicates that a combination of conditions is involved. Research studies since 1943 have emphasized the relationship between vitamin B_2 (riboflavin) and its effect in the prevention of periodic ophthalmia. More recently, reports by many investigators have suggested that the leptospiral micro-organisms may play a role in this disease of horses.

The microscopic lesions seen in equine eyes affected with periodic ophthalmia have been recognized as being similar to those seen in experimental animals that have been fed a diet deficient in vitamin B_2. Attempts to reproduce the naturally occurring condition in horses by feeding them rations containing little of this vitamin have not succeeded.

Evidence obtained by T. C. Jones and his coworkers at the Army Remount Depot, Front Royal, Va., however, indicated that the daily addition of a small amount of this vitamin to the ration of horses with normal eyes markedly lowered the number of new cases. This finding has led to the use of riboflavin as a supplementation to help prevent new cases of the disease. Adding the vitamin to the feed of animals that had periodic ophthalmia did not prevent further attacks and did not alleviate the symptoms in studies done by the Army.

Foreign and North American reports indicate that many horses having a history of periodic ophthalmia also have a much higher content of blood serum leptospiral antibody than do horses with normal eyes. This has aroused considerable interest in the possible relationship between the leptospira group of micro-organisms and periodic ophthalmia. Attempts to reproduce periodic ophthalmia in horses by injection of cultures of leptospira have not been successful.

Treatment of periodic ophthalmia is primarily one of reducing the ill effects. Prompt attention by a veterinarian to the attacks as they occur may prolong the sight.

The symptoms can be alleviated in several ways: By cold applications in the form of compresses to the eye; the administration of drugs to dilate the pupil in order to prevent adhesions between the iris and lens or cornea; and mild laxatives to lower the pressure within the eyeball.

The animal should be placed in a dark stall and kept out of strong sunlight during the acute stages. We know of no successful treatment for advanced cases in which extensive, irreparable damage has occurred.

T. O. ROBY *is a veterinarian employed by the Animal Disease and Parasite Research Branch of the Agricultural Research Service, where he has been engaged in work on anaplasmosis of cattle and infectious anemia of horses.*

L. O. MOTT *is a veterinarian in charge of the Viral and Rickettsial Disease Section of the Animal Disease and Parasite Research Branch. He received the doctor of veterinary medicine degree from Kansas State College.*

Equine Influenza

E. R. DOLL

DISEASES described as equine influenza are known also as pinkeye, shipping fever, stockyard fever, catarrhal fever, and epizootic cellulitis. The names have been applied to a complex group of contagious respiratory and systemic infections of horses, mules, and asses.

Two different filterable viruses are known to be involved in this disease complex. The viral infections often are complicated by superimposed or secondary bacterial infection. Streptococcic infection is the most frequent bacterial complication.

The most serious cost of respiratory diseases is the loss of work by draft animals and the interruption of training, racing, or showing of pleasure horses. Abortion is the main economic loss in breeding establishments.

One virus has been known for 30 years as the equine abortion virus. In sucklings and weanlings and in susceptible older horses, it causes a short period of fever, which is accompanied by symptoms of a mild respiratory catarrh.

The disease may become severe when it is complicated by bacterial infection. On breeding farms the disease is commonly referred to as colds. The term "influenza" is often used at racetracks and training stables. Pregnant mares seldom show symptoms but may abort 3 weeks to 3 months after infection by the virus.

The second virus causes high fever, symptoms of severe generalized illness, and respiratory and intestinal disturbance. The virus causes severe losses from abortion when pregnant mares are infected. The specific lesion it causes is a necrosis of the small arteries (arteritis). Other lesions and the symptoms result mainly from damage to the arteries.

The disease caused by either virus and the bacterial complications associated with infection by each have been described as equine influenza.

RESPIRATORY INFECTIONS occur frequently in horses and mules that pass through sales barns, remount depots, stockyards, fair stables, training stables, racetracks, and other establishments where many animals from separate sources are brought together.

Respiratory infections spread rapidly in large groups of horses and may become highly virulent and cause severe illness or death. Respiratory disease occurs sporadically on farms. Often it is mild and usually is introduced by a newly acquired horse. Farm horses that are stabled and pastured separately may escape the disease.

The signs of the different virus infections and the bacterial infections that follow as complications often are similar. Diagnosis depends on careful consideration of signs and lesions and laboratory tests.

Abortion virus infection can be distinguished from infection by the virus causing arteritis by complement-fixation tests or serum neutralization tests. Serum samples should be tested in pairs, one taken during the acute febrile stage and the other 2 to 3 weeks later.

Fever (103°–106° F.), watery discharges from the nostrils and eyes, inflamed eyes and nostrils, depression, weakness, and rapid breathing are early signs of infection by the virus causing arteritis of horses.

Difficult breathing is common. Exhalation is accompanied by a heave line and in more severe cases a pronounced abdominal lift.

Swelling of the legs, abdomen, mammary glands, scrotum, and sheath due to edema (accumulation of fluid) is a frequent symptom.

The term "pinkeye" refers to the swelling and congestion of the inner membrane of the eyelids, which may be so severely swollen that the eye is closed completely.

Severely affected animals are depressed, lose sensation to commands and physical pain, eat and drink erratically, and may finally refuse feed altogether.

Some animals are restless, move about without purpose, and frequently shift weight from one foot to another with cracking noises in the joints.

In critical cases the respiratory rate increases, the nostrils are flared, and breathing is accompanied by sounds that indicate edema of the lungs and accumulation of fluid in the chest and abdomen.

Some horses develop colic and profuse diarrhea and suffer great loss of weight. The horse becomes prostrate. Death occurs within 4 to 8 days after the onset of fever in acute cases.

Some horses have only a fever and slightly reduced activity and appetite. They recover promptly and the disease is not apparent to a casual observer.

In mild or moderate cases, without complications, the temperature returns to normal in 3 to 6 days and complete recovery follows promptly. The fever persists 7 to 9 days in severe cases and is followed by gradual recovery, which may take a week or longer. The mortality in uncomplicated cases is usually less than 1 percent, but may be as high as 5 percent. In the severe intestinal form it may be 10 percent or higher.

A second rise of temperature, often fluctuating, usually signals the development of complicating bacterial infections. They may affect the lungs, causing pneumonia; the intestinal tract, causing profuse fetid diarrhea; or the lymphatic system, causing abscess formation.

Other complications are inflammation of the nervous system, with severe depression, paralysis, twitching, or excitability; inflammation of the kidneys, resulting in frequent, scanty urination; and degeneration of the heart muscle, with serious changes in the character and rate of the pulse and prolonged or permanent weakness. Severely affected eyes may develop a keratitis, corneal ulcers, and cataracts. Laminitis and swelling of tendon sheaths may occur.

RESPIRATORY DISEASES are spread mostly by direct contact between infected and susceptible horses.

The viruses may be spread by objects with which the sick come in contact—mangers, troughs, feed, water, salt boxes, pails, cars, trucks, utensils, brushes, and brooms. They may be airborne in infected stables. Apparently healthy carriers of the viruses probably occur. The virus apparently dies in a short time in unoccupied stables.

Newly acquired animals should be held in rigid quarantine in an isolated stable, with separate attendants, for 15 to 30 days. The same practice should be used for horses being returned to a farm from fairs, shows, or racing circuits. The viral diseases are contagious, and sanitary precautions are not likely to prevent their spread through an infected stable. Strict isolation of an infected stable and adequate sanitary practices often prevent spread to other units on a farm.

Horses that are to be shipped may be protected to some degree against complicating bacterial infections (which follow viral respiratory diseases) by repeated injection of bacterins.

No specific vaccines or antiserums are available for the viral diseases. Temperatures should be taken twice daily of horses that are in transit and after arrival at fairgrounds or racetracks, so that isolation and treatment can be started promptly.

At the first sign of illness, usually a fever, the animal should have absolute rest in a clean, well-bedded, well-ventilated stall. It should have access to good hay and clean, fresh water. It should be fed lightly with grain and given light exercise after the temperature returns to normal. Exercise is important for reducing and preventing swelling of the legs.

Affected horses should not be returned to work until a normal physiological state is established. In mildly and moderately affected horses with uncomplicated recovery, a good rule would be 3 weeks after the temperature has returned to normal. Severely affected horses and those that develop complications may need more time.

Medicinal treatment should be prescribed by a veterinarian. Early treatment, at the first appearance of fever, may include the use of one or several antibacterial drugs to prevent development of complicating bacterial infec-

tions. Often no other treatment is necessary. Severe cases may require medication for regulating the bowels. Cardiac and respiratory stimulants may be necessary. Prostrate animals require artificial feeding and administration of fluids, salts, and nutrients intravenously.

E. R. DOLL, *a native of Missouri and graduate of the University of Missouri and Michigan State University, since 1943 has conducted research on antibiotic therapy for bacterial diseases of foals, breeding problems of mares, hemolytic disease of newborn foals and pigs, virus abortion of mares, and viral respiratory infections of horses at the Kentucky Agricultural Experiment Station.*

Breeding Problems

E. R. DOLL

DIFFICULTIES in reproduction are a major problem in raising work stock and pleasure horses. They include any cause of infertility or sterility of mares or stallions, breeding practices, abortions, foaling difficulties, and some diseases of foals.

General good health of breeding animals is important.

Brood mares must have adequate housing, balanced nutrition, regular exercise, and proper attention for the control of parasites and infectious diseases. About 50 percent of mares that are bred under ordinary circumstances without consideration of these principles have healthy foals. On specialized breeding farms where each animal receives careful attention, 60 to 80 percent of the mares bred produce healthy foals.

Breeding efficiency is improved when mares are bred in accordance with

their natural breeding habits. Wild horses usually breed during the spring months. Conception rates are higher late in the spring after mares have grazed new grass, have shed their winter hair, and are gaining weight.

The animal's sexual behavior, activity of the genital organs, maintenance of pregnancy, and mating are regulated by hormones secreted mainly by the pituitary gland, ovary, and testicle.

Abnormal secretion of the sex hormones may result in sterility or reduced fertility in either sex. In the male it may be manifested by impotency or temporary or permanent sterility. The impotent animal has no sexual desire or activity. The infertile or sterile animal is active sexually but is unable to reproduce. Effects on the female may be irregular sexual rhythm, failure to conceive, abortion, or complete cessation of sexual activity.

The egg usually is expelled from the ovary and passes to the uterus about 24 to 48 hours before the end of the heat period. Spermatozoa—the sperms— live 12 to 48 hours in the mare's genital tract. It is desirable, therefore, to breed 1 or 2 days before the mare goes out of heat. The length of the heat period of the mare usually is 18 to 21 days. Most mares are in heat 2 to 5 days. Mares tend to have uniform estrual cycles. If records are kept on the length of the heat periods of individual mares, the proper time for breeding is easily determined. Conception rates are higher for mares bred on the last day of the heat period. If the stallion breeds only 12 to 15 mares, mares may be bred every other day through the heat period with good conception rates.

Improvement of the conception rate results from having sperm available for fertilization at the time of ovulation. A stallion usually is permitted to breed 35 to 40 mares each breeding season and to serve a mare only once at each heat period. Excessive use of a stallion reduces his fertility and results in lowered conception rates.

Some mares have irregular heat periods that vary in length from 2 to 30 days. Others come in heat, but an egg is not produced by the ovary. Some have regular sexual cycles but do not show heat. Frequent examination of the genital tract of mares that have quiet or irregular heat periods enables the veterinarian to determine the correct time for breeding and will spare services of valuable stallions on mares that do not ovulate.

Hygienic practices during breeding and foaling and systematic veterinary examination of mares are largely responsible for the success of specialized horse breeding farms.

Barren and maiden mares should have veterinary examination during the fall to determine their soundness for breeding. Early detection of abnormalities permits adequate time for treatment and recovery of the mare before breeding the following spring.

The examination consists of thorough cleansing of the hind parts of the mare and inspection with a speculum of the vagina and cervix for infection or abnormalities. Infection is indicated by inflammation and abnormal secretions. If infection is present, a bacteriological culture is made to identify the infecting organism. Also, a manual examination of the ovaries and uterus is made by palpation through the walls of the rectum to determine if there are abnormalities that would prevent conception or response to treatment.

Infected mares may be given medicinal treatment appropriate for correcting specific infection. If necessary, the upper part of the vulva may be closed by surgical operation. Surgical closure of the vulva is the most effective single procedure for correcting uterine infections.

Similar examination should be made of the genital organs of foaling mares. Their genital organs usually return to normal within 7 days, and they come in heat 7 to 12 days after foaling. Examination of the genital tract should be made on the seventh or eighth day. Mares should not be bred at this heat period if the placenta was retained more than 3 hours; if any lacerations have not entirely healed; if severe bruises of the cervix, vagina, or vulva occurred; if purulent secretion or urine is found in the vagina; if the vagina or cervix are discolored or congested; or if the vagina or uterus lacks normal tone.

Some mares with young foals will not manifest heat. They must be examined with the speculum every 2 or 3 days, starting about 25 days after foaling, to detect heat and ovulation. Many horsemen prefer not to breed on the foaling heat but to wait for the second heat period. This practice lessens the risk of future troubles, such as genital infections, abortions, and diseased foals.

The placenta, or fetal membranes, normally are expelled in entirety within 2 hours after the foal is born.

The membranes should be inspected by a veterinarian to determine if all parts come out. Retention of a part or all of the placenta for longer periods indicates abnormalities.

Systematic hygienic practices should be employed in the breeding shed. Mares showing signs of infected genital organs should not be admitted for service.

In preparation for breeding, the external genitalia of the mare are washed with soap and water. The lips of the vulva are swabbed clean with cotton moistened in a mild antiseptic and rinsed with water. The tail is wrapped with a clean bandage. The mare should be restrained properly to prevent accidents or injury to attendants or the stallion. Breeding hobbles, a neck guard for the mare, and a nose twitch usually are enough. Owners of valuable animals usually do not use breeding stocks.

Before service, the penis of the stallion is washed with soapy water, swabbed with an antiseptic solution, and rinsed with clean water. The stallion is cleaned again after service.

Mares that have sutured vulvas must be protected from tears during breeding. This is done by use of a surgical stitch through the vulva at the lower margin of the repaired portion and use of a breeding roll, which restricts the depth of insertion of the stallion's penis.

Many breeders have the stallion's semen examined following each service to determine viability or abnormalities of the sperm and the presence of pus cells. A stallion having pus cells in the semen, indicating inflammation or infection of the genital organs, should be withheld from service.

When artificial insemination is practiced, semen is collected with an artificial vagina or in a breeder's bag. Semen from one ejaculate may be divided for insemination of 4 to 8 mares. This practice may prevent spread of some genital diseases, but may also result in genital infection unless conducted with scrupulous cleanliness.

A veterinarian can diagnose pregnancy by rectal examination 40 to 45 days after breeding. Pregnancy also may be determined 42 to 120 days after breeding by injecting mare's blood serum into laboratory animals or by chemical tests on mare's urine. Early examination for pregnancy is most valuable for detecting mares that did not become pregnant, so that measures can be taken to continue breeding or correct causes of their failures to conceive. Most specialized breeding establishments prefer to have pregnancy diagnosis made by manual examination, as reasons for failure to conceive may be determined at the same time.

About 50 percent of abortions in mares result from bacterial and viral infections. The cause of about 40 percent of abortions is unknown. A few are caused by injuries.

It is estimated that one-third of mares that become pregnant abort or have a weak or diseased foal when husbandry practices are no better than average. Properly managed breeding establishments have few such losses.

Streptococci alone cause nearly 20 percent of all abortions. Abortions from this infection are frequent in early pregnancy, but may occur at any stage of gestation. Some foals are born with streptococcic infection that was acquired before birth.

Diagnosis of streptococcic abortion is made by bacteriological examination of the aborted fetus, of the fetal membranes, or of the genital tract of the mare after abortion.

Abortion often results from infection of the uterus and fetal membranes without invasion of the fetus by the streptococci.

Mares become infected with streptococci after foaling or during mating or when a poor conformation of the genital organs permits air or feces to enter the genital tract. Difficult foaling, injury of the genital tract during foaling, and retained placenta predispose to infection.

Stallions rarely transmit the disease

except mechanically from infected mares.

Streptococcic abortion cannot be avoided by vaccination or medicinal treatment of pregnant mares.

Many losses can be prevented by breeding only noninfected mares and stallions and using hygienic precautions during breeding.

Examination of the mare's genital tract before breeding is essential. Bacterial cultures should be made from the cervix or uterus of any mares that show abnormalities. It is best to take cultures during a heat period. For foaling mares, the examination should be made on the seventh or eighth day. Medicinal douches and instillation of antibacterial drugs into the uterus may eliminate the infection.

Surgical closure of the upper part of the vulva is the most dependable corrective procedure. Strict sanitary precautions at foaling time and avoiding nonprofessional manipulation of the genital tract will do much to prevent infection. Ninth-day breeding should be avoided.

CONTAGIOUS equine abortion is caused by the bacterium *Salmonella abortivo-equinus*. Abortions caused by this organism may occur at any stage of pregnancy, but usually they happen from the fourth to eighth month. Mares get the infection by ingesting the infectious organism on pasture or with feed or water. Mares may show signs of generalized illness preceding or following abortion.

Diagnosis may be made by cultural examination of the aborted fetus, the fetal membranes, and the genital tract of the mare and by testing the mare's blood for specific agglutinins about 2 weeks after abortion.

Vaginal discharges, dead fetuses, and fetal membranes should be buried deeply or burned. Stalls and equipment in contact with a mare that aborts should be cleaned and disinfected. Aborting mares should be kept isolated and not bred until the genital tract is free of the infection.

The disease may be effectively controlled by eliminating reacting mares and stallions and systematic vaccination of pregnant mares with a specific bacterin.

OTHER INFECTIOUS micro-organisms cause fewer than 3 percent of known abortions.

Shigella equirulis, an organism causing septicemic infection of newborn foals, sometimes invades the uterus and causes abortion.

Escherichia coli, an enteric organism, occasionally causes uterine infection and abortion.

Staphylococci, the common wound infection organism, and *Corynebacterium equi*, which causes pneumonia of foals, also cause uterine infection and abortion.

Organisms less frequently found are *Pseudomonas aeruginosa*, *Klebsiella genitalium*, and flavobacteria.

Specific diagnosis can be made only by bacteriological examination of the fetus. Some of these micro-organisms cause serious infection of the genital tract and prolonged or permanent sterility.

ABORTION may result from certain drugs, including cathartics and worm repellents, and from eating poisonous plants, chemicals, and moldy or spoiled feeds. Severe illness from infectious diseases, with high fever, an attack of colic, or extensive suppurative wound infection, may cause abortion.

Twin pregnancy in the normally uniparous mare is pathological and nearly always results in abortion.

Twisted navel cords impair blood circulation in the membranes and nutrition of the fetus, with consequent abortion.

Malformations may be incompatible with development of the fetus and cause its death and abortion. Faulty attachment of the placenta causes undernourishment, death, and abortion of the fetus.

Other causes of abortion are genetic factors, hormone imbalances, kicks or blows over the abdomen, and severe exertion, fatigue, and exposure.

Pregnant mares should have light work each day or freedom for exercise in a pasture.

In areas where horses are raised extensively, about 40 percent of abortions result from unknown causes. These abortions are sporadic, noninfectious, and noncontagious. Usually they do not interfere with subsequent breeding and foaling.

VIRAL ABORTION was identified originally as a disease of the equine fetus. Later research disclosed that the virus causes a fever and mild respiratory catarrh of horses. Infection and abortion of the fetus is a phase of the disease in pregnant mares.

Viral abortions occur from the 5th through the 11th month of gestation. Relatively few abortions occur from the 5th through the 7th month.

Then about 14 percent of abortions occur in the 8th month, 33 percent each in the 9th and 10th months, and 15 percent in the 11th month of gestation. Viral abortions occur from September through May. They are most frequent from December through April, when 94 percent of outbreaks and 95 percent of abortions occur. The number of abortions per farm usually varies from 1 to 3, but on some farms 25 to 90 percent of pregnant mares abort.

Affected mares usually show no signs of impending abortion or ill health. They have no history of recent illness. Expulsion of the fetus comes about and progresses rapidly. The membranes usually are expelled with the fetus or soon thereafter. The mares usually suffer no ill effect from the abortion. The genital tract returns to normal as readily as after normal foaling, and they breed equally as well as after normal foaling.

Mares that abort from viral infection may experience any accident or complication associated with foaling or a stillbirth from other causes. These include tears, bruises, or lacerations,

retention of the membranes, abnormal position of the fetus, and prolapse of the uterus. These incidents are no more frequent in viral abortion than in abortion from other causes.

The incubation period—the time from exposure until abortion—varies from 20 to 90 days. An outbreak usually runs its course within 60 days after the first abortion.

Occasionally foals are born alive at full term with infection that was acquired before birth. Such foals live a few hours to several days. Signs are severe weakness and depression, difficult and rapid breathing, rapid heart rate, and foamy nasal discharge. Complications, particularly infection by streptococci and *Shigella equuli*, are frequent.

The fetal carcass reveals hemorrhages on the surfaces of the oral cavity, nasal passages, pharynx, larynx, trachea, esophagus, stomach, intestines, and the internal surfaces of the chest and abdomen.

Diagnostic findings are excessive fluid in the chest cavity, severe edema of the lungs, and focal necrosis of the liver. The fluid in the chest cavity is relatively clear and serumlike, and is present in quantities from a slight excess to 2 quarts or more. The lungs are pale, firm to the touch, and heavy. The interlobular spaces are widely separated by the edema. Liver lesions are present in 50 to 75 percent of infected fetuses and consist of tiny foci of necrosis that are gray or white in color and depressed below the liver surface. Lung lesions are present more regularly than liver lesions.

Laboratory diagnosis is made from gross lesions, by exclusion of bacterial infection, and by the presence of intranuclear inclusion bodies in tissue sections. Lung, liver, and spleen are the most suitable tissues for microscopic detection of inclusion bodies.

The intranuclear inclusions are found in the bronchial epithelium and alveolar cells of the lungs, in the hepatic cells, and in the reticuloendothelial cells of the spleen.

CONTROL PROCEDURES during outbreaks of viral abortion include strict application of sanitary practices and restricting caretakers and equipment to the affected barn. Manure and bedding should not be moved to other areas.

A mare that aborts should be left in the barn where the abortion occurred, unless she can be moved to an isolated point or placed with other horses not having contact with pregnant mares. Manure and bedding in a contaminated stall should be soaked with a strong disinfectant and left in the stall a few days before it is removed.

There is a distinct pattern of behavior of the abortion virus on breeding farms of central Kentucky. An epizootic in which signs appear only in sucklings and weanlings occurs each fall and winter. Infection by the abortion virus in the young horses causes a fever of 1° to 4° F. that lasts 1 to 6 days and a mild conjunctivitis and respiratory catarrh, which is accompanied by a watery nasal discharge. Some foals develop a mucopurulent inflammation of the nasal passages as a complication of the viral infection. Others are affected so mildly that the disease is not noticed. A pharyngitis and cough are frequent in some outbreaks. Signs of pneumonia are seen in some foals.

Infection of sucklings and weanlings usually begins in August or September, with an increasing incidence in October, but the highest incidence is in November. It recedes in December. Brood mares show no signs of the disease during the time it is present in their sucklings and weanlings. Many mares, however, are infected, but only a few abort. Abortions usually occur 1 to 3 months after the disease becomes evident in the young horses.

Horses may be affected severely when assembled from isolated areas into large groups. Continuous introduction of susceptible animals provides opportunity for increased virulence of the virus and the bacteria that are involved in secondary infections. Pharyngitis, pneumonia, abscess formation, enteric disturbances, and other aberrant forms are frequent. Then the disease closely resembles the conditions usually diagnosed as influenza.

E. R. DOLL, *who has a degree in veterinary medicine from Michigan State University, has been a member of the staff of Kentucky Agricultural Experiment Station since 1943.*

Diseases of Foals

E. R. DOLL

SOME of the diseases that may attack a newborn foal are strictly problems of management. Others are acute infections that require the prompt attention of a veterinarian.

The breeder who supervises foaling and carefully watches the foal during its first 3 days of life will be able to correct minor disturbances before they become serious. Early detection of illness and correct treatment have saved the lives of many foals.

The life of the mare or the foal may be lost during birth from a lack of attendance.

Normally a foal is born within 20 to 30 minutes after actual labor begins. Longer periods of labor usually indicate that foaling is not progressing properly and that help may be needed.

In normal birth the front feet appear first. The foal's nose is between its knees and its back is toward the back of the mare. The feet and nose usually appear 5 to 10 minutes after the water breaks.

Signals of trouble are the appearance of only one foot, failure of the nose to appear, more than two feet showing, feet turned upside down, failure of the foal to appear soon after the water breaks, and prolonged labor. A veterinarian should be summoned immediately.

Membranes should be freed from the foal's head after the head has cleared the birth canal. Some breeders allow the navel cord to be broken naturally. Others prefer to break it by pulling at the constricted part 2 or 3 inches below the stump. The cord should not be cut or tied. The cord should be disinfected after it is broken. Mild tincture of iodine is suitable. An effective means of application is to pour about 1 ounce of the disinfectant in a small jar, hold the jar firmly against the foal's abdomen, and shake it so that the antiseptic is in contact with the navel for about a minute.

After the delivery, the mare and foal should be permitted to rest and get up of their own accord. A foal ordinarily will be up and nursing within 1 or 2 hours. Foals that are not up and nursing in 3 hours need help in rising and assistance in standing while nursing. If the weakness persists for 5 to 6 hours, it is wise to call a veterinarian, because weak foals often have developed bacterial infections before birth.

Meconium, the fetal feces, may be impacted in the bowels, and an enema is required to remove it. Enemas are not necessary for every foal. Normally the foal begins to pass the meconium in a few hours. Retention of the meconium is indicated when the foal carries its tail high, strains frequently without bowel movement, and has colicky symptoms.

Enemas, warm water or 2 ounces of glycerin in 1 quart of water, should be given with a small, soft rubber tube, which is inserted 10 to 14 inches into the rectum. No more than 1 quart of enema fluid should be used. Excessive or too frequent enemas may cause a diarrhea. Syringes with metal or hard rubber barrels should not be used, because they may puncture the wall of the rectum. If the impaction of the meconium is persistent, professional assistance should be called in.

A CONDITION known as 9-day scours often causes worry among inexperienced horsemen. Foals often develop a diarrhea some 8 to 12 days after birth. Usually it is mild and persists for only a few days. The cause is thought to be a change in the milk that occurs in association with the mare's ninth-day heat period.

Rupture of the urinary bladder is infrequent in young foals. The cause is not known. The rupture nearly always is lengthwise and on the upper surface of the bladder. The foal cannot urinate. All urine is deposited in the abdominal cavity. The affected foal becomes sluggish. The abdomen is distended by the accumulation of urine. Death occurs in 3 to 5 days. Most foals recover after the abdomen is drained and the urinary bladder is closed by surgery.

CONTRACTED TENDONS, crooked legs, and aberrations of the feet are frequent in young foals. Any of these conditions may persist or become worse and affect the future soundness of the horse. Treatment consists of surgery on the affected tendons, use of braces, and corrective trimming of the feet.

BACTERIAL INFECTIONS cause various diseases of foals, among them navel-ill, joint-ill (or arthritis), pneumonia, scours, generalized infections (or septicemia), tetanus, and wound infections.

The micro-organisms involved most frequently are *Shigella equirulis* and streptococci. Organisms found less often are *Salmonella abortus-equi, Corynebacterium equi,* staphylococci, *Escher-*

ichia coli, and *Salmonella typhi-murium*. Almost any one of the organisms can produce one or more of the symptoms associated with bacterial infections of young foals.

Shigella equirulis infection is the most important single cause of illness and death of newborn foals. The organism exists in the digestive tract of horses. Infection may occur before or after birth. Symptoms frequently appear 1 to 3 days after birth. Then the disease is generalized and has little tendency to localize in joints or organs. The onset is rapid.

Symptoms are an early rise of temperature, increased pulse and respirations, congested membranes, slightly swollen joints, dullness, weakness, rapid prostration, and early death. In foals more than a week old, the course of the disease is slower, and visible joint involvement is frequent. In foals less than 3 days old, lesions of an acute generalized infection, inflammation of the intestines, and a slight excess of joint fluid are the only postmortem findings. The kidneys in older foals usually contain many small abscesses, which usually are specifically diagnostic for the disease.

STREPTOCOCCI are second only to *Shigella equirulis* as a cause of illness and death of foals. Infection often is present when a foal is born, but pronounced symptoms may not appear for a week or longer.

Infection also is acquired after birth. Prenatal infection often results in abortion or death of the foal within a few days after birth. Foals dying during the first few days usually have generalized infection or pneumonia and the joints are involved slightly. In foals a week or more old, joint troubles are more frequent and more severe, and the course of the disease is slower. Symptoms are similar to those associated with *S. equirulis* infections, but the course of the disease is slower. Foals sometimes live 2 or 3 weeks before dying.

Streptococci frequently are found in abscessed navels and are the commonest cause of infection in wounds or injuries of young foals.

Staphylococci usually are found in infected wounds or with streptococci in respiratory infections.

Tetanus, or lockjaw, is associated with infected navels or puncture wounds. Use of 3,000 units of antitoxin following puncture wounds and proper care of wounds will prevent tetanus. Annual immunization of pregnant mares with tetanus toxoid should provide passive colostrum antibody protection for the foal for a month or longer after birth.

Escherichia coli infections cause acute septicemia. Symptoms are nervous disturbance and rapid prostration. The mortality rate is high. Death usually occurs in 1 to 4 days. Peritonitis and enteritis are frequent lesions. Occasionally the joints are involved. Many affected foals are weak or ill at birth— an indication of prenatal infection.

Corynebacterium equi usually affects foals 1 month old or older and causes pneumonia and abscesses of the lungs. The infection may spread and cause abscesses in the lymph nodes and other internal organs. Treatment usually is unsatisfactory.

Salmonella typhi-murium infections are sporadic. Foals may be affected over a wide range of age. Symptoms are high fever, profuse diarrhea, and rapid dehydration and prostration. Lesions are those of acute generalized infection and inflammation of the intestines.

THE CONTROL of infectious diseases of newborn foals begins with hygiene and correct selection before the mares are bred. Infection of the genital tract may be present before breeding, or introduced when the mare is bred, or acquired later. Mares with genital infections fail to become pregnant, abort, or produce a weak or dead foal.

Manipulation of the genital tract, except by a veterinarian, should be avoided. Mares with anatomical defects that permit entry of air or foreign matter into the vagina should have the vulva repaired surgically. Such mares must be opened before foaling to prevent injury of the external genitalia.

Infections after birth may gain entrance to the body through the navel cord, but circumstances indicate that infection is more often acquired by ingestion and from the alimentary tract. Rigid sanitation should be practiced in the foaling stalls and stables that house brood mares.

Bacterins and serums have little or doubtful value in the treatment of the bacterial infections of newborn foals. Sulfa drugs are of benefit for some intestinal disturbances. Streptococcic infection may yield to treatment with several of the sulfa drugs. Early in the course of the disease, streptococcic and *Shigella equirulis* infections respond satisfactorily to treatment with selective antibiotics or combinations of antibiotics. Dosages should be in accordance with instructions on the packages of the product used.

In acute cases, antibiotic treatment must be started before an irreversible damage has occurred in the vital organs. Cases of longer standing, with multiple involvement of the joints or localizations of infection in other parts of the body, do not respond well to treatment with antibiotics.

HORSE and mule foals are subject to hemolytic anemia and jaundice (icterus), a disease that occurs when the mare becomes immunized against the red blood cells of her fetus. The blood type of the fetus apparently is the same as the type of its sire. This disease is somewhat like the Rh disease of human infants.

Synonyms for hemolytic disease are neonatal isoerythrolysis, icterus gravis, hemolytic icterus, jaundiced foals, and isohemolytic disease of newborn foals.

It happens only when a mare is carrying a fetus with a blood type different from her own, and then only if there is a leakage of red blood cells or their components from the fetal tissues into the mare's tissues.

When the leakage occurs, the mare's body reacts and develops a substance—an antibody—which is capable of destroying the red blood cells of the fetus. This reaction is known as isoimmunization. The same reaction and disease are produced by injecting vaccines containing horse tissues into mares. In the absence of vaccination, the isoimmunization is infrequent.

The antibody does not pass through the fetal membranes in horses, and the foal cannot be affected before it is born. The antibody is transferred from the blood to the mammary gland as the mare prepares to foal. The first milk—the colostrum—contains 4 to 8 times more antibody than the mare's blood. In the absence of other diseases, foals of immunized mares are perfectly healthy when born. They remain healthy until they suckle the first milk. Antibody from the colostrum is absorbed from the intestine into the foal's blood stream, where it attacks and destroys the red cells. Hemoglobin from damaged red blood cells is converted by the liver into bile pigments, which bring about jaundice.

The foal's movement becomes sluggish soon after it sucks the colostrum. It nurses infrequently, spends much time lying down, becomes progressively weaker, and may be prostrate within 16 to 24 hours after birth. The membranes of its lips, mouth, and eyes become pale. The heart rate and respirations are rapid. The body temperatures are normal or subnormal. Jaundice often appears within 30 to 40 hours and progressively becomes more severe for several days. The urine may be stained with blood pigments in the early stages of very acute cases. Later the urine becomes deep yellow.

The severity of hemolytic disease varies with the amount and antibody potency of the colostrum suckled by the foal. Many foals develop critical anemia and die in 16 to 30 hours. In others, 2 to 5 days are required for red cells to reach the lowest levels. Death may occur 1 to 9 days after birth, but most fatalities occur on the third or fourth days. Mildly and moderately affected foals often show no ill effects except lack of normal vigor.

Hemolytic disease should be suspected when severe anemia and jaundice develop during the first week after birth. Laboratory tests are necessary for confirming the diagnosis and estimating the need for treatment.

The mare's serum and colostrum agglutinate horse cells of the same type as her foal. Blood cells from an affected foal do not react satisfactorily with the mare's serum.

Agglutination (clumping) of the foal's cells in the antiglobulin sensitization test is proof of hemolytic disease. The test employs an antiserum for horse globulin and washed red cells from the affected foal.

Hemolytic disease may be confused with bacterial infections of newborn foals. Anemia and jaundice are absent or slight in bacterial infections, and the agglutination tests are negative.

Management and treatment of the sick foal varies with the time the disease is discovered. Usually the foal has removed all of the colostrum from the mare in 8 to 24 hours. Unless laboratory tests are available, the affected foal should not be muzzled to prevent nursing.

Blood counts indicate the need for blood transfusion, which is the only successful treatment. Blood transfusion is not necessary if the foal's red cell count is 6 million or higher. Foals with red cell counts between 4 million and 6 million will survive without treatment, but blood transfusion speeds recovery. The cell counts between 3 million and 4 million are critical. When the cell count falls below 3 million, death may be expected.

The blood donor must be selected carefully to obtain red cells that are compatible with the antibody in the mare's serum. Acutely affected foals must not be transfused with cells that agglutinate in its dam's serum, because that intensifies the disease. Transfusion with the mother's blood is likely to kill the foal.

Severely affected cases need an exsanguination transfusion, in which blood volumes of 1 pint are alternately injected into and withdrawn from the foal. The amount of blood transfused should raise the red cell count to approximately 7 million. That usually requires injection of 6 to 7 quarts of compatible blood and removal of 5 to 6 quarts from the foal.

The response to blood transfusion is rapid. Prostrate foals may be up nursing the mare in 20 minutes after a transfusion is completed. Foals with hemolytic disease of moderate severity often respond satisfactorily to transfusion of 2 or 3 pints of blood.

The disease can be prevented after a mare is known to have jaundiced foals. Two methods may be used.

The mare's serum may be tested with blood of stallions to select a compatible sire for future foals. Hemolytic disease will not develop in a foal with red cells that are compatible with the antibody in the mare's serum.

If a compatible stallion cannot be found, it is necessary to watch for foaling and muzzle the foal before it nurses. The antibody-laden colostrum is removed by hand milking the mare for 24 hours, after which it is usually safe for the foal to nurse. While the mare is being milked by hand, the foal should be fed milk from another mare or a dehydrated formula as used for babies. One tablespoonful of dehydrated formula is mixed with 2 ounces of water. The foal is fed 4 to 6 ounces every 5 or 6 hours.

This practice should be followed for all foals from immunized mares unless laboratory testing is available. Some foals inherit the blood type of the mare and will not develop jaundice even if they suck the colostrum. When these foals are identified by laboratory tests, milking the mare is not necessary.

FOALS THAT ARE MUZZLED and withheld from nursing do not receive the natural protective and laxative properties of colostrum. Without the protective colostrum, the foals are quite susceptible to intestinal disturbances and bacterial infections. Careful attention must be given to regulation of the bowels, and antibiotic drugs should be administered as directed by a veterinarian for 3 or 4 days to prevent bacterial infections.

E. R. DOLL, *who joined the Department of Animal Pathology, Kentucky Agricultural Experiment Station, Lexington, in 1943, has two degrees from the University of Missouri and the degree of doctor of veterinary medicine from Michigan State University.*

Equine Infectious Anemia

C. D. STEIN

INFECTIOUS anemia is known also as swamp fever, malarial fever, slow fever, and mountain fever. It affects horses, mules, and donkeys. Its prevalence in the United States has been declining with the substitution of motorized equipment for horse power in industry, agriculture, and the Army, but it is still of grave concern the world over to the establishments that handle large numbers of horses.

Infectious anemia is most prevalent in poorly drained, low-lying sections, but it has been found in wooded sections and marshy pastures at high altitudes. It also appears to be more prevalent when biting insects are most numerous and in wet years more than in dry seasons.

The active form of the disease appears in May or June, reaches its height in midsummer, and usually declines late in the fall. Chronic cases may be seen in the winter.

Outbreaks in the United States have been chiefly sporadic—isolated cases confined to small areas and showing little tendency to spread. Small outbreaks have been reported from time to time in parts of Idaho, Oregon, Nevada, Montana, Mississippi, Wyoming, Louisiana, and Texas.

A number of severe outbreaks have occurred at establishments where large numbers of horses are assembled, and

maintained, such as Army posts, breeding farms, dude ranches, and biological institutions. A serious outbreak occurred in 1947 in a large group of Thoroughbred race horses in New England, but it was promptly controlled by destroying affected animals and applying strict sanitation.

A chronic form, formerly prevalent among mules on large cotton plantations in the Mississippi Delta, has abated because tractors have replaced many mules.

The cause is a filterable virus—which under natural conditions appears to affect only horses, mules, and donkeys. The virus may persist in an infected animal for years. It is apparently present in the blood and body tissues of affected animals at all times and may be eliminated with some of the secretions or excretions, such as the milk, semen, saliva, eye and nasal secretions, urine, and manure.

The exact nature of the virus remains a matter of discussion. It has not been cultivated in vitro (outside the animal body) and cannot reproduce itself consistently in other animals.

Experiments by investigators in the Department of Agriculture with strains of virus from different areas indicated that it varies greatly in virulence. Among the factors that apparently influence the virulence are the susceptibility of the host, frequency of passage (that is, transmission of the disease from one animal to another in series at short intervals), method of exposure, source of virus, character of the inoculating substance (the inoculum), and debilitating factors affecting the host.

The virus shows considerable resistance to disinfectants, heating, freezing, and drying.

Findings of investigators as to the action of heat and chemicals on the virus have been put into practical use in formulating requirements for the treatment of antiserums prepared from horses, thus safeguarding against dissemination of the disease through the use of such biological products.

Biological supply houses operating under Government license are required to heat all antiserums prepared from horses at 58° to 59° C. (136.4° to 138.2° F.) for an hour. The heat destroys any infectious anemia virus they may contain.

In the experiments conducted in the Department of Agriculture, only horses and donkeys were found to be susceptible. Attempts to infect calves, sheep, swine, dogs, cats, rabbits, guinea pigs, rats, mice, and pigeons failed.

Although the disease can be transmitted experimentally by injecting infectious material, by insect vectors, and by ingestion of contaminated material, we do not know how it spreads naturally.

Ordinarily the disease appears to spread slowly and sporadically. Outbreaks may occur, however, when infected animals are moved into new territory and when conditions are favorable for transmission and for the exposure of large numbers of susceptible horses.

Studies made during the outbreak among race horses in New England in 1947 indicated that biting flies may have been responsible for the early spread of the disease from carriers to healthy horses and that the use of unsterilized hypodermic needles and instruments spread it further.

The disease seems to spread more rapidly among animals on pasture than among those kept in stables, especially when biting insects abound.

Experimental evidence has led to several conclusions. The disease is transmitted readily by the injection of blood or tissue emulsions from affected animals into susceptible ones. Minute doses of the virus are infective for susceptible animals. The body secretions or excretions may contain the virus.

Infected mares may transmit the disease to their offspring and therefore should not be used for breeding.

THE CLINICAL SYMPTOMS of infectious anemia are variable and depend largely on the form of the disease.

It may occur as an acute, rapidly fatal disease or more commonly as a chronic affection, characterized by intermittent attacks of fever, loss of weight, progressive weakness, marked depression, and dropsical swellings on the lower parts of the body and legs.

The disease may also exist in a form—the subclinical form—in which no clinical symptoms are apparent though the affected animal carries virulent virus in the blood stream.

In the acute form the incubation period—time elapsing between exposure and first appearance of symptoms—usually is about 12 to 15 days, but it may vary from a few days to 3 months or longer.

The onset is sudden and brings a rise in temperature, which usually goes to about 105° F. but may reach 108°. The febrile attacks usually are severe and may be more or less continuous.

Respiration is accelerated and frequently is of the abdominal type. The animal is dejected, the head hangs low, leg weakness is marked, the body weight is shifted from one leg to another, and the hind feet are frequently placed well forward under the body.

The membranes of the eyes show congestion, followed by brownish to yellowish discoloration (icterus). Feed is refused. There may be a slight watery discharge from the eyes and nose and, if the weather is extremely warm, profuse sweating. Urination may be frequent, and in severe cases diarrhea may develop.

The attack usually lasts 3 to 5 days, after which the temperature returns to normal and the animal appears to be well except for a marked loss of weight. Occasionally, however, the initial attack may persist until the animal dies.

Dropsical swellings of the sheath, the legs, the chest, and the under surfaces of the body may occur at any time. Subsequent attacks usually follow. Normal periods of a few days to many weeks or months may intervene. When the intervals between the attacks of fever are short, the animal seldom lives more than 15 to 30 days. During the attacks of fever and immediately afterward, the number of red corpuscles in the blood drops. During the periods of normality between attacks, the count of red corpuscles is normal in most cases.

The subacute and chronic forms differ from the acute in that the attacks are less severe and the intervals between them are longer. The subacute cases may end in death during or following one of the attacks, or the reactions may grow less frequent and the animal may finally develop into a chronic case or a clinically recovered carrier.

The chronic form generally is manifested by unthriftiness, rough coat, underweight, sluggishness, weakness, dropsical swellings of the lower parts of the body or on the legs, muddy discoloration of the visible mucous membranes, and small hemorrhages of the third eyelid, or haw.

As the disease progresses, evidence of anemia may develop. The count of red corpuscles may be extremely low. The blood may appear thin and watery. The visible mucous membranes may become pallid in the later stages. The pulse may be slow and weak. The heart action may become irregular. A jugular pulse may be visible. The pulse may slow down quickly after exercise. Muscular weakness is manifested by a wobbly or rolling, staggering gait or by partial paralysis of the hindquarters. Animals that have the chronic form may eat constantly if they have access to feed but nevertheless lose weight steadily.

Animals with the chronic form can do some work if handled carefully but they are subject to recurring attacks, characterized by extreme weakness, knuckling, and inability to walk in a straight line. Sometimes the horse is so weak that it cannot stand by itself.

With good attention, rest, and supportive treatment (which includes abundance of good food, administration of liver extract, stimulants, and tonics), it usually overcomes the periodic attacks and may go back to routine work. Each attack takes its toll of flesh and strength, however; frequent attacks will weaken the animal, make it useless, and finally bring about death by exhaustion.

AN INACTIVE, or latent, stage may follow the first attack, but usually it is preceded by several attacks of fever. This form is observed in animals that apparently have recovered from the acute, subacute, or chronic types of the disease. Animals affected with the latent form show no clinical symptoms and are known as clinically recovered carriers. Their temperature remains normal. There is no reduction in the red corpuscles or any sign of disease over a period of months or years, and yet the infectious agent is always present in the blood stream and the tissues and may be eliminated with the body excretions.

Such animals are a menace to other horses that may be near them. The inactive form of the disease may become active at any time and present all the characteristics of the acute or subacute form. Unusually hard work or any debilitating influence may reactivate the infection. Complete recovery of carriers with a disappearance of virus from their blood rarely occurs. It has also been observed that the virulency of the blood of some carriers may diminish with time.

The Department of Agriculture had under observation two virus carriers that were good examples of the inactive form of the disease. These horses were first infected in 1935. A series of inoculation tests proved that one of the animals harbored the virus in its blood stream for more than 15 years and the other for more than 18 years.

DIAGNOSIS is usually difficult. The only definite means is the horse inoculation test. A tentative diagnosis based on history, clinical symptoms, blood examinations, and autopsy can be made in active cases with some certainty. A history of rapid loss of flesh, loss of spirit and energy, evidences of muscular weakness, attacks of fever, congestion of the membranes of the eye with some degree of jaundice, and dropsical swellings of the lower parts of the body, strongly suggest infectious anemia.

The diagnosis would be further strengthened if after the temperature reaction an examination of the blood shows a decrease in the volume of the red corpuscles, an increase in the sedimentation rate, and a decrease of hemoglobin. The postmortem and microscopic findings in animals that die furnish additional evidence on which to base a tentative diagnosis.

A tentative diagnosis, especially one when large numbers of horses are involved in an outbreak, should always be confirmed by a positive horse inoculation test. In carrying out this test, whole blood samples or preferably filtered blood samples collected aseptically from suspected cases are injected subcutaneously (under the skin) in 50 cc. amounts into young healthy test horses. The test horses are held under observation for 60 days in an isolated unit and their temperatures are taken and recorded twice daily. If the test horses develop clinical symptoms of infectious anemia during this period, the test is declared positive.

The inactive form is ordinarily not detected, because no clinical symptoms are present to cause suspicion.

In acute cases occurring in the field, death may occur before the usual train of symptoms develops. The disease in the acute form may be confused with anthrax, influenza, acute equine encephalomyelitis, and other acute febrile conditions.

The subacute and chronic forms may be mistaken for trypanosomiasis (dourine, murrina, and surra) or a heavy infestation with strongyles (intestinal parasites).

The possibility that some of those maladies may be the source of the trouble can be eliminated by laboratory examination.

Since the development of a reliable means of diagnosis is important from the standpoint of control, much experimental work on diagnostic procedures for the detection of infected animals was carried out by the Department of Agriculture investigators. Results obtained with many different types of laboratory tests, which have been advocated by investigators in the diagnosis of the disease, were frequently indefinite or nonspecific and, therefore, undependable.

Indefinite results were likewise obtained with the so-called tongue test for diagnosis, in which observations in suspected cases are made for the presence of minute hemorrhages on the under surface of the tongue. This test has been reported as a valuable aid to diagnosis (especially in carriers) by investigators in the Soviet Union, Sweden, and Switzerland. None of the tests was sufficiently satisfactory to warrant adoption as a standard diagnostic method.

No SPECIFIC TREATMENT or vaccination has been discovered for infectious anemia. In searching for an effective treatment, investigators have tried numerous agents, but none of the preparations had any appreciable influence on the course of the disease. None freed the infected animals of the virus.

In localities where the disease is constantly present, veterinarians employ supportive treatment—the use of arsenical compounds (mainly sodium cacodylate) with tonics, rest, and abundance of good feed, and efforts to eliminate intestinal parasites and other debilitating factors. Such treatment brings about some clinical improvement, but it has no lasting value, for the animal remains infected, is subject to fever, and may be a virus carrier.

When a definite diagnosis of infectious anemia has been made, it is advisable to kill the animal and dispose of the carcass by cremation or deep burial to prevent further spread of the infection. This method of control has been followed in small, isolated outbreaks and in establishments keeping large numbers of horses, and it has been effective in preventing the spread of the disease. This method is impracticable in areas where the disease is widely distributed and exists chiefly in a mild, chronic form.

Infected animals should be isolated from healthy animals. Flies and mosquitoes should be controlled.

The greatest care always should be taken to prevent transmission of the disease from animal to animal by the use of unsterilized instruments.

Only horses known to be free from the disease should be used as donors for blood transfusions. All antiserums of equine origin intended for treatment of horses should be heated to destroy the virus.

Mares and stallions suspected of being affected should not be used for breeding purposes. Horses from areas where the disease exists should be isolated, have their temperatures taken and recorded daily, and be kept under observation for 60 days after being brought on premises where normal horses are kept.

In areas where there is reason to believe that many animals are affected with the disease in either a chronic or an inapparent form, the maintenance of good sanitary conditions, provision for a supply of pure, fresh drinking water and attention to the feed, care, and handling of animals will help to hold the ill effects of the disease to a minimum and retards its spread.

C. D. STEIN, *a graduate of the University of Pennsylvania, joined the Department of Agriculture in 1911 and served in three divisions of the former Bureau of Animal Industry. For many years he has contributed important researches on anthrax, equine infectious anemia, and other infectious diseases of livestock. He was a veterinarian in the Animal Disease and Parasite Research Branch when he retired in March 1956.*

Equine Encephalomyelitis

M. S. SHAHAN AND H. W. SCHOENING

EQUINE encephalomyelitis killed tens of thousands of horses and mules in the United States in the 1930's and early 1940's. The incidence of the disease in horses has since dwindled to a few thousand or fewer annually for three reasons: The equine population is much smaller; vaccination and other means of prevention are used; and large numbers of animals have developed immunity from exposure in previous outbreaks.

Commonly called horse encephalitis (inflammation of the brain), sleeping sickness, staggers, blind staggers, or brain fever, the disease has occurred in nearly all parts of the United States and in Canada, Mexico, Central America, South America, and the Caribbean area.

Scientists discovered in 1931 that it is caused by a filterable virus, but very likely equine encephalomyelitis occurred in the United States for at least two decades previously. Then, as later, the disease appeared sporadically for several years, flaring up at intervals in widespread epizootics, first in one part of the country and then in another.

Once scientists believed it affected only horses and mules, but now it is known that equine encephalomyelitis may occur in other species, from birds, both domestic and wild, to man. The known range of natural hosts of the virus includes the horse, mule, ass, deer, pheasant, pigeon, prairie chicken, purple grackel, other birds, and people.

Many other species develop encephalomyelitis, quite like that in the horse, when the virus is injected into the brain. In fact, almost all animals may be so infected—cattle, swine, sheep, goats, chickens, ducks and other birds, and the usual laboratory animals, such as monkeys, guinea pigs, rabbits, rats, mice, and hamsters. But, as far as we know, none of those mammals is naturally infected, although birds and possibly some species of wild rodents are suspected of being natural reservoirs of the virus.

The virus responsible for equine encephalitis is one of the smaller viruses. The particle is larger than that of foot-and-mouth disease, but much smaller than the elementary bodies of smallpox.

Two immunologically distinct types of the virus have been identified in the United States: The western type, so called because of its general occurrence west of the Appalachians, and the eastern type, which usually appears east of the Appalachians. The western type thus is more widely distributed

than the eastern type, which has been concentrated along the eastern seaboard and the gulf coast.

Encephalitis caused by one type of the virus is indistinguishable clinically from that induced by the other, but (as in other diseases with more than one immunologic type of virus) recovery from infection with one type results in immunity to that type only and not to others.

A third type of equine encephalomyelitis virus, known as the Venezuelan, has been identified in Venezuela and other countries of northern South America, Central America, and the Caribbean area. This type never has been found in the United States.

THE DISCOVERY in 1933 by R. A. Kelser, of the Veterinary Corps of the United States Army, that mosquitoes could transmit equine encephalomyelitis under laboratory conditions led to a long series of investigations. Dr. Kelser's work was an outstanding contribution to the study of equine encephalomyelitis and other neurotropic virus diseases (those affecting nerve cells).

EQUINE ENCEPHALOMYELITIS virus is one of the arthropod-borne *encephalitis viruses*, that is, it may be carried from one animal to another by various species of arthropods, including in this case mosquitoes and ticks of different species, as well as chicken mites (*Dermanyssus gallinae*), mites of wild birds (*Lyponyssus sylvarium*), and chicken lice (*Eumenacanthus stramineus*).

Mosquitoes of the genera *Culex*, *Aedes*, *Mansonia*, and *Culiseta* are regarded generally as the chief vectors. They and mites and lice can transmit the virus in birds, which seem to be an important reservoir of the virus, especially the western type.

Some species of mosquitoes appear to transmit either type of equine encephalitis virus with equal facility. Others may transmit one but not the other.

The Venezuelan type apparently is

transmitted by species of mosquitoes that are not common in the United States.

The western virus has been isolated from the bloodsucking conenose, or assassin bug (*Triatoma sanguisuga*), but because of geographic distribution and other factors, the bug is not considered to be an important common vector of equine encephalomyelitis.

St. Louis encephalitis, another of the arthropod-borne viral infections that affects man, is as widely distributed as the western equine encephalitis virus among certain western mosquitoes, especially *Culex tarsalis*.

Horses have been artificially infected with the St. Louis virus and they, as well as other animals, may have an important part in perpetuating the disease. As the virus of western equine encephalomyelitis has been transmitted experimentally by the tick *Dermacentor andersoni*, so has the virus of St. Louis encephalitis been transmitted by the tick *D. variabilis*. Likewise the virus may be carried over into the eggs. Naturally infected ticks have not been found, however, and whether they are important vectors of either disease is open to question.

Japanese B encephalitis, still another one of the mosquito-borne neurotropic viruses, affects people especially but may involve horses. The disease has been found in Japan and other areas in Asia and the Pacific. It has not been found in the United States.

Russian spring-summer encephalitis is carried by ticks in Russia and parts of western Europe. It has not occurred in the United States. It is essentially a disease of people. Horses and other animals may be involved in its spread, although the ticks themselves appear to be the reservoir of the virus. Like the other arthropod-borne diseases, it occurs during the time of the year when the vectors are prevalent. In this instance the ticks (*Ixodes persulcatus* and *Ixodes ricinus*) are more numerous and active in the spring and early summer in contrast with mosquitoes, which generally are more prevalent in most lo-

calities during the late summer and early fall. There appears to be a relationship between this virus and that of louping ill of sheep.

Like poliomyelitis in human beings, equine encephalomyelitis attacks and actually infects many subjects that reveal little or no evidence of the disease. Mild or severe symptoms of involvement of the central nervous system— brain and spinal cord—may occur in 1 to 100 horses and mules in every thousand, depending on the severity of the epizootic. The occurrence of antibodies in the blood (as may be demonstrated by laboratory tests), however, is evidence that other animals are exposed and become infected.

MORTALITY AMONG HORSES and mules that develop unmistakable clinical signs of infection varies generally from 20 to 25 percent in the case of western-type virus and averages 75 to 90 percent in epizootics caused by the eastern virus. Some surviving animals retain aftereffects of the disease. Epidemics in man result in higher mortality from eastern-type virus than from the western type, and complications may persist in survivors.

Outbreaks in confined pheasants have occurred repeatedly, particularly in the northeastern part of the United States. Generally these outbreaks accompany outbreaks of the disease in horses—suggesting that the same vector is probably to blame. Some species of mosquitoes are known to feed on both birds and mammals, and transmission among more than one species (such as birds and horses, or horses, birds, and people) is to be expected.

Whether in horses, people, or birds, the peak of incidence of the infection usually occurs in late summer and early fall, preceded by a gradual acceleration beginning in the spring and followed by a rapid recession in cases about the time of the first frost. In milder climates the disease may continue into the winter, but such cases generally are few in number.

In pheasants, however, the disease

may persist into the winter. Such occurrences may be due to cannibalism, which is common in confined pheasants. The disease may be controlled by debeaking the birds.

A VIREMIA, or presence of the virus in the blood, occurs in all susceptible species—particularly during the early stages—when the infection is induced experimentally. Generally this state is rather fleeting, but the virus nevertheless can usually be found if persistently sought at appropriate times.

Finding virus in the blood of natural cases is more difficult, because the virus usually has moved to the brain by the time nervous symptoms appear.

NERVOUS SYMPTOMS usually develop 2 to 7 days after artificial inoculation of virus of equine encephalomyelitis. The time varies with the route of inoculation and the type and concentration of the virus. The incubation period under natural conditions seems to vary from 7 to 10 days, but may be longer.

The first indication of equine encephalitis is fever, which is present in nearly all cases. The temperature varies from 102° to 107° F. During the early part of the febrile stage, nothing more than lack of spirit or slightly peculiar actions may be noticed, but the virus multiplies rapidly in the blood at that time.

If the infection is of the so-called inapparent, silent, or occult type, it ends there. Otherwise the disease progresses and causes distinct symptoms of involvement of the brain and spinal cord, constituting what is known as a "frank" case.

Both types of attack constitute true infections, and recovery results in substantial immunity to reinfection with the same type of the virus. In affected stables, either or both types of the disease occur, but usually more animals show mild or no symptoms at all than develop signs of brain affliction. Ordinarily no more than 10 percent of a given group develops clear signs of encephalomyelitis.

Sluggishness and drowsiness are early symptoms of the brain disease.

The lips are loose and dropped or tensed and wrinkled and sometimes drawn to one side. Groups of muscles about the head, shoulder, or flank may twitch spasmodically.

As the disease progresses, the sick animal stands dejectedly and moves reluctantly with an awkward stumbling or staggering gait. The legs are sometimes crossed. Some affected animals are inclined to back up persistently. Others walk stumblingly in a circle, usually in one direction, the tail switching as they move. Such animals may stumble blindly into obstructions in their paths. Whinnying and sensitiveness to the slightest touch, as shown by flinching or jerking muscular contractions, are common.

Most affected animals become stupid and unusually untractable, but some become wild, as in rabies. Sexual excitement sometimes occurs.

The dejected "sleeper," when it is aroused, may exhibit momentary interest in his surroundings, feed, or water, only to lapse into a stupor, with unchewed food in the mouth or water trickling from the lips or the nostrils. The tongue may be paralyzed and is not retracted if it is pulled from the mouth. If a water bucket is held up to his head and he is repeatedly aroused, the horse may succeed in swallowing a considerable quantity of water, a little at a time. Often, however, affected animals seem unable to swallow.

Grinding the teeth and stretching the head and neck are common. The mouth becomes foul smelling because of putrefaction of accumulated secretions and unswallowed feed. If the eye is examined carefully, the membranes usually may be seen to be of a yellowish or muddy color and sometimes sprinkled with small hemorrhages.

Gauntness increases as the illness progresses. Often a prominent ridge develops along the lower abdominal wall because of muscular tenseness. The digestive and excretory processes are retarded; some constipation results. Urine collects in the bladder, which may be greatly distended. Dribbling of urine may occur without normal periodic voiding.

In about 1 of every 4 or 5 cases caused by the western type of virus and as many as 9 of 10 cases caused by the eastern type, weakness progresses for a few days until the animals collapse. Of the cases that lose their footing and cannot regain their feet without help, few recover.

Before it dies, the animal may lie quietly on its side, breathing with a snoring sound, or it may thrash about violently. Some animals in the delirium dig up the earth through rhythmic or off-and-on running movements. Marked bruising and swellings occur on the parts of the body in contact with the ground.

If the prostrate animal lies quietly, the body temperature usually remains near normal, but fever may be high if there is much struggling or if pneumonia or some other complicating organic disease develops.

Some of the animals that survive suffer permanent damage to the brain and become what are commonly called "dummies."

Other diseases may be confused with equine encephalomyelitis. Almost any infection, intoxication, or organic change in the brain and spinal cord may produce several similar symptoms. Rabies is among the first infectious diseases to be considered in cases suggestive of equine encephalitis.

Other systemic infections, such as influenza, anthrax, infectious anemia, and even tetanus, must be distinguished if the case at hand is to be managed properly and appropriate control measures are to be taken.

Among the intoxications to be considered are moldy corn poisoning (encephalomalacia or softening of the brain); botulism; azoturia (Monday morning sickness); poisoning by such minerals as barium, lead, arsenic, phosphorus, and selenium; and poisoning by plants, such as whorled milkweed, yellow tarweed, poisonhemlock, locoweed, Senecio (or ragwort), horsetail, and ergot-infected paspalum grass.

Certain tumors and abscesses in the brain, heatstroke, and lightning may cause spasms, convulsions, or paralysis that may be confusing.

Close study and searching inquiry usually enable the veterinarian to establish at least a tentative diagnosis on the basis of seasonal occurrence, history, and other circumstances.

Often, however, laboratory examinations must be made to establish the exact cause of the trouble.

VACCINATION is the most practical means of preventing equine encephalitis. The vaccine consists of formalin-inactivated virus that has been propagated in embryonated chicken eggs.

For greatest effectiveness, vaccine should be injected in the spring or early summer, before the epizootic season begins. Two doses, given 7 to 10 days apart, are required for maximum protection. Vaccine to be used in the West should be made from western-type virus; that in the East, from eastern-type virus. In some areas where both types are known to have existed, both are included in the vaccine, which is then known as bivalent.

Every practical means should be used to keep animals from exposure to mosquitoes, the chief vectors of the disease. Drainage of swamps, marshes, and sloughs will reduce or eliminate breeding of many species of mosquitoes. Spraying of ponds and lakes with products designed to kill mosquito larvae is also helpful. Oil, kerosene, DDT, and lindane (the gamma isomer of benzene hexachloride) are among the substances used for this purpose.

Pasturing of animals on high, open pastures tends to lessen exposure to mosquitoes, as does stabling at night, when the insects are apt to be most active. Screens on stables will keep many insects out. Periodic spraying with repellents and insecticides, such as DDT and lindane, is also helpful.

Sick animals should be isolated in screened quarters and sprayed at intervals to limit opportunities for bloodsucking insects to get to them.

Transmission by insects from animals dead of the disease is unlikely, but it is wise nevertheless to bury such cadavers and disinfect quarters the sick animals used before they died.

A specific antiencephalomyelitis serum is commercially available. If such serum is administered in time to animals in affected stables, some may be protected. Effectiveness of the serum is limited, however, both as to degree and to duration. The preventive effect of the serum diminishes to practically nothing within 2 or 3 weeks.

Injections of fluids intravenously, rectally, or by stomach tube are considered advantageous in combating extreme dehydration.

Good nursing practices, such as repeated grooming, turning prostrate animals from side to side every hour or so, and protection from the elements and self-injury are helpful.

Antiencephalitis vaccines have been developed for protection of man. They have been used in laboratories to prevent accidental infections. Under proper conditions—which should be determined only by public health or laboratory officials—they may be applicable in epidemics.

M. S. SHAHAN *in 1953 became director of the Plum Island Animal Disease Laboratory of the Department of Agriculture.*

H. W. SCHOENING *was graduated from the School of Veterinary Medicine, University of Pennsylvania, in 1907, and served in the Department from 1907 to 1955, except during a period of military service.*

Mange and Lice of Horses and Mules

F. D. ENZIE

MANGE, barn itch, scab, scabies, and itch are general terms applied to a group of contagious skin diseases caused by minute, insectlike parasites called mites. Horses and mules may be affected with three different types of these pests, Sarcoptes, Psoroptes, and Chorioptes. The diseases they produce are known as sarcoptic, psoroptic, and chorioptic mange, respectively.

The mites spend their entire life cycles in or on the skin of the host animal. Each type of mite, as it carries on the various processes of life, produces lesions—injuries—that are more or less characteristic.

The three kinds of mange usually are transmitted by direct contact between healthy and infected animals, although the mites may be transferred on currycombs, brushes, blankets, and other equipment.

Ordinarily the disease spreads fastest in winter when the animals may be closely confined or crowded together.

In the warmer seasons, when the animals are on pasture or are otherwise exposed to sunlight, the disease tends to disappear or lie dormant. It becomes active again under conditions of winter management.

Sarcoptic mange is the type most commonly found among horses and mules in the United States. The mite *Sarcoptes scabiei equi* causes it. The mature female is about one-fiftieth of an inch long. The male is a little smaller. They are just visible to the unaided eye.

These white or yellowish parasites

are round or slightly oval, like a horseshoe. They have four pairs of short, thick legs. Only the first two pairs of legs, on either side of the bluntly rounded head, extend beyond the margin of the body.

The sarcoptic mites burrow in the upper layer of the skin and form tunnels, in which they mate and lay eggs. Each female may deposit 25 eggs in about 2 weeks. The young mites that develop from the eggs mature in 14 or 15 days. A new generation of mites therefore is produced about every 2 weeks, a factor of importance in determining the intervals between treatments with medicinal agents.

The mites cannot complete their life cycle off the host, but the adults may survive for a month or more if temperature and moisture are suitable.

The burrows extend to the deep, sensitive layers of the skin. There the activities of the mites cause intense irritation and itching. The horse seeks relief by rubbing the affected places against any available object and other animals. Blisters and small lumps or ridges develop. The skin becomes swollen and inflamed. The constant rubbing causes the vesicles, or blisters, to rupture and discharge serum. The serum, mixed with scurf and other foreign matter, becomes dry and forms scabs. Bacterial infections occasionally become established under the scabs and make the condition worse.

The mites constantly move from the edges of the lesions to the surrounding healthy skin, and so the condition spreads over the body. The lesions may progress rapidly or slowly, depending on the animal's general physical condition and the amount of care and attention it receives.

As the disease advances, the areas first affected become dry, rough, and bare. The skin in the final stages is greatly thickened, wrinkled, and leathery. The mites are inactive then and hard to find, but the skin remains leathery. The skin may continue to be unpliable for some time after the mites are destroyed.

The first lesions generally occur on the head, neck, and shoulders, but they may start on any part of the body. From the primary injuries, the disease spreads to other parts of the skin surface. Furthered by the animal's scratching and rubbing, the lesions may extend over much of the body within a few weeks, particularly if the animal's general resistance is low on account of a heavy burden of internal parasites or a poor nutritional state.

Sarcoptic mange is contagious to horses of all ages and classes. It also is transmissible from one class of livestock to another and from animals to people. It is tremendously important therefore to have an accurate, early diagnosis, to isolate affected animals from all other livestock, and to undertake treatment and other control measures promptly.

To diagnose sarcoptic mange positively, one has to find the mite. That is done by microscopic examination of skin scrapings from the edge of fresh, active lesions. Because the mites live in burrows in the skin, deep scrapings must be made in order to find them, often to the point of drawing blood. In the advanced stages of the disease, when the skin has become dry and leathery, the mites are hard to find.

PSOROPTIC MANGE MITES, *Psoroptes equi equi*, are oval and somewhat larger than those that produce common scab in horses and mules. The male and female are one-fiftieth and one-fortieth of an inch long, respectively. Against a black background they are visible without magnification. The elongate, tapering head and the four pairs of legs extend well beyond the margin of the body.

The psoroptic mites do not form burrows in the skin but live in colonies on the surface. They pass their entire life cycle on the host. A female may lay 15 to 25 eggs. The young mites, which hatch in about 4 days, reach the egg-laying stage 10 to 12 days later. Psoroptic mites may live a year or more in barns or sheds, but probably they cannot survive more than a few weeks when exposed to the sun.

The first lesions of psoroptic mange generally appear on the poll, under the mane, or at the base of the tail, but they may start on any part of the body that is thickly covered with hair. Itching is intense.

Serum accumulates in the hair from ruptured vesicles and papules, becomes mixed with foreign matter, and dries to form crusts and scabs. Irritation of the lesions is increased by the bacterial infections that often become established under the scabs. The mites constantly move toward the healthy skin near the edges of the wound.

Some mites migrate to other areas where they may start new lesions. The itching continues, and the skin becomes mutilated from the constant rubbing and biting. The skin over large areas of the body finally becomes thickened, wrinkled, bare of all hair, and covered with thick and adherent scabs.

Psoroptic mites are more host specific than those that produce common mange. The variety that affects horses and mules is not transmissible to man or to other livestock. Among horses, however, psoroptic mange is more highly contagious and spreads faster than sarcoptic mange. Infections usually are acquired by contact with infected animals, but indirect transfer of mites may occur from equipment or contaminated stalls and sheds.

The diagnosis of psoroptic mange is established by identifying the characteristic mite obtained from skin scrapings. As these mites live on the surface of the skin, comparatively superficial scrapings usually are enough. In the early stages of the disease, the mites generally are most plentiful around the edges of fresh wounds. After the condition is well established, the mites may be found also near the edges of scabs or in the furrows between folds of skin.

THE CHORIOPTIC MITES, *Chorioptes equi*, resemble the psoroptic mites in many respects. They have the same general conformation, live on the surface of the skin, and produce similar (though generally less extensive) lesions.

These mites usually attack the lower part of the legs and generally remain below the hocks and knees. The condition therefore is commonly called foot mange.

The lesions occur oftenest on the hind legs and are like those of the psoroptic mange in most ways. Infected animals exhibit the same general restlessness and irritation as in other types of mange and attempt to allay the itching by pawing, rubbing, licking, or biting the affected parts.

PREVENTION of infestation with mange mites and other external parasites is largely a matter of employing good husbandry practices.

Clean quarters, regular grooming, and a balanced diet are important in maintaining and promoting general health and preventing the development and spread of all parasitic skin diseases. Blankets, saddles, and harnesses should be cleaned and disinfected regularly. Currycombs and brushes should be cleaned thoroughly immediately after use.

Mange in horses and mules can be eradicated by dipping or spraying with suitable chemical agents.

Dipping is preferable because it assures thorough coverage of the animal—to be effective, the medicament must be brought into direct contact with the parasites. All horses on the premises should be treated whether or not a specific diagnosis is established in each animal.

Two dippings 10 to 12 days apart ordinarily will be enough to cure psoroptic and chorioptic mange.

Three or more treatments may be necessary for sarcoptic mange because of the location of the mites in burrows in the skin.

Animals that have chorioptic mange may be driven through a shallow wading tank if the lesions are confined to the lower parts of the legs.

Dipping is not feasible during severe winter weather. It is impractical when only a few animals are involved. Spraying is a useful alternative method. It is effective if the entire body surface is completely wetted.

With either method, advanced lesions that are covered with hard scabs or crusts should be thoroughly soaked and softened by hand with warm dip or spray before treatment.

Besides rotenone and the standard lime-sulfur and nicotine dips, several newer treatments are used against the three kinds of mange affecting horses and mules. They include lindane, benzene hexachloride, benzyl benzoate, and tetraethylthiuram monosulfide.

TWO KINDS OF LICE, a bloodsucking species called *Haematopinus asini* and a biting louse known as *Bovicola equi*, infest our horses and mules.

The sucking lice are the more injurious, because heavy infestations mean a heavy loss of blood that seriously weakens the animal.

Lice occur in largest numbers in winter, when the hair is long and the animals generally are closely confined.

The sucking lice are easily told from biting lice by their larger size, pointed heads, and bluish bodies. Mature adults are about a third as broad as long, and the overall length is about one-eighth inch.

The much smaller biting lice have a white or yellowish body and a red or brown head, which is short and blunt.

Sucking and biting lice pass their entire lives on the host animal. They are generally transmitted by direct contact between animals.

The eggs, or nits, of the sucking louse usually are close to the skin and attached firmly to the hairs. Most of the eggs hatch in about 2 weeks. The young lice reach maturity about 12 days later.

The eggs of the biting louse are deposited in the same general manner, but have a shorter incubation period. When they are removed from the host, most of the biting lice die in less than a week, although some may survive as long as 10 days if kept on tufts of hair. The sucking lice cannot survive more than 2 or 3 days away from the host animal.

Sucking lice mostly prefer the head, neck, back, and inner surface of the thighs, but they move about on the skin and hair when they are not feeding. They get nourishment by piercing the skin and sucking blood and fluids.

Biting lice may be found anywhere on the body, although they seem to occur in largest numbers around the withers and base of the tail. They do not suck blood but feed on hair, scales, and exudations from the skin.

The commonest method of transmission is by direct contact between clean and infested animals.

Hair and scurf from grooming equipment and hair clipped from infested horses should be collected promptly and burned. The ground or floor on which the clippings accumulated should be thoroughly sprayed with an effective insecticide, such as DDT, lindane, or methoxychlor. Infested stables and yards should be cleaned thoroughly by removing accumulations of litter and manure. The stables should be sprayed also with insecticide.

Treatment of infested animals may be by dipping, spraying, washing, or dusting with insecticidal preparations. The best method in any particular case depends on the number of horses to be treated, prevailing weather conditions, and the available facilities.

Dipping is most effective, because it assures thorough coverage of the animal. It is preferred where winters are mild and a large number of animals is involved.

Methoxychlor, DDT, lindane, benzene hexachloride, chlordane, and toxaphene are effective against both sucking and biting lice.

F. D. ENZIE *has been concerned with investigations of parasite treatment since 1942. He joined the Department of Agriculture in 1940. He is a parasitologist in the Agricultural Research Service.*

fur-bearing animals

Infectious Diseases of the Rabbit

KARL W. HAGEN, JR.

THE INFECTIOUS agents that are responsible for diseases in the rabbit belong to the same major groups that are found in man—bacteria, fungi, viruses, and protozoa.

High on the list of the infections, which are steadily growing in importance as more and more rabbits are raised commercially, is pasteurellosis.

The acute infection by *Pasteurella multocida* is marked by a septicemia and is like the hemorrhagic septicemia of farm animals. It is most common in adult females. It can cause death in 24 to 48 hours. Autopsy reveals a congestion of blood vessels. The surface of the intestine and tissues just under the skin show hemorrhagic areas. Often the spleen is enlarged.

The chronic form is not necessarily fatal, but it can detract from the ani-

mal's appearance and value. Breeders refer to it as "a cold" or "snuffles." A nasal discharge may persist and may spread to a large proportion of the stock if conditions favor it. The animal may become a carrier if the mucous discharge subsides.

Abscesses under the skin on various parts of the body are also typical of the chronic form. The abscesses contain a thick, creamy pus.

Pasteurellosis of the reproductive tract is usually a chronic infection. It produces a purulent discharge from the sex organs. The infection may be spread among other animals in the process of mating.

The introduction of a suitable or virulent bacteria into the uterus will not produce this reproductive infection. The change that takes place in

559

the pregnant or falsely pregnant uterine tissue is necessary before the bacteria can become established in the uterus.

Since the doe has two uteri, it is possible that one uterus is infected while the other uterus is healthy and carrying young. The animal becomes sterile if both uteri are infected.

When the infection is not well established in the uterus, it is possible for the purulent material (pus) to be evacuated from the reproductive tract. When it is free of this material, the uterus can carry a normal litter.

The prevention of pasteurellosis depends mainly on the degree of sanitation maintained in the rabbitry, careful isolation and quarantine of all newly acquired animals, and prompt disposal of sick or diseased animals. Regular cleaning and disinfecting of hutches are measures that help to reduce all infectious diseases.

A clean water supply and properly stored feed are important.

Isolation of new animals will prevent exposure to potential carriers and reduce the possibility of introducing disease into a clean rabbitry. All animals that show symptoms of disease should be isolated immediately or be slaughtered and properly disposed of by burning or deep burial.

No vaccine is available. Antibiotic preparations, such as streptomycin and penicillin, and sulfaquinoxaline are effective, but the cost of such therapy must be weighed against the value of the individual animal.

STATISTICS of the United States Rabbit Experiment Station, at Fontana, Calif., show that pneumonia is the greatest single cause of death in mature rabbits. It was present alone in 53 percent of all losses in mature rabbits in 1947–1949. Among the developing rabbits, 10 percent showed primary pneumonia at death. One-third of all autopsied cases showed pneumonia either alone or with other pathology, such as enteritis. Primary pneumonia was found in 5 percent of the unweaned young. The highest death rates from pneumonia alone were during the third week, when the young were emerging from the nestbox, and during the 11th week.

The major predisposing factors to pneumonia in mature does were pregnancy, parturition, and heavy lactation. In the 6- to 12-week-old rabbits, enteritis, abscesses, and long teeth were the main factors. In the nestbox babies, exposure and improper care were the main causes.

Rabbits with pneumonia lack appetite and breathe with difficulty. The head is thrown back, and the nostrils are elevated. They literally gasp for air during the later stages. There may be a watery or a purulent discharge from the eyes and nose. The color of the ears and eyes is not pink, but bluish, and the body temperature is elevated above the normal (102.5° F., with a variation of one-half degree).

When such animals are opened after death, the lobe or lobes of the lungs appear mottled with patches of gray and red. The tissue in advanced cases may have the consistency of liver.

Frequently the bronchi and bronchioles fill with a thick pus. An entire lobe in advanced cases may be replaced by this cheeselike matter, which is characteristic of a *Pasteurella* infection.

In primary pneumonia cases, *P. multocida* was isolated in 65 percent of the animals; when the pneumonia was secondary to enteritis, the *Pasteurella* isolates were only 15 percent and were not found in cases of infant pneumonia. *Alcaligenes bronchisepticus* and a *Streptococcus* species were found infrequently in primary pneumonia, but in secondary pneumonia they each accounted for 35 percent of the isolates In infant pneumonia the two species occupied equal importance.

Rabbits should be housed in well ventilated hutches that provide protection from dampness, drafts, and extremes of heat and cold. Units should have good head space and allow some sunlight to enter. Overcrowding should be avoided.

Intramuscular doses of penicillin are effective against many cases of pneumonia if given early enough. Late cases with advanced pathology are fatal. Reducing feed concentrates and providing fresh greens often will help the animal resist the infection.

INFECTIOUS MYXOMATOSIS (mosquito disease) is a specific, rapidly fatal disease that is caused by a filterable virus, *Molitor myxomae*. It was first discovered in domestic rabbits in Mexico when some laboratory animals were shipped from Lower California to San Diego, Calif., in late 1927. By 1937 it had spread along the entire west coast. It is called mosquito disease by some rabbit growers, because it is found frequently in low, marshy areas where mosquitoes are numerous.

The disease is highly infectious among rabbits, but it does not appear to be transmissible to other animals or to man. Mosquitoes transmit the virus by carrying blood or exudate from the eye or nostril of an affected animal to a noninfected rabbit. Direct contact between animals also spreads the infection. Biting flies and fleas can transmit the virus, but the insect vector is purely mechanical, as no life cycle is required in the vector.

Myxomatosis is characterized by tumors, which appear in the subcutaneous tissues around the eyes, mouth, nose, and sex organs. Conjunctivitis, edema of the eyelids, and a nasal discharge occur. The ears swell and become pendulous and heavy—a characteristic symptom.

The central nervous system is invaded by the virus from the blood stream, breathing becomes labored, and the animal enters coma. Artificially infected animals show symptoms in about 10 days and die 4 or 5 days later. Mortality may be as high as 95 percent in animals more than 60 days old. The young are affected less.

Internal changes at autopsy are not characteristic. If the soft tumors are cut, the surfaces are white, gelatinous, and glistening. The lungs are usually congested. The spleen is dark, enlarged, and pulpy. Infected epithelial cells in or near the tumors contain cytoplasmic inclusion bodies.

Rabbits recovering from myxomatosis are immune to the disease, but vaccine protection has not proved to be efficient. Antibiotics have no effect on the course of the infection.

The best method of control consists of early recognition and immediate destruction of all animals with symptoms. Screening units and reducing mosquito populations by drainage and spraying also are effective measures.

The reservoir of infection is not known. The virus neutralization antibodies and complement-fixation tests were negative in a Public Health Survey of cottontail and jackrabbits in San Diego County, Calif.

SPIROCHETOSIS (or true vent disease) of domestic rabbits is caused by *Treponema cuniculis*, which is transmitted from one animal to another by mating.

The micro-organism closely resembles the spirochete of human syphilis, but there is no antigenic relationship between them. Spirochetosis is not prevalent nor is it of great importance, but its resemblance to *T. pallidum* makes it worth mentioning here.

The first symptoms are small vesicles, or blisters, around the vent and the external sex organs. The vesicles rupture and become covered with scabs, or crusts, which usually are confined to the external genitalia but may spread to the lips, eyelids, or hocks. Affected animals usually remain in good physical condition and exhibit no other symptoms of the disease if there are no complications.

Spread of spirochetosis can be prevented by examination of the external genitalia of both animals before mating and not using for breeding purposes any animal that shows lesions.

An effective ointment consists of 3 parts lanolin and 1 part of colomel, which is rubbed well on the affected areas 3 to 4 times a week. The lesions usually heal within 10 to 14 days. The animals can be bred after they have healed entirely.

TULAREMIA, or "rabbit fever," is an infectious disease that affects people and many species of animals. It occurs in wild rabbits, but it has never been found as a natural infection in domestic rabbits.

Domestic rabbits are susceptible to the disease, but the usual manner in which they are raised does not expose them to the insects (ticks, lice, and fleas) involved in the spread of the disease. Cannibalism also spreads the infection among wild animals.

Laboratory infections with *Pasteurella tularense* produce a fatal septicemia in the rabbit.

The bacteria are susceptible to the action of streptomycin, Aureomycin, and several sulfa drugs.

RABBITS occasionally are affected with a parasitic fungus disease, known as favus. The head and feet usually are attacked, but some rabbits are more susceptible than others.

Favus may be caused by members of the genus *Trichophyton* or *Achorion*, both of which cause similar infections in other domestic animals and man.

Circular or oval plaques appear on the face and ears. These lesions are covered with scaly crusts, and small red points appear about the hair follicles. After these lesions have been established for some time, the fur breaks off at the skin surface, and a raised scaly surface is left.

Rabbits with favus should be isolated from the others. The fur should be trimmed away from the lesions and should be burned. Daily applications of tincture of iodine or a 10-percent solution of salicylic acid in alcohol should be applied for a week.

MATURE FEMALES frequently develop a staphylococcic or streptococcic infection of the mammary tissue. The rabbit grower often calls it "blue breast," because the tissue turns black and blue. Some cases appear to be highly contagious and can be spread by transferring young from one infected doe to another. The breasts are red and flushed in early cases, and the animal's temperature goes above normal. Appetite and activity may be poor. As the infection spreads, the breasts become bluish or black and firm or congested.

Intramuscular injections of 150,000 units of procaine penicillin, if given early, will cure the infection.

Reducing feed concentrates and substituting fresh, green succulent foods will help.

Injuries to the lactating breasts, caused by improper nestboxes or dirty bedding materials, should be prevented.

ENTERITIS, or "bloat," in one or another of its forms, is responsible for more deaths among unweaned rabbits than any other disorder. Its incidence in any herd may vary, but detailed statistics over a 3-year period indicated that 50 percent of the unweaned mortality cases showed this disorder. It is seldom observed until after the fourth week of life, and the incidence is highest during the seventh week.

The cause of enteritis is not known. All efforts to reproduce the disease experimentally have failed. Observations indicate it is not infectious and that sanitary measures have little effect in controlling it. All attempts to isolate an etiological agent have given negative results. Some technicians believe that enteritis is a nutritional or biochemical problem.

Characteristic symptoms are lack of appetite, lusterless and squinting eyes, rough fur, and grinding of the teeth. Animals may display an intense thirst and drink often. Sometimes the abdomen becomes distended with gas—hence the name "bloat." The temperature generally is subnormal.

Predominating symptoms divide enteritis into three major groups. When a thick, gelatinous discharge is voided or fills the large intestine, the enteritis is called mucoid. Extreme fluidity of the bowel contents or a profuse watery diarrhea are characteristic symptoms of diarrheal enteritis. When free blood is found in the lumen of the intestine and cecum, the enteritis is called hemorrhagic. It is the most acute. There may be no noticeable symptoms.

Diarrheal enteritis occurred in 80 percent of all cases; mucoid enteritis in about 15 percent; and hemorrhagic enteritis in about 5 percent. The average age at death was lowest with hemorrhagic and highest with diarrheal. The course of the disease in animals with diarrheal symptoms ranged from 24 to 72 hours. In the mucoid stage it was 4 to 10 days.

The stomach at autopsy is filled with fluid, and ulcerations in the pyloric region are often noted. Fluid, gaseous, or mucoid intestinal contents are found throughout the entire alimentary tract. Formed droppings are not found in the large intestine. Adhesions are not uncommon in the intestinal loops. Sloughing off of the mucosa and submucosa of the small intestine and necrosis of the epithelium of the colon is noted. Pathological changes are limited to the gastrointestinal tract.

Antibiotic feed supplements (Aurofac-A, Penbac, and Terramycin-5) and vitamin B_{12} incorporated in pelleted rations have been effective in reducing mortality from enteritis. In one series of tests, enteritis mortality was reduced by 75 percent by the addition of 5 pounds of Aureomycin supplement per ton of feed.

The administration by mouth of 25 milligrams per pound body of weight of Aureomycin or Terramycin to sick animals also has reduced enteritis mortality.

KARL W. HAGEN, JR., *is a member of the Animal Disease and Parasite Research Branch, stationed at the United States Rabbit Experiment Station in Fontana, Calif. He is a graduate of the University of California in Los Angeles and has studied rabbit diseases since 1950.*

Parasites of the Domestic Rabbit

EVERETT E. LUND

DOMESTIC RABBITS raised commercially in this country are usually maintained in individual hutches, each of which contains at most a doe and her litter of unweaned young. The degree of isolation secured by this practice, together with the employment of reasonable measures of sanitation, has been effective in controlling parasitism in our domestic rabbits. There are, however, a few parasitic diseases that still become troublesome.

Coccidiosis is the most prevalent of all parasitic diseases of domestic rabbits. It is caused by microscopic one-celled parasites that invade the lining of the intestine, multiply prolifically, and eventually leave the body of the rabbit in the droppings. At this stage they are in a resistant form and are called oöcysts. When conditions of temperature and moisture are favorable, the minute oöcysts develop to an infectious stage within a few days. They are then ready to attack another rabbit, if taken in with feed or water or as the animal washes itself.

At least four species of coccidia live entirely in the lining of the intestine of domestic rabbits, save for their passage from one animal to another. Not all are equally harmful. Rabbits tolerate moderate numbers of any of these species without suffering measurable damage. Excessive numbers of the larger species produce soft droppings or diarrhea, indisposition to feed, a consequent loss in rate of gain, and at times death.

There is no positive means of diagnosing intestinal coccidiosis without a microscopic examination of the droppings, the intestinal or cecal (blind pouch) content, or the intestinal wall. Even then, experience is needed to judge whether the number of parasites present is great enough to account for the symptoms, because other disorders, particularly mucoid enteritis, may produce similar symptoms and be present at the same time.

The control of intestinal coccidiosis in domestic rabbits rests largely on the employment of management practices that minimize the danger of fecal contamination of feed, water, hutch floors, and other equipment. Self-cleaning floors that permit droppings to fall through, out of reach of the animals, reduce to about one-tenth the hazard that is presented by soil or floors on which manure accumulates. Feeders about 4 inches above floor level, provided with guards to keep animals from perching in them, also are necessary. If watering cannot be accomplished with automatic valves placed 8 to 9 inches above floor level, the water containers must also be provided with guards.

Handling of animals must be reduced to a minimum. Equipment—brushes, scrapers, pails, and other utensils—should never come in contact with one hutch after another. The oöcysts are quite resistant to all usual disinfectants but are susceptible to drying. If the hutch floors and other equipment are kept clean and dry, infections heavy enough to be of economic significance are unlikely.

Even the best substances used for treatment have only transitory effects on the intestinal coccidia, but some-times they may be useful in subduing severe outbreaks. A pelleted ration containing one-half pound of sulfaquinoxaline per ton of feed (0.025 percent concentration) may be offered in place of the regular ration for 2 or 3 weeks to reduce the incidence of intestinal coccidiosis to a point at which control by suitable management practices is sufficient. The intestinal coccidia develop a tolerance when the drug is used continuously.

One species of coccidium, *Eimeria stiedae*, multiplies in the liver of domestic rabbits. Like the other species, it enters the intestinal wall but lodges in the liver before reproducing. Infections more than 16 days old are easily recognized by the creamy-white, circular nodules produced on the liver. Because infections of any degree disfigure the liver, making it unmarketable, and prejudice the marketing of the entire carcass, liver coccidiosis is always of economic significance.

Liver coccidiosis by itself does not produce diarrhea or any other external symptoms, except in the most extreme cases. Then the liver may be so greatly enlarged as to distort the body of the animal. Some animals affected to this extent die; usually ruptured livers, peritonitis (body cavity inflammation), or pneumonia are complications. A technician with experience can diagnose some cases of liver coccidiosis by a microscopic examination of the droppings, but the disfiguring lesions remain on the liver several weeks after the last evidence of oöcysts in the fecal pellets, so only internal symptoms can be entirely trustworthy.

Liver coccidiosis is acquired in the same way as intestinal coccidiosis. The control measures also are the same. Liver coccidiosis can be held to much lower incidences than can intestinal coccidiosis with the same control measures. In well maintained commercial rabbitries, 2 to 10 percent of the animals may have light cases of intestinal coccidiosis, while liver coccidiosis is either absent or present in less than 0.5 percent of the herd.

A ration containing 0.025 percent of sulfaquinoxaline is more than 90 percent effective against the liver coccidium. Its effectiveness continues, so the ration can be fed indefinitely. But this is not necessary, and if the drug is used at all, it should be used only as an emergency measure, until management control can be effected.

EAR MANGE is probably the second most important parasitic disease of domestic rabbits. It is caused by a small mite, usually *Psoroptes communis cuniculi*, which is just visible to the naked eye. Studies conducted in California in 1948 and 1949 revealed that 45 to 80 percent of the commercial rabbitries visited had been troubled with ear mange. The incidence among mature animals was found to range as high as 84 percent, but averaged 11 percent.

Ear mange is usually contracted by close or prolonged contact with animals already infected or by placing animals in quarters recently occupied by affected ones.

The tiny mites that are able to find their way into the auditory canal at the base of the ear pierce the skin with their sharp mouth parts, feed, and permit the escape of the clear serum. The serum hardens into scales, beneath which the mites continue their activity, feeding, mating, laying eggs, producing more layers of scales, and spreading. Finally thick crusts are formed, and the area involved extends far up the inner surface of the ear and occasionally even to the head and neck near the ear.

Intense itching is provoked by all this activity. Affected rabbits shake their heads, rub their ears with their front feet, and scratch vigorously at the base of their ears with their hind feet. Parallel scratches one-fourth to three-eighths inch apart at the base of the skull or on the neck are self-inflicted by the nails of the hind feet and are indicative of ear mange. By looking into the ear, one can see yellow crusts of dried serum, sometimes tinged with blood. Their presence can be accepted as almost certain evidence of ear mange.

Treatment consists of cleaning the ear first with a bland oil, such as ordinary vegetable oil used in cooking, and then swabbing the entire inner surface of the ear with medicated oil. Enough oil should be applied so that it runs into the auditory canal and wets all surfaces thoroughly. Cases of long standing have such heavy encrustations that it is necessary to extend the cleaning over a period of 2 or 3 days, so that the heavy cakes can soften before one attempts to extract all of them. A mixture of 1 part of iodoform, 10 parts of ether, and 25 parts of vegetable oil is effective. It may be prepared by any druggist. A second application of this mixture should be made 7 to 10 days after the first, to kill recently hatched mites, or ones having strayed from the area. A 0.25-percent solution of lindane in vegetable oil is effective and inexpensive, but should not be used unless the operator wears rubber gloves or can otherwise avoid prolonged contact with the solution while it is being applied. The drug is harmful when absorbed through the skin.

All animals near the affected ones, recently in contact with them, or in quarters recently occupied by such animals should be treated, except does within 10 days of kindling. These should be treated after they have kindled, to avoid restraining them at a time when abortion may be induced, should they struggle violently. It is unnecessary to treat unweaned animals, but any being saved beyond the age of 8 or 10 weeks should be treated.

Once a herd is free of mange it is not difficult to keep it so. All new introductions to the herd and animals being returned to it after contact with other rabbits should be treated as a routine practice in all rabbitries.

Ear mange does not often cause mortality, but it makes its victims unthrifty and seriously interferes with production. It particularly influences lactation and the care of the young.

Occasionally mites penetrate the eardrum, so that infections arise in the middle ear. The organs of balance in the inner ear may be affected; the animal turns its head to one side and may even roll over in an effort to orient itself to gravity. This condition is called wry neck and can result from any of several causes, but ear mange is a common one. Animals showing wry neck may live, but they are useless and should be destroyed or marketed, if no other infection is present.

BODY MANGE of domestic rabbits is also caused by tiny mites of other species. This disorder is not common, but when it is present the areas first involved are usually the back and the neck, although it may occur anywhere.

The affected areas lose the hair, and the skin is red, with an abundance of white scales. Diagnosis depends on finding the mites or their eggs on hair plucked at the margins of the bare areas. A microscope or a good lens may be needed to make sure of that.

Treatment of body mange is tedious. If the areas involved are not numerous, treatment may be practical for animals of more than ordinary value. One should clip the hair from an area at least one-half inch beyond that which is obviously affected and swab the skin thoroughly with vegetable oil or a mixture of 1 part of flowers of sulfur in 3 parts of vegetable oil. The iodoform preparation mentioned for the treatment of ear mange is also satisfactory, but the lindane preparation should not be used if more than 5 to 6 square inches of skin are to be swabbed, because there would be danger of too great absorption of the toxic drug.

Body mange is spread by contact, through the use of infected hutches, and by the shed hair as it blows or is carried about, as on the clothing of the attendant. Hutches that are clean and dry and free from hair cannot harbor mites capable of establishing infection more than a few days at summer temperatures and hardly more than 2 weeks in cold weather.

PINWORMS are fairly common in domestic rabbits, especially in old does. The glistening white worms, one-half inch long, often are seen on the surface of freshly passed droppings or shining through the wall of the cecum (blind gut) of mature animals that are slaughtered.

Ordinarily pinworms do little or no harm. They may become numerous, especially in animals 2 to 3 years old. Mature worms usually become sufficiently inactive to be swept out of the cecum from time to time with its normal movement of contents.

The worms manage to stay next to the intestinal wall in most instances and in that way escape from the rabbit on the outside of the droppings, rather than become sealed up within the mucus-covered pellets. Worms voided in that way often crawl away from the droppings (unless they are on concrete, sheet iron or some dry, unresponsive surface) and dry up; the females then liberate the hundreds of microscopic eggs that fill almost their entire bodies. The eggs become infective after several days, and some are consumed with feed and water or as the animals wash.

Pinworms infrequently perforate the cecum, permitting bacteria to infect the body cavity. Death from peritonitis may result.

Pinworms rarely become a serious problem if management methods necessary for the control of coccidia and other intestinal disorders are observed.

Phenothiazine is effective in ridding rabbits of pinworms if administered at the rate of 0.2 gram per pound of body weight on each of 2 days, with 3 or 4 days intervening. Rabbits are able to detect the drug in the ration, but it can be given in gelatin capsules. This is such a nuisance it can be recommended only when the grower is particularly desirous of freeing an animal of worms for some special reason.

TAPEWORM LARVAE—developmental stage—sometimes disfigure the livers of rabbits with irregular, creamy-white streaks. The streaks are the scars of the paths taken by the larvae as they migrate through the liver. The larvae finally come to rest as little glistening beads of jellylike material on the membranes supporting the intestine.

Each such little bead is an embryonic tapeworm, which must now await consumption by a carnivorous animal, such as a dog. In its intestine the embryo will grow into a mature tapeworm; its eggs later escape in the dog's droppings and can infect another rabbit.

Disfigured livers are objectionable and often prejudice the value of the entire carcass. To prevent this type of infection in rabbits, the owner has to keep all feed, water, nest-box straw,

equipment, and everything the rabbit may touch entirely free of possible contamination with droppings of carnivores, particularly dogs. He should never permit a dog to sleep on feed sacks and bales of hay or straw or to contaminate anything that will reach the rabbits. And, conversely, to keep the dog from becoming infected, he should not allow it to feed, on the viscera of infected rabbits.

EVERETT E. LUND *is a parasitologist in the United States Department of Agriculture. He received his training at Iowa State College and the University of California at Berkeley. After having taught several years in universities here and abroad, he joined the Department of the Interior in 1944 and the Department of Agriculture in 1946.*

Diseases and Parasites of Minks

JOHN R. GORHAM

THE BOTULISM bacterium, *Clostridium botulinum*, produces a potent toxin in contaminated meat. Such meat, fed to minks, can kill them in 18 to 96 hours. Almost immediately the animals suffer muscular incoordination and stiffness. Paralysis of the front or hind legs follows. The muscles used in breathing become paralyzed by the toxin, and the minks die.

The carcasses of sick horses and spoiled feed that has had a chance to become warm for a time should never be used.

The treatment of minks affected with botulism often is to no avail. Prompt recognition by the rancher will give the veterinarian a better chance to save the minks that have not eaten enough of the poisoned food to show symptoms. The owner should throw away immediately all the contaminated, frozen, stored food and the uneaten ration in the pens.

Antitoxin that contains toxin-neutralizing antibodies against the three common types of toxins, designated A, B, and C, should be administered to every mink on the ranch as soon as possible.

For prevention, a toxoid—preventive inoculation—offers fair promise of being helpful. The first work on botulism toxoids for minks was done in Sweden. Following the disastrous outbreaks of botulism in this country when spoiled whale meat was fed, research workers in Utah and Wisconsin and at the Department of Agriculture Fur Animal Disease Station developed an experimental toxoid, which is available commercially. It is emphasized, however, that care in management and selection of feed is the best insurance for preventing this malady.

ANTHRAX is a fatal disease of minks caused by the bacterium *Bacillus anthracis.* Minks die within a few days after eating meat from an anthrax-infected cow, pig, or horse. The animals show few if any signs of sickness before death.

An autopsy discloses that the spleen is enlarged, blue black, and easily torn. Because other disease conditions in minks seem to be similar to anthrax, a diagnosis can only be made on bacteriological examination in a laboratory. The surest prevention is to avoid feeding meat from sick animals.

Penicillin injections have been given to affected minks with good results.

People may become infected by handling pelts removed from minks that died from anthrax. Because the spores—the resistant stage of the bacterium—survive the tanning process, dead animals should be burned and not pelted. Premises once contaminated remain infected.

ABSCESSES caused by Micrococcus and Streptococcus and by *Klebsiella ozaenae* are common in minks. Often slivers of bone or barbed grasses injure the animal and carry the bacteria into the skin or lining of the mouth. Pus accumulates, and an abscess, or boil, is formed.

When the abscess feels hot and swollen and is fluctuating to the touch, one should make a vertical incision long enough to drain away the pus with a sharp, sterile blade. The cavity should be washed out with a mild disinfectant, such as dilute hydrogen peroxide, and dusted with sulfa powder, such as sulfathiazole or sulfanilamide. A veterinarian can demonstrate this simple technique. In all cases, an injection of 100,000 to 200,000 units of penicillin should be given.

STREPTOCOCCUS organisms—the small bacteria which, when viewed under the microscope, occur in chains like a string of beads—may cause other troubles. Ranchers may notice that the top and sides of the head, nose, and upper neck region of some of their minks have suddenly become swollen. This condition is called cephalic cellulitis. The minks are sluggish and refuse food. If they are not given an inoculation of penicillin at this time, death will ensue.

These types of bacteria may also cause fatal septicemia (blood poisoning) in young minks. The symptoms are not apparent, and the animals are found dead in their nest boxes. Penicillin is the antibiotic most frequently recommended for treating streptococcal infections.

Pseudomonas aeruginosa causes a rare but deadly disease in minks. This bacterium is introduced into the herd through contaminated drinking water. Most minks are sick only an hour or two before they die—they may look healthy in the evening but are found dead the next morning. Pneumonia is the most significant finding at autopsy.

Streptomycin and polymyxin are the antibiotics of choice. As these drugs are highly toxic to minks, information as to the dosage and manner of treatment should be obtained from a veterinarian.

PASTEURELLA MULTOCIDA is found in cases of mink pneumonia. The disease often appears in the spring and fall when the weather is damp and the temperature is subject to rapid change. The nest boxes should be constructed so that they can be kept dry and well ventilated. Minks can stand freezing temperatures, but they cannot tolerate wet nest hay and boxes.

Rapid, shallow breathing, as evidenced by a heaving of the flanks, is the most important clinical sign of the malady.

For treatment, injections of penicillin, Aureomycin, or Terramycin can be given. Treatment is not always successful because the animal is often too far gone by the time it looks ill.

GANGRENE occasionally develops in wounds and after contaminated tissue vaccines have been injected. Various bacteria have been isolated—Clostridium, Streptococcus, Micrococcus, and Actinomyces.

Animals that have been given contaminated vaccine drag the inoculated leg. Gas bubbles form in the muscle and a foul discharge is noted later.

The broad-spectrum antibiotics, such as Aureomycin and Terramycin, are used for treatment.

PLEURITIS, or inflammation of the lining membranes of the chest cavity, often causes death. When the ribs are cut and the chest cavity is opened, a large amount of thick, grayish-yellow pus is seen. The lungs are compressed and covered with adhesions.

Many bacteria have been isolated from this pus, including Streptococcus and Micrococcus species, coliforms, Norcardia species, *Actinomyces necrophorous*, and organisms like pleuropneumonia.

Animals sick with pleuritis are rarely treated, because they usually are found dead with no signs of illness.

ENTERITIS, an inflammatory condition of the small and large intestine, is commonly observed on mink ranches in the United States and Canada.

Spoiled food, corrosive chemicals, and a specific virus can cause it. Many bacteria have been suspected, but the actual cause in many instances is unknown. The disease is more apt to develop in the summer months.

Affected minks often have a big appetite. Beneath their pen is seen a large accumulation of black, tarry, or grayish-white droppings. Usually only a few minks on the ranch are affected.

When the whole herd is involved, prompt veterinary assistance is required, because sulfa drugs or high levels of antibiotics will have to be added to the rations.

WHEN DISTEMPER is mentioned, mink ranchers everywhere have cause for alarm, for it is very serious in minks throughout the United States.

Although almost all of the minks get the disease in any given outbreak, some animals do not show any symptoms. The number of deaths may vary from one outbreak to another. The loss may be as high as 90 percent in young mink, but the average loss in older mink is 30 to 40 percent. Kittens as young as 3 weeks may be infected. Outbreaks can occur at any time.

The incubation period—the interval between the time the virus first enters the mink and the appearance of disease—is about 9 to 14 days.

The first sign of the disease is swollen, watery eyelids. The lids become crusty and stick together in 2 or 3 days. The minks may have an excellent appetite at this time.

Next the feet may swell—the so-called "snowshoe" foot. Small, brownish, granular scabs can be seen on the surfaces of the pads. The minks may die at this time or appear to recover, but these "recovered" individuals may later die of what the rancher calls the "screaming fits." In this type of distemper, the virus has invaded the brain, causing the minks to froth at the mouth, chew violently on the wire netting, roll about the pen, and scream sharply. These convulsive seizures may last a short or a long time. The mink usually dies after one or two attacks.

The virus is spread from animal to animal through the air. In the normal breathing process, minks that show distemper (as well as the apparently healthy carriers) emit millions of small, virus-containing droplets into the air. The virus also is found in the saliva, nasal secretions, and skin scurf shortly before and during an attack. A mink may also shed virus into the air after the signs disappear.

Distemper can be transmitted among mink by indirect means, such as contaminated mitts and food pans.

A diagnosis often can be made by observing affected animals, but sometimes laboratory tests are necessary.

Microscopic slides can be made of tissue from the bladder and trachea (windpipe) and stained with special dyes. Distemper leaves rather characteristic marks, called inclusion bodies, in those tissues. They are small stained "dots," or specks, which represent distemper virus.

The surest way to obtain a diagnosis is to remove the spleen from the suspected distemper-infected mink, grind it in a liquid suspension, and inject it into a ferret. If the spleen from the animal in question contains active virus, the ferret, which is almost 100-percent susceptible to the virus, will become infected.

Every precaution must be made to keep distemper away from the ranch. New breeding stock or minks returned from fur shows should be quarantined for 2 months, as they may carry the virus into the herd.

Infected dogs are a dangerous source of distemper virus for minks.

Two general types of distemper vaccine are on the market—the killed-virus vaccines and the living modified-virus vaccines.

The killed-virus vaccines, prepared from a spleen containing virulent virus of an animal dead of the disease and treated with formalin to inactivate the virus, have some disadvantages. Animals inoculated with them develop immunity rather slowly. The immunity seems to leave the animal, and so revaccination is necessary.

Living-virus vaccines, which are made by growing the virus in chicken embryos, have been more successful in controlling outbreaks.

VIRUS ENTERITIS has been considered a serious threat to minks in the United States. It has been found in Ontario and has been reported on a few ranches in Wisconsin and Illinois. The disease may kill as high as 80 percent of the kitten crop. It spreads rapidly on a ranch.

The first indication of sickness, within a week after the minks are exposed, is a sudden loss of appetite. If the feces are examined, a slightly pink to grayish-white "slug" (intestinal cast) can be noticed. The animals that do not die within 4 or 5 days recover, but may never reach maximum size. When the dead animals are opened, the intestines appear bright red.

Minks that have recovered from the disease should be pelted in season, because they may harbor the disease as "silent" carriers and serve as a source of virus for the kitten crop of the following summer.

Because virus enteritis might be related to feline panleukopenia virus, cats and visitors and other traffic should be excluded from the mink yards. Research workers have tried to develop a vaccine.

Good sanitary practices are the only control measures.

NURSING SICKNESS, a common condition of nursing minks, appears before the fifth or sixth week of lactation. Affected females are first noticed in late June at about the time the young minks are weaned, but the disease may appear after the kits have been taken away.

Symptoms of nursing sickness include lack of appetite, loss of flesh, weakness, and incoordination. Death follows a period of coma. Some females, although apparently starving, fill their mouths with feed but do not swallow it.

The carcass is extremely thin—there is almost no body fat. A yellow, easily torn liver is often observed. Usually the gall bladder is distended with bile—evidence the animal has not been eating—and the stomach is empty.

Ranchers have considered the prevention of this condition a management problem. The nursing females should be carefully watched. If any become thin and dehydrated, the kittens should be given to another female if they are too small to be weaned. Another help is to make food and water easily available to the young kits from an early age onward.

Dr. G. R. Hartsough, of the Great Lakes Ranch Service, has suggested that the cause of nursing sickness may be a depletion of salt in the diet. He has recommended the addition of 0.5 percent of table salt to the feed from late May until the middle of July. Because some commercial mink cereals contain salt, caution should be used when adding more salt, as minks are susceptible to salt poisoning.

URINARY CALCULI, called "gravel" or "stones" by the rancher, causes heavy losses. The disease is observed rarely in the Pacific Northwest, but calculi are a major problem among the mink herds of Wisconsin and other North Central States.

Most deaths occur in pregnant, whelping, or lactating females. Losses of females on some ranches have exceeded 15 percent.

Bladder stones often hinder the passage of young through the birth canal. After prolonged labor, the female becomes weak and dies within a day or two. Sometimes ranchers report straddling gait, difficult urination, and paralysis. When stones are found at autopsy and have caused death of the mink, the calculi are frequently accompanied by a discharge of blood and pus.

In male minks, small calculi can lodge at the penis bone and block the flow of urine to the outside.

The cause is unknown. The stones are almost pure magnesium ammonium carbonate. Because a calculus of this type is thought to form in alkaline urine, investigators believe this alkalinity has a role in the disease. Experiments have been started in an attempt to find out whether the bacteria in the bladder or the ration itself cause an alkaline urine.

Observations have indicated that the feeding of ammonium chloride from the first of April through June may help control the disease, because the drug helps to establish a more neutral urine. It is important that the animals be given ample water.

STEATITIS (yellow fat) has been recognized as a disease since 1942. The malady undoubtedly occurred before that time but was diagnosed as something else.

It affects only young minks and occurs in the summer and fall. The disease gives no warning—a fat kitten, apparently in the best of health, refuses the night feeding and is dead in the morning. Before the cause was known, it forced many ranchers to go out of business.

Young minks succumbed when they were fed rations containing high percentages of fish scrap that had been in storage for a long time. Storage horsemeat that has quantities of untrimmed fat also caused the disease. Observations of field outbreaks and laboratory experiments have revealed that these diets have a high content of unsaturated fats and are deficient in vitamin E. Apparently those two factors work together to form the characteristic yellow-brown color of the fat and eventual death.

Often the ailment occurs soon after weaning; therefore the dam, as well as her kits, should have a diet that contains ample vitamin E. This vitamin may be obtained in many different forms (stabilized powder, wheat germ meal, wheat germ oil, and purified tocopherols).

It has been our experience that the stabilized powder is the most satisfactory.

It is possible that the liquid preparations are more readily oxidized by the rest of the ration, so that some of the vitamin E is withdrawn. Vitamin E is a dietary essential that the body is unable to synthesize (manufacture) and must be obtained from outside sources. It is also called the antisterility factor and tocopherols. Vitamin E protects other vitamins from the destructive effects of oxygen and is thought to be necessary for normal reproduction in some animal species.

Ranchers should supplement the diet of the young growing kits so that the amount of wheat germ meal or synthetic preparations in the ration provide 15 milligrams of vitamin E per day per mink.

In an outbreak, the owner should lower the level of fish or storage horsemeat, substitute fresh, unfrozen horsemeat and liver, and add wheat germ meal or stabilized vitamin E powder to the diet. Each affected kit should receive an inoculation of 15–20 milligrams of vitamin E a day for 3 days or more. The preparations can be obtained at drugstores or from veterinarians. They are sold under such names as injectable tocopherols.

HYDROCEPHALUS, or "water head," is a hereditary disease that causes death in minks.

The distended head, malaise, incoordination, and lack of growth are readily seen when the litters are first checked after whelping.

The accumulation of fluid within the cavities of the brain forces the brain tissue against the soft developing skull bones and pushes them outward. Little brain tissue is found when the young mink is examined after death.

Because the affected kitten usually dies before it is 6 weeks old, it should be removed from the litter, as it will take nourishment from the dam.

The dam, sire, and littermates of the hydrocephalic kit should be pelted the following winter. Both parents are sure to carry the recessive genes that are responsible for the disease, and all or most of the littermates may carry it. This manner of control, if followed annually, should eventually eliminate the malady from the ranch.

THE CAUSE OF WET BELLY in male minks is unknown. The constant dribbling of urine causes a loss of hair and a severe inflammation of the skin and underlying tissues in the region of the penis. Frequently 10 percent of the males on a ranch may be affected.

When the animal is pelted and the skin stretched on the board to dry, the damaged area is readily visible. Because those pelts bring lower prices at auction, the condition is a cause for concern.

The addition of molasses and fresh liver to the ration has been recommended.

SPORADIC AILMENTS may plague mink ranchers. Fatty or yellow liver is often found in a postmortem examination. It should not be considered a separate disease, but rather an abnormal finding, which accompanies such diverse conditions as nursing sickness, food poisoning, poisoning by chemicals, pregnancy disease, and uremia.

Minks often are addicted to fur chewing. They have a lionlike appearance, because they chew off all hair they can reach. Sometimes a mink will chew off its entire tail—hair, flesh, and bone—and continue chewing until it kills itself.

Hot, humid, still days can cause the death of old and young minks alike. If the female is whelping or if the kits are only a week or two old, the losses are high. The female refuses to nurse the kits, or she may become so restless that the young minks are dragged about until dead.

Mink farmers should never feed chicken byproducts without making sure that the chicken heads do not contain diethylstilbestrol (caponizing) pellets. Diethylstilbestrol, even in small amounts, will cause breeding failures in male and female minks.

(Diethystilbestrol is a synthetic hormonelike substance that depresses the development of male characteristics and, in females, interferes with the normal reproductive cycle. It has been used to bring about increased weight gain in steers and feed-lot heifers and to stimulate the rate of gain in fattening lambs. It is frequently used in turkeys and chickens to reduce their activity and to increase weight gains.)

A condition causing death in minks that carry the Aleutian gene—that is, Aleutian and Sapphire color phase mutations—results in occasional losses. The affected individual may exhibit bleeding at the mouth, become extremely thin, and succumb in a month or less. To increase the hardiness of this beautiful mutation, many ranchers outcross them with standard black minks. No effective treatment is yet known.

The gray fleshfly (of *Wohlfahrtia* species) is responsible for the death of many young minks. The female fly deposits eggs, which are quickly transformed into moving maggots on the skin of the young kitten. The maggots bore into the skin and leave a deep sore behind them.

The young minks become extremely restless and cry pitifully. Infection, lack of appetite, and exhaustion frequently lead to death.

The kits that have maggots should be removed and treated by injecting hydrogen peroxide, chloroform, or ether into the opening—these substances usually make the maggot back out. The wound should then be treated with an antiseptic, such as mild tincture of iodine.

JOHN R. GORHAM, *an employee of the Agricultural Research Service, is in charge of the Fur Animal Disease Research Laboratory at Pullman, Wash. Dr. Gorham is a graduate of the State College of Washington and the University of Wisconsin.*

Diseases and Parasites of Foxes

JOHN R. GORHAM

THE IMPORTANCE of cleanliness in the care of foxes cannot be overemphasized. With them, as with many other animals, it is easier to prevent a disease than to cure it.

Foxes are hearty, vigorous animals and rarely are sick if they have an adequate diet and healthy conditions in which to live. They must be reared in pens with woven-wire bottoms. That method of husbandry disrupts the life cycle of many disease agents and parasites, because the feed does not become tainted with droppings.

To make the use of disinfectants easier, the equipment and construction should be designed to save labor.

Simple, handy pens, kennels, feed houses, and feeding equipment are best. Because fecal matter and other organic material harbor bacteria and viruses, cleaning should precede disinfection. One agent can do both jobs.

When routinely cleaning and disinfecting pens and kennels, ordinary lye solution is an effective and economical disinfectant. One can of lye, which contains 13 ounces, is enough to make 15 gallons. If large areas must be covered, the lye can be bought as caustic soda and each pound will make about 20 gallons of solution. The solution does not have to be heated.

Besides acting as a disinfectant, lye solutions cut grease and partly dissolve and penetrate fecal material, but lye has some disadvantages.

Concentrated lye is a poison. It is destructive to aluminum, paints, and clothing. It does not harm wood or iron in the dilute concentration recommended. The dilute solution as recommended is not harmful to the animals in the amounts which might remain in the pens. Quantities of the solution should not be left unguarded where the animals might drink it. The solution may be slightly irritating to the hands and face of the operator. Since exposure to the air soon converts lye into a relatively inactive substance, containers should be tightly covered.

SALMONELLOSIS, an important bacterial disease of foxes, causes many losses in the pups during the late spring and early summer. The feeding of calves infected with salmonella organisms has brought the malady to the fox ranch.

Adult foxes may harbor the bacteria in their intestines. The bacteria pass out in their feces, which convey the infection to the young.

The disease is marked by such signs as lack of appetite, dullness, rough coat, a humped-up appearance, and eyes that appear sunken and show a discharge. Diarrhea is only occasionally noticed. Autopsy reveals an enormous enlargement of the spleen. Depending upon the circumstances of the outbreak, the veterinarian may use streptomycin, Aureomycin, Terramycin, or sulfa drugs. Often combinations of sulfa drugs and antibiotics are employed.

Distemper in foxes is caused by the same virus that causes distemper in dogs, minks, ferrets, and raccoons. It is transmitted through the air from fox to fox or by indirect contact by caretakers, who carry the virus on their shoes among pens or who handle healthy foxes after handling affected ones.

The first signs include a marked thirst and a dry, hot nose—signs of a high temperature. Foxes that usually are active at feeding time show no interest in their food and stay in their kennels. Next, a purulent discharge appears from the eyes and nose. The eyes may become glued shut with discharge. A diarrhea and pneumonia often occur. The fox either dies at that time or may seemingly recover and later die in a convulsion—barking fits.

Vaccination of the weaned pups before they are placed on the range or pens is advocated. The living egg-adapted vaccine seems to be superior to older methods of vaccination. The sulfonamides and antibiotics can pre-vent secondary complications of distemper but do not act specifically against the virus.

Fox encephalitis (infectious hepatitis) is found wherever foxes are raised and remains a disease problem for long periods of time on large fox farms. The death rate is 2 to 40 percent of the foxes on a ranch.

About 6 days after infection has taken place, the illness begins with a violent convulsion. Then the animal appears to be "walking as though asleep." A period of apparent normality follows, but convulsions occur again, followed by a somnolent state. Flaccid paralysis is another common sign. Recovered foxes are apparently immune for life.

For prevention, the killed-tissue vaccine used for immunization of dogs against infectious hepatitis should be administered shortly after weaning. Because the resultant immunity is not permanent, revaccination at yearly intervals is recommended.

Salmon disease, a rickettsial disease of foxes caused by the consumption of infected salmon, is a common malady where salmon, trout, and steelhead of the Pacific Northwest are fed. The affected fox loses its appetite, is severely depressed, and has a fever of 104° to 106°. Near the terminal stages, a yellowish or a bloody diarrhea is apparent.

The most striking finding at autopsy is a generalized enlargement of the lymphoid tissue. The veterinarian will confirm the diagnosis by finding the rickettsia in microscopic sections.

There is no vaccine for this condition. Penicillin, broad-spectrum antibiotics (Aureomycin, Terramycin), and some sulfa drugs (sulfanilamide, sulfamerazine) have been used successfully to treat the condition.

Rickets and Chastek paralysis are nutritional diseases of foxes. Both conditions are also reported in mink.

Rickets is a disease of young animals and is usually noticed a short time after weaning. It is caused by a deficiency of vitamin D, which upsets calcium and phosphorus metabolism. The usual source of this vitamin for foxes and mink is in fish oils or it may be formed by the action of the ultraviolet rays of sunlight on the skin.

Foxes with rickets have an enlargement of the ribs at their attachment to the sternum and a grotesque enlargement of the face bones. Affected animals with their short bodies and curved leg bones often have a difficult time getting around.

When rickets is suspected, the condition should be corrected by including high-potency vitamin D fish oils, together with a supplement containing calcium and phosphorus. All affected pups should have plenty of sunlight.

Chastek paralysis occurs on ranches where certain types of fish are fed in excess of 10 percent of the total ration. Fish such as fresh-water carp, Atlantic-coast whiting, Pacific-coast mackerel, quillbacks, mullets, suckers, northern pike, and Great Lakes herring have been found to cause the disease. There seems to be a factor in these fish that inactivates vitamin B_1 (thiamine).

After several weeks on such rations, the foxes lose their appetite. Next, some of the foxes appear stiff and exhibit nervous signs—spasms, paralysis, and convulsions. If symptoms have appeared, daily injections of thiamine should be given. Most foxes recover if treatment is begun early.

The fish should be cooked, because heat destroys the thiamine destroying factor. If cooking of fish is not possible, one should alternate fish feeding with rations containing no fish. Ample vitamin B_1 in the form of brewer's yeast will also help control the disease.

Roundworms, or ascarids, are common intestinal parasites in young foxes. The infection is seldom as heavy in adults. Affected pups are restless, have a poor appetite, and have a potbellied appearance. Diarrhea and convulsions are rather common. The worms are occasionally passed in the droppings or may be vomited from the stomach. Prevention depends on rigid sanitary practices. Portable kennels, wire-bottomed runs, and frequent removal of feces will help in control. Tetrachlorethylene—capsules, to be had from a veterinarian or a drugstore, are used for treatment. The veterinarian will also give instruction for using a capsule "gun"—a convenient instrument for administering worm pills.

On ranches where these roundworms are prevalent, the treatment of pups 4 to 5 weeks old, followed by another administration 2 weeks later, is a routine practice. Pregnant females should not be wormed. Tetrachlorethylene should be given to the adult breeders as soon as freezing temperatures prevail. Cold weather seems to retard the development of hookworm and roundworm eggs while they are in the soil, thus reducing reinfection.

Hookworms cause damage by embedding their heads in the lining of the intestine. By sucking blood they cause injuries and hemorrhages that lead to severe anemia.

Hookworms are difficult to see in the feces, as they are slender and about three-fourths inch long.

Fox pups heavily infected with hookworms are very thin and have dry harsh fur and pale mucous membranes. The droppings are dark and blood streaked.

Good sanitation and treatment with tetrachlorethylene are used for control. Treatment is as for roundworms.

Lungworms may be found in the larynx, windpipe, bronchial tubes, and lungs. A few worms cause no trouble, but large numbers lead to chronic bronchitis or pneumonia in young foxes.

Because of the location of the parasite in the lungs, treatment is ineffective. The enforcement of strict sanitary measures, such as raised wire pens, is the best safeguard.

JOHN R. GORHAM *is a veterinarian in the Department of Agriculture with the Animal Disease and Parasite Research Branch at the State College of Washington, Pullman, Washington.*

index

Abomasum, *see* Stomach
Abortion(s), goats, 211; hyperkeratosis, 274; trichomoniasis, 277; horses, 537; mares, 538; mares, causes, 539; sheep, 425
Abortion virus infection, horses and mules, 534
Abscesses, 30; shipping fever, 258; swine, 382; minks, 568.
Acanthocephala, defined, 31; 344
Acariasis, 292
Accredited tuberculosis-free areas, 5
Acetone, 121
Acetonemia, 38; infection, 244; defined, 245; 262
Aconitine, 120
Acriflavine, 85
Act(s) of 1884, 2, 66; May 29, 1884, 68; August 30, 1890, 68; February 2, 1903, 66, 68; March 3, 1905, 66, 68, 69; June 29, 1906, 69; June 30, 1906, 69; March 4, 1913, 69; May 31, 1920, 68; August 24, 1935, 70; February 28, 1947, 68; June 16, 1948, 68
ACTH, ketosis, 251; 252; 254; 255; pregnancy disease, 429
Actinobacillosis, cattle, 265–268; deer, 267; guinea pigs, 267; man, 267; mice, 267; rabbits, 267; rats, 267; sheep, 267; swine, 267
Actinobacillus, 384
Actinomyces, 384
ACTINOMYCOSIS AND ACTINOBACILLOSIS,[2] 265–268
Adrenal cortex, ketosis, 252
Adrenal glands, 106
Adrenocorticotrophic hormone, *see* ACTH
Adsorbate bacterin, 377; erysipelas, 476
Africa, 7, 15, 28, 32, 229, 269, 271, 418
African blue louse, 412
African sleeping sickness, 32
African tickborne fever, 15
Agglutination test, leptospirosis, 228; trichomoniasis, 281; vibriosis, 426; pullorum disease, 448; paratyphoid, 454
Agglutination-lysis test, leptospirosis, 227
Agricultural Marketing Act of 1946, 70
Agricultural requirements, 1975, 9
Agricultural Research Center, 350, 354, 378, 388, 399
Agricultural Research Service, 6
Airplanes, insecticides, 179, 181
Air-sac infection, 457, 476, 479
AITKEN, W. A.,[1] 255
Alabama, 273, 299, 362, 489

Alaska, 16
Albumin globulin, 262
Alcohol, 72
Aldrin, 87; toxicity, 137; 144
Aleutian gene, minks, 572
Alfalfa, 104; saponins, 109; 143; 430
Alkaligrass, 120
Alkaloid, defined, 119; 120
Alkyl dimethyl benzyl ammonium chloride, 102
ALLEN, REX W., 389, 399
Allergic reactions, 39
Allergy, bloat, 111
Alsike, 430
Alveoli, defined, 291
Ameba (amoeba), described, 33
American dog tick, 159, 272
American Q-fever, 160
Amino acids, 250, 253; pregnancy disease, 429
Aminosol, 254
Ammonium chloride, 104
Ammonium magnesium phosphate, 104
Amygdalin, 121
Anaerobic, defined, 332
Anaplasma, 269
Anaplasmosis, 157, 160, 170, 177, 233
ANAPLASMOSIS OF CATTLE, 268–273
Anatipestifer infection, ducks, 498
ANDERSON, W. A., 427
ANDREWS, JOHN S., 335, 338, 350
Anemia, 34; anaplasmosis, 268, 269, 270; from roundworms, 284; from stomach worms, 285; baby pigs, 379; goats, 390, 393, 394, 397; sheep, 390, 392, 394, 397; poultry, 495; pets, 504; horses, 545
Anesthetics, 74
Animal and Poultry Husbandry Research Branch, 109
Animal Disease Research Laboratory, 106
Animals, nematodes, 35
Anorexia, defined, 251
Antelope, rabies, 195; tapeworms, 154
Anthelmintics, 81; gastrointestinal parasites, 403
ANTHRAX, 229–235
Anthrax, 2; 3; 18; 56; 170; chronic, 230; symptoms, 230; diagnosis, 232; control, 232; treatment, 234; 258; blackleg, 264; 373; 423; 549; minks, 568
ANTIBIOTICS, 94–96
Antibiotics, 84; action, 94; administration, 94; defined, 94; salts, 94; allergic reaction, 95; toxicity, 95; limitations, 96; mastitis, 249; blackleg, 264; 266;

anaplasmosis, 271; pinkeye, 314; calf pneumonia, 324; swine disease, 383; sore mouth, 415; pullorum, 450; typhoid, 452; paratyphoid, 455; ornithosis, 460; CRD, 478; IS, 479; dogs, 516; distemper, 524; leptospirosis, 526; feline distemper, 528; foals, 544; rabbits, 560; gangrene, 569
Antibiotic feed supplements, rabbits, 563
Antiblackleg serum, 265
Antibodies, 52; defined, 89; 366; infectious bronchitis, 480
Antidotes, 139; chlorinated hydrocarbons, 139
Antigens, diagnostic, 90; brucellosis, 205; pullorum, 449
Antiglobulin sensitization test, equine, 545
Anti-hog-cholera serum, 358
Antiseptics, 74
Antiserum, procedures, 89; anthrax, 233; equine, 547
Antitoxins, 89; enterotoxemia, 424; minks, 567
Antrypol, 300
Apatite, 113
Aphthous, *see* Foot-and-mouth disease
Apoplexy, 422
Appetite, mastitis, 246; ketosis, 251, 254; shipping fever, 257; wheat-pasture poisoning, 261; blackleg, 263; coccidiosis, 315; mucosal disease, 328; loss of, goats, 397, 400; sheep, 397, 400, 418, 423, 434; ewes, 428
Argasidae, 157, 158
Argasids, 157, 158
Argentina, 24, 459
Argyrol, 314
Arizona, 124, 128, 299, 302, 418
Army Remount Depot, 533
Arrowgrass, 119, 121
ARS–53–6, 450
ARS–53–8, 450
Arsenic, toxicity, 132; swine dysentery, 364
Arsenic poisoning, livestock, 113
Arsenical dip, 4, 132; for lice, 307
Arsenical poisoning, acute, 132
Arsenicals, 85
Arteritis, horses and mules, 534
Arthritis, losses, 13; 376; calves, 320, 430; baby pigs, 380; lambs, 430; sheep, 436
Arthropoda, defined, 31
Arthropods, parasitic, 36
Artificial insemination, 203, 225; and trichomoniasis, 279; 282
Ascarids, swine, 340; poultry, 487; 504
Asia, 8, 15, 20, 28, 229, 373
Asiatic Newcastle disease, 64
Aspergillosis, ducks, 497
Assassin bug, 552
Asses, *see also* Mules
tetanus, 237; infectious anemia, 546
Aster, 119
Atrophic rhinitis, losses, 13; baby pigs, 381; swine, 382
ATROPHIC RHINITIS IN SWINE, 350–354
Atropine, 120
Aujesky's disease, baby pigs, 381
Aureomycin, *see* Antibiotics
Australia, 16, 19, 24, 104, 229, 313, 354, 394, 396, 405, 416, 417, 427
Autogenous bacterin, calves, 325
Avian diphtheria, 464

---

[1] Names of persons in this section are those of authors of chapters.
[2] Titles of chapters are printed in small capitals.

Avian leukosis complex, 467
AVIAN LYMPHOMATOSIS, 466–474
Avian monocytosis, 463
Avian spirochetosis, 157
Avianpox, 464
Avitaminosis A, in swine, 385
Azaleas, 122
Azoturia, 38, 554

Babesiosis, 157; dogs, 527
Bacillary white diarrhea, 447
Bacillus Calmette-Guerin vaccine, 17
Bacitracin, see Antibiotics
Bacteria, defined, 30; virulence, 40; 47; mastitis, 245
Bacterial infections, foals, 542
Bacterin(s), production, 89; shipping fever, 259; blackleg, 264; erysipelas, 377; enterotoxemia, 424; paratyphoid, 455; equine respiratory diseases, 535; foals, 544
Bacteriophage, 50
Badger, rabies, 195
Balanoposthitis, sheep, 434
Bang's disease, see Brucellosis
Barley, 104
Barn itch, 292; horses and mules, 555
Barns, 170
Bats, rabies, 20, 195, 198
Bayer compound 21/199, poisoning, symptoms, 141
Bayer L 13/59, 87; effects, 140; 171
BCG, 17
Beans, 143
Bear, rabies, 195
Beef animals, 296
Beef cattle, trichomoniasis, 277; lice control, 309; pinkeye, 314
Beef measles, 22
Beef tapeworm, 18; life cycle, 21; control, 22
Beet tops, 104, 115
Belching mechanism, 109
Belgium, 8, 192, 278
Beltsville Research Center, see Agricultural Research Center
BENNETT, PAUL C., 382
BENSON, EZRA TAFT, v.
Benzaldehyde, 121
Benzene, 143
Benzene hexachloride, see BHC
Benzol, 303
Benzyl benzoate, mange, 519
BHC, 85; 86; toxicity, 134; 144, 163; mange, 296; 348; 308; lice, 346, 413, 492; kidney worms, 340; scabies, 406
BIESTER, H. E., 239
Big jaw, 266
Bighead, sheep, 127, 421
BINNS, WAYNE, 113, 118
Bioassay procedures, 143
Biological products, 88–93
Biological Products Licensing Section, 92
Bipolar bacillus, 256
Bird tick, 161
Birdpox, 466
Birds, see also Poultry
ticks, 157; anthrax, 230; scabies, 292; erysipelas, 374; fowl typhoid, 452; lice, 490; esophageal worm, 507
Birth, foals, 542
Bison, flukes, 150
BITING GNAT, 181–182
Biting lice, cattle, 307; 411; equine, 558
Bitter actinea, 122
Bittern, pullorum disease, 446
Bittersweet, 122
Bivalent bacterin, 265
Black art, 151
Black blowfly, goats, 175; sheep, 175

Black disease, cattle, 262; sheep, 435
Black muzzle, 405
Black nightshade, 122
Black quarter, 263
Black scours, see Trichostrongylosis
Blackfly(ies), 181, 498
Blackhead, 487
BLACKHEAD OF TURKEYS AND CHICKENS, 441–444
BLACKLEG, 263–265
Blackleg, 2, 3, 233, 236, 258; sheep, 433
Blackleg bacilli, 263
Black-legged tick, 159, 272
Blacktongue, 526
Bladder stones, mink, 571
Bladderworm, 21; losses, 22; 23; prevention, 23; cattle, 154, 155; dogs, 154, 155, 508; goats, 154, 155; people, 155; sheep, 154, 155
Blind staggers, 41
Blindness, ewes, 428; horses and mules, 531
Blisters, in vesicular exanthema, 369
Bloat, acute, 108; cattle, 108; chronic, 108; sheep, 108; treatment, 111; rabbits, 562
BLOAT IN RUMINANTS, 108–113
Bloating, milk fever, 244; blackleg, 264
Blood, bluetongue virus, 419
Blood calcium, 244
Blood parasites, ducks, 501
Blood plasma vitamin A, 275
Blood serum tests, CRD, 478
Blood sugar, 243, 254, 427, 428
Blood testing, paratyphoid, 454
Blood transfusions, anaplasmosis, 271; scours, 321
Bloodsucking lice, cattle, 307
Blowflies, 389
Blue comb, 38
BLUE COMB, 463–464
Blue-bag, 433, 434
Bluebonnets, 120
Bluetongue, cattle, 311, 327; sheep, 331
BLUETONGUE OF SHEEP, 418–422
Boars, brucellosis, 209; dysentery, 363
Body lice, 412, 491
Bone, growths, 106; actinomycosis, 265
Bonemeal, 104
Boston, 26
Botfly, 407
Botulism, 14; ducks, 496, 499; 554; minks, 567
Boutonneuse fever, 15
BOVINE COCCIDIOSIS, 314–317
Bovine malignant catarrh, 330
BOVINE MASTITIS, 245–250
Bovine shipping fever, 255
Bovine tuberculosis, 17
Bovoflavin, 281
Bowel worm, large-mouthed, 390
BOWMAN, GEORGE W., 314
Boynton's Tissue Vaccine, 361
Brachial nerve, 468
Brachial plexus, 107
Bracken, 126, 127, 128; poisoning, 128
Brain fever, equine, 551
Braxy-like disease, 422
Brazilian spotted fever, 15
Breeding, for disease resistance, 58; cows, timing, 321
BREEDING PROBLEMS, 536–541
Breeding problems, trichomoniasis, 277
Breast, cancer, 105
British Isles, 252
Broad fish tapeworm, dogs and cats, 510
Broad tapeworm, 24

Broadleaf, 122
Bromthymolblue test, mastitis, 247
Bronchitis, infectious, chickens, 480; dogs and cats, 508
Brood mares, management, 536
Brooder houses, 443
BROWN, R. W., JR., 245
Brown dog tick, 158, 161, 272, 519
Brown winter tick, 160
BRUCELLOSIS, 202–213
Brucellosis, 2; 5; cattle, 5, 202; costs, 12; losses, 13, 18; extent, 18; goats, 18, 202, 211; sheep, 18; swine, 18, 202; 19; treatment, 208, 274; baby pigs, 380; 425
Bubonic plague, 3
Buccal capsule, 394
Buffalo gnats, 181
Bulgaria, 8
Bull nose, 353
Bulletin No. 1, 3, 268
Bullnettle, 122
Bulls, urinary calculi, 103; brucellosis, 203; vibriosis, 224; trichomoniasis, 277; reproductive system, 278; mites, 294
Bureau of Animal Industry, 2, 3, 6, 66, 359
Burma, 8
BURMESTER, B. R., 466
BUSHLAND, R. C., 131, 172, 175, 345, 411
Buttercup, 120
Butterfat, mastitis, 246
Butyric acid, 254
Buzzards, fowl typhoid, 452

Cadmium salts, 82
Cajenne tick, 161
Calcium, 104; milk fever, 243; wheat-pasture poisoning, 262; deficiency in tetany, 326
Calcium carbonate, 104, 123
Calcium gluconate, wheat-pasture poisoning, 261
Calculi, cattle, 103; mink, 103; sheep, 103
Calf barns, ventilation, 322
Calf diphtheria, 332
California, 4, 10, 17, 63, 64, 108, 112, 127, 258, 299, 300, 302, 318, 326, 327, 329, 369, 416, 418, 456, 508
California black-legged tick, 159
California influenzalike disease, 329
Caltrop, 120
Calves, warts, 106; tapeworm, 154; Johne's disease, 154; shipping fever, 256; wheat-pasture poisoning, 261; blackleg, 263; anaplasmosis, 271; small hairworm, 285; coccidiosis, 314; pinkeye, 314; diseases, 317–326; influenza, 329; white muscle disease, 429; ornithosis, 460
Camel, rabies, 195
Canada, 16, 17, 63, 64, 65, 186, 300, 304, 327, 350, 416, 417, 427, 501, 551
Canaries, pullorum disease, 446; paratyphoid, 453
Canarypox, 464
Cancer, 105; eye in Herefords, 105; uterus, 106
Canine hepatitis, 524
Canine typhus, 526
Canker, 464
Cannibalism, ducks, 499; pheasants, 553; wild animals, 562
Capillarids, 390; poultry, 489
Car sickness, dogs and cats, 529
Carbohydrates, in rumen, 251; deficiency, 427
Carbolic acid, scabies, 406
Carbon tetrachloride, 81, 303; roundworms, 398, 487

Carbonate of lime, 123
Cardia, 109
Carnivore tapeworm, in pets, 25
Carotene, 104
Carrier animals, defined, 41; 272
CARTER, ROSCOE H., 143
Cartilage, growths, 106
Cat flea, 25, 521
Cat louse, 523
Cat scratch fever, 19
Catarrh, dogs, 524; respiratory,
  horses, 541
Catarrhal fever, malignant, cattle,
  327, 330, 418; horses and
  mules, 534
Cats, see also Feline
  rabies, 19, 195; transmission of
  diseases to man, 19; urinary
  calculi, 103; ticks, 159;
  foot-and-mouth disease, 187;
  tuberculosis, 216; anthrax,
  230; tetanus, 238; blackleg,
  263; internal parasites, 503;
  roundworms, 503, 505;
  anemia, 504; hookworm,
  504; bladderworm, 508;
  bronchitis, 508; eyeworm,
  508; lungworm, 508; tapeworm, 509; broad fish tapeworm, 510; coccidiosis, 510;
  flukes, 510; external parasites, 517; mange, 517; ear
  mange, 518; fleas, 521; infectious diseases, 523; lice,
  523; catarrh, 524; epileptiform fits, 524; paresis, 524;
  rhinitis, 524; skin eruption,
  524; distemper, 529; hair
  balls, 528; hernia, 528; intestinal obstruction, 528;
  miscellaneous ailments, 528;
  heat exhaustion, 528; motion
  sickness, 529; wounds, 529
Cattle, 1; losses, 1954, 11; 13;
  brucellosis reservoirs, 18; allergic reactions, 39; urinary
  calculi, 103; adrenal tumors,
  106; bloat, 108; fluorides,
  114; lead poisoning, 114;
  molybdenum poisoning, 115;
  nitrate poisoning, 116; salt
  poisoning, 116; selenium poisoning, 117; fescue poisoning,
  129; lameness, 129; liver
  flukes, 148; tapeworms, 153;
  bladderworms, 154, 155; ticks,
  157; hornfly, 167; stablefly,
  168; mosquitoes, 177; gnats,
  181; vesicular stomatitis, 182,
  184; foot-and-mouth disease,
  187; rabies, 197; brucellosis,
  202; tuberculosis, 216; Johne's
  disease, 223; vibriosis, 224;
  226; leptospirosis, 226; anthrax, 229, 230; malignant
  edema, 235; listeriosis, 241;
  ketosis, 250-253; shipping
  fever, 255; grass tetany, 260-
  262; wheat-pasture poisoning,
  260; blackleg, 263; actinobacillosis, 265-268; actinomycosis, 265-268; anaplasmosis, 268; hyperkeratosis, 273;
  trichomoniasis, 277; roundworms, 284; stomach worms,
  284; strongyles, 288; internal
  parasites, 290; stephanofilariasis, 298; miscellaneous diseases, 327-334; mucosal diseases, 327; Indiana virus diarrhea, 328; Iowa mucosal disease, 328; rhinotracheitis, 329;
  malignant catarrhal fever, 330;
  bluetongue, 331, 419, 420;
  nasal granuloma, 331; red
  water disease, 333; scabies,
  404; 551
Cattle fever tick, 162

CATTLE GRUBS, 300-306
CATTLE LICE, 307-309
CATTLE SCABIES, 292-298
Cattle tick, 269
CATTLE TICK FEVER, 310-313
CAUSES OF DISEASE, 29-40
Cecal coccidiosis, poultry, 438
Cecal strongyle, ducks, 500; geese,
  500
Cecal worm, blackhead, 442, 487;
  chickens, 488
Central America, 19, 198, 551
Cephalic cellulitis, minks, 568
Cercariae, 149
Chagas disease, 32
Chalk, 123
Chastek paralysis, foxes, 574
CHEMICAL POISONING, 113-117
Chemicals, antiparasitic, 79; and
  parasites, 80; germicidal value,
  101
CHEMOTHERAPEUTIC AGENTS FOR
  EXTERNAL PARASITES, 85-88
CHEMOTHERAPEUTIC AGENTS FOR
  INTERNAL PARASITES, 80-85
Cherry seeds, 121
Chick bronchitis, 480
Chicken louse, large, 491
Chicken mite, 493
Chickens, see also Poultry
  selenium poisoning, 117; vesicular stomatitis, 184; rabies,
  195; brucellosis, 212; tuberculosis, 216; listeriosis, 240;
  coccidiosis, 437; blackhead,
  441; pullorum disease, 446;
  typhoid, 451; paratyphoid,
  453; Newcastle disease, 455;
  ornithosis, 459; bluecomb,
  463-464; fowlpox, 464; lymphomatosis, 466; leukemias,
  469; erysipelas, 474; chronic
  respiratory disease, 476; infectious bronchitis, 480;
  infectious laryngotracheitis,
  483; tapeworms, 484; roundworm, 486; gapeworm, 487;
  gizzard worm, 488; globular
  roundworm, 488; hairworm,
  488; stomach worm, 489;
  eyeworm, 490; lice, 490;
  hepatitis, 497; fowl cholera,
  498
Children, bovine tuberculosis, 17;
  Wilm's tumor, 107; tuberculosis, 217; mites, 295
China, 64
Chinchillas, vesicular stomatitis,
  184
Chloramphenicol, 95
Chlordane, 85, 86; toxicity, 135,
  144, 169, 303, 308; for hog
  lice, 346; swine mange, 348
Chlorinated hydrocarbons, toxicity,
  138
Chlorinated hydrocarbon insecti-
  cides, hog lice, 346
Chlorinated naphthalene, and
  hyperkeratosis, 276
Chloroform, 72
Chloromycetin, see Antibiotics
Chlorothion, 87
Chlorothion sprays, effects, 140
Chokecherry, 121
Cholera, 9; swine, 2, 3, 4, 354-362
Chorioptic mites, cattle, 292, 557
Chorioptic scabies, 292
Chronic bloat, 108
Chronic fluorosis, 113
Chronic mastitis, 246
Chronic respiratory disease, see
  CRD
CHRONIC RESPIRATORY DISEASE IN
  CHICKENS, 476-478
Chronic selenium poisoning, 117
Ciliates, described, 33
Cirrhosis, sheep, 151
Civet cat, rabies, 198

Civil War, 9
CLABORN, H. V., 143
CLARKSON, M. R., 7
Cleanliness, foxes, 573
Climate, and parasites, 78
Clover, 143
Clover, silage, 430
Clump, defined, 448
Coal tar-creosote, for hog lice, 346;
  scabies, 406
COBBETT, N. G., 292, 345, 347, 407
Coccidia, 42; cattle, 315; 387;
  poultry, 437; dogs and cats,
  511; rabbits, 563
Coccidiosis, shipping fever, 257;
  268; cows, 314; calves, 324;
  enteritis, swine, 365; 423; in-
  testinal, 438; ducks, 499;
  geese, 501; dogs and cats, 510;
  dogs, 516; liver, rabbits, 564
COCCIDIOSIS OF CHICKENS AND
  TURKEYS, 437-441
COCCIDIOSIS OF SHEEP AND GOATS,
  387-389
Cockroach, 490
Colchicine, 120
Cold, in calves, 322
COLE, T. W., 310
Colon, cancer, 105
Colorado, 123, 129, 212, 299, 257,
  258, 304, 418, 423, 424, 427
Colorado rubberweed, 122
Colorado tick fever, 157, 159
Columbian spotted fever, 15
Commissioner of Agriculture, 2, 62
Common liver fluke, 148
Common salt, poisoning, 116
Complement-fixation test, lepto-
  spirosis, 228; anaplasmosis,
  272; 328; ornithosis, 459, 461,
  462
Complex, defined, 362
Conception rate, mares, 537
Concrete floors, 170
Conenose bug, 552
Congress, 162, 194
Conjunctivitis, calves, 329; horses,
  541
Connecticut, 2, 62, 327, 416
Constipation, sheep, 423; dogs and
  cats, 524
Contagious abortion, goats, 211; 262
Contagious ecthyma, see Sore
  mouth
Contagious equine abortion, 539
Contaminated water, 426
Control programs, 6
Convulsions, blackleg, 264
Cooperias, 390
Cooperids, cattle, 285; sheep, 285
Copper sulfate, flukes, 152; round-
  worms, 398; foot rot, 432;
  ulcerative dermatitis, 435
Copperweed, 126
Corn, 104, 143
Corn Belt, trichinae, 26; 256; 338
Corncockle, 121, 122
Cornea, 532
Corneal vascularization, 532
Corpus luteum, 277, 282
Corticosterone, 254
Cortisone, metabolism, fat, 254
Cottonseed meal, 104
Coughing, shipping fever, 258;
  virus diarrhea, 328; swine,
  336; swine influenza, 366;
  goats, 401; sheep, 401; infec-
  tious bronchitis, 481.
Coughs, calves, 322
Cow, abdomansum, disease transmission, 17; 109; dorsal sac,
  110; duodenum, 110; esophagus, 110; reticulum, 110;
  rumen, 110; stomach, 110;
  rabies, 195; tuberculosis, milk,
  217; vibriosis, 224; tetanus,
  238; wheat-pasture poisoning,
  261; contagious abortion, 262;
  reproductive system, 280

Cowpox, 18
Coyoes, 16; rabies, 195, 198; flukes, 510
CRD, chickens, 476
Creep-feeding, beef calves, 288
Creeping eruptions, 15
Cresols, 85
Creosote, for lice, 307
Cresylic compounds, 101
CROOKSHANK, H. R., 260
Cropworm, poultry, 489
Crotalaria, 120
Cryolite, 113
Cube powder, grubs, 304; lice, 414
Cud, 257
Curacao, screwworm experiment, 175
Cyanogenetic glucosides, 121
Cyanogenetic plants, 118
Cyprus, 418
Cystercercosis, 19
Cystic ovaries, 252
Cysticercus, 21

Dairy cattle, see also Cattle, Cows
milk fever, 243; trichomoniasis, 277; sprays for lice, 309; pinkeye, 314
DALE, C. N., 382
Darnel, 119
DAVIS, C. L., 105, 265, 414, 422, 427
DAVIS, LEONARD REID, 314
DAVIS, R. E., 260
DDT, 85, 86; toxicity, 133; 138; residues, 143; 163; 169; 176; 179; 181; 275; 303; 308; for hog lice, 346; dip, for lice, 413; for lice, 492; for mites, 495; for ticks, 521
Death losses, causes, 11
Deathcamas, 120
Deer, liver flukes, 149; 152; tapeworms, 154; vesicular stomatitis, 184; foot-and-mouth disease, 187; rabies, 195; actinobacillosis, 267
Deerflies, 170
DELAPLANE, JOHN P., 459
Delivery, mares, 542
Demodectic mange, 294
Demodectic mites, cattle, 292
Denmark, 18, 192, 193, 354
Dental fluorosis, 114
Dermatitis, see also Skin disease 15; goats, 395; sheep, 395; ulcerative, sheep, 434
Derris powder, for grubs, 303
Detergents, 98
Dextrose, pregnancy disease, 429
Dhurrin, 121
Diagnostic test, anaplasmosis, 272
Diarrhea, 19; chronic, 114; shipping fever, 257; hyperkeratosis, 274; roundworms, 284; nodular worm, 287; coccidiosis, 315; septicemia, 319; virus, 327; mucosal disease, 328; rhinitis, 352; in sheep and goats, 388, 390, 395, 397, 423; paratyphoid, 454; and blue comb, 463; tapeworms, 484; dogs, 507; in dogs and cats, 524; mares, 543
Diazinon, toxicity, 139; 171
Dichloro-diphenyl-trichloroethane, see DDT
Dieldrin, 87, 137, 144
Diet, 61; for sheep, 79; cows, 244, 318; in ketosis, 253; and threadworms, 343; pregnant ewes, 428; dogs, 513; dogs and cats, 518; minks, 571
Diethylcarbamazine, 83
Digestive ketosis, 252
Digestive tract, roundworms in, 389
Dilan, toxicity, 138
DILLARD, W. M., 528
Diphtheria, calves, 324, 332

Dips, cattle, 296; for grubs, 303; ticks, 319; hog lice, 346; swine mange, 348; scabies, 406; lice, 412, 492, 558
Dipterex, 140
Disease organisms, common, 14
Diseases, see also Specific disease and bacteria, 29; viruses, 29; causes, 29–40; defined, 30; produced by worms, 36; spread, 40–45
DISEASES AND PARASITES OF FOXES, 573–575
DISEASES AND PARASITES OF MINKS, 567–573
DISEASES OF BABY PIGS, 377–381
DISEASES OF CALVES, 317–326
DISEASES OF DUCKS, 496–499
DISEASES OF FOALS, 541–546
Disinfectants, action, 98; 341; 455; 573
DISINFECTION, 98–102
Distemper, dogs, 523; vaccination, 524; minks, 569
Docks, 123
Dogs, persons bitten by, 14; reservoir of infections, 15; and hydatid, 16; urinary calculi, 103; tapeworms, 153; bladderworms, 154; ticks, 159, 162; screwworms, 173; vesicular stomatitis, 184; foot-and-mouth disease, 187; rabies symptoms, 196; brucellosis, 212; tuberculosis, 216; leptospirosis, 227; anthrax, 230; tetanus, 238; blackleg, 263; roundworms, 503; internal parasites, 503; anemia, 504; hookworms, 504; roundworms, 505; heartworm, 506; whipworm, 506; esophageal worm, 507; eyeworm, 507; intestinal threadworms, 507; vomiting, 507; bladderworms, 508; bronchitis, 508; dropsy, 508; giant kidney worm, 508; lungworm, 508; tapeworm, 509; broad fish tapeworm, 510; coccidiosis, 510; flukes, 510; salmon poisoning, 510; giardiasis, 510, 511; kala azar, 511; leishmaniasis, 511; piroplasmosis, 511; diet, 513; vitamin deficiency, 513; mange, 517; external parasites, 517; sarcoptic mange, 517; demodectic mange, 518; ear mange, 518; brown dog tick, 519; wood ticks, 519; black-legged tick, 520; gulf coast tick, 520; Rocky Mountain spotted fever tick, 520; fleas, 521; distemper, 523; infectious diseases, 523; lice, 523; catarrh, 524; epileptiform fits, 524; infectious hepatitis, 524; paresis, 524; rhinitis, 524; skin eruption, 524; enteritis, 525; tonsillitis, 525; leptospirosis, 525, 526; jaundice, 526; anemia, 527; babesiosis, 527; cough, 527; diarrhea, 527; fever, 527; histoplasmosis, 527; nausea, 527; nocardiosis, 527; tularemia, 527; intestinal obstruction, 528; miscellaneous ailments, 528; heat exhaustion, 529; motion sickness, 529; wounds, 529
Dog flea, 25, 521
DOLL, E. R., 534, 536, 541
Donkeys, see Mules
Double-pored tapeworm, 509
Douche method, 280
DOUGHERTY, E. III, 496
DOUGHERTY, ROBERT W., 108, 250
Dourine, 5, 549
Doves, ticks, 158; pullorum disease, 446; Newcastle disease, 456

DOYLE, L. P., 362
Drainage, and equine encephalitis, 554
Dropsy, shipping fever, 258; dogs, 506, 508
Drugs, action, 72
Ducklings, see Ducks
Ducks, pullorum disease, 446; fowl typhoid, 451; paratyphoids, 453; Newcastle disease, 456; ornithosis, 459; lymphomatosis, 467; erysipelas, 474; tapeworms, 484; cropworm, 489; lice, 490; aspergillosis, 497; infectious serositis, 498; fowl cholera, 498; leucocytozoon infection, 498; botulism, 499; coccidiosis, 499; louse, 499; eye inflammation, 499; salt poisoning, 499; prolapse of oviduct, 499; paralysis of penis, 499; water belly, 499; tumors, 499; cecal strongyle, 500; parasites, 500; worms, 500; blood parasites, 501; leucocytozoon disease, 501; intestinal flagellate, 502
Duodenum, defined, 484
Dusts, for ticks, 163; for lice, 492; lice, equine, 558
Dutchmans-breeches, 120
Dwarf tapeworm, in people, 24; in rats and mice, 24
DYE, JOSEPH A., 250
Dysentery, swine, 363

Ear, tick damage, 161
Ear mange, dogs and cats, 518
EARL, F. L., 350
Earthworms, 336, 339, 368
East Coast Fever, 78
Echinococcis, in Canidae, 16; dogs, 16; Herbivora, 16; people, 16; sheep, 16; swine, 16
ECONOMIC LOSSES FROM ANIMAL DISEASES, PARASITES, 11–14
Ecthyma, contagious, see Sore mouth
EDDY, GAINES W., 172, 175
Edema, malignant, 233; 235; shipping fever, 258; cattle, 291; baby pigs, 379; goats, 390, 397; sheep, 390, 397; equine influenza, 535; viral abortion, 540
Eggs, in diets, 9; abnormal, infectious bronchitis, 481
Egypt, 8
Elk, flukes, 150; rabies, 195; tapeworms, 154; ticks, 157
ELLIS, N. R., 103, 377
ELY, RAY E., 143
Emaciation, 34; hyperkeratosis, 274; roundworms, 284; tick fever, 310; goats and sheep, 390, 397
Embryonal nephroma, 107
Emetine hydrochloride, lungworms, 403
Encephalitides, in birds, 19
Encephalitis, 177; foxes, 574
Encephalomyelitis, 160, 177
England, 39, 112, 350, 417, 459, 497
Enteric disorders, baby pigs, 378
Enteritis, 19; defined, 362; dogs, 525; mares, 543; rabbits, 560, 562; minks, 569
ENTERITIS COMPLEX, THE, 362–365
Enterohepatitis, infectious, poultry, 441
ENTEROTOXEMIA OF SHEEP, 422–424
Enucleation, defined, 282
Environment, 47
Environmental conditions, and urinary calculi, 103
ENZIE, F. D., 503, 517, 555
Enzootic, diseases, 8; defined, 15

579

Epidemic, swine influenza, 367; ornithosis, 459
Epileptiform fits, dogs and cats, 524
Epithelial, defined, 298
Epizootic cellulitis, horses and mules, 534
Epizootics, 7
EPN, 139
EQ–335, 174, 177
EQUINE ENCEPHALOMYELITIS, 550–555
Equine encephalomyelitis, 41; people, 551
EQUINE INFECTIOUS ANEMIA, 546–550
EQUINE INFLUENZA, 534–536
EQUINE PERIODIC OPHTHALMIA, 531–533
Ergot sclerotia, 129
Eructation, 109
Erysipelas, losses, 13; swine, 360, 475; turkeys, 474–476
Erysipeloid lesions, erysipelas, 475
Erythroblastosis, chickens, leukemia, 469
Esculin, 121
Esophageal worm, dogs, 507
Estate acetonemia, 252
Estrus, see Oestrus
Eupatorium, 126
Europe, 8, 229, 304, 330, 373, 405, 427, 459
European hare, 18
Ewes, pregnancy disease, 427; ornithosis, 460
Export trade, 1
EXTERNAL PARASITES OF DOGS AND CATS, 517–523
EXUDATE, defined, 532
Eye, cancerous, 105; inflammation, 313; inflammation, ducks, 499; horse and mule, 532
Eye tumors, 106
Eyeworm, poultry, 489; dogs, 507

FARR, MARION M., 437, 500
Fasciculations, 138
Fat metabolism, 254
Favus, rabbits, 562
Feces, examination, roundworms, 396
Federal indemnity, scrapie, 417
Federal meat inspection, 6, 12
Feed, and disease, 38; urinary calculi, 103; mastitis, 249; supplemental in wheat-pasture poisoning, 262; swine, 336
Feed supplements, rabbits, 563
Feeding, and parasites, 78; milk fever, 245; 248
FEEDING AND MANAGEMENT, 60–62
Feline, see also Cats
    distemper, cats, 528; enteritis, infectious, cats, 528
Ferrets, vesicular stomatitis, 184
Fever, anaplasmosis, 268; coccidiosis, 316; calf pneumonia, 323; hog cholera, 357; swine influenza, 366; vesicular exanthema, 370; sheep, 418, 420; horses and mules, 534
Filariasis, 177
FINCHER, M. G., 317
Finches, paratyphoids, 453
Finland, 18, 192
Fish, tapeworm, 24; giant kidney worm, 508
Fish and Wildlife Service, 201
Fistulas, horses, 212; actinomycosis, 266
Fitweed, 120
FITZGERALD, PAUL R., 277
Flagellates, described, 32
Flatworms, 34; swine, 335
Flavones, defined, 111
Flax, 121
Flea powder, 522

Fleas, dogs and cats, 521; control, 522
FLEECEWORMS, 175–177
Fleeceworms, activities, 37; goats, 175; sheep, 175
Flies, 298; among ducks, 496
FLIES THAT AFFECT LIVESTOCK, 166–172
Florida, 198, 273, 299, 311, 362, 489
Fluff louse, 491
Flukes, people, 16; described, 34; dogs, 510
Fluorine, 113
Fluorine poisoning, 38
Fluorspar, 113
FMD, see Foot-and-mouth disease
Foaling heat, 537
Foals, diseases, 541; bacterial infections, 542; streptococci, 543
Follicle method, fowlpox vaccination, 465
Follicular mange, cattle, 294
Food, consumption, 7; in U. S., 9
Food and Agriculture Organization, 7, 212
Food poisoning, 19
FOOD SUPPLIES AND ANIMAL DISEASES, 7–10
Foot ailments, sheep, 435
FOOT-AND-MOUTH DISEASE, 186–194
Foot-and-mouth disease, 4; 12; 182; cats, 187; cattle, 187; deer, 187; dogs, 187; goats, 187; hogs, 187; people, 187; sheep, 187; swine, 187; types, 188; control, 191; prevention, 191; 381
Foot bath, copper sulfate, 432
Foot lice, 412
Foot mange, cattle, 292
Foot rot, sheep, 431; 435
Foot scabies, see Scabies, chorioptic
Formaldehyde, ulcerative dermatitis, 435; fumigation, 456
FOSTER, AUREL O., 75, 80
Fowl, blackleg, 263
Fowl cholera, ducks, 498
Fowl paralysis, 158, 468
Fowl plague, 3
Fowl tick, 158; 165; 272
FOWL TYPHOID, 451–452
FOWLPOX, 464–466
Fowlpox, 177
Foxes, 16; rabies, 195; bladderworm, 508; flukes, 510; encephalitis, 525, 574; diseases and parasites of, 573–575; Chastek paralysis, 574; rickets, 574; salmon disease, 574; salmonellosis, 574; hookworms, 575; roundworms, 575
France, 192, 350
FRANK, A. H., 224
Frogs, anthrax, 230; esophageal worm, 507
Fructose, in ketosis, 254
Fulmars, ornithosis, 459
Fumitory, 120
Fur Animal Disease Station, 567
Fur animals, losses, 1954, 11, 13
Fur-bearing animals, diseases and parasites of, 559–575
Fur chewing, minks, 572
Furazolidone, for fowl typhoid, 452

Gall sickness, 268
Gallbladder, growths, 106
Gangrene, shipping fever, 258; minks, 569
Gangrenous stomatitis, 332
Gannets, Newcastle disease, 456
Gapeworms, poultry, 487, 489, 500
Garbage, and hog cholera, 358; vesicular exanthema, 371
GARDINER, J. L., 484, 486
Garget, swine, 384, 433
Gas, in stomach, 108, 109

Gas gangrene, 14
Gastroenteritis, swine, 363; pigs, 381; parasitic, defined, 390
GATES, DANIEL W., 268
Geese, pullorum disease, 446; paratyphoid, 453; Newcastle disease, 456; tapeworm, 484; lice, 490; hepatitis, 497; fowl cholera, 498; cecal strongyle, 500; gizzard worm, 500; parasites, 500; roundworms, 500; coccidiosis, 501
Genes, 47
GENETICS AND DISEASE, 46–54
Genetics, defined, 46; pig diseases, 377; blue comb, 463
Genital infections, mares, 537
Georgia, 124, 273, 362
Germany, 39, 111, 120, 350
Germs, see Bacteria
Giant liver fluke, 150
Giardiasis, dogs, 510, 511
GIBBONS, W. J., 243
Gid bladderworm, in sheep, 35, 154
Giddy, 155
Giemsas stain, 226
GILTNER, LEIGH T., 88
Githagin, 121
Gizzard worm, poultry, 488, 500
Gland, parathyroid, 244
Glanders, 5, 18
Globular roundworm, poultry, 488
Gluconeogenesis, 250
Glucose, 121, 250, 251, 254
Glucosides, 120
Glycerol, 254
Glycogen, ketosis, 251, 428
Gnats, cattle, 181; bluetongue, 419
Goats, losses, 13; liver flukes, 149; tapeworms, 153; bladderworms, 154; fleeceworms, 175; black blowfly, 175; secondary screwworm fly, 175; green-bottle fly, 175; vesicular stomatitis, 184; foot-and-mouth disease, 187; rabies, 195; brucellosis, 202, 211; contagious abortion, 211; Malta fever, 211; tuberculosis, 216; Johne's disease, 223; leptospirosis, 227; anthrax, 230; blackleg, 263; small hairworm, 285; coccidiosis, 387; roundworms, 389; haemonchosis, 392; nematodirosis, 394; strongyloidiasis, 395; nodular worms, 399; lungworms, 401; scabies, 403, 406; head grubs, 408; lice, 411; sore mouth, 414
Goiter, pigs, 379
GOLDBERG, AARON, 401
Goldenrod, 124
GOODE, E. R., JR., 202
GOODING, C. L., 62
Gopher, rabies, 195
GORHAM, JOHN R., 567, 573
Goslings, coccidiosis, 501
Gram stain, 266
Grass, 143
GRASS TETANY AND WHEAT-PASTURE POISONING, 260–262
Gravel, minks, 571
Gray fleshfly, minks, 573
Grease, and disease, 38; hyperkeratosis, 275
Greasewood, 123
Great Britain, 290, 416, 427
Greece, 8
Green-bottle fly, 175
GREENE, J. E., 523
Groundsels, 119
Growths, in actinomycosis, 267
Grubs, 13; cattle, 300
Guinea fowl(s), pullorum disease, 446; fowl typhoid, 451; paratyphoids, 453; Newcastle disease, 456; fowlpox, 466; tapeworms, 484; gapeworm, 489; stomach worm, 489

Guinea pigs, vesicular stomatitis, 184, tuberculosis, 216; anthrax, 230; listeriosis, 239; blackleg, 263; actinobacillosis, 267, 551
Gulf coast tick, 161
Gullet, heelfly, 301
Gullet worms, 390
Gut, inflammation, 362

Haemonchosis, goats and sheep, 392
HAGEN, KARL W., JR., 559
Hair balls, cats, 528
Hair lungworm, 401
Hairlessness, baby pigs, 379
Hairworm, cattle, 285; intestinal, 390; stomach, 390; poultry, 488; ducks, 500
HALL, WALTER J., 451, 463
Halogens, 100
Halogeton, 123
HAMMOND, DATUS M., 277
Hamsters, vesicular stomatitis, 184, 551
Hares, liver flukes, 149; rabies, 195
Harvest fever, 226
Hawaiian Islands, 272
Hawk, rabies, 195
HEAD GRUBS OF SHEEP, 407–411
Head lice, 491
Head scab, 405
Heart, growths, 106; injury in calves, 430
Heart block, 245
Heartworms, 504; dog, 506
Heat, mares, 537
Heat exhaustion, dogs, cats, 529
HEATH, M. K., 528
Heavers, 432
Hedgehog, rabies, 195
Heelflies, cattle, 300
Heifer, vibriosis, 224; trichomoniasis, 277
Hemolytic anemia, foals, 544
Hemolytic icterus, 544
Hemorrhages, intestinal, 34, 256; shipping fever, 258; scours, 320; red water disease, 334; swine, 336; gland, hog cholera, 357; coccidiosis, 439
Hemorrhagic enteritis, calves, 325
Hemorrhagic enterotoxemia, calves, 325
Hemorrhagic ova, 451
Hemorrhagic septicemia, 256, and blackleg, 264; swine, 382, 423
Hens, fowlpox, 464
Hepatitis, necrotic, 435; infectious, dogs, 524
Heptachlor, 87; toxicity, 137, 144
Herbivora, defined, 16
Heredity, and disease, 46; and bloat, 111, 248; and mastitis, 249
Hereford, cancer eye, 105, 139
HERL, OREN E., 88
HERLICH, HARRY, 284
Hermaphroditic, defined, 148
Hernia, cats, 528
Hexachloroethane, 81; roundworms, 398
Hexamita, 445
HEXAMITIASIS OF TURKEYS, 444–446
Hides, 13; damage to, 37; damage by flies, 302
High temperature, shipping fever, 258
Histomonads, 32
Histomoniasis, poultry, 441
Histoplasmosis, dogs, 527
HOG CHOLERA, 354–362
Hog cholera, spread, 10; losses, 13; 54; 55; 227; acute, 233; symptoms, 357; vaccines, 361; 379; baby pigs, 381
Hog Cholera Research Station, 359
HOG LOUSE, THE, 345–346
HOG MANGE, 347–350

Hogs, see also Swine
losses, 1954, 11; 12; salt poisoning, 116; selenium poisoning, 117; foot-and-mouth disease, 187; rabies, 195; blackleg, 263
Hog's potato, 120
Holland, 8
Honeycomb, 108
Hookworm, 15; human type, 15; cattle, 286; swine, 335; goats and sheep, 394; dogs and cats, 504, 512; foxes, 575
Hormone, ketosis, 251; imbalances, horses, 539; 572
Hornflies, 13, cattle, 167
Horse inoculation test, 549
Horsebrush, 126, 127
Horsechestnut, 121
Horseflies, 170, 271
Horses, 1; losses, 1954, 11; 13, 18; sleeping sickness, 41; worms, 43; urinary calculi, 103; fluorides, 114; nitrate poisoning, 116; selenium poisoning, 117; flukes, 150; ticks, 157; vesicular stomatitis, 184; rabies, 195; fistula, 212; poll evil, 212; tuberculosis, 216; leptospirosis, 227; anthrax, 230; malignant edema, 235; tetanus, 237; blackleg, 263; diseases and parasites of, 531–558; periodic ophthalmia, 531; abortion virus infection, 534; influenza, 534; respiratory infections, 534, 535; breeding problems, 536; viral abortion, 540; foal diseases, 541; pharyngitis, 541; contracted tendons, 542; jaundice, 544; hemolytic anemia, 544; infectious anemia, 546; encephalomyelitis, 550; lice, 555, 558; mange, 555; mites, 557
Host, defined, 21
HOURRIGAN, J. L., 418
Housefly, 166, 170, 171; baits, 171; insecticides, 171
Houses, ticks in, 521
HOW DISEASES AND PARASITES ARE SPREAD, 40–45
HUFFMAN, WARD T., 118
Human beings, see People
Human flea, 25, 521
Hump sore, 300
HUTCHINGS, L. M., 362
Hydatid disease, control, 16
Hydatid tapeworm, in animals, 23; people, 23; dogs and cats, 509
Hydatidworm, 154
Hydrocephalus, minks, 572
Hydrogen cyanide, bloat, 110
Hydrogen peroxide, 85
Hydrophobia, see Rabies
Hyena, rabies, 195
Hygienic practices, mares, 538
Hyperimmune serum, cholera, 359; erysipelas, 376
HYPERKERATOSIS, 273–276
Hypocalcemia, 262
Hypocalcemia, parturient, see Milk fever
Hypochlorites, 101
Hypoglycemia, 38; ketosis, 250, 251; 262; pigs, 379; 427
Hypomagnesemia, 262
Hypophosphatemia, 262
Hypopituitarism, swine, 383
Hysterectomy, swine, 354

Iceland, 24
Icterus, foals, 544; equine, 547
Icterus gravis, 544
Idaho, 127, 299, 362, 418, 546
Illinois, 267, 273, 276, 416, 497
Immunity, defined, 29; anaplasmosis, 271; Newcastle disease, 458; feline distemper, 528
Immunization, swine, 89; 328; hog cholera, 358

Immunological techniques, 76
Inbreeding, and distemper, 524
Inclusion bodies, shipping fever, 258
Incoordination, 253
Incubation period, defined, 330
Incubators, disinfecting, 450, 456
India, 300, 331
Indiana, 416, 418
Indiana virus diarrhea, 328
Indigestion, 252
Indonesia, 8
Infectious abortion, see Brucellosis
Infectious anemia, horses, 546, 549; 554
INFECTIOUS BRONCHITIS, 480–482
Infectious bronchitis, 457
INFECTIOUS DISEASES COMMON TO ANIMALS AND MAN, 14–20
INFECTIOUS DISEASES OF DOGS AND CATS, 523–527
INFECTIOUS DISEASES OF THE RABBIT, 559–563
Infectious hepatitis, foxes, 574
INFECTIOUS KERATITIS, OR PINKEYE, IN CATTLE, 313–314
INFECTIOUS LARYNGOTRACHEITIS, 483
Infectious papilloma, 106
Infectious rhinotracheitis, and shipping fever, 258
Infectious serositis, ducks, 498
INFECTIOUS SINUSITIS IN TURKEYS, 479–480
Infertility, rams, 212
Inflammation of brain, equine, 550
Influenza, 255; swine, 366; horses and mules, 534; 554
Inhalation, 74
Inheritance, and mastitis, 249
Injury, mechanical, swine, 385
Insect pests, 13
Insecticide, Fungicide, and Rodenticide Act, 143
Insecticides, see also Name of Insecticide
85; toxicity, 131; for ticks, 163; fleeceworms, 176; from planes, 181; chlorinated hydrocarbon, 303, 308; for lice, 308, 492; for mites, 495
Insects, 36, 37
Inspection activities, 64
Intercostal nerves, 107
Internal parasites, 13; of cattle, 290; swine, 342
INTERNAL PARASITES OF DOGS AND CATS, 503–517
Intestinal catarrh, tapeworms, 484
Intestinal disorder, 262
Intestinal flagellates, ducks, 502
Intestinal obstruction, dogs and cats, 528
Intestinal parasites, horses, 549
Intestinal roundworm, in man, 28
INTESTINAL THREADWORM, THE, 343–344
Intestinal threadworm, in calves, 286
In vitro, defined, 546
Iodides, soluble, 85
Iodine, for pigs, 379; navel infection, 436
Iodophores, 101
Iowa, 9, 328, 359
Iowa mucosal disease, cattle, 328
Ireland, 111, 354
Iridocyclitis, horses and mules, 533
Irrigated pastures, mosquitoes, 178
Isohemolytic disease, 544
Isoimmunization, 544
Isonicotinic acid, 17
Isopropanol, 253
Israel, 418
Italy, 192
Itching, 292; in sheep, 404, 416; dogs, 518; horses and mules, 555
Ixodoidea, 157

Jackal, rabies, 195
Japanese B encephalitis, 552
Jaundice, tick fever, 310; swine, 341; dogs, 526; foals, 544; horses, 545
Jimmyweed, 124
Johne's disease, 57; 221; cattle, 223; calves, 223; sheep, 223
Johnin test, 222
JOHNSON, HOWARD W., 213, 221
Johnsongrass, 121
JONES, L. MEYER, 94, 96
JUNGHERR, E. L., 480
Jungle yellow fever, 20

Kala azar, dogs, 511
Kansas, 54, 117, 259, 295, 299, 338, 418
KATES, KENNETH C., 153, 344, 389
Keel, ducks, 496
KEMPER, H. E., 403
Kentucky, 541
Kenya typhus, 15
Keratin, defined, 273
Keratitis, cattle, 313
Ketogenesis, defined, 251
Ketone bodies, 252, 428
Ketosis, 38; in ewes, 427
KETOSIS IN CATTLE, 250–255
Kidney, growths, 106
KIDNEY WORMS OF SWINE, 338–340
Kidney worms, 335; 504; giant, in dogs, 508
Kids, tapeworms, 154
Kittens, see Cats
KNIPLING, E. F., 29, 85, 166
Knotty gut, goats and sheep, 399
KUTTLER, A. K., 202
Kwashiorkor, 7

Lactation ketosis, 252
Ladino clover, bloat, 108, 430
Lambing paralysis, 38, 427
Lambs, losses, 11; tapeworms, 154; white muscle disease, 429–431
Lameness, virus diarrhea, 328; sheep, 431
Lancet fluke, 150
Land snail, 151
Large American fluke, 150
LARGE INTESTINAL ROUNDWORM, THE, 340–342
Larkspur, 119, 120
LARSEN, AUBREY B., 221
Larval tapeworms, 153
Larvicides, mosquitoes, 179
Laurels, 122
Laws, and disease, 62; 28-Hour, 67; digest of, 68; Virus-Serum-Toxin, 89; foot - and - mouth disease, 191; tick fever, 310; garbage-cooking, 372
Lead, 114
Lead arsenate, 81, 83; arsenate, tapeworms, 154
Lead poisoning, cattle, 114; calves, 324
Leather, 37; warts, 106, 299
Leather ticks, 158
LEE, AUBREY M., 29, 60, 273
Leg mange, cattle, 292
Legislation, see also Laws
Legislation, Federal, 63
Legs, crooked, horses, 542
Legume pastures, 110
Leishmaniasis, dogs, 510, 511; 516
Leptospira, 19, 226
LEPTOSPIROSIS, 226–228
Leptospirosis, 15; 18; 19; 258; calves, 324; baby pigs, 380; dogs, 525, 526
Leucocytozoon disease, ducks, 498, 501
Leukemias, chickens, 469
Lice, 45; insecticides, 308; swine, 345–346; dips, 412; sprays, 413; poultry, 490; dogs and cats, 523; equine, 558
LICE OF SHEEP AND GOATS, 411–414

Life cycle approach, 77
Limberneck, ducks, 499
Lime, milk fever, 243
Limestone disease, 128
Lime-sulfur, toxicity, 132; for scabies, 296; swine mange, 348; dips for scabies, 406
Linamarin, 121
Lindane, 85, 86, 144; for mange, 296; 303; for hog lice, 346; swine mange, 348; dips, scabies, 406; lice, 413, 492; for mites, 495; for ticks, 521
LINDQUIST, ARTHUR W., 40, 177, 181, 300
LISTERIOSIS, 239–242
Listeriosis, pigs, 380; swine, 384; sheep, 417; 423
Litter, care, 440; and infectious bronchitis, 481
Liver, growths, 105; damage, swine, 341
Liver disease, poultry, 467
Liver flukes, sheep, 148, 436; cattle, 148; control, 151
LIVER FLUKES OF CATTLE AND SHEEP, 148–153
Liver glycogen, 250, 251, 254
Livestock, industry, 1; diseases, losses from, 1954, 6; production, history, 8; population, problems, 10; fluorine poisoning, 38; mechanical injury, 39; arsenic poisoning, 113; flies, 166; screwworms, 172; gnats, 181
Livestock Sanitary Association, 204, 362
Lizards, ticks, 157
Lobelia, 120
Lockjaw, 237; horses, 543
Locoweed, 126, 554
Lone star tick, 160
Long Island, 2, 497
LOTZE, JOHN C., 268, 387
Louisiana, 299, 332, 460, 546
LUCKER, JOHN T., 298
Lumbar nerve, 468
Lumen, 285
Lumps, pullorum disease, 447
Lumpy jaw, 266
LUND, EVERETT E., 441, 444, 563
Lung, cancer, 105
Lung fluke, swine, 337
Lung inflammation, swine, 351
Lung parasites, 290
LUNG PARASITES OF SWINE, 335–337
Lungers, 432
Lungworm, pneumonia, cattle, 291
Lungworm disease, calves, 324
LUNGWORMS IN SHEEP AND GOATS, 401–403
Lungworms, swine, 335; 368; 504; cat, 508; dogs, 509
Lupines, toxic, 120
Lye, 98
Lymph glands, 105
Lymph nodes, 215
Lymphomatic leukosis, poultry, 467
Lymphomatosis, 13; poultry, 466–474
Lysol, head grubs, 409

McCRORY, B. R., 418, 422
MACDONALD, A. D., 446
McDUFFIE, WILLIAM C., 157, 166, 177, 181
McINTOSH, ALLEN, 157
MACKELLAR, WM. M., 310
McKERCHER, D. G., 418
McLean County system, 342
McMaster egg-counting slide, 396
Mad itch, baby pigs, 381
Maggots, 105; screwworm, 174; 300
Magnesium, 104; milk fever, 243; wheat-pasture poisoning, 262; tetany, 326
Maine, 327

Malaria, 3, 8, 177, 268; equine, 546
Malathion, 87; lice, 492; mites, 495
MALIGNANT EDEMA, 235–237
Malignant edema, blackleg, 264
Malignant lymphoma, 107
Malignant stomatitis, 332
MALLMANN, W. L., 98
Malnutrition, and distemper, 524
Malta fever, goats, 211
Mammitis, 433
Man, see People
Management, mastitis, 247, 248; trichomoniasis, 282; turkeys, 443
Management and feeding, 60
Mange, see also Scabies
3, 292; demodectic, swine, 347, 349; hog, 347–350; sarcoptic, swine, 347; follicular, swine, 349; dogs and cats, 517; sarcoptic, equine, 555; ear, rabbits, 565; body, rabbits, 566
MANGE AND LICE OF HORSES AND MULES, 555–558
Manitoba, 24
MANTHEI, C. A., 202, 226, 327
Mares, heat, 537
Marketing, and diseases, 10
Marmot, rabies, 195
MARSH, HADLEIGH, 425, 431
Martins, Newcastle disease, 456
Maryland, 2, 124, 299
Massachusetts, 2, 26, 54, 62, 338, 497
Massage, 74
Mastitis, 8, 10, 12, 252; defined, 245; acute, 246; tests, 247; mange, 295; swine, 384; sheep, 433
Measles, 155
Meat, production, 7; in diets, 9
Meat inspection, volume, 6
Meat Inspection Branch, 266
Meat inspectors, 12
Meconium, 542
Medicines, 72
Mediterranean, 16
Melanotic pigmented tumors, 107
Mendelian heredity, 48
Meningitis, tuberculous, 214
Merozoites, 388
Mesenteric nodes, 215
Metabolic acidosis, 319
Metabolic diseases, defined, 38
Metabolic requirements, ketosis, 255
Metabolism, milk fever, 244; white muscle disease, 431
Metallic arsenates, 83
Methemoglobin, 115
Methoxychlor, 85, 86; toxicity, 137; 138; 144; 167; 169; 303; 308; dip for lice, 413; spray for lice, 413
Methyl bromide, worms, 340
Methylbenzene, 83
Metritis, defined, 244
Mexico, 3, 12, 63, 64, 65, 186, 198, 310, 311, 551
Mg./kg., defined, 133
Mice, zoonoses, 19; 24; vesicular stomatitis, 184; malignant edema, 236; anthrax, 230; actinobacillosis, 267
Michigan, 124, 299, 416
Microfilariae, defined, 298; heartworm, 506
Middle East, 16, 20
Midges, 298
Milk, in diets, 9; pasteurization, 213
Milk cistern, 246
MILK FEVER, 243–245
Milk fever, 38, 262; swine, 383
Milk flow, hyperkeratosis, 274
Milk substitutes, for calves, 319
Milk sugar, mastitis, 246
Milk-colic, 422
Milkers nodules, 18

Milk-ring test, 5; brucellosis, 205
Milksickness, 124
Milkweeds, 122; poisoning, 123
Milo grain, 104
Minerals, in diet, 60; elements, 104; hypopituitarism, swine, 383; imbalance, blue comb, 463
Minks, urinary calculi, 103, 571; giant kidney worm, 508; botulism, 567; diseases and parasites, 567; cephalic cellulitis, 568; pneumonia, 568; streptococcus organisms, 568; abscesses, 568; anthrax, 568; distemper, 569; enteritis, 569; gangrene, 569; pleuritis, 569; nursing sickness, 570; virus enteritis, 570; steatitis, 571; Aleutian gene, 572; fur chewing, 572; hydrocephalus, 572; sporadic ailments, 572; wet belly, 572; gray fleshfly, 573
Minnesota, 11, 279, 302, 441
Miracidia, 510
MISCELLANEOUS AILMENTS OF CATS AND DOGS, 528–530
MISCELLANEOUS DISEASES OF CATTLE, 327–334
MISCELLANEOUS DISEASES OF SWINE, 382–386
Mississippi, 108, 299, 489, 546
Mississippi Basin, 24
Missouri, 11, 124, 418
Mites, 36; cattle, 292; chorioptic, 292; demodectic, 292; disease, 292; psoroptic, 292; sarcoptic, 292; follicle, 349; scabies, 403; equine, 555; psoroptic mange, equine, 556; chorioptic, equine, 557
MITES ON POULTRY, 493–496
Mohair, damage, 13
Molasses, ketosis, 254
Moldy corn poisoning, 554
Molybdenosis, 125
Molybdenum poisoning, 115
Mongoose, rabies, 195
Monkeys, rabies, 195; 551
MONLUX, A. W., 265
Montana, 127, 198, 299, 302, 304, 418, 433, 546
Moon blindness, 531
Moose, tapeworms, 154; ticks, 157, 160
MORAN, EDWARD A., 118
Morphine, 119
Mosquito disease, rabbits, 561
Mosquitoes, cattle, 177; people, 177; insecticides, 179; 271; 298; 551; 552
MOSQUITOES ON LIVESTOCK AND MAN, 177–180
Motion sickness, dogs and cats, 529
MOTT, L. O., 182, 327, 531
Mountain fever, equine, 546
Mouse, rabies, 195
Mucosal disease, 258; cattle, 327
Mud fever, 226; of turkeys, 463
Mules, see also Horses
losses, 1954, 11; 13; worms, 43; ticks, 161; rabies, 195; tuberculosis, 216; anthrax, 230; tetanus, 237; periodic ophthalmia, 531; diseases and parasites of, 531–558; abortion virus infection, 534; influenza, 534; respiratory infections, 534, 535; breeding problems, 536; viral abortion, 540; contracted tendons, 542; jaundice, 544; encephalomyelitis, 550; hemolytic anemia, 554; lice, 555, 558; mange, 555; psoroptic mange mites, 556; chorioptic mites, 557
MULHERN, F. J., 369
Murine typhus fever, 19
Murrina, 549

Muscle, growths, 106; deterioration of, lambs, 430; deterioration of, calves, 430
Muscovies, hepatitis, 497
MUTH, O. H., 429
Muzzling, foals, 545
Myeloblastosis, chickens, leukemia, 469
Myelocytomatosis, poultry, 469
Mystery-grass, 120
Myxomatosis, infectious, rabbits, 561

Nagana, 8
Nasal cavity, inflammation, dogs, 524
Nasal discharges, in calves, 322; infectious bronchitis, 481
Nasal granuloma, cattle, 331
Nasal septum, 350
National Poultry Improvement Plan, 449, 479
National Turkey Improvement Plan, 449
Natural immunity, 52
Navel cord, inflammation, pigs, 380
Navel infection, sheep, 436
Nebraska, 9, 104, 295, 299, 338, 370, 418
Nebraska, laws, quarantine, 54
Necrosis, defined, 362
Necrotic enteritis, 365
Necrotic laryngitis, 332
Necrotic rhinitis, baby pigs, 380; swine, 382
Necrotic stomatitis, 332; baby pigs, 380
Nemathelminthes, defined, 31
Nematodes, described, 35; diseases produced by, 36; in dogs, 503
Nematodirosis, goats and sheep, 394
Neomycin, see Antibiotics
Neonatal isoerythrolysis, 544
Neoplastic conditions, 467
Nervous symptoms, equine, 553
Nervous system, inflammation, 535
Netherlands, 39, 192, 262
Neural lymphomatosis, poultry, 468
Neurosis, scrapie, 416
Nevada, 127, 299, 546
New duck disease, 498
New Jersey, 2, 456
New Mexico, 124, 127, 128, 299, 305, 404, 418
New wheat disease, 463
New York, 2, 26, 285, 299, 302, 319, 327, 416, 456, 497
New York Random Sample Test, 466
New York State Mastitis Control Program, 247
New York virus diarrhea, cattle, 327
New Zealand, 16, 24, 112, 129, 416, 417, 430
NEWCASTLE DISEASE, 455–458
Newcastle disease, losses, 13; 64
Nicotine, 85, 120; for lice, 307
Nicotine sulfate, toxicity, 131; scabies, 296, 406; roundworms, 398, 489; for mites, 495
Night blindness, in swine, 385
9-day scours, horses, 542
Nitrate poisoning, 115, 124
Nitrites, in blood, 116
Nitrofurazolidone, paratyphoid, 455
Nits, 558
Nocardiosis, dogs, 527
Nodular worms, calves, 287, 390
NODULAR WORMS OF SHEEP AND GOATS, 399–400
Nodules, defined, 285, 399; sheep and goat intestines, 399
Noninfectious diseases, defined, 38
Nonscutate ticks, 158

NORDQUIST, A. V., 11
North American fever tick, 311
North Carolina, 10, 54, 124
North Dakota, 302
Northern fowl mite, 494
Norway, 18, 351
Norway rat, 226
No-see-ums, 181
n-propyl isomer, 309
Nursing sickness, minks, 570
Nutrition, people, 9; pig diseases, 377; ewes, 427
Nutritional deficiencies, baby pigs, 378; swine, 384; Newcastle disease, 457
Nutritional factors, 61
Nymphs, lice, 307

Ocular lymphomatosis, poultry, 468
Oestrus (estrus), after trichomoniasis, 277
Office of Virus-Serum Control, 89
Ohio, 3, 299, 350, 405, 416
Oil Meal, poisonous, 119
Oils, swine mange, 348
Oklahoma, 260, 273, 299, 418, 433
OMER, C. R., 416
Omphalitis, baby pigs, 380
Ontario, 256
Oöcysts, 315, 387, 437, 563
Ophthalmia, periodic, equine, 531
Opium, 120
Opossums, ornithosis, 460
Oregon, 127, 299, 416, 418, 427, 546
Organic insecticides, toxicity, 132
Organic phosphorus insecticides, 139
Oribatid mites, 153
ORNITHOSIS AND PSITTACOSIS, 459–462
OSTEEN, O. L., 373, 455, 474, 476, 483
Osteopetrosis, poultry, 469
OTHER DISEASES OF SHEEP, 431–436
OUR BATTLE AGAINST ANIMAL DISEASES, 1–7
Outline of Disinfection Procedures for Poultry Service Personnel, 451
Ovarian lesions, 447
Ovary, growths, 106
Overgrazing, and poisonous plants, 118
Owls, rabies, 195; Newcastle disease, 456
Oxalacetate, 251
Oxalic acid, 123
Oxyhemoglobin, 116

Pacific coast tick, 272
Pajaroello tick, 159
Palestine, 418
PALS, C. H., 11
Pan American Veterinary Congress, 18
Panleukopenia, feline, 528
Paperflower, 126
Parakeets, pullorum disease, 446; ornithosis, 459; psittacosis, 460
Paralysis, blackleg, 263; in swine, 384; sheep, 423; dogs, 521
Parasite control, principles, 75–80
Parasites, in animals and man, 14; defined, 31; bloodsucking, 37; on animals, 37; spread, 40–45; external, 78; internal, chemicals for, 80; external chemicals for, 85; internal, cattle, 290; and distemper, 524
PARASITES AFFECTING DUCKS AND GEESE, 500–502
PARASITES OF THE DOMESTIC RABBIT, 563–567
PARASITES THAT ATTACK ANIMALS AND MAN, 21–28
Parasitic amebas, 42
Parasitic gastroenteritis, 390

Parasitism, 75; in beef calves, 288; pigs, 381; ducks, 496; dogs, 511; cats, 511
Parathion, toxicity, 139
Parathyroid, milk fever, 244
PARATUBERCULOSIS (JOHNE'S DISEASE), 221–223
Paratyphoid, swine, 364; 423; poultry, 453–455; ducks, 496
Paresis, dogs and cats, 524
Parrots, paratyphoid, 453; Newcastle disease, 456; parrot fever, 459; ornithosis, 459; erysipelas, 474
Parturient hypocalcemia, see Milk fever
Parturient pariesis, see Milk fever
Paspalum grass, 554
Pasteur Institute, 196
Pasteur treatment, 88
Pasteurella, shipping fever, 256; 259; minks, 568
Pasteurellosis, swine, 382; ducks, 498; rabbits, 559
Pasteurization, brucellosis, 213
Pastures, 41; contaminated, 43, 57; 60; community, and brucellosis, 208; rotation, 291, 340, 389
Pathogenic, defined, 46
PATTERSON, W. C., 182, 369
Paunch, 108
Peafowl, tapeworms, 484; eyeworm, 490
Peas, 143
Penicillin, see also Antibiotics and infection, 15; 95; CRD, 476; for minks, 568; foxes, 574
Penis, inflammation, 279; sheep, 434
Pennsylvania, 2, 9, 310, 330
Pens, for calves, 316
People, glanders, 5; and epidemics, 7; food, 9; diseases of, 14–20; roundworms, 16; tapeworms, 16; flukes, 16, 34; bovine tuberculosis, 17; brucellosis, 18, 213; parasites, 21–28; tapeworm carriers, 22; pork tapeworm, 23; fish tapeworm, 24; virus diseases, 31; African sleeping sickness, 32; nematodes, 35; insects, 37; tumors, 105; milksickness, 124; bladderworms, 155; ticks, 157, 159, 162; stablefly, 168; mosquitoes, 177; foot-and-mouth disease, 187; rabies, 201; tuberculosis, 216; leptospirosis, 226; anthrax, 230, 232; listeriosis, 239; influenza, 255, 366; actinobacillosis, 267; scabies, 292, 517; follicle mites, 349; cholera, 356; vesicular exanthema, 371; erysipelas, 374; sore mouth, 415; paratyphoids, 453; Newcastle disease, 455; ornithosis, 459; hookworm, 505; threadworms, 507; eyeworm, 508; hydatid tapeworm, 509; equine encephalomyelitis, 551; poliomyelitis, 552
Pericarditis, 460
Peritonitis, 252; swine, 345; blackhead, 442; mares, 543
Perthane, 87, 137
PESTICIDE RESIDUES IN ANIMAL PRODUCTS, 143–148
PETERSON, H. O., 403, 411
Petrels, ornithosis, 459
Petroleum, toxicity, 131; for hog lice, 346; mites, 495
Phage, 50
Phaseolunatin, 122
Pheasants, pullorum disease, 446; fowl typhoid, 451; Newcastle disease, 456; ornithosis, 459; fowlpox, 464; lymphomatosis,

467; erysipelas, 474; cannibalism, 553
Phenothiazine, defined, 81; for roundworms, 289; lungworms, 291; roundworms, 397; nodular worms, 400; blackhead, 443; cecal worms, 488
Philippines, 8
Phosphates, milk fever, 243
Phosphoric acid, 104
Phosphorus, 104
Photosensitization, 421
Physical therapy, 74
Physostigmine, 120
Pigeon(s), rabies, 195; malignant edema, 236; pullorum disease, 446; paratyphoids, 453; Newcastle disease, 456; ornithosis, 459; fowlpox, 464; erysipelas, 474; tapeworms, 484; lice, 490
Pigeon capillarid, poultry, 487
Pigeonpox, 464
Pigs, see also Swine losses, 1954, 11; vesicular stomatitis, 184; ascarids, 340; pig typhoid, 365; diseases of baby pigs, 377–381; enteric disorders, 378
Pimply gut, sheep and goats, 399
Pingue, 122
Pinkeye, cattle, 313; equine, 534
Pinworms, 390; rabbits, 566
Piperazine compounds, 82; for dogs, 514
Piperonyl butoxide, 309
Piroplasmosis, 269; dogs, 510, 516
Placenta, 538
Plant poisoning, 423
Plants, poisonous to animals, 39
Platyhelminthes, defined, 31
Pleurisy, losses, 13
Pleuritis, minks, 569
Pleuropneumonia, 2, 3, 9
Pleuropneumonialike organisms, 462, 476, 479
Plum Island Animal Disease Laboratory, 194
Pneumonia, losses, 13; 244; 258; 262; hyperkeratosis, 274; calves, 320, 323, 430; rhinitis, 350; baby pigs, 380; swine, 383; lungworms, 402; sheep, 420, 430; 432; dogs and cats, 507, 508; rabbits, 560; minks, 568
Poison in feed, 38; plants, 39
Poison sego, 120
POISONOUS PLANTS, 118–130
Poisons, swine paralysis, 385
Poland, 8
Polecat, rabies, 195
Poliomyelitis, people, 552
Polyborate, for kidney worms, 340
Polymyxin, 96
Polyp, 267
Poppy, 120
Porcupine, rabies, 195
Pork, tapeworm, 22; trichinosis, 25
Portable pens, 288
PORTER, DALE A., 153, 284
Posthitis, sheep, 434
Potassium, wheat-pasture poisoning, 262
Potassium nitrate, 115
Potassium permanganate, 496
Potatoes, 122
Poultry, losses, 1954, 11; worms, 43; immunization, 89; fluorides, 114; ticks, 157; tuberculosis, 215, 219; coccidiosis, 437; diseases and parasites, 437–502; blackhead, 441; blue comb, 463; and visceral lymphomatosis, 467; neural lymphomatosis, 468; ocular lymphomatosis, 468; osteopetrosis, 469; roundworms, 486; ascarids, 487; hair-

worms, 488; spiral stomach worm, 489; capillarids, 489; mites, 493
POULTRY AND THE PARATYPHOIDS, 453–455
Poultry houses, 440, 486
POULTRY LICE, 490–493
Poults, see also Turkeys management, 443; hexamitiasis, 444; paratyphoid, 454; Newcastle disease, 455; blue comb, 463; and IS, 480
Powders, for fleas, 522
Pox, 3
Pox diseases, swine, 385
Pox vaccine, 466
PPLO, see Pleuropneumonialike organisms
Precipitation, and parasites, 78
Precipitin test, 281
Pregnancy, mares, 538
PREGNANCY DISEASE, 427–429
Premunize, defined, 271
Prenatal infections, 271
Preparturient paresis of ewes, 427
Prepatent period, defined, 269
Prevention of disease, 71–102
PRICE, EMMETT W., 148, 503
Proglottids, defined, 21, 153
Programs, control, 6
Propylene glycol, 254
Prostate, cancer, 105
PROTECTION AGAINST TRANSMISSIBLE DISEASES AND PARASITES, 54–60
Proteins, 60, 254
Protozoa, defined, 31; 387, 503, 510
Prussic acid poisoning, 262
Pseudorabies, baby pigs, 381
Psittacosis, see also Ornithosis ducks, 19; turkeys, 19
Psoroptic mites, cattle, 292; 557
Public health, echinococcis, 16; brucellosis, 18; swine diseases, 19; brucellosis, 213
Public Health Service, 17, 201
Public Law 518, 143
Puerto Rico, 311
Pullet disease, 463
Pullets, coccidiosis, 438; fowl typhoid, 451
Pullorum, losses, 13
PULLORUM DISEASE OF CHICKENS AND TURKEYS, 446–451
Pulmonary edema, cattle, 291
Pulmonary parasitism, swine, 335
Pulpy kidney, 422
Pulse, anaplasmosis, 270
Punkies, 181
Puppies, see Dogs
Purdue University, 328
Purpura hemorrhagica, 233
Pyemia, losses, 13
Pyometra, 277, 282
Pyrethrins, for lice, 307; 309
Pyrethrum, 85, 86, 167, 309

Q-fever, 18, 19
Quail, ticks, 158; pullorum disease, 556; paratyphoid, 453; Newcastle disease, 456
Quarantine, 4; imported cattle, 6; 59; foot-and-mouth disease, 192; tick fever, 310; vesicular exanthema, 371
QUARANTINING, 62–70
Quarter ill, 263
Quaternary ammonium compound, 99

Rabbit Experiment Station, 560
Rabbit fever, 562
Rabbit tick, 161
Rabbits, domestic, losses, 1954, 11; losses, 13; liver flukes, 149; rabies, 195; tuberculosis, 216; malignant edema, 236; listeriosis, 239; actinobacillosis,

267; tapeworms, 509; infectious diseases, 559; pasteurellosis, 559; "snuffles," 559; pneumonia, 560; management, 560; mosquito disease, 561; infectious myxomatosis, 561; spirochetosis, 561; bloat, 562; enteritis, 562; favus, 562; tularemia, 562; coccidiosis, 563; diarrheal enteritis, 563; parasites, 563; liver coccidiosis, 564; ear mange, 565; body mange, 566; pinworms, 566; tapeworms, 566

RABIES, 195–202

Rabies, costs, 14; control program, 15; cats, 19; 41; Pasteur treatment, 88; 195; hare, 195; rabbit, 195; rat, 195; mouse, 195; jackal, 195; badger, 195; marmot, 195; woodchuck, 195; weasel, 195; porcupine, 195; hedgehog, 195; mongoose, 195; raccoon, 195; gopher, 195; owl, 195; hawk, 195; chicken, 195; bats, 195; stork, 195; pigeon, 195; polecat, 195; elk, 195; bear, 195; camel, 195; antelope, 195; deer, 195; monkey, 195; skunk, 195; hyena, 195; coyote, 195; foxes, 195; wolf, 195; hog, 195; goat, 195; sheep, 195; mules, 195; horse, 195; cow, 195; cat, 195; squirrel, 195; furious form, 197; dumb form, 197; vampire bat, 198; control, 200; vaccine, 201; 554

Raccoon, rabies, 195
Race horses, 547
RADELEFF, R. D., 131
Ragworts, 119
Rams, urinary calculi, 103
Range paralysis, 468
RANNEY, ALBERT F., 213
Rapid whole-blood test, for chickens, 448
Rat bite fever, 19
Rat tapeworm, in people, 25; in rodents, 25
Rations, urinary calculi, 103; ketosis, 254; and scours, 318; swine, 383; lambs, 424
Rats, zoonoses, 19; 24; urinary calculi, 103; vesicular stomatitis, 184; rabies, 195; 226; anthrax, 230; malignant edema, 236; actinobacillosis, 267
Rattlebox, 120
Record-of-Performance tests, 351
Red lungworm, 401
Red mange, dogs, 518
Red spots, dogs, 518
Red water disease, cattle, 333
Redroot, 115
Regional Poultry Research Laboratory, 467, 470
Regulations, sanitary, 64
Relapsing fever, 157
Repellents, mosquitoes, 180
Reproduction, trichomoniasis, 277; horses and mules, 536
Reproductive system, bull, 278
Residual insecticides, 308
Resinoids, 122
Resistance, defined, 29
Respiratory diseases, calves, 322; horses and mules, 534, 535
Restraint table, 410
Reticulum, 108, 252
Rhinitis, swine, 350; dogs, 524
Rhinotracheitis, cattle, 329
Rhizopoda, described, 33
Rhododendrons, 122
Riboflavin, periodic ophthalmia, 533
Ricefield fever, 226
Rickets, foxes, 574
Rickettsialpox, 20

Rift Valley fever, 18
Ringworm, in pets, 15, 18
Rio Grande, 311
Road oils, 275
ROBERTS, IRWIN H., 292, 300, 307, 490, 493
ROBY, T. O., 268, 531
Rock phosphate, 113
Rocky Mountain spotted fever, 3, 20, 157
Rocky Mountain spotted fever tick, 159, 272
Rodents, 14; tularemia, 527
Rome, 8
Rotenone, 85, 86; for grubs, 303; for lice, 307, 414; mange, 519; for ticks, 521; for fleas, 522
Roundworm, filarial, cattle, 298; saprophytic, 300; swine, 335; large intestinal, swine, 340–342; in people, 27; goats, 389; sheep, 389; large intestinal, pets, 505; in cats, 503, 512; in dogs, 503, 512; foxes, 575

ROUNDWORM PARASITES OF THE DIGESTIVE TRACT OF CATTLE, 284–290

ROUNDWORMS, 486–490

ROUNDWORMS OF THE DIGESTIVE TRACT, 389–399

Rubberweeds, 122
RUBIN, ROBERT, 290
Rumania, 8
Rumen, 108; digestion, ketosis, 251; 252; 253; 257; bacteria in, 321
Rumen inoculation, pregnancy disease, 429
Ruminants, bloat, 108; tapeworms, 153
Russia, 8
Russian spring-summer encephalitis, 552
Russian-thistle, 115

Saliva, 110
Salmon disease, foxes, 574
Salmon poisoning, dogs, 510
Salmonella diseases, 452
Salmonellosis, 18, 19, 380; in fox, 574
Salt, poisoning, 38; 116; ducks, 499
Sandflies, 181
Sanitary regulations, 64
Sanitation, to control stablefly, 169; and housefly, 170; tuberculosis, 220; calf barns, 324; in cholera, 358; baby pigs, 380; swine diseases, 382; control of nodular worms, 400; poultry, 439; pullorum, 450; Newcastle disease, 458; roundworm, 487
Saponins, 109
Saprophytic roundworms, 300
Sarcoptic mange, 293
Sarcoptic mites, cattle, 292
Scab, see also Scabies 3, 292; dermatitis, 299; horses and mules, 555
Scabies, 4; cattle, 292; psoroptic, sheep, 403; transmission, 404; chorioptic, sheep and goats, 405; demodectic, goats, 405; psorergatic, sheep, 405; sarcoptic, sheep, 405; horses and mules, 555

SCABIES IN SHEEP AND GOATS, 403–407

Scales, mange, swine, 347
Scaly-leg mite, 494
Scandinavia, 16, 350
SCHOENING, H. W., 29, 40, 195, 550
Schwannomas, 107
Schwann's cell, 107
SCHWARTE, L. H., 239

SCHWARTZ, BENJAMIN, 21, 29, 40
Sciatic nerve, 468
Sclerotia, 129
Scolex, defined, 35
Scotland, 416, 431
Scouring, from stomach worms, 285
Scours, coccidiosis, 314; calves, 317; causes, 319; prevention, 320; in swine dysentery, 363; in pigs, 365, 378
SCRAPIE IN SHEEP, 416–417
Scratching, cows, 295; swine, 346
Screaming fits, minks, 569
Screwworm(s), 160; in livestock, 172; in sore mouth, 415
SCREWWORMS THAT ATTACK LIVESTOCK, 172–175
Screwworm fly, 37
Scrofula, 214
Scrotum mange, cattle, 292
Scutate ticks, 158
Secondary ketosis, 252
Secondary screwworm fly, goats and sheep, 175
Secretary of Agriculture, 63, 66, 67, 92, 310, 370, 467
Selenium, 124
Selenium poisoning, 117
Semen, stallion, 538
Septicemia, 19; 30; 256; acute, in calves, 318, 319; erysipelas, 475
Septicemic disease, fowl, 453
Seroagglutination tests, brucellosis, 205
Seroagglutinin titers, 206, 210
Serological tests, erysipelas, 376; dogs, 526
Serum, production, 89; cholera, dosage, 360
Serum-neutralization test, 328
Serums, 71
Sex hormones, horses, 536
Shaft lice, 491
SHAHAN, M. S., 186, 550
SHALKOP, W. T., 105
Sheath, inflammation, 279; sheep, 434
Sheep, 1; losses, 11, 13; gid bladderworm, 35; urinary calculi, 103; adrenal tumors, 106; bloat, 108; fluorides, 114; molybdenum poisoning, 115; nitrate poisoning, 116; poisoning, 123; bighead, 127; liver flukes, 148; cirrhosis, 151; tapeworms, 153; bladderworms, 154; black blowfly, 175; fleeceworms, 175; greenbottle fly, 175; secondary screwworm, 175; vesicular stomatitis, 184; foot-and-mouth disease, 187; rabies, 195; tuberculosis, 216; Johne's disease, 223; leptospirosis, 227; anthrax, 230; malignant edema, 235; tetanus, 237; listeriosis, 240; black disease, 262; blackleg, 263; actinobacillosis, 267; roundworms, 284, 389; small hairworm, 285; coccidiosis, 387; haemonchosis, 392; nematodirosis, 394; strongyloidiasis, 395; nodular worms, 399; lungworms, 401; scabies, 403–407; head grubs, 407; lice, 411; sore mouth, 414; scrapie, 416; bluetongue, 418; enterotoxemia, 422; vibriosis, 425; pregnancy disease, 427; foot rot, 431; miscellaneous diseases, 431–436; progressive pneumonia, 432; blackleg, 433; mastitis, 433; ulcerative dermatosis, 434; venereal disease, 434; black disease, 435; arthritis, 436; navel infection, 436

585

Shield ticks, 158
SHIPPING FEVER, 255–260
Shipping fever, 262; 327; horses and mules, 534
SHOPE, RICHARD E., 366
Shore birds, ornithosis, 459
SHUMAN, RICHARD D., 350, 373, 377, 474
SHUPE, J. LEGRANDE, 277
Silica, 104
Silver nitrate, ulcerative dermatitis, 435
SIMMS, B. T., 54, 71
Skellysolve B, 143
Skin disease, cattle, 292, 298; swine, 347; dogs and cats, 524
Skunk, rabies, 195, 198
Sleeper, equine encephalomyelitis, 553
Sleeping sickness, 20, 550
Slobbering, calves, 333
Slow fever, equine, 546
Small-farm acetonemia, 252
Smear, 62, 174
SMITH, C. L., 307, 490, 493
SMITH, CARROLL N., 517
Snails, 149
Snakes, ticks, 157; esophageal worm, 507
Sneezing sickness, 350
Snoring disease, cattle, 311
Snowshoe foot, minks, 569
Snuffles, rabbits, 559
Soap plant, 120
Sodium fluoride, 81, 82, 307, 342, 492
Sodium propionate, 254
Sodium salts, 101
Soil, spores in, 40
Solanine, 120, 122
Solvents, toxicity, 131
Sore mouth, 19, 332, 415, 421, 435, 526
SORE MOUTH IN SHEEP AND GOATS, 414–415
Sorehead, 464
Sorghum, 104, 119, 121
Sorrels, 123
South Africa, 19, 78, 110, 330, 421, 427
South African tick-bite fever, 15
South America, 15, 16, 19, 28, 32, 44, 198, 229, 459, 551
South Carolina, 124, 310
South Dakota, 117, 299, 303, 304, 306
Southern cattle fever, 268
Soviet Union, 549
Sows, brucellosis, 209; threadworms, 343; dysentery, 363; milk fever, 383
Spain, 8, 192
Sparrows, 446, 453, 456
SPECIAL PRINCIPLES OF PARASITE CONTROL, 75–80
Spermatozoa, 537
SPINDLER, LLOYD A., 60, 340, 343
Spinose ear tick, 159, 262
Spirochete, 526, 561
Spirochetosis, rabbits, 561
Splenic fever, see Anthrax
Spore vaccine, anthrax, 234
Sporozoans, described, 32
Sporozoites, 315, 388
Spraying, dangers, 133; equipment, 306; and equine encephalitis, 554
Sprays, for ticks, 163; mites, cattle, 297; grubs, 304; lice, dairy cattle, 309; hog lice, 346; swine mange, 348; lice, 413, 492, 558
Squirrels, 120; rabies, 195
Stablefly, 168
Staggers, 427, 551
Stallion, service, 537
Stamping out, foot-and-mouth disease, 191
Staphylococcal infections, 463

Staphylococcus infections, 18; mastitis, 250; rabbits, 562
Starlings, 456
Steatitis, minks, 571
STEELE, JAMES H., 14
Steers, urinary calculi, 103; wheat-pasture poisoning, 261; water belly, 262; virus diarrhea, 328
STEFFERUD, ALFRED, VII
STEIN, C. D., 229, 235, 237, 263, 546
Stephanofilariasis, in cattle, 298
Sterility, 12, 106, 536
Sterilized flies, 174
Stick method, fowlpox vaccination, 465
Sticktight flea, 521
Stiff lamb disease, 429
Stillbirths, pigs, 378
Stillborn calves, hyperkeratosis, 274
St. Louis encephalitis, 552
Stockyard disease, 256
Stockyard fever, horses and mules, 534
Stomach, cancer, 105; bloat, 108; 252; roundworms, 284; parasites, 290
Stomach worm, common, 284; large, 390; spiral, poultry, 489
Stones, minks, 571
Storage fat, 250
Stork, rabies, 195
Strain 19 vaccine, 5, 18, 205
Stray dogs, 15
Streptococcal infections, 463; rabbits, 562
Streptococci, 384
Streptococci, mastitis, 245; abortion, mares, 538; horses, 542
Streptomycin, see also Antibiotics and infection, 15; mastitis, 434
Stress conditions, shipping fever, 256
Stress factors, CRD, 478
Strip cup, test, 247
Strobane, 87, 136
Strongyloid, poultry, 488
Strongyloidiasis, goats and sheep, 395
Strychnine, 119
Stuttgart's disease, 526
Subclinical, defined, 270
Suckers, defined, 35
Sucking lice, 411, 523, 558
Sudangrass, 121
Sugar (sugars), 254
SUGG, R. S., 313
SULFA DRUGS, THE, 96–98
Sulfa drugs, see also Sulfonamides 84; infectious bronchitis, 481; infectious serositis, 498; foals, 544; rabbits, 562
Sulfonamides, see also Sulfa drugs 84; discovery, 96; production, 96; toxicity, 97; value, 97; action, 97; mastitis, 249; shipping fever, 257; actinomycosis, 266; coccidiosis, 316, 389; erysipelas, 475; fowl cholera, 498; dogs, 516
Sulfur, 85, 132; coccidiosis, 389; for lice, 492
SULLIVAN, J. F., 476, 479, 480
Suramin, 300
Swamp fever, 177, 233, 546
Swans, Newcastle disease, 456
Sweden, 18, 192, 327, 431, 549, 567
Sweetclover, 430
Sweetclover poisoning, 233, 264
Swellhead, 479
Swellings, in shipping fever, 257; blackleg, 263; in cattle, 265; hyperkeratosis, 274; dogs, 506; dropsical, equine, 547, 548
Swine, 1; African swine disease, 8; disease losses, 12; brucellosis, 18; worms, 43; tumors,

107; fluorides, 114; liver flukes, 149; vesicular stomatitis, 183; foot-and-mouth disease, 187; brucellosis, 202; tuberculosis, 216; leptospirosis, 227; anthrax, 230; tetanus, 238; listeriosis, 240; actinobacillosis, 267; lung parasites, 335; diseases and parasites of, 335–386; icterus, 341; intestinal threadworm, 343; thorn-headed worm, 344; lice, 345; mange, 347; atrophic rhinitis, 350; enteritis, 362; dysentery, 363; influenza, immunity, 367, 381; vesicular exanthema, 369; diamond skin disease, 373; erysipelas, 380, 475; swinepox, 381, 385; miscellaneous diseases, 382–386; plague, 382
SWINE ERYSIPELAS (DIAMOND SKIN DISEASE), 373–377
SWINE INFLUENZA, 366–368
Switzerland, 192, 549
Symptomatic anthrax, 263
Synergist, defined, 309
Syria, 418

Tail louse, 307
Tall fescue, 129
Tapeworm(s), in man, 16; occurrence, 34; people and animals, 35; cattle, 153; goats, 153; sheep, 153; antelope, 154; calves, 154; deer, 154; kids, 154; elk, 154; lambs, 154; moose, 154; ducks, 500; cats and dogs, 509; rabbits, 566
TAPEWORMS AND BLADDERWORMS, 153–156
TAPEWORMS OF CHICKENS AND TURKEYS, 484–486
Tariff Act of June 17, 1930, 63
Tariff Act of 1930, 70
Tartar emetic, 300
TDE, toxicity, 137; 176; 181; dip for lice, 413
Teat (teats), mastitis, 246
Teething, 268
Temperature, and parasites, 78
Tendons, contracted, horses, 542
Tennessee, 273, 299, 362, 416
Terramycin, see Antibiotics
Tests, serological identification, 328
TETANUS, 237–239
Tetanus, 14; pigs, 380; horses, 543, 554
Tetanus antitoxin, 90, 238
Tetanus toxoid, 238; mares, 543
Tetany, calves, 326
Tetrachloroethylene, 81; roundworms, 398, 487
Tetracycline, see Antibiotics
Texas, 4, 45, 83, 104, 124, 198, 260, 261, 273, 276, 299, 302, 310, 311, 416, 418, 433, 546
Texas fever, 2, 269, 310
Therapy, defined, 71
Thirst, sheep, 417; dogs and cats, 524
Thistle, 115
THOMPSON, CLARENCE H., 476, 479
THORN-HEADED WORM OF SWINE, 344–345
Thoroughbred horses, 546
Thread lungworm, 401
Thread-necked strongyles, cattle, 287; sheep, 288
Thread-necked worms, 390
Threadworm, 390; poultry, 487; ducks, 500
Threadworm, intestinal, swine, 335, 343; dogs, 507
3-day scours, 319
Tick fever, 3, 10, 233, 269, 310
Tick-infested area, 1956, 311
Tick paralysis, 157, 159

586

Tick(s), eradication, 4; 36; 45; birds, 157; cattle, 157; elk, 157; horses, 157; lizards, 157; moose, 157; 160; poultry, 157; snakes, 157; toads, 157; turtles, 157; wild animals, 157; doves, 158; life history, 158; quail, 158; turkeys, 158; cats, 159; dogs, 159, 162, 516, 519; 520; people, 159, 162; anaplasmosis hosts, 272; American dog, 520; Rocky Mountain spotted fever, dogs, 520; lone star, dogs, 520; gulf coast, dogs, 520
TICKS THAT AFFECT DOMESTIC ANIMALS AND POULTRY, 157–166
Timothy hay, 275
Toads, ticks, 157
Toluene, 81, 83
Tonsillitis, dogs, 525
Tonsils, actinomycosis, 267
TORREY, J. P., 354, 382
Toxaphene, 85; 86; toxicity, 136; 144, 163, 176; for mange, 296, 303, 308; for hog lice, 346; dip, for lice, 413
Toxemia, cats, 529
TOXICITY OF INSECTICIDES, 131–142
Toxins, 14; defined, 30, 111; anaplasmosis, 269
Transportation, and diseases, 10
TRAUM, J., 186
Trauma, 105
TREATMENT OF DISEASE, 71–75
Trematodes, dogs, 510
Trembles, 124
Tremetol, 124
Tremors, 138; sheep, 416
Trichinae, 25
Trichinosis, 19; in people, 25, 27; symptoms, 26
Trichomonads, 32; 42; 277; rhinitis, 351
Trichomonal antigen, 111
Trichomoniasis, 463
TRICHOMONIASIS OF THE REPRODUCTIVE TRACT, 277–283
Trichostrongylosis, sheep and goats, 394
TROMBA, FRANCIS G., 338
Tropical cattle tick, 162
Tropical horse tick, 160
Trypaflavin, 281
Trypanosomiasis, 19, 549
Tsetse fly, 8
Tubercle bacillus, described, 214
Tuberculin testing, 17
TUBERCULOSIS AND ITS ERADICATION, 213–221
Tuberculosis, 2, 3; cow, 5; eradication, savings, 6; costs, 12; bone, 214; forms, 214; joint, 214; poultry, 215; avian, 219; poultry, 219; swine, 220
Tularemia, 20; 157; 170; 520; dogs, 527; rabbits, 562
TUMORS, 105–107
Tumors, 40; skin, 107; swine, 107; 470; ducks, 499; equine, 554
TUNNICLIFF, E. A., 431
Turbinates, 350, 352
TURKEY ERYSIPELAS, 474–476
Turkey gnats, 181
Turkeys, see also Poultry 11; ticks, 158, 418; coccidiosis, 437; blackhead, 441; hexamitiasis, 444; pullorum disease, 446; fowl typhoid, 451; paratyphoids, 453; Newcastle disease, 455; ornithosis, 459, 461; blue comb, 463; fowlpox, 464; lymphomatosis, 467; infectious sinusitis, 479; tapeworms, 484; roundworms, 486; cecal worm, 488; hairworm, 488; gizzard worm,

488; gapeworm, 489; stomach worm, 489; eyeworm, 490; lice, 490; chicken mite, 494; fowl cholera, 498
Turkeypox, 464
TURNER, JAMES H., 389
Turtles, ticks, 157
28-Hour law, 67
Typhus, 3
Tyrothricin, see Antibiotics

Udder, mange, 292
Udder inflammation, sheep, 433
Ulcerative stomatitis, 332
Ulcers, hyperkeratosis, 274
Unthriftiness, pigs, 340; swine, wormy, 339
Uremic poisoning, baby pigs, 379
URINARY CALCULI, 103–105
Urinary calculi, 262; minks, 571
Urine, 15; sugar in, sheep, 423
Urine colloid system, 104
Urolithiasis, 103
Uruguay, 24
Use of Disinfectants on the Farm, 451
Utah, 123, 127, 279, 299, 362, 418, 433, 567
Uterus, cancer, 106

Vaccination, 58; foot-and-mouth disease, 193; brucellosis, 206; Strain 19, 208; leptospirosis, 228; anthrax, 233; malignant edema, 236; blackleg, 264; erysipelas, 377; sore mouth, 415; bluetongue, 419, 421; blackleg, sheep, 433; fowl typhoid, 452; infectious bronchitis, 482; distemper, 524; equine encephalitis, 554
Vaccine(s), Strain 19, 5; and infection, 15; BCG, 17; use, 59; 71; bluetongue, 91; distemper, 91; fowlpox, 91, 465; hog cholera, 91, 361; killed-virus, 91; Newcastle disease, 91, 457; rabies, 91, 201; wart, 106; brucellosis, goats, 212; shipping fever, 259; blackleg, 264; anaplasmosis, 271; black disease, 436; lymphomatosis, 473; laryngotracheitis, 483
Vaccinia virus, swine, 386
Vaginal discharge, sheep, 425
Vaginitis, 252
Vagus nerve, 468
Vampire bat, rabies, 198
VAN HOUWELING, C. D., 1
VAN NESS, G. B., 226, 229, 463
V. E., see Vesicular exanthema
VEGORS, HALSEY H., 284
Venezuela, 551
Ventilation, calf barns, 322
VERMINOUS DERMATITIS, 298–300
VERMINOUS PNEUMONIA OF CATTLE, 290, 291
Vesicles, defined, 361
Vesicular diseases, 331, 369
VESICULAR EXANTHEMA, 369–372
Vesicular exanthema, 10, 12; baby pigs, 381
VESICULAR STOMATITIS — V. S., 182–186
Vesicular stomatitis, 18; cause, 183; types, 183; cattle, 184; chickens, 184; chinchillas, 184; deer, 184; dogs, 184; ferrets, 184; goats, 184; guinea pigs, 184; hamsters, 184; horses, 184; mice, 184; rats, 184; sheep, 184; treatment, 185; pigs, 381
Vetch, 430
VETERINARY BIOLOGICAL PRODUCTS, 88–93
Veterinary Division, 2
Vibriosis, costs, 12; losses, 13; 18
VIBRIOSIS OF CATTLE, 224–225

VIBRIOSIS OF SHEEP, 425–426
Viral abortion, mares, 540
Viremia, equine, 553
Virginia, 2, 124, 273, 299
Virus(es), defined, 30; 47; diarrhea, 258; influenzalike, 322; hog cholera, 355, 360; vesicular exanthema types, 370; contagious ecthyma, 415; scrapie, 416; bluetongue, 418; ulcerative dermatitis, 435; hepatitis, ducks, 497
Virus diseases, differences, 41
Virus-Serum-Toxin Law, 89
Visceral gout, 463
Visceral lymphomatosis, poultry, 467
Vitamin A, and urinary calculi, 104; shipping fever, 256; in hyperkeratosis, 274; cows, 318, 321; dogs, 513
Vitamin D, 104; for foxes, 574
Vitamin E, for calves, 431; lambs, 431; minks, 571
Vitamins, in calf feed, 319; for baby pigs, 379; pregnancy disease, 429; for poultry, 468
Vomiting, in sheep, 423; dogs, 507, 524; cats, 524
V. S., see Vesicular Stomatitis
Vulva, 278; inflamation, 328; sheep, 434
Vulvitis, sheep, 434

Wallows, medicated, for swine, 348
Warbleflies, 300
Wart, common, 106; vaccine, 106
Wartlike lesions, hyperkeratosis, 274
Washington, 127, 299, 305, 306, 338
Water belly, 103, 262
Water head, minks, 572
Waterlily, 120
WATERS, NELSON F., 46, 466
Weasel, rabies, 195
Weather, and bloat, 111
WEHR, EVERETT E., 437, 500
Weight loss, coccidiosis, 315
Weil's disease, 226, 526
West Germany, 192
West Indies, 3, 310
West Virginia, 2
Western duck sickness, 496
Western Utilization Research Branch, 109
Wet belly, minks, 572
Wheat bran, 104
Wheat-pasture poisoning, 260
Whipworms, 390; in dogs, 506
White grubs, swine, 345
White mouse, foot-and-mouth disease, 187
WHITE MUSCLE DISEASE IN LAMBS AND CALVES, 429–431
White ragweed, 115
White scours, 320
Whiteside test, mastitis, 248
Whole-blood antigen, 449
Whorled milkweed, 122, 554
Wild animals, ticks, 157; scabies, 292
Wild birds, Newcastle disease, 455
Wildcats, 14
Wild chokecherry, 121
Wild dogs, 14, 16
Wild ducks, 496
Wild fowl, paratyphoids, 453
Wild hogs, 345
Wild onion, 120
WILLIAMS, J. E., 446, 453
Wilm's tumor, 107
Wing lice, 491
Winter tick, 272
Wisconsin, 11, 112, 273, 299, 567, 571
Wolves, 16; rabies, 195; 300
Womb, 244
Wood preservatives, 275

Wood tick, dogs, 519; control, 521
WOODARD, G. T., 131, 143
Woodchucks, flukes, 151; rabies, 195
Wooden tongue, 267
Wool, damage, 13
World Health Organization, 17, 212
World War, Second, 8

Worms, parasitic, 34, 42, 57; swine kidney worms, 338
Wounds, blackleg germs, 263; swine erysipelas, 374; dogs and cats, 529
Wrights eupatorium, 128
Wyoming, 124, 288, 299, 362, 370, 418, 433, 546

X-disease, 273, 463

Yearlings, blackleg, 263
Yeasts, in mastitis, 245
Yellow body, 282
Yellow fat, minks, 571
Yellow fever, 3, 177, 226
Yellow tongue, 267

Zoonoses, defined, 14
ZUMBRO, PAUL B., 446
Zygadinine, 120

SCIENTIFIC NAMES

Achorion, 562
Actinobacillus lignieresi, 265, 267
Actinomyces bovis, 265, 267, 268
  lignieresi, 268
  necrophorus, 365, 569
Aedes, 178, 551
  aegypti, 178
  atlanticus, 177
  canadensis, 177
  dorsalis, 178
  infirmatus, 177
  nigromaculis, 178
  sollicitans, 178
  squamiger, 178
  sticticus, 178
  taeniorhynchus, 178
  varipalpus, 178
  vexans, 177, 178
Aerobacter aerogenes, 245
Agrostemma githago, 122
Alcaligenes bronchisepticus, 560
Aleurostrongylus abstrusus, 508
Amaranthus retroflexus, 115, 124
Amblyomma, 159, 160, 520
  americanum, 160, 520
  cajennense, 161
  maculatum, 157, 161, 520
  varium, 157
Amidostomum anseris, 500
Amoebotaenia sphenoides, 485
Amsinckia intermedia, 124
Anaplasma centrale, 271
  marginale, 268
  marginale var. centrale, 271
Anatoecus dentatus, 499
Ancylostoma, braziliense, 15, 27, 504, 505
  cannium, 504, 505
  duodenale, 15
Anopheles, 178
Aplopappus heterophyllus, 124
Aporina delafondi, 485
Argas persicus, 158, 272
Ascaridia galli, 487
Ascaris lumbricoides, 28
Asclepias, 122
  eriocarpa, 122
  fascicularis, 122
  labriformis, 123
  pumila, 122
  subverticillata, 122, 123
  verticillata var. geyeri, 123

Aspergillus fumigatus, 497
Astragalus, 124, 126
  drummondii, 126
  tetrapterus, 126

Babesia bigemina, 76
  canis, 162, 511, 527
Bacillus anthracis, 229, 233, 234, 568
  monocytogenes, 239
Bacterium monocytogenes, 239
  tularense, 527
Balantidium coli, 33
Bdellonyssus sylviarum, 494
Beta vulgaris, 124
Bikukulla cucullaria, 120
Boophilus, 159, 162
  annulatus, 76, 159, 161, 162, 269, 272, 311
  annulatus var. microplus, 311
  decoloratus, 157
  microplus, 76, 159
Bovicola bovis, 307, 309
  caprae, 412
  ovis, 412
Brucella, 202, 203, 204, 205, 210, 212
  abortus, 202, 203, 204, 205, 209, 210, 211, 322
  melitensis, 202, 204, 209, 210, 211, 212
  suis, 202, 203, 209, 210, 211
Bunostomum phlebotomum, 286
  trigonocephalum, 390

Callitroga hominivorax, 172
  macellaria, 175
Capillaria aerophila, 508
  annulata, 489
  bovis, 390
  brevipes, 390
  caudinflata, 488
  contorta, 489, 500
  felis-cati, 508
  obsignata, 487
  plica, 508
Chabertia ovina, 390
Cheilospirura hamulosa, 488
Chelopistes meleagridis, 491
Choanotaenia infundibulum, 485
Choerostrongylus pudendotectus, 335

Chorioptes bovis, 405
  bovis var. bovis, 292
  equi, 557
Cicuta vagans, 122
Cionella lubrica, 151
Clostridium botulinum, 499, 567
  chauvoei, 263
  chauvoei-septicus, 265
  chauvoei-septicus bacterin, 236
  hemolyticum, 333
  novyi, 262, 436
  perfringens, 325
  perfringens Type D, 422, 423
  septicum, 235
  septicum bacterin, 236
  tetani, 237
  welchii, 325
Cochlosoma anatis, 502
Coenurus cerebralis, 154, 155
Conium maculatum, 120
Cooperia curticei, 285, 390, 395
  oncophora, 285, 390
  pectinata, 285, 390
  punctata, 285, 286, 390
Corydalis caseana, 120
Corynebacterium, 313, 382
  equi, 539, 542, 543
  parvulum, 239
  pyogenes, 246, 322
Crotalaria sagittalis, 120
Ctenocephalides canis, 16, 521
Cuclotogaster heterographus, 491
Culex, 178, 551
  pipiens, 178
  quinquefasciatus, 178
  tarsalis, 37, 178, 552
Culicoides, 181, 419
Culiseta, 178, 551
Cyathostoma bronchialis, 500
Cysticercus bovis, 21, 154, 155
  cellulosae, 23
  ovis, 154, 155, 156
  tenuicollis, 154, 155

Dasypterus floridanus, 198
Davainea meleagridis, 484
  proglottina, 484
Delphinium barbeyi, 120
  menziesi, 120
  occidentale, 120
Demodex canis, 518
  folliculorum bovis, 294

Demodex canis—Continued
  folliculorum suis, 349
  phylloides, 349
Dermacentor, 159
  albipicus, 157, 159, 160, 272
  andersoni, 159, 520, 552
  (andersoni) venustus, 272
  nigrolineatus, 159, 160
  nitens, 159, 160
  occidentalis, 160, 272, 520
  variabilis, 159, 272, 520, 552
  venustus, 159, 160
Dermanyssus gallinae, 493, 551
Derris eliptica, 303
Desmodus rotundus murinus, 198
  rufus, 198
Dicentra cucullaria, 120
Dicrocoelium dendriticum, 34, 150, 151
Dictyocaulus filaria, 401
  viviparus, 290
Dioctophyma renale, 508
Diphyllobothrium latum, 24, 510
  mansoni, 510
  mansonoides, 510
Diptera, 300
Dipylidium, 516
  caninum, 16, 25, 509
Dirofilaria immitis, 506
Dispharynx nasuta, 489

Echidnophaga gallinacea, 521
Echinococcus granulosus, 16, 23, 154, 509
Eimeria, 314
  acervulina, 438
  adenoeides, 439
  alabamensis, 315
  anseris, 502
  arloingi, 32, 388
  auburnensis, 315
  bovis, 84, 315
  brunetti, 438
  canis, 511
  dispersa, 439
  ellipsoidalis, 315
  faurei, 388
  gallopavonis, 439
  hagani, 438
  innocua, 439
  maxima, 438
  meleagridis, 439
  meleagrimitis, 439
  mitis, 438
  necatrix, 438
  ninae-kohl-yakimova, 388
  nocens, 502
  parvula, 502
  praecox, 438
  subrotunda, 439
  tenella, 438
  truncata, 501
  zurnii, 315
Elaeophora schneideri, 82
Entamoeba polecki, 33
Erysipelothrix, 242
  rhusiopathiae, 373, 474, 475

Escherichia coli, 49, 51, 100, 245, 539, 543
Eupatorium rugosum, 124, 128
  wrightii, 128

Fasicola gigantica, 150
  hepatica, 18, 148, 149, 150
Fascioloides magna, 150
Felicola subrostrata, 523
Festuca arundinaceae, 129
Filaroides osleri, 509
Formica fusca, 151
Fossaria bulimoides, 149, 152
  cubensis, 149
  ferruginea, 149
  hepatica, 152
  modicella, 149, 150
  modicella rustica, 150
  ollula, 150
  parva, 150
Franseria discolor, 115, 124
Fumariaceae, 120

Giardia canis, 511
Gongylonema ingluvicola, 489
Goniocotes gallinae, 491
Goniodes gigas, 491

Haemaphysalis, 159, 161
  chordeilis, 161
  leporispalustris, 161
Haematopinus eurysternus, 307
  quadripertusus, 307
  suis, 345
Haemonchus contortus, 284, 289, 390
  placei, 284
Halogeton glomeratus, 123
Helicella candidula, 151
  ericetorum, 151
Helodrilus, 336
Hemophilus bovis, 313
  influenzae suis, 366
Hepatozoon canis, 162
Heterakis gallinae, 442
  gallinarum, 488
Heterodoxus longitarsus, 523
Hexamita meleagridis, 444
Histomonas meleagridis, 441
Histoplasma capsulatum, 527
Hymenolepis, 485
  carioca, 485
  diminuta, 25
  nana, 24
  tenuirostris, 501
Hymenoxys odorata, 122
  richardsoni, 122
Hypoderma bovis, 45, 300
  lineatum, 300

Isospora bigemina, 511
  felis, 511
  rivolta, 511
Ixodes, 159
  cookei, 159
  pacificus, 159, 520
  persulcatus, 552
  ricinus, 552

scapularis, 159, 272, 520
soricis, 157

Klebsiella genitalium, 539
  ozaenae, 568
Knemidokoptes laevis var. gallinae, 494
  mutans, 494

Leishmania donovani, 511
Leptospira canicola, 15, 226, 227, 526
  grippotyphosa, 227
  icterohemorrhagiae 15, 19, 227, 526
  pomona, 226, 227
  sejroe, 226, 227
Leucotozoon simondi, 498, 501
Linognathus africanus, 412
  ovillus, 412
  pedalis, 412
  piliferus, 523
  stenopsis, 412
  vituli, 307, 309
Linum usitatissimum, 121
Lipeuris caponis, 491
Listeria, 242
Listerella hepatolytica, 239
  monocytogenes, 239, 384
Lonchocarpus nicou, 303
Lupinus luteus, 120
Lymnaea acuminata, 150
  natalensis, 150
  traskii, 149
Lymnaeidae, 150
Lyponyssus sylvarium, 551

Macracanthorhynchus hirudinaceus, 344
Mansonia, 178, 551
Marshallagia marshalli, 390
Menacanthus stramineus, 491
Metastrongylus elongatus, 335
  salmi, 335
Metroliasthes lucida, 485
Micrococcus, 382
  pyogenes, 245
Microsporum canis, 15
Moniezia benedeni, 153
  expansa, 153
Moraxella anatipestifer, 498
  bovis, 313
Muellerius capillaris, 401
Multiceps multiceps, 155
Mycobacterium, 214
  paratuberculosis, 222
  phlei, 222

Nematodirus abnormalis, 390
  filicollis, 390
  helvetianus, 287, 288
  spathiger, 287, 288, 390
Neorickettsia helminthoeca, 510
Nicotiana attenuata, 120
Notoedres cati, 518

Oesophagostomum columbianum, 390, 399
  radiatum, 287, 289
  venulosum, 390, 399
Oestrus ovis, 407
Ornithodoros coriaceus, 159
  hermsi, 158
  (Otobius) megnini, 159
  parkeri, 158
  talaje, 158, 159
  turicata, 158, 159
Ornithostrongylus quadriradiatus, 488
Ostertagia circumcincta, 390
  occidentalis, 390
  ostertagi, 284
  trifurcata, 390
Oxylipeurus polytrapezius, 491
Oxyspirura mansoni, 489
Oxytenia acerosa, 126
Oxytropis, 126
  lamberti, 126

Paracolobactrum, 453
Paragonimus westermanii, 335, 337
Pasteurella, 560
  hemolytica, 256, 257
  mastitidis, 433
  multocida, 245, 256, 322, 382, 383, 498, 559, 560
  tularensis, 159, 562
Peganum harmala, 120
Phaenicia sericata, 175
Phormia regina, 45, 175
Physopsis africana, 150
Pomatiopsis lapidaria, 337
Protostrongylus rufescens, 401
Prunus virginiana, 121
  virginiana var. demissa, 121
  virginiana var. melanocarpa, 121
Pseudomonas, 382
  aeruginosa, 245, 351, 539, 568
Pseudostertagia bullosa, 390
Pseudosuccinea columella, 149, 150
Psilostrophe, 126
  sparsiflora, 126
Psorophora, 178
  confinnis, 177
  necrophorus, 415
Psoroptes communis, 565
  equi equi, 556
  equi var. bovis, 292
  equi var. ovis, 403
Pteridium aquilinum, 127
Pulex irritans, 521

Raillietina cesticillus, 484
  echinobothrida, 484
  tetragona, 484
Rhabditis, 300
Rhinosporidium, 332

Rhipicephalus, 159, 161
  sanguineus, 162, 272, 511, 519
Rickettsia akari, 20
  ruminantium, 88

Salmonella, 19, 326, 364
  abortivo-equinus, 539
  abortus-equi, 542
  anatum, 453
  bredeney, 453
  cholera suis, 364, 365
  derby, 453
  gallinarum, 451
  newport, 453
  paratyphi, 100
  pullorum, 53, 446, 450
  senftenberg, 453
  typhimurium, 51, 453, 455, 543
Salsola kalitenufolia, 115
  pestifer, 124
Sarcobatus vermiculatus, 123
Sarcocystis rileyi, 502
Sarcoptes scabiei canis, 517
  scabiei equi, 555
  scabiei var, bovis, 293
  scabiei var. ovis, 405
  scabiei var. suis, 347
Schistosoma japonicum, 16, 18
Senecio, 119, 120
Setaria cervi, 82
Shigella equirulis, 539, 542, 543
Silybum mariamum, 115, 124
Simulium, 181
Skrjabinema ovis, 390
Solanum, 122
  carolinense, 122
  dulcamara, 122
  nigrum, 122
Solenopotes capillatus, 307
Sorghum halepense, 121
  vulgare, 121
  vulgare var. sudanense, 121
Spherophorus necrophorus, 332, 382
Spirella minus, 20
Spirocerca lupi, 507
Stagnicola bulimoides techella, 149, 150
  palustris nuttalliana, 150
Stanleya, 124
Stephanofilaria stilesi, 298
Stephanurus dentatus, 338
Streptococcus, 382, 560
  agalactiae, 245, 247
  dysgalactiae, 245
  uberis, 245
Strongyloides, 343, 507
  avium, 488
  papillosus, 286, 288, 390

ransomi, 36
  stercoralis, 507
Strychnos, 119
Syngamus trachea, 489, 500

Taenia, 516
  hydatigena, 155
  ovis, 155
  pisiformis, 35, 509
  saginata, 18, 21, 154, 155
  solium, 22
  taeniaformis, 509
Tetradymia, 127
  canescens, 127
  glabrata, 127
Tetrameres americana, 488
Theileria parva, 78
Thelazia californiensis, 507
Thysanosoma actinioides, 154
Torquilla frumentum, 151
Toxocara canis, 16, 505
  cati, 505
  leonina, 505
Treponema cuniculis, 561
  pallidum, 561
Triatoma sanguisuga, 552
Tribulus terrestris, 124
Trichinella spiralis, 25
Trichomonas, 351
  foetus, 32
Trichophyton, 562
Trichostrongylus axei, 285, 390
  capricola, 390
  colubriformis, 285, 390
  tenuis, 500
  vitrinus, 390
Trichuris discolor, 390
  globulosa, 390
  ovis, 390
  vulpis, 506
Triglochin maritima, 121
  palustris, 121
Tritrichomonas foetus, 279
  (Trichomonas) foetus, 277
Troglotrema salmincola, 510
Trypanosoma cruzi, 162
Tyzzeria anseris, 502
  perniciosa, 502

Uncinaria stenocephala, 504

Vibrio, 224
  fetus, 224, 225, 425, 426

Wohlfahrtia, 573

Xylorrhiza parryi, 124

Zebrina detrita, 151
Zigadenus, 120

PERSONS WHOSE WORK IS CITED IN THIS YEARBOOK

Abelein, R., 281
Allen, E., 502

Baker, J. A., 322, 525
Bang, Bernard, 202
Bankowski, R. A., 370
Barner, Ralph D., 313
Bartlett, David E., 278, 281
Beach, J. R., 464
Beaudette, F. R., 474
Bell, Wilson B., 275
Bentley, O. G., 259
Biffen, R. H., 53
Billings, W. A., 476
Boda, J. M., 244
Bortree, A. L., 275
Bourne, R. F., 427
Braend, M., 351
Britton, J. W., 125
Broadfoot, D. I., 481
Bruce, David, 202
Buck, J. M., 5
Byrne, J. L., 351, 353

Card, L. E., 53
Carter, G. R., 256, 257, 352
Chandler, Asa C., 152
Chivers, W. H., 328
Cole, H. H., 244
Cole, R. K., 53, 463
Cooley, R. A., 162
Cotton, W. E., 5
Couch, James F., 126
Crawford, A. B., 370
Creech, G. T., 373
Cunningham, I. J., 129
Curtice, Cooper, 3, 311

Dale, C. N., 356
Darlington, P. B., 269
Davis, D. J., 267
Davis, Gorden E., 158
Davis, R. E., 276
Deem, A. W., 424
Delafond, 55
Dickinson, E. M., 475
Dinaburg, A. G., 399
Donham, C. R., 350
Dorset, Marion, 89, 359, 361
Dougherty, E., III, 502
Doyle, L. P., 350
Doyle, T. M., 456
Dryere, H., 243
Dzenis, L., 351

Ellis, N. R., 276
Evans, Alice, 5

Farley, Herman, 259, 313
Flatla, J. L., 351
Fosterman, A. A., 373
Fox, F. H., 327
Frenkel, H. S., 193

Gallagher, C. H., 313
Gibbons, W. O., 275
Goodman, A. A., 129
Goss, H., 125

Gowen, J. W., 53
Graham, W. R., 258
Green, W. W., 379
Greig, J. R., 243, 416
Grey, C. G., 376
Gwatkins, R., 350, 351, 353

Hansel, William, 275
Hanson, R. P., 184
Haring, C. M., 17
Harrison, E. S., 322
Hartsough, G. R., 571
Harwood, Paul D., 134
Hawn, M. C., 480
Hayes, F. M., 17
Heath, M. K., 526
Hibbs, J. W., 245
Hoffman, Robert A., 309
Hudson, C. B., 474
Hutchings, L. M., 350
Hutt, F. B., 53

Jellison, William L., 160
Johnson, A. G., 275
Jones, T. C., 533
Jones, T. L., 353

Kaplan, M. M., 17
Kelser, R. A., 551
Kerr, W. R., 322
Kilborne, Fred L., 3, 268, 311
King, N. B., 259
Klosterman, E. W., 259
Knipling, E. F., 174
Knox, C. W., 53
Koch, Robert, 55, 213, 373
Kristjansson, F. K., 350

Lambert, W. V., 53
Lamont, H. G., 322
Lamson, G. H., Jr., 307
Larin, N. M., 525
Leith, T. S., 376
Leuckart, Rudolph, 149
Lindahl, Ivan, 276
Lindley, C. E., 104
Link, Roger P., 276
Löffler, F. A. J., 373
Looss, Arthur, 44

McAuliff, John, 323
MacCallum, A. C., 327
McEntee, Kenneth, 275
McKay, K. A., 352
McNutt, S. H., 376
Madin, S. H., 370
Melvin, A. D., 359
Mendel, Gregor, 47
Meyer, K. F., 269, 459
Miles, A. A., 242
Miller, R. C., 275
Mohler, John R., 5
Moritz, 55
Moynihan, W. A., 259
Muth, O. H., 427

Newsom, I. E., 423
Niles, W. B., 359

Olafson, Peter, 273, 275, 327
Olson, Carl, Jr., 242, 275
Osteen, O. L., 376

Palotay, J. L., 257, 259
Parker, Joseph W., 4
Parker, R. R., 161
Parry, H. B., 525
Pasteur, Louis, 55, 58, 88, 373
Perroncito, 55
Phillip, C. B., 157, 160
Phillips, P. H., 275
Plummer, P. J. G., 353
Pomeroy, B. S., 481
Pounden, H. D., 245

Quigley, G. D., 463

Ramsey, F. K., 328
Reber, E. F., 276
Renoux, Paul, 212
Rhubarth, Sven, 525
Roberts, E., 53
Roberts, F. H. S., 284
Robinson, W. O., 275
Rosenwald, A. S., 475

Salmon, D. E., 2
Schalk, A. F., 480
Schmidt, Hubert, 275
Schmidt, S., 193
Schoening, H. W., 275, 376
Schofield, F. W., 351
Scott, J. P., 259
Shaw, J. N., 427
Sikes, Dennis, 275
Sippel, William, 275
Smiley, R. S., 350
Smith, Theobald, 3, 213, 268, 311, 373
Smith, Wade M., 481
Stanley, W. M., 50
Stearns, T. J., 129
Stover, D. E., 463
Stunkard, H. W., 153
Switzer, W. P., 351, 376

Telford, A. S., 134
Theiler, Arnold, 157, 269
Thomas, A. P. W., 149
Thomas, D. L., 259
Thuillier, M. L., 373
Toissant, 55
Traum, Jacob, 5, 17, 202, 369

Udall, D. H., 319
Underbjerg, C. K., 376

Vandeplassche, M., 278, 281

Waldmann, O., 193
Walker, R. V. L., 327, 353
Waters, Nelson F., 53
Welch, Howard, 134, 135, 136, 137
Wellmann, G., 374
Wilkins, H. F., 160
Wilson, G. S., 242
Wood, M., 370

591